International Acclaim for

THE LACUNA

"[Kingsolver] stands up for the enduring and redemptive power of a good story to teach and, above all, to give us reasons to believe in the possibility of change."
—*The Times* (London)

"Rich . . . impassioned . . . engrossing."—*Chicago Tribune*

"Masterful. . . . A reader receives the great gift of entering not one but several worlds. . . . The final pages haunt me still."—*San Francisco Chronicle*

"A lavishly gifted writer. . . . Kingsolver [has a] wonderful ear for the quirks of human repartee. *The Lacuna* is richly spiked with period language. . . . This book grabs at the heartstrings."—*Los Angeles Times*

"[Kingsolver] writes with a sharp political edge that gives the novel a superb authenticity. Her canvas is as monumental and colourful as a Diego Rivera mural."
—*The Courier-Mail* (Australia)

"Tender, tragic, optimistic, sometimes depressing—but always com~
word and twist has earned its place in this provocative and h
—*The New Review*

"A sweeping mural of sensory delights and stimula   ᴀment,
identity, and history. . . . Readers will feel the sting o   ᴠeen then and
now."—*Seattle Times*

"[Kingsolver's] playful pastiche brings to vivid life the culture wars of an earlier era."
—*Vogue*

"Marvellous. . . . Only a writer of exceptional skill and daring can hold together such an ambitious undertaking."—*Sydney Morning Herald*

"Insightful and very entertaining."—*The Irish Times*

"As in *The Poisonwood Bible*, Kingsolver perfects the use of multiple points of view. . . . This is her most ambitious, timely, and powerful novel yet."
—*Library Journal*

"Readers will love it."—*The Sunday Telegraph*

"Shepherd's story in Kingsolver's accomplished literary hands is so seductive, the prose so elegant, the architecture of the novel so imaginative, it becomes hard to peel away from the book."—*Pittsburgh Post-Gazette*

"A sweeping narrative of utopian dreams and political reality. . . . A stirring novel. . . . Intimate and pitch-perfect."—*San Diego Union-Tribune*

"Kingsolver deftly combines real history and the life of the fictional protagonist. . . . A sweeping tale."— *Atlanta Journal-Constitution*

"[Kingsolver] stirs the real with the imagined to produce a breathtakingly ambitious book, bold and rich . . . hopeful, political, and artistic. *The Lacuna* fills a lacuna with powerfully imagined social history."— *The Kansas City Star*

"[*The Lacuna*] achieves a rare dramatic power. . . . Kingsolver masterfully resurrects a dark period in American history with the assured hand of a true literary artist."
—*Publishers Weekly* (starred review)

THE LACUNA

Also by Barbara Kingsolver

Fiction

Prodigal Summer

The Poisonwood Bible

Pigs in Heaven

Animal Dreams

Homeland and Other Stories

The Bean Trees

Essays

Small Wonder

High Tide in Tucson: Essays from Now or Never

Poetry

Another America

Nonfiction

Animal, Vegetable, Miracle: A Year of Food Life
(with Steven L. Hopp and Camille Kingsolver)

Last Stand: America's Virgin Lands
(with photographs by Annie Griffiths Belt)

*Holding the Line: Women in the Great Arizona
Mine Strike of 1983*

THE LACUNA

A Novel

Barbara Kingsolver

HarperCollins*Publishers*Ltd

Published by HarperCollins Publishers Ltd.

First published in Canada in a hardcover edition by HarperCollins Publishers Ltd: 2009
This trade paperback edition: 2010

HarperCollins books may be purchased for educational, business,
or sales promotional use though our Special Markets Department.

HarperCollins Publishers Ltd
2 Bloor Street East, 20th Floor
Toronto, Ontario, Canada
M4W 1A8

www.harpercollins.ca

Library and Archives Canada Cataloguing in Publication information is available

ISBN 978-1-55468-476-2

RRD 10 9 8 7 6 5 4 3 2 1

A Note on Historical References

All articles and excerpts from the *New York Times* used in this text appear as originally published, reprinted with permission.

Diego Rivera, "Rivera Still Admires Trotsky; Regrets Their Views Clashed," April 15, 1939.

"U.S. Forbids Entry of Trotsky's Body; Soviet Calls Him Traitor," August 25, 1940.

"2,541 Axis Aliens Now in Custody," December 13, 1941.

Samuel A. Tower, "79 in Hollywood Found Subversive, Inquiry Head Says," October 23, 1947.

"Truman Is Linked By Scott to Reds," September 26, 1948.

The following article excerpts are also used with permission.

Anthony Standen, "Japanese Beetle: Voracious, Libidinous, Prolific, He Is Eating His Way across the US," *Life*, July 17, 1944.

"Peekskill Battle Lines," *Life*, September 19, 1949.

Frank Desmond, "M'Carthy Charges Reds Hold U.S. Jobs," *Wheeling Intelligencer*, February 10, 1950.

All other newspaper articles in the novel are fictional. Historical persons are portrayed and quoted from the historical record, but their conversations with the character Harrison Shepherd are entirely invented. This is a work of fiction.

❀

The author gratefully acknowledges the usefulness of Alain Dugrand, *Trotsky in Mexico, 1937–1940* (Manchester, England: Carcanet, 1992); Leon Trotsky, *My Life: An Attempt at an Autobiography* (New York: Pathfinder Press, 1970); *The Diary of Frida Kahlo: An Intimate Self-Portrait* (New York: Harry N. Abrams, 2005); Malka Drucker, *Frida Kahlo: Torment and Triumph* (Albuquerque: University of New

Mexico Press, 1995); Hayden Herrera, *Frida: A Biography of Frida Kahlo* (New York: Harper & Row, 1983); Walter Bernstein, *Inside Out: A Memoir of the Blacklist* (Da Capo, 2000); William Manchester, *The Glory and the Dream* (Boston: Little, Brown, 1973); Martha Norburn Mead, *Asheville: In Land of the Sky* (Richmond, Va.: Dietz Press, 1942); and Hernando Cortés, *Five Letters of Cortés to the Emperor*, trans. J. Bayard Morris (New York: Norton, 1969), as well as the estates of Lev Trotsky, Dolores Olmedo, Frida Kahlo, and Diego Rivera for opening these persons' homes and archives. *Gracias* to the Instituto Nacional de Antropología e Historia (INAH) for its meticulous care of Mexico's historical treasures (notably the Rivera murals) and enduring dedication to public access. Finally, special thanks to Maria Cristina Fontes, Judy Carmichael, Terry Karten, Montserrat Fontes, Sam Stoloff, Ellen Geiger, Frances Goldin, Matt McGowan, Sonya Norman, Jim Malusa, Fenton Johnson, Steven Hopp, Lily Kingsolver, and Camille Kingsolver.

THE LACUNA

PART I

Mexico, 1929–1931

(VB)

Isla Pixol, Mexico, 1929

In the beginning were the howlers. They always commenced their bellowing in the first hour of dawn, just as the hem of the sky began to whiten. It would start with just one: his forced, rhythmic groaning, like a saw blade. That aroused others near him, nudging them to bawl along with his monstrous tune. Soon the maroon-throated howls would echo back from other trees, farther down the beach, until the whole jungle filled with roaring trees. As it was in the beginning, so it is every morning of the world.

The boy and his mother believed it was saucer-eyed devils screaming in those trees, fighting over the territorial right to consume human flesh. The first year after moving to Mexico to stay at Enrique's house, they woke up terrified at every day's dawn to the howling. Sometimes she ran down the tiled hallway to her son's bedroom, appearing in the doorway with her hair loose, her feet like iced fish in the bed, pulling the crocheted bedspread tight as a web around the two of them, listening.

It should have been like a storybook here. That is what she'd promised him, back in the cold little bedroom in Virginia North America: if they ran away to Mexico with Enrique she could be the bride of a wealthy man and her son would be the young squire, in a hacienda surrounded by pineapple fields. The island would be encircled with a shiny band of sea like a wedding ring, and somewhere on the mainland was its gem, the oil fields where Enrique made his fortune.

But the storybook was *The Prisoner of Zenda*. He was not a young

squire, and his mother after many months was still no bride. Enrique was their captor, surveying their terror with a cool eye while
eating his breakfast. "That howling is the *aullaros*," he would say, as
he pulled the white napkin out of its silver ring into his silver-ringed
fingers, placing it on his lap and slicing into his breakfast with a fork
and knife. "They howl at one another to settle out their territories,
before they begin a day of hunting for food."

Their food might be us, mother and son agreed, when they huddled together inside the spiderweb of bedspread, listening to a rising
tide of toothsome roars. *You had better write all this in your notebook*,
she said, *the story of what happened to us in Mexico. So when nothing
is left of us but bones, someone will know where we went.* She said to
start this way: In the beginning were the *aullaros*, crying for our
blood.

Enrique had lived his whole life in that hacienda, ever since his
father built it and flogged the *indios* into planting his pineapple fields.
He had been raised to understand the usefulness of fear. So it was
nearly a year before he told them the truth: the howling is only monkeys. He didn't even look across the table when he said it, only at
the important eggs on his plate. He hid a scornful smile under his
moustache, which is not a good hiding place. "Every ignorant Indian
in the village knows what they are. You would too, if you went out in
the morning instead of hiding in bed like a pair of sloths."

It was true: the creatures were long-tailed monkeys, eating leaves.
How could such a howling come from a thing so honestly ordinary?
But it did. The boy crept outdoors early and learned to spot them,
high in the veil of branches against white sky. Hunched, woolly bodies balanced on swaying limbs, their tails reaching out to stroke the
branches like guitar strings. Sometimes the mother monkeys cradled
little babes, born to precarious altitudes, clinging for their lives.

So there weren't any tree demons. And Enrique was not really a
wicked king, he was only a man. He looked like the tiny man on top

of a wedding cake: the same round head with parted, shiny hair, the same small moustache. But the boy's mother was not the tiny bride, and of course there is no place on that cake for a child.

When Enrique wanted to ridicule him after that, he didn't even need to mention devils, he only rolled his eyes up at the trees. "The devil here is a boy with too much imagination," he usually said. That was like a mathematics problem, it gave the boy a headache because he couldn't work out which was the wrong part of the equation: being a Boy, or being Imaginative. Enrique felt a successful man needed no imagination at all.

Here is another way to begin the story, and this one is also true.

The rule of fishes is the same as the rule of people: if the shark comes, they will all escape, and leave you to be eaten. They share a single jumpy heart that drives them to move all together, running away from danger just before it arrives. Somehow they know.

Underneath the ocean is a world without people. The sea-roof rocks overhead as you drift among the purple trees of the coral forest, surrounded by a heavenly body of light made of shining fishes. The sun comes down through the water like flaming arrows, touching the scaly bodies and setting every fin to flame. A thousand fishes make the school, but they always move together: one great, bright, brittle altogetherness.

It's a perfect world down there, except for the one of them who can't breathe water. He holds his nose, dangling from the silver ceiling like a great ugly puppet. Little hairs cover his arms like grass. He is pale, lit up by watery light on prickled boy skin, not the scaled slick silver merman he wants to be. The fish dart all around him and he feels lonely. He knows it is stupid to feel lonely because he isn't a fish, but he does. And yet he stays there anyway, trapped in the below-life, wishing he could dwell in their city with that bright, liquid life flowing all around him. The glittering school pulls in at one side and pushes out the other, a crowd of specks moving in and out like one great breathing creature. When a shadow comes along, the mass of fish darts instantly to its own center, imploding into a dense, safe core, and leaving the boy outside.

How can they know to save themselves, and leave him to be eaten? They have their own God, a puppet master who rules their one-fish mind, holding a thread attached to every heart in their crowded world. All the hearts but one.

The boy discovered the world of the fishes after Leandro gave him a diving goggle. Leandro, the cook, took pity on the flutie boy from America who had nothing to do all day but poke around in the cliffs along the beach, pretending to hunt for something. The goggle had glass lenses, and was made with gum rubber and most of the parts of an airman's goggle. Leandro said his brother used it when he was alive. He showed how to spit in it before putting it on, so it wouldn't go foggy.

"*Andele.* Go on now, get in the water," he said. "You will be surprised."

The pale-skinned boy stood shivering in water up to his waist, thinking these were the most awful words in any language: *You will be surprised*. The moment when everything is about to change. When Mother was leaving Father (loudly, glasses crashing against the wall), taking the child to Mexico, and nothing to do but stand in the corridor of the cold little house, waiting to be told. The exchanges were never good: taking a train, a father and then no father. Don Enrique from the consulate in Washington, then Enrique in Mother's bedroom. Everything changes *now*, while you stand shivering in the corridor waiting to slip through one world into the next.

And now, at the end of everything, this: standing waist-deep in the ocean wearing the diving goggle, with Leandro watching. A pack of village boys had come along too, their dark arms swinging, carrying the long knives they used for collecting oysters. White sand caked the sides of their feet like pale moccasins. They stopped to watch, all the swinging arms stopped, frozen in place, waiting. There was nothing left for him to do but take a breath and dive into that blue place.

And *oh God* there it was, the promise delivered, a world. Fishes mad with color, striped and dotted, golden bodies, blue heads. Societies of fish, a public, suspended in its watery world, poking pointed noses into coral. They pecked at the pair of hairy tree trunks, his legs, these edifices that were nothing to them but more landscape. The boy got a bit of a stiffy, he was that afraid, and that happy. No more empty-headed bobbing in the sea, after this. No more believing in an ocean with nothing inside but blue water.

He refused to come out of the sea all day, until the colors began to go dark. Luckily his mother and Enrique had enough to drink, sitting on the terrace with the men from America turning the air blue with their cigars, discussing the assassination of Obregón, wondering who would now stop the land reforms before the *indios* took everything. If not for so much mezcal and lime, his mother might have grown bored with the man-talk, and thought to wonder whether her son had drowned.

It was only Leandro who wondered. The next morning when the boy walked out to the kitchen pavilion to watch breakfast cooking, Leandro said, "*Pícaro*, you'll pay. A man has to pay for every crime." Leandro had worried all afternoon that the goggle he brought to this house had become an instrument of death. The punishment was waking up with a sun-broilt spot the size of a tortilla, hot as fire. When the criminal pulled up his nightshirt to show the seared skin on his back, Leandro laughed. He was brown as coconuts, and hadn't thought of sun burn. But for once he didn't say *usted pagará*, in the formal language of servants to masters. He said *tú pagarás*, you will pay, in the language of friends.

The criminal was unrepentant: "You gave me the goggle, so it's your fault." And went back into the sea again for most of that day, and burnt his back as crisp as fat rinds in a kettle. Leandro had to rub lard on it that night, saying "*Pícaro*, rascal boy, why do you do such stupid things?" *No seas malo*, he said, the familiar "you," language of friends, or lovers, or adults to children. There is no knowing which.

On Saturday night before Holy Week, Salomé wanted to go into town to hear the music. Her son would have to go too, as she needed an elbow to hang upon while walking around the square. She preferred to call him by his middle name, William or just Will, conditioned as that is on future events: You *will*. Though on her tongue of course it sounded like *wheel*, a thing that serves, but only when in motion. Salomé Huerta was her name. She had run away at a young age to become an American Sally, and then Sally Shepherd for a while, but nothing ever lasted long. American Sally was finished.

This was the year of Salomé pouting, her last one in the hacienda on Isla Pixol, though no one knew it yet. That day she had pouted because Enrique had no intention of walking around with her on the zocalo, just to show off a frock. He had too much work to do. Work meant sitting in his library running both hands through his slick hair, drinking mezcal, and sweating through his collar while working out colonnades of numbers. By this means he learned whether he had money up to his moustache this week, or only up to his bollocks.

Salomé put on the new frock, painted a bow on her mouth, took her son by the arm and walked to town. They smelled the zocalo first: roasted vanilla beans, coconut milk candies, boiled coffee. The square was packed with couples walking entwined, their arms snaking around one another like the vines that strangle tree trunks. The girls wore striped wool skirts, lace blouses, and their narrow-waisted boyfriends. The mood of the fiesta was enclosed in a perfect square: four long lines of electric bulbs strung from posts at the corners, fencing out a bright piece of night just above everyone's heads.

Lit from below, the hotel and other buildings around the square had eyebrow-shaped shadows above their iron balconies. The little cathedral looked taller than it was, and menacing, like a person who comes into the bedroom carrying a candle. The musicians stood in the little round belvedere whose pointed roof and wrought-iron railings were all freshly painted white along with everything else, including the giant old fig trees around the square. Their trunks blazed in the darkness, but only up to a certain point, as if a recent flood of whitewash through town had left a high-water mark.

Salomé seemed happy to float with the moving river of people around the square, even though in her elegant lizard-skin shoes and flapper crepe that showed her legs, she looked like no other person there. The crowd parted for her. Probably it pleased her to be the green-eyed Spaniard among the Indians, or rather, the *Criolla*: Mexican-born but pure nonetheless, with no Indian blood mixed in. Her blue-eyed, half-American son was less pleased with his position, a tall weed growing among the broad-faced townspeople. They would have made a good illustration for a book showing the Castes of the Nation, as the schoolbooks did in those days.

"Next year," Salomé said in English, pinching his elbow with her fierce crab claws of love, "you'll be here with your own girl. This is the last *Noche Palmas* you'll want to walk around here with your old wrinkle." She liked using American slang, especially in crowds. "This is posalutely the berries," she would announce, putting the two of them inside an invisible room with her words, and closing the door.

"I won't have a girlfriend."

"You'll turn fourteen next year. You're already taller than President Portes Gil. Why wouldn't you have a girlfriend?"

"Portes Gil isn't even a real president. He only got in because Obregón was iced."

"And maybe you will likewise ascend to power, after some girl's first *novio* gets the sack. Doesn't matter how you get the job, ducky. She'll still be yours."

"Next year you could have this whole town, if you want it."

"But you'll have a girl. This is all I'm saying. You'll go off and leave me alone." It was a game she played. Very hard to win.

"Or if you don't like it here, Mother, you could go somewhere else. Some smart city where people have better entertainments than walking in circles around the *zocalo*."

"And," she persisted, "you'd still have the girl." Not just a girl but *the* girl, already an enemy.

"What do you care? You have Enrique."

"You make him sound like a case of the pox."

In front of the wrought-iron bandstand, the crowd had cleared a space for dancing. Old men in sandals held stiff arms around their barrel-shaped wives.

"Next year, Mother, no matter what, you won't be old."

She rested her head against his shoulder as they walked. He had won.

Salomé hated that her son was now taller than she was: the first time she noticed, she was furious, then morose. In her formula of life, this meant she was two-thirds dead. "The first part of life is childhood. The second is your child's childhood. And then the third, old age." Another mathematics problem with no practical solution, especially for the child. Growing backward, becoming unborn: that would have been just the thing.

They stopped to watch the mariachis on the platform, handsome men with puckered lips giving long kisses to their brass horns. Trails of silver buttons led down the sides of their tight black trousers. The *zocalo* was jammed now; men and women kept arriving from the pineapple fields with the day's dust still on their feet, shuffling out of the darkness into the square of electric light. In front of the flat stone breast of the church, some of them settled in little encampments on the bare earth, spreading blankets where a mother and father could sit with their backs against the cool stones while babies slept rolled in a pile. These were the vendors who walked here for Holy Week, each woman wearing the particular dress of her village. The ones from the south wore strange skirts like heavy blankets wrapped in pleats, and delicate blouses of ribbon and embroidery. They wore these tonight and on Easter and every other day, whether attending a marriage or feeding pigs.

They had come here carrying bundles of palm leaves and now sat untying them, pulling apart the fronds. All night their hands would move in darkness to weave the straps of leaf into unexpected shapes of resurrection: crosses, garlands of lilies, doves of the Holy Spirit, even Christ himself. These things had to be made by hand in one night, for the forbidden Palm Sunday mass, and burned afterward, because icons were illegal. Priests were illegal, saying the mass was illegal, all banned by the Revolution.

Earlier in the year the *Cristeros* had ridden into town wearing bullets strapped in rows like jewelry across their chests, galloping around the square to protest the law banning priests. The girls cheered and threw flowers as if Pancho Villa himself had risen from the grave and located his horse. Old women rocked on their knees, eyes closed, hugging their crosses and kissing them like babies. Tomorrow these villagers would carry their secret icons into the church without any priest and light the candles themselves, moving together in single-minded grace. Like the school of the fish, so driven to righteousness they could flout the law, declare the safety of their souls, then go home and destroy the evidence.

It was late now, the married couples had begun to surrender dancing space to a younger group: girls with red yarn braided into their hair and wound around their heads into thick crowns. Their white dresses swirled like froth, with skirts so wide they could take the hems in their fingertips and raise them up to make sudden wings, like butterflies, fluttering as they turned. The men's high-heeled boots cut hard at the ground, drumming like penned stallions. When the music paused, they leaned across their partners in the manner of animals preparing to mate. Move away, come back, the girls waggled their shoulders. The men put handkerchiefs under their arms, then waved them beneath the girls' chins.

Salomé decided she wanted to go home immediately.

"We would have to walk, Mother. Natividad won't come for us until eleven, because that's what you told him."

"Then we'll walk," she said.

"Just wait another half hour. Otherwise we'll be walking in the dark. Bandits might murder us."

"Nobody will murder us. The bandits are all in the *zocalo* trying to steal purses." Salomé was practical, even as a hysteric.

"You hate to walk."

"What I hate is watching these primitives showing off. A she-goat in a dress is still a she-goat."

Darkness fell down on everything then, like a curtain. Someone must have shut off the lights. The crowd breathed out. The butterfly girls had set glasses with lighted candles onto their braid-crowned heads. As they danced, their candles floated across an invisible surface like reflections of the moon across a lake.

Salomé was so determined to walk home, she had already started in the wrong direction. It wasn't easy to overtake her. "Indian girls," she spat. "What kind of man would chase after that? A corn-eater will never be any more than she is."

The dancers were butterflies. From a hundred paces Salomé could see the dirt under these girls' fingernails, but not their wings.

Enrique was confident the oil men would come to an agreement. But it could take some time. The oil men had come to Isla Pixol with their wives; they all took rooms in town. Enrique tried to persuade them to stay at the hacienda, since the advantages of his hospitality might work in his favor in the negotiations. "That hotel was built before the flood of Noah. Have you seen the elevator? A birdcage hanging from a watch chain. And the rooms are smaller than a cigar tin."

Salomé shot her eyes at him: How would he know that?

The wives wore bobbed hair and smart frocks, but all had entered the third of what Salomé called the Three Portions of Life. Possibly, they'd entered the fourth. After dinner, while the men smoked Tuxtlan cigars in the library, the women stood outside in point-heeled shoes on the tiled terrace with their little hats pinned against the wind and cheek-curls plastered down. Holding glasses of *vino tinto*, they gazed across the bay, speculating about the silence under the sea. "Seaweeds swaying like palm trees," they all agreed, "quiet as the grave."

The boy who sat on the low wall at the edge of the *terraza* thought: These budgies would be disappointed to know, it's noisy as anything down there. Strange, but not quiet. Like one of the mysterious worlds in Jules Verne's books, filled with its own kinds of things, paying no attention to ours. Often he shook the bubbles from his ears and just listened, drifting along, attending the infinite chorus of tiny clicks and squeaks. Watching one fish at a time as it poked its own way around the coral, he could see it was talking to the others. Or at any rate, making noises at them.

"What is the difference," he asked Leandro the next day, "between talking and making a noise?"

Salomé hadn't yet learned Leandro's name, she called him "the new kitchen boy." The last *galopina* was a pretty girl, Ofelia, too much admired by Enrique, given the sack by Salomé. Leandro took up more space, standing with bare feet set apart, steady as the stuccoed pillars supporting the tile roofs above the walkways of this yellow-ochre house. A row of lime trees in large terra-cotta pots lined the breezeway between the house and kitchen pavilion. And like a tree, Leandro was planted there for most of each day, cutting up chayotes with his machete on the big work table. Or peeling shrimps, or making *sopa de milpa*: corn kernel soup with diced squash blossom and avocado. *Xochitl* soup, with chicken and vegetables in broth. Salads of cactus nopales with avocado and cilantro. The rice he made with a hint of something sweet in it.

Every day he said, *You could pick up that knife and stop being a nuisance.* But smiling, not the way Salomé said "nuisance." Not the way she said, "If you come in here with those sandy feet your name is mud."

Regarding the difference between talk and noise, Leandro said, "*Ca depende.*"

"Depends on what?"

"On intention. Whether he wants another fish to understand his meaning." Leandro considered his pile of shrimps solemnly, as if they might have had a last wish prior to execution. "If the fish only wants to show he is there, it's a noise. But maybe the fish-clicks are saying 'Go away,' or 'My food, not yours.'"

"Or, 'Your name is mud.'"

Leandro laughed, because in Spanish it sounds funny: *Su nombre es lodo.*

"*Exacto*," Leandro said.

"Then to another fish, it's talk," the boy said. "But to me it's only noise."

Leandro needed help—too many mouths to feed in this house, the Americans liked to eat. Also it was Salomé's birthday, and she wanted squid. The oil men's wives' eyes would swing like the pendulum of a clock beneath their cloche hats when they saw squid *a la Veracruzana.* But the men would eat tentacles without noticing, enthralled with their own stories. How their hired guns had put down the rebellion in Sonora and sent Escobar running like a dog. The more mezcal went into their glasses, the faster Escobar ran.

After supper Leandro said *El flojo trabaja doble*, the lazy man has to work double, because the boy tried to carry all the dishes to the kitchen at once. He dropped two white plates on the tile, shattering them all to buttons. So Leandro was right—sweeping up took twice as long as making an extra trip. But Leandro came out and helped pick up the mess, kneeling beneath the Americans' gaze as they commiserated on the clumsiness of servants, here is one thing that's the same in every country.

Afterward Salomé tried to get them all to cut a rug. She cranked up the Victrola and waved the mezcal bottle at the men, but they went to bed, leaving her fluttering around the parlor like a balloon of air, let go. It was her birthday, and not even her son to whom she had given life would cut a rug with her. "For God's sake, William, you're tedious," she diagnosed. Nose in the books, you're nothing but a canceled stamp. *Flutie, green apples, wet blanket*, this is only a small sample of the names that came to mind when Salomé was stewed to the hat. He did try to dance with her after that, but it was too late. She couldn't hold herself up on her own stilts.

Salomé is airtight, the men liked to say. Copacetic, the cat's meow, a snake charmer. Also a fire bell. One of the oil men said that to his wife, when the others were outside. Explaining the situation. *Fire bell* meant still married, to the husband in America. After all this time not divorced, some poor sod in D.C., an administration accountant. She had the affair right under his nose with this Mexican attaché, she couldn't have been more than twenty-five at the time, and with that child already. Left the other fellow flat. Be careful of this fancy Salomé, he warned his wife. She's a disappearing act.

On *Cinco de Mayo* the village celebrated with fireworks, commemorating the victory over Napoleon's invasion in the battle at Puebla. Salomé had a headache, one last gift from the night before, and spent the day in her little bedchamber at the end of the hall. She called it Elba, her place of exile. Lately Enrique had been retiring early and closing the heavy door to his own bedroom. Today she was in no mood for noise. Today, she complained, they were making more explosions in the campo than it probably took to scare off Napoleon's army in the first place.

The boy did not walk into town for the celebration. He knew that in the long run Napoleon's generals still came back and cuffed Santa Ana, and took over Mexico long enough to make everyone speak French and wear tight pants until 1867, or something near it. He was supposed to finish the book on Emperor Maximiliano, from Enrique's library. That was Salomé's program for him, Reading Moldy Books, because there was no school in Isla Pixol suitable for a boy who was already taller than President Portes Gil. But the best place for reading was in the forest, not the house. Under a tree by the estuary, twenty minutes' walk down the trail. And the book on Maximiliano was enormous. So it only made sense to carry *The Mysterious Affair at Styles* instead.

The biggest *amate* tree had buttresses like sails reaching out from the trunk, dividing out little rooms furnished with drapes of fern and patchouli. A rooming house for dragonflies and ant thrushes, and once, a coiled little snake. Many trees in that jungle were as broad around their bases as the huts in Leandro's village, and held their branches too high to see. There was no knowing what lived up there. Once the saucer-eyed devils had howled for blood, but maybe those branches were only the balconies of monkey hotels, and nesting places for *oropéndola* birds, whose gurgling song sounded like water bubbling out of a tin canteen.

In Enrique's library, every wall was covered with wooden cabinets. The room had no windows, only shelves, and all the book cabinets had iron grilles covering their fronts like prisoners' windows, locked over shelves packed with books. The square openings between the welded bars were just large enough for a fine-boned, long-fingered boy to put his hand through, like slipping on an iron bracelet. He could reach in and touch the books' spines, exactly as Count Dantès in *The Count of Monte Cristo* had reached through the bars to touch his bride's face, when she came to see him in prison. Carefully he could slide one book from its place in the packed shelf, and with both hands put through the bars he could turn and examine it, sometimes even open it, if the shelf were deep enough. But not remove it. The grilles had iron padlocks.

Every Sunday Enrique brought out the skeleton key, unlocked the case, and took out four books exactly, which he left in a pile on the table without discussion. Invariably historical, stinking of mold, these were to be a boy's education. A few were all right, *Zozobra*, and also *Romancero Gitano*, poems by a young man who loved gypsies. Cervantes held promise, but had to be puzzled out in some ancient kind of Spanish. One week only with Don Quixote, before turning him in to be locked up again and exchanged for a new week's pile, had felt like a peek through a keyhole.

And anyhow not a single one of those books could hold eight minutes to Agatha Christie or the others he'd brought from before, when they came here on the train. His mother had let him carry two valises: one for books, one for clothes. The clothes were a waste, outgrown instantly. He should have filled both with books. *The Mysterious Affair at Styles*, *The Count of Monte Cristo*, *Around the World in Eighty Days*, *Twenty Thousand Leagues Under the Sea*, books in English that didn't stink of mold. He'd already read most of them now, more than once. The Three Musketeers still called out to him, waving their swords, but he always shoved them back in the valise. Because what would be left, when all these books were in the past? He lay awake nights dreading it.

The program of a real school was vague in Salomé's convictions, and frankly in his own: dank memories of wool coats and rough boys, and *sport*, a terrible thing, daily enforced. One lady in a brown sweater used to give him books to keep, that was the best thing he recalled from home. But that is not what we call home now, Salomé said, "We're here and there isn't a school so you'll just have to read every book in that damned library, if we're allowed to stay." If not, her program became less certain.

The library often stank, from the oil men in there smoking Tuxtlan cigars all night. Salomé hated all of it: cigars, men talking. Also locked-up books, or any other kind it seemed, and flutie boys who read them too much. But even so, she bought him a notebook from the shop by the ferry docks, on the day they'd tried to run away from Enrique and cried because of having absolutely nowhere to go. She sat limp on the iron bench in her silk-crepe dress, shoulders shaking, for such a long time he'd had to wander over to the window of the tobacco stand and leaf through magazines. There he'd found the pasteboard notebook: the most beautiful book ever, it could become anything.

She came up behind him while he was looking at it. Set her chin on top of his shoulder, wiped her cheek with the back of a hand, and said, "We'll take it, then." The man wrapped it carefully in brown paper, tied with a string.

That was the story she had wanted him to begin, to tell what happened in Mexico before the howlers swallowed them down without a trace. Later on, many times, she would change her mind and tell him to stop writing. It made her nervous.

At the end of that day, after running away, buying a notebook, and eating boiled shrimps from a paper cone while standing on the pier watching ferries leave, they'd gone back to Enrique, of course. They were prisoners on an island, like the Count of Monte Cristo. The hacienda had heavy doors and thick walls that stayed cool all day, and windows that let in the sound of the sea all night: *hush, hush*, like a heartbeat. He would grow thin as bones here, and when the books were all finished, he would starve.

But no, now he would not. The notebook from the tobacco stand was the beginning of hope: a prisoner's plan for escape. Its empty pages would be the book of everything, miraculous and unending like the sea at night, a heartbeat that never stops.

Salomé for her part was not worried about running out of books, only of having her clothes go out of fashion. *You can't buy a thing on this island. Unless he wants me to be a she-goat, wear skirts down to the ground.* A trunk with her nicest things had been mailed overland from Washington, D.C., last year, according to the lawyer who was supposed to be taking care of these matters. But both the trunk and the divorce seemed to have lost their way. Enrique said they might see that trunk one day, *ojalá*, if the Lord is willing. Meaning if the Lord is not, the Zapatistas held up the train and took everything. The boy cried, "Oh yes, imagine it! The Zapatistas in their gun belts, reading Miss Agatha Christie by the campfire. Eating off Mother's Limoges and wearing her dressing gowns."

Enrique pinched his moustache and said, "*Imagine it!* Too bad you can't sell daydreams like that for money."

"Revolution in Mexico is a fashion," he announced to the oil men at supper on their last night. "Like the silly hats worn by our wives. I don't care what they told you in Washington, this country will work hard for the foreign dollar." He raised his glass. "The heart of Mexico is like that of a loyal woman, married forever to Porfirio Díaz."

The deal was made, the oil men went away. The next morning Enrique let Salomé sit on his lap at breakfast and give him a kiss like a trumpet player. A sign of progress, she declared, after he'd gone out to inspect a new packing house. "Did you hear him say that, hats worn by *our wives?*" Her first project now was to get herself moved back into his bedroom. Her second one was to fire his maid.

The boy's best plan on any day was to make himself scarce. Walk out the back through the kitchen, down a long lane of *mulata* trees with red skin peeling away from their trunks, exposing smooth black skin underneath. Cut across the sand trail through the pineapple field, over the low rock wall out to the sea, carrying a rucksack with a book and a packet of tortillas for lunch, the diving goggle and a bathing costume. No one would see but Leandro, whose eyes following him down the sand trail could make him feel naked when he was not. Leandro, who came barefoot up the lane every morning carrying the smoky smell of breakfast fires from his village, but wearing a clean shirt laundered by his wife. Salomé said Leandro already had a wife, a child, and a baby. As young as he is, she clucked, happy that someone had wrecked his life even faster than she had wrecked hers. If Leandro was already in the Second Portion of Life (the part with children), it was going to be short.

Out on the reef, the fish came every day for the scraps of tortilla the boy brought from the kitchen and tore into pieces, casting his bread upon the waters. One fish had a mouth like a parrot's beak and a fire-red belly, and was always the first in line to come banging up for the day's handout. So really it wasn't a friend. It was like the men who came to visit for the free eats and their eyes full of Salomé in a V-neck satin dress.

Salomé formulated her plan of attack. First, she instructed Leandro, we make only Enrique's favorite foods every day. Starting with break-fast: cinnamon-flavored coffee, tortillas warm from the griddle, pine-apple with ham, and what she called Divorced Eggs, two of them crowded onto a plate, one with mild red salsa and one with spicy green. Salomé maintained her own perspective on romance.

The kitchen was connected to the house by the passageway of lime trees. It had low brick walls, planks for work counters, and was open all around to the sea air so smoke could escape from the firebox of the brick stove. Posts in the corners held up the roof, and the brick bread oven hunched in one corner. Natividad, the oldest servant, who was nearly blind, came out every dawn to sweep out the firebox and light it again, feeling his way to the flame, laying the sticks side by side like tucking children to bed.

When Leandro came he would push the fire to the sides, keeping the heat away from the center of the heavy iron griddle. He mopped the griddle with a rag dipped in the lard jar so the tortillas wouldn't stick. Next to the lard jar he kept a big bowl of sticky corn dough, pinching up balls of it and pressing them flat by hand. The heat made a necklace of black pearls on each white tortilla as it cooked. In the thick ones, the *gorditas,* he cut ridges as they cooked, for holding the bean paste. But for empanadas he made them thin, folding the torti-lla over the filling and sliding it into a pan of hot grease.

Most of all, Enrique cared for *pan dulces* made with wheat-flour dough. Puffy and soft with a grit of coarse sugar on top, filled with pineapple, sweet and tart from the oven's wood smoke. Many a cook had been fired by Enrique, before this Leandro arrived from heaven. *Pan dulce* is no easy trick. The vanilla has to be from Papantla. The flour is ground in a stone metate. Not like masa for tortillas, corn soaked in lime water that's ground up coarse and wet. Any Mexican can do that, Leandro said. Dry flour for European bread is a different matter. It has to be ground so fine it comes up into the air in clouds. The hard part was mixing in the water, going too fast. Dumping water on the flour in a cold gush, causing a catastrophe of lumps.

"*Dios mio*, what have you done there?"

The boy's excuse: the bucket was too heavy.

"*Flojo*, you're as tall as I am, you can lift the bucket."

The dough had to be thrown away, and everything started over. Leandro from heaven, angel of patience, paused to rinse his hands in the wash bucket and dry them on his white trousers. Let me show you how to do this. Begin with two kilos of the flour. Make a moun-tain on the counter. Into this mound, with your fingers, crumble the flakes of butter, the salt and soda. Then pull it out like a ring of vol-canic mountains around a crater. Pour a lake of cold water in the cen-ter. Little by little, pull the mountains into the lake, water and shore together, into a marsh. Gradually. No islands. The paste swells until there are no mountains left, and no lake, only a great blob of lava.

"There. Not just any Mexican can do that, *muchacho*."

Leandro flopped the dough over gently on the counter until it was smooth, fluid and solid at the same time. It would sleep overnight in a covered bowl. In the morning he would roll it flat, cut it with a ma-chete into squares, spoon a dot of pineapple filling on each one, and fold it in a triangle, sprinkled with sugar grains soaked in vanilla. "Now you know the secret for making the boss happy," Leandro said. "Cooking in this house is like war. I am the *capitan* of bread and you are my *sergente mayor*. If he throws out your mother you might still have a job, if you can make *pan dulce* and *blandas*."

"Which are the *blandas*?"

"*Sergente*, you can't make this kind of mistake. *Blandas* are the big soft ones he's crazy for. Tortillas big enough to wrap a baby in, soft as an angel's wings."

"*Si, señor!*" The tall boy saluted. "Big enough to wrap angels in, soft as a baby's crupper."

Leandro laughed. "*Small* angels," he said. "Only baby ones."

On the twenty-first of June, 1929, a giant iguana climbed up the mango by the patio, causing Salomé to stand up from her lunch and scream. And on that day the Three Years Silence ended, though the iguana had nothing to do with it.

It was a declaration signed by the president, ending the three-year ban on saying the mass. The war with the Cristeros ended. The church bells rang all day on Sunday, calling back the priests with their gold rings, landholdings, and sovereignty intact. Enrique took it as proof: Mexico falls on her knees at the altar, ready to return to the days of Porfirio Díaz. True Mexicans will always understand the virtues of humility, piety, and patriotism. "And decent women," he added pointedly to Salomé, quoting Díaz: "Only in her home, like a butterfly in a glass jar, can woman progress to her highest level of decency." He expected her to take herself and her son to town for the Reconciliation Mass.

"If he wants a butterfly, he should let me stay home in his damn glass jar," she fumed in the carriage on the way to church. Salomé was all for the Three Years Silence. In her opinion the mass could only be more tedious if they made you wear cotton stockings. She too had lived under the reign of Porfirio, ruled by a dark supremacy of nuns who showed no mercy to a businessman's cheeky daughter who came to school with her ankles showing. Salomé had maneuvered a miraculous escape, like the Count of Monte Cristo: a study tour in America, where she enlisted a claims accountant in her father's firm who was helpless before her charms. She'd solved the mathematical problem of age sixteen by saying she was twenty. At twenty-four she'd said the same thing again, balancing the equation. She became Sally, confirmed in the church of expediency. Even now, as they approached the cathedral in town, she rolled her eyes and said, "Opium of the masses," parroting the men in government who'd tried to rout the priests. But she didn't say it in Spanish, for the driver to hear.

The cathedral was packed with solemn children, farmers, and old women on tree-trunk legs. Some worked their way through the Stations of the Cross, orbiting around the crowd's periphery as deliberately as planets. A long line of townspeople waited to receive communion, but Salomé walked to the head of the line, accepting the host on her tongue as if this were a bakery line and she had plenty of other errands.

The priest wore gold brocades and a pointed hat. He had managed to keep his clothes very nice, during his three years hiding out. All eyes followed him like plants facing light, except for those of Salomé. She left as soon as possible and walked straight for the carriage, snapping at Natividad to get going, fiercely digging in her beaded bag for her aspirins. Everything about Salomé came from a jar or a bottle: first, the powder and perfume, the pomade for her marcel wave. Next, the headache, from a bottle of mezcal. Then the cure, from a bottle of Bellans Hot-Water-Relief. Maybe some other bottle gave her the flapper-dancing, crank-up-the-Victrola Twenty-Three Skidoo. Stashed under a table drape in her room, something to help her keep it up.

If Enrique didn't love her, she now announced in the carriage, it was not her fault. She didn't see how God was going to help any of this. Enrique's mother didn't approve of a divorcée, so that was one person to blame. And the servants, who did everything wrong. She would like to blame Leandro but couldn't. The white-flour dough he made for the pastries was perfect, as silky as Salomé's white dress that could be poured out of a pitcher, in which she still hoped to be married one more time.

The problem must be this long-legged son, bouncing with the bumps in the road, brushing hair out of his eyes, staring off at the ocean. No place on the top of the wedding cake for a boy already as tall as the president, who was not, himself, elected.

To get to the oil fields in the Huasteca, Enrique had to take the ferry to shore, then the *panga* to Veracruz, then the train. If he had to be gone one day, he'd be gone a week, or better yet a month. Salomé wanted to go with him to Veracruz, but he said she would only want to buy things. Instead, he allowed them to come in the carriage to the pier in town, to watch him leave on the ferry. In the flattering morning light she waved her handkerchief from the dock, elbowing the son to wave as well. They both had roles in the play called *Enrique Makes Up His Mind*. "Pretty soon he'll say the word, and then we can let our hair down, kiddo. Then we'll think what to do about you." Enrique had mentioned a boarding school in the Distrito Federal.

The pasteboard notebook was running out of pages, the book called *What Happened to Us in Mexico*. He asked to purchase a new one at the tobacco stand. But Salomé said, "First we'll have to see if there's more to the story."

When the ferry was gone, they ate lunch on the *malecón* across from the shrimp jetty, watching seabirds wheel in circles trying to steal food. Out on the water, men in small wooden boats pulled in their nets, crumpling up mounds of gray netting that rose like storm clouds from each hull. By late morning the trawlers were already docked with their rusted hulls all listing the same direction along the dock, double masts leaning like married couples, equally drunken. The air smelled of fish and salt. The palm trees waved their arms wildly in the sea wind, a gesture of desperation ignored by all. The boy said, "There is always more to the story. This lunch will be the next part." But Salomé said what she always said now: *You need to stop doing that, put the book away. It makes me nervous.*

On the way home she directed the driver to stop at a little village near the lagoon. "Drop us off here and come back at six, never mind for what," she said. The horse knew how to go everywhere, and it was a good thing, because old Natividad was nearly blind. That was a good thing also, as far as Salomé was concerned. She wanted no witnesses.

The village was too small even to have a market, only an immense stone head in the town square, left over from a century when the Indians had huge ambitions. Salomé stepped down from the coach and strode past the great head with the beard of grass under its chin. At the end of the lane she said, "It's this way, come on," and turned up a path into the forest, walking fast in her sling-back shoes, her lips pursed, chin tilted down so the marcel wave hung forward like a closed curtain. They came to a plank footbridge suspended on ropes over a ravine. Slipping off the pointed white shoes and dangling them from a hooked finger, she stepped out in her stockings onto the bridge over crashing water, then paused to look back. "Don't come," she said. "You should wait here."

She was gone hours. He sat at the end of the plank bridge with his notebook on his lap. An enormous spider with a fire-red belly came along lifting one foot at a time, slowly pulling its entire body into a tiny hole in one of the planks. What a terrible thing to know: every small hole could have something like that inside. A flock of parrots shuffled in the leaves. A toucan looked down its long nose, shrieking: *a mi, a mi!* Squatting by the chasm, he believed again in the tree-devils. And so at dusk, howling, they arrived.

When Salomé returned, she took off her shoes again to cross the bridge, put them back on, and strode toward the village. Natividad was already waiting, a stone head himself, letting the horse graze. She climbed in the carriage and never spoke at all.

❈

It was a form of revenge to steal the pocket watch. Something he could keep from his mother, for refusing to tell why she'd gone into the jungle. He did it on the day the tailor rode out from town, eager for Salomé's opinion about fabrics for Enrique's new suit. Enrique was away. It was only good manners for the tailor to take a glass of *chinguirito* with Salomé, and then another one. There was plenty of time for a boy to creep into her room to look at the Father Box. It was covered with dust, shoved underneath the cabinet where she kept her toilet pot. She hated the man that much.

No use crying over a spilt father, she always said. Only once had she let him look at the things in this box: a photograph of a man who had been his father somehow. A bunch of old coins, fobs, jeweled cuff links, and the pocket watch. He craved the watch. That first time, when she'd let him sit on the floor and touch everything in the box while she lay on her bed, propped on one elbow watching him, he'd dangled it on its chain in front of her eyes, making it swing, like a hypnotist: *You are getting very sleepy.*

She said, *"El tiempo cura y nos mata."* Time cures you first, and then it kills you.

Strictly speaking, these things are yours, she'd told him. But strictly speaking they were not even hers, she'd scooped them up in a hurry without asking, when she left and ran off to Mexico. "In case we needed something to sell later on, if we fell on hard times." If they fell on something harder than Enrique, she must have meant.

Now the watch she'd stolen was stolen again: a double-cross. He'd crept in her room and taken it while she was in the parlor laughing at the tailor's jokes, lolling her head back on the silk sofa. Among all the treasures in the box, he'd only needed that one. The time that cures you first, and later stops everything that's happening in your heart.

The blue fog of Tuxtlan cigars came out of the library and filled the whole house. Two Americans had come back with Enrique this time, to fumigate the southern shores of Mexico with their smoke and endless talk: the election campaign, Ortíz Rubio, that disaster Vasconcelos. Gringos always made Enrique nervous, and Salomé excited. She poured cognac in their glasses and let them see her chest when she leaned over. One looked, the other never did. Both were said to have wives. At midnight they went out for a walk on the beach, in their fedoras and leather shoes. Salomé collapsed in a chair, all the flapper draining out of her.

"You should go to bed," she announced.

"I'm not a child. *You* should go to bed."

"No bunk, mister. If he gets any more cross, we'll both be hoofing it out of here."

"Where would we go? Hoofs can't walk on water."

One of the men was Mr. Morrow, the ambassador, and the other was an oil man like Enrique. According to Salomé, that second one was high-hatty, but she could make him produce the cash if she wanted to. "He's richer than God," she said.

"Then he must have sunrise in his pocket. And mercy in his shoes."

She stared. "Is that from one of your books?"

"Not completely."

"What do you mean, not completely?"

"I don't know. It sounds like it would be in *Romancero Gitano*. But it isn't."

Her eyes grew wide. She had put her hair in a shellacked wave, hours ago, but now it was coming apart, the short curls across her forehead coming loose from the rest. She looked like a girl who had just come in from playing.

"You made that up, sunrise in his pocket and mercy in his shoes. It's a poem." Her eyes clear as water, the points of her hair just touching her brows. The candlelight found long, narrow lines of satin in the cloth of her dress, a pattern that would never show up in ordinary daylight. He wondered how it would be to have a mother, really. A lovely, surprised woman like this, who looked at you. At least once, every day.

"You do need another book, don't you? To write down your poems."

But already he was on the last page. The scene of his mother in the candlelight filled most of it, and the ending wasn't good. When the men came back, they cranked up the Victrola, and the one called "I Could Make Him Produce the Cash" tried to dance the Charleston with Salomé, but his shoes had no mercy in them at all. You could tell they pinched his feet.

ARCHIVIST'S NOTE

These pages record the early life of Harrison William Shepherd, a citizen of the United States born in 1916 (Lychgate, Virginia), taken by his mother to Mexico at a young age. The words are those of H. W. Shepherd, vouchsafed. But the pages preceding are plainly not from the hand of a boy. He came to his powers early, that is well known and many have remarked on it, but not so young as thirteen. He did acquire a notebook that year for making a journal, a habit kept on through life. The endeavor of it has passed unexpectedly from the author to myself, and all here collected.

In January 1947 he began a memoir that was to be made of the early diaries. The pages here previous came to me from his hand, to be typed and filed as "Chapter One." I took it for a book's beginning. There was no call to doubt it, for he had written other books by then. He'd made what he could of that first pasteboard notebook mentioned, purchased on a dock in Isla Pixol, and probably disposed of it afterward. It was his habit, when he rewrote anything, to shed himself of all earlier versions. He kept a clean house.

A few months afterward, he left off all intention of writing his memoir. Many were the reasons. One that he gave was: the next little notebook in the line had gone missing, his second boyhood diary, and he became discouraged of recalling what it contained.

I believe he did remember a good deal of it, but I'll comment no further on it. He had concerns.

There is a peculiar thing to tell about that second diary. He said he couldn't find it, and that was a fact. It only came to light in 1954. It turned up in a trunk of his things that had been stored many years in the home of an acquaintance in Mexico City. They found it after her death caused the household to be shuffled around. The diary is leather-bound, smaller than a sandwich (approx. 3 x 5 in.), easy to overlook. It was inside a trouser pocket, wrapped in a handkerchief. So it was never kept with all his later diaries, lying there lost a long while. He never did lay eyes on it again. It had no name inside it, only a date and heading on the first page as will be shown. It was only by luck and a certain letter of instruction that the trunk was recognized as his, and sent here to me. He was of course by that time gone. Without its surprising resurrection, that missing piece of the tale, there would be none to tell. Yet here it is. The writing is his for certain, the hand, style, and heading. He wrote similar things at the start of his notebooks even when much older.

The difference in style, from the writer's memoir to the child's diary, the reader will shortly encounter. A man of thirty wrote the previous pages, a boy fourteen wrote the diary herein to follow. All the diaries after it show the normal progress of age. In all, he showed a habit that claimed him for life: his manner of scarcely mentioning himself. Anyone else would say in a diary, "I had this kind of a supper," but to his mind, if supper lay on the table it had reasons of its own. He wrote as if he'd been the one to carry the camera to each and every one of his life's events, and thus was unseen in all the pictures. Many were the reasons, again not mine to say.

The little leather-bound booklet lost and found, then, was a diary he kept from 1929 until summer of 1930, when he left Isla Pixol. That one was a toil to transcribe, the nuisance being its size: small. He penciled it in the empty portions of a household accounts book. It was evidently a common type of booklet they had in the 1920s, stolen from a housekeeper, he plainly states. He hadn't yet the strong habit of putting a date to his entries.

The third diary runs from June 1930 until November 12, 1931. He took more faith with dating the entries after enrolling in school. That one he kept in a hardbound tablet of a type used by schoolchildren of the time, purchased in a Mexico City bookshop.

The rest follow in order, many notebooks in all, an odd lot for shape and size but all one gloss within. No man ever set a greater store in words, his own or others. I have taken pains to do the same. His penmanship was fair to good, and I was no stranger to his hand. I believe these texts to be loyal and stanch to his, apart from some small favors to a boy's spelling and grammars. And small is the need, for a boy that took his lessons from *The Mysterious Affair at Styles* and so forth. I took some reliable help with translating the Spanish, which he used now and again, probably without full understanding of the difference when young. He spoke both languages as a routine. English with the mother, Spanish with most others until his return to the United States. But sometimes he twixed the two, and I've had to guess on some.

The common custom is to place a note such as this at a book's beginning. Instead, I let his own Chapter One stand to the fore. He plainly meant it to be the start of a book. I stand behind the man, with ample reason in this instance. I had good years to learn the wisdom of it. My small explanations here are meant to introduce the remainder. I have set upon the whole of it certain headings, for organizing purposes. These I marked with my initials. My only hope is to be of use.

—VB

Private journal Mexico North America

Do not read this. El delito acusa.

2 November, Dead People's Day

Leandro is at the cemetery to put flowers on his dead people: his mother and father, grandmothers, a baby son that died when it was one minute old, and his brother who died last year. Leandro said it's wrong to say you don't have a family. Even if they are dead, you still have them. That isn't nice to think about, ghost people standing in rows outside the windows, waiting to get acquainted.

Leandro, wife, and dead people are having their party at the grave-yard behind the rock beach on the other side. Tamales in banana leaves, *atole*, and *pollo pipian*. Leandro said those are the only foods that could attract his brother away from a lady. He meant Lady of the Dead, who is called Mictec-something—Leandro couldn't spell it. He can't read. He didn't cook the tamales this time. At his house, the wife is Captain of Tortillas, and the *sergentes* are his nieces. When he leaves here, he goes home to a mud thatch house and women who cook for him. Maybe he sits in a chair and complains about us. No one comes to take off his boots. None to take off.

All the maids went off also for *Día de los Muertos*, and Mother had to warm the *caldo* for lunch herself. She complained about Mexican servants running off for every excuse. In Washington, D.C., who ever heard of the kitchen help having to go throw marigolds on a grave? She says the *indios* have so many gods they have an excuse to stilt out of work every day of the year. *These Mexican girls.* But

Mother is one herself. A good thing to remind her, if you want a slap on the kisser.

This morning she said, *I am no mestizo, mister, and don't you forget it.* Don Enrique is proud of no *indios* mixed up in his blood, Pure Spanish only, so now Mother is proud of that too. But she has nothing to celebrate, because of no Indian gods. Not even the God of Pure Spaniards, she doesn't like him either. She said *chingado* when she burned her hand after the maids went to their party. *Pinche, malinche.* Mother is a museum of bad words.

Don Enrique brought back the accounts books from a shop in Veracruz so we can keep track of the truth around here. He told Mother, *Desconfía de tu mejor amigo como de tu peor enemigo.* Trust your loved ones as you trust your worst enemy. Write. Everything. Down. He slapped the little books on her dressing table, making her jump and the sleeves of her dressing gown tremble. He calls them Truth Books.

Here is the truth. One booklet was pinched by the household thief. Mother was finished with it anyway. She started, but then Cruz took over the job of writing down which days Mother pays them. Otherwise Mother says she paid but really didn't, because she was juiced. Don Enrique told Cruz to keep tabs whilst he is away in the Huasteca. He says money runs out of this house like blood from a wound.

7 November

Seventy-two seconds, longest time ever. If Mother could hold her breath that long she could be divorced. But that time does not really count, it is on land only. On a bed *cercado de tierra*, locked by land. Kneeling by the pillow with a pinched nose, holding the watch up to the candle to see the seconds. It's harder to go that long in the water, because of cold. One way is to breathe a lot first, very fast, then take in one large breath and hold it. Leandro says *in the name of God don't try that when you're diving, it's a good way to faint and drown.*

Leandro used to dive for lobster and sponge for his living, before he was a cooking boy.

That is some slide down the stairs, from a soldier's life out there diving to a *galopino. Cookie! That's as dangerous as sucking on a nurse's tit!* It was a very rude thing to say this morning to Leandro, who isn't allowed to be angry. He came back from the Day of the Dead with his hair tied in a special way, the horse-tail in back wound with henequen string. Probably his wife did that.

Leandro said his brother who made the diving goggle was drowned last year whilst diving for sponge. He was thirteen, *younger than you and already supporting his mother.* Leandro said that without looking up, hitting the knife hard against the board, chopping onions.

Natividad came in then with the tomatoes and epazote from market, so there was no chance to say *No lo supe.* Usually there is something terrible you don't know.

Or for Leandro to say, *You don't know anything.*

From the exciting life of diving, his brother got to be dead. *That is the truth about soldiering, in case you want to know something*, Leandro said. *Cooking won't kill you.*

This morning low tide was early. The village boys collecting oysters came into the cove and said this beach belonged to them. They screamed *Vete rubio*, go away blond boy, scramble away like a crab over the coral rocks. The path by the lagoon makes a dark tunnel through mangrove trees to the other side of the point. The beach over there is only a thin strip of rocks, and disappears when the tide comes up. This morning the tide was lowest ever. Knobs of the reef cropped out of the water, like heads of sea animals watching. That side is too rocky for boats. No one goes there. No oyster boys to scream at a *rubio* who is not rubio, with hair as Mexican black as Mother's. When they look, do they see anything at all?

Floating on the sea is like flying: looking down on the city of fishes, watching them do their shopping. Flying away *como el pez volador.* Like a flying fish. The bottom falls, and in deep water you can soar, slipping away from the crowded coral-head shallows to the quiet dark blue. Shadows of hunters move along the bottom.

At the back of the cove on that side, a rock ledge rises up from the water. You can see that cliff from the ferry. It has long white stripes of guano, banners marking the roost holes where seabirds think they are hiding. At the base of that cliff, something lay under the water that can't be seen from a boat. A dark something, or really a dark nothing, a great deep hole in the rock. It was a cave, big enough to dive down and crawl into. Or feel around the edges and go a little way inside. It was very deep. A water-path tunneling into the rock, like the path through the mangroves.

An unexpected visit from Mr. Produce the Cash. Mother was in a mood when he left. His fancy shoes must have pinched her also. She started a spat with Don Enrique.

24 November

Today the cave was gone. Saturday last, it was there. Searching the whole rock face below the cliff did not turn it up. Then the tide came higher and waves crashed too hard to keep looking. How could a tunnel open in the rock, then close again? The tide must have been much higher today, and put it too far below the surface to find. Leandro says the tides are complicated and the rocks on that side are dangerous, to stay over here in the shallow reef. He wasn't pleased to hear about the cave. He already knew about it, it is called something already, *la lacuna.* So, not a true discovery.

Laguna? The lagoon?

No, lacuna. He said it means a different thing from lagoon. Not a cave exactly but an opening, like a mouth, that swallows things. He opened his mouth to show. It goes into the belly of the world. He says Isla Pixol is full of them. In ancient times God made the rocks melt and flow like water.

It wasn't God, it was volcanoes. Don Enrique has a book on them.

Leandro said some of the holes are so deep they go to the center of the earth and you'll see the devil at the bottom. But some only go through the island to the other side.

How can you know which is which?

It doesn't matter, because either one can drown a boy who thinks he knows more than God because he reads books. Leandro was very angry. He said stay away from that place, or God will show you who made those holes.

⊠ The Tragic Tale of Señor Pez ⊠

Once there was a small yellow fish with a blue stripe down his back, Señor Pez by name, who lived in the reef. One unfortunate day he was caught by the bare hands of a monstrous boy, the God of Land. Sr. Pez wanted to eat the tortilla offered by the Hands of God, and so the beggar earns his fate. He was carried to the house in a diving goggle and put in a brandy glass of seawater on the windowsill in the Bedchamber of God. For two days Sr. Pez circled the glass with trembling fins, grieving for the sea.

One night Señor Pez wished himself dead. In the morning his wish was granted.

He was to be given a Christian burial under the mango at the end of the garden, but the plan was spoilt by the cleaning girl. The maid Mother hired this time is named Cruz, which means Cross, which she is, most of the time. She came into the Bedchamber of God to pick up the God's Foul Stockings whilst he was outside reading. She must have found the floating body, and decided to throw him out. God returned to his room to find no corpse, no brandy glass, and Señor Pez gone to the garbage jar with the kitchen scraps for the pigs. Leandro said it was true. He saw Cruz throw it in there.

Leandro helped dig through the scraps to find Señor Pez. The Boy God had to hold his nose for the stink, and felt stupid and flutie because he almost cried when they couldn't find it. Thirteen years old, crying for a dead fish. Not for that really, but its being buried in a slop of onion peels and slimy seeds of a calabaza. Our meals are made from the other part of these rotten things. The food inside us must also rot in the same way, and nothing is truly good or stays here because every living thing goes to rot. A stupid reason for crying.

But Leandro said, There now, *no te preocupes,* we know Señor Pez is in here somewhere. Then he had an idea that was very good: why don't we dig a big hole in the garden and bury everything together? And they did. Together the two friends made a noble burial as in times of old for the Azteca kings, the slop bowl providing the departed Señor Pez with everything needed for his journey into the second world, and a little more.

25 December

The village wakes up in a hurry, whilst the sun seems to struggle with the job as Mother does. Last night was the party for Christmas Eve. Today she will sleep until noon, then wake up with one hand across her forehead, the frilled elbows of her dressing gown shuddering. Her voice like a Browning machine rifle sending the house girls running for her headache powders. And everyone else out of the house.

On the road walking to the village for Christmas mass, a lot of people passed by, nuggets of family in brown shells. A man leading his pregnant wife on a burro, like Joseph and Mary. Three long-legged girls in dresses straddling one gray mare, their legs hanging down like a giant insect. A peevish rooster that ought to have been in a better mood, because look here my friend: at the roadside butcher stand, all your comrades hang upside-down ready for roasting. Sausages also were slung over the line like stockings, and a whole white pig skin just hanging, as if the pig went off and left his overcoat. His wife the sow was alive, tied to a papaya tree in the yard with her piglets rooting all round. They could be free to run away, but don't, because of their mother chained on the spot.

The little church in the village has no bell, only copal-tree incense floating out the open windows to mix with the fish-rot smell of ocean. Leandro was there with his family, resting one hand on each of his children's heads, like grapefruits. Later at the fiesta he didn't ever say *Feliz Navidad* or *Hello friend I come to your house every day*. He only clapped together his small son's hands for the piñata strung from the fig tree. There were firecrackers for the holy babe snapping blue smoke in the road, and amongst all the nut-brown families, one invisible boy.

1 January 1930: First day of the year and decade.
Every *cabeza* in the house is full of headache powders. Shattered glasses in twinkling pools on the terraza. No word is heard from the turkey that chased children from the yard all December. He greets the New Year from the kitchen, a carcass of bones attended by his audience of flies.

A fine day to go out looking for a tunnel to another world. Perhaps to meet the devil. Mother called out *Callete malinche dios mio don't slam the door!* Not even the usual warning about sharks, let them have boy-flesh if they want. Clear sky, empty beach, and the water like a cool pair of hands, begging. Even the reef fishes didn't speak today.

The lacuna was there again, a dark mouth in the rock. This time the opening was deeper below the surface, but it was still possible to dive down and feel between the lips of rock into a gullet that broadened in darkness. It was the last day of the world then, time to swim inside, thinking of Leandro's dead brother. Stroking through cold water, counting the pounding heartbeats: thirty, forty, forty-five, one half of ninety. Waiting that long before turning around, feeling the way back toward the entrance, swimming with aching lungs back to the light.

Sun and air. Breathing. Alive, after all. The hand of the watch returned to the top for one more year of life, stolen back.

5 January

Tomorrow is Feast of the Kings. Only here it will be the Feast of Don Enrique's Sisters and Mother, who came over on the ferry. Leandro has to cook for them all. Cruz and the others went to their villages for the fiesta, but Mother is determined to have a feast for the guests, with or without servants. She pretends she and Don Enrique are married, and the señora is to be called *abuela*. The so-called grandmother in her chic frock lights a cigarette, crosses her legs, blows smoke out the window.

Mother wants green and red *chalupas*, and scrambled egg *torta* with sugar. Leandro would like to be with his family. He's put out with Mother for making him stay, so he made fun of the señora. A scandal. But he knows he won't be caught. The *capitan* and his *sergente* have a conspiracy.

The *rosca de reyes* is hardest to make: the cake called Ring of the Kings, using white-flour dough, the same as for Baby's Crupper tortillas. A blob of dough fit for a king, rolled out on the table, as long and fat as a sea slug. *Como pene.* Poking it and laughing: *Como bato.* Leandro is normally much more pious.

Weiner! Jaker!

Pachango!

Thing! *Thing of the King!*

Leandro had tears in his eyes and said Mother would kill us. He crossed himself and prayed for both souls. He made the cake into a ring by putting the thing-of-the-king in a circle and pressing the ends together. The token goes inside, a small clay baby Jesus that looks like a pig. Leandro said really it's not even Jesus, it's the boy-god

Pilzintecutli. He dies when the days grow dark in December, then rises again on February 2, which is Candlemas. The ancients were concerned with light and darkness. We are in the dark days now, he said. Whoever finds the token in the cake will have good luck, when the light returns.

All the rest of the year, the clay token sits in a jar in the cabinet waiting to go into this cake. Leandro took the little pig Jesus out of the jar and kissed it before putting it in the *rosca*. Round jellied fruits go on top, but he put a square piece where the token was inside, his secret way of marking it. Reach for that one, he said, when the dish of cake is passed around.

Is it still lucky if you cheat, instead of getting the token by chance?

Mi'jo, Leandro said. Your mother can't even remember the day she gave you birth. If an orphan boy is going to have any luck, he will have to make it himself.

What kind of orphan has two living parents? You said everyone has family even if they are ghosts. Or forget your *cumpleaños*.

Leandro took the orphan's cheeks in his hands and kissed him on the mouth, and then spanked his crupper like a child, not a boy as tall as a man. A boy with terrible thoughts of kissing a man as a man. Leandro meant nothing by it. A *beso* for a child.

Leandro went home after the feast. All servants have fled, leaving kitchen scraps, bad moods, and dust. What is the use of good luck in an empty house?

2 February, Candlemas

Leandro was gone nineteen days, now back. He has to make a hundred tamales for Candlemas, without his *sergente*. It's better to hide in the *amate* tree all day reading, a book won't run off to its family any time it wants. Leandro can't even read. Let him make tamales all day.

Today begins a year of perfect luck protected by Pilzintecutli, the clay-pig Jesus.

13 February

Today the lacuna appeared, a little below the surface. It's near the center of the cliff below a knob where a hummock of grass grows out. It should be easy to find again but best to look early, with sun just up and the tide low. Inside the tunnel it was very cold and dark again. But a blue light showed up faintly like a fogged window, farther back. It must be the other end, no devil back there but a place to come up on the other side, a passage. But too far to swim, and too frightening.

One day Pilzintecutli will say, *Go ahead lucky boy. Vete, rubio*, swim toward that light. Go find the other side of the world where you belong.

The strangest thing. Mother believes in magic. She went back to the village of the giant stone head. After sending Natividad away with the carriage, she said, "This time we both go." She took off her shoes again to cross the footbridge, then followed a path through the forest right around the edge of a lake. Yellow-winged *jacanas* flapped up from the water and an alligator rested at the edge, covered with waterweed up to its bulging eyes. Then back into the jungle, under giant trees. We were going to see a *brujo*, she said finally, because someone has put a bad eye on us both, and that's why she can't get another baby. Probably it was Don Enrique's mother.

The *brujo*'s bamboo hut stood in a clearing, inside a circle of stones. It might have been made a thousand years ago. The door was a curtain of snail shells strung together that made a wooden tinkling sound when his hand pulled it aside. Inside was an altar covered with little clay figures, and branches with leaves standing in jars, and cockleshells of burning copal gum, the same incense as in the church. He said to take off our shirts, which Mother did immediately, down to her silk underthings. The *brujo* didn't look at her, his eyes went to the roof of the hut and he began to sing, so he truly was a *brujo*, not just a man.

He seemed as old as a person could be, and still living. His chant was quiet and fast, *Echate, echate*. He walked all around Mother first, swatting her body gently with a branch of leaves dipped in a jar of leaf-water, shaking drops of it on her hair, breasts, and belly, then everything else, son included. Then he blew smoke over her, from the cockleshell of burning gum. With his knotted old hands he held up a figure cut from thin paper, a small catlike man-shaped thing, and burned it in the flame of a candle. Some of the carved figures on his altar looked like a man's thing, his organ. Stone *pachangos*.

When he finished Mother paid him in coins. She didn't speak until after crossing the bridge back to the village. The square was deserted, except for the great stone head. Natividad hadn't come back. "Enrique can't be told about this," she said. "You know that, of course."

"Does he want you to get a baby?"

She straightened her dress and pulled at the back of her stocking. "Well. It would change things, wouldn't it?"

Leandro's baby girl died in January after Feast of the Kings, and no one here knew. Cruz told Mother today. He was gone three weeks, not because he was angry with his *sergente*, but to bury a child. The two small grapefruit heads in church: only one now. Cruz had a fight with Mother because what Don Enrique pays is not enough for feeding a chicken. She said Leandro's wife couldn't get her milk, and the baby died.

How can he go home to a family with nothing to eat, then come to this house to make one hundred tamales? He behaves as if he had no dead children. The real Leandro never comes here. He only pretends.

9 March

Today the lacuna is gone. Directly below the knob in the cliff, nothing. If it is there, then buried below too much ocean. The grass hummock on the cliff face is very low to the water now. Or rather, the sea is higher.

Don Enrique is away in the Huasteca, and Mother has taken up kitchen knives. She waved one around this morning. Not to chop onions but to show she means business about keeping her secrets. Not just the *brujo*, but also Mr. P. T. Cash. So, no mention here about another surprising visit from him, while the master was away. Anyway Mother is too lazy to lift up a mattress and find this little book.

13 March

The lacuna came back. In the afternoon the rock opened its mouth and swallowed the boy down its gullet. But it was hard to swim, the water was rushing out. It was the same as before, lungs bursting, turning back too soon. Leandro's brother whispering, *Come live with me here*, but a brain hungry for oxygen loses courage and wants air.

Tomorrow will be the day.

Last Will and Testament

Let it be known. If HWS drowns in the cave, he leaves nothing to anyone. His earthly possessions are stolen things: pocket watch. This book. One year of good luck.

He leaves his body for the fishes to eat.

He leaves Leandro to wonder where he has gone.

He leaves Mother and Mr. Produce the Cash to enjoy the company of the devil.

Dios habla por el que calla.

14 March

The cave has bones inside. Bones of humans! Things on the other side.

This is how it feels when you are nearly drowned: the brain pounds like a pulse in red and black. The salt water burns your eyes, and you nearly go blind following the light until you come to the air, breathing.

At the end of the tunnel the cave opens up to light, a small saltwater pool in the jungle. Almost perfectly round, as big across as this bedchamber, with sky straight up, dappled and bright through the branches. *Amate* trees stood in a circle around the water hole like curious men, gaping because a boy from another world had suddenly arrived in their pool. The *pombo* trees squatted for a close look, with their knobbly wooden knees poking up out of the water. A tiger heron stood one-legged on a rock, cocking an unfriendly eye at the intruder. San Juan Pescadero the kingfisher zipped back and forth between two perches, crying, "Kill him kill him kill him!"

Piles of stone blocks lay in a jumble around the edges of the pool, a broken-down something made of coral rock. Vines scrambled all over the ruin, their roots curling down through it like fingers in sand. It was a temple or something else very ancient.

The light through the trees was shadowy at midday, but the water was clear. Belly-dragged up on a flat stone, sitting at the edge looking back in, it was plain to see the bottom of the cave dropped down to make a sort of room down there, huge and deep. Stones were piled like a sand castle underwater, with bits of shining things mixed into the pile. Maybe yellow leaves, or gold coins. It was like coming up inside a storybook. An ancient temple in the forest, and a pirate's treasure below. The treasure was mostly shells and broken pottery covered with sea moss, mostly too deep to dive down and reach.

It took hours to explore everything. Some of the broken blocks of the ruin had designs carved on them, a script of lines and circles or perhaps the portraits of gods. One looked like a skeleton, its arms flung open, the skull smiling wide. A water snake slipped off a rock and made a sliding S shape across the top of the water. The jungle vines were tangled like fishing nets. It was the type of forest with a watery floor, and no good way to walk out of there. And no good way to swim back out of that cave, either. No way back from this story, it seemed. Nothing left to do but slide like a turtle into the pool, sink down, and sit on slime-covered rocks and the treasure of ancient times.

That is where the bones were! Leg bones, wedged in the rocks. It made for such a shock, it was hard to breathe after seeing them. Floating in the pool was also not very easy because now the tide pulled downward, dropping lower and sucking against the stones around the edge of the hole, hissing a song of drowning: *ahogarse, ahogarse.* The ocean pulled hard, dragging a coward explorer back from the secret place, sucking him out through the tunnel and spitting him into the open sea.

Out there again gasping, it was plain that the tide had turned and gone out. Now it was extremely low. Coral knobs poked out like heads. A great round moon hung on the eastern horizon, just coming out of the sea, white as an oyster.

Then it seemed the bones and temple could not have been real, and this cave would vanish again. Only the moon was real, as big and whole as breathing.

A book in Don Enrique's library says the pagans of old built their castles on this island. Not as tall as the great pyramids of the Azteca, but small stepped temples with platforms for sacrifice. They carved pictures of their gods, which were many in number. The book said the same things Leandro says, that the ancients watched light and signs to tell them when to plant corn, when to get married. But it also told more terrible things: they made sacrifices by throwing gold and sometimes girls (alive) into water holes in the forest. The cave must be that kind of hole, a *cenote.* Because of the bones.

The book was written by a priest, not very good, but interesting at some parts. Hernán Cortés sent an expeditionary force to destroy the pagan city here and build the cathedral in town. If the ruin in the jungle is really part of that ancient city, then for certain the cenote has gold and treasure in its depths, along with the bones of unlucky girls. Leandro might know something about it, but can't be asked. There is no trusting his allegiance, he might tell Mother. So he will never know about going inside the lacuna.

24 March

First, the cave wasn't there today. Or so it seemed. But really it was, nearly two meters down from the surface, buried by tide, with a strong current flowing out of it.

The last time, it was morning when the current inside the cave pulled inward toward the jungle-hole. During the hours of exploring the tide must have turned, so at evening it was easy to swim out. The moon was just rising then. The tides are the cause. The time to go in is just before the tide turns. Otherwise, more bones on that pile.

25 March

The tide was wrong completely, the current flowed out of the cave all day. On the day of the full moon, everything was right.

Don Enrique says a full moon pulls up the highest tides of the month, at midday and midnight. And it pulls them down to their lowest ebb when it is rising or setting. So says a man in a frock coat and breeches who, if he tried to row a boat, would fall out instantly and drown. But Leandro said the same thing about the moon and high tide, so it might be true.

How can you know if the moon is going toward full, or disappearing?

This evening the moon was half, and Leandro said it's dying away. You can tell because it's shaped like the letter C, not curved forward like D. He says when the moon is D like Dios, it is growing to fill God's sky. When dying away it is C, like Cristo on the cross. So, no good tides again for many days.

12 April

Today was the full moon, perfect tide, and the bad luck of slicing the end of a finger with the kitchen knife. Blood everywhere, even in the masa, turning it pink. It had to be thrown out. *Oh no, let's serve it to Don Enrique and Mother! A* clayuda *of her son's blood, like the Azteca sacrifices to their gods.*

Leandro said, Pray God forgives you for such talk. Get busy and make more masa.

Tonight the moon rose, the beach was quiet, and no one swam into the lacuna. The three Musketeers would have done it, diving in with scabbards in their teeth, not bandages on their fingers. But they were three, all for one and one for all.

Tonight a shadow passed across the moon. Don Enrique says an eclipse. But Leandro says it is El Dios and El Cristo putting their heads together, crying over everything that happens down here.

2 May

Birthday of Santa Rita de Casia. Mother needed cigarettes, but there wasn't any market today because of the fiesta. All the women went to the procession in long ruffled skirts, their hair braided with ribbons and flowers. Boys carrying beeswax candles as tall as men. The old woman who sells nopal in the market was at the front, dressed like a wrinkled bride. Her old groom shuffled beside, holding her arm.

Leandro says they couldn't have this fiesta last year because of the Silence against the church. But that Santa Rita de Casia is not really a saint, but a woman-god. Nothing is ever what they say, and no one holy one hundred percent.

12 May

Perfect tide today. Into the cave and back out. The water pushed, all the way in, to touch those bones again. Tomorrow the tide should be almost perfect again. But only a few more days this month, to look for the treasure hidden from Hernán Cortés.

13 May

Mother says tonight. In just a few hours we leave on the ferry. It isn't possible just to go away from here, but she said, Oh yes it is. Leave everything.

Tell no one, she said: Don Enrique will be furious. Not even Cruz can know, don't pack anything from your room yet because she would notice. Wait till it's almost time. Take only what fits in one rucksack. Two books, only. Not those huaraches, don't be ridiculous, your good shoes.

She said: *Bueno*. Very fine. If you want to stay here, stay. On this stupid island so far from everything, you have to yell three times before even Jesus Cristo can hear you. I will happily go without you, and light a candle for you in the Catedral Nacional when I get there. Because when Enrique finds out, he'll kill you instead of me.

Mr. Produce the Cash is meeting us on the mainland.

You will not say one word to Leandro. Not one word, mister.

Dear Leandro, here is the note you won't read because you can't read. The pocket watch is in the jar in the cabinet, with the clay Pilzintecutli. It's a gift to find next year when you have to make the *rosca* with no *sergente* to help mix the flour. The watch is gold, maybe you can take it to monte de piedad and get money for your family. Or keep it to remind you of the pest who is gone.

Mexico City, 1930 (vb)

11 June

La luna de junio, first full moon in June, a day to dive for treasure.
But the nearest thing to ocean here is the rot-fish smell on Saturdays
after all the wives on the alley cooked fish the day before, and their
garbage is waiting for the slop-cart man. The ocean is the last dream
in the morning before noise from the street comes in. Motorcars, police on horses, the tide goes out, the prisoner awakes on a new island.
An apartment above a bakery shop.

Mother says a *casa chica* means probably his wife knows about
her but doesn't mind, because a Small House doesn't cost too much.
The maid doesn't even sleep here, no room. The water closet and gas
cooking eye are in the same room. The main kitchen is downstairs
in the bakery, passed through from the street, with a key. No library
and no garden here, in a city that stinks of buses. Mother thinks it is
all wonderful and reminds her of childhood, even though that was a
long time ago and not this city. And if it was so wonderful, why did
she never go back to see her father and mother until dead?

"Quit your moping, mister, finally we're off that island where
nothing was ever going to happen. Here you don't have to yell three
times before Jesus Cristo can hear you." Probably because after the
second yell, Jesus would look down in time to see you get coshed by
a trolley.

But, she says. God has a swell house here, the biggest cathedral
in the world. One of the high marks of the Distrito Federal. So far
we've seen only one high mark, La Flor, the shop where Mr. Produce

the Cash and his friends go for coffee. We went there alone, in defiance of orders. His businessman friends don't yet know about his new enterprise, the secret kept in a small box, the *casa chica*. The lid of the box is mother's hush money, which she says is not very much. So probably she will not be very quiet.

She needed to go to La Flor to have a look-see at how they dress here, so she won't be a low-lid dumbdora like people on that island. On the streets you can see which men are farmers who've come to the city for the day: white trousers, rolled to the knees. The men taking coffee at La Flor were all black-trouser men. The ladies wore cloche hats and smart, short dresses like Mother's, but with black stockings for modesty. The waitresses had white aprons and eyes wide with fright. This city is like Washington, and it isn't. It's difficult to remember real places from the book places. The patio had giant fern trees like the forest in *Journey to the Center of the Earth*, and very good chocolate. Cookies called cat's tongues. The cat's meow, Mother said, but really the cat's not-meow. Our alley has so many, with a slingshot you could get a good supply of tongues.

Mother was in a jolly mood, and finally agreed to stop at the stationer's on the way home, for a new notebook. She pouted: You love that little book more than me, you'll go in your room and forget me.

But just now she came in and said, You poor thing. You're like a fish that needed water. I didn't even know.

Today the cathedral. It took all morning to reach the central plaza, the Zócalo, two buses and then a trolley to get there from the outside edge of the Distrito Federal. The *casa chica* is located in an unfashionable neighborhood south of the bullfighting plaza on a dirt alley that runs into Insurgentes. According to Mother, we reside halfway between the Capitol of Mexico and Tierra del Fuego, South America.

The Zócalo is a huge square with palm trees like parasols. Facing one side is the long Palacio Nacional of pink stone, with small windows all the way down it like holes in a flute. The brick streets leading into the Zócalo are narrow as animal burrows in tall grass, the buildings close on both sides, as far as you can see. Downstairs are shops and people live above, you can see the women leaning on their elbows on the iron balconies watching everything below. Bicycle carts, horses, and automobiles, lines of them, sometimes going both ways in the same street.

The cathedral is immense as promised, with gigantic wooden doors that look as if they could shut you out for good. The front is all warbly with carvings: the Ship of the Church sailing over one door looked like a Spanish galleon, and over the other, Jesus is handing over the keys to the kingdom. He has the same worried look the bakery-shop man had when giving Mother the key to come through his shop to our apartment upstairs. Mr. Produce the Cash owns the building.

Inside the cathedral you have to pass the great Altar of Perdón, all golden with angels flying about. The black Christ of the Venom hangs there dead in his black skirt, surrounded by little balconies, maybe for the angels to land on when they get tired. It was such a monument of accusation, even Mother had to bow her head a little as she crept past it, sins dripping from her shoes as we walked around the nave, leaving invisible puddles on the clean tiles. Perhaps God said her name was mud. He would have to yell that more than three times, for her to hear.

Around the back outside the church was a little museum. A man there told us the cathedral was built by Spaniards right on top of the great temple of the Azteca. They did it on purpose, so the Azteca would give up hope of being saved by their own gods. Just a few pieces of temple left. The man said the Azteca came to this place in ancient times after wandering many hundred years looking for a true home. When they got here they saw an eagle sitting on a cactus, eating a snake, and that was their sign. A good enough reason to call a place home, better than all of Mother's up to now.

The best artifact was the calendar of the ancients, a great carved piece of stone as big as a kitchen, circular, bolted to the wall like a giant clock. In the center was an angry face looking out, as if he'd come through that stone from some other place to have a look at us, and not very pleased about it. He stuck out his sharp tongue, and in taloned hands he held up two human hearts. Around him smiling jaguars danced in a circle of endless time. It might be the calendar Leandro knew about. He would be happy to know the Spaniards decided to keep it when they bashed up everything else. But Leandro can't read a letter, so there is no use writing him anything about it.

Mr. P. T. Cash is to come on Mondays, Thursdays, and Saturdays. Mother could put a sign on her door like the bakery shop downstairs.

They discuss The Boy's Future: P. T. says the Preparatoria in September, but Mother says no, he can't get in there. It's supposed to be difficult, with Latin, physics, and things of that kind. What will they make of a boy who has only attended the school of Jules Verne and the Three Musketeers for five years? Her idea is a little school organized by nuns, but P. T. Cash says she is a dreamer, the Revolution did away with those when the priests fled Mexico. If they know what's good for them, he said, those schoolteacher nuns got married. Mother insists she saw a school on Avenida Puig south of here. But Preparatoria is free, and a *católica* school would cost money, if one could be found. We will see who wins: Mr. Produce the Cash or Miss No Cash Whatever.

24 June

St. John's Day, all the church bells ringing on a Tuesday. The maid says it's a signal for the lepers to bathe. Today is the only day of the year they are allowed to touch water. No wonder they smell as they do.

❀

On the way back from the Colonia Roma dress shop today, it started to rain like pitchforks, and we bought paper hats from the newspaper boys. When it rains, they give up on shouting about the New Bureaucratic Plan and fold it up into something useful. Then we lost the way home and Mother laughed, her hair stuck like little black ribbons to her face, for once happy. For no reason.

Standing under an awning to hide from the rain, we noticed it was a shop of books, and went inside. It was fantastic, every sort of book including medical ones, the human eye drawn in cross-section and reproductive organs. Mother sighed for the slim chances of gaining entrance to the no-cost Preparatoria. She told the shopkeeper she needed something to put her boy on the Right Track, and he showed her the section of very old, worn-out ones. Then took pity on Mother and said if we brought them back later, he would return most of the price. Huzzah, something new to read. For your birthday, she said, because it passed almost a week ago and she was sorry for not celebrating. So pick out something for turning fourteen, she said. But still no adventure novels. Pick something serious, history for example. And no Pancho Villa, mister. According to her, if he hasn't been dead twenty years, he isn't history.

The Azteca are dead for hundreds, so we got two books about them. One is all of the letters written by Hernán Cortés to Queen Juana of Spain, who sent him off to conquer Mexico. He sent back plenty of reports, starting each one with "Most Lofty Powerful and Very Catholic Empress." The other one is by a bishop who lived among the pagans and drew pictures of them, even naked.

More rain, a good day for reading. The great pyramid under the cathedral was built by King Ahuitzotl. Luckily the Spaniards wrote buckets about the Azteca civilization before they blew it to buttons and used its stones for their churches. The pagans had priests and temple virgins and temples of limestone blocks ornamented on every face with stone serpents. They had gods for Water, Earth, Night,

Fire, Death, Flowers, and Corn. Also many for War, their favorite enterprise. The war god Mejitli was born from a Holy Virgin who lived at the temple. The bishop wrote how curious it was that just like our Holy Virgin, when she turned up expecting a baby, the Azteca priests wanted to stone her but heard a voice saying: "Fear not Mother, thy honor is saved." Then the war god was born with green feathers on his head, and a blue face. The mother must have had quite a fright that day, all round.

Because of all that, they gave her a temple with a garden for birds. And for her son, a temple for human sacrifice. Its door was a serpent's mouth, a lacuna leading deep into the temple where a surprise waited for visitors. Towers were built from all their skulls. The priests walked about with their bodies blackened with the ashes of burnt scorpions. If only Mother had brought us here five hundred years sooner.

Every day it rains buckets, the alley is a river. Women do their washing in it. Then it dries up, flotsam everywhere. The maid says it's a law that everyone has to clean a section of the street, so we should pay her husband for that. Mother says no dice, if we have to huddle like pigeons upstairs we aren't paying any damn street cleaner.

Mother's room has a tiny balcony facing outward to the alley, and this room is opposite, facing a courtyard inside the block of buildings. The family across keeps a garden there, hidden from the street. The grandfather wears white cotton trousers rolled to his knees, tending squash vines and his pigeon house, a round brick tower with cubbyholes around the top where his pigeons roost. The old man uses a broom to chase away parrots eating his flowers. When the moon is *D como Dios*, his pigeons cry all night.

Cortés is an adventure story, better than the Three Musketeers. He was the first Spaniard to find this city, which was Tenochtitlan then, capital of the Azteca empire. Somehow it was in a lake at that time. They had causeways crossing the water, wide enough for Cor-

THE LACUNA ❋ 55

tés and his horsemen to ride abreast. He heard of the great city and sent messages first so the Azteca wouldn't kill him the minute he arrived. A good plan. King Moteczuma met him with two hundred nobles all dressed in nice capes, and gave Cortés a necklace made of gold prawns. Then they sat down to discuss the circumstances. Moteczuma explained that long ago their ancient lord went back to his native land where the sun rises, so they were expecting one of his descendants to come back any time and subject the people as his rightful vassals. Cortés had sent messages about being sent hither by a great king, so they thought he must be their natural lord. That was good luck for Cortés, who rejoiced and took leisure from the fatigues of his journey. Moteczuma gave him more gold things, and one of his daughters.

The Azteca in other cities were not so friendly to the Spaniards, and killed them. One was a big troublemaker, Qualpopoca. Cortés demanded him brought in for punishment, and to be safe decided to put Moteczuma in chains, but on a friendly basis. Qualpopoca arrived fuming, insisting he was a vassal of no Great King from any-where, and hated all Spaniards. So he was burned alive in the public square.

Mother is tired of hearing bits of the story. She says she is not the damned queen of Spain, put the candle out before it falls on the bed and burns you alive.

She says we can't keep the book even if it is the best adventure ever. And a birthday present. It is too long to copy the whole story out, only the main parts. Cortés let Moteczuma go free again and they were still friends, which seems strange. He showed Cortés the build-ings and marketplaces, fine as any in Spain, and stone temples higher than the great church of Seville. Inside some, the walls were covered with the blood of human sacrifice. But the people had great culture and politeness of manners, with good government everywhere main-tained, and stone pipes to bring water down from the mountains.

Moteczuma had a grand palace and lattice houses where he kept every manner of bird, waterfowl to eagle. It took three hundred men to look after them all.

But really Cortés wanted a tour of the gold mines. Playing dumbdora, he told Moteczuma the land looked very fertile, so the Great King should like to have a farm there (over the gold mine). They fixed it up with maize fields, a big house for His Majesty, even a pond with ducks. Crafty Cortés.

Next, the Governor of Honduras grew very jealous and sent eighty musketeers over to Mexico, declaring he had the true authority of Spain to conquer and suborn the natives. Just when Cortés was having such a grand time, he had to go with all haste back to the port of Veracruz to defend his position, then rush straight back to save the men he'd left at Tenochtitlan. For the people there finally got wise to Cortés, and his name was mud. The populace advanced upon his garrison, and they fought for their lives. King Moteczuma climbed a tower and shouted for everyone to stop, but he was struck in the head by a rock and died three days later. Cortés got out of that place by the skin of his neck. He had to leave behind almost all his golden shields, crests, and other such marvellous things as could not be described nor comprehended. That is what he wrote, but probably he was too embarrassed to describe or comprehend them because one-fifth share of the booty was supposed to go to her Extremely Catholic Majesty the Queen.

Almost the whole night reading and copying, until the candle burned out. This morning Mother said stop being lazy and run to the market. We need coffee, corn meal, and fruit, but really cigarettes. Mother could go for one year without food, but not one day without her lip sticks.

The Piedad market had no cigarettes. The old women there were smoking cigarettes but said they didn't have any because it's Friday. They said, Try the one south of here, the Melchor Ocampo market. Just walk south on Insurgentes to the next little town from here, Coyoacán. Take the lane called Francia. That market has everything.

Mother is right about the city ending just south of where we live. It isn't South America, but the streets turn to dirt lanes and it's like a village, with families living in wattle huts around dirt courtyards, children squatting in the mud, mothers making fires to cook tortillas. Grandmothers sit on blankets weaving more blankets for other grandmothers to sit on. Between the houses, gardens of maize and beans. From the last bus stop after two maize fields is Coyoacán as the women said, a market with everything. Cigarettes, piles of squash blossoms, green chiles, sugarcane, beans. Green parrots in bamboo cages. A band of *leprosos* walking north toward the city for their morning begging, like skeletons with skin stretched over the bones, and tatters of clothes hanging like flags of surrender. Begging with whatever parts of hands they still had attached.

The next thing to come along was an iguana as big as an alligator, strolling with a frown on its face and a collar on its neck. Attached to the collar a long rope, and holding the rope, a man with no teeth singing.

Señor, is it for sale?

What isn't, young friend? Even I could be yours, for a price.

Your lizard. Is it food or a pet?

Mas vale ser comida de rico que perro de pobre, he said. Better to be the food of a rich boy than the dog of a poor one. But today there was only enough money for fruit and cigarettes. Anyway the maid cries enough already, without having to cook a lizard for lunch. It took a long time to walk back, but Mother wasn't angry. She'd found a couple of dinchers in the pocket of her yellow dress.

Sunday is the worst day. Everyone else has family and a place to go. Even the bells from the churches have a conversation, all ringing at once. Our house is like an empty cigarette packet, lying around reminding you what's not in it. The maid, gone to mass. Mr. Produce the Cash, to the wife and children. Mother rinses her girdles and step-ins, flings them on the rails of the balcony to dry, and finds herself with nothing left to live for. Sometimes when there isn't anything in the house to eat, she says, "Okay, kiddo, it's dincher dinner." That means sharing her cigarettes so we won't be hungry.

Today she pinched the Cortés book and hid it because she was lonely. "You just read your books and go a hundred miles away. You ignore me."

"Well, you ignore me whenever Produce the Cash is here. Go find him."

The door to her bedroom slammed, rattling its glass panes. Then opened again, she can't stay cooped. "A person could go blind from reading so much."

"Your eyes must be good, then."

"You slaughter me, cheeky Charlie. And that notebook is giving me the heebie-jeebies. Stop it. Stop writing down everything I say."

E-v-e-r-y-t-h-i-n-g. S-h-e. S-a-y-s.

Finally tonight she had to give up Cortés in exchange for the cigarettes, because she was going to die without them.

The market in Coyoacán is not like the Zócalo downtown, where everything comes ready-made. The girls in blue shawls sit on blankets with stacks of maize they just broke from the field an hour before. While waiting for people to come, they shell off the kernels. If more time passes they soak the corn in lime water, then grind it into wet *nixtamal* and pat it out. By day's end, all the corn is tortillas. *Nixtamal* is the only kind of flour they use here. Even our maid doesn't know how to make white-flour bread.

While the girls make tortillas, the boys cut bamboo from marshes by the road and weave it into birdcages. If no one comes to buy a cage, they will climb up trees and steal birds from their nests, to put in the cages. You have to come before ten in the morning if you want whole maize ears or an empty birdcage. By the end of the week they will have made a world. And on the seventh day rest, like God.

The old lizard man comes every day. He and his creature look the same, with whitish scaly skin and wrinkled eyes. The man is called Cienfuegos, and his beast is named Manjar Blanco: creamed chicken.

On the plaza near the Melchor market the palace of Cortés still stands. He ruled from there after conquering the Azteca. First it was the garrison where he gathered his musketeers and schemed to take over Tenochtitlan; a plaque on the square tells about it. This very place Cortés described in his third letter to the Queen. How strange to read of a place in a book, and then stand on it, listen to the birds sing, and spit on the cobbles if you want. Only it was on the shore of the lake then. The great city had dikes to hold back the waters, and sometimes the Aztecas removed stones from the dikes, causing floods to rush over Cortés and his men as they slept. They had to swim for their lives.

21 July
The question of school lurks. Exams for entering the Preparatoria are a few weeks away, tomorrow we will go back to the bookshop for more Improving Texts. The letters of Cortés will be traded for something else, and it's no use tearing a fit to keep it. Tonight is the last chance to finish and copy out the good bits.

The last siege of Tenochtitlan: Cortés tried to block the causeways across the lake and starve them out. But the people threw maize cakes at him and said: We are in no want of food, and later, if we are, we shall eat you!

He made his men build thirteen ships in the desert and dig a canal to move them to the lake, so he could attack both by land and water: the final assault. He bore his ship straight into a fleet of canoes hurling darts and arrows. "We chased them for three leagues, killing and drowning the enemy, the most extraordinary sight in the whole world," he told the Queen, and mentioned how it pleased God to raise up their spirits and weaken those of the enemy. Also the Spaniards had muskets.

The people fought him as the bitterest of foes, including women. Cortés was dismayed by their refusal to submit. "I was at pains to think in what way I could terrify them so as to bring them to knowledge of their sins, and the damage we were in a position to do them." So he set fire to everything, even the wooden temples where Moteczuma kept his birds. He was much grieved to burn up the birds, he said. "But since it was still more grievous to them, I determined to do it."

The people uttered such yells and shrieks that it seemed as if the world was coming to an end.

22 July

The new book is nowhere near as good: *Geographical Atlas of Mexico.* The City of Mexico is two and a half kilometers above sea level. In ancient times it was different islands built on stone foundations in a salt lake, connected by causeways. The Spaniards drained the lake with canals, but it is still a swamp, the old buildings all tilt. Some streets still run like canals when it rains. The motorcars are like ancient canoes, and the people flow from one island to another. And rulers still make grand buildings with paintings on the outside. The newspapers call them Temples of the Revolution. Modern people are just like ancient ones, only more numerous.

4 August

A victory for Mother: being seen in the daylight with Mr. P. T. Cash. He took us in his automobile to have lunch at Sanborn's, downtown near the cathedral in the Casa Azulejos. The grand lunch room at the center of the building has a glass ceiling so high that birds fluttered under it, indoors by accident. One wall was covered with a painting of a garden, peacocks and white columns. Mother said it portrayed

Europe. Her cheeks were pink, because of meeting the important friends.

Waitresses in long, striped skirts brought carts of rainbow-colored juices: pomegranate, pineapple, guayabana. The Important Friends paid no attention to the pretty juices, discussing the federal investment plan and why the Revolution will fail. Mother wore her smartest silk chiffon, a blue helmet hat, and ear drops. Her son wore a dress coat too tight and short. Mr. P. T. Cash wore his Glenurquhart plaid suit and nervous expression, introducing Mother as his niece visiting for the year. The friends were oil men with oiled hair and one old doctor named Villaseñor. His wife, a Rock of Ages in high lace collar and pince-nez. All gringos except the doctor and wife.

The oil men said the sooner the Mexican oil industry collapses, the better, so they can take it over and make it run straight. One told his theory about why America is forward and Mexico is backward: when the English arrived in the New World, they saw no good use for Indians, and killed them. But the Spaniards discovered a native populace long accustomed to serving masters (Azteca), so the empire yoked these willing servants to its plows to create New Spain. He said that was their mistake, allowing native blood to mingle with their own to make a contaminated race. The doctor agreed, saying the mixed-race mestizos have made a mess of the government because they are smoldering cauldrons of conflicting heritages. "The mestizo is torn by his opposing racial impulses. His intellect dreams of high-minded social reforms, but his brute desires make him tear apart every advance his country manages to build. Do you understand this, young man?"

Yes, only, which half of the mestizo brain is the selfish brute: the Indian or the Spanish?

Mother said her son intends to be a lawyer, causing everyone to laugh.

But it wasn't a joke. Cortés and the Governor of Honduras were tearing one another apart before they'd even got started. Cortés burned people and birds alive, to be terrifying. The Azteca priests smeared their churches with blood, also to be terrifying.

The oil man named Thompson told Mother she should make a military man of that one, not some snake of a lawyer. President Ortiz Rubio sends his two sons to the Gettysburg Academy in America, just the ticket.

Mother asked the doctor's wife if there were any little schools left, run by the Catholic Sisters. The Rock of Ages nearly started to cry, saying they are all gone due to the Revolution. But they still have a place for the ones who aren't clever enough for the Preparatoria. The government has let Acción Catolica take over the schools for the deaf mutes, cretins, and children of bad character.

Mrs. Doctor said the Revolution has wrecked everyone's morals and turned the churches into newspaper offices or moving-picture theatres. She told Mother they used to have laws to restrict things like gambling, concerts, divorce, and somersaulters. In the time of Porfirio a person didn't have to see all that.

Mother might quite like to see some somersaulters and divorce. Her favorite song is "Anything Goes." But she put her hand on Mrs. Doctor's lace sleeve. As a helpless mother trying to raise a young boy alone, she needed advice.

13 August
Feast of St. Hippolitus, and entrance exams at the Preparatoria. It was a scorching: most terrible of all, the maths. Latin was a guessing game. Outside the window, noisy green parrots came all afternoon to tear apart a patch of yellow tube-shaped flowers.

25 August
Today begins the year of all suffering at the School of Cretins, Deaf-Mutes, and Boys of Bad Character on Avenida Puig. The classroom is like a prison hall full of writhing convicts, its iron-barred windows set high along one wall. Small boys and monkeys for pupils. No one

else there could be fourteen or anything near it, they're the size of baboons. The Holy Virgin feels very sorry but remains outside, on her cement pedestal in the small tidy garden. She has sent her son Jesus in with the other wretches, and he can't flee either. He is pegged to his cross on the wall, dying all the day, rolling his eyes behind the back of Señora Bartolome, even He can't stand the look of her clay-pipe legs and those shoes.

She teaches one subject only: "Extricta Moralidad!" The tropical climate inclines young persons of Mexican heritage to moral laxity, she says.

Señora Bartolome, *perdon*: We are at an elevation of 2,300 meters above sea level here, so it isn't tropical, strictly speaking. The average monthly temperature ranges from twelve to eighteen degrees Centigrade. It's from the *Geographical Atlas*.

Punished for insolence. Bad Character accomplished, the first day of term. Tomorrow perhaps Deaf-Mute. After that, one could aspire to Cretin.

1 September

No reading in class. Señora Bartolome says a book will distract from her lessons of hygiene, morality, and self-control. *You'll sing a different song in the administrator's office.* She hints it may contain iron maidens and the wresting rack.

After lunch the older boys fall into sword fights, and smaller ones play at Hawks and Hens. If one pupil stilts out for the afternoon, subtracting from the bedlam, the señora could only be the happier. Mother doesn't notice either. Too busy fuming about P. T.'s big house with nineteen maids in Colonia Juárez, which we will probably never see because of P. T.'s wife. Mother's big plans, washed out. Like flotsam in the alley after it rains.

Saturday is the best day at the Melchor Ocampo market. One old cigarette seller named La Perla is boss of that place, telling the girls to tidy their flower stalls. *Guapo, ven aqui*, take this money and go buy me a *pulque*. I see you here every day, *novio*, are you too good-looking for the schoolroom?

Handsome! To an old woman with the face of a lizard.

13 September

P. T. Cash came today to the *casa chica*, but left early. Everyone in a foul mood, God included. The rain kept pouring until it seemed the whole sky would drain like a tide. First Mother cried, then drank tea like a foreigner, trying to drown her Mexican passions. He shouted that her head is in the clouds, he is a man, not a fountain of money, the PNR is falling apart and everything he worked to build is running away like the water out in the streets. The American businesses will run across the border like Vasconcelos did. Mother knows this small house could fall at any moment. And we shall be beggars looking for scraps at the market. Bathing on St. John's Day.

15 September

Independence Day, the town boiling with parades for the Revolution. At school the cretins performed in costume: traditional dances, impaired by the absence of girls. The teachers made a Patriotism Banquet: rice in the colors of the flag, red and green salsa. Cups of rice water, sugared almonds, a little of everything, and of nothing quite enough. At the head of the table by the bowl of pomegranates, Señora Bartolome had put a note: Take only one, our Lord Jesus is watching!

A second note appeared at the foot of the table beside the sugared almonds: Take all you want, Jesus is looking at the pomegranates. The other boys laughed and spit rice water. The prank earned great approval and a whipping. But the administrator has a weak arm. Halfway through, he had to sit and rest, saying, *this squalid school, is there no better place for you?*

16 September

Stilted out of school before morning roll call. North on Avenida Puig and straight on, past the Hospital for Lepers. Past the Plaza Santo Domingo, where the scribes write letters for the people who can't. Many blocks of *multifamiliares* with tiny balconies like ours, each building painted pink, blue, or ochre. The wooden trolleys run in straight lines: north to south, east to west. The Azteca built it this way, with the Templo Mayor the center of everything. The Spaniards couldn't change what's underneath.

The Zócalo was crowded with men selling ices, women in long braids selling vegetables, charlatans selling miracles. The scent of copal. Music from the organ grinders. A man selling *carnitas*, the hungry boys following him like dogs. Some Preparatoria students put on a play in the street about Ortíz Rubio and Calles: the president was a puppet on strings, and old dictator Calles was his puppet master. The Preparatoria students had also stilted out from school.

The shortest way home was to walk by the Viga canal, filled with floating newspaper pages and one dead dog, swelled up like a yellow melon.

29 September

Today at the Melchor market, a fantastical sight. A servant girl with a birdcage on her back, full of birds. She wore her blue shawl wrapped around the cage and tied in front to hold it. The willow cage must have been very light because she was not bent over, yet it towered over her head, with turrets like a Japanese pagoda. And full of birds: green and yellow, flapping about like dreams trying to escape from a skull. She looked like an angel moving down the rows following her mistress, looking at no one.

The mistress had stopped to haggle with a man and buy another bird. She was so tiny, from the back she also looked like a servant girl. But when she turned, her skirts and silver earrings whirled and her face was very startling, an Azteca queen with ferocious black eyes.

Her hair was braided in a heavy crown like the Isla Pixol girls, and her posture very regal, though she wore the same ruffled skirts as her maid. She gave the vendor his money and took two green parrots, slipping them neatly into the cage on the girl's back. Then moved off quickly toward the street.

The old market woman La Perla said, "Don't fall in love with that one, *guapo*, she's taken. And her man carries a gun."

Which one is married? The servant girl, or the queen?

La Perla laughed, and so did her friend Cienfuegos the lizard-man. "That's no queen there," she said. More like a *puta*, was La Perla's opinion.

But Cienfuegos didn't agree. "It's her husband who chases women, not the other way around." The two of them argued about whether the tiny Azteca queen was a harlot. The lizard found and consumed a scrap of tortilla in the street. Finally Cienfuegos and La Perla agreed on one thing: the regal little woman is married to the *discutido pintador*. The much-discussed painter.

Who discusses him so much?

Cienfuegos said: "The newspapers." La Perla said: "Everyone, *guapo*, because he is a Communist. Also the ugliest man you ever saw."

Cienfuegos asked how she knew what he looked like, did he come around courting her? La Perla said she saw him once at the Plaza Caballito, down there with the troublemakers when the workers had their strike. He was as fat as a giant and horribly ugly, with the face of a frog and the teeth of a Communist. They say he eats the flesh of young girls, wrapped in a tortilla. "He's a cannibal. And from the look of her, I would say his little bride there might also eat children for lunch."

"From the look of things today, they're having parrot stew."

"No, *guapo*," La Perla said. "Not to eat! Those birds are for his paintings. He paints pictures of the strangest things. If he gets up in the morning and wants to paint the hat of an Englishman, his wife has to go find him the hat of an Englishman. Small or big, if he wants to paint it, *eso*. She has to run to the market and buy it."

"She must be carrying a lot of money in her purse then," said Cienfuegos, "because the newspaper says right now he's painting the National Palace."

6 October

Mother reached a diplomatic compromise with P. T. Cash. She gets to visit his house in Cuernavaca next week, and maybe some parties. Mother wants to learn the new dances. The Charleston is for dead hoofers, she says, only the meatballs are doing that now. In this city the smooth girls put on long skirts to do the *sandunga* and *jarabe*.

Suddenly the butterfly girls with long skirts and braided hair are in fashion. Mr. Cash does not agree; he says only nationalists and out-laws let their girls do those dances. But Mother bought a phonograph record for practicing the *sandunga*. Finally the Victrola is unpacked from its box, finding its outlaw voice.

15 October

Mother in Cuernavaca all week with P. T. Cash. She has agreed to the theory that looking for some jobs is better than staying at the school of cretins. Because of the oil men's money running over the border like water. None yet, except running errands for La Perla, which is work but no job. Trying to hire as a scribe to write letters for people in Plaza Santo Domingo was a bad idea. The men with stalls there howled like monkeys, defending their territories. Even though lines are long, and people wait all day. For two days the baker downstairs needed help with mixing the dough, while his wife was away. But now she is back, and he says Run away, we don't need a beggar boy here.

18 October
Mother is back in fine feather, with extra hush money. She bought one of the newspapers that carries the long adventure of Pancho Villa. The story is told a little each Saturday, so you'll have to buy another paper. But when people finish, you can pick it up from the sidewalk for free. Yesterday's heroes fall beneath the shoes of the city.

On Saturdays the university students have their *carpas* in the street, like a Poncho and Judas play, only with Vasconcelos and the president. Vasconcelos is always saving Mexico for the Mexican people: in a country school he takes down the cross from the wall, routs the nuns, and teaches the peasant children to read. He should come to Avenida Puig. President Ortíz Rubio gets to play more various roles: a puppet of gringos, or a baby in a basket, or a hairless *escuincle* dog. Everything but an iguana on a leash. Some newspapers agree with the students that the president is a villain, and others say he saved us from Vasconcelos, the foreigners, and the Russians. The newspapers only agree on the much-discussed painter: he covers the walls of our buildings with colors like a tree produces flowers. One newspaper showed a picture of him. La Perla was right: ugly!

They say he's making a huge painting on the stairwell of the National Palace, the long red building on the Zócalo with windows like holes in a flute. Cienfuegos and La Perla disagree whether you can walk in and have a look. The old lizard man says they have to let you, because it's courts and public offices. "Tell them you're getting married."

La Perla said, "Stupid old man, that won't work. Where is his wife?"

"All right," Cienfuegos said. "Tell them you're getting a divorce."

24 October
Dios mio. The paintings pull you right up the walls. Cienfuegos was right, they're inside, but you can walk through the main door into the courtyard with a flying-horse fountain and a portico all the way

around. In all the little offices, men stand in shirtsleeves recording marriages and tax accounts. Outside their doors on the hallway walls, Mexico bleeds and laughs, telling its whole story. The people in the paintings are larger than the men in the offices. Dark brown women among jungle trees. Men cutting stone, weaving cloth, playing drums, carrying flowers as big as brooms. Quetzalcoatl sits at the center of one mural in his grand green-feathered headdress. Everyone is there: Indians with gold bracelets on brown arms, Porfirio Díaz with his tall white hair and French sword. In one corner sketch, a native *escuincle* dog growls at the European sheep and cattle that have just arrived, as if he knows the trouble ahead. Cortés is there too, in the hallway outside Property Assessment. The painter has made him look like a white-faced monkey in his crested helmet. Moteczuma kneels, while the Spaniards make their mischief: fat monks stealing bags of gold, the Indians enslaved.

But Cortés was not the beginning of Mexico or its end, as the books say. These paintings say Mexico is an ancient thing that will still go on forever, telling its own story in slabs of color, leaves and fruits and proud naked Indians in a history without shame. Their great city of Tenochtitlan is still here beneath our shoes, and history was always just like today, full of markets and wanting. A beautiful lady lifts her skirt, showing her tattooed ankle. Maybe she is a *puta*, or a goddess. Or just someone like Mother who needs an admirer. The Painter makes you see that those three kinds of women might all be the same, because all the different ancestors are still inside us and don't really die. Imagine being able to tell such stories, whispering miracles into people's brains! To live by imagination alone, and get paid for it. Don Enrique was wrong.

Where was the Much-Discussed Painter? The guard said usually he's here day and night, any hour he can get his plaster mixers and pigmentists to show up. Every day but not today.

The mural on the wall behind the grand staircase was enormous. And not even half finished. Ladders and platforms covered most of the wall, so he could reach the highest parts. The guard looked up there at the planks for a while, as though he expected to find the Painter sleeping there. But today, no.

"Maybe he shot someone," the guard said. "Come back tomorrow. He has a lot of friends here at the ministry. He always gets out of prison."

25 October

Today the Painter came to work. He was already on the scaffolds at nine o'clock. High up on the planks, hard to see, but plainly he was there because workers swarmed around him like his own hive of bees. The assistant boys were running all over the courtyard with water and plaster, planks and ladders. They mix plaster in buckets and haul it up to him on a rope. It's not just a painting, these boys explained with proper scorn. A *mural*. Hard to say that in English: a wall-made. Not wall or painting but both combined, made at the same time so the picture will never fall off unless the wall itself tumbles. A Plaster Captain up on the scaffold works continuously at the Painter's side, spreading the last thin coat of white paste. Not too quickly or too slow, so the Painter can put his pigments in the plaster as it dries.

"Those two have worked together since God was sucking his mother's tit," the boys said. They seemed more afraid of the Plaster Captain than the Painter, though both men shouted down like God sending commandments: too much water in the plaster, or not enough. Today every boy was stupid.

The problem was the man in charge of plaster mixing, named Santiago but today named mud, because absent. They said he broke his head in a fight over a woman. And according to the Painter, without Santiago none of these boys could mix plaster any better than his grandmother's dog.

I can mix plaster.

Go ahead, then.

It was like mixing the flour for *pan dulce*: how could it be so different? The powder they called *cal* has the same fine grind, floating up in white clouds around the boys when they dumped bags of it into the mixing buckets. Their eyelashes and the backs of their hands were white, and the edges of their nostrils, from breathing it. They were dumping powder into the water, not the other way around.

Wait. Spread a canvas on the floor, make a mountain of the powder. Pour water in the center, a lake in the volcano. Mix the lagoons with your fingers into marshes, making the paste thick. Gradually, or there will be lumps.

Even the old Plaster Captain up on the platform stopped working to watch. It was terrifying. "Where did you learn that?"

"It's like making dough for *pan dulce*."

That caused the plaster boys to laugh. Boys don't make bread. But they were in trouble, so got quiet again. One asked, "Like *nixtamal* for tortillas?"

"No, the white flour dough. You use it for European bread and sweet buns."

Ha ha ha, Sweet Buns! So the new job has a new name to go with it. But the Plaster Captain and Painter both remarked on the plaster. The plaster captain is Señor Alva, the painter is Señor Rivera. He is even more fat than he looked in the newspaper, and feared by the boys, so it might be true he eats flesh. But when he climbed down from the scaffold to go make his water, he said, "Hey, Sweet Buns, come over here! Let me have a look at the boy who's mixing this good plaster."

He said, "Come back tomorrow. We may need you again."

29 October

The Painter keeps boys running as late as the last trolley runs. Sometimes you mix, or tie ropes, or carry things up the scaffolds. The Palacio has spiked iron lanterns hanging from the ceiling, you have to watch your head or could crown yourself. The stairwell mural is the size of two walls, one above the other. It is meant to be finished before the end of the year.

A coarse plaster full of sand goes on first, to cover ridges and bumps in the brick wall. Next, three more layers, each smoother and whiter, more marble dust and less sand. The bumps are erased, like forgetting, and the painter begins the story new. Each day he leaves more history on the wall, and boys leave with more pesos in their pockets.

Today Señor Alva came down from the scaffold as fast as a monkey to fight with one of the guards. They are rude about the paintings. Four boys in *tejano* hats came in and said they would throw tar on the wall after the Painter goes home, to defend Mexico and save her national symbols from insult. Señor Alva shouted at the guards to keep those boys away. But the Painter seems not to care what they say. He keeps painting.

10 November

Señor Rivera is gone. And the wall only half painted. Indians and horsemen ride above white air. The mountains have no ground beneath them. The coal sketches on the rough white wall remain half alive, waiting. This can't be the end, but Señor Alva says for sure he's gone. To San Francisco to paint for the gringos. The only work now is to take apart the scaffold and clean the splatters of plaster off the floor. That's it, boys, he said. The pesos have gone to San Francisco too.

18 January 1931, Feast of San Antonio

The priest did the blessing of animals. The society ladies brought parrots and canaries to church, clutching the cages against brocaded bosoms, baby-speaking to their birds with bird-pursed lips. Or holding cats that wriggled violently, hopeful of eating a parrot. Or hairless *escuincles* that watched with big disapproving eyes popping out of their dog skulls. At the back of the church, villagers waited with goats and burros on ropes. After dogs and parrots were satisfactorily blessed, the farm women were allowed to lead their beasts down the aisle, all eyes upon the burro blessings dropped on the floor.

One old man brought a sack of dirt over his shoulder that was crawling with ants and caterpillars. When he marched to the altar, all the women in smart hats leaned away from the aisle, their long strands of pearls all swaying to one side as if the deck of a ship listed beneath them. The priest in his clean hems backed away from the altar as the farmer heaved his sack onto it and black ants swarmed all over. "Go on, make these pests into Christians!" the farmer shouted. "I'll take them home to convert the others, so they'll stop chewing on my crops and leave me a living."

Cienfuegos came with Manjar Blanco on his leash. The ladies did not know how to pray for a Christian lizard. Their little dogs are probably still barking about it.

31 March

School or a job is the only choice, Mother says. So it's school again, murderous. Today there was a body! Draped in black cloth, lying across four wooden chairs lined up side by side in the administrator's office. The administrator was still out having his lunch when the Penitent was sent in for a minor infraction involving spittle, and had to wait there a long time, examining The Body. Its feet stuck out from beneath the drape, plainly the feet of a dead person. Man or woman, it was impossible to tell, but nothing was breathing under that cloth. No scent of corpse gas either. Detective novels often mention that. But perhaps it was recently dead and hadn't had time to decay. Or perhaps there was corpse gas, the whole school smelled of piss, and it might be similar. The hour passed horribly, measured in held breaths.

Twenty minutes. It couldn't be Señora Bartolome under that black drape. Too slim. And not the administrator—everyone saw him leave for his lunch. What kind of school punishes boys by making them sit in a room with a corpse?

Fifty minutes. Outside in the sun the Holy Mother stood on her pedestal in the garden, sorry but unsympathetic. The usual position of mothers.

Fifty-eight minutes: the administrator returned in a high mood, smelling a little of pulque. At the sight of the Penitent he fell into his chair, abruptly depressed. Lately he can summon little courage for the beatings. "Oh, it's Shepherd, our troublesome foreigner. What is it today?"

"Reading in the class again, sir. And participating in a contest of sorts."

"Of what sort?"

"Of spitting to hit a mark on the floor, sir."

"Anything that might improve your character? The reading, I mean."

"No, sir. Booth Tarkington."

The administrator leaned so far back in his chair, it appeared he might fall out of it, or else begin a nap. He made no mention of the draped form. Who could it be? It seemed taller than the stunted type of boy inclined to this school. But hard to judge, lying down.

"Sir. Is it possible to ask, has any of the teachers been ill?"

Sitting near enough the body that he could reach over to box its ears, the administrator replied, "All as hale as can be expected for women of their age and temperament." He sighed. "Which is to say, probably immortal. Why do you ask?"

"One of the students, then? Has any boy turned up, well, dead?"

The administrator now seemed unlikely to nap. *"Dead?"*

"Perhaps subjected to an overly long punishment by accident, and perished?"

The administrator now sat up. "You are an imaginative boy. Are you also a suspicious one?"

A glance at the feet that poked from under that drape. "No, sir."

"You should write stories, boy. You have the disposition for a romantic novelist."

"Sir, is that a good or bad disposition to have?"

The administrator smiled and looked sad, both at once. "I am not certain. But I'm sure of one thing, you don't belong in this school."

"No, sir. That seems certain to me also."

"I've spoken of it to Señora Bartolome. She says your competence at learning the Latin lessons has surpassed her competence to teach them. It isn't fair to the others, for her to teach so much. They struggle with conjugating their shoes and stockings."

A long pause.

"We discussed a transfer to the Preparatoria next year."

"Sir, the entrance examinations are murder. At least, for anyone who's missed learning everything they teach after the sixth-grade primary."

"Indeed. How did that happen to you?"

"A drastic home life, sir. Something like a novel."

"Well, then. One can only hope you are writing it all down."

"No, sir, only some of it. On the interesting days. On most of the days it's along the lines of a bad novel with no character learning any moral."

The administrator placed his elbows on the desk and touched his fingers together, making his hands into a flower bud. The unanswered question of the corpse still lay beside him. This was more of an interesting day.

"Back to the classroom with you then, young Shepherd," he said, finally. "I will tell Señora Bartolome you have my permission to read adventure novels as much as you like, in preparation for your writing career. But I'll advise you to pay attention during the maths. They could turn out more useful than they seem."

"Yes, sir."

"One thing more. We are aware your attendance is casual."

"I had a bit of work, sir. But lost it again."

"Well, I expect there is little I can do about keeping you here. But please come on Friday. Before we dismiss for Easter week, our school will be leading the processional down the street to St. Agnes. We need six of our older boys for carrying the Santo Cristo. You may be the only one who can remember which way to walk."

"For carrying the what?"

The administrator leaned out from his desk and yanked the silk drape from the corpse, exposing a bloody head and naked shoulders. "Our crucifixion figure. We've just had it cleaned and varnished, ready to carry into the chapel."

"Oh. Indeed sir, *corpus Deum*. He lives."

School is closed for Holy Week, but Mother is in an unholy frame of mind, due to the predicted collapse of the Mexican oil industry. According to P. T., production has fallen to less than a quarter what it was when the Americans first came in. They thought they were tapping a deeper vein, he said.

"So did I," Mother says.

In a jam, she asked the doctor's wife for guidance. As usual, it was suggested that God might provide, so Palm Sunday mass at the cathedral is part of the plan. The place was a forest of palm leaves standing upright, swaying in the windless air, held up by villagers with pleading eyes and hungry children. Mrs. Doctor was dressed up in a silver fox stole like Dolores del Rio. She pulled Mother toward the front pews, away from the odors of poverty. The kneeling lasted hours, but Mother wrestled through.

The streets outside afterward were like a festival. People pouring in from the provinces, maybe some even from Isla Pixol. All eyes turn to the Virgin as she is conveyed about town in many different processions, dressed in her jeweled diadem and many new frocks at once.

Uninteresting days without number. A *National Geographic* pinched from the bookshop. It had a photograph of a Hindu with six hundred pins inserted in his body. Two skewers through his abdomen, one through the tongue. Dressing each morning takes him one hour and a half. For overcoming life's catastrophes, he walks through fire.

8 May

The administrator called Mother in for a talk before school ends. She would sooner walk through fire, yet she put on her worst dress and went. The administrator told Mother it was in the boy's interest that he should attend a different school next year. There were choices—technical, professional—but his advice was the Preparatoria. He lectured Mother using many conjugations of the verb "to prepare." Preparation for Preparatoria. But Mother prepares for nothing. She informed him it was none of his business, but her son was going to the United States to live with his father, and she was certain the schools there were of higher caliber.

Is it true? On the angry walk home, she refused to say.

10 June

The angel servant girl of the birdcage reappeared at the Melchor market. This time she was without the birdcage, but again followed hastily behind the Azteca queen, accepting every form of purchase that dark little woman could shove in her arms. Clay bowls, sacks of beans, a devil's head made of papier-mâché. The mistress limped slightly but otherwise was exactly the same, snapping her fingers at the servant girl and everyone else as she moved down the rows. Measuring every object with fearsome black eyes.

La Perla recognized them too: *That scandal, the painter's wife*, she called her. "They went away, but see, they're back, probably kicked out by the gringos. It will be in the newspapers. The Communists always make trouble so they can get in the papers."

24 June, St. John's Day

The lepers bathe again.

La Perla was right, the Painter is in the newspapers. The president wants him to finish what he started on the Palacio stair wall. All the top-level men want this Painter now, Ambassador Morrow hired him to paint his palace in Cuernavaca. Mother claims she saw it when she was there, and the ambassador also, who is now a senator of the United States. She says she spoke to him on the street, and why not, they're acquainted. Ambassador Morrow came to visit Don Enrique, it was the time she made P. T. Cash dance with her in his black-and-white shoes. Now she thinks Morrow would have been the better bet.

6 July, cumpleaños. *Fifteen years of age.*
No birthday fiesta, but Mother said to take some extra coins from her purse and buy some *carne asada* or something nice at the market. Only, no coins.

The Painter's wife was there today buying buckets of food, getting ready for a fiesta at her house from the looks of it. But no servant! The little queen looked like a burro under all her baskets. Two bananas fell on the street behind her as she walked. Down at the end of the market, men were unloading a wagon of green-tamale corn in the husk, stacking the ears in tall pyramids. The queen pointed through her bundles, making a man fill a big sack for her.

La Perla said, "Stop staring, *guapo.* Just because it's your birthday, you don't get any girl you want. Your eyes will roll in the street behind her like those bananas."

"How is she going to carry that corn? She'll collapse for sure."

"So, go talk to her. Tell her for ten pesos you'll carry it. She'll pay you, she's rich. Go on, *go.*" La Perla pushed with her little hands like knives. Crossing the street was like walking through water.

Señora Rivera. Would you like some help carrying something?

She set down her two baskets, picked up the great bulging sack, and handed it over with a thump. "Go ahead. Anybody has the right to make a kite from his pants."

There was no further discussion. Following behind her was a whole conversation by itself: her swirling skirts, her short legs walking as fast as a little dog's, her proud head crowned with its circle of braids. Make way for the queen, pulling a boy behind like a kite on a string. Her house was down four streets and over one, on Londres at the corner of Allende. She walked through the tall front door without saying "Follow" or "Stop here" or anything, sweeping past an old woman with her apron bunched up in one hand, who took the sack of corn and went away. But the Queen stood where she was, framed in the entry by bright sunlight beyond. The high wall enclosed a beautiful courtyard inside, with the rooms of the house all around it.

It was impossible to turn away from the sight of her strange little figure there, the palms and fig trees waving behind her like fans. The courtyard was a dream. Birds in cages, fountains, plants sprawling from their pots, vines climbing the trunks of the trees. And in that jungle, the Painter! Sprawled in a chair in the sun, wearing the wrecked clothes of a beggar and the glasses of a professor. He was smoking a cigar and reading a newspaper.

"Oh! Good morning, sir."

"Who is it?" He barely glanced up. His wife gave a warning look.

"Sir, the nation rejoices in your return."

"The nation considers me to be worth approximately two peanuts, at most."

"Nevertheless, sir. Do you need a plaster mixer?"

Now the paper dropped onto the round belly and he looked up, taking off his glasses, his bulging eyes like two boiled eggs in that enormous head. He glared for a moment, then brightened: "Sweet Buns! How I've missed you. Those other boys are hopeless."

The Queen stood staring with such a fierce frown, her dark eyebrows joined in a handshake over the bridge of her nose. But her mouth remained amused as she watched her husband get up to clap this strange boy on the back, hiring him on the spot.

❊

The great mural grows down the staircase day by day, like a root into the ground. Presidents and soldiers and Indians, all coming alive. The sun opens its eyes, a landscape grows like grass, and today fire came out of the volcano. Señor Alva says the Painter is working his way toward the beginning of time, at the mural's center, where the eagle will sit on a cactus and eat the serpent, home at last.

Señor Rivera makes charcoal sketches over the wall, and every day begins a new section. He frames the scene with long lines sloping to a point on the distant horizon, the Vanishing Point. Then holds the picture in his head as he works to paint in shadows, then color, finishing a panel as fast as we can mix plaster for the next one. The slake-lime paste burns our hands, white marble dust becomes the air we breathe. Today he scolded the pigmentist because the blue paste was too blue. But the plaster was perfect.

14 October

Ambassador Senator Morrow died in his sleep while his wife was playing golf. All the newspapers are about him, Best friend of Mexico. His daughter's husband is Charles Lindbergh, so he only has to wave his cap at the crowd and everyone cheers, or mourns. Mother says she had that ambassador pegged from the start: the type to love his wife and die young. She's sore because P. T. did not produce the cash after all.

26 October, luna de octubre

Some of the boys at work say the Painter is going away again. Señor Alva says they want to make a big show of his paintings in a museum in New York. But his paintings are on the walls of Mexico. How could they leave here?

12 November

He's gone. He took Señor Alva with him. In the forgotten white land at the bottom of our wall, the eagle has no cactus, no snake for his lunch, he can't find home. The story of Mexico waits for its beginning.

PART 2

Washington, D.C.

1932–1934

(VB)

1 January 1932

For a son on the wrong track, Mother has found a different set of rails and packed him off on them. *Lock, stock, and barrel*, she said with a raised glass. Describing a firearm in its entirety.

This train runs north from the city. At the little struggling desert towns, children run alongside, reaching toward the windows. Then come the rocky flatlands where the towns give up altogether. Spiked maguey plants reach out of the ground like hands. A great clawed creature trapped underground. At evening, the light drained and the land went from brown to umber, then dried blood, then ink. In the morning the pigments reversed, the same colors rising out of a broad, flat land that looks like a mural.

This compartment has one other person, an American named Green who got on at Huichapan. Not old, but he stares out the window like an old person, rocking in rhythm with the suitcases over his head and water in a glass in his hand. He sips a little every hour, as if it's the last water on earth. Overnight some flames appeared in the distance, each standing alone like a candle. Oil wells, burning to remove the gases.

Last night the conductor came through to say we were three hours from the border and it was twelve o'clock; his privilege was to wish us a prosperous New Year. He moved down the car repeating the same news and the same privileged wish.

Happy new year, Mr. Green.

Just before the border were pecan orchards, dark blocks of trees with their boughs half bright and half shadowed, lit by the electric lights of the shelleries. People working there in the dead of night, New Year's morning. The train sighed and stopped at the border, waiting for the customs agents to arrive at their offices. The whitening sky showed a thin stretch of river with dogs skulking along its shores, their up-curved tails reflected on the gray surface. The riverbank is a dumping ground: planks and metal, flaps of tarred paper. At daybreak children began walking from the scrap piles, not a dumping ground after all but a terrible kind of city. Women came out of the shacks too, and last the men, straightening to unfold themselves, placing both hands against their backs, shifting their trousers and pissing in the ditches. Squatting to splash their faces at the river's edge.

Old men thin as bones walked along the stopped train, looking in the windows. They lingered at the rear until police came with sticks to beat them away from the iron-sided cars. These people look as poor as could ever be, worse than the beggars and *borrachos* of Mexico City, who at least always have a ballad of the Revolution to sing into their shirt collars as they lean on a doorway. Here is the end of Mexico, end of the world and Chapter One. This train ride is like the long, narrow cave in the sea. With luck it might open on the other side into someplace new. But not here.

6 January

Five days and the train has passed through many underworlds. Grass hills, dark swamps of standing trees. And now, almost nothing but fields of dead sticks, immense as the sea. Not a green leaf anywhere. The gringos read magazines, failing to notice their world has nothing left alive in it. Only the Mexicans look out the windows and worry. A woman and four children are the only others who have come this same unimaginable distance, from Mexico City. Today when the train crossed a bridge over a high river gorge, she made the children sing for the Feast of the Kings so they wouldn't cry. She took a *rosca* cake from her bag, crumbling out of its paper wrappings into the worn velvet seats. The family huddled together, locking their small holiday from the inside.

7 January: Federal District of North America

Lock, stock, and barrel the human cargo arrived today at Union Station, delivered into such fierce cold, stepping off the train felt like being thrown into water and commanded to breathe it. The Mexican mother reached her little foot down from the doorway like the feeler of a snail. The freezing air set her to panic, rolling her children up in shawls like tamales, pushing them ahead of her into the station, *adios*.

Would he be here? And if not? Mother had suggested no other plan, if the father should fail to arrive and claim his baggage. But now here he was: a painful clap on the shoulder, the blue eyes measuring, how strange, a relative with pale eyes. Who could have picked *that* one, from just the one tinted photograph? Of course, he must have been experiencing similar disappointments in the son. "Your train was an hour late."

"Sorry, sir." Ragtag boys rushed past like pigeons flushed from the bush, coshing people's suitcases into their knees.

"A bunch of little tramps on the rods," he said.

"On the rods?"

"They ride into town on the outside of the train."

The cold was killing, every breath prickling into needles of nostril-ice. And clothes itching like mange after so many days. People in long coats, the howling steam engines. Finally it dawned, what he'd said: these ragged boys rode *outside* the train. *Dios mio.* "Where will they go now?"

"Bunk on their ears in some hobo jungle. Or else they'll go listen to the Christers. Accept the Lord for one night in exchange for a mulligan."

"Is mulligan a kind of money?"

His laugh was a loud burst, like notes exploding from a mariachi trumpet. He was amused by this empty bank of bewilderment, his son. The inside of the station was like the cathedral: so much space overhead, a great dome rising toward heaven, but not enough room down here for all the people jammed in. A grand marble doorway opened to the street, but outdoors the sun was cold, shining without heat, like an electric bulb. Crowds hurried along, unconcerned their star had no fire.

"Where is everybody going?"

"Home, son! Time for a two-bit square and a working man's nap. This is nothing. You should see it Monday morning."

Could a street hold more people? Inside the station the trains were still shrieking, the sound of digestion in the belly of that monument. Like an Aztec temple drinking blood. Mother's parting advice: Try to put a positive face on things, the man hates whining, let me tell you.

"Union Station looks like a temple."

"A temple." Father gave a sideways look. "How old are you now, fourteen?"

"Fifteen. Sixteen this summer."

"Right. Temples. Built with government money by Hoover's swindlers." He scowled at the trolley stop, as if the city had slyly shifted around behind his back while he was in the station. A freckled, pink-ish man, the pale moustache discolored along its bottom edge. The photograph hadn't recorded the unheroic complexion—that skin would broil to a crisp in Mexico. One mystery solved.

He dodged into the crowd and moved fast, leaving no choice but to tuck-chin like a boxer and watch out for horse droppings, tugging the behemoth trunk. Mother's driver had put it on the train; porters carried it after that. No more help now, America was help-yourself.

"They're planning to put up a whole string of your *temples* here on the south side of Pennsylvania. See that eye-popper? Washington's Monument." He pointed into a leafless park, the pale stone rising above the trees. A memory rose with it: the long, narrow box of hallway rising like a dark mouse tunnel. An echoing argument in the stairwell, Mother's hand pulling downward, back to safety.

"We went in there, didn't we? One time with Mother?"

"You remember that? Small fry. You got the screaming heebies on the stairs."

He'd stopped at a corner, panting, emitting breath in bursts of steam like a kettle. "They've put an elevator to the top now. One more temple to Hoover's swindlers, if you ask me." He chuckled, tasting his clever remark again after the fact, like a belch. People were gathering here, a trolley stop. An officer clopped past on a huge bay horse.

"Mother said *you* worked for President Hoover."

"Who says I don't?" A hint of ire, suggesting he might not. Or not in any capacity Mr. Hoover would know about. A bean counter in a government office, Mother said, but one of the last men in America with a steady job, so it serves him right to get his boy sent him on the train.

"President Hoover is the greatest man ever lived," he said, overly loud. People looked. "They've just had a telephone put in on his desk, for calling his chief of staff. He can get MacArthur quick as snapping his fingers. You think your president of Mexico has a telephone on his desk?"

Mexico will be held as a grudge, then. Probably for reasons to do with Mother. Ortíz Rubio does have a telephone; the newspapers say he can't make a move without ringing up Calles first, at his house on the Street of Forty Thieves in Cuernavaca. But Father didn't want to hear about that. People ask without wanting to know. He boarded the trolley through the brew of people, shouldering his way toward the seats. The trunk wouldn't fit under the wooden bench, but hunched in the aisle: an embarrassment. People coming on the trolley flowed around it like a river over a boulder.

The ride was long. He stared out the window. It was impossible to imagine this man in the same room with Mother, the same bed. She would swat him like a fly. Then call a maid to wipe up the residue.

The men here wear suits like businessmen in Mexico City, but with more layers due to the cold. The women have complicated stuff, long scarves and things to put their hands in, hard to name. One had a shawl around her neck made from a whole fox with its head still on, biting its tail. If Cortés came here, he could write the Queen a whole chapter about the ladies' clothes.

After many stops, Father said: "We are going out to the school. They said it's the best to start right away, in your situation." He spoke slowly, as if "situation" meant a boy with a damaged brain. "It's bread and board. You'll bunk there with your pals, Harry."

"Yes, sir." (*Harry*. It will be Harry now?)

"That'll be a barrel of laughs." He bit his moustache, then added, "It better be."

Meaning, it is costing some money. *Harry. Harry Shepherd looked out the window.* Whoever pays the bill, names the boy.

Scenes passed by: marble edifices, parks of skeletal trees, boarded warehouses. Pale white men in black suits and hats. And then the opposite: dark-colored men in pale shirts and trousers, no hats at all. They were digging a long trench with pickaxes, their muscled arms bare even in this cold. In all Mexico there is not one Indian so black as those men. Their arms had a shine, like the rubbed wood of black piano keys.

At the end of the trolley ride, a motorbus. The great trunk occupied its own seat, with a window for viewing the scenery of mansions strung along a river. Father took long fishing expeditions into his pocket to find his watch, pull it out, and frown at its face. Did he remember the other watch, the one Mother took, later on pinched again from her jewelry case? The memory of it feels like a sickness now, not for the sin of thievery but for the dreadful longing pinned to it. For this man. This father.

17 January

Most Lofty Excellent Empress, the place called Potomac Academy is marvellous bad. A prison camp in brick buildings built to look like mansions, where native leaders called Officers rule over the captives. The Dormitory is a long house of beds like a hospital, with every patient required to go dead at Twenty One Hours. Lights Out means no more reading or else. In the morning the corpses rise again on command.

The strangest thing: the captive boys don't seem to wish for escape. In class they take their orders and knuckle under, but the minute the officer leaves the room, they commence to rapping heads with inkwells and aping the language of radio men named Amos and Andy. In the dormitory they gawk at someone's eight-pager with a girl called Sally Rand in it, naked with feathery fans. She looks like a cold baby bird.

The captives are released Saturday afternoon, no classes or exercises for once, and the dormitory empties out. Boys go to homes if they have them. The morning is Chapel first, then Mess Hall, then Freedom.

All the other boys in form nine are younger. But taller than the cretins anyway, and less spittle. Form nine was a compromise, because of being too tall to go all the way back to form six. The officers teach Latin, maths, and other things. Drill and psychomotricity. Best is literature. The officer recommended a pass to the form-eleven literature class, Samuel Butler, Daniel Defoe, and Jonathan Swift. Who gives a fig if they are Restoration or neoclassicists? New books in endless supply.

Drill is cleaning and display of firearms, not so different from cleaning dishes.

Mathematics: the worst. Nothing past the *tablas de multiplicar* will ever fit in this calabash. Algebra, a language spoken on the moon. For a boy with no plans to go there.

Sunday, January 24
Notes on how to speak in America:

> *1.* Do not say "Pardon me." People in books say it constantly. Here, they ask who sent you to prison.
> *2.* Shouting "Go fry asparagus!" won't make them leave you alone, as it would in Spanish.
> *3.* "Beat it" means Go fry asparagus.
> *4.* "Punk" means fluter. Also: chump, ratso, and "sure it ain't the YMCA."
> *5.* "Mexico" is not a country, but a name. Hey Mexico, comeer.

The United States is the land of the square deal and the working stiff. Even though the newspapers say nobody has a job, and deals are not very geometric.

The boys move in cloudish groups, like schools of fish on the reef. In the hallways the groups approach, pass by, and join up again behind, as if you were a rock, not a sentient being. A splay-legged thing dangling in the wrong world.

February 21
So many people are sore at President Hoover, he had to chain up the gates to the White House and lock himself in. According to the boy named Bull's Eye. Yesterday a one-armed vet tried to break through the gate, got his ass beat up, and was hauled off to the hoosegow, where the one-armed man received his first square in a fortnight.

> *6.* A square is a meal.

Bull's Eye pinches newspapers and cigarettes from the Officers' Mess. When he pulls the papers out of his jacket in the lavatory, the boys crowd around. They can't wait for him to read his made-up headlines in the loud voice of a news hawker: EXTREY, HEXTREY! CHICKEN LIVER HOOVER CRAWLS UNDER PRESIDENTIAL BED! MRS. HOOVER TO GET SOME PEACE AT LAST!

The real name of Bull's Eye is Billy Boorzai. He isn't a regular student. He was, until his pop lost his job at a radio shop and his mam lost her marbles. Now he takes classes only half the day, then works in the kitchen and mops the lavs. At night he reads what he has swiped from teachers' desks, getting his education on the lam, he says.

Bull's Eye has admirers but no friends in here, he says, his friends are all on the outside. He gets to leave the grounds because of his job in the kitchen (*the mess*). The cooks send him to the butcher's, the canvas man's, even the gunsmith's sometimes. He says the cooks need firearms for self-defense, the food is that bad.

February 28

A logic problem: is the tedium of maths class better or worse than the tedium of maths detention? Being held prisoner in the library with an algebra book is not improving. But, that great hall full of books is not punishment, either. For certain it is safer than outdoors with boys shoulder-banging at American football, screaming in the language of Gee Whiz and Your Old Man.

March 13

Every morning Bull's Eye stands naked in the lav, shaving his face. He looks twenty. He says he's only the same age as everybody else here, plus a few hard knocks. He says you grow up fast when the South Sea Bubble bursts and your dad gets the boot. He doesn't go home either. We have that in common: dads who won't look a son in the eye. He says it's good as any reason for friendship.

It's the only one so far. The boy called Pencil in the next bed will talk if no one else is around. The Greek boy named Damos says, "Hey Mexico, comeer," but he also says, "Hey Brush Ape." Bull's Eye told them to watch out, the kid from Mexico is ace at firearms, maybe he used to ride with Pancho Villa.

Now they use that name: Pancho Villa. It took a while to recognize it because they pronounce it something like Pants Ville: *Hey, Pants-ville, comeer!* It sounds like a location, one of the hanging-laundry neighborhoods you see from the train to Huichapan.

March 14
Lucky Lindy's baby is kidnapped, and everyone is afraid, even boys locked up in a brick school. For the hero who flew across the ocean, a terrible crash. The newspapers say any child is in danger if Lindbergh could be that unlucky. But this country already had bad-luck people everywhere, sleeping in the parks, wearing newspapers for coats. The people who have good cloth coats look out the trolley windows and say, *Those bums need to buck up.* Unlucky Lindy makes them afraid because it happened to a hero.

March 20
Bull's Eye smells like peeled potatoes, cigarettes, and the mop bucket. When the others go home on Saturday, he says, "Hey-Pancho-Villa, you are cor-di-ally invited to assist me with my labors." These include scrubbing the lunch mess, running with the wet mop in the commissary, jumping on it, and sliding across the floor between the long tables. And so forth. The assistant receives no pay except getting his head squeezed inside Bull's Eye's elbow and his hair scrubbed with knuckles. That is how boys touch here, Bull's Eye especially.

March 27
Military strategy is interesting. Running an army is similar to running a household of servants. Mother is good at that kind of warfare, she has instincts for reconnaissance and the surprise attack. Officer Ostrain says the United States has the sixteenth largest army in the world, ranking leagues behind Great Britain, Spain, Turkey,

Czechoslovakia, Poland, Romania, and many others. (Mexico was not mentioned.) Our poorly equipped military seems to offend Officer Ostrain to the limits of his brass-buttoned endurance. He says it's a disgrace that General MacArthur and Major Eisenhower have to stand on Pennsylvania Avenue waiting like common citizens for the Mt. Pleasant trolley car, to get to the Senate chambers.

The boys say they have seen them and Major Patton also, playing polo on Saturdays at Myer Field. They want to grow up to have ponies like the generals, and sport them around polo fields on Saturdays with Sally Rand riding behind, her breasts bouncing like footballs. That is why they never plot an escape from the academy.

April 10

The K Street market is like a piece of Mexico. The fish hawkers sing the same as on the *malecón*, but in a kind of English: *four-bits a mack-rel, la-yay-dies!* Old women with teas and herbs promise to cure any ailment. The air smells like home: charred meat, salt fish, horse dung. Going there today was like bursting through the surface of water and finally breathing. After being in a tunnel of dark, for thirteen Sundays.

The outer part of the market has stalls selling leather goods, teakettles, every earthly thing for anyone that still has a nickel to rub against a dime. Inedibles are sold on the outside of the market, comestibles in the interior. The knife grinders with big naked arms stand at the entrance to the butchers' avenue. Oystermen in white aprons wheel full carts up from the wharves. The *cilindro* man has one missing ear, and a monkey in a blue cap to dance to his organ music. Women sell figs and roses, eggs and sausages, chickens and cheese, racks of dressed rabbits, even live birds in cages like the market in Coyoacán. One woman sells *conejillos de Indias*. Bull's Eye says they are not called Indian rabbits here, but Guinean pigs. He has no good explanation for it, and agrees they are probably more rabbit than pig.

This morning he told the head cook he needed an assistant for his errands at the market. Have a heart, Bull's Eye told her, you're asking for more than one poor sod can carry. His first destination is the Atlantic and Pacific Tea Company, which he calls the A and P, and which sells more than tea. The week's supply of rice, beef, flour, coffee, and fifty more things for the Potomac Academy go into crates from there onto a horse-truck every Saturday. The week's changes to the list have to be brought in person, the shop men want a boy to help with the boxing up. Other things are purchased from the rest of the market. The boy for the errand is Bull's Eye, and now his assistant Pancho Villa.

It took hours to get to the A and P. With so many swell things to look at on the way, dogs to be fed, friends to cuff on the shoulder. Blue-black workmen to be stared at as they pick open a trench as long as Pennsylvania Avenue. Where do they come from?

"Africa acourse," was Bull's Eye's reply.

"From Africa, all that way, just for the job of digging ditches?"

"No, you lob. They were slaves first. Before they all got put free by Abe Lincoln. Didn't you ever hear of the slaves?"

"Maybe. But not like these. Mexico didn't have them."

A lob is a *pendejo*. But Bull's Eye will answer questions that can't be asked of other boys. Those dark men and their wives can't shop here or ride the trolleys, he said, it's against the law. Even to get lunch in a restaurant. If one of them needs to make water whilst digging the ditch on Pennsylvania Avenue, or get a drink, he has to walk two miles out Seventh Street to find a restaurant that will let him touch a glass or use the lav.

It's a strange way. Being a servant, making a bad wage, that is no puzzle. All the richest men in Mexico were once lifted from the cradle by servants. But they all drink from the same water jar that fills the master's glass, and they use the same chamber pot, still warm from the piss of the *patrón*. In Mexico nobody ever thought to keep those streams flowing separately.

April 17

School is closing two weeks for Easter holiday. Then comes the end of the term soon, and summer. Most of the boys will go home, but not all. Some have to stay for remedial maths and repeating Virginia history in the sweat of July. Living here in the sock-stinking dormitory, and not with Father. He clearly explained that, in his letter about coming to visit while school is closed for Easter holiday. That will be swell, he says, a visit with old Dad. Swell enough for two weeks, not the whole summer.

Nothing here counts for anything now but Saturdays. Going to the market with Billy Boorzai. The rest is just coasting with half-closed eyes through another week.

May 3

Father's explanations made no mention of a lady. She must have cleared out of his apartment in a hurry, to make way for the Easter visitor. On the Q.T., Father is putting on the feedbag with a dame. Dust-colored stockings hang like cobwebs on the bathroom radiator, a lipstick winks like gossip on the bureau. Why would he hide her? Does he not know about Mother and her swains? He should listen through her wall some night, if he thinks his son is unacquainted with bedroom jolly-ups and pig fights.

Or he would lose some bargaining score if the Dame is reported back to Mexico. He and Mother are still not divorced because of the Mexican paperwork. "Divorce," he pronounces like a taste of soup with too much salt. Her name, he says like the Lord's taken in vain. Sometimes he says "Mexico," and the word has nothing in it at all. A wall with no colors painted on it.

May 5

A Trip to the Museum with the Father Figure. The weather has gone from freezing to broiling, with some talk of cherry blossoms in between. People on the trolley press against you in a crush, men in white linen suits, girls in sailor dresses and felt turbans. The smell of perspiration is different here. Cortés could write about that also: Most Excellent Empress, the sweat of the Northern People has a redolent stench. Maybe because of so many layers of clothes. Father's white suit hangs limp from his shoulders, wilting by the minute, like the moonflowers in the garden in Isla Pixol.

Smith Sonian is the name of the museum, a brick castle containing the stuffed, dead skins of every species but our own. Why not a few humans too? Father laughed at that one, like a man in some kind of a show, with an audience. His mood has shifted. Now he seems to take his son as a joke, rather than a serious offense. The museum had rooms of things from Tenochtitlan and other ancient sites of Mexico, fabulous artworks in gold that Cortés did not manage to carry off. Now in Washington, instead.

On the ride back to Father's apartment the trolley passed a long park, a row of warehouses, and then the most amazing spectacle: a city of tents and shacks roiling with people. Cooking fires, children, laundry hanging on lines, like a Mexican village of the very poorest kind set down in the middle of Washington City, surrounded by office buildings. A hand-lettered sign said: BONUS EXPEDITIONARY ENCAMPMENT. The American flag hung about in multiples over the shacks like laundry, blending in with the laundry really. The flags were as sun-faded as the upside-down trousers on the lines. The size of the camp was astonishing, a whole nation of beggars arrived in the capital. "That lot," Father spat through his moustache. "They've run their hobo jungle all the way down Pennsylvania. I have to pass through all that to get to work every morning."

A woman in a headscarf held up a naked baby toward our trolley. The baby waved its arms. A hobo jungle is unlike other jungles, where monkeys howl through the leafy air. "What do they all want?"

"What does anybody want? Something for nothing acourse." In that moment Father sounded like Bull's Eye.

"But why so many of them? And all the flags?"

"They're war veterans. Or so they say, because vets are entitled to a soldier's bonus. They want their bonus."

Ragged men stood at military attention every few meters, like fence posts all along the edge of the camp facing the street. Veteran soldiers, you could tell it from the placement of feet and shoulders. But their eyes searched the passing trolley with a terrifying hunger. "They've been here all week? What do the families live on?"

"Shoe leather soup, I'd say."

"Those men fought in France, with mustard gas and everything?"

Father nodded.

"We studied the Argonne. In Military Strategy. It was very bad."

Another nod.

"So, can't they get their money now, if they fought in the war?"

"I'd have been there too, in the Argonne," he said, suddenly turning pinkish, "if I could have been. Did your mother tell you I wouldn't fight in the war?"

A subject to steer around. "What's the soldier's bonus supposed to be?"

Surprisingly, Father knew the answer: $500 a man. He is a bean counter for the government. Five hundred bucks for risking a life in the war, so they could begin a new one here. Congress turned them down, decided to pay out the bonus later when these men are old. So they've come here from everywhere, wishing to take the matter up with the president.

"Does Mr. Hoover mean to meet with them?"

"Not on your life. If they want to talk to him, they better use the telephone."

May 14

Going with Bull's Eye to the market, that first time, was like Mother's first cigarette in the morning. Now every minute is a long piece of waiting, fidgeting out the minutes, pecking the desk, trying to think of something else until Saturday. Living in dread of not being asked again. On Friday nights the boys raise a cloud of stink in the barracks, throwing dirty drawers in satchels to get ready for the weekend, and then they fall down asleep. Leaving only the sound of one cricket ratcheting, a slant of puny moonlight. An hour or two for thinking: Billy Boorzai. Will he ask tomorrow? Or not?

Who cares. A person could prowl the library instead, in peace for once. Find some book that's better than noisy K Street. Keeping up with that big rough-elbowed dodger is worse than American football. It takes forever to get anywhere, Bull's Eye knows every third fellow he sees, not just boys but men of all sorts. And then has to renew the acquaintance with shoulder jabs and insults while the tagalong stands watching, like a pet dog. What does it matter if he asks or not?

June 17

The barracks have emptied; almost all the boys went home for summer, collected by servants in fancy carriages or mothers in horse-drawn taxis. It was entertaining to see which ones were rich or not. They all act like imperial kings when the parents aren't here.

Tomorrow begins a real job, for pay. Pearl diving, Bull's Eye calls it. Washing dishes in the mess hall. Father arranged it to cover board over the summer. But this afternoon, nothing yet to do in the empty barracks but take out every pair of pants from the foot locker and fold it up again. Or sit on the bed with *The Odyssey*. Until the head of Bull's Eye appears around the door. All ears and smile, the half-bit haircut. "Heya bookworm. Too busy lollygagging, then?"

"Too busy for what?" The book claps shut.

"Noodle juice and cookies with Mrs. Hoover. Whatcha think, for what? An ankle excursion."

"K Street?"

The smile disappears because the whole boy disappears. *The Odyssey* can be reopened to any page, it doesn't matter which. And then he is back, that grin. The scion of a ruined family, delighted with himself. This hurts, an ache in the groin, wanting so badly to see that smile and follow it somewhere. It keens like Mother waiting for the next cigarette. That is how she loves men, too. It must be. But in this case, can't be.

"What doesn't kill you," Bull's Eye likes to observe while scrubbing pots in the mess, "will make you piss on your shoes."

June 28
President Hoover asked the treasury secretary for a nickel to telephone a friend.

Secretary Mellon said, "Here's a dime. Phone both of them."

According to Bull's Eye, two million Americans are on the road. Half are probably just boys, not lucky enough to scrub pots for three squares and a plunk. Or farmers. Radio repairmen, teachers, nurses, or they finished school and no job anywhere. "It gripes my soul, truly it does," says Bull's Eye. He is steamed about the relief bill passed by the Congress, then knocked right down by the president because it's an Unexampled Raid on the Public Treasury. That was the news headline. Hoover says it's no crisis, only depression, everyone down in the dumps feeling sorry for themselves. If the gloomy people would buck up and smile, this mess will go away.

July 16
Only twenty-two boys are taking summer classes, most of them living at home. In the long, echoing barracks it's only Bull's Eye and Pancho Villa in the two end beds, and all the others empty. It feels like a hospital at the conclusion of a plague.

Bull's Eye has a friend living in the Bonus Army encampment. Nickie Angelino, a cousin of his mother's from Pennsylvania. Sometimes Nickie can be tracked down in the tent village, sometimes not. There are so many there now, acres of humankind, and people living under tarpaper tend to move around a good deal. Everyone at the camp knows Nick Angelino though. Famously, he scaled the White

House fence without arrest and left a gift on Hoover's doorstep: his medals from the Argonne, and a picture of his family. Angelino has a girl he calls his wife, but she looks too young, in her thin, short dress. To cover her breasts she wears a green nobbled sweater, even in the heat. Their baby wears old shirts torn up for nappers. He was born last month, here in the encampment. The girl won't talk about it.

The smell of the Bonus Expeditionary Force always comes first: cooking smells, latrine smells. *Phew.* A clock on the head from Bull's Eye, for saying that.

"What? It stinks!"

"Nothing." Bull's Eye gets angry easily, at the camp.

"What *nothing*? You hit me."

"*Phew*, says you. Here's a hundred thousand men that served your country."

"My country is Mexico."

"Damn you."

"Okay, they served our country."

"And here's their girls and kids with nothing and no place. All they want is what the government says they got coming. And you say *phew.*"

"Well, crap stinks. Even if it came from a hero's ass."

"You know what it said in the paper? The bonus marchers are not content with the pensions already received, although seven or eight times those of other countries. The *New York* goddamn *Times.*"

"What pensions already received?"

"None. They got no red cent so far, after discharge."

"How could the newspaper say that if it's a lie?"

"Lob. If the president lies, why wouldn't they?" Bull's Eye frowned, scanning the crowd for Nickie.

"How can the government refuse to pay, if they served?"

"They got VFW certificates they're supposed to cash in. But now they have to wait ten more years, because of the bank crisis. That wasn't the deal when they shipped out. If Congress can't pay the soldiers, they shouldn't be declaring war on the Krauts."

"Gee whiz."

"See those two behind the bread truck? They're the men from the VA, checking papers on the people waiting for the free bread. They won't turn a guy away anyhow. But they said it's running ninety-four percent."

"Ninety-four percent what? Certain your old man's your dad?"

"Lob. I talked to them yesterday. That many have got Army or Navy discharge papers. Or wives of men with records. One in five disabled."

Bull's Eye decided to look in the warehouse district. Men with families are starting to move their broods up there now, into the old brick hulks on Pennsylvania, camping out in condemned buildings. Blue and white flags of laundry hung out of almost every warehouse window. Kids ran out of the big open doors, and so did smells: cooking, cabbage, the inside of a shoe. Bull's Eye followed the bread wagon up Pennsylvania, hoping to spot Nickie in the crowd that pressed around the truck.

The bread comes from a bakery in New York, he says, a bunch of vets with jobs who got together and send it here for free. Even though the papers say these men are "rioters." Unpatriotic to help rioters. If a reporter came down here, he might notice there isn't any riot. Only Nick Angelino climbing the fence to leave a picture of his baby.

Angelino was located at last, carrying a loaf of bread and his wrapped-up son of about the same size. He tried to wave, looking as if he might drop one or the other. Bull's Eye went loping to catch him. He loves Nick's stories of riflemen and trenches and gas and men going blind in the war. The Argonne is a fantastic story these men all marched through together, and in the end it led here.

July 22

Summer more than half gone. Soon the Boy Army will return to take the place over again, making it loud. But for now the dormitory is still a camp for two tramps on the rods. Bull's Eye pretends he's a hobo, pulling out his Hoover flags, empty pockets turned inside out. Sometimes for a joke he covers himself with Hoover blankets, his newspapers. When it's hot he sits on his bed with nothing on at all, pumping his muscles like a wrestler, talking half the night, smoking fags he's pinched from the officers' mess.

Tonight the moon is five days past full, bleeding white blood into the sky, C *como* Cristo. Nobody else, only Bull's Eye, sitting there naked as Sally Rand, behaving as if he thinks he's quite worth looking at, too. Eye to eye, holding that stare as he leans back against the wall. The moon lighting up the smoke over his head like storm clouds. Every place the light touches his skin, he is a statue made of marble. All but the hairs on his chest.

"Whaddayou staring at?"

"Nothing."

"Go back to Mexico then."

"All right, sure. It's going to happen."

Bull's Eye stared. "When?"

"What do you care?"

He came over and sat on this bed, took the lit fag out of his mouth. "Smoke this. It makes you dizzy, but then you feel good."

"Okay."

But the dizziness was there already. Dizziness and ache. From seeing everything the moon was allowed to touch.

July 25

Staying on for fall term is contingent on passing the summer classes. Bull's Eye says they should pay us more for pearl diving.

"We should go and march with the Bonus Army."

Bull's Eye laughs. "Tell it to Sweeney."

July 28

Today was terrible. The end of summer term should be a fine day, and instead, people killed. If you ever think a day is fine, you weren't paying attention. Probably somebody was getting clapped bloody while you ate your breakfast. It happened right in front of us. The heat was bad on K Street, but Bull's Eye kept yelling to hurry up, into the thick of the encampment. Men standing on the back gate of the bread truck were passing out loaves into all those hands, like in the Bible. Loaves floating from hand to hand.

The encampment has changed shape all summer, it started at the riverbank but grew and swelled up into the warehouses on Pennsylvania, where the whole thing started today. With Bull's Eye scooting right toward the fight, *acourse*, a moth to the candle, and there is no keeping up with him. But the moth at the candle dies. He survives every time. Yelling his head off that it was going to be a real sockdolager. It was the police superintendent on his blue motorcycle, sent down to kick the Bonus Army families out of the warehouses. They're supposed to be tearing those down, to build more temples.

Bull's Eye said Glassford's in a jam. The superintendent. Hoover is on his neck for letting people get in the warehouses in the first place, and wants them kicked out today. Some people who'd been watching since early morning said two companies of marines in their helmets had already come to do the job, sent down there by Vice President Curtis—on trolley cars! And Glassford sent them back, ready to spit, because the vice president has no authority over military troops.

"Is that true?"

"Asking me? You seen me in government class?"

Now the superintendent was sweating in his brass-buttoned uniform, taking off his helmet and wiping his forehead a lot as he talked with the Bonus Army men. His job on the line. But those families, on a worse line surely. The crowd of gawkers was growing. Two men in white suits arrived in a limousine, also sweating, and had words with Glassford, gesturing at the building. Bull's Eye pushed to get closer, nearly tipping an old man with a shopping basket on his arm. The old man was mad as bugs, shouting at the police. *Where was you in the Argonne, buddy?* You wouldn't have guessed the fellow had so much air in him.

Other people picked it up, shouting things too. "They risked life and limb in France! You're running them out like dogs!" But mostly the crowd was quiet, waiting to see how it would go. A banner painted on a bedsheet furled out a second-story window: God Bless Our Home.

"All right then, we're off to K Street," said Bull's Eye suddenly, and off he headed toward the A and P. For once, his magnet for trouble failed him, and he was putting sacks of corn grits in a crate at the back of the store when the showdown started. A woman came running in the front door screaming that Officer Glassford had been shot. Bull's Eye took off at a lope. The story changed many times before we could get to the scene: Glassford was dead, or else he wasn't. He'd finally ordered the area cleared, and got hit with a brick thrown out a window of the warehouse. That was how it went, people talking and running for the scene, and at the warehouse it was bedlam. Women streaming out the door carrying cookpots and children, a lot of crying and screaming. Some Bonus Army men lay bloody in the street. Shot, maybe dead.

Bull's Eye looked ready to murder. More men were roaring up from the main encampment by the river, they'd gotten wind and come running with bricks to defend their women and kids, and Glassford's men returned fire with bullets. They weren't even ashamed, scads of people saw them do it, the whole crowd was screaming. Like Cortés and the Aztecs: one side always better armed.

An ambulance sounded from far away, probably stuck. The mob was like an ocean now, shifting from side to side. Nothing could get through, the only thing running fast was rumors: Hoover had called up MacArthur to put on his whipcord britches, get down here with troops, and rout the Bonus Army. Half the city stood jammed together on the hottest day of the year; offices were letting out, all eyes watching to see what would happen to these women and men. They stood on the step of a wrecked building, clutching what was left of their lives in a wad at their bellies, and every shopper and business-man, idler and schoolboy felt a horror rise, wondering the same thing: Where can they go?

A grumbling sound like thunder seemed to come out of the street.

An out-of-breath newsboy grabbed the corner of a building as he came round it and flung himself against the wall, gasping. "It's a tank!" he shouted. "The treads are turning the pavement into gravy!"

It seemed a fair time to leave, but escape was impossible. The front of the crowd began backing up from the street, shoving the rest of us against the window of a telegraph office, jammed between men in straw boaters and secretaries in point-heeled shoes. Two girls in cloche hats, one white hat and one black, stepped out of the door of the telegraph office and said, "Gee, what's the story?" People were pouring out of buildings with nowhere to go, milling in the street across from the Bonus Marchers.

The cavalry arrived just then, clopping up the street. It was Ma-jor Patton. Probably he'd arrived ahead of MacArthur's tanks be-cause the horses could dodge around the stalled motorcars choking up Pennsylvania Avenue. The horses reared and pranced sideways, spooked by the crowd. Their riders had long sabers, held high in their right hands. Behind them came a machine gun detachment, audibly marching in step.

"Gee *whiz*," said the white-hat girl again. Bayonets appeared, bristling above the heads of the crowd. People pressed back harder against the buildings as the tanks rolled up, their treads chewing the road as they came. The Bonus Marchers were lined up across the street, standing steady. Women struggled to hold babies, but all the men stood at attention, like the soldiers they are. They saluted the cavalry's color guard, and one small ragged boy on a man's shoulders pumped his own little flag in the air. A lady in the crowd of onlookers raised up a high shout and the whole throng took it up: *Three cheers for our men who served, hurrah! Hurrah! Hurrah!*

Patton's horsemen wheeled and charged the crowd.

Everyone ducked and shoved, the white-hat girl screaming, stepping sideways with her pointed white shoe, stabbing like a knife, and everyone tumbled. "Pull her up quick!" Bull's Eye said, helping from his side to drag her up by the elbows, but she seemed to be swooning. A man fell against her, someone else against the man, and then it was a whole smash-up of secretaries and bean counters. With flat hands pressed against the stone wall of the telegraph office, it was possible to inch back up to standing. Bull's Eye began to swim with his elbows *toward* the street, while everyone else pressed back, and that was a good time to say so long to Bull's Eye. Between the stone wall and the crush of shoulders, it was hard to breathe. Over the sea of heads and hats you could catch sight of cavalrymen leaning down from the waist, on their horses, flailing their saber blades against whatever was below them.

Against *people*. That hit with a shock. They were beating at the Bonus Army men and women with the razor-sharp blades of sabers.

Someone pushed into the near crowd with a bloody face, the meat of his cheek sliced back and bone shining. Roar after roar rose from the crowd in front, leaving those at the rear to guess and dread the cause of it. The cavalry men kept shouting to clear out, but the crowd shouted "Shame! Shame!" until it became a chant. The Bonus Army had linked arms to form a colonnade across the street, and the cavalry flung their horses through the line, snapping bones. The crowd howled, screams erupting with every charge of horsemen into flesh.

Bull's Eye suddenly reappeared: "Come on!"

"We can't get through. I'm smashed potatoes."

Bull's Eye swung open the door of the telegraph office and, like a magician pulling a scarf through a ring, yanked us both through the knot of people into the office. The people trapped inside all looked up, the same shocked face.

"Back to the alley," Bull's Eye yelled, but no one else made for it as he threaded through the desks and clerks to the washroom, climbed onto the radiator, and popped open the window. Outside, the alley-way was surprisingly empty. Trash heaps and crates of sodden lettuce, it must be a restaurant next door—it was a stench to beat the band. Not one other person had thought to escape from the melee by this route. Bull's Eye turned south at a hard trot.

"School's the other way."

"Right!" he said, without slowing up.

A burning stench began to choke out the restaurant smell. "God," Bull's Eye croaked. "It's gas. Come on, this way or we're cooked."

People came into the alley with hands over their faces, coming from the direction of the river. What followed was the sight of blindness itself coming on, and a feeling exactly like trying to breathe salt-water. Like swimming into the cave, the longest possible held breath. Every gulp of air tasted like poison. People were stumbling over trash heaps and people heaps. A newsboy curled like a fetus on his big stack of papers; suddenly the whole pile was old news.

"Come on," Bull's Eye said, "he's not dead. You don't die of gas."

Bull's Eye's face was purple as liver, his eyes streaming tears, but he still moved at a clip that wasn't easy to follow. An ambulance entered the alley, and people mobbed it. Between two buildings a tableau of the riot appeared: an infantryman pulling a blue bottle from his belt, uncorking it, and hurling it into the haze.

July 29

It's all in the newspapers today. Bull's Eye sat reading on his bed without a word, handing the papers over when he finished reading each part.

Gallinger Hospital filled to overflowing with the casualties. Any Bonus Marchers who made it to the Eleventh Street bridge joined the ones at the riverbank encampment. Mr. Hoover sent orders for troops to stop at the bridge, but MacArthur "couldn't be bothered with new orders," so he mounted machine guns on the bridge and led a column of infantry across the Potomac into the encampment. They set flaming torches to the canvas and pasteboard homes. Exactly as Cortés said it: Much grieved to burn up the people, but since it was still more grievous to them, he determined to do it.

It was shameful to read those newspapers, to feel any eagerness for knowing each awful detail of the massacre. How the artillery marched right over the camp on the riverbank, destroying the hobo jungle of fruit crates, chicken coops, tarpaper shacks, and dirt-colored tents. God Bless Our Home. Families must have been kneeling in there, praying for any miracle a tightfisted God might have left for them.

The Bonus Army families had crops planted in their camp. Every Saturday this summer Bull's Eye had pointed those out—how we cheered for the measly corn rows sprouting by the Potomac. They made the encampment look like Mexico. A real village, where people might live and eat. Hungry kids were waiting for those almost-ready ears—after months of porridge, sweet corn roasted in the coals. To think of MacArthur's horses trampling it on purpose: somehow that small part of the story made tears come.

Bull's Eye never came to bed after lights-out. He turned up hiding in the infirmary, sitting hunched on the side of a bed, smoking. With more newspapers.

"Look at this." He threw it.

The penalty for prowling around after lights-out is severe, but the infirmary was deserted. The late extra: After sunset yesterday the flames in the Anacostia encampment rose fifty feet in the air and spread to the surrounding woods. Six companies of firemen were required to defend adjacent property. The president observed from the White House windows an unusual glow in the eastern sky, and conceded MacArthur was right to proceed with the routing. In his opinion the Bonus Army consists of Communists and persons with criminal records.

The editorial writer applauded MacArthur for sparing the public treasury: The nation is being bled dry by persons like these who offend the common decency.

"Why would the paper say they're criminals?"

"They were treated like criminals," Bull's Eye replied. "So people want to think it. The paper says whatever they want."

It was no use reading more, but hard to stop. The late extra had photos. A society page. While soldiers poured gasoline on the shacks, the upper crust were cruising the river on their yachts, watching MacArthur spare the public treasury. A Mrs. Harcourt required medical attention after she saw a small boy receive a bayonet through his lower body. Senator Hiram Bingham of Connecticut was badly jostled on the street in front of the warehouse while attempting to leave his office. His injuries were not mortal, but earned as many newspaper inches as all the others together, including a woman in the Anacostia camp who lost her sight to flaming gasoline thrown in her face, and the vets from the Argonne shot dead in their own country. A dozen kids got shattered limbs or broken skulls. Two infants died of inhaling gas.

"Was one of them Nick's baby, do you think?"

Bull's Eye kept his head turned away. "For Christ's sake," he said. "A gas bomb costs more than a hundred loaves of bread."

ARCHIVIST'S NOTE

The next journal after this one will not appear to the reader, for it was destroyed in 1947. This note presents an intrusion, and I beg pardon for it. The notebook was burned in a metal tar bucket outdoors on a September evening, at the start of a rain. Mr. Shepherd watched through an upstairs window. The one doing the burning was myself.

It was a slim book of lined paper and cotton-duck binding with "Potomac Academy" stamped on it, a type of thing issued to the boys there, probably in great number. But this one in particular he had used for a diary, in 1933. It isn't my place to give an opinion about the burning. I'm a typist. But he made it plain he didn't want that little book to reach the public view. Nor any of these personal writings, truth be told. He was averse to making himself known. Even when greatly misunderstood. He liked to say, *"Dios habla por el que calla,"* meaning God speaks for the silent man. If he believed that, after all that happened, I am not sure how.

So, any regrets over the missing "Potomac Academy" 1933 would not be his. Evidently the notebook had something in it to disturb him, and he decided to destroy it. Later he would make the same judgment about all the rest of his diaries. But that particular one he plucked out first from among all the notebooks and pages he kept in portmanteau bindings on a shelf in his study. I won't try to say why a man would write pages he meant no one to see, let alone keep them nice in bindings. The sole place he let his words be seen was in the books published with his name on their spines. Harrison Shepherd. You might think of him as your friend, when closing one of these books. Many did. But he never let any photograph of himself go on the dust jacket, to encourage that kind of feeling. Even though he was a good-looking man, well groomed with dark hair and Roman features, about six feet and five inches in height. He did not have physical deformities, as has been said. The height alone was unusual.

But maybe you'll not have heard of him at all, nor have any idea why you should have. Until reading all this here.

The notebook that burned, then. People who make a study of old documents have a name for this very kind of thing, a missing piece. A lacuna, it's called. The hole in the story, and this one truly missing still, I know it is gone and won't turn up later in any trunk, as that first little leather-bound one finally did. The burned book from the Potomac Academy probably described his friendships and so forth until his leaving the school in 1934, midway through the graduation year. I didn't read it, before putting it to the flame. I am not concealing any scandal. Mr. Shepherd spoke of having made a disaster of his schooling, but said little else of it. He went back to Mexico then to live with his mother, who had abandoned her liaison with the American and found work as a seamstress in a Coyoacán dress shop. Mr. Shepherd and his mother accumulated some disagreements. He took a position again with the painter Diego Rivera, as a plaster-mixer to start. By late in the year 1935 he was paid as a member of their household staff.

Some writings did survive from his time at the Potomac Academy, sheafs of typewritten pages describing battle scenes and dialogues he later used in his novel *Vassals of Majesty* (1945). But as to the journal, his express wish was to see it removed from this earth. In time, with full voice and sound mind, he expressed that same wish for the other journals too: all these now collected in a volume.

I didn't make this plain at the beginning. I do so now. If you're of the mind to honor a dead man's wishes, always and regardless, be now fairly warned. If you feel it is best or kindest, then put these pages down and read no more.

—VB

PART 3

San Angel and Coyoacán

1935–1941

(VB)

Directions for making empanadas dulces

They can be triangular, or curled like snails with the filling inside. The dough is the same, either way: white flour with lard and a little salt rubbed in. Beat egg yolks into a little cold water (as many eggs as Olunda will spare), then mix the liquid lake into the volcano of flour. Exactly like mixing plaster.

Roll the dough in a rectangle as wide as the whole counter in this kitchen, which is so small, if two ants are in the sugar it's already too crowded in here. Next, with a clean machete cut the dough into squares like little handkerchiefs. Spoon some filling on each one and fold it diagonally to make a triangle. The square of the *hipotenusa* can go to hell. The filling can be custard or pineapple. For the custard, heat a liter of milk and some sugar with pieces of cinnamon. Beat seven egg yolks with some corn starch and pour it in a thin stream into the boiling milk. Stir until your arm is falling off. The *lechecilla* will be yellow and very thick.

For pineapple filling, cook the fruit with brown-sugar syrup and star anise.

The other way to make them is to spread the filling over the whole rectangle of dough and roll it into a log, then cut off round pieces, each one like a snail. For that, use the pineapple filling. The custard will make a devil of a mess.

Bake the pastries in the oven, if you live in a normal house. If you live in a supermodern house dreamed up by an idiot, go next door to the San Angel Inn. One of the cooks there, Montserrat, will meet you at the back door and take your trays to bake in the kitchen. She'll send one of the hotel girls to tell you when they're done.

Those are the instructions. If your boss has the appetite of an elephant and a kitchen the size of an insect, this is how to keep your job. Do it exactly this way, because he said, "Write out the recipe, *mi'ijo*, in case you ever leave me the way she did. You're the only person who knows how to cook like my wife."

What he doesn't know is the servants did the cooking, not her, right from the beginning when they still lived with her parents. After they moved here, secretly she had most of the meals picked up from the San Angel next door.

The girl Candelaria is the angel of the birdcage, sighted years ago in the Melchor market hurrying behind her mistress. It took a few days of working here to be sure she is the same servant. It's not a face you forget. Smooth skin, the countenance of a village girl, hair that reaches her knees. Olunda makes her tie her braids in loops, for safety and hygiene. Her mistress the Azteca Queen is gone. But Candelaria remains.

Could there be an uglier house in all Mexico than this one? *Functionalismo*, architecture as ugly as a fence made of dung. Except the fence here is the nicest part: a row of organ cactus surrounding the courtyard, planted so close together you can only see cracks of light between them. From upstairs you can look over it to the inn across the road, and a field where some cattle graze. San Angel is only two bus stops from the edge of the city, just one from Coyoacán, yet here is a farmer working in his field with an iron-bladed hoe that looks like it was forged during the reign of Moteczuma. When he stops to rest, that poor old man has to raise his eyes to this modern mess of glass and painted cement that looks like a mistake. It looks like a baby giant was playing with his blocks when his mother called him, so he ran away and left his toys lying in Calle Altavista.

Two blocks: the big pink one and small blue one standing separately, each with rooms stacked one above the other, screwed together by a curved cement staircase. The big pink block is the Painter's domain, and his studio on the second floor is not so bad. That window is the size of a lake, a whole wall of glass looking down at the neighbor's trees. The planks of the floor are yellow, like sun on your face. That room feels like someone could be happy in it. Everything else feels like being shut up inside a crate.

The small blue block is meant to be for the small wife. Servants are only allowed up the staircase as far as the kitchen (which is not worth the trip). Her rooms above it are sealed like a crypt since the Queen moved out. Good riddance, says Olunda. "She won't be back, I promise you. I'll eat a live dog if she ever shows up here again. After she caught master with his pants down as usual, but this time, humping her own sister!"

What a strange couple. Why would a man and wife live in separate houses? With only a little bridge between them, red pipe railings connecting one roof to the other. You can see it from the inn across the street. Functionalist *tonteria*. *He* is the one who eats, but the kitchen is on *her* side. If you manage to cook anything, you have to carry it down the staircase, which is like the inside of someone's ear, outside into the blazing sun to cross the gravel courtyard, then up the other cement ear to the studio where the master stands with his pants belted high on his giant dumpling belly, waiting to be fed.

And now he says she's coming back, he wants her greeted with empanadas and *budines* and *enchiladas tapatías*. He has never put his two giant feet in this tiny kitchen or he would know, you might as well try to make enchiladas in a peanut shell. Mixing plaster was easier. But living with Mother was not. So he'll have his enchiladas.

November 30
Live dogs beware of Olunda. The mistress has come back after all. Moved back in with her furniture and strange collections packed into

the rooms above the kitchen. It was like a surgery to carry her bed up the stair and through the narrow cement doorways without breaking out a glass-block wall. Candelaria and Olunda went up to help, and came back with hair standing on end. She has a pet monkey, they swear. He hides and leaps on your back when you carry food into her studio. Olunda moved her cot out of the little salon below the kitchen, because the mistress wants that space for a dining room. Olunda would rather sleep in the laundry closet under the house, anyway. The monkey is the least of it. The little queen has a temper like Mother's.

This servant's quarter out in the courtyard is probably the safest place to be, even with César the Flatulent for a roommate. He says this little block house wasn't meant to be a servant's quarter: they put it in the corner of the courtyard for keeping the motorcar, but the Painter decided to let the motorcar reside on Altavista Street, to make room for its driver in here. He says the architect planned for no driver or servant's quarters because he was a Communist, like the Painter. Olunda agrees. They said it was to be a revolutionary house, free of class struggle, no servants' rooms because they didn't believe in laundry maids or cooks.

Nobody does, really. Why should they? Only in having clean clothes, clean floors, and *enchiladas tapatías*.

4 December 1935: The Queen Takes Notice

She was on her throne, the chair at the head of the mahogany dining table. It's a wonder of the world she has fit her parents' furniture into that room, including a cupboard for dishes. The old carved chairs are so enormous she looks like a child, feet swinging below her ruffled skirts and not quite reaching the floor. She was in a foul mood, sneezing, wrapped in a red shawl and scribbling away, putting names in the ledger book where she means to keep better track of expenses and sales of her husband's paintings. One more thing she has taken over from Olunda, since moving in. All the names go in the book now, including the new kitchen boy, and what he is paid.

"*Xarrizzon Chepxairt!*" She grasped her throat when she said it, like choking on a chicken bone. "Is that really what people call you?"

"Not many people, señora. It sounds better in English."

"I was saying it in English!"

"Sorry, señora."

18 December: Second Audience with the Queen

She's sick in bed still; Olunda says she's twenty-five with the ailments of ninety. Kidneys and leg at the moment. Nevertheless she was propped up on pillows and dressed like an Indian bride: ruffled blouse, lip rouge, earrings, at least one ring on every finger, a crown of ribbons braided around her head. But she still looked half dead, staring up at the little windows at the top of the wall. Her bedroom is like a cement box, only slightly larger than the bed.

"Señora, sorry to disturb. Olunda sent me to get your plates from lunch."

"No wonder she won't come fetch the dishes herself, she's ashamed of that *jocoque*." She glanced up. "Olunda la Rotunda. Do they still call her that?"

"Not if they're still alive, señora."

"How does she get so fat on her own cooking? Look at me, I'm vanishing."

"Fried bread with syrup is her secret."

She made a little puzzled scowl. "And you, skinny creature. What's your name?"

"It didn't please you much the first time. When you wrote it in the ledger."

"Oh shit, that's right, you're that one. The unpronounceable." She seemed to wake up, sitting up straighter. When she looks at you, her eyes are like lit coals inside the hearth of those shocking eyebrows. "What does Diego call you?"

"Muchacho, mix some more plaster! Muchacho, bring me my lunch!"

She laughed. It was a good impersonation: it's all in his eyes, the way he opens them wide and leans forward when he bellows.

"So, you make plaster for Diego's lunch?"

"Never, señora. On my honor. He hired me first as a plaster boy, and a few months ago he moved me in here, to work in the kitchen."

"Why?" She cocked her head, like a beautiful doll propped on the pillows. One among many, in fact. The bookshelf behind her bed was full of porcelain and cloth dolls. All of them, like her, look dressed up for some party that will be noisy for certain.

"He likes my *pan dulce* and *blandas*, señora. I'm good at soft dough, in general. On the plaster crew they used to call me Sweet Buns."

"You can make *blandas* in this house? In that stupid little kitchen with the *fuego electrico*? You must be the Son of God. Tell Olunda to put you in charge of *everything*."

"She wouldn't take that kindly."

"What do you think of that kitchen?"

A pause, for guessing the right answer. It's well known that the Painter likes the house; a wrong answer in this interrogation could prove deadly. It felt like being back at the academy, but with a different category of officer.

"Everyone says it's an outstanding house, señora."

"Everyone will say horse shit smells like flowers," she stated, "if they want to be popular with a horse's ass."

"And your opinion, señora, if I may ask?"

She frowned at the white wall, the metal-cased window. "Bauhaus," she said, like a dog barking twice. "It's a monstrosity, isn't it? How do you even fit in that kitchen?"

"The same way you fit in your water closet. It's the same size room, directly underneath."

"But you're twice my size!"

"Standing in the center of the kitchen, it's possible to touch all four walls, exactly."

"It's that *pendejo* Juan O'Gorman showing off his modern ass. I don't know what he and Diego were thinking, it's like a hospital." She gestured with the back of her ring-ring hand. "And stairs! To get up to that stupid bridge and go across to Diego, I'm supposed to go out the window and climb little steps up the side of the house like an acrobat. What shit. He's not even worth it, I would kill myself, *chulito*. Who are you? Say it again, I swear I'll try to remember."

"Harrison. Shepherd."

"Christ, I'm not going to call you that. Diego calls you what, again?"

"Sweet Buns."

"The crew is very unkind to the plaster boys. As you know. But honestly, XARrizZON! It sounds like strangling. What kind of a name is that?"

"It was a president, señora."

"Of what? Some place where they don't have any oxygen?"

"Of the United States."

"As I said."

One more country is now to be held as a grudge, then. The mother country, the fatherland, two is all you get. Best to keep quiet, and stack the lunch dishes onto the tray. In two minutes César and Olunda would be fighting over everything left on those plates.

"You're from Gringolandia, then," she pressed.

"Born there, yes, señora. A half-citizen on my father's side. My mother sent me back there to be educated, but it didn't work."

"Why not?"

With the examination ending now, a quick last grasp at redemption: "The school kicked me out."

"Really."

It was a good guess: now even the ribbons in her hair curled forward to hear more. All the dolls stared. "Kicked out for what, *chulito*?"

"For a scandal."

"Involving?"

"Another student."

"Another student *and?*" Her hair practically standing on end.

"*Conducta insólita.* Irregular conduct. Señora, no more can be said. You would have to put me out on the street if you knew the rest."

She crossed her arms and smiled. "That's what I'm going to call you: Insólito."

The examination: passed, with highest honors. The prize: a possible ally in this impossible house.

5 January 1936

After weeks lying in bed existing on air and pink bananas, the Queen has risen. She came down the stairs, ribboned and ruffled like a Oaxacan saint's day, to reclaim her rightful place in this house and terrorize the staff. She announced a hundred people are coming for the Feast of the Kings tomorrow. Later she said, "Really only sixteen are coming, but cook for one hundred in case." Chalupas, flautas, tacos, *gaznates*, and macaroons. The dining room is the only place Candelaria and Olunda can sit to cut up vegetables without poking out one another's eyes. And the *rosca*: the mistress started screaming when she remembered that, "Tell César to get the car and take you into the city to find a *rosca*, they'll all be gone already from the bakeries here in San Angel." But Candelaria told her we have one already: "This boy knows how to make it."

Señora gawked as if a fish had arrived in her home, wearing an apron. "Insólito. It's just as I said. You're the oddest egg. A boy who makes *rosca*."

"Odd egg, go upstairs and get me a bowl," commanded Olunda, rolling her eyes. She had argued against making a *rosca* in the first place. (Too much trouble. Not enough space.) Then she insisted there was no Pilzintecutli to hide in the cake. When Candelaria retrieved the porcelain figure from a storage chest, Olunda stomped out. Now the Christ Child himself was contradicting her.

It's a new year in a house turned upside down. The mistress hangs bright, fluttery paper banderas over the Bauhaus windows, making the house embarrassed, like a plain girl in too much makeup. On the heads of her husband's Azteca idols she puts red carnations, turning them into altars, and she sets the table the way a priest prepares the tabernacle: white lace tablecloth from Aguascalientes reverently unfolded from the cupboard, blue or yellow plates set out, each one blessed by her fingertips, then the Kahlo grandmother's silverware. Finally, the flowers and fruit piled in the center of the table like a sculpture: pomegranates, bananas, *pitahaya*, everything chosen for color and shape. She was finishing the arrangement this morning when the monkey scuttered in and snatched out the bananas. The mistress bellowed, tiny as she is, and chased him out into the courtyard with a mimosa branch she was using in the centerpiece: "*Wicked child!*"

The diagnosis of Olunda is that this hairy child is the best the señora can hope for. Only twice pregnant in six years of marriage and both times the baby bled out, one at a gringo hospital, the other one here. They say it's because of a trolley accident years ago that ruined her woman parts and is "too horrible to discuss," though Olunda and Candelaria still manage to do so. By their accounting, in the last two years she's had two miscarriages, four surgeries, thirty doctor visits, and a giant fit over her husband's affair: she broke a lot of the *talavera* crockery before she moved out. It took her all of last year to forgive him. "And that was only the affair with her sister Cristina, we're not even counting women outside the family. Listen, how do you make the dough shiny like that?"

"You brush it with softened butter and then the white of one egg."

"Mmph." Olunda folded her arms across the mountain range of her bosom.

"Where did the señora live? Before she moved back in here?"

"An apartment on Insurgentes. Candelaria had to go clean it

sometimes. Give me those dried figs, *mi'ija*. Tell him about the mess, Candi, it was even harder to clean up over there than here."

"It was because of the paintings," Candelaria explained.

"He painted, in her apartment?"

"No, she did."

"The Mistress Rivera is also a painter?"

"If you can call it that." Olunda was shredding chicken breasts for the chalupas, grunting as she worked, settling an old grudge with those hens.

Candelaria said once she went to the señora's apartment and found a sheet of metal covered with blood. "I thought she had cut herself while setting it up on the easel, or else murdered someone. Probably her husband, considering. But then the mistress sat down with her red pigments, whistling, and happily applied more blood on the picture."

"Enough gossip," said Olunda, who was clearly jealous not to have seen this sight herself. "Candi, you have to peel every tomato in that bucket, and you, Odd Egg, I want to see you chopping onions until tears come out of your ass."

2 February

Eight kinds of tamales for the feast of Candlemas. Even César was ordered to help. He threatened all day to quit, as he is "a chauffeur, not a peon for women's work." He's been angry since October because of having to share his room with an Odd Egg, and now he even has to put on an apron, the world may end soon. The Painter says he's sorry, but that's how it is, Frida rules the house. "And besides, old comrade, you're getting too old for driving, so you better get used to peonage." It's true, yesterday César got lost four times on the way to the pharmacist's. The mistress calls him General Wrong Turn.

Even more than aprons he despises this notebook. He calls it "the espionage." He is adamant, shutting off the lights on pen and paper. But most nights, by the time every dish in the house has been scraped, cleaned, and put away, he's already snoring like a whale. The spy may do his work here unless the whale is roused from stupor. It is like being in a *casa chica* again with Mother, *Put out the damn candle before you burn us all.*

19 February

Candelaria doesn't remember that day when she carried the parrot cage on her back through the Melchor market. She says she must have just come from the village then, the Painter and Mistress hired her when they were newlyweds, living at the Allende Street house with the señora's parents. Candelaria doesn't remember the parrots, or why they were purchased, or how long the couple lived in that place with the fantastic courtyard, before building this house. She couldn't say if she liked it better there. She seems to forget almost everything. The secret to surviving the storms of Rivera service.

2 March

The señora is making a painting in the little studio next to her bedroom. It's not such a mess, she uses a cloth under her chair. At the end of the day, it looks like it rained blue, red, and yellow. She cleans her own brushes and knives, a hundred times tidier than the Painter, who throws everything on the floor and stomps out in his cowboy boots. But Candelaria and Olunda refuse to carry her lunch upstairs, saying her temper is even worse when she's painting. She never says *gracias* because life is made of survival not grace, she says, and servants are paid to bring what they're asked. Today she demanded stuffed chiles, more blue pigment, and surprisingly, advice.

"The painting looks good so far, señora." When people ask for advice, this is what they want. "Good progress too. We'll see that finished by the end of the month."

"We will?" She gave a fierce, quick smile like a cat showing itself to another cat. "As the fly said, sitting on the back of the ox, 'We are plowing this field!'"

"Sorry."

"It's okay, Insólito. If anybody says it's ugly, I'll tell them 'we' painted it."

The painting has people floating in the air, connected by ribbons. She asked, "Do you like art? I mean, do you understand it?"

"Not really. Words, though. Those are nice. Poems and things like that."

"What did you study in school?"

"Awful things, señora. Drill and psychomotricity. It was a military school."

"*Dios mio*, you poor skinny dog. But they didn't succeed in enslaving you, did they? I notice sometimes you still piss on the shoes of the master."

"Excuse me, señora?"

"I've seen you reading the newspaper to the girls down in the dining room. Changing the headlines to make them laugh. Your little insurrections." She still faced the painting, speaking without turning around. Was this going to be a dismissal?

"It's just to pass the time, señora. We still do our work."

"Don't worry, I'm a revolutionist. I approve of insurrections. Where did they send you to school, Chicago or something? One of those freezing places?"

"Washington, D.C."

"Ah. Throne of the kingdom of Gringolandia."

"More or less. The cornfields outside the throne of the kingdom. The school was in the middle of farms and polo fields."

"Polo? That's some kind of crop?"

"A game. Rich people play baseball riding ponies."

She put down her paintbrush and turned around. "Isn't it crazy? Rich people in the United States don't even know how to use money properly." She peeked at her lunch plates now, inspecting the *rellenos*. "They don't mind throwing big parties while people stand outside in the street with nothing. But then they serve puny little foods at the party! And live in houses stacked on top of one another like chicken crates. The women look like turnips. When they dress up, they look like turnips in dresses."

"You're right, señora. Mexico is the better place."

"Oh, Mexico's going to the devil too. The gringos steal a little more of it every week, replacing the beauty of our campos and our Indios with the latest fashion in ugliness. Probably they'll turn our maguey into fields for pony-*beisbol*. It can't be helped, I suppose. The big fish always eats the little one."

"Yes, señora."

"Little dog, don't give me this '*si señora*.' I'm sick of that."

"Sorry. But it's right, what you said. My mother is Mexican, but all she's ever wanted to do is dress like an American lady and marry American men."

The eyebrow went up. "A *lot* of them?"

"Well, one at a time. And really she only succeeded once, with my father. The other slippery fish all got away."

She laughed, shaking her head full of ribbons like a flag in the wind. She would never be converted to a turnip. "Insólito, you should come out and piss more often."

"Olunda keeps my rope tied very short, señora."

"You have to stop calling me señora. How old are you?"

"Twenty this summer."

"Look, I'm practically the same as you, twenty-five. It's Frida, only. César calls me that so you can too, it's not a crime against the state."

"César is like your grandfather."

She tilted her head. "You're not afraid of me, are you? Just shy, right?"

"Maybe."

"You don't have a lot of heat in your blood, is the problem. You're not completely Mexican, and not all gringo either. You're like this house, Insólito. A double person made of two different boxes."

"That might be true, señora, Frida."

"In the house of your mother, a taste for beauty and poetry. Secret passions, I suspect. And in the gringo side, a head that's always thinking and surviving."

"True, maybe. Except my house is only a kitchen, it seems. And very small indeed."

"The kitchen of your house is ruled by Mexico, thank God."

4 March

Our Lord Jesus has not yet risen. How do we know this? Olunda grumbles about another day of Lenten meals. But they can be some of the best: lima bean soup, potatoes in green sauce, fried beans. At supper this evening the Painter hinted he needs more boys on the plaster crew, and the mistress scolded him: "*Sapo-rana!* The way you eat, you should know we need your plaster boy here." Toad-frog, she calls him, then gets up, walks over to him, and kisses his toad-frog face. They are the strangest couple. And why do these Communists observe Lent, in any case?

The Painter's new mural in the Palacio Bellas Artes has the newspaper reports flying so fast, their pages might combust. He's copying the mural he did in the United States that created a scandal and had to be torn down before completion. It frightened the gringos that badly. Scaring gringos can make a hero of any Mexican. Other artists now come to the house every night, crowding around the Riveras' dining table with two colors of paint still in their hair. Writers, sculptors, bold women in makeup who want the vote, and students who are evidently waiting for San Juan Bautista to bathe, along with the lepers. Some are too old to be students, so who knows what they do. (If anything.) One is a Japanese in gringo clothes, arrived here to make a mural in the new Mercado.

The only place big enough for washing that many dishes is in the laundry closet under the stair. Down in the courtyard you can still hear them up there drinking their way to an agreement, sometimes all night, like the men who used to visit Don Enrique. But this crowd wants to kick out all the American oil men. The señora shouts: "Save Mexico for the Mexicans! Save the Mexicans for Mexico! The two commandments of our revolution!" Then they all jerk back their heads, swallowing tequila for Mexico.

Tonight the Painter explained, for the benefit of servants trying to slide behind the guests' chairs to clear the dinner plates, that this was a famous quote from Moses.

"Señor Rivera, Mexico is in the Bible?" Poor Candelaria, the Painter sometimes makes a sport of her. Possibly in more ways than one.

A different Moses, he told her. Moisés Sáenz, in 1926. "Ten years of revolution may not have saved all the Mexican children, but at least we've saved them from the pope and the Italian Renaissance."

"The Renaissance had its good points," his wife maintained.

"Honestly, Friducha. Who needs all those fat little cherubs flying around?"

As a matter of fact she is painting one with cherubs now. They look like unruly children with wings. She never seems happy with what she's painting, and talks to herself: "Oh boy, that won't work. What a lot of shit. That looks like it came out of the ass of a dog." Candelaria won't go near her. Next to Mother's Museum of Bad Words, Señora Frida could construct a pyramid.

But in her husband she has perfect confidence. She always says to the guests: "Damn all other artists to hell, Diego *is* the cultural revolution!" Even when some of her guests are among the damned. One time in her studio she said, "He's very great. Don't forget that, if you think you're looking at a fat frog who won't pick up his pants from the floor. His work is the whole thing. He's doing what nobody could do before." Maybe she heard Olunda complaining about him. Voices carry in this strange cement house.

She says Mexicans have trouble making friends with their history because we're many different nations: Toltec, Aztec, Mayan, Oaxacan, Sonoran, all fighting each other from the very beginning. That's why the Europeans and gringos could come in and walk over everything. "But Diego can take all those different people and make them into one Mexicanized *patria*," she said. He paints that on the wall, so big you won't forget.

It explains a lot, what she said. Why he is much-discussed. And why some people want him torn down, not just gringos but also the Mexican boys in *tejano* hats who don't want anyone saying they were born from between the legs of an Indian woman. He makes people feel things. How thrilling it must be, to tell the story of La Raza in bold colors and no apology: Indians walking out of history into the present, all in a line with their L-shaped noses, marching past Cortés into the vanishing point of their future.

9 April

President Cárdenas agrees with the Rivera dinner guests, it's time to kick out the oil men. Mexican oil for the Mexican people now. The newspaper says the workers will only have to work eight hours a day from now on, and get a share of profits. Cárdenas even kicked out Big Chief Calles, boss of every Mexican president since the rocks of the earth were still warm. Now he can enjoy the company of his gringo business friends more than ever, because the president had him arrested and put on a plane to New York. "What a Boy Scout, that Cárdenas," Olunda said. "Usually they just assassinate their rivals."

It was also a day of liberation for the peons of the Kitchen of Microscopia. The señora wants a huge Easter party, and decided to have it at a regular house with a real kitchen: her father's house on Allende Street. It's where they lived before, near the Melchor market, with the jungle courtyard. She had César drive the staff there to get started cooking for Saturday, assisted by that house's ancient housekeeper and two girls. The dining table was piled with newspapers; the Painter still gets a lot of mail there. The others begged to be entertained with dramatic readings while cutting up one thousand tomatoes. Candelaria is tender-hearted, but Olunda only wants the motorcar plunges into the canyons of Orizaba, so the kitchen readings always involve some compromise. The Allende Street house staff were an easier audience: old Perpetua seems deaf, and the two girls laughed at anything: *Upon arrival in New York City, Calles told reporters . . . "I was thrown out of Mexico because I forgot my pants and wallet in the bedroom of a* puta *on Avenida Colón."* Candelaria and the girls shrieked and giggled.

Mistress Frida appeared in the doorway, completely unexpectedly. Olunda threw down the fork she was using to mash avocados and cupped her hands over her fleshy ears. The house girls ardently peeled the nopales without looking up.

"My concern is for your ignorance," the señora snapped. "This is a historic day. Read it to them correctly."

"Yes, señora."

She stood, waiting.

"Upon arrival in New York City, the former Jefe Maximo told reporters, 'I was exiled because I opposed the attempts to create a dictatorship of the proletariat.'"

"Very good. Keep going." She swirled and walked out to attend to her father, leaving the kitchen proletariat to absorb the real news of the day. The State Department of Chiapas, responding to the Syndicate of Indigenous Workers, has voted to raise the wages of all coffee workers throughout the state. In a formal declaration to the Congress, President Cárdenas stated, "In the new democracy, organized laborers exert a genuine influence on the political and economic leadership of our country."

Olunda's eyes darted from her avocados to the doorway, to the newspaper, and back to her bowl. Dreaming, perhaps, of a Syndicate of Avocado Mashers.

19 April

The mistress is having a relapse of difficulties with her back, an infection of her eyes, kidney stones, and an affair with the Japanese sculptor. So says Olunda, but it hardly seems possible: when would she have time? But Candelaria has evidence: the last time she let the Japonés through the gate, the Painter came barreling down the spiral stair with his pistol out. The sculptor is no longer welcome in either half of the double house.

22 April

The señora packed herself off to the hospital, taking paintbrushes and some dolls. Today she sent word she also needed chiles rellenos, so the master dispatched the male servants to the hospital with her lunch. Possibly to see if the Japonés is lurking there, attempting sexual liaisons with a woman in a plaster spinal corset. César got lost twice on the way, then remained in the car to nap and recover himself for the voyage home.

"Insólito!" she cried from her hospital bed. "Look at your poor Friducha, falling all to pieces and dying. Let me have that basket." She wore only half the usual pirate's chest of jewelry today, but her hair was pinned up the usual way. She must have nurses and stretcher-bearers at her command at the Hospital Inglés.

"Did you stop by my father's house to give him some of this?"

"Of course. Señor Guillermo sends you his heart."

"He's going to starve, with Mother gone. She's the only one who ever ordered those servants to get up off their *nalgas*." She pulled out the napkins and silver, arranging her bed for dining as carefully as she sets the table at home.

"With respect, señora, his housekeeper is the same one who managed to keep you alive through your childhood."

"My point exactly. She's ancient. It's like an archaeological ruin over there."

"Everything is fine at Allende Street, you shouldn't worry. Perpetua hired two new housegirls. Belén and something. Today they were planting lilies in the courtyard."

"Lilies! The whole house needs repairs and a good coat of paint. I would make it plumbago blue. With red trim. What's the news from home?" she asked, tearing into the rellenos. She had an excellent appetite for a dying woman.

"You don't want to know."

"*Meaning?* Has Diego replaced me already?"

"Oh, no, nothing like that. It's all the same people coming over in the evenings."

"The painters?"

"Mostly the writers and the theater ones."

"The Contemporáneos. Oh boy, you're right, I don't want to know about them. Villaurrutia with his *Nostalgia for Death*! Just go ahead and drink the poison, *muchacho*, get it over with. I think he and Novo are having an affair with each other, they're both impervious to flirtation. And Azuela is just gloomy."

"Mariano Azuela? That's him? The author of *Los de abajo*?"

"The one. Don't you find him gloomy?"

"He's a very great writer."

"But very cynical, don't you think? Look, that character Demetrio in *Los de abajo*: What kind of hero is he? Fighting in the Revolution without a single idea in his head about *why*. Remember the scene where his wife asks him why he's fighting?"

"Of course. He throws a rock into the canyon."

"And the two of them just stand like a pair of dummies, watching the rock roll all the way down the hill."

"It's a moving scene, Señora Frida. Isn't it?"

"Maybe if you're a rock. I'd like to think I'm being pulled through history by something more than the force of gravity."

"But gravity is winning. Look how short you are."

"This is no joke, I'm warning you, Sóli. Be careful of your heart going cold. The Mexican writers are cynics. Our painters are the idealists. Take my advice, if you ever need a party to cheer yourself up, invite the painters, not the writers."

She cocked her head, like a cat inspecting a mouse prior to

consumption. "But . . . you are a writer, aren't you? You write at night."

How could she know that? Now they will make it stop.

"Pages and pages. César told me that. He said it's like you're possessed."

No confession.

"I also believe you find it *most* interesting that Novo and Villaurrutia are sleeping with boys instead of girls? Don't you."

None.

"I'm not charging you with crimes, you know."

"No. No secrets, Señora Frida."

"What a lot of *mierda*. You always call me señora when you're lying. So tell me, how are things in the soap opera of Los de Kitchen?"

"The same, Frida. We're just tedious little servants."

"Sóli, you are neither small nor tedious. Sooner or later you're going to have to confide in me, one pierced soul to another. Sleep on it, Sóli. Consult your pillow."

4 May

A visit with Mother, to take her to La Flor for her birthday. She was dazzling as always in a violet frock and dyed-to-match wool cloche. Her new plan is to win the heart of an American engineer contracting for the government. She describes him as "plenty rugged." Also plenty married: they met when he came in the dress shop to buy a gift, not for his wife but his mistress. "Former mistress," Mother calls her hopefully.

"It's inspiring, Mother. You never shrink from competition."

"What about you? That girl came in the shop again last week. This is the Rebeca I told you about, the friend of that little jelly bean you took to the Posadas last winter, and if you ask me, this Rebeca is ten times prettier. If the other one is a wet sock, that's your good luck. She was a half-portion, if you ask me. But the friend is really swell."

"I didn't ask you."

"Rebeca, this one is. Write it down, *mi'ijo*, at least pretend you're interested. Or am I going to have to hire a *puta* to get a woman in your little *pinche* life?"

"A *pinche* life full of women, thanks all the same. One more and it might split open like a pomegranate."

"I mean a woman in *bed*."

"That house is ruled by a woman in a bed. Completely."

"*Mi'ijo*, you exasperate me. This Rebeca, look, she's a smart one like you. She wants to go to university, but right now she's a seamstress. Did she stop in? I told her where you're working. I didn't tell her the kitchen, of course, I said you were some kind of a secretary. Intending to become a lawyer. It isn't a lie to say you're *intending*."

"Let's go back to your love life. It's more interesting."

"It had better get that way soon, let me tell you. Forty! Look at me, I'm a rock of ages." She covered her face with her hands. Then peeked through, because the watermelon salad arrived. "And you, almost twenty! It's unbelievable."

"Half a rock of ages."

"And what will you be doing on your twentieth birthday, mister?"

"Cooking, probably. The señora has the same birthday. She doesn't know it."

"Listen, if we go anywhere together now, you are not to say you're my son, do you hear me. Look at you, a *man*! How could you do that to me? That's it, mister. The men nowadays want fillies and pips and sweet patooties and no-o-o dotie brodies."

She has moved on from oil men, there was no future in that stock. Don Enrique has lost everything in the nationalization. Mother reports that the hacienda on Isla Pixol has been appropriated, turned over to the people of the village as a communal farm. They turned the house into a school.

"Well, good. One provincial school will have some books in it, anyway."

"You would be on their side, wouldn't you? Houseboy for the pinkos."

"The point of the appropriation law is restitution, Mother. Meaning Don Enrique or his family must have taken that land from the villagers in the first place."

"But look, were they really using it? Your Leandro is probably the president of the collective now, trying to work out how to put on a pair of shoes."

"*My* Leandro? He had a wife. The only man in that house who did."

"Ooh, you slay me. Poor old Enrique, he got his sock chorus, didn't he? Can you imagine the scrow, when they put him off his own place? And his mother! Holy moly, that must have taken the army." Mother took a nibble of her watermelon salad.

"Consorting with Americans has improved your English."

"As far as I care, Enrique and his relatives can go chase themselves, and you can put that in your hat. There's some jazz talk."

"And you can put this in your hat, Mother. Washing the dishes of pinkos doesn't make someone a pinko. It's not like an influenza."

"I'm just razzing you. I'd take up with a pinko in two toots, if he was famous and had a wad of tin. That artist's little girlfriend is one lucky duck."

"The little girlfriend is actually his wife."

"Like I said. But what a piece of calico, all spuzzed up like an Indian. She's no Garbo. How'd she get lucky?"

"He's fond of the way she dresses. They're nationalists."

"No soap!" She shook her head. "To me she looks like a corn-eater."

"You used to ask, What kind of man would chase after that? In Isla Pixol, remember? Now you know."

"Hey, you got a gasper?" She took a cigarette and lit it, pushing away her unfinished lunch. Poor Mother, still living from one gasp to the next. She removed a piece of tobacco from her tongue, and announced: "A corn-eater will never be any more than she is."

It was no use reminding Mother of her temporary craze for learning the *sandunga*. If corn-eaters are now having their day in nationalist Mexico, in Mother's estimate they will soon lose the race to fillies and sweet patooties. The afternoon crowd at La Flor had waned, but she kept glancing around the patio, always on the alert.

"What's become of Don Enrique, then? Is he begging on the streets?"

"Oh golly no. He's living in one of his other places. Up in the oil fields somewhere in the Huasteca. Enrique could always pull more money out of his *nalgas*. No matter how much he complained to us about our spending."

She leaned forward and looked up with big eyes under the brim of her cloche hat, and suddenly there she was: the other Mother. The mischievous girl, drawing another child into her conspiracy. "Don't worry about Don Enrique, *mi'ijo. Dios les da el dinero a los ricos, porque si no lo tuvieran, se morirían de hambre.*"

God gives money to the rich because if they didn't have it, they would starve.

1 July
The Riveras' wad of tin must not be as big as Mother thinks. Señora Frida had to make a strategy for financing her birthday party: she painted a portrait of the lawyer's wife and sold it to him. The party will be at the Allende Street house to hold all the people, as she has invited three quarters of the Republic, including mariachis. The painters and the gloomy writers are coming. Olunda is in a frenzy. Chicken *escabeche*, pork and nopales in *pipián* sauce, *mole poblano*. Sweet potatoes mashed with pineapple. Tomato and watercress salad. The pork-rib and tomato stew she calls "the tablecloth stainer." At last report she also wants shrimps and marinated pigs'

feet. The señora might have to paint portraits of the guests as they come in, and sell them on the way out, to pay the butcher after this fiesta. A wearying twentieth birthday expected for the cook.

14 July
Housecleaning. Eight paintings moved from Señora Frida's cramped studio into the storage room on the Painter's side. The nice painting of her grandparents, the odd one of herself and the monkey, and the bloody one that Candelaria talks about, from when she lived in the apartment on Insurgentes. Each title has to go in the ledger before it's moved upstairs: the bloody portrait of the stabbed girl is called *A Few Little Pokes*. She painted it after a man in the Zona Rosa stabbed his girlfriend twenty-six times, and when the police came and found her dead, the boyfriend said, "What's the problem? I only gave her a few little pokes." The story was in all the newspapers. Señora said, "Insólito, you'd be amazed what people will buy."

Did she mean the painting, or the man's story?

5 August
The people who come to dinner with paint in their hair now have a name for themselves: the Syndicate of Technical Workers, Painters, and Sculptors. After the plates are cleared they bring the typewriter from the Painter's office and make a newspaper right on the dining table. The writer in charge, Señor Buerrero, was the pigmentist on the mural crew. They argue about everything: Which is better, art or philosophy? Easel art for the bourgeoisie, or murals for the public? Which is the more nationalist, pulque or tequila? The servants get an earful, better than any school yet. Tonight they argued about how to defeat fascism in Spain. Mexico opposes the Fascists, even though the gringos and British think a stern fellow like Franco is just the thing to straighten up Spain. The Riveras' old friend Siqueiros is there now, fighting alongside the Spaniards.

But he was strange, Alfaro Siqueiros. The type to find a fight anywhere, war or no war. When he used to come to supper, Olunda would pull out her crucifix and say, "*Dios mio*, don't use the good *talavera*, it will be in pieces before the pastry." Rivera calls him a bang-bang artist, making murals with a spray gun and airplane paints. Siqueiros called Rivera a high-flying Communist, getting commissions from gringos and robber barons. Then Rivera would say, Look at your friend Stalin if you want to see the robber baron *maximo*, and usually that was when the *talavera* became endangered.

Really, those two have only one fight: Who is a better painter, Siqueiros or Rivera?

19 August

The señora in the hospital all week; it seems very serious. They moved her again to the Inglés. It's a long drive to take her lunch. On the way back today we brought food to the Painter in the Palacio Bellas Artes, where he's touching up that mural after they put some electric wires in the wall behind. It's the re-creation of the one that frightened people in New York so badly. Last summer the plaster boys made bets it would show monsters with devils' heads, or worse. Seeing it now, it's hard to guess which part is frightening. No monsters. Maybe the white and dark-skinned workers side by side. In the United States they require different bathrooms. But the Painter says no, it was only the face of Lenin, leader of the Russian Revolution.

The boys on the plaster crew are all different ones from last summer, so no one there today remembered Sweet Buns. That name is gone. Sometimes the past can vanish.

25 August

Señora Frida is still in the hospital. The house is both dull and chaotic, the blue side ruled by the monkey lurking on the stairs, awaiting the return of his mistress. He hangs by one hand from the stair rail, scratching his *nalgas*. The Painter, on his side of the house, is doing approximately the same. She is the center of everything.

29 August

The Painter is working like a madman in his studio. Candelaria refuses to take him his food or clean the studio while he's in there, for reasons she won't disclose. An acceptable reason would be: it looks as if a giant dog, after a large lunch of food, socks, paints, trousers, and pencils, walked into that room and vomited everywhere.

It's no easy trick to clean up around him. The man takes up a lot of space. He seems to be painting landscapes. Unlike his wife, he does not ask for a servant's opinion on his work. He interrogates. Yesterday: "How long have you been in this house?"

"All day, señor. My bed is in the little carriage house, shared with César."

"I know that. And you used to be on the plaster crew. Sweet Buns, they called you. I'm asking how long you've been with us here in San Angel."

"Living here, since last October, sir. Before that, two times in the summer when you had those gatherings and needed an extra cook. You hired me full-time after a girl left. Olunda recommended me to your service. Probably she regrets it now."

"Why is that?"

A pause. "Modesty should prevent my saying it, but my bread is better than hers. Beyond that, Olunda views life in general as a regrettable contract."

"I see your point. That's enough for now."

But today he launched a second interrogation, even more blunt. Beginning with: "Your name is Shepherd, and you're a foreigner. Is that right?"

"Only one-half foreign, sir. Mexican mother, gringo father."

"He lives in the United States? Doing what?"

"Keeping track of money in a government office. Building and road repairs."

"I see. And are you trustworthy?"

"It's a hard question to answer, sir. Saying 'yes' could prove either case."

He seemed to like that answer, smiling a little.

"Half American does not mean half loyal, Señor Rivera. Your household is generous and inspiring. A worker could not ask for much more."

"But workers do, every minute. I understand you're a writer."

"Señor, what on earth gives you that understanding?"

"One person. By name, César."

"He does?"

"He says you scribble every night. Are you reporting on us to someone?"

César is a perseverant snitch. "It's nothing like that. Just a diary of kitchen nonsense and little stories. Romantic adventures set in other times. Nothing of consequence, meant for no one else's eyes."

"César says you write in English. Why is that?"

"With respect to your old comrade driver. How does he know it's English?"

The Painter considered this. "Meant for no one else's eyes, including César's."

"You could understand the need for privacy."

His toad-frog face broadened helplessly. "You're talking to a man who smears his soul on the walls of public buildings. How would I understand?"

"Well, no sir. But consider how your wife views her art, something she does for herself. It's more like that. But of course it isn't art, these little notebooks, there's no comparison. What she does is very good."

"Don't panic, I'm not going to fire you. But we have to start being careful about security. We can't have a spy in our midst."

"Of course not." A long pause. Clearly it is important not to ask why. Does he want more reassurance, something personal? "About the English, sir. It's a habit from school. They taught us to use typewriters, which are very handy, I have to say. But they didn't have the Spanish characters. So a story begun in English keeps going in English."

"You know how to use a typewriter?" He seemed quite surprised.

"Yes, señor. When the question of Spanish characters came up, the officer at school said no typewriter anywhere has characters beyond those needed for English. But it isn't true. The one you sometimes leave on the dining-room table has them."

"Those gringos. What jingoists."

"That was the problem at school. You can't get far on a story without the accents and *eñe*. You begin with Señor Villaseñor in the bath, reflecting on the experience of his years, but instead he is *'en el bano, reflexionando en las experiencias de sus anos.'*"

The Painter laughed, throwing a streak of blue across his big belly. Olunda will offer up some curses over those trousers. The big toad has a wonderful laugh. That must be what women like about him, besides the wad of tin. Not his face, for sure. But his joy, the way he gives himself up entirely. As he said, a soul smeared on walls.

The suspect was then released, carrying a pile of dirty plates from the room of interrogations. If César can read his name here, let him worry. Let him fret all day over Senor Villasenor in the bath, reflecting on the experiences of his anuses.

3 September

Señora Frida is back from the hospital, but not well. Both master and mistress are in the house now, requiring service day and night. Candelaria, forced to choose between devil and dragon, has chosen the one that needs her hair combed. Just as well, because the other devil needs a typist. The Communist Party has thrown him out over the never-ending argument of who is better, Stalin or Stotsky or Potsky or what. The other Communists won't come over for supper and do his typing anymore. And the mistress seems angry with him over some private matter. Olunda has plenty of theories. Poor toad-frog Diego, losing people faster than he can paint new ones on a wall.

14 September

Today General Wrong Turn got lost on the way to the house in Coyoacán where he lived for forty-one years. The errand was the usual, taking food to Señor Kahlo. When César first began driving Guillermo Kahlo around for making his photographs, it was in a carriage. Not a motor coach in all Mexico City, he says, and those were the good days. It's true that horses have certain advantages: namely, knowing the way home.

It's strange every time, returning to the Allende Street house where Señora Frida marched home from the Melchor market that birthday long ago, a stranger, with a shy boy carrying her bags because Every Man has the Right to make a Kite from his Pants. And in the courtyard inside, the Painter sat under the trees reading his newspaper, waiting to be found, all on a chance. How strange that a boy could make a kite of his pants, fly them around the world, and somehow arrive back at the house where everything began.

1 October

A tiresome day. Being the Painter's typist is harder than mixing his plaster. The worst of it isn't the typing but his interrogations. He says cleverness in a servant is not always a good thing. Candelaria, for example, could straighten all the papers on his desk and come away with no more idea of what's written there than Fulang Chang the monkey. And the master doesn't hold Fulang Chang entirely above suspicion. Only the illiterate, wide-eyed Candelaria. "How about you?" he needled. "What did you see just now, while you were typing the invoice letters?"

"Nothing, Señor Rivera."

"Nothing, including the official letterhead of the President of the Republic? You didn't notice a letter from Cárdenas?"

"Señor, I have to admit, that did catch my eye. The seals are outstanding. But you're an important person. Commissions from the government are nothing exceptional. I didn't care enough to read the letter, that's the truth. I'm uncurious about politics."

He closed his newspaper, took the glasses off his nose, and stared across the room from the armchair where he likes to sit while reading and dictating. *"Uncurious?"*

"Señor Rivera, you stand for the people, anyone can see the good of that. But leaders all seem the same, no matter what they promise. In the end they'll let the poor people go to the dogs."

"A cynic! A rarity, in revolutionary Mexico. In your age group, anyway."

"I didn't go to university. Perhaps that's helped me maintain my position."

"A severe young man. You allow for no exceptions?"

"Exceptions haven't presented themselves. I read the newspapers a little. Which I take from your studio when you're finished, señor. I offer that confession."

"Here, take this one too, it's nothing but junk." He folded it and tossed it at the desk. "Did you ever hear of a man named Trotsky?"

"No, sir. Is he a Pole?"

"A Russian. There's a letter from him over there as well. In the same stack with the president's."

"That one I did not see, Señor Rivera. I swear it's the truth."

"I'm not accusing. The point I want to make is that you're wrong, idealism does exist. Have you heard of the Russian Revolution at least?"

"Yes, sir. Lenin. He got you in trouble with the gringos on your mural."

"That one. Leader of the Bolsheviks. He sent the monarchs packing, along with all the rich bloodsuckers living off the workers and peasants. He put the workers and peasants in charge. What do you say about that?"

"With no disrespect, señor, I would say, how long did he last?"

"Through the revolution and seven years after. He did what was best for his people, until death. All the while living in a rather cold little apartment in Moscow."

"It's admirable, señor. And then he was murdered?"

"He died of a stroke. With two men poised to succeed him: one with scruples, the other with cunning. I suppose you'll say it's predictable, the cunning one took power."

"Did he?"

"He did. Stalin. A selfish, power-mad bureaucrat, everything you seem to require in a leader of men."

"I'm sorry, sir. It's not that I want to be right about this."

"But I contend you are not. The other one, with scruples, could just as easily be in charge now. He was Lenin's right hand and best friend. Elected president of the Petrograd Soviet, a populist, certain to succeed Lenin. Different in every way from Stalin, who was infatuated with party bureaucracy. How could the people fail to support the populist over the bureaucrat?"

"And yet they failed to do so?"

"Only thanks to an accident of history."

"Ah. The populist with scruples was murdered."

"No, to Stalin's frustration, he remains alive in exile. Writing strategic theory, organizing support for a democratic People's Republic. And avoiding Stalin's ant colony of assassins, who are crawling over the earth right now looking for him."

"It's a good story, señor. Strictly from the point of view of plot. May I ask, what was the accident of history?"

"You can ask the man himself. He'll be here in a few months."

"Here?"

"Here. It's the Trotsky I mentioned, the letter lying over there on the desk under Cárdenas. I've asked the president to grant him political asylum under my custody."

So. For this, all the questions and mystery. The Painter stood grinning, his hair in an unruly halo around his head, or perhaps it was a devil's horns. His smile underlined by double chins. "Well, my young friend. Do you remain *uncurious?*"

"Señor, I confess, I maintain that position with increasing difficulty."

8 October

Sometimes when the Painter is reading over the day's typing, there's time to look at the books in his library. The whole wall is shelves. On the bottom are Frida's wooden-spined box folders where she files the household papers. Each one she has identified with a picture drawn on its spine: a naked woman, for Diego's personal letters. The Evil Eye, for hers. The one for accounting has only a dollar sign.

The rest is books, a wall of them about everything: political theory, mathematical theory, European art, Hinduism. One shelf the length of the room is devoted to Mexico's ancient people: archaeology, mythology. Scientific journals on the antiquities, which look tedious. But others are fascinating. The Painter took one down to show it off: a codex. Made a hundred years ago by monks, who labored to make exact replicas of the ancient books the Mexica people made on thick tree-bark paper. It didn't have pages exactly, but was one long folded panel like an accordion. The ancient language is pictures, little figures. Here, a man cut in half. There, men standing in boats, rowing.

He said it was the Codex Boturini, about the peregrinations of the Azteca. On the advice of gods they left Aztlán in search of their new home, and took 214 years to find it. The long page was divided into two hundred fourteen small boxes, each one recording the main thing that happened in that year. Not good, mostly. A head hanging on a rotisserie over a fire! A man with eyeballs falling out! But most of the years showed simply their search for home. Anyone could feel the anguish of this book—what longing is keener? Pictographs of weary people walking, carrying babies or weapons. Small, inked footprints trailed down the full length of the book, the sad black tracks of heartache. When completely unfolded, the codex stretched almost the whole length of the studio. That is how long it is possible to walk, looking for home.

November 2

Day of the Dead. The señora made altars all over the house to recall her beloved dead: ancients, half-born children. "Who are your dead, Insólito?" she keeps asking.

They request a suspension of all writing, this notebook put away. César will enforce the ruling. They set their trap and pounced in the Painter's study at lunchtime, husband and wife in one room for once, for this purpose. *For security. No more of your little notes. We've promised extraordinary measures for the Visitor, you can't imagine how frightened he is.* Devil and dragon in one lair, the Painter sitting at his desk, and she pacing the yellow floorboards with rippling skirts, a tiny tempest. *Not even a market list.* They claim César is becoming agitated, convinced he's sleeping in the same room with an agent of the GPU. "Poor old General Wrong Turn, I know he's confused," she said. This woman who has said many times: *Sóli, to stop painting would feel like being dead.* She understands what she's asking. To stop writing and be dead.

"It's for safety," he added. A man who throws paint in the face of safety.

Where are your dead, Sóli? Here, and the devil take it, a notebook for the altar of the dead in this lonely house. Dead and gone, the companionship of words.

Report from Coyoacán

This record of events will be submitted to Señora Frida for weekly inspections, or at any other time she requires, for purposes of security. According to her authorized instruction it is to harbor no opinions, confessions, or fictions. Its purpose is: "To record for history the important things that happen." The señora's sympathy for record-keeping is noted with gratitude—HWS, 4 January, 1937.

9 January: Arrival of the Visitor
The petrol tanker *Ruth* arrived from Oslo at dawn this morning to discharge its only passengers at the Tampico docks. The landing party were brought from the ship by a small launch, under the watch of Norwegian guards, and welcomed onto Mexican soil by the following persons: Sra. Frida, Mr. Novack (American), and General Beltrán representing the government of Mexico. Diego R. still hospitalized with an infection of the kidneys. The Visitor and party were taken by government train to the capital.

11 January: Arrival of the Visitors in the House at Coyoacán
He is to be known here as "Lev Davidovich." His wife: "Natalya." Because of the danger of assassination, a welcoming party assembled at the San Angel house to distract attention while Lev and Natalya were secretly brought here to Coyoacán. Their secretary of many years is expected to arrive here in the coming week. He did not travel together with them, but through New York.

12 January

The visitors are settled in the house, the former dining room serving as their bedroom with Lev's study in the adjacent small room. Lev in extraordinary spirits, despite his years of travails fleeing from Stalin and recent twenty-one days at sea. He steps through the glass doors of his study into the sunny courtyard and stretches himself, flexing his arms: a compact, muscular man, truly the Russian peasant to lead a revolution of peasants. He seems built for a life of work rather than confinement. When he's working at his desk, his broad hand clasps a pen as if it were an ax handle. When he smiles, his eyes shine and his cheeks dimple above the little white beard. Delight appears to be his natural state. Does a man become a revolutionary out of the belief he's entitled to joy rather than submission? This surprising man looks up at the bright Mexican sky, remarking that with only one country on earth that will have him now, he's glad this is the one.

He could leave this house for a stroll if he liked, though of course he would have to be guarded. In Norway they were indoors under house arrest since last September, Natalya said. Stalin threatened trade sanctions against Norway unless the government rescinded his asylum. And we can be sure, Stalin already knows he is here.

14 January

Arrival of the secretary: to be known in this record as "Van." Tall, blond, broad-shouldered as a footballer, it's good he traveled separately. Such a d'Artagnan as this fellow could hardly walk down a street without attracting attention, as the señora will shortly see for herself.

Lev's study and bedroom are the most secure part of the house, as they form an interior wing jutting into the courtyard. Good light from the portico doors facing the courtyard and magnolia tree. Van is keeping very busy there today, unpacking books.

16 January

Sra. Frida will be shocked to see her childhood house so transformed. It was a good choice to move her father to San Angel, all Sr. Guillermo's things are packed away. The exterior walls have been painted plumbago as requested, so it is the Blue House she wanted. But really, a Blue Fortress. The courtyard wall is raised to a height of seven meters, and the masons are moving their scaffolds now to begin bricking up the windows. The men agree these security measures are needed. From the tall wooden doors on Londres Street, visitors now enter through a guarded vestibule into the courtyard garden.

The courtyard is still the jungle it was; the masons haven't trampled the flowers completely. The house retains its original U shape, with the long front room facing Londres Street (fireplace and leaded-glass windows intact) to be used for dining and political meetings. Lev's bedroom and study make the other long wing. The string of tiny rooms across the back, connecting the two main legs, will house everyone else: Perpetua, the house girls Belén and Carmen Alba, the secretary Van, the cook HS, bodyguards Octavio and Felix. The windows in these small rooms face the exterior on the Allende Street side, so all are being closed by the brickmasons, making them dark little cupboards. One guard is posted out on Londres at all times. Sr. Diego is now feeling well enough that he brought over his Thompson machine gun.

The kitchen retains good light and air, extending outward as it does on the Allende Street side to enclose the back of the courtyard. The masons agreed to leave windows open for ventilating the wood fires in the stoves, after voluble argument from Perpetua, who warned of *cocineras ahumados*, the kitchen girls smoked like hams. Perpetua is confused and worn out from the changes, and resigned to her new position as assistant to a male head cook, HS, who vows to do his best by this duty. This kitchen is a wonder, with its extravagance of blue and yellow tile, woodstoves as long as divans, and the welcome sight of large wooden tables for rolling out dough. It will be a pleasure preparing the daily repast here for the visitors, and any feasts required for evening gatherings.

Household directives noted here: No food from unknown sources to be served, under any conditions. No unknown person to enter the house. HS is to assist the Visitor with typing and correspondence (recommended by Diego R.) and to retain this written record of events (requested by Sra. Frida). The first report from Coyoacán is here complete for the week Jan. 9–16, submitted for inspection.

19 January

The Coyoacán house is proving a good accommodation. Old houses have their wisdom. Despite the bricked-up exterior, the main rooms are comfortably lit by the courtyard. That jungle enclosed by high blue walls is a comforting world for visitors who are not at great liberty to roam elsewhere. Perpetua is taking care with her lilies and figs; it remains a cheerful world, in no way resembling a prison. Perpetua said Guillermo had this house built for his family more than thirty years ago, and through all those years no one saw a need for turning it upside down, until now. (Her resentment of the current upheaval is understandable.) The deep adobe walls keep a good temperature all day. The contrasts between this house and the modern one built by the Riveras in San Angel are many, most particularly their *kitchens*. But on that subject no opinion is given here.

Sra. Frida's choice of blue walls is greatly approved by all here.

A note on meal preparations: The visitors prefer tea over coffee. Another exceptional preference is unsweetened bread cut into thin slabs, toasted in the oven until somewhat hard, as if stale. Otherwise they are generally agreeable to normal foods. Natalya made plain their disinterest in pickled fish, after a long Norwegian winter of almost nothing else. They request mashed turnips and a green vegetable unknown to these parts, translated by Van as "the Sprouts of Belgium." Tomorrow Perpetua will be driven into the city on a search, as the Melchor market here has neither tea nor turnip. But they are adapting well to customary foods: sugared fritters, baked guava, and fermented cream are all favored. This morning they took enchiladas with eggs, and tea.

On days when no special meals are scheduled, all hands go to helping Lev unpack and arrange his study. He is curious about Mexico: the altitude of mountains, population of the city, its history, and so forth. Perpetua on her trip to town is to fetch the *Geographic Atlas* owned by HS, from his mother's apartment. It is outdated but will serve for now; Pico de Orizaba has not changed its height in a decade.

Lev communicates with help from the secretary Van, since Lev's Spanish and English are rudimentary, and clever Van seems to speak everything possible: French, Norwegian, Russian. He claims both French and Dutch as native tongues. He makes a point of moving the largest crates, insisting no extra help is needed in Lev's office. It can't be argued really; Van is tall and strong as an ox. (Though more handsome.) He complains sometimes in English about the "native typist," apparently not realizing HS also has two native tongues. But Lev is agreeable to having an extra fellow to help him. Plainly, Van has a habit of protecting his chief from outsiders, which is natural. He first became Lev's assistant in France, where they lived from 1933 until 1935. That was before Norway. Prior to that, Lev and Natalya were hiding in Istanbul, and before that, Kazakhstan. Lev Davidovich has been living in exile under threat of death since 1927. "I am a man in a very large world," he said slowly today, "with a very small place to be."

Mexico is fairly good sized, sir. You'll see.

Van said, "He's speaking metaphorically. He means that he lives in the planet without a passport."

21 January

A telegraphed message came this morning, delivered by Diego wearing his holster and gun. The message was in a code. Lev spent many hours in his study working it out, rejecting even Van's offers of help, with Natalya the whole time walking between the study and the kitchen, pulling on her fingers, making Perpetua burn the milk. The message concerns the son in Paris. Van says there are two sons; the younger was taken to prison camp three years ago, almost certainly dead. Two daughters are also dead.

Lev is not very sure of the message except for one important part: the telegram is definitely from Lyova, so he is alive. They have a code for his identity that is known to no one else on earth, not even Natalya. Lev speculates that GPU killers in France have tried to assassinate Lyova, and we can expect the newspapers to report him killed. To spare distress, he wanted his parents to know he is alive, in hiding.

They seem little spared from distress, though. If her son escaped murder this time, Natalya asks, what about the next? Lev rages that his children have done nothing to earn a death sentence from Stalin. The younger one, Sergei, only ever cared for books, sport, and girls, but ended in a concentration camp. "And now Lyova. His crime is to be the son of his father. Who can change the things that brought him into the world?"

23 January

Diego arrived early, upset, with the bundle of newspapers he receives by special post. Two report the death of Lyova, as predicted, but they know this is false. There is worse news yet: headlines declaring L. D. Trotsky found guilty of crimes against the Soviet Union. His trial in Moscow has been going on for weeks, with the accused in absentia. Van says Lev petitioned to go there and stand trial, for the chance to defend himself, but Stalin wouldn't lift the exile order. The aim of the trial is to discredit anyone who ever spoke against Stalin. Some of Lev's friends are also declared guilty: men named Radek, Piatakov, and Muralov, all three imprisoned now in Moscow.

The charges are strange and diverse: derailing trains, collaborating with Rudolf Hess and the Nazis, acting as agents of the Japanese emperor, stealing bread. Attempting to assassinate Stalin by poisoning his shoes, and his hair cream.

Stalin uses hair cream?

"Careful, lad," said Lev. "That knowledge alone could get you the firing squad."

The penalty for the charges against Lev is death. Yet he seems in good spirits, despite the newspapers from France and the United States calling him a villain, and the Mexican ones calling him a "villain in our midst." The editorials speculate on why he betrayed his principles. These newspaper men have never met Lev, yet confidently they discuss his innermost feelings and motives! They take it on faith that the treacheries were all committed. They don't even wonder how a man could derail so many Russian trains after he was put on a cargo boat for Prinkipo Island.

The security regimes here are strictly maintained, as the news makes clear Stalin intends to have Lev assassinated. The guard in the street changes hourly. Lorenzo organizes drills in which Lev and Natalya must be hidden very quickly. When Diego comes in the car, Lev has to move to one of the inner rooms before the court gates are opened to let the car drive in. Snipers could be in Allende Street, waiting for a line of fire into the courtyard. And if any unknown person comes to the door, even a grocer's boy delivering eggs and flour, the intruder is patted down, relieved of belt and shoes, and made to open all packages for inspection. The GPU will certainly strike, and no one knows how they will do it. (Though entering in the guise of a grocer seems unlikely.)

Lev says he has been a revolutionary from the age of seventeen, with a gallows waiting for him somewhere for forty years. His friends will know these new charges against him are invented. "And my enemies know it also. Which of these has written anything new?" He threw the newspapers aside and made Natalya come and sit on his knee. She obeyed him, but with a frown on her bottom lip, like the little dogs that have long wool in their eyes and a flattened nose. Lev took off his round-rimmed spectacles and sang to her in Russian. He asked to hear some songs of the Mexican revolution. Perpetua knew a surprising number. For such an old cook, her voice is steady.

24 January
Lev and Natalya went for a stroll in the Melchor market, their first venture outside the house since arrival. Between all the guards and Diego's machine gun, Coyoacán village must have entertained a commotion. But the so-called Villain in Our Midst means to hold his bearded chin up to the world without shame.

With Lev and Natalya out strolling and all the guards escorting, the house was quiet. A slow afternoon passed, helping Van file cartons of Lev's letters and published writings. It's hard to believe such an outpouring of words could come from one man—"the Commissar," Van calls him. He works each day as if the calendar on his desk were on its last page, which it could well be. Today while he was out, Van took the opportunity to ask many questions, not friendly. Place of birth, education, and so forth.

He revealed some scraps of his own life: a difficult childhood, the French mother losing her citizenship for marrying a Dutch husband, who died soon after Van's birth. Van has a weakness for what he calls Nederland licorices. They look like black glass beads, in a packet he keeps in the desk drawer, guarded rather anxiously, as he is sure they can't be bought in Mexico.

Here are two fatherless boys, then, eager to be anything for Lev, with his own two sons so far gone from him, and the man so kind. Already Lev remembers which assistant takes sugar in his tea. He puts everyone through stretching exercises so they won't get backaches while typing what he himself stayed up all night to write. But Van will always be the favored son, of course. He has served Lev so long.

Van was surprised to learn the "native typist" is also of hybrid origin, half gringo. He changed to speaking English after that. His Spanish is very imperfect. He needs help with interpreting at the political meetings, especially when the talk flies around the table like a flock of crows. Last evening it flew from Russian to English (for Mr. Novack), then Spanish (for the Riveras' colleagues), then back to Russian, with some French thrown in by Van, just for show, it seemed. Excuse this opinion, if it is one, but as Sra. Frida can plainly recall, no one at that meeting needed French.

All papers filed today were letters from the past four years, most in French but some typed in Russian, pages of characters in that strange alphabet lined up like rows of little men doing bending exercises. So it's untrue that typewriters are restricted to characters of the English language. Van cracked his composure and smiled at the story of Officer Gringo and the Potomac Academy typewriters. He understands Spanish well enough to laugh at the joke about Señor Villanueva and his *anos* in the *bano*. Or he pretended. He seems fearful of losing his position as his commissar's sole interpreter.

With apologies here to Sra. Frida, because the last paragraph undoubtedly contains at least one opinion. But not a fiction. The second weekly household report from Coyoacán is herein submitted for her inspection.

30 January

A wire came from Paris: Radek, Piatakov, and Muralov were executed in Moscow. Lev's spirits flag—more of his friends are dead—but he stays absorbed in work. What the newspapers say about Lev is shocking, charges more improbable every day. Lev said that when the public nerve is aroused, the most impressive capacity of man is his skill for lying. Van said, "It's good to hear you indignant, Commissar."

But Lev maintained he was not at all indignant. He was holding a Russian newspaper with such ink-stained fingers he could be a printing press. "I'm speaking as a naturalist, stating fact. The urge to lie is produced by the contradictions in our lives. We are made to declare love for our country, while it tramples our rights and dignity."

"But newspapers have a duty to truth," Van said.

Lev clucked his tongue. "They tell the truth only as the exception. Zola wrote that the mendacity of the press could be divided into two groups: the yellow press lies every day without hesitating. But others, like the *Times*, speak the truth on all inconsequential occasions, so they can deceive the public with the requisite authority when it becomes necessary."

Van got up from his chair to gather the cast-off newspapers. Lev took off his glasses and rubbed his eyes. "I don't mean to offend the journalists; they aren't any different from other people. They're merely the megaphones of the other people."

"It's true, sir. The newspapers are like the howlers on Isla Pixol."

Lev seemed interested in the comparison, and changed from English to Spanish. "What are these howlers?" he asked.

"A kind of monkey, very terrifying. They howl every morning: first one starts, then a neighbor hears it and starts his own howl, as if he can't help it. Soon the whole forest is bellowing, loud as thunder. It's their nature, probably they have to do it, to hold their place in the forest. To tell the others no one has gotten the best of them."

"You are a naturalist also," Lev said. He struggled but was determined to continue the conversation in Spanish. Van left the office. "Where are these creatures?"

"Isla Pixol. It's a coastal island, south of Veracruz."

"A monkey does not swim. How did they become isolated?"

En isla, he said. Probably he meant, *en una isla*, on an island.

"It wasn't always an island, an isthmus of rocks connected it with the mainland, but they dredged it for a shipping channel. It was during Maximilian, I think. The monkeys that had gone out there couldn't get back."

22 February

The jacaranda in the courtyard has put on its bloom. This purple can't be ignored, it's like a tree singing. The walk down Londres Street to the market is a concert: the small jacaranda on the corner hums the tuning note, then all others in the lane join in. Even Perpetua has a light in her eye, holding one hand to her flat old bosom as she takes the cucumbers out of the market basket, one by one.

From Lev's study, the view from the end window is a solid blaze of purple. Van sits there to take dictation from the Ediphone, with his square profile framed against the window like Poseidon in a purple sea. Or some Teutonic god who causes all he touches, and the air itself, to burst into purple flames. It is not a fiction or opinion to report that he is breathtaking. Perpetua is not the only one in this house thinking of cucumbers.

1 March

Octavio apprehended a man with a repeater, in the alley. After every fresh newspaper rant on the villain residing in Coyoacán, these men show up. So far it's only citizen-desperados vowing to protect their wives. Lev fears more sophisticated men, Communist Party operatives working under command of Stalin's GPU. But a bullet from a barefoot soldier is no less deadly than from a well-paid one. Lorenzo sleeps in the front dining room now. Those lovely windows will have to be closed with brick. The masons have made a mess, and Van had to move into the tiny cupboard with HS, close quarters for two. Though he left his multitude of serge jackets in a trunk in the other room.

This week is too hot for early spring. And this week the household staff are banned from the front of the house due to the government officials negotiating there, late into the night. The heat in this bricked-up cloister is unbearable. Van is dismayed at being held out of the meetings, but Diego says it's sensitive. President Cárdenas is expected here himself, to help arrange the Commission of Inquiry for Lev.

After cooking and serving supper, washing up, tidying, and sweeping, nothing is left for the staff but to sit on cots in these tiny rooms in undershorts and gob shirts, smoking panatelas, telling exaggerated stories to pass the time. It's like being at school. These are not brotherly feelings Van inspires. Mother would say: Van is plenty rugged.

March 3

The guards spend every long evening all in one small room, breathing the same exhaled air and drinking one another's spit from one warm jug of pulque. Playing cards for pesos, boredom games. Earlier this evening, the usual one: name your one wish if you could have it, then die tomorrow. Boys at school played this, reliably coming round to getting hands on some celebrated pair of *tetas*. Van from his high place added to the earnest list, "success of the Commissar's revolution." He was on the cot and everyone else on the floor, passing the cigarette packet. "You, Shepherd. Name yours."

"To make something beautiful, that people would find very moving."

"*Pendejo*, you do that every day in the kitchen."

"I mean a work of art that isn't in the toilet pot by the next day. A story, or something like that."

"Like the murals of Rivera, commanding men to rise from their knees and fight!" Lorenzo said. Stewed or not, loyal to the cause.

"Or smaller, like the paintings she does. Something people would find . . . dear."

"*Querido*. That's all you want, sheepdog!"

"Our shepherd," Van said, leaning out to pat a shaggy head as if it belonged to his dog. In front of the other men. The small dog panted.

10 March

A wire from Mr. Novack, now back in New York: he has persuaded Professor John Dewey to chair the commission of inquiry. Some

American journalists will follow the story to Mexico. Diego and Lev are extremely happy, as it will give Lev opportunity to answer Stalin's charges, for the world to hear.

Noted: That Sra. Frida, after inspecting last week's record of events, repeats her request that it remain objective, especially with regard to the secretary Van.

April 6

Professor John Dewey of Columbia University arrived today by train from New York. He will preside over the joint Commission of Inquiry into the Charges Made Against Lev Davidovich Trotsky in the Moscow Trials. He and seven journalists will reside for the month at the San Angel Inn. The opening press conference will be there, honoring Professor Dewey's wish for fairness and no contact with the defendant prior to hearings.

The proceedings will be held here, because of special needs for Lev's security. The attorney for Lev's defense, Mr. Goldman from Chicago, arrives by train tomorrow. Sandbags are being laid across Londres to close the neighborhood to traffic. Extreme publicity is expected during the trial. The Mexico City newspapers are already having a run of extras on the subject of the Villain in Our Midst.

April 10: First Session of the Joint Commission of Inquiry

Professor Dewey opened. Thanked Mexican government for its political democracy, stated no man should be condemned without a chance to defend himself. "I have devoted my life to the business of enlightening minds, in the interest of society. I accept my responsibilities in this commission for one reason: to do otherwise would be false to my life's work." The responsibility is to investigate charges of sabotage and sedition brought by Stalin against the defendant.

Defendant is Lev Davidovich Trotsky, b. 1879. Fought as anti-tsarist from age seventeen, led the Bolshevik Revolution, elected president of the Petrograd Soviet in 1917. Author of the manifesto of the Third

International Comintern, 1919. Expelled from the Soviet Communist Party in 1927. Forced into exile in Kazakhstan at that time.

At the table with the defendant are his wife, his lawyer, and Van, who has the job of producing requested documents. At a table near it, two Americans and HS, who are to translate and record all questions posed to Lev, and his answers. A man named Glotzer (American) is official court reporter and knows a language (shorthand) that allows writing everything very fast, but only if he understands the words. So all proceedings go to English for his sake, and of course for Professor Dewey's. Therefore HS has the duty to record and translate any questions asked or answered in Spanish.

None today, only testimony. Cross-examination begins tomorrow.

12 April

One question in Spanish today, from Sr. Pontón of the Sociedad de Naciones, translated as follows: "Sir, for our Mexican correspondents I beg you the trouble of answering: your persistent charge against Stalin is a lack of democracy. Is that correct?"

Lev answered: "Correct. A rank of party workers has been created who enter the government and renounce their own opinions. Or at least any open expression of them. Every page on their desks comes from above. They behave as if the hierarchy had already created all party opinion and decisions. From this hierarchy, every decision affecting the country stands in the form of a command."

When Lev isn't speaking he puts his feet on the table and leans back in his chair. Today he reached such an extreme backward angle, it seemed the GPU might not be needed to crack the man's head. But he was still listening. He looks down his Russian nose and his whole lower face crumples into his collar when he concentrates. He has no consciousness of how he must look to others, only aiming his mind with such a ferocious focus that it could set all those bureaucrats' papers to flames. This must be the countenance of a revolutionary.

This daily record complete and submitted: 4/12/37.

13 April

Sr. Pontón's question and Lev's answer have gone on the front page of today's *Washington Post*! Exactly as translated by HS, and quoted again on the editor's page, in a discussion of the Moscow Trials and the commission. The article even used the description of Mr. Trotsky leaning in his chair, and the headline in very bold letters was: THE COUNTENANCE OF A REVOLUTIONARY.

These were only some notes and doodles submitted with the translation transcript, Sra. Frida. This is a shock, and a terror. The very first try at translation, and some notes jotted on a whim, now on display for the world to read? It was hard to think about breakfast this morning. Perpetua said, "Sit down and stop shaking, *mi'ijo*. It's a bad start to the week for a man who's hanged on Monday."

Hanging is what it feels like! A twenty-year-old *galopino* who knows nothing about politics could have mistaken yes for no, a *renunciar* for a *renacer*, and then what? History could hang on it. Lives could be lost, for the sake of a wrong word. No wonder writers are pessimistic. Better to be a cook, where a mistake will only send someone away hungry, or at worst, to the WC.

But Van complimented the translation. He read the article to Lev and Natalya at breakfast, translating it back to Russian as he went. They listened to the words of a cook, while eating toasted bread for which the same nervous cook had already burned his knuckles.

14 April

After the day's hearings closed today, Lev went to the front door to see the huge crowd gathered there. Not only newsmen but workers of all sorts, even laundrywomen. No barefoot soldiers want to kill him anymore, after hearing his fiery defense of the worker and peasant reported in the news. Now he's afraid they'll want to knock Jesus off the pallets of the Holy Week processions this week and put Trotsky up there instead. A group from the miners' syndicate walked here all the way from Michoacán.

He spoke to the crowd in Spanish, slowly but well. "I am here because your country believes with me in democratic government and the worker-control of industry. Our efforts cannot succeed in an empty space." (Probably he meant "a vacuum.") "True change will come from an international organization of workers for world revolution." The crowd has been quiet all day, but at those words they roared.

Nearly every day he takes small pauses from his writing to practice Spanish with the native typist. Van doesn't like the distraction, pointing out that translators are always at the ready. And Lev says, "Trust an old revolutionary to trust no one completely." He was teasing, it seemed. But today as he spoke directly to the crowd, his purpose was clear.

15 April

A long day of hearings. Mr. Dewey says it's nearly concluded, but the crowd still grows, both the number of foreigners inside and the Mexicans outside. Lev has such a passion for this hearing, he wouldn't mind if it went on until the sun burned cold. Van seems content beside his chief, undaunted by the army of observers: Mexican and foreign reporters in fedoras and rolled-up shirtsleeves, magazine writers, even some novelists, watching Van's every move as he fishes into the paper caverns of the files with his long fingers, retrieving whatever obscure page Lev might need, indicated only by a word, a date, or a person's name. They are like father and son. Lev and Van.

Very few questions in Spanish today. Sr. Pontón of the Sociedad de Naciones has the most. Today he had two. The first: "Sir, is it your position that a worker's state could genuinely honor suffrage and all democratic rights, as in a social democracy?"

Lev's reply: "Why should it not be so? Even now, in all the capitalist countries, Communists take part in the parliamentary struggle. When we achieve a worker's state, there is no difference in principle in the way we will use suffrage, freedom of the press, assembly, and so forth."

Second question: "Sir, you say the Soviet Union under Stalin is a degenerated workers' state, controlled by an undemocratic bureaucracy. You predict this corruption will be overthrown by a political revolution, establishing a democracy of the working class. Or that it will continue to degenerate under world pressure into a purely capitalist state. In either case, can you rationalize the costs to society?"

Lev answered: "Young man, you make a point. Humanity has never succeeded in rationalizing its history. Much harm comes from leaders who insist that for every advance, someone else must slide backward. The dictatorship of the Soviet Secretariat came about because of the backwardness and isolation of the country, for so long imposed on us by the tsar. We were accustomed to the rationalizing of a despot. People accept what they have already known. When mankind is exhausted, he creates new enemies, new religions. Our best task is to move forward without seeking to do so."

April 17

The commission has ended its work after thirteen sessions. If it went another day, the dining room of this house would crack like an egg. Lev closed with his usual vigor: "The experience of my life has not destroyed my faith in the clear, bright future of mankind. At age eighteen I entered the workers' quarters of Nikolayev with nothing but a boy's belief in reason, truth, and human solidarity. My faith since then has become more mature, but no less ardent."

Every hand stopped; the reporters looked as if they might need handkerchiefs. Mr. Dewey said, "Sirs, anything I could say after that would be a waste of breath."

Mr. Dewey and colleagues will consider the evidence and find the defendant guilty or not guilty. They will take many weeks before releasing their written verdict. But Lev is jubilant. Before the world, he has answered the charges.

28 April

The house is calming to the previous routines. If "calm" describes a man who works like three, signaling the typist to finish a letter and bring a book while he dictates political theories into the microphone of the wax-cylinder recording machine. It's very warm, even working in shirtsleeves. Van is always last to remove his tweed jacket. An unexpected brush of his hand, when he reaches for a book, feels like boiling water. Van and Lev are both men of northern temperaments, yet Van seems agitated by Mexico's vivid sun and landscapes, while Lev seems enlivened. He even loves the cactus.

1 May

Sra. Frida has continued her daily visits here since the hearings ended, making sure Lev is content. Let it be noted here: bringing Fulang Chang "to cheer the place up" may not be helpful. Natalya despises the monkey and yesterday, while Sra. Frida was in the kitchen, gave him a whack on the skull with a Conservative Party newspaper.

Lev is energized by the news of the workers' uprising in Barcelona, citing it as a sign that the Third International agreement between Stalin and the world's other communist parties has collapsed. Lev has been asked to write a fourth set of Internationalist agreements, hence his frenetic rush of words congealed into wax cylinders from his Ediphone. The alternative to Stalin's Comintern now sits in jars on the desk, waiting to be transformed into typewritten words, and then the actions of men.

To celebrate, the household staff is complying with Sra. Frida's requests to prepare for her "Fourth International party." Sr. Rivera is more worried about security than table decoration.

2 May: The Dance

Lev was already in his study when Sra. Frida arrived this morning to take over the dining room, before Natalya had eaten her breakfast.

So she ate in the kitchen. Begging pardon, but please let it be noted: this is Natalya's only home. Lately she has mentioned feeling like an unwanted guest.

Begging a second pardon, señora, but it was impossible not to laugh at the sight of you standing there at the table, decorating it for the party, with red carnations in both hands and one in your mouth. You looked like Carmen.

What are you laughing at? You think it's so simple to create history? Long skirt sweeping the floor like a broom, moving around the table, carefully laying out the long-stemmed carnations on the white tablecloth. The pattern looked like a huge eye, the long stems as eyelashes radiating outward like rays of the sun.

It's true, dining tables are part of history. The Painter's walls and Lev's wax cylinders are not the whole story. The Sra. frowned, already picking up the flowers again before the design was finished. Commanding: *Fetch the scissors!* without even looking up. Snipping the heads of the carnations from their stems, working so quickly that trails of blood might have begun flowing from her fingertips, like one of her paintings.

Then she put a hand on her hip and held up the scissors, menacing the air. "We're going to have dancing tonight. A lot of handsome artists. Belén and Carmen Alba told me you dance the *sandunga* and *jarabe*, perfectly. I will not even ask how they know this. But how did you learn?"

"From my mother."

"Your mother, a nationalist? I had a different impression."

"She would deny it now. She had a flirtation with it when we first came to the city. But now she's moved on to the age of swing, and well-paid engineers."

"And do you renounce us also? Or would you dance with an Indian girl?" She held out her hand and moved like liquid, rolling herself up into the arm that received her, making a flirtatious snip with her scissor like a flamenca dancer with her castanet.

Señora Frida is a confusion of terms: sometimes like a stern little man, then suddenly a woman or a child, but in every form demanding that you remain in love with her. Commanding even her giant of a husband, until he runs off to be rescued by softer, pillowy women. This is the truth and not an opinion: her cat smile, those hands, the paintbrushes. Any one of them can be like a slap across the chest.

After an hour's work she was satisfied with the arrangement of red flowers on white linen. "Here will be Lev's place," she said quietly, "and here. Natalya's." Uttering that second name as if her place at the table were a concession.

Jealous, of Natalya? Frida, is it possible?

It's a lot of work to use flowers as paints. By the time the party ends, they'll be a mess of wilted petals. Stains on your white tablecloth that could have been prevented. But you whirled around at that suggestion, looking fierce: lips pursed, the hand on your red rebozo, those silver earrings caressing your shoulders like hands.

"Unnecessary stains and dead flowers! Sóli, excuse me but what else do I have for making my marks on life, if not *lo absurdo y lo fugar.*"

You wanted to know how to say that in English. "The absurd" is easy. The other is more difficult. *Fugar* means things that run away with time. What would we do without the absurd and the running away?

That was the moment when the door flew open *bang!* and of course it was Diego. Carrying books and jacket, dropping things as he went, his boots hitting the tiles like cracks from a rifle as he crossed the room, kissed you, took the flowers away, and began to rearrange everything. All your work, you, everyone in the room—it all vanishes in the presence of Diego. Always right, because he is always riveting. For La Frida there is El Diego and nothing else.

A long time ago at school there was a boy like that, Bull's Eye, always right even when he was wrong. Once you said it would be necessary to confide in you, Frida, sooner or later, one pierced soul to another. That maybe you could help. Since you are the only one reading this report each week, here is the confession you requested: the scandal of irregular conduct. For the Insólito there was Bull's Eye and nothing else. *Insólito* means ridiculous. It means all those things you said, absurd and running away. Where would you be without *lo absurdo y lo fugar*. Maybe you're also lonely in this house, and you were asking: My friend, what would I do without you?

16 May
The press reports that Mr. Browder of the American Communist Party has come here to warn Mexican Communists against any communication with Trotsky. He says "unity at all costs" means supporting Stalin. Lombardo Toledano and many other Mexican party leaders have dined at the Riveras' table, eaten the food of this kitchen. But Diego's membership in their party is now revoked. They all ignore his invitations to come here and meet with Lev.

The heat is unbearable. Van goes out to a bar at night, the Golden Earring, just to get some air, he says. Lorenzo goes along, hoping to meet girls. *Do you want to come too?* Van asked. But probably the bar would be just another airless place.

1 June
The commander in chief of the Red Army, executed for treason. Tukhachevsky had expressed support of Trotsky's position, and for this reason only he is dead. Lev dreads there will be a purge, thousands of officers affected. Nothing else here to report.

4 June
A telegram this morning from Lyova, as always in code. The purges in the Soviet Union are terrible. The chief of the Soviet Secret Service has resigned his post in protest of the killings, and announced his loyalty to Trotsky and the Fourth International.

Lev fears for the safety of Chief Reiss, but is cheered by news he has broken from Stalin. A congenial day in the office, despite swelter-ing heat. Lev had the big red worktable from his office carried out-side to the courtyard. The commissar was quite a sight, working in his big straw hat and old-fashioned balbriggans. Even Van has finally stripped from gob shirts to Vee Lines, and over the course of the day his great Dutch shoulders began to glow. Tonight they are nearly the same maroon color as the desk.

This afternoon he knocked over the ink bottle and laughed about it, for a change. His sympathies are improving. He gratefully accepted help with changing the typewriter ribbon, and later with a repair of the electrical cord of the Ediphone. He complimented a small correc-tion in a translation, saying we make a fine team. Who knows where else the pair of us might work, outside of these walls, if such a day should come.

5 June
Señora Frida's wish this evening was to dine intimately with the Visi-tors. Natalya is not well and remained in bed. Van went out for the evening.

8 June
Let it be noted: Every time Sra. Frida brings out a tray of tea, the commissar lights up like the sun. He used to bear interruptions with polite tolerance. Now he glances up often to see if it's time yet for an-other. Listening for the jingle of bracelets. Van agrees, Lev's behavior is strange. Today Lev and the señora went in the automobile to Sra. Cristina's house on an undisclosed mission, and stayed several hours, not for the first time. The lack of security is extremely worrisome. Frida, this is not an opinion.

10 June

Today while Lev was out for the afternoon, he instructed the office should be well cleaned and the table moved back indoors. Rains are expected.

Evidently the commissar didn't expect such a thorough tidying-up. Van found a box of letters that worry him greatly. The nature of these letters may be known to Sra. Frida. *The new workers need not only your husband's murals, but also what you offer: beauty, truth, passion. True art and revolution are joined at the lips and the heart.* Some letters, even more explicit, had been placed inside books he's borrowed from Sra. Frida. He means to return these later, evidently. The letters remain in place.

Tonight Van paces like a prisoner around his cot in this tiny cupboard of a room. He sucks on licorice pastilles when he is anxious, after first laying out the evening's ration end-to-end as Mother used to do with her cigarettes.

"Can we say anything about this, to anyone?"

"How could we?"

Van is desperate for his chief's safety. And feels loyalty to Natalya as well; he has lived with them so many years. He wants this behavior explained. But not the explanation.

"For the sake of heaven," he keeps saying, alternately pacing and slumping onto his cot. His broad shoulders and white V-shirt glow in the darkness of this bedroom with its closed-up windows. "I thought she looked up to him as a father. For the sake of heaven, she calls him El Viejo."

"The *old man* is only five years older than Diego. Maybe she says that to disguise her feelings."

Bricked into this tiny cell: two men wrapped in heat like a blanket, whipped into two entirely separate frenzies. At the root of each man's distress, although from entirely separate quarters: the damages wrought by love, the cruelties of sexual attraction.

He hasn't any notion. In a moment he will be naked, it happens every night. Innocently he lays out his body, piece by piece like a banquet. His long, flat belly like a white-flour tortilla. His beautiful feet extended beyond the wildest hopes of his little cot.

"How can they be so foolish?" he keeps asking.

"Love can be like a sickness, Van. They didn't want it to happen."

11 June

Four of Sra. Frida's paintings will be included in an exhibition at the National University. Likely she is happy about it, though she has not mentioned this, or anything else of a personal nature, since the last inspection of this journal. She comes to the house almost daily to see Lev, but avoids the staff. Most especially she avoids Van.

The personal confidences of her cook, for which she has earnestly asked on several occasions, have gone unnoticed here, or at any rate passed without comment.

12 June

An unforgettable outing: strange and wondrous, but in the end, bitter humiliation. The confidences of this report have been used against their author. Fact, not opinion.

The workings of a household are like those of the world. The Russians tolerate Stalin's tyranny, Lev says, only because they know nothing else, from centuries of isolation under the Tsar. So it may be here, as well. So it may be with a mistress whose cruelty merely contains her past. Cruelties imposed on her by a husband, or life itself.

Yet, as Lev said at his trial: our best task is to move forward without insisting others slide backward.

The authorized reporting of history, then: Sra. Frida proposed the outing as a kindness to all, "to escape this insufferable heat." But Natalya of course is still unwell, and Diego too busy even to be told about the outing. The escapees included only herself, Lev, and his two secretaries—two pairs, like playing cards in her hand. She arranged it with more than the usual secrecy and drove the motorcar herself because César can't keep his mouth shut, she said. And that much is true.

A long drive to the dusty edge of the city, out to the embarcadero. Xochimilco is a strange village, farm fields that appear to float on the water. Really they are built-up islands, farmed since the time of the Azteca, when this city still stood in a lake. The canals and square farm-islands are the last evidence of what lies beneath all this history and claptrap called Mexico City. Sra. Frida lectured with great flair during the drive, sometimes letting go of the steering wheel to wave her hands, telling how the ancients supplemented their diet of frogs by making these islands for growing vegetables. How the layers of water lily leaves and fertile mud are built up inside a fence of inter-laced reeds, until the island gets above water level and the farmer can plant his crop.

Now it is a mad maze of colors and cool water. Squash and corn-fields, floral explosions, with waterways running on a perfect grid between the island fields. Angel's trumpets dangle their pink bell-flowers over the water, and white herons stand one-legged among the reeds. Giant old poplars tower along the borders of each field, shading the watery lanes. You can see how it's all constructed; they begin by planting these poplar saplings in a rectangle under the wa-ter, for anchoring the interlaced reeds and poles that will become the island's perimeter. Now the saplings planted long ago are ancient, leafy giants, with coral beans crowding in thickets between them. Some islands have the farmers' reed-thatched huts built right upon them, with children running and swimming from one to the next, naked as fish. Women cast lines into the water or hawk jugs of pul-que to the boaters passing by. Every side channel offers another thrill-ing glimpse, a long ribbon of shining green water overarched with a tunnel of trees.

The passenger boats made for the canals are broad, flat-bottomed *trajineras*. Gaudy ducklike things, every one is painted up in red, blue, and yellow, with an arch across the front of each one spelling out a

woman's name in flowers. Made to order with each hire. Frida and
Lev had a dispute when they hired the boat: she wanted to call it
Revolución. Not the best (Van pointed out) for the security of our
comrade guest. Lev prevailed, and the boatman spelled out *Carmen*,
Sra. Frida's first name. She snuggled up happily with the "old man"
on the bench on their side, with Van and HS on the other bench, two
pairs facing one another across the plank-table. All the boats have
one, a long, narrow table for picnicking bolted right in, running from
prow to stern. Ours was painted the brightest yellow, which seemed
to suit Frida's mood. She would know a name for this color. The canals were jammed with these boats, all painted with similarly violent
imagination, bobbing with couples and families escaping the city's
heat, pushed along by boatmen with poles. The farmers in canoes
full of vegetables had some trouble poling between the traffic jams,
making their way out to the marketplaces of the city.

A canoe swept by carrying marimba players, two men in white
shirts standing side by side at their long instrument of wooden
blocks, rolling their hands over the rippling wooden notes. Frida
tossed the marimba men a few pesos to play "The Internationale."
Other boatloads of musicians bobbed past also; the place was filled
with them, even a whole mariachi band standing up in their canoe,
entirely precarious, balancing the enthusiasm of song with their will
to keep dry.

It was a wild, floating marketplace. Men selling flowers, women
with giant aluminum pots balanced in tiny boats, pulling up alongside
to sell you a lunch: roasted corn, *pollo mole*, *carne asada* and tortillas,
handed up into your boat on crockery that would be washed afterward in the canal. Lev bought a bunch of red roses and tucked them
one by one into Frida's crown of braids. He poured glasses of red wine
for all of us, and then refilled them. He paid a band to play "Cielito
Lindo" and then twelve or fourteen other songs, all about the heart
and not one concerned with the Revolution. When he leaned out over
the water to pay the musicians, he forgot to let go her hand, which he

was holding under the table. The lovers were quite on display, cuddling all the afternoon, her little elbow folded neatly against his.

Van looked away, listing various sights as we passed by them in a childish way that was very unlike him, thanks to his discomfort. It would have been just as well to stare at these two; they make a better physical match than the little dove and the toad-frog. A more pleasing alignment: the Indian girl and her compact Russian peasant. Across from them, the Nordic god and native typist were shoved so close together on the bench, every turn of the boat pressed some part of a leg or shoulder against another. The air was breathlessly still, a cottony hot roar that swallowed everything: heat and music, a pounding pulse. Van close enough to touch his cheek, or clasp his knee. It took everything not to do it.

Then suddenly, loud screaming split the quiet. Our sleepy boatman raised his pole in alarm, but it was only a boatload of schoolgirls. They came alongside, waving wildly, with another boat following behind in right pursuit. That one, of course, filled with schoolboys, splashing and hurling flowers at their victims.

"It's a war of flowers!" the girls shrieked, launching back long-stemmed arrows across the water. They fell short every time, like the Azteca warriors uselessly slinging arrows at Cortés, just before their hearts were blown apart with cannon fire.

"*En garde!*" cried Frida, arming herself from the bower encircling her head, tossing roses in every direction. Lev also threw some flowers: a probable first in his long career as a militant. Frida reached into the water to catch a long-stemmed carnation and pointed it like a sword, swiping Lev's cheek and then his chest.

"I am hit!" he cried, clasping his chest in mock drama, falling back against the bench. "Struck in the breast by a posey. What do you call this one?"

"*Encarnado*," she said.

"*Descargado por encarnado*," he said. Carnal wounds. Injury may be mortal.

She kissed his cheek. Van looked carefully at the trees. The two boatloads of warriors moved away down a side canal, leaving the water behind them clotted with their colorful ammunition. Another canoe approached, and a man selling toys climbed aboard our boat, his pockets filled with trinkets of woven palm leaves. "Any children here?"

"No," Frida said, and Lev said "Yes" at the same time. Van explained, "I'm afraid the children have all gotten away."

"Well, this one is indispensable for people of any age." The man pulled from his pocket a long, woven tube. "A *trapanovio*. You had better try it, señorita." He held it toward Frida, who obligingly put her finger in the end of the tube and then made a show of not being able to escape. Everyone knows this trick. The weave of the tube holds tighter, the harder one pulls away.

"Señor, you'll have to buy it now, and hold on to the other end yourself," the man told Lev, extracting from him five pesos. "Otherwise she'll have this dangerous device for catching boyfriends, entirely at her disposal. Who else here needs to trap a few *novias*? You, young men?"

"That one maybe," said Frida laughing, pointing across the table. "He's desperate to trap a particular *novio*."

There was no need to say it like that. *Novio*, the masculine form.

"But forget about the other one." She tugged her trapped finger free of Lev's grip, its long prosthesis still attached, and shook it at Van as if he were a naughty child. "He needs no devices for trapping girls, apparently he has his own equipment. What time is it now, four o'clock? They're already lined up waiting for him at the Golden Earring."

"What is this?" Lev sat forward. "You go to that bar at night?"

"Not every night. And the girls don't make a queue."

"Oh, I've heard some stories!" Frida said. She seemed quite intoxicated, but maybe it was an act. She can seem that way at any time, for her own reasons. The toy man sensed that he had stepped in the pie, and scurried back to his canoe.

"What is this, Van?" Lev asked again, seeming interested but not disapproving. "You didn't tell me about any girls."

Van blushed acutely. "Not *girls*. One girl. Her name is Maria del Carmen."

"Maria del *Carmen*," Frida sang. "So this boat named Carmen carries more than one torch. Tell me about this young lady. Is she a bar girl?"

"A waitress. But educated at university. She tutors me in Spanish sometimes in the evening."

"Oh, very good, very good," Frida said, smiling ferociously, a cat with the mouse beneath its paw. "University educated and pretty, I have no doubt. Tutoring you in Spanish! Have you learned this one yet, *esternón?*" She touched her breastbone, leaning forward, and then cupped her own breasts in her hands. "What about *pezónes?*"

Van's complexion gave over completely to his blush. His ears and even the back of his neck. "I know the words. If that's what you are asking."

She stood up and leaned across the table, close to his face: *"Y besos suaves?"*

Lev pulled her back by the hand. "Frida, he's a man, not a child. If he has a lover in the town, it's not your concern."

"Everything is my concern, *mi viejo*. Lovers, most of all." The looks she gave to Van were smoldering. She worked the woven boyfriend trap gently off of her finger and studied it for a moment, before tossing it across the table to the object of no one's desire.

"Insólito, you're the one who needs this. Better go trap yourself a different fish."

14 June

The household has exploded. Diego and Natalya learned of their spouses' affair, leading to the unpleasantness one could reasonably expect. Lev left this morning for a house in the desert at San Miguel Regla, loaned on short notice by trusted friends of Diego. When Sra.

Frida came to the house today, Natalya made a very painful spectacle of her anger. Poor Belén was so frightened she dropped a plate of fritters.

Of course Van went with him, and Lorenzo also, but not the other bodyguards. Lev says he can't impose an army on the hospitality of the Riveras' friends, even if they support the Fourth International. Diego fears the place can't properly be guarded. And to complicate the arrangement, Diego may count himself among those lined up to assassinate his comrade guest.

Frida seems both disconsolate and unrepentant. A strange mix. Surely, señora, you don't blame anyone but yourself? You wanted to be discovered, that was obvious. Remember what you asked for in these pages: a history without deceit.

17 June

In the kitchen, the stories burn hotter than the stove. Perpetua says Señora Frida went up to San Miguel Regla yesterday, on the excuse that she needed to give some money to the Landeros family for taking Lev in their house. Perpetua clucked her tongue. "What business could she have up there except monkey business? But once you're on the horse you have to hold on, I suppose. Even if he bucks."

"That old man must have spice in his sauce yet," said Carmen Alba.

"*Old?*" Perpetua spat. "He's not even sixty. You girls are children, you don't know. The longer the sauce cooks, the spicier it gets."

Belén kept a nervous eye on the kitchen door, fearing the wife of the sauce in question.

30 August

A telegram came yesterday: Lev's former secretary Erwin Wolf, murdered in Spain by the GPU. Natalya felt someone should take the sad message to Lev. It was a quiet drive to San Miguel; César seems more than ever suspicious, even though he no longer has to share his room with a notebook-keeping spy.

The road to Regla passes near the great pyramids of Teotihuacán. Then through little mountain towns, steep streets filled with taverns, donkeys and dust, and pink colonial mansions from an earlier time, before it was shameful in Mexico to be rich. Now the mansions are all apartments, displaying laundry from their balconies.

Lev's place at San Miguel Regla is a small apartment at the back of a large hacienda. It seems safe enough, a high wall and Lorenzo posted at the window, in a desert outpost visited mostly by vultures. The Landeros are rarely in residence, the family and servants in any case asked not to approach the rear of the house. With no women around, the rooms shared by Van, Lev, and Lorenzo look like drawers in a giant cabinet, the beds swimming among notebooks, pistols, shoes, and inkwells. If Lev stays much longer, he may drown in his river of paper.

Lev finds the desert air invigorating and takes long walks each morning on the empty roads. He has fallen in love with cactus, finding a hundred varieties populating the dry ravines. To Van's dismay he digs them up, wraps them in burlap coats, and carries them home on his shoulder. Somehow, he plans to make a garden of these bizarre, prickled creatures. Van seems prickled also. Maybe missing life at the Golden Earring.

The return trip was even slower due to César's somnambulant driving and the anticipation of Natalya's poor eager face, the small bulldog sniffing for her absent master. She'll have to be told; Lev indicated no plans for returning soon. He doesn't mean to neglect her; it's only his pure fascination with life as it is, however it is. For any homeless wanderer he is a miracle of instruction: now that he is exiled from every place on earth except a desert wilderness, he declares a passion for cactus.

Here, very little is to be done. Cooking for unemployed bodyguards and Natalya, who hardly eats. She has survived six weeks now on lemon-juice tonics and Phanodorm. Every afternoon at two o'clock she parks her black shoes like two tiny automobiles beside her bed and lies down, fully dressed, to survive the remainder of the day.

One of the messages carried to Lev concerned a visit from Joseph Hansen, a comrade from the Trotskyist Party of the United States. Natalya sees hope in it: Lev's true appetite, she says, is for his work. The arrival of Hansen will bring him back.

8 September
Lev returns, as predicted, and with him the flood tides of paper. Idle days gone. Van works all day transcribing the wax cylinders, while Lev generates more. The typing is endless, interrupted only by the security drills.

Our menage is stirred like a soup: Diego wants Mr. Hansen and his wife Reba to have one of the connecting rooms. So all the guards will now share one tiny room, unless one would share a bed with old Perpetua, who snores like a boar pig. The house girls made a pallet under the fig in the courtyard so they can get some peace.

Members of the staff feel more than ever like inmates, because of the crowding and extreme security measures. The threats are real—this is understood, but not easy. Belén and Carmen Alba can't visit their mothers. The door is rarely opened; even a trip to the market has to coincide with the change of guards, so as to interfere less with Lev's work schedule. Van has ceased his nocturnal visits to the tavern. The bodyguards sleep with pistols in their belts, the possibility of death waiting behind every knock. The heat of summer has abated, and nothing is as it was.

12 September
Arrival of Joseph Hansen and his wife Reba. Lev and Joe are so happy to meet, they stayed up all the night talking. Reba helped make up extra beds, stuffed mattresses on the floor of a tiny room where now five men will sleep when not on duty. Reba apologized terribly and offered to share Perpetua's bed. Diego didn't forewarn her about the number of people already living here, probably because he neglected to notice it himself. She nearly wept. "And tomorrow you'll have to

feed us all. You must be tired of salvaging these men who are saving the world."

Hansen means to write a biography of Lev. In that case, this recording of events may no longer be necessary. Mr. Hansen understands politics far more perfectly, and can record conversations objectively, not laced with an ignorant cook's prejudices for sweet and salt. History can fall into more capable hands.

In any case, a record maintained to another person's standard is no real comfort to the spirit. Let it here be said, the writer understands this assignment was intended as a kindness, for which he is grateful. But the task has no freedom in it. A record meant for another's eyes is not recording, but spying.

September 16
Frida.

Carmen Frida Kahlo de Rivera, to be precise. And Van.

Were discovered sleeping on the pallet under the fig tree, where the house girls usually sleep but were tonight sent home to their families for the national holidays.

Recorded here for history: the couple lay with limbs entwined, his great white arm sheltering her small, curved body. Her black hair surrounded both of them, rooting them to the bed as if they were growing there, a single plant. They seemed consoled by sleep, unaware of an observer who had consumed some beer, earlier in the evening during the Independence fiesta, and hoped to deposit a secret piss in the geranium bed. The pair did not know they had been discovered. Apparently they still do not. The observation is here reported. Some madness of penned dogs infects this camp.

November 7
The Dewey Commission formally acquitted Lev of every accusation from the Moscow Trials. After months of deliberation they have re-

leased their written verdict to every nation. Of course Stalin still wants him murdered, more than ever. And the American and European newspapers that made him guilty in the first place have barely reported the Dewey Commission. Diego says the gringos are watching Hitler with a nervous eye, especially now with the Anschluss and the Rome-Berlin axis. He says Britain and the United States will want Russia on their side, if there is a war. So they can't let Trotsky be right about Stalin being a monster. They are going to need that monster.

Still a cloud has lifted, in time to celebrate Lev's birthday and the October Revolution. The Riveras made the largest-ever fiesta, hired marimbas, the patio and house filled entirely. The security men nearly exploded from nerves. The guests are not artistic Communists any more but peasants, white-trousered men in huaraches, unionists who support Lev. The women entered shyly with their heads down, braids nearly sweeping the courtyard stones. A few brought live chickens as gifts, their feet tied nicely with henequen ribbon. But the cooking for this fiesta started a week ago.

Señora Frida was especially extravagant in a gold Tehuana blouse, green skirt, and blue shawl. She arrived with a large parcel wrapped up in paper: a portrait of herself, a birthday gift for Lev. Somehow it did not get presented, in the middle of so much celebration. People were already sleeping on chairs and window ledges, and it was halfway to morning when she came in the kitchen demanding, "For the love of Petrograd, can anybody tell me why we celebrate the October Revolution on the seventh goddamned day of November?"

"Belén asked Van the same question. Apparently it took more than a month for the Russian proletariat to overthrow seven centuries' worth of oppression."

"Well, according to Diego you should go to bed now. He says it's inappropriate to have the servants spend more than one day making so much food to honor the ten million starving peasants."

"Don't worry, all the other oppressed cooks have already gone to bed. I was just cleaning the chocolate pots. And I'm sorry to report it, but the cooking for today started a week ago. What does Diego expect? For you to do that kind of work yourself?"

She sank delicately into one of the wooden chairs at the yellow table, perched like a canary. "Oh, Sóli. You know that frog and me. We can fight about any stupid thing."

"Not to mention the things he doesn't know about."

You looked up then with a child's dread, clutching your shawl as if it might protect you from bullets or ghosts. How interesting, to discover the power to frighten you. *When mankind is exhausted, he creates new enemies*, Lev says. The qualities of cruelty are spontaneous. *Our best task is to move forward.*

"Frida, forget it. Nobody will tell Diego about you and Van. It only went in the book so you would know you've been seen. You can tear out that page. But as the wife of a man who keeps a Luger next to his dentifrice? You could be more careful."

"I thought you would be furious. Because of Van."

"Fury demands a fire. For Van and me, no hope of a fire. As you pointed out that day on our boat outing. Had you already been with both of them, back then?"

"You make me sound like an animal. 'A madness of penned dogs,' that's cruel."

"It wasn't you who surprised me, only Van. And Lev too, they seem such moral fellows. Forgive me for putting it that way."

For once your eyes stayed steady, trained on the question, not looking for the door. "What do you know about love?"

"Nothing, apparently. That it winks on and off like an electric bulb."

You seemed to be excavating your soul to locate some kindness. "People want to be consoled. You're so young. You still have a lot of time for being moral."

"You're only a few years older. As you've said."

"But old anyway, with all my patched-up parts. I'm as doomed as all these men, for lesser reasons of course."

The pots were all shining now. Nothing more to do.

"Sóli, there's an ache in this house. Tomorrow anybody could get a bullet in the head. Men like Diego and Lev have to make their vows of sacrifice. 'Better to live on your fucking feet than die on your knees,' and all that. But under all that fatalism, they want life."

"Who doesn't want life?"

"But they do, more than most. They want it so badly they shake the world until its teeth fall out. It's why they're the men they are."

"And Frida can help them to be alive. When she feels like it."

"It was only that one night, with Van. I think he had a lot to drink. But you can never tell with the big, quiet ones. He's dying of loneliness."

"Who is, Van?"

"Yes. Did you know he had a wife?"

"Van is married?"

"He was. To a girl in France. They were very young when they met, I gather, both working for the Party. They had a little boy. The wife's name is Gabrielle. She wanted to come here but Natalya wouldn't have it—apparently they had quite a row. You know how protective Natalya is, she thinks of Van as her son."

"It's understandable. After all they've been through. Her losses."

"You're right. Forget about Diego, I think Natalya would kill me if she found out about Van and me."

A wife. Van had a wife named Gabrielle. He has a son. This is what it means to be alone: everyone is connected to everyone else, their bodies are a bright liquid life flowing around you, sharing a single heart that drives them to move all together. If the shark comes they will all escape, and leave you to be eaten.

This is the last report. November 7, 1937.

Coyoacán notebook

Mother is gone. Dear God in whom she never could believe, please let her not be alone in some drear heaven without men or music. Salomé, motherless mother, never more than a child herself. Dead, with her heart in the wrong place.

In the beginning were the howlers, mother and son joined in terror of the devils stalking from above. No matter how many times men told her, "It's nothing. It's a practical matter." *Write down the story of what happened to us*, she said. *Promise me. So when nothing is left but bones and scraps of clothes, someone will know where we went.* She said to begin this way: They are crying for our blood. But how can the story end so soon, and so bitterly? Salomé in a shattered sedan with her heart dislocated one last time. Nothing left but bones and scraps of clothes. Who can say where she went?

The new beau was a foreign-news correspondent. They were dashing to the airfield to catch a glimpse of a daredevil pilot said to be landing there for just a few hours. A stunt flyer, planning later this year to circle the world. These men with their great plans. The correspondent is an Englishman, Lewis. Probably he promised Mother the chance to meet famous people at the airfield. Instead they met head-on with a truck coming from Puebla, carrying cattle to market. Some cattle escaped. Lewis suffered a broken collarbone and lacerations from flying windshield glass. But it was on Mother's lap that the engine of his Studebaker came to rest, causing what the doctor called a spontaneous pneumothorax. It means that a hole ripped in one lung suddenly let out all the air, pulling the heart into the right half of her chest. Tearing it thus from the position it held for forty-two years, without ever settling in completely. Maybe for those last few shivering beats it was at rights. Maybe her heart stopped yearning to be somewhere else.

Lewis told what he remembered of it, offering condolences from a bed in the English hospital. His head was bandaged like a mummy from the films. "You're the son," the mummy observed. "She said you were planning on university, to be a solicitor." He had only known her a short while. Didn't feel entitled, really, to say anything at a funeral. Diego, with usual generosity, paid for the casket and a special mass despite his atheism. And despite Mother's. The mistake passed unnoticed among the few friends gathered, none of whom had known her in life. Just the one son, bearing up the weight of his own bones and damp unmanly grief. What a raging, salted wound, that sad little passage, what arrogance the world holds against women like Salomé. So many salons she has entered on the arm of a beau, always ready to charm the necessary bureaucrats of this world. Yet in the end, not one proved willing to escort her out of it.

How could a life of such large hopes be so small in the end? Her last apartment: one room above a lace-and-girdle shop. One trunk of frocks and phonograph records, donated to a coworker. Every *casa chica* was smaller than the one before. Were the beaux less generous over time? Her assets less marketable? If she had lived to be old, would she have resided in a teacup, to be sipped at intervals beneath some gray moustache?

At least she made the papers, departing as she did. A small note in the big News Extra about a daredevil flyer called Howard Hughes: "Among the press mobs, a foreign correspondent was injured and female acquaintance killed in a collision while speeding to the site on the Viaducto Alemán." Her mark on history: the female acquaintance.

26 April

Lev couldn't attend the mass of course, for safety, but continues to say he was sorry for that. His whole body winced the morning of the news. He and Natalya are raw at every edge since Lyova's murder in February. In a Paris hospital, where in heaven's name any person should be safe. They have no children left now, only the grandchild Seva from the eldest daughter. Lev's supporters are falling to a pogrom, everyone in the Vorkuta labor camp executed on the same day. And yet the United States claims Stalin as an ally, *still*. They have offered to help extradite Lev, for the purpose of execution.

Ever since Cárdenas expropriated the American oil, the news promises sanctions will come, and maybe war. Francia Street last week filled up with students shouting: "Let the gringos come. We already turned back Napoleon!"

Natalya takes Phanodorm morning and night, and cups of tea one after another: drowning her sorrows, as Frida would say, until the damn things learn to swim. But maybe some sorrows can't be borne. When Lev pauses in his work to stare out the window, his eyes are as cold as his children's bodies. The clear, bright future he once saw so plainly must now be charcoal lines, drawn down to a vanishing point.

Last night he came out to the courtyard to smoke a pipe and talk, just memories, not necessarily ordered. He told about a dinner he had with Stalin many years ago, when no one yet saw the man as anything more than an ambitious, irritating young bureaucrat. They were sharing a bottle of wine with Kamenev and Dzerzhinsky, talking nonsense as young men do, and the question came up: What did each like best in life?

Lev said the question exhilarated Stalin. "He leaned forward on the table gripping his knife like a pistol, leveling it at each one of us, and said: 'To choose your victim, to prepare everything, to revenge yourself pitilessly. And then to go to sleep.'"

11 August

Teotihuacán is the place where gods live. Xipe Totec, who rules over lust and birth. Round-eyed Tlaloc who brings the rain. Even in the times of the Azteca this mysterious city of pyramids was already ancient, lying in ruins northwest of the lake when Cortés arrived. The priests showed him the gigantic temples and told him it was where the gods had lived while creating the world. It was only logical, to assume they had needed a central office.

The Avenue of the Dead runs down the center of the ancient city, with the Pyramid of the Moon standing mighty against the sky, and the Pyramid of the Sun opposite, even taller. Temples flank the central avenue all the way down its length, some with great carved snakes undulating across their facades. Coral bean trees sprout from between the huge pavement stones, reaching for the sky with their blood-red fingers of blossom. Really, no one knows who lived and died in Teotihuacán, to what end. Walking wide-eyed and human among the great temples, though, it was easy to imagine blood and flesh, hearts ripped out to appease a terrible destiny.

Going there with Frida made it seem an especially likely setting for human sacrifice: her usual custom for picnics. Strangely, it was the opposite. A day for the history books. She showed up at the Blue House after breakfast, leaning her head into the kitchen doorway and motioning to come outside quickly, as if hiding something.

"You have to come with me to Teotihuacán," she announced. "Right now. For the day." She looked ready for any possibility, dressed in a gabardine overall rolled to the knees, and the usual full-body armor of jewelry.

"I have a lot of work to do, Frida."

"Sóli, this is important. You call yourself a Mexican, and you've never seen the pyramids of Teotihuacán."

"I haven't had affairs with all Mexico's elite, either. Poor citizenship, I suppose."

"Look, you and I have things to talk about."

"We do. And it seems we won't."

"I have the Roadster out on Allende Street. It's just you and me—I'm driving, not César. Are you going to be a big prick about this?"

"Sorry, Frida. I have a very large snapper in here, and he's a good joe but he refuses to shed his scales and bathe himself in tomatoes and capers without supervision. There's a dinner tonight. Twelve people coming to hear Diego and Lev and Mr. Breton present their paper. In case you've forgotten."

"They can use their big paper to collect bird defecations for all I care. And Perpetua can cook that snapper—you're not as important here as you think."

"Are you firing me?"

"If that's what it takes to get some goddamn company for the day. Okay. I'm going to smoke while you make up your mind."

She leaned against the wall and lit a cigarette, in plain sight of the men if they bothered to look out the window of Lev's study. Lev is adamantly old-fashioned about a few things. One of them: women shouldn't smoke. Another: he doesn't like women in trousers. Frida was diving from the steeple today.

"So. Here's the story." She slid her eyes toward the office window, exhaling a long plume. "Do you remember Gamio? He's that friend of Diego's, the Professor of Ancient Shit who excavated the pyramids. According to himself, he's discovered something astonishing."

"What a mood you're in. A person would be crazy to get in a car with you."

"Fine, stay here with Diego and the Old Man and Monsieur Lion-Maned Poet so full of himself he makes me want to piss in his wineglass. I'm certain you will be dazzled by their Manifesto on Revolutionary Art for the *pindonga Partisan Review*."

"Well, I already know what it says. I typed it."

"And?" Suddenly she was interested. Maybe she hadn't been allowed to read it. But flying on a trapeze between Diego and Frida could end in a smashup. It would pay to be cautious.

"Mostly it condemns the restrictions Stalin imposed on artists in the revolutionary state. No surprise there. I thought Diego discussed everything with you."

"Mrs. Breton, Mrs. Trotsky, and Mrs. Rivera are not a part of this historic conversation. Ever since that bedbug poet showed up here, it's a boy's club."

"You're not exaggerating about that. It's noticeable."

She pursed her lips. "At least Jacqueline likes to smoke and gossip. Otherwise we would have died of boredom up at Lake Pátzcuaro. While our husbands spent every damn minute working on their *chingado* paper."

"You could have written it yourself, Frida, it's no big manifesto. 'The artistic imagination requires freedom from coercion. Artists have an inalienable right to choose their own subjects.' That kind of thing."

She whistled. "What genius. Fulang Chang could have written that."

"There's also a bit about surrealism. How Mexico is destined to become the true place of surrealist-revolutionary art, because of its flora and dynamism and all that. The mix of races. So what's the astonishing discovery from the professor?"

"Okay, listen. He said they were putting back a wall of a temple that fell down or something. And accidentally uncovered a mass grave. This is *old*, Sóli. Diego adores all that ancient crap, Gamio knows it, so he invited us to come up and have a look before they have to move the bones and everything. But Diego has this meeting. So I'm going, as soon as this cigarette is finished. You have twenty more seconds to decide."

It was a lively trip in the Roadster. Frida had more than her ordinary jittery energy, tugging at her necklaces and offering a steady stream of half-invented history lessons mixed with urgent personal advice. "Sóli," she declared suddenly, "I have to teach you to drive this car. César isn't going to live forever. You know, I've been thinking maybe he died already. He's been looking mummified all this year."

The car was headed northwest at a fairly breakneck pace. The city's outskirts trailed out into villages like the ones on the southern edge, tucked between lime orchards and stony stretches of desert. Hens picked through the roadside litter, and here and there a rooster stood in the center of the road with the authority of the police. Mangoes spread their leaves like umbrellas. The car shuddered when Frida abruptly veered to avoid a boy chasing an emaciated cow in the road. Mother's death loomed large, an apparition.

"I'm serious," Frida said, after relocating the road with the majority of the Roadster's tires. "You have to learn to drive. I'm commanding you, as your boss."

"Promoted! From secretarial assistant of the world's leading political theorist, to Señora Rivera's driver."

"I'm trying to do you a favor. You could have more freedom."

"A knowledge of driving, with no hope of ever owning a car. An interesting formulation of freedom. Maybe you should present a paper."

"When did you become such a big *sangrón?* You used to be nice."

She kept her mouth closed for several kilometers, which improved her driving. Running through the speeds in the Roadster with the gear-shifter on the floor looked simple, compared to the Model T with its hand-grip levers for running the accelerator and clutch. Even so, Frida grinds the gears like a butcher. The Chevrolet even has a gauge showing the gasoline level, so you don't have to guess when it's running out. Sometimes César forgets and lets the Model T run so low he has to back it up a hill, to drain out the last of the fuel from the tank under the seat. That would be Frida's style as well.

Eventually she pulled over in a village, asked directions, and came back determined to get in on the passenger's side. The driving lesson that followed was successful, until too successful.

"You can't go this fast," she admonished, though we moved at a fraction of her former speed. "You have to move the shifting thing across to the other side first."

"We're in the highest gear."

"Well, you must not be doing it right. It's supposed to make a sound when you put it into high."

"Not if you double-punch the clutch. Watch this, you stop the shifter in neutral, that's the cross-part of the H, and let the clutch all the way out, then put it back in again to match the gear speed."

"Bastard. How did you know that?"

"I've spent a thousand hours in the car with César, trying to keep him from wandering off the end of the earth. I learned the gears. What else was there to do? Listen for the one-millionth time to the story of Pancho Villa in Sanborn's?"

Frida laughed. "Poor old Cesár. Drinking a citrate of magnesia in the presence of Pancho Villa. And that's the best war story he'll ever have."

"At least with his slow-motion driving you can see how everything works. He treats the transmission like a woman. He'd rather cut off his fingers than grind the gears the way you do, Frida."

"Screw yourself."

Pupil and teacher were relieved when the tops of the pyramids rose into sight, looming over the tile roofs and palm trees of San Juan Teotihuacán. The archaeological site was closed because of the excavations, and the crew had vacated for a long lunch. Their trowels and notebooks lay about every which way. While awaiting Gamio's return, Frida decided to climb to the top of the Pyramid of the Sun, to get a perspective on the place. It took half an hour because of the steepness and number of steps: two hundred twenty-eight. She dragged her bad leg up every one, counting them with a hail of obscenities: cuarenta-y-*dos*-chingada, cuarenta-y-*tres*-chingada. Sometimes the steps were so steep she had to climb "on all four paws," but she never accepted a hand. "I might be a damn cripple but I'm not dead yet," she spat. "If my heart stops, fine, you can carry me back down." Still angry from the driving lesson.

The view from the pinnacle could stop any heart: the complex geometric forms of the ancient city revealed themselves below, and beyond them, a landscape of black volcanic mountains. The pyramids of lava rock seemed to rise straight from the land, rather than having conquered it. And in fact, a half hour later when we stood on a platform in the ancient city's central plaza looking back at the Pyramid of the Sun, you could plainly see what she called "the joke of the ancient guys." The profile of the Sun Pyramid—its staircases, balustrades, and rounded top—perfectly follows the shape of the volcanic mountain rising behind it. A giant monument playing copycat to a mountain.

"They were laughing. The joke is on God," she said, and sat down on the dusty plaza to make a sketch of the pyramid and mountain.

"If you say so. But it's a joke with years of planning behind it, and terrible labors. Probably people died building it. Why throw away life to play a joke on God?"

She held a spare pencil in her mouth, and didn't look up from her drawing.

When Dr. Gamio arrived, he had plenty of theories on the subject. The people wanted greatness. They worked hard to be remembered by eternity. Alignment was a sacred matter, as important as water and bread. He escorted Frida to the excavation site holding her arm, warning her against tripping over every pebble. His first words were to say how sorry he was that Diego couldn't come, but he was not sorry. He was enamored of her, like everyone else.

The excavation lay open: a mass grave, protected under a temporary tin roof set on posts. Down a few dirt steps, there they were, skeletons of men lying in a row like fish in a box, their narrow, dust-colored bones only faintly lighter than the reddish dirt in which they were embedded. Oddly, the skeletons were perfectly flattened, as if all these humans had been pressed under a hot iron. It took a moment for the eye to adjust to the increments of dust, discerning the human from nonhuman elements. The dead wore jewelry that had survived where flesh did not, bracelets loosely encircling bones. Most peculiar of all: around each neck, a sort of cravat or necklace made of human lower jaws, with the teeth still in place! It was a riveting sight, these bizarre, scalloped strands of mandibles strung together, looping low across the former chests, a fashion beyond anything even Frida might wear. The professor pointed out cut marks here and there on the bones, butchery marks, which he claimed as proof that these unfortunates were sacrificed.

A cool breeze whistled past our ankles, causing the tin roof to tremble. A storm was rising in the distance, but this cool air seemed to come from beneath the ground. The professor said in fact, it did. The place has lava tubes, long caves where the molten earth once ran as rivers. The ground beneath the whole ancient city is laced with them.

"Tunnels, you mean? Like the water caves out on the coast?"

He said it's different rock but a similar formation. The ancients were directed by their gods to look for a doorway from the earth, and here they found them.

The professor talked and talked without releasing Frida's elbow. She shot a few trapped glances before the final escape, a quick getaway down the Avenue of the Dead while Gamio was distracted by a student volunteer. To avoid the dazzling heat, Frida suggested leaving the ancient stone pavement and climbing down the bank of the little San Juan River. It was nearly dry, a trickle in the bottom of a grassy ravine. She flung out a tablecloth in a grove of old pepper trees with gnarled trunks and birds singing from their drooping fernlike boughs. She collapsed on the ground, panting, "Help, we're saved! I thought I would be a human sacrifice. Bored to death by Theories of Antiquity." Then set about unpacking the heavy picknick basket she'd brought from home.

"Why do you think they made necklaces like that, of human mandibles?"

She fingered her own necklace, huge jade stones, a wedding present from Diego.

"Fashion," she said. "Diego showed me pictures of that before. Most of the people weren't important enough to collect real human teeth, you know, the regular low-class citizens. So they made fake ones, flint teeth stuck into clay jawbones." She pulled a bottle of wine from the basket and uncorked it, pouring it into two good crystal glasses that probably shouldn't have risked the journey. But that is Frida, using her best, the devil can take the shards.

"Isn't it awfully sad to think that's all history amounts to, just following the next stupid fashion?"

"Fashion isn't stupid," she said, handing over a glass, spilling a dark red splash on the knee of her overall.

"It's worse than stupid. There's damage in it. Mother lived and died in dread of wearing last year's frock. And look at what Lev loses, every time the newspapers jump in line to call him a villain. When one says it they all have to say it, for fear of being left behind. It's all the same thing more or less. Following fashion."

"*Fashion* is not the same as *idiocy*."

She produced an impressive meal from her basket: pork tamales in banana leaves, stuffed chayotes, prickly pear fruits fried in batter.

"Don't tell your professor boyfriend, but I agree with you about the pyramid copying the shape of the mountain. It's a joke. They were just people. We come here to be dazzled by sculptures of giant snakes, imagining the ancients labored for us, so we will remember them for all time. But maybe they just liked the look of snakes."

"When did you have this big revelation?"

"Today."

"I told you, every Mexican has to come here."

"Look, Frida. I'm going to tell you something, and it doesn't even matter if you make fun of me. Ever since I was fourteen and read Cortés, I've been writing a story about the Azteca. Mostly in my head, but a lot is on paper. And now I can see I've had the story wrong, all this time. I've spent years writing something really stupid."

She nodded, biting into a tamale. "Tell me in what way it's stupid."

"My impression was from books. The ancients seemed to be . . . what the professor said. Locked in the struggle for greatness. Heroes and battles, mythic kings."

"Well, nobody knows how they were, so you can make up anything you want." She pawed through the basket for napkins. She brought the blue-and-yellow ones. "A story is like a painting, Sóli. It doesn't have to look like what you see out the window."

"Well, the ancients might not have been very heroic. Most of them were probably like Mother, crouched somewhere trying to work out how to make fake jawbone jewelry that would look like the real thing."

"That's a better story, to tell you the truth," she said. "Greatness is very boring."

The prickly pear fruit was delicious: thick slices, lightly fried with sugar and anise. "Did you cook all this today, this morning?"

"Montserrat, at the San Angel Inn," she said with her mouth full. She chewed thoughtfully. "I mean it. Your idea for the story sounds good."

"Well, it doesn't matter because I can't be a writer."

"Dumb kid, you *are* a writer. Cesár tried to get you fired for always writing in your notebooks, and Diego tried to make you stop, too. It killed me to see him try. Now these men want to make you an efficient secretary. But you keep writing about soft hearts and scandal. The question is, why do you think you can't be a writer?"

"To be a writer, you need readers."

"I'm no painter, then. Who ever looks at my dumb little pieces of shit?"

"An American movie star, to name one. Diego told me that fellow looked at all your paintings and bought a couple."

She was pouring more wine but glanced up, under her dark brows. "Edward G. Robinson. He bought four of them, if you want to know. Two hundred dollars each."

"*Dios mio.* You see?"

"I see nothing. I see a boy who chews off the ends of his fingers and bleeds ink."

"A dumb kid, is what you said."

"Let's get back to the topic of your story. What do you think people want, if it's not greatness and to be remembered for all time?"

There was hardly anything left of that huge lunch but greasy fingers and a crackle of anise between the teeth. The wine bottle was empty. "Mostly? I believe people want to eat a good lunch, and then take a good piss."

She was digging in that basket again, and unbelievably, produced another half-bottle of wine, recorked from some previous adventure. "And love, Sóli, don't forget that. We are bodies, sometimes with dreams and always with desires."

"Love. But the pure kind of love, what Lev has for humanity, I don't think that comes very often. Most of us are ordinary. If we do anything great, it's only so we'll be loved ourselves. Maybe just for ten minutes."

"Love is love, Sóli. We give greatly to receive. Don't spit yourself out like a seed all the time. When Lev was your age, he was probably more like you than you think."

"All right. People are ruled by love, and our kidneys. That's my opinion, and now I really do have to take a piss. Don't watch, please."

"Hey, you could have found a bigger tree," she called out. "A skinny guy like you, and you're not even halfway hidden."

"You could allow a gentleman the privacy of his piss."

Frida in her dungarees lay back against the bank, looking through her black eyelashes. It's impossible to explain how or why, but she had completely transformed. From venomous snake to friend. "If you want to write romantic novels about the Azteca," she said, "I mean, if that's what moves you, then you should do it."

It was a true conversation. About whether our ancestors had more important lives than we do. And how they've managed to trick us, if they did not. Frida felt it helped them not to put anything in writing. The people at Teotihuacán had no written language, according to Dr. Gamio. "So we can't read their diaries," she pointed out, "or the angry letters they sent their unfaithful lovers. They died without telling us their complaints."

She is right about that. No regrets or petty jealousies. Only stone gods and magnificent buildings. We only get to see their perfect architecture, not their imperfect lives. But it's a strange point to argue for an artist whose paintings are rants and confessions. Without regrets and jealousies, she would have blank canvas.

"You'd better burn all your paintings then, Frida. If you want people in the future to think you were heroic."

She fingered her beads and knit her eyebrows. Raised her glass up to the light and rolled the red liquid around, studying it. "I think an artist has to tell the truth," she said finally. "You have to use the craft very well and have a lot of discipline for it, but mostly to be a good artist you have to know something that's true. These kids who come to Diego wanting to learn, I'll tell you. They can paint a perfect tree, a perfect face, whatever you ask. But they don't know enough about life to fill a thimble. And *that's* what has to go in the painting. Otherwise, why look at it?"

"How does an artist learn enough about life to fill a thimble?"

"Sóli, I'm going to tell you. He needs to go rub his soul against life. Go work in a copper mine for a few months, or a shirt factory. Eat some terrible greasy tacos, just for the experience. Have sex with some Mexican boys."

"Thank you for the advice. You seem to favor foreigners."

"Never mind about me. I've done everything already—nothing is left for these bones but the grave." She drained her glass. "You've been so angry with me. Why?"

"Good God, Frida. Because you treat me like a child."

She looked truly startled.

"I understand. I'm not an important person like you. Or Van, for that matter. But working for you and Diego, sometimes I don't even feel human. I'm a mouse creeping around the shoes of giant people, trying not to get stepped on."

"Look, if I don't flirt with you, you should take that as a compliment. I don't always respect myself, but I almost never respect men. They're like flowers, all showy, a lot of color and lust. You pick them and throw them on the ground. But you I respect. I always did. From the first day I saw you."

"You don't even remember the first time you saw me. It was before I ever came to work in the house, years before. On your birthday."

"In the Melchor market." She tilted her head, but without the coy smile. "You asked if you could help me carry a bag of corn. I told you any man has the right to make a kite from his pants."

She is a marvel or a trickster, a brilliant, terrifying friend. She divines the unknown. There will never be another Frida.

"I approve of your program, Sóli."

"What program is that?"

"Cortés and the Azteca. Writing a true history of Mexico. I think you're right, you should crack open the mute culture, give those boring heroes some sweat and piss."

"Do you think?"

"Look, there's no sense pretending history is a goddamn Homeric Odyssey."

A brilliant red bird landed overhead, the same color as the coral-bean blossoms, resting briefly on the swaying branch before it flew away. Frida packed up the last of the meal. "It's good we talked today. We don't have a lot of time."

"What do you mean?"

"I have to get ready for a show. I'm having a real show, my own paintings entirely. Can you imagine?"

"That's wonderful."

"Sóli, it's terrifying. It feels like I've been lying in the bathtub all this time admiring my own curly *pendejos*. And now a hundred people are looking in through the curtain, applauding."

"Oh. When is the show?"

"When is not the question. *Where* is the question. New York. I'm going at the end of summer. The show opens in October, and after that I'm going to do another one in Paris. It was Mr. Lion-Maned Poet who set up the show in Paris, to tell you the truth. André. I should try to be nicer to him. Anyway." She seemed out of breath.

"Are you all right?"

"A little afraid, I guess. I'm leaving Diego for a long time. Leaving everybody, but in a different sense, leaving Diego."

"I don't believe that. You and that frog can't breathe without each other."

"Well, we'll see. Anyway, I wanted to repair some damages, before I go."

She lay back and closed her eyes. After a minute she asked, "How do you know it was my birthday, the day we met in the Melchor market?"

"Because it was mine too."

She sat up and her eyes opened wide, like a doll. "We have the same birthday?"

"Yes."

"All this time?"

"Every year, in fact."

She stared, recalculating history. "All those parties and birthday fiestas. You've been working like a slave on your own *cumpleaños*."

So after all, she cannot divine everything.

She lay back again and closed her eyes. "*Mi vida*, don't keep secrets from me. You shouldn't even try, you see how we're connected? It will always be the case. We came into life through the same passage."

With damages repaired to her satisfaction, she fell asleep almost immediately, leaving one strange landscape for another, her dreams. Soon she would leave this place altogether—Diego, Mexico, the house and everyone in it.

The bones of the ancient city radiated heat, but the little river ran a cool thread through its belly. A lizard moved in the grass of the bank, running into the shade of a ledge, coming to rest near a stone that seemed rounded and glossy, even in shadow. That stone was smooth to the touch, and when turned over, revealed itself not as an ordinary pebble but a small, carved figurine. A little man made of jade or obsidian, something ancient, small enough to hide inside a closed hand. A remarkable artifact. It should be turned over to the professor. Obviously it would be wrong to take it from this place.

Every detail of the little figure was perfect: his rounded belly with indented navel, his short legs and fierce face. A headdress that resembled a neat pile of biscuits. Eyes deeply indented under arched brows. And inside his rounded lips, a hole for a mouth, like a tunnel from another time, speaking. *I am looking for the door to another world. I've waited thousands of years. Take me.*

The New York Times, *April 15, 1939*

Rivera Still Admires Trotsky; Regrets Their Views Clashed

Artist Explains He Quit Fourth International So as Not to Embarrass Leader—Reveals Letter Caused Their Rift

By Diego Rivera

MEXICO CITY, April 14—The incident between Trotsky and myself is not a quarrel. It is a lamentable misunderstanding which, going too far, brought about the irreparable. That compelled me to break my relations with a great man for whom I always had, and I continue having, the greatest admiration and respect. I am very far from harboring the silly presumption of engaging in a polemic with Trotsky, whom I consider the center and the visible head of the revolutionary movement that is the Fourth International.

The Mexican proverb says, "He who does not block the way helps a lot." In the future, my personal actions and opinions, should I have any, will block neither Trotsky's nor the Fourth International's path.

The incident between Trotsky and myself had its origin in a letter addressed by me to my friend, the French Poet André Breton. That letter was typed in French for me by one of Trotsky's secretaries. Trotsky happened to see a copy that had been left on the secretary's desk, according to the written declaration that he sent me, and the concepts I expressed in my letter, in reference to the general situation of the Leftist forces in the world, to the social role of artists and to their position and rights within the revolutionary movement, besides some personal allusions to him, so displeased Trotsky that he expressed opinions against me which I found unacceptable and which compelled me to split with him.

Trotsky toils without respite, helping continually with his mental effort the slow and difficult work in preparation for the liberation of the workers of the entire world. About him he has a general staff of young secretaries, volunteers come from the four corners of the earth, to help in this work. Meanwhile, other voluntary workers watch day and night over the safety of the man who, together with Lenin, gave its victory to the proletariat of Russia. These and all the other thousands of heroes of October now, from the exile imposed upon them by Stalin's counter-revolution, continue to labor for the future victory of the workers of the entire world.

The enemies, the "organizers of defeat," Stalin and his GPU, persecute the man of October. Everywhere they have tried to hurt him, to annihilate him psychologically through the extermination of his family. . . . Meanwhile his closest collaborators, persecuted and threatened, are murdered, one after another. It is natural that this state of things and the accumulation of sufferings it produces have had their effect upon the man of October, despite his enormous will power and self-assurance. It is natural that Trotsky's disposition should have become more and more difficult, despite his huge reserve of goodness and generosity.

I regret that fate should have decreed that I should collide against that difficult side of his nature. But my dignity as a man precluded my doing anything to avoid it.

※

Casa Trotsky, 1939–1940 (VB)

On the morning Lev and Natalya moved out of the Blue House, an egret came down from the sky, its broad white wings spread like a parachute, and landed in the courtyard. It extended the S-curve of its long neck until nearly as tall as a man, turning its long-beaked head this way and that, peering at each person present. Then it strode across the bricks to the front gate, lifting its long legs at the knee like a man riding a bicycle. The chief guard shoved the gate open, just a crack, and four men with pistols in their belts stood watching an egret cross Allende Street, disappearing around the corner.

Frida would have claimed it as an omen on Lev's departure. But she is not here, she's in Paris where everyone is an idiot, according to her reports. Natalya, unprepared to trust in signs, was swaddled in the same woolen suit and hat she wore the day they arrived on the ship from Norway. Lev was less armored, in a white shirt open at the collar. Each carried one small suitcase. Van, who has been inattentive since falling in love again (this time she's American), kept his eyes down and stayed busy moving crates of papers into the car sent by Diego. Diego himself was not present.

Every person may have felt some accusation in the heron's glare, for which member of the household was blameless? Frida went away, leaving Diego and Lev with only their needles of irritability to fill a space evacuated of desire. And Diego, poor man, can only be the person he is. An organizer who can't get to meetings on time, a secretary who forgets to answer letters. He has the heart of an anarchist, not a party functionary.

Some blame of course goes to Stalin: his threats hanging over this house, the murders of Trotsky's children, peers, and collaborators, the annihilation of his whole generation in Russia. Stalin's cruelties have pressed the souls of this household flat as ancient skeletons in the dust.

But most to be blamed: the careless secretary who unraveled everything.

Diego wrote the newspapers about his split from Trotsky, reporting his desire to stand out of the way of a great man. "An accumulation of sufferings have had their effect," he wrote, without naming them all: the affair with Frida, for example, though that's said to be forgiven. The note he dashed off to Breton complained, "The bearded old goat is serious every minute. For God's sake, can't he let the Revolution rest for a night and get drunk with a friend who risked everything? Who's housed and fed his entourage for two damn years? How can any mortal tolerate these overcast Russian temperaments?"

He scribbled the note in Lev's own office and gave it over to be typed, a hasty act of bravado, while Lev was elsewhere. The letter should have been posted to France immediately. Instead, the preoccupied secretary, in his haste to get the evening's cooking started, left it lying on the Ediphone table, where Lev later found it. The old man came in the kitchen later with his glasses off, rubbing his eyes, too tired, he said, for supper. Just a piece of toast, perhaps. Bed early, plans to make tomorrow.

What a knot of history one mistake can become. Trotsky was meant to succeed Lenin as president of the Soviet, but a small accident caused the job to fall to Stalin instead. Diego never told what the accident was. Only that small caprices alter fate. One letter, left out by accident. If Diego and Lev had kept their alliance, they might have forged a movement to overthrow Stalin. The peasant armies of Mexico worship Diego, but they need Lev's strategic intelligence.

From Michoacan, blazing through the brigades of Spain into all of Europe, the world might yet take up Lev's dream of socialist democracy. But a careless mistake has torn this league asunder.

Why did Diego call his friend a goat? He expected the word to vanish with the afternoon post, that's why. Bitter words normally evaporate with the moisture of breath, after a quarrel. In order to become permanent, they require transcribers, reporters, complicit black hearts. Diego meant nothing by that letter; his respect for Lev is undying. He had an eye infection that week, a cramp in his stomach after a lunch of too many pork sandwiches. From somewhere in that roil, a few poisonous sentences erupted. Now the world has them.

And the secretary? Was his sin sloth, or pride? The letter was in French, but why couldn't he have asked for Van's help to change the words, and type a tactful version? And why didn't he post it at once, as requested? A remembrance of last year's jacaranda in the window, the sound of something breaking in the kitchen—for no good reason he forgot, and left the letter on the table.

The mistake has left him panting like the victim in a crash: his loyalty to Lev bent like pieces of metal around his chest. The wrecked engine of Rivera spewing petrol, threatening flames. He must extricate himself by making a choice. Diego says stay, as typist-cook and errand boy, for the same coins that have rained down steadily since the first bewildered day of mixing plaster on the floor of the Palacio Nacional. But Lev also asks for continued service. He needs a trusted secretary more than ever, because of the perilous relocation, and Van's increasing distractions. Lev offers a room and cot in a house of clear, bright dreams, which could all be murdered tomorrow. The Painter offers money, asking only to be worshipped.

At seven this morning, after a brief rainstorm, Lev Trotsky lifted his suitcase, stepped across the puddles in the brick walk, and left the Blue House for the last time. He and his wife climbed into the back of the car with Lorenzo the guard, his rifle lying across their knees, and Van in the front passenger's seat, also armed. The driver sat very straight, as if his body were pierced like a Hindu's with a thousand nails of guilt.

"We are ready, my son. Drive," Lev said, and together the small party traveled six blocks to a wrecked, vacant house on Calle Viena, rented from a family called Turati, where they will make their new home.

If any brokenhearted man ever made a better show of good cheer, it could only have been in the moving pictures. Lev's efforts to make the best of the new arrangement have buoyed everyone. Natalya has put away Phanodorm and taken up housecleaning: sweeping cobwebs from the high, pale green ceilings of this Porfirian mansion, washing its leaded-glass windows and arranging furniture. Sometimes she ties on an apron and makes Lev's breakfast. Today she painted chair rails and all the wooden cabinets in the dining room, a nice combination of yellow and brown that Frida would have called boring. What a relief, that she is no longer reading these pages.

The Americans, Joe and Reba Hansen, have come here from the apartment where they had retreated from Rivera hospitality and Rivera complications. A new couple has arrived also, Mr. O'Rourke and his off-beat girl friend Miss Reed. Everyone seems relieved to gather over simple suppers in the main room here, with an old yellow-checked tablecloth on the long table and no one worrying about wine spills. Debating the day's news instead, under no secret storm clouds of household intrigue. Van plays music programs on the wireless and whistles along while typing, when no one else is in the office. His happiness, as always, seems to be linked to a girl.

Only Lorenzo is cheerless, but that's nothing new. He frets, whether on or off duty, a worried monument pulling on his huge black moustache, his face burned to red leather from the hours spent staring out at the menacing world. His forehead, a startling white above the line made by his hat, when he removes it for supper. Protecting Lev has been a terrifying charge since the day they walked off the planks at Tampico. Lorenzo has apprehended dozens of threats, not only the barefoot vigilantes but also the cool plots of Mexican Stalinists. Lately Toledano has been going to unionists' meetings, offering cash to any man willing to put a bullet in Trotsky. Most men these days need the money.

Everything is reported to Lev but not Natalya. She only learns the worst of it when the police are forced to arrest someone and the story makes the newspapers, wedged between the usual confabulations about the "Russian Traitor in Our Midst." Lorenzo and the three young guards take six-hour shifts on the roof, around the clock, walking the perimeter on the brick parapet. The black rock wall around the courtyard was three meters tall to begin with, but the masons have raised it higher still, with brick turrets and notches for rifle bores. It will be good if Lev can purchase the house, because of the need for these alterations. Joe Hansen says money is coming from the Trotskyist party in the United States. The Socialist Workers.

The kitchen here is very adequate: a gas stove with four eyes, a plank counter and icebox. And within the high walls, the courtyard offers a bright relief of trees, shaped as a triangle between the main house and the long, narrow brick guard house running opposite at an angle. Here at last, guards and secretaries may have some privacy, the guard house has four rooms in a row downstairs and four above. The garden is shaded by an old jacaranda and some figs. Lev wants to retrieve the cactus specimens he collected in San Miguel Regla, which stand potted in some forsaken corner at the Blue House, so he can make a cactus garden. Today after lunch he pointed out where he intends to plant each one, with stone paths for roaming between the bits of garden, a park in miniature. It's an impossibly small space for such an elaborate plan. But this tiny plot, measured in meters, is Lev's last remaining homeland.

It seems an airy enough estate, from inside. The strange spectre of confinement becomes striking only from the outside, when one

walks home to it from the market, for example. The compound oc-
cupies a flat-iron shaped lot in Coyoacán where Calle Viena and Rio
Churubusco meet at an angle. The high, dark walls enclosing it come
together at a point, looking exactly like the dark prow of an ocean
liner: the great, slow ship of Trotsky's fate setting sail down Churubusco, as if it were still a canal in the city on a lake, as Cortés found
it. As if one could still build a ship in the desert, and set one's sights
on a new world.

Lorenzo's mother came this week from the country, bringing one
more pair of eager eyes for guard duty: her daughter's boy, Alejandro.
Also, two pairs of rabbits and some checkered hens. Lev is as happy
as a lad with his new livestock. The rabbits now have hutches near
the entry gate, but Lev says the chickens are "emancipated travelers,"
free to roam the courtyard. Natalya objected on grounds of sanita-
tion, and the hens' safety.

"Nataloschka," her husband said, "no wolves live here. The chickens are the only ones without the worry of a predator. Let them have
an open visa." Of course she conceded. In Lev's new study, he sets
his chair so he can see out the window into the courtyard where they
scuttle around, cocking their heads at beetles in the dust.

Perpetua has walked down the street from the Blue House twice this
week, to deliver some pottery Natalya liked especially. Her favorite
is the white glazed platter with fish leaping over it, a gift from Frida
when they first arrived. Natalya thanked Perpetua and put it away in
a cabinet, but today she has brought it out and set it against the wall.
In the years with Lev her world has been so constrained, with so few
objects of beauty in it. She is not a bulldog, only a woman pressed
into the shape of a small jar, possibly attempting to dance in there. It
shows in the way she places a seashell on a window sill, a red-painted
chair in the corner: she is practiced in the art of creating a still life and
taking up residence inside it.

❋

Lorenzo's nephew, Alejandro, is the youngest of the guards, nineteen or twenty perhaps. From a tiny village near Puebla, he's the only one of the guards who is not from the political movement, but Lorenzo guarantees his loyalty. Lev welcomes a new recruit.

Alejandro seems happy just to escape a certain village misery. He has a shy, odd manner, precisely what Frida would call a queer duck. She would say she approved, then make sure everyone watched him like a fish in a bowl. Probably she can't help that, she's been watched that way herself since marrying Diego.

In New York and Paris when she flew high, the newspaper stories tried to shoot her down. Now that she is coming home, apparently washed up, what they say about her is worse. Like Natalya, she must feel the need to retreat into a small space, making still-life creations and painting herself inside. She doesn't have to hide from assassins, but being Much-Discussed appears to be its own kind of prison.

The chickens are not the only emancipated ones here. Lev allows writing of any kind. While he himself works tirelessly on Lenin's biography and a dozen political articles at once, he confessed that really no book can beat a good novel. He wishes he could write one himself.

What a strange discovery. He came in the office late this evening to look for a dictionary, surprised to find one of his assistants still banging at a typewriter.

"Young Shepherd! What business could keep you so late in headquarters?" Headquarters of the Fourth International is his name for the big office next to the dining room. Natalya moved in all three typewriter tables and her roll-top desk, the telephone, bookshelves, file cabinets, and all. It was her idea to make a separate office so all can work here—herself, Van, the Americans who've come to study with Lev—without driving the commissar out of his mind. Lev keeps to his little study in the other wing by their bedroom, writing in peace until he needs someone to come and take a dictation.

"I'm sorry, sir." *Gather up the pages quick, put them in a folder. No confession unless forced.* "It's nothing that will liberate the people."

He waited for more, standing wide-eyed at the doorsill in his shirt and tie. His white hair stood on end from a long day's work. He pulls his hair while he thinks.

"Sir, I'm reluctant to say."

"Oh, no. Some secret report to the adversary?"

"Please don't suggest such an awful thing."

"What, then? A love letter?"

"It's more embarrassing than that, sir. A novel."

The muscles of his face collapsed like a dumpling, all dimples and wrinkled eyes behind the beard and round glasses. Lev's smile is like no other. He pulled out Natalya's desk chair and sat in it backward, straddling it like a horse, leaning his elbows on its back and laughing until he nearly wept. "Oh, this is a *mechaieh*!"

There was nothing to do but wait for a more comprehensible verdict.

"I've been worrying where it is you go, my son. When your mind is not here." He clucked his tongue, said some words in Russian. "A novel! Why do you say this won't liberate anyone? Where does any man go to be free, whether he is poor or rich or even in prison? To Dostoyevsky! To Gogol!"

"It surprises me to hear you say it."

His halo of white hair was lit from behind by the blue blaze of the street lamp outside. The windows facing the street are bricked up halfway, but light comes in from above. It looked like a setting for a detective film. He stood and walked to the back bookshelf, making his way between tables and the recording machine cabinet with its cords snaking across the floor. He clicked on the lamp near the bookshelf.

"I want to show you something. My first published book. An account of a young man only twenty-seven years old, imprisoned by the tsar for being a revolutionist, maneuvering a bold and dramatic es-

cape to Europe where he plotted his return with the People's Army."
Lev found the book and tapped it thoughtfully with his thumb.
"This was a popular sensation among the workers of St. Petersburg.
The entire Soviet, eventually. If a Russian can read, he has read this
one."

"A novel, sir?"

"Unfortunately, no. Every word of it is true." He opened the book
and turned a few pages. "And since then, only theory and strategy.
What a bore I've become."

"But your life is still a potboiler. Stalin's assassins lurking, the
Communist Party and Toledano scheming to poison your name. I
hate to say it, but the newspapers might get on your side if you wrote
it that way. They could carry your saga in weekly installments, the
way they did for Pancho Villa during the war."

"Getting the newspapers on our side, oh, my boy. That is a career
for circus acrobats and worthless politicians."

"Sorry, sir."

He smiled. "Well, it would win the Russians. Our brains have
a weakness for morose and thrilling plots." He snapped the book
closed. "What is the subject of yours?"

He listened carefully to the idea of a historical adventure about
ancient Mexicans, even if it is more adventure than history, and will
never be any good. He pulled a pile of books out of his shelf that
might inspire a novelist just starting off.

"Do you read Russian? No. Well, Jack London, certainly. And
Colette, for the female view. Oh, and this one by Dos Passos, it's
called *The Big Money.*" He also offered one of his typewriters, the
spare one that only needs a little oil to get working again, and a small
table for use as a writing desk in the guardhouse room at night. "So
you won't again have to creep into headquarters on the sly," he said.
"With Lorenzo as nervous as he is, he might shoot you through the
window by mistake. A fine potboiler you would make of yourself
then, my son. And who would write it?"

✳

Alejandro, the village boy, almost never speaks. Yet claims he wants to learn English. One quiet assertion at a time, he begins: *I am. You are.* His room is the one at the opposite end of the guard house, but he comes to this one every morning at four, after finishing his shift of pacing the roof with his rifle cocked in darkness. This room that has housed no secrets up to now, except for a box of things hidden under the bed: a small stolen idol. A partly written, entirely dreadful novel. The little woven finger toy called a *trapanovio*, souvenir of a remarkable humiliation.

Alejandro is the first one to see the *trapanovio* since that day in Xochimilco, and he didn't laugh when he heard the story. He inhaled sharply, fists on his face, and wept.

At four o'clock while the world sleeps off its judgments, reliably he arrives. *He has, they have.* A strange kind of love it is. Or no kind of love at all. A solace of the soft tissues only, not the first or last of anything, grateful and urgent and terrified by turns. Afterward, in plain sight of his unsettled accomplice, Alejandro prays.

Frida is home a month, and unraveling like a yarn doll. Diego wants a divorce. She suspected it last autumn, but her plan was to stay away so long, he would learn he couldn't live without her. Such plans rarely succeed. She's moved out of the Double House, living in Coyoacán now, and it's odd to see the Blue House filling up with her things. She has layered on more paint, the colors of blood and the depths of the sea. The bedroom that was Lev and Natalya's, spare as a servant's back then with its woven rug and neatly made bed, now is crammed with her dressing table, jewelry, doll shelves, and trunks of clothes. Lev's former study holds her ruckus of easels and paints. It should not seem strange, as it was her house all along, and her father's before she was born.

This morning Perpetua sent Belén running down the block for help because the mistress had gone mad. Frida spends madness the way she spends money; it was all over by the time help could arrive. Perpetua answered the gate, pointed without a word, and returned to the kitchen. Frida sat on a stone bench in the courtyard with her hair all cut off. It lay in thick black parentheses on the bricks, all around her feet.

"Natalya sent me to ask if there's anything you need."

Frida smiled insincerely at the lie, revealing new gold caps on her incisors. It seemed she might have been drinking, even at this early hour.

"What I *need* is to castrate the son of a bitch and be done with it." She made some menacing snips at the air with her scissors, startling the black cat that had been disguised in the nest of hair. It stood and arched its back.

It seemed pointless to mention she has also been having affairs, in New York and Paris. At least, such things were much discussed in the press. A handsome Hungarian photographer. "Sorry, Frida. But with Diego and women it's nothing new, right?"

"Is this the kind of *mierda* you walked over here to tell me? I've been miserable for a long time already, so I should be used to it now? Thank you, my friend."

"Sorry." The cat slunk away into the laurel bushes.

"Sóli, you'll never guess: now I have fungus on my hands. A new ailment! One thousand operations, plaster corsets, medicines that taste like piss, collapsed organs, and there's still something new that can go wrong with me. Maybe I could be a little miserable about this?" She held up her hands, mottled pink, raw and dreadful.

"All right. If you need permission."

Even in her disconsolate state she looked like a peacock, perfectly dressed in a green silk skirt and enough jewelry to sink a boat. Even drowning, Frida would cling to vanity. "Don't forget Paris and New York, Frida. They loved your show. Yesterday Van showed me a fashion magazine with you on the cover."

"The opinion of me in Paris and New York, if you want to know, was the same as for a talking pony. Imagine it, a Mexican girl who dresses funny and curses like a soldier! Every day was, what do you call it? A bowl of fish."

Translating Frida is no easy trick. "A kettle of fish? That means you're in bad trouble. Or else a goldfish bowl, which means people are looking at you all the time."

"Both. I was in a kettle of goldfish. People pointed on the street."

"Because you're famous. People saw your paintings."

"Listen, don't ever become famous. It's killing. You should see what they wrote in the papers, those reviewers. They hardly bothered to look at the paintings, they only wanted to write about the painter herself. 'She should be making nice pictures of nature instead of these nightmares. And always *herself*—she's not even that good looking!'"

"We saw the reviews. A lot of them were good. Diego says Picasso and Kandinsky think you're a bigger talent than both of them combined."

"Okay, but that cockroach André Breton didn't bother to pick up my paintings from the customs house until I got there and screamed at him. And it's true what I'm telling you about the reviews. They write what *they* think you should be painting."

That courtyard seemed more than ever like a fairy-tale house, with tree leaves for its ceiling and an ivy-covered floor. White calla lilies rose up through the ivy carpet, all of them bending their hooded heads toward Frida, like charmed cobras.

"Obviously you had a miserable time. But you can't blame anyone for seeing you as a spectacle."

She looked puzzled. Her earrings today were a pair of heavily embossed golden snakes, but with her newly shorn, glossy head she looked like a sea lion. With gold teeth. "What spectacle?"

Carmen Frida Kahlo de Rivera. Who could explain her to anyone, least of all herself? "You play a certain role. You have to admit that. Mexican peasant, queen of the Azteca or what. You don't dress to blend in."

Her gold incisors flashed. "If I don't choose, they choose for me: Wife of the Much-Discussed Painter. The newspapers would wrap me in gauze and make me a martyred angel, or else a boring jealous wife. Above all, a victim—of Diego and life. Of disease. Look at this leg." She yanked up the green silk to reveal her naked, lame leg. It was a more awful sight than the infected hands: thin as a stick because of the childhood polio, bent and scarred from the accident, years of limping and indignities uncountable.

"You've never seen it, have you?" she asked.

"No."

"How long have you known me?"

"Nearly ten years."

"And in that time, have you thought of me as *this*?"

It was hideous: the leg of a leper, a street beggar, a veteran of wars. Anything but the leg of a beautiful woman. "No."

She tossed the long silk skirt back down, like covering a corpse. "People will always stare at the queer birds like you and me. We only get to choose if they'll stare at a cripple, or a glare of light. The jewelry and everything makes people go blind. The gossips will say a million things, but they never ask, 'That Mexican-Indian-Azteca girl, why does she always wear long dresses?'"

With the points of her naked toes she carefully set about pushing the locks of hair on the ground into a round pile. Everything with her is an artful project, flowers laid out on a table, even her own self-destruction. "So," she said, "how is your wonderful story, the scandals of the ancients? Are you working on it every day?"

It was tempting to tell her about the writing desk in the guard-house room, a newly oiled typewriter, a pile of pages growing higher every night. It would excite Frida to make her an accomplice. But she is no good at secrets. "What do you mean, queer birds like us? Nobody is staring at me."

"So you think."

The cat circled warily near her feet, eyeing the strange black pelt.

"And your dear comrade Van. How is he these days?"

"Not staring at me. That is for sure."

The cat decided the new animal between his mistress's feet was neither predator nor prey, so he crept away over the ivy, lifting his feet as if walking through shallow surf.

"Being a peacock is not the only way to hide yourself, Frida. A pigeon can hide."

"Is that what you are? A pigeon hiding in a little hole in the bricks?"

"I'm a typist. And a cook. Sometimes now I get to clean rabbit cages."

She sighed. "What a waste of time. I thought you had *chispa*. A spark, or some kind of discipline. It turns out you're a little gray pigeon." She smoothed her skirt over her leg and pulled her shawl around her shoulders, composing herself against what she had revealed.

"I'm sorry about your leg. I'd heard different things."

"Sóli, let me tell you. The most important thing about a person is always the thing you don't know."

Twelve people living in this household now, and only one bathroom. Miss Reed calls it The Dance of the Hours. The four Americans always stay up late—the strange, funny Miss Reed (who dresses like a boy) and her husband sleep in one of the guard-house rooms but rarely retire to it until dawn, the same time Lev rises for his morning exercise. Joe and Reba still have their apartment, and take field trips to its bathroom. For everyone else the clock is ruled by quick dashes and rationed cups of coffee. Lorenzo and the other three guards have been known to piss over the side of the roof, declaring that the GPU must be defeated by every known weapon. But some weapons they hold in reserve. The competition of morning is not for the weak-hearted.

The secret hour is seven forty-five. Lev has long finished his ablutions by then, and Natalya as well. The late risers are no threat as yet, and the morning shift are still holding off, respecting Natalya's privacy. It's possible then to slip from the dining room into Lev and Natalya's wing, tiptoe through Lev's study. Lev will soon be in there, as surely as the map of Mexico will be on the wall. But at seven forty-five he's still outside feeding the chickens.

The narrow bathroom runs alongside Lev's study and bedroom under a tin shed roof, added on the house some time between Porfirio Diaz and modern plumbing. Its fixtures stand in a row like soldiers at attention: the bathtub on clawed feet, the lavatory on its pedestal, the cabinet with Lev's medicines and everyone's shaving things in a jumble. The pitcher and bowl on a stand. The dreadful hairy rug someone should throw out. Lev should write a paper: "The Political Challenge of a Commonly Held Bathroom: No One Has the Authority to Throw Out the Rug." And at the end, the captain of this army: the commode. Its tank above, the pull chain awaiting the private's salute.

Rather than exiting by the door into Lev's study (he might be there now), it's less awkward to exit through the empty end room Natalya calls "Seva's room," still hoping their orphan grandson can be brought here from Paris. For now it houses a wooden wardrobe of coats and jackets. This morning it also contained Natalya, standing at the laundry table folding a pile of Lev's striped silk pajamas. Awkwardness sometimes cannot be escaped.

"Good morning."

"Good morning."

It seemed necessary to say something else. "Lev has a lot of pajamas."

"Yes, he does."

"Nice ones. Most people don't dress as well, even during the day."

She said, "Most people don't have to think of dying in their pajamas. And being photographed for the papers."

"Dear God."

"Don't apologize. We're accustomed." She lifted her eyes briefly, a pair of gray stones, then looked back to her work. "I've been wanting to tell someone, and probably rather than Van, I should mention this to you. His blood pressure is higher."

"Lev's blood pressure? How high?"

"Extremely. The doctor yesterday was very worried."

"Is Lev worried?"

She folded the last pajama. "Lev thinks a bullet will find him before the stroke arrives. If that answers your question."

"But you wanted someone else to know. Understandably."

"Probably there's nothing you can do. He gets terrible headaches."

"He seems calm."

"Oh yes, Lev is calm, calm is Lev. What I said about wearing good pajamas when he is murdered. It's not photographs he worries about. I don't mean he is vain. I just cannot think of the word. My English."

"The word is *dignity*, maybe?"

"Dignity, yes."

"He could rest a little more. He's out every morning taking care of the chickens, but any of us could do that."

"Oh, he is crazy for those animals. I haven't seen him so affectionate for something since Benno and Stella. Two dogs we had in France." She grew quiet, visiting memories of dogs, and maybe living children. "I think the animals relieve him," she said finally. "Something in the world he can keep safe."

"But maybe it wouldn't hurt to offer some help?"

"Yes. To you, he might listen. He calls you 'son.' You notice it, of course."

"Of course. Lev has a large heart. He's father to the whole world, it seems."

"He said he finds you steadying."

"He does?"

"In your manner you resemble Sergei. He wouldn't have mentioned that, but it's true. Sergei was quiet. Always paying attention. He was for the good of other people."

"You must miss him. All of them."

She shook her head side to side, looking out the window, her lips tightly closed.

Outside, the morning was cool, with puddles still standing from a rain in the night. In the far corner of the courtyard against a blaze of red bougainvilleas covering the wall, Lev stood in a circle of hens. He tossed out grain and clucked softly in some form of gallinaceous Russian, apparently engrossed. He looked up, startled.

"Oh! Have you come asking my friends for proof of their dedication?"

"No eggs needed just now. Breakfast is nearly ready."

"Now you see, I was thinking, the hens make only a collective contribution. But the rabbits are fully dedicated, when called to serve. We may have two factions here."

"Like the Mensheviks and Bolsheviks."

He pursed his lips and nodded. "The Omelletscheviks. And the Hassenpfefferviks."

"Natalya thought you might need help with the animals."

"No, no." The flat shovel was out of the tool rack, leaning against the rabbit hutch beside a filled manure bucket. He had cleaned the little shed where the hens roost at night. Later he would take the manure and bury it around the garden.

"You're a very great thinker, sir. You shouldn't be doing farm work."

"You're wrong about that, my son. Everyone should do farm work. Your name is Shepherd. Did you ever tend sheep?"

"No, sir."

He took the shovel in hand, watching the hens make their excursionary expeditions into the garden. "Do you know that Stalin is murdering farmers now?"

"Why?"

"His idea for feeding the masses is to create enormous farms. Like factories, with vast machines and armies of unskilled labor. Rather than trust the wisdom of men of the land. He's imprisoning yeoman farmers, trying to destroy their class."

One of the hens caught a lizard, and it writhed wildly in her beak. She ran helter-skelter with all the others in zealous pursuit. Their aptitude for carnivory was impressive.

"That is enough talk of Stalin before breakfast. My young friend Shepherd with no sheep. I meant what I said. Everyone should get dirt on his hands each day. Doctors, intellectuals. Politicians, most of all. How can we presume to uplift the life of the working man, if we don't respect his work?"

Lev carefully folded the garment he wears to greet the animals each day: an ancient green cardigan with holes at the elbows. Evidently he does not expect to be assassinated while feeding chickens. Or it's his best hope. He took off his glasses and turned his face to the sun for a moment, boots planted wide, the peasant brow facing heaven. He looked the very image of the People's Revolution in one of Diego's murals. Then the former president of the Petrograd Soviet put away the manure shovel and went to his breakfast.

Today Van was married. Who could have imagined it two years ago, this very day, on a painted picnic boat in the canals of Xochimilco? Frida was correct, of course, Van didn't need the *trapanovio* to catch his true love. Nor did Lev, it seems. He holds hands with Natalya, and together they stand on the deck of this ocean liner, a ship with trustworthy friends and cactuses planted in its hold, and they watch the sun set behind the high wall that encloses them. Frida has been less lucky in love or anything else, declining to get out of bed for weeks now. Her body threatens to fold up shop, and good riddance, she says, since Diego no longer wants it.

Van and his American girl Bunny were wed this morning in city hall, in the nuptial office whose door happens to be directly under Diego's mural of the ancient Mayans harvesting cacao, though the lovers probably didn't notice. They plan to move soon to an apartment in New York. Natalya shed a few tears, as tiny and undramatic as her black shoes. She has always known she would lose this son, along with every other.

Lev was more jovial, congratulating the couple with formal toasts and Russian love poems recited from memory. Bunny wore a crown of twined flowers, some old-world notion of Natalya's, and somehow procured a bag of Van's beloved licorice for a wedding present. In the courtyard he stood blue-eyed beside his bride making disheveled toasts, absent his shoes for some reason. When Bunny reached on tiptoe to set her floral crown on Van's head, he smiled so broadly his molars gleamed. So grateful for her affection. He has no idea that everything about him can stop a heart: his shrug, like a little Dutch boy, shoulders raised high and then dropped. His beautiful white feet.

Celebrations are rare in this house, maybe all the more joyful for that reason. And if joy did not fill every quarter, at least no one spent the whole day cooking.

Britain has entered the war. Winston Churchill sent an Expeditionary Force into France, thousands of soldiers to defend the Maginot Line and prevent all of Europe falling to Hitler. Every evening after the plates are cleared, Lev turns on the radio receiver, and everyone goes quiet. All the boisterous opinions that normally fill this room are quashed by one thin voice quivering out of the air from some other world into the yellow-painted dining room. Why should Lev believe the wireless reports, when all others fail him? He struggles with the question himself. But is so hungry for knowledge, he casts his net wide and picks through the catch, hoping he can tell fish from flotsam.

It seemed impossible that this singular man, Hitler, could pull the whole world into the cauldron of his ambitions. Now it's only a question of the order in which nations are pulled. And what unexpected arrangements, as nations find themselves shoulder to shoulder with others, or face to face against: Canadians on the soil of France, Germans in Poland, Russians and Finns on the shores of the Baltic Sea.

Even in the horror of war, Lev is optimistic; he says it will make internationalists of us all. A modernized proletariat will unite, because war so conspicuously benefits rich men and kills the poor ones.

"Surely the French munitions worker can see how his labors fill the pockets of war financiers in the city of London." He says the factory worker and peasant of every nation will discover that their common enemy is the factory owner, exploiting their labor, keeping them poor and powerless.

But this boy in a French or British factory, standing in his leather overall welding the casing on a metal bomb: what can he see? That thing will fly through the air, fall hundreds of miles away, and kill boys in leather overalls in a German factory. The reports will roar victory or defeat, and boys will never know how alike their lives have been.

Seva has arrived from Paris, to put his arms around his grandparents for the first time in his memory. He calls Lev "Monsieur Grandfather," it breaks Natalya's heart. The Rosmers, who brought him, are their oldest friends: Alfred the cartoon Frenchman with his long neck, moustache, and beret, and round Marguerite, clasping everyone to her bosom. Lev says he and Alfred have fought Stalin together since Prinkipo. The Rosmers will stay some months now in Mexico, they are renting a house. France is uncertain, to say the least, and the boy needs time to adjust. He's lived with the Rosmers most of the time since Zinaida died, after Marguerite located him in a religious orphanage. Lev never talks about any of that. Zinaida was his eldest, the story unfolds a little at a time: tuberculosis, leaving the USSR with her baby for treatment in Berlin. Her visa revoked by Stalin, the husband Platon disappearing in a prison camp.

Seva is now thirteen, a tall schoolboy in short pants and leather sandals. He speaks Russian and French and not a word of Spanish, and walks carefully around the courtyard watching the hummingbirds that hover at the red flowers. Marguerite wanted to know what they are called. In France, she said, they don't have such things. It must be true, because Seva dashed in red-faced with excitement over the creature. Marguerite made him slow down so she could translate his desires. A net or a pillowcase, he wanted. Anything in which he could capture it.

Natalya hugged him hard, already torn with remorse over the forces that govern this family. "No, Seva, you won't be allowed to capture it," she said. "Your grandfather believes in freedom."

On Your Leaving

Praise the Vanguard, because it says your name. Van evanescent, servant of the advance, praise any word that could hold you. Praise your jacket that hangs on the peg, still holding one shoulder aloft, slow to forget the comrade it embraced.

Praise all but the vanishing point where we stand now, not quite parted. Already memories fall like blows. But soon they will be treasure, dropped like gold through a miser's fingers as he makes his accounts: the years at a desk, elbow to your elbow. The Flemish lilt of your words, like the shift and drop of a typewriter carriage, every sentence luminous and careful: a library with poppy fields inside. The times our teacups crossed by accident, the shock of tasting your licorice there. The brotherhood of small rooms in locked-up houses, the drift of quiet words while waiting for sleep, a restlessness we cast over blended boyhoods: the captured fish in a glass, the spaniel that ran away in a Paris park. You were always first to escape. The sight of you, falling like rain into your own beatific slumber.

Praise each insomniac hour, kept wide awake by your glow. Sleep would only have robbed more coins from this vandal hoarded store.

—HWS, OCTOBER 1939

Folded into an envelope, it was another letter left lying in the office for someone to see, this time not an accident. With Van's name typed on the outside, and then for good measure the address also, it looked like one of the endless messages delivered in the courier's bag. A memorandum to be filed. A cowardly disguise, yes, but who in this world who ever wrote a love poem wants to stand by blushing while the lover reads it? Such things should be tucked in a coat pocket and read in a different room, or somewhere else altogether. He and Bunny leave tonight on the evening train.

His valises were all packed and his mind too; he seemed halfway in New York when he came into the office looking for his black shoes. He took the jacket off the peg by the door, one last time, and put it on as he always does, shifting it across his shoulders to get it settled. The shoes were located, absurdly, on top of the file cabinet. Probably set there by Natalya when she swept.

"Well, comrade Shepherd. We have had a go at the world together in this little headquarters, have we not?"

"We have. It has been very great, Van. You taught me worlds of things. It's hard to say how much."

He shrugged. Glanced at the envelope on the corner of the desk. "More filing, on a Sunday?"

"I think it's old, maybe from Friday."

"But it's for me, you're sure? Not for the commandant?"

"It's your name on it. Probably just a news clip or something. It couldn't be very important."

He smiled and shook his head, sliding his eyes toward the dining room where Lev plowed his way through the daily quotient of newspapers. "Long live the Revolution and work that never ends. But mine here is done."

He dropped the envelope in the wastepaper basket.

The rains have ended. Soon the migrant birds will come back from the north.

The Trotskyist Party in the United States continues to send migrants too, a small, steady flow of young men eager to work for Lev. They are good boys with plenty of heart and muscle, put to work mostly as rooftop guards and kitchen help. Socialist Workers, they call their party, and most are from what they call the "Downtown Branch" in New York. Jake and Charlie were first to arrive, with a fat, smuggled envelope of cash, support from the worldwide movement that is well put to use in this household. As was the bottle of brandy they produced in time for Van's wedding.

The newest one is Harold, who "bunks" with Jake and Charlie, speaking their same language of *conk* and *dig me* and *togged to the bricks*. Mother would have adored these boys, though she'd probably lose patience with their praise for the common man.

With Van gone, letters and drafts are starting to pile in a backlog inside Lev's brain, but he won't let these boys help much with secretarial work. He says it requires special skill; the best secretary to a writer must be a writer himself. ("Even, perhaps, a novelist," he conspires with a twinkle.) Lev's study table is mounded with papers, ink bottles, boxes of wax cylinders from the Ediphone. The calendar lying open on his desk must be excavated each morning, to turn the page on a new day. The books mount in polyglot piles: Russian, French, Spanish, and English all in one stack, representing different strata in his miraculous brain. A layer for each new country in his journey.

Now he means to add another: the United States. He is invited to travel there as a witness, in a trial before the Congress. A man named Dies wants him to testify against the American Communist Party. Lev is eager to do it. Their devotion to Stalin must be checked, he says. The American Communists still believe all Stalin's charges against Lev, but when they know the truth, he says, they will shift their allegiance to the movement for socialist democracy in Russia. He believes this Dies Committee could be used to engage the world war as a platform for world revolution.

Jake and Charlie say it's a trap, and Novack sent telegrams warning Lev not to cross the border. The United States seems ready to get in the war, most likely on Stalin's side, against Hitler. What a goodwill gift Lev Trotsky would make, delivered to Stalin in chains. Natalya is terrified; the U.S. press uniformly say Lev is a monster. But still he makes plans to go. The Dies Committee has issued his papers and promised police protection for the journey. But won't grant a visa for Natalya, or any Mexican assistant.

Lev can work around any obstacle. He plans to bring a secretary and translator whose legal status is without reproach: who has never belonged to any political party. Who holds a U.S. passport because his father is a citizen, working in a government accounting office. Lev even assumes the father will offer hospitality in Washington during the hearings, which will last several weeks.

If Father even recognized his son at his door, he would likely send him off to go and bunk with the Christers. And if Stalin has offered a bounty on Lev's head, Father would gladly collect it. But Lev won't believe it, this man to whom paternal affections come as naturally as beating to a heart. No dictionary has words that can make Lev understand estrangement between a father and son. Departure is set, November 19.

The bags are all packed, filled with papers. Natalya had to remind Lev to bring some clothes and a coat. It will be cold in the north. Important files have been excavated from the time of the Dewey Commission, in which Lev already worked hard to prove his innocence. His belief in justice still burns so brightly, it's hard to watch.

Lorenzo will drive the car to the train station in the morning. Mexican police will provide bodyguards to the U.S. border. Marguerite Rosmer made a party here this evening for bon voyage, though Natalya finds little to celebrate. But Marguerite always cheers her, and so did the presence of other friends: the Hansens, Frida, and Diego of course. He and Lev get along famously now that they're no longer friends.

And Frida: if anything can get her out of bed, it's a party. She showed up in a wild *tehuana* dress with a bodice of ribbons, and her short hair brushed out in a wave like a motion picture star. She brought her sister's two children, who adore Seva. Diego arrived late, wearing a hat like Pancho Villa's. The children had firecrackers and caused Lorenzo a near collapse, he was so nervous about the possibility of an attack. He stopped the party four times, forcing everyone to clear the courtyard and go into the bunkhouse because the guards on the roof had sighted a strange vehicle in the street. Once, it was the Buick that dropped off the Rosmers. The car belongs to their friend Jacson, a young Belgian they've befriended who sometimes drives them places. Marguerite told a story during the party about how this same young man once chased Frida around Paris. "He won't admit it," Marguerite said. "But his girlfriend Sylvia says he was infatuated. Do you recall him? Apparently he followed you for days, trying to meet you."

"How could I remember which one he was?" Frida asked, tilting her head so one gold earring danced against her black hair. There was no smile or dazzle, she was play-acting at being coy, a habit without feeling.

"On the day your show opened, Jacson apparently waited all afternoon outside the gallery with a bouquet the size of a Dalmatian. When you finally came, you told him to make a kite from his pants, and threw the flowers in the gutter!"

"The poor man," Diego said. "Frida destroys them all."

The look that passed between them held such awful sadness. If either of the two had painted such a thing, it would have to be torn down from the wall.

Marguerite was still in the thrall of her story, imagining this boy on the street with his broken flowers. "That's true! He probably didn't know she was married."

Frida says the divorce will be final before the year's end.

✳

Natalya is ecstatic, Lev is irate, and everyone else holds an intermediate position. There will be no journey, no testimony. Lev didn't even get on the train. Somehow the Dies Committee must have caught wind of his revolutionary intentions, or sensibly guessed them. At the last possible moment the Department of State wired a permanent revocation of his visa. He is *never* to be allowed to enter the United States.

Already the newspapers have their story. They interviewed Toledano and also the artist Siqueiros who is in league with him now, both of whom know less than Lev's chickens about what really happened. But still they had plenty to say: Lev was foiled in a plot against the people, financed by the oil magnates and the American FBI.

Alejandro's English improves, but not his conversation. His shyness suffocates him like a caul. But like any child he fights to be born, to land himself in the tribe of men. With the other guards around, he can piss off the roof with the best of them. He swears loyalty to the Fourth International, and also to Jesus, especially at Christmas and other holy days of obligation.

Lev counsels Lorenzo and the other guards to be lenient, the lad will develop a revolutionary discipline. Give him time. Alejandro is unschooled, afraid of being wrong.

February is the hardest month for Lev. Too many deaths have left their stains on its walls. On some days he drifts into memories, visiting with beloved ghosts of so many he's known—his young first wife, friends, daughters and sons, coworkers and comrades, all murdered by Stalin, many of them for no better reason than Lev's anguish. He and Natalya have frank talks about where she can go, if Lev is the next in that line. Joe and Reba vouch they can get her safely to New York; Van of course is already there. "Take me along for burial," Lev said. "The United States would gladly admit me as a corpse."

What a vast tapestry Lev must have woven in sixty years of living, the meetings of minds and bodies, armies of joined hands and pledged oaths—and now this household is nearly all that's left of it. Only these few could tell a story of him from memory when he is gone. It's such a small measure to stack against the mountain of newsprint fables, the Villain in Our Midst. What will people find in libraries one day, if they go looking? So little hope he will be honestly remembered. No future history in this man.

Today he turned over a handwritten letter to be typed. It seemed more private than public, some sort of will or testament. The heading said only: "February 27, 1940."

"For forty-three years of my thinking life I have been a revolutionary; for forty-two of those years I fought under the banner of Marxism. If I had to start all over again, I would of course try to avoid this or that error, but the general course of my life would remain unchanged. I will die a proletarian revolutionist. My faith in the communist future of mankind is firmer today than it was in the days of my youth.

"Natalya has just come up from the courtyard and opened my window so the air may come in. I can see a wide strip of green grass along the wall, the pale blue sky above, and sunlight on everything. Life is beautiful. Let the future generations cleanse it of all evil, oppression and violence, and enjoy it to the full."

Natalya declared today it was time for a "walk." It's the name she and Lev use for outings, long drives into the country where Lev can scramble through cactus-filled ravines while Natalya spreads a picnic blanket in a grapefruit grove. "He needs to get out of this coffin," she said at breakfast, even though she worries herself sick whenever he leaves the fortress. But she knows his hungers. With every passing month lived outside of Frida's shadow, Natalya seems to be more of a person, a wife. That blue house was a mouth that swallowed her down. Or a dark necessity they passed through together.

Some words that have meaning in this house: Forgiveness. Trust.

As the Commissar of Picnick, she commanded the kitchen troops in the packing of lunch, while the Steering Committee of Outings spread out maps on the dining room table and made a reconnaissance. Keeping to deserted roads would be safe. They decided on Cuernavaca, by a route that would afford good views of the volcanos Popocatapetl and Ixtaccihuatl. It was noted that the American Faction would amuse the Mexican Faction by trying to pronounce these names.

The Rosmers were telephoned, as this adventure would require two automobiles: the old Ford on permanent loan from Diego, and their friend Jacson's Buick. He appears willing to take his friends anywhere on short notice, probably because he likes being inside that immense car. Reba and Joe, Miss Reed, Lorenzo, food, wine, blankets, and one machine gun all fit in the Buick, along with the Rosmers. In the smaller Ford, the bodyguards Alejandro and Melquiades crammed into the front seat with the driver, who contained his displeasure with the cantankerous Ford. (Oh, for Diego's Chevrolet Roadster, its powerful engine and smooth gearshift.) Lev and Natalya sat in back with their excited grandson, and the equally wide-eyed lad Sheldon, newest volunteer from the States.

Lev kept his head down as always, lying across the others' laps in the back seat until the car was well outside the city, climbing a dirt road out of the dusty central valley. Large stretches of land lay uncultivated, studded with spiny plants fiercely defending their territory from no one who wanted it. Stockmen in wide-rimmed hats rode along the roadsides driving their cattle, whose large, down-turned ears gave them a look of hopeless sadness in the inhospitable landscape. Nopal plantations and occasional sugarcane fields gave the only glimpses of green.

"Shepherd, I was thinking," Lev said, after it was deemed safe for him to sit up and look about. "We should always have a second driver in the vehicle. Do you think you could teach Melquiades?"

"Yes, sir." Lev meant: in case the first driver is shot by a sniper.

The passengers would need the protection of escape. It's the kind of horror Lev needs to anticipate and solve daily, like working out the finances or fixing a broken hinge.

In time the road gained purchase on the shoulder of the mountain. Rolling fields of brown grass and oaks gave way to dry pine forest. The plan was to avoid the city of Cuernavaca, taking rugged roads to a gorge near Amecameca. The day was *jueves santo*, the Thursday before Easter, so every village church in the land was cloaked in a purple drape, mourning the dead Christ who was expected to return shortly. Alejandro crossed himself each and every time a church was passed. He did it inconspicuously, probably embarrassed in the present company: just a tiny movement of a curled hand at his chest, the smallest possible gesture that might still be visible to a sharp-eyed God.

At certain bends in the road, the pine forests opened onto breathtaking views of Popocatapetl and Ixtaccihuatl, the dazzling snowy peaks of the twin volcanoes. "Killer!" Sheldon sighed from the back seat. This boy was already known to Jake and Charlie when he arrived, from "the Downtown Branch," and had never traveled outside New York before. Now he remarked on each vista, as unfailingly driven to it as Alejandro was to cross himself at each church. "Popo, po—" Sheldon tried, and gave up, which was just as well. The others were tired of laughing.

"Try Cuernavaca," offered Seva, into whose mouth both Spanish and English have run like water in a faucet, since the day the Rosmers brought him.

"*Cornavaca!* Thanks, pal! And now I think I'm done in for the day."

The little boy is especially fond of Sheldon, quick to come to his defense when the other guards tease. It's no wonder Seva wants to follow him around, Sheldon is such a good joe: first to volunteer for the worst guard shifts, never taking offense at a joke, never taking a second *pan dulce* off the plate until they've gone around. On his first great adventure, Mexico has struck Sheldon star-eyed. Mexico, he says, is *keen*.

"The Aztecs called the city Cuauhnahuac," Lev said. "It means, 'near the woods.'" Who. knows where Lev learns such things? He reads everything.

"But Grandfather, Cuernavaca means cow horn, yes?" Seva asked. "Why did the Spaniards change it?"

Melquiades suggested that the Azteca changed it themselves to keep from laughing to death when they heard the Spaniards try to say "Cuauhnahuac."

The destination was a forested ravine with a shaded glen and a cold, rushing stream for swimmers with strong hearts. Lev took his grandson on a hike and they came back triumphant, Lev carrying his burlap-wrapped prize like a stout log over his shoulder. It was his favorite cactus, the *viejito*, "little old man" they call it because it grows long white hair instead of spines. Melquiades and Lorenzo together hefted the cactus into the trunk of the Buick and swear it weighed thirty kilos, at least. Stalin and high blood pressure notwithstanding, Lev may outlive us all.

His happiness, when it comes to him, is so pure. He has a ridiculous old straw hat he wears only for these outings. No one could remember when they'd seen it last, or his smile. Or the camera. For a change, here was a day worth remembering, and Lev wanted to record everything: Natalya and Marguerite on a blanket at the feet of pines, setting out plates of batter-fried chicken. Natalya in her little brimmed hat, seated on a rock by the water, smiling at the camera. The bodyguards clowning. Seva in his swim trunk posing on the cliff for a high dive he did not—under a hail of alarmed Russian from Natalya—actually execute. Sheldon took the camera and made Lev get in most of the photographs. Of the many vicissitudes to be recorded that day, most important was Lev's joy.

An hour before sundown the party elected an Executive Committee of Packing Up, and everything went into the cars. A white egret picked through the minor leavings of lunch strewed on the ground. This bird had spent the afternoon stalking snails along the riverbank, ignoring the acrobatics of bodyguards leaping off rocks, shaking water from their ears, and complaining of frozen *cojones*. It looked like the same bird that strangely appeared in the courtyard of the Blue House, the day Lev left it. That day had felt like a sad, terrible pageant: the Children of God cast from Eden. But it was not Eden; that leavetaking was a good one for Lev and Natalya. And of course the egret today looked like that other one. All egrets look the same.

Of all things, a letter has come from Father. Dated in April but arrived today in May, on Mother's birthday, by strange coincidence. Its arrival at all is a miracle; it was addressed to the house in San Angel, care of Diego, and anything that falls to the care of Diego could well be shoved under the leg of a wobbling table, or put in a sandwich. That address must have been sent him by Mother years ago, when she was still living.

Father didn't have a great deal to say. He was ill last year, and has bought a car. He mustered two paragraphs describing the car, and none of the illness. Synchromesh in the lower gears, floor-mounted shift lever and clutch on the floor. A Chevrolet Roadster like Diego's, apparently, but a later model, and white. He closed with the hope that Mother's passing might provide occasion for a closer rapport between father and son. Rather than use his own address, because he said he intended to be leaving his apartment shortly, he gave the address of his solicitor, located on I Street in Washington, D.C.

"A closer rapport" could mean, for example, one letter in every year divisible by four. It's worth considering.

24 *May*

They must have parked somewhere down Viena Street and crept toward the house, two hours before dawn. The men wore city police uniforms, Lorenzo swears, so he was confused when they approached in the usual friendly way and then forced his arms behind his back, tying and gagging him. Alejandro was near the gate on the other side, taken at the same time in the same way. They held a pistol to his head and asked about locations of the telephone lines. He told them nothing, but the men still found and cut them quickly, along with the new electric alarm. They knocked on the gate, and Sheldon opened it, not understanding Alejandro's distress when he gave the password at gunpoint, or perhaps failing to ask for it. Alejandro can't clearly remember.

The gunmen rushed through into the courtyard, opening fire on the guardhouse where the thunder of machine guns woke everybody at once. Round after round also went through the windows of the main house into Lev and Natalya's bedroom. The *tat-tat-tat* kept going, for as long as it took to scramble under a bed in the blackness, feel the cold floor, and consider the end of life. Outside in the courtyard was a peculiar glow, not the moon or the streetlight. The air smelled of gunpowder, and then came the scent of riot gas—a bizarre memory. Incendiary bombs, thrown into the house.

Natalya and Lev had rolled onto the floor beside their bed and lay flat. Natalya says she kept her hand on Lev's chest the whole time, to know if his heart was beating. The doorway from their room to Seva's filled with flames. A black silhouette of a man appeared there for a few seconds. They watched him raise a pistol and fire, four times, into the blankets that lay in a jumbled pile on their bed.

Seva, Seva, she said when the phantom had gone, Seva must be dead or they've taken him. It was the most horrible sound, and also a terrible relief, when she heard her grandson scream. She crawled to the doorway and found him bleeding from his foot, under his bed. He was already there, he said, when he'd seen the man's feet come in. The gunman had fired into Seva's bed too. One bullet went through, striking Seva's foot.

One at a time, the bodies in the guard house stood up from the floor, put their hands on their own heartbeats, and struggled to put life back on like a suit of clothes ripped away. Every body alive. We have survived. Only Sheldon is missing. Alejandro believes he might have been shot—he thinks he saw him collapsed by the gate, maybe dragged away by the assailants. Seva won't stop asking where he is. If we are alive, he insists, then Sheldon is alive.

Lorenzo says the man who nearly broke his arms out on the street was a person he recognized. Wearing a false moustache, but it was the muralist, Diego's old friend who became his enemy: Alfaro Siqueiros. No one quite believes it. But Lorenzo is not a fanciful man, and he is sure.

The police came today and used kitchen knives to dig the lead slugs from the walls of Lev's bedroom. Seventy-six bullets. The pocked, crumbling wall, what's left of it, looks like the face of a leper. Bullet holes only centimeters from Lev's pillow. The officers worked all day, collecting evidence. The survivors stood in the ruined court-yard blinking at the light, with eyes unprepared to see the life that is spared into their custody.

Survival, by itself, is not reason enough to rejoice. If life was a suit of clothes momentarily ripped away and put back on, the tearing has ruined it. Today seems harder than yesterday. Night is worse than day, and day is bad. No one has slept. The whistle of a teakettle causes every heart to lurch. Natalya's arms are bandaged, she burned them putting out the fire in Seva's bed. She sits in a chair with tears in her eyes, holding her arms forward as if to embrace a ghost. Lev paces, his thoughts scrambled. With so many others already dead, he must see this assault as a rehearsal for the inevitable. Everyone else in the house must surely harbor secret thoughts of leaving here. Those thoughts layer the misery of guilt upon the misery of terror.

Lorenzo is furious over the breach, and now tediously repeats the security drills everyone knows too well already. "When the horse is gone, it's too late to shut up the barn," Lev warns gloomily. "They won't come by the front gate next time." But Lorenzo can't stop himself, driven by anger or embarrassment at his failure. "When the bell rings for changing the night guard, the man inside is to pull one bolt only. *Are you listening? One bolt only!* The bolt that opens the grille. Ask the pass word. If correct, the entrant may pass *only into the vestibule.*" But the vestibule is controlled by an electric button, and the electricity was cut. Alejandro was blind with panic. And whatever Sheldon's excuse for opening the gate, he can't defend it.

The newspapers have been unspeakable. They say it was a pantomime, mounted by Trotsky himself to gain publicity. The police questioned everyone here, and poor Alejandro they held for two days, probably guessing his vulnerability. Keeping him awake, shoving a rifle butt into his shoulder, the police interrogated him about the so-called fake attack: if it had been real, they asked again and again, how could anyone have survived it? How could seventy bullets fill a room, and every one miss its mark?

In desperate logic, Alejandro pointed out that Seva was actually hit. It was only on the toe, but still. If this were staged, what grandfather would choose a child as victim?

The police reported his words to the press, neatly turned: *The ruthless villain chose his innocent grandchild as the victim in his charade!* In their haste to repeat the scurrilous story, some of the papers even reported Seva dead.

Alejandro is beside himself now, feeling that he caused these vicious reports. He was never quick to come to words, but now he won't ask for coffee at the breakfast table. He is wrung out and sick over his poisoned words, and may not speak again.

28 May

The Rosmers have departed for home, or whatever they find in Europe. Marguerite looked miserable to be leaving her friends at this moment, not so concerned with France's upheaval, as with Natalya's. But the passage is booked and can't be changed. But good news— when they came to the house this morning to say good-bye, they managed to talk Natalya into coming with them as far as the seaport. A small vacation on the coast. Reba went with her, they will come back next week on the train. Natalya's burns are almost healed. She didn't want to part from Lev, but he insisted. This is perfect, they don't even have to take the train to Veracruz: Jacson agreed to drive them in his beautiful Buick, of course.

The good-byes in the courtyard were unmercifully long. Every kiss now between Lev and Natalya is heavy with grief. And Marguerite hugs everyone twice. By the time it all finished they had nearly lost their driver. Jacson was finally located in the house with Seva, playing with a model glider.

25 June

Sheldon Harte has been found, in the village of Tlalminalco, at a house owned by relatives of Siqueiros. Seva hasn't been told yet, but his friend Sheldon will not be back. The police found him under four feet of quicklime in the bottom of a pit.

Thirty people have been arrested, including Siqueiros, though he will probably be allowed to leave the country. The Mexican newspapers are calling him a "half-mad artist" and "irresponsible pirate." Guilt and blame in this story are already established—Trotsky did it himself—and so finding a true culprit creates some awkwardness. In a strange extension of their logic, one newspaper suggested the mad painter had sold himself to Trotsky, who paid him for the simulated attack. "*The* simulated attack," no longer even posed as a speculation, but the fact of the matter. Once a truth is established in newsprint, none other can exist.

Sheldon was a good joe. A *friend*: one more word that has sprouted leaves of meaning in Casa Trotsky.

Diego is gone, already in San Francisco. While the police were busy avoiding any trail that actually led to the Stalinist culprits, they accused Diego of participating in the attack. Now the charge is moot, with Siqueiros in custody, but the presses are locked in their own frenzy: the much-discussed painter a murderer! What reporter could contain his enthusiasm for that particular theory? Diego had to leave without a farewell, and Lev is sad of it. Through all its stages, the camaraderie of these men is remarkable.

Now Lorenzo is behaving like a madman: he installed metal doors three inches thick, on both entrances to Lev and Natalya's bedroom. Lev says going to bed now is like getting in a submarine. Lorenzo also has drawn up plans for a bomb-proof redoubt, three new brick turrets to overlook the streets, and barriers of barbed wire and mesh that will withstand grenade attacks.

Lev is plainly tired of mentioning the barn and the horse already escaped. He says they won't come in the same way again. "Lorenzo, my friend, if they were that foolish, you would have nothing to worry about."

The gloom may yet lift. Natalya has taken out her summer dresses finally, and put away her ancient Russian fur-trimmed coats. Of course, the weather in this city is exactly the same in any month, give or take a chance of rain. Yet Natalya follows the seasons scrupulously, wearing light-colored prints in the spring, dark coats in autumn. Her sense of order is still ruled by the weather of Paris, or Moscow. And because of it, she survives. Lev survives. The past is all we know of the future.

Another good sign: Natalya accepted guests for tea. In the Melchor market Reba ran into the faithful chauffeur Jacson and his girlfriend Sylvia. On a whim she suggested they stop by, so Natalya could thank Jacson for driving them all to Veracruz. Reba worried whether it was right to ask without Lev's permission, but Natalya said of course it was fine, the Rosmers have known Sylvia for years and Jacson has shown a thousand kindnesses in recent months. Natalya seemed to enjoy Sylvia and Jacson. She said they should come again, bringing a little diversion into this fortress.

Lev seems to have his own opinion of the couple. He took an unusually long time to check on the chickens before coming in to join the visitors for tea. Natalya grew a little exasperated and sent a messenger to get him.

"Pardon, sir, but your wife is wondering why it would take forty-five minutes to feed eleven hens."

"Tell Natalya these hens are more interesting company than her guests. No, no, don't tell her that. He's a good sort, this Jacson. But he fancies himself a writer."

"What's he writing?"

"Well, that's the problem. He doesn't know. He showed me a draft. It's supposed to be some sort of analysis, Schachtman's theory of the Third Camp. But really it's a tedious mess. His thinking is very shallow, if he's thinking at all."

"Oh."

"And he'll want me to critique it."

"That's difficult."

"Difficult. Oh, my son. I have faced the GPU and the gulag. But somehow I cannot face a young man who has been very kind to my wife, and say to him, 'Well, my friend, you are a shallow thinker. And tedious.'"

"Would you like me to tell Natalya the hens are extremely hungry today?"

He sighed, rattling the grain scoop. The hens tilted their heads, watching his every move. "Look at this. In 1917 I commanded an army of five million men. Now I command eleven hens. Not even a rooster at my service."

"More often than not, Commissar, it's the roosters that give the trouble."

He chuckled.

"If you'd like a little help with passing the time here, sir, I have a question to ask you. About being commander of the Soviet. I've been wanting to ask for a long time."

"Well, then, don't wait. The doctor says my blood pressure is through the roof. What can this question be?"

"Diego told me you were meant to succeed Lenin. You were his second in command, with the people's support. You would have led the revolution to a democratic Soviet Republic."

"This is the case."

"Then why did Stalin come to power instead of you? The books say 'an unsettled transition,' that kind of thing. But Diego said it differently."

"How did he say it?"

"An accident of history. Like a coin toss, that could have gone either way."

Lev was quiet for an extremely long time. It seemed likely that Jacson and Sylvia would leave before this conversation moved forward at all. It was a bold question, possibly even rude. Van had said many times that Lev hates to talk about this, and won't.

But finally he did. "Vladimir Lenin died in 1924, this you know. He had a stroke, soon after the Thirteenth Party Conference. He was exhausted by that conference, and I was also. I had been ill many weeks and came down with pneumonia during the sessions. Natalya insisted we go to the Caucasus afterward for a rest. She was right, I might have died otherwise. The conference concluded, and I embraced my comrade and friend Vladimir before departing."

He paused, took off his gloves, and wiped his eyes.

"Natalya and I were on the train to the Caucasus. In the dining car, having a cup of tea. The porter came and handed us a telegram: Lenin was dead of a stroke. Stalin had sent the wire. 'Dear comrade Lev,' he said, or some such thing. In friendship and full solidarity he shared my grief, and gave details of a funeral. He said for various reasons, mostly for maintaining calm, the family and secretariat had decided against a large state funeral. They would hold a private burial the very next day. There was no time for me to return, of course, but Stalin assured that I should not worry. The family understood. In due time, they would want me to eulogize Lenin in a state ceremony."

"And so you went to the Caucasus."

"We proceeded to the Caucasus, for a week of rest. And before the end of it, learned that Stalin had lied. The information he sent in the wire was false. The funeral had not been immediate or small. It was a large state funeral, three days after the wire. I could have managed to return in time, had I known. I should have been the one to speak there. To calm people, because it was a frightening time. With Lenin gone so suddenly, it was chaotic. People were very uncertain about the future."

"But instead of you, Stalin spoke at the funeral."

"The newspapers said I had refused to come, declining to be disturbed from my vacation. He told that story openly. But not from the platform, of course. At the funeral he spoke of leadership and reassurance. How he accepted the mantle of the people's trust, when others had shirked it. . . . Everyone knew of whom he spoke."

"You had their loyalty, a few days before. Did that count for nothing?"

"They were so afraid. In that moment their keenest desire was to lean on someone who seemed unfailingly strong."

His eyes fixed on the sky, above the wall that enclosed him. No wound to his flesh could have pained Lev more than this memory. It was cruel to raise the subject, Van had been right about that.

"Sir, you couldn't have known. It was not your mistake."

"The mistake was to believe him. To accept the sympathy of a friend extended in a telegram. I was very ill of course, with a fever, Natalya reminds me of that. And the loss was disorienting, no one expected it so suddenly. But to take Stalin at his word, look what has come of this. A hundred thousand deaths. The whole revolution betrayed."

"How long did it take you to get back to Moscow?"

"Too long. That is the simple truth. Stalin moved so quickly to fill the bureaucracy with men who swore loyalty to him. These were supposed to be neutral positions, men dedicated only to the country. But loyalty to Stalin guaranteed the future of Stalin. It's hard for a nation to retrieve itself from such a change of guard."

"But people desire fair government. You say that constantly."

"They want to believe in heroes, also. And villains. Especially when very frightened. It's less taxing than the truth."

Lev scrutinized the doorway to the dining room. The visitors were leaving. He waved the grain scoop. Jacson and Sylvia waved back. Natalya stood on the patio with a raincoat pulled over her shoulders like a cape. The sky was dark with a threat of rain.

"So that was the accident of history. A false telegram on a train."

"It was no accident."

22 August
This impossible thing cannot be. Something should have stopped this.

In the morning he was in the best spirits. He transplanted four cactus plants in a new garden. He was pleased about devising a new cactus-planting technology involving a canvas hammock, chicken wire, and a counterweight. "From now on *everything* will go faster!" he declared, as if he had invented internal combustion.

By lunchtime he'd finished revising the next-to-last chapter of his book on Stalin. In the afternoon he dictated an article on the American mobilization. From three thirty to four it rained pitchforks, and the day remained overcast. At five he took a break to have tea with Natalya, as always, and afterward asked for help with the rabbits. Two females had given birth to litters, in the same hutch. He needed to move one family lest the mothers cause trouble with one another's young. Cannibalism is always a possibility.

Lev had one of them by her nape, the big spotted one called Minuschka, when Jacson arrived unexpectedly from the gatehouse. Lev handed over the hare with instructions on where to move her kits.

Jacson also appeared to have his hands full: a folder of papers, his hat, a raincoat over his arm. He was leaving for New York shortly, he said. But had finished his first article. Please, could Lev give it an honest critique?

Lev looked back, shooting a certain feckless glance, nearly comic: *Help! I would sooner face the gulag!* But he said, "Of course. Come into my office."

They went in the house, he probably asked Natalya to make a cup of tea for the visitor, and then they must have proceeded to Lev's office. It's easy to picture: Lev sitting down, rooting out a clearing on his desk to set down the pages, collecting the patience to read it and make some tactful comment. The future waits. The world revolution waits, while Trotsky gives his full attention to a shallow-thinking but hopeful fellow, because nothing wondrous can come in this world unless it rests on the shoulders of kindness.

He would have asked Jacson to sit down opposite him in the arm-chair. But instead he stood, probably a little nervous to have this great man examining his syntax and logic. Fidgeting, annoying Lev to no end. Fingering things on Lev's desk: the glass paperweight, wedding gift from Natalya. Cartridge cases in the pen tray, souvenirs of the Siqueiros raid in May. Jacson laid his raincoat on the table.

And we heard the roar. A scream or a sob but really a roar, indignation.

Joe and Melquiades scrambled down the ladder from the roof, and everyone else from everywhere. Natalya cried out from the kitchen, "Lev?" Two baby rabbits fell to the ground and squirmed in the dust. The strangest sight had appeared in the window of Lev's study: Lev standing with his arms around Jacson—he seemed to be embracing the man—and screaming. There was blood. Joe and Lorenzo and Natalya all were shouting at once. Somehow Joe got there first, on his long legs, and already had Jacson pinned to the floor, and Natalya was white as chalk, collapsed against the door. Lev was seated now at his desk, glasses off, his face and hands covered with blood. On the floor lay a strange small pickax, with its handle cut short. Not a kitchen tool. Some other thing.

"You're going to be all right, old man," Natalya said quietly. Melquiades had his rifle cocked, trained on the writhing man on the floor. Joe was kneeling on Jacson's chest, grappling to control the man's flailing arms.

Lev spoke: "Don't let Seva in. He mustn't see this."

And then Lev said to Joe, or Melquiades, "Don't kill him."

"Lev," Joe said, almost sobbing the word. He had Jacson's wrists pinned now, his own large knuckles white against the stained floor. Lorenzo eased the Colt .38 out of Lev's desk drawer. It was always kept there, with six bullets in the magazine. A .25 automatic had also been lying on the table by the Dictaphone, within easy arm's reach of where Lev had sat reading Jacson's paper. And the security alarm bell is wired under the desk. They don't come the same way again.

Melquiades didn't lower the rifle. Both guns were trained on the man on the floor, aimed at his head. Intermittently he bucked and twisted under Joe's knees.

Lev held his hands away from his face and stared at the blood. There was so much of it. His white cuffs were soaked like bandages. It dripped onto the papers, this morning's typed drafts. Very slowly he repeated, "Don't kill him." It was an impossible spectre, an impossible request.

"It's no time for mercy," Joe said, his voice strange.

Lev closed his eyes, obviously struggling for words. "There is no hope they will . . . tell the truth about this. Unless. You keep that man alive."

When the Green Cross ambulance came, Lev was alive but half paralyzed, his body suddenly seeming terribly thin and strange to the touch, colder on that side when lifted onto the stretcher. Reba, Alejandro, and most of the others stayed at the house with Seva. Natalya rode in the back of the ambulance. It was dark. Streetlights were on.

At the hospital Lev began to speak in French, and later in Russian, just before they took him to surgery. Languages fell away, a long exile peeled from him like the layers of an onion.

The surgeons found that the blade had penetrated through Lev's skull, seven centimeters into the brain itself. He died the next day without waking again. Yesterday.

His last sentence in English had begun, "There is no hope." Natalya remarked later that those words were so strange to hear, from a man who lived decades on nothing but hope. But hope was not the issue, nor was mercy. There is no point discussing it with Natalya or Joe, but that was a clear instruction: No hope they will tell the truth, unless you keep that man alive.

He meant the newspapers. A dead assailant could become anyone, a victim himself. Another mad artist hired by Trotsky in a plot gone wrong, his final practical joke. Lies are infinite in number, and the truth so small and singular.

Lev was right; the man lives, and the world will know what he was. The police have him, already they're starting down the trail that now spools backward through our memories as a terrible thread: Reba running into him in the Melchor market last week, not by chance. Driving Natalya to Veracruz, not a whim but a calculation. The gift he gave Seva that day, the little glider: a chance to get inside the house, memorize the rooms. His attachment to the Rosmers' old friend Sylvia, and then befriending the Rosmers themselves. Driving them everywhere in his elegant Buick. Even his possession of the Buick. Where did he get such money? We didn't think to ask.

In custody he admitted it proudly, right away: he is a trained agent of Stalin, in the pay of the GPU for many years. Jacson is not his only name, or his real one. How many avenues did he have to try, before finding one door ajar? The trail goes back years, even back to Paris, his stalking of Frida, waiting outside her gallery with the bouquet of flowers. So much careful work, for the chance to sink a blade into the brain of Lev Trotsky.

The New York Times, *August 25, 1940*

U.S. Forbids Entry of Trotsky's Body

No Specific Reason Is Cited, but Fear of
Demonstration Is Believed Cause

SOVIET CALLS HIM TRAITOR

PRESS SEES DESERVED END FOR EXILE— ACCUSED SAYS HE HAD NO ACCOMPLICES

Special to The New York Times

WASHINGTON, Aug. 25—The State Department announced today that the body of Leon Trotsky would not be permitted to be brought to the United States from Mexico.

There was no reason offered, but it was assumed that the possibility was foreseen of Communist and anti-Communist demonstrations, if the body were brought here.

"In response to an inquiry from American Consul George P. Shaw in Mexico City," the announcement said, "the department has informed him that it perceives no reason for bringing Trotsky's body to the United States and that it would not be appropriate to do so."

SOVIET CHARGES PERFIDY

MOSCOW, Aug. 24 (AP)—The Soviet press, giving the Russian people their first word today of the death of Leon Trotsky in Mexico City last Wednesday night, proclaimed it the "inglorious end" of a "murderer, traitor and international spy."

It was the first mention of the attack since a brief dispatch on Thursday reported that an attempt had been made on the life of the exiled Communist leader by one of his followers.

The Communist party organ, *Pravda,* charged Trotsky with sabotaging the Red Army during the civil war, plotting to kill Lenin and Joseph Stalin in 1918, organizing the slaying of Sergei Kiroff and plotting to kill Maxim Gorky, and with having served in the secret service of Britain, France, Germany and Japan.

"Trotsky, having gone to the limits of human debasement, became entangled in his own net and was killed by one of his own disciples," said Pravda. "Thus, a hated man came to his inglorious end, going to his grave with the stamp of murderer and international spy on his forehead."

The Train Station Notebook, August 1940 (VB)

Today is a Saturday, the last of August. This train rocks, sliding north. It's four in the afternoon and the sun is bright on the left side of the train, beaded like a salt crust on the dirty windows, so that much is sure: the train is headed north. The last ten days are like shreds in a bag of scraps. Nothing in memory makes sense. Everything is gone, pockets full of ashes.

Lev was right to the end. The story of Jacson Mornard is so vile, the newspapers have been bound to tell it. President Cárdenas has condemned Russia and the United States as well, a league of foreign powers that dishonored our country with the attack. Three hundred thousand Mexicans walked down Paseo de la Reforma in the funeral procession, after walking here from mines and oil fields, from Michoacán and Puebla. Half made the journey without shoes. A quarter of them might not be able to say the name of Lev Davidovich Trotsky. Only that he was one of the generals in their Century of Revolution, as the president says. A man cut down by outsiders who refuse to believe the people can succeed.

On which day was the funeral? The attack was on a Tuesday, his death on Wednesday, and everything else is gone. Papers, books, clothes, and every memory ever recorded in a notebook. The police took everything from the guard house rooms, confiscated as evidence. The only hope of sorting out anything now is to put it in this little book. Starting with today, working backward: Day Last in Mexico, the train slides north; the train begins to move; the train is boarded at the Colonia Buenavista station; a packet of sandwiches and a small notebook bound with a wire coil are purchased at the new Sanborn's in the downtown station, using pesos out of the little purse from Frida.

Already the rest is a jumble. On which day was that, when Frida handed over the purse with the money and the documents for getting her crates through customs?

It was after the murder, but before the funeral. After the interrogation at the police station. They even questioned Natalya, for two hours. Everyone else they held for two days at least. Frida was ready to bite those men for making her sleep on a cot in that cold, stinking room. She was nowhere near, on the day of the murder. Joe gave the best statement, he remembers the most, even though he was on the roof when Jacson arrived, so didn't see him come into the courtyard.

No one else saw that: his nervous smile when asking the favor, one more critique of this paper he'd written. The raincoat over his arm: the weapon must have been underneath his coat. No one else saw Lev's silent glance back over his shoulder: *I would rather face the gulag!* His plea. A secretary's only work is to protect his commissar— Van would have done it. Any small discouragement could have sent Jacson Mornard away: Sorry, but as you know, Lev is awfully busy. He has to finish his article on the American mobilization. Maybe if you could just leave your paper, he'll have a look at it when he gets the chance. That could have happened. Lev could have been saved.

Now Miss Reed sits on the side of the bed holding Natalya's hand, whether it is Tuesday or Sunday, morning or midnight. Joe and Reba are in Lev's study packing up the papers and files. In that room only, the police left everything in place. They didn't take much from the house, either. But from the guard house: everything. It was astonishing. To be driven home from a blank brick cell at the police station, walk through the gate, and see Lev's cactuses still standing in place as if nothing had happened, the hens waiting to be fed. And then the guard house: the doors to every room standing open and nothing at all inside, only blank brick cells. The metal cots, the mattresses. The floors swept as clean as the day of moving in. The little table loaned from Lev was still there, but nothing on it, not even the typewriter. The books, gone. The trunk and boxes under the bed, gone. Clothes, tooth powders, the few photographs of Mother. And every one of the notebooks from the very beginning, from Isla Pixol. Also the box of typed pages that had grown to weigh as much as a dog, and had been that kind of faithful friend at the close of each day. The stack of pages growing fatter and more certain all the time. It doesn't matter. None of that matters.

Frida says the police are stupid cockroaches, they confiscated anything written in English because they couldn't tell what it was, the idiots couldn't see it's only diaries and stories. The Scandals of the Ancients, evidence of no crime except Mistaken Identity: a young man possessed of the belief he was a writer. So distracted by his dreams, he was a careless secretary, the type to leave letters lying around. Or leave his boss at the mercy of a tedious visitor, one more deadly supplicant with a badly written article.

Joe and Reba will pack up what's left of Lev, his thoughts crammed on paper, so it all can be sent to a library somewhere, sold for enough money to help Natalya get away. Van might arrange the sale, if he can be found. His last letter came from Baltimore; he was teaching French. He may not even know about Lev's death. Unthinkable. All of this is unthinkable, however much Lev and Natalya did think of it, anticipating death with each day's dawn. To think is not always to see.

Natalya will finish out the bottle of Phanodorm day by day, holding tight to Miss Reed's hand until she can open her eyes and walk on a ship and sail away. The United States won't let her come back with Joe and Reba. So Paris, then, to live with the Rosmers. She has to go. Lorenzo believes she's now a target, a highly watched symbol of her husband. She can't sleep for fear of the GPU, the wolves of her dreams.

Frida is going to San Francisco, where Diego is already. As usual she has a plan: her friend Dr. Eloesser will cure all her illnesses, and Diego will want her back. Melquiades plans to go south where he has relatives, Alejandro may go that way too. San Francisco, Paris, Oaxaca, the four winds—everyone scatters. Lev's writings will be kept together somewhere, but what of the secretaries who recorded them, their small contributions to his logic? Or even the contribution of a good breakfast, the satisfied stomach on which the greatest plans were launched, who will remember that? The New York boys versus the Mexicans in courtyard football, Casa Trotsky is gone, as if it never existed. The house will be swept and sold to new owners who will tear down the guard towers, puzzle over Lev's cactus gardens, and give away his chickens, or eat them.

This household is like a pocketful of coins that jingled together for a time, but now have been slapped on a counter to pay a price. The pocket empties out, the coins venture back into the infinite circulations of currency, separate, invisible, and untraceable. That particular handful of coins had no special meaning together, it seems, except to pay a particular price. It might remain real, if someone had written everything in a notebook. No such record now exists.

Frida says everybody had better knock the Trotsky dust off their shoes and get out of here. "Sóli, I have a plan for you," she said, seated at the little wooden desk in her studio. She'd sent Perpetua running down the street with an urgent summons—Frida wants to see you right away. "We have to get you away from here, you're not safe. The police took everything from your room, even your socks. It's because of all those things you wrote. I'm sure they're watching you." The police took many things from many people, but she believes words are the most dangerous. She says maybe Diego was right about "your damn diaries," the confiscated notebooks might put their author in jeopardy.

But she has a plan. She needs to send eight paintings to the Museum of Modern Art in New York, for a show: *Twenty Centuries of Mexican Art*. And after that another show is planned, *Twentieth-Century Portraits*. Frida has become a fixture of her century. The Levy Gallery may be interested as well. She needs a consignment marshal. "Or whatever the hell you call it in English," she said; she'll look it up for the documents. *Pastor de consignación* is what she called it, a "shipping shepherd," a legally authorized agent to accompany the paintings on the train all the way to New York. "Your passport is already fixed up. You were ready to go with Lev last fall, for that hearing."

"Frida, the police won't allow an emigration. Not with a murder investigation still open."

"Who says you're emigrating? I already talked with them about this. Leaving the country for a short time is okay, as long as you're not a suspect. I told them you're my consignment marshal."

"You already talked with the police?"

"Sure. I told them you have to oversee this delivery because I can't trust anybody else to do it," she said, tapping her pencil against the wooden desk. This plan had no complications at all, in her mind, beyond selecting which portraits to send for the show.

"And then?"

"No *and then*. You'll have to carry all these customs forms, one for each painting. You show them at the border, and get each one stamped. Declarations of value and all that. You have to be really careful to hold on to all the receipts from the lockup."

"The lockup?"

"Don't worry, you're not going to jail." Her hair has grown back, just barely long enough to coronate herself again, with the help of plenty of ribbons. When did she cut it off? The conversation of that morning is gone, that notebook is gone. Every time it hits like a rock. In Frida's studio, in front of the window, exactly where Van used to sit for dictation, she now had a half-finished portrait on her easel: Frida in a man's suit, cutting off her hair. *Keeping your damn diaries*, but these paintings are her own version of it.

Today she rattled like a gourd full of seeds, talking and fidgeting with the things on her desk. "Okay, the porter captain on the train will make the guys bring the crates to a special part of the baggage car, where they have a cage. You follow him in there to see him do it. He'll lock the crates inside and give you a receipt for getting them back. So you don't want to lose that."

"A cage?"

"Not the kind of cage for lions. Well, maybe they would put lions in there if they were expensive ones." She seemed desperate to be cheerful. She picked up tubes of paint, like big silver cigars with brown paper labels around their middles, then fingered the brushes standing together in a cup. She was afraid. It took a while to understand that this was the problem: fear. Not for herself but for her friend, whom she had thrown to the lions many times before. This time she wants him saved.

"Oh. So the paintings won't just be in a big suitcase or something?"

"Oh my God, wait till you see. They build a traveling crate for each one. Diego has a man who does this, he's very expert. He wraps them in layers and layers of kraft paper like a mummy and then fits each painting in two wooden crates, one inside the other. There's a space in between that's stuffed with straw, to prevent damage during shipping. The crates are huge. You could get inside one yourself."

That was on a Friday, because Perpetua was cooking fish. The day before the funeral? How long did it take to build those crates?

The police returned a few things the following week, but not much, not even clothing. Knowing those pigs, she said, they stole anything useful and burned the rest. Reba had to ask Natalya to open the wardrobe and pass around Lev's shirts, so the possessionless guards could have something to wear. His shirts were so familiar. It was startling to see them from the back, walking through the garden. Of all of us, they fit Alejandro best: small devout Alejandro, no one would guess they were the same size. Lev was so much larger than his body.

One day (which?), Frida said she went to the police station and screamed until they returned a few more items. Probably the officers locked the doors in terror, and threw things out the windows. So she had a small suitcase of items to hand over, along with the documents, for the trip to New York. That was yesterday. In the dining room of the Blue House, after one last look round the place, those mad blue walls and yellow wicker chairs. That glorious kitchen. Embraces from Belén and Perpetua.

"The police already had destroyed a lot of your things," Frida said flatly when she produced the suitcase. "This is what you'll need for the trip, and the rest you wouldn't want. There were some really old clothes and things, but you won't need that junk right away. I had it packed up and stored in a trunk at Cristina's."

"Anything else? Papers?"

"Only some books I think you borrowed from Lev, so I gave them to Natalya. Your room was all in a big metal box marked 'C,' maybe the third one they tore apart. I could tell because it was your clothes. There was hardly anything else, just some old magazines. We can send you the trunk after you get an address in Gringolandia. Sóli, jump! You're going to be a gringo!"

"This is all?"

She had packed the suitcase herself. It was hard to look inside: the unbearable persistence of hope. Of course there were no notebooks, no manuscript. Only shirts and trousers. A lot of woolen sweaters; Frida believes the sky of New York flings down snow at all times, even August. Also milk of magnesia, aspro gargle, and Horlick's powder for nerves, furthering Frida's vision of Gringolandia. Toothbrush, razor. She says it's not a good idea to bring more than this. A large trunk would draw suspicion.

"Remember, this is not an emigration."

But her embrace was like a child's farewell, dramatic and desperate. She didn't want to let go. "Look, okay. I brought you two presents. One is from Diego. He doesn't know yet. But I'm sure he would

THE LACUNA * 257

want you to have this. For Sóli, the drifter between two houses, to commemorate your journey. Look, it's the codex!"

It was the codex. The ancient book of the Azteca, a long tableau in pictures on accordion-folded paper, describing their journey from the land of the ancients, wandering until they found home. It was a copy, of course, not the original. But probably worth some money. Diego might not be pleased about this. It can always be returned.

Her face brightened. "The other one is from me. I made a painting for you!"

Frida only gives paintings to people she has loved. It was unexpectedly hard to keep from crying as she fetched the crate from the other room and lugged it in. It must be a small portrait; the outer crate is only the size of a suitcase, easily managed with regular baggage. But heavy as lead, for its size. She must have put a lot of paint on that canvas.

"Unfortunately you can't see it, I've already packed it up to go. I hope you'll like it. Write and tell me what you think. But you have to wait until you arrive in your new life. This is very important, okay? You mustn't peek. This is my gift, so don't defy me. Don't open this damn thing until you get to your father's house, or wherever you end up. Okay, promise?"

"Of course. Who would defy you, Frida?"

"And don't get it mixed up with the others. Look, I had the man print your name on the outside of the crate to be sure. You have papers in the folder to get it through customs, the same as the others. But don't give it to the museum by accident."

"Are you crazy? I won't forget."

"Yes, I am crazy, I thought you knew." She stared at the crate. "Look at that, it's an omen. You and I came into life through the same doorway, and now you are supposed to go through this one for me. It's your destiny."

"What makes you think so?"

"Your name. For me you're just Sóli, I forgot you're Shepherd. You were meant to be the *pastor de consignación*." The shepherd of the shipment.

Eight paintings, a suitcase of Viyella socks and milk of magnesia. And two gifts, from people whose faces already slide backward from memory as the train climbs north.

Oh, the little stolen man. Forgotten until just now. Even he is left behind, the police must have taken him in the sweep, with everything. It's a pity. This train might be just the thing he was looking for, those thousands of years. A long, narrow channel through darkness, a tunnel through the earth and time. *Take me away to another world*.

More memories bubble up every day. The sea cave in Isla Pixol, cold water on prickly boy-skin. Images, conversations, warnings. The first time seeing Frida in the market with Candelaria: What was she wearing? Mother in the little apartment on the alley off of Insurgentes. Billy Boorzai. The first days in Mexico City. Isla Pixol, the names of villages and of trees. Recipes and rules for life from Leandro: What were they? Whom did Mother love, and what made her so happy that day in the rainstorm? The reef full of fishes, what were their colors? What lay at the bottom of the cave? How long did it take, exactly, to swim through it without drowning?

The notebooks are gone. It must have been like this for Lev at the end, with his past entirely stolen. A lifetime of people, unconfirmed by their living presences, or photographs or descriptions in a notebook, can only skulk in the corners like ghosts. They shift like chimeras. Careful words of warning reverse themselves like truth and newspaper stories, becoming their own opposites. An imperfectly remembered life is a useless treachery. Every day, more fragments of the past roll around heavily in the chambers of an empty brain, shedding bits of color, a sentence or a fragrance, something that changes and then disappears. It drops like a stone to the bottom of the cave.

There will not be another notebook after this one. No need. No more pages piling up. Oh, the childish hope of that. As if a stack of pages could someday grow high enough that a boy could stand on top of it and be as tall as Jack London or Dos Passos. That is the sorest embarrassment: those hopeful hours of typing through the night shift while Lorenzo's boots tapped overhead on the roof, all of our hearts bursting with the certainty of our own purposes. No more of that, never another typewriter. Accumulating words is a charlatan's career. How important is anything that could burn to ash in a few minutes? Stuffed into an incineration barrel at the police station, set on fire on a chilly August evening—maybe an officer warmed his hands, and that is the use of that. Better to roam free like a chicken with no future and no past. Searching only to satisfy the hunger of the present: a beetle or lizard snapped up, or perhaps one day, a snake.

Harrison W. Shepherd leaves Mexico with his pockets full of ash. An emancipated traveler.

PART 4

Asheville, North Carolina

1941–1947

(VB)

My name is Violet Brown. *Was*, I will say. When you read this I'll not be living. I will explain that directly.

If I sound colorful, I am not. It's nought but a pair of names, stamped on me by two people who never met. First, my mother. She was fond of romantic novels with "Violets" in them. She was tubercular and passed when I was young. The second name was from my husband Freddy Brown, who came and went quickly through his time also: lost in the great flood of 1916. The swell of the French Broad River wrecked most of Asheville that time, including the Rees Sons Tannery, where he worked. I was widowed the same year as married, yet still am known to this day as Mrs. Brown. A woman can be marked by others: *embossed* is a good word for it, one of a great many taught me by Mr. Shepherd. He remarked once that I had been embossed with names like an address on a package, by people who didn't know the contents but still got to decide how it would be sent.

Mother pined to see me married before she passed, and it happened soon after, when I was fifteen. Now I am older than she ever did get to be, and can see other paths are worthy. I've lived a maiden's life and found happiness, including being helpmeet to a man. I served greatness. I don't wish for more. That is the beginning and end of what needs be said about me. The purpose of this is to make known the life of Mr. Shepherd. When this book lies open he is dead, and so be I. Our argument at rest, if such it was.

He was given to a secretive temperament, and it gained the better of him when he fled Mexico. He stopped keeping his journals and became hopeless of the written word and its consequence. He told me that, later on. Every scrap of his writings lost, things he'd kept track of since boyhood. He let go the hope of becoming a man of letters. I can attest. We were acquainted at that time, and if pressed to say what this young man might become, I'd think first of the kitchen, or any profession that suits one who keeps to himself. But a well-known writer of books? No. He read them. But most did, in those days.

He never went back to his notebooks exactly as before, probably due to the change in situation. He kept carbon copies of his letters, and filed the clippings of news that attracted him. And still did write personal things, on any day that stirred him. I've seen him go in his study and type out memory of a whole event, in a kind of a fury. I expect if he'd been married he would have ranted the tale to his wife. But he didn't have any wife, so his typewriter did the listening. Often it was whole conversations he'd had. His memory for conversation was shocking, I suppose due to his years of taking dictation from impatient men. But he must have had a knack for it, before. Then he'd file it in one of his leather folders and be done with it. You could call it a letter to himself, or God. He had that saying, God speaks for the silent man. That must have been the One he was talking to.

Mr. Shepherd seldom let me see the personal writings. He knew how to file something himself. If a man can cook, he can file. He was the most bashful person I ever did meet, very pained to speak forthrightly of his feelings.

We met soon after the travel mentioned, from Mexico to the United States. The murder unsettled and wrenched something in him badly, I know that much. He never wanted to talk about that time in his life. He spent a few months in the city of New York, I only know because it was winter that he came on south and settled here. I haven't any record of what he did in New York, save for one exception. He visited the father of Sheldon Harte, the boy that was killed in the raid, to give condolence and tell that man about his son's last days, since no other soul ever would. The newspaper reports had been awful, young Sheldon accused of being an accomplice in the "staged attack." That he had turned on his friends and run off, that kind of thing.

It troubled Mr. Shepherd that there were no photographs of Sheldon Harte in Mexico, to give to the father. He mentioned that, more times than you'd think. The boy always would take the camera in his own hand and urge others into the photograph. Now I've pondered why that was troubling to Mr. Shepherd, because he used his notebooks in like fashion, always portraying others, not himself. At the end of all this, when I struggled with my conscience over Mr. Shepherd's wishes, I used his sentiments on Sheldon Harte to help guide my hand. He was sad that Sheldon had perished without being in any photographs. It struck him as wrong that a man should disappear.

His task in New York was delivering important paintings to the galleries, and this he did in a perfectly satisfactory way. Probably he stayed to see the paintings hung so he could make reports to Mrs. Kahlo Rivera. His friendship with her remained an anchor for a time, yet she herself had a great many friends and may have felt anchored elsewhere. That is an opinion. She and Mr. Rivera remarried that same year, returned to Mexico, and resumed life as before. To my knowledge she never offered Mr. Shepherd encouragement to return to Mexico. His only shred of a plan, arriving here in '40, was to go to Washington, D.C., with the address of a lawyer's office in hand and ask where his father was living.

The office happened to be on the same street where he'd ducked the tear gas in the riots, years before. He said he took it as no portent. The father had written he would be moving soon to a new place, and for that reason gave a lawyer's address. The son went with expectations of making some peace, this being all the family he had left. If all went well, he could find a place nearby and perhaps look after the father in old age.

Well, what a surprise he found at the lawyer's office. His father had moved, to the sweet hereafter. The illness mentioned offhandedly in his letter was in truth a malignancy of the intestines he failed to survive. The lawyer explained how the man had come to him to put earthly matters in order, so he knew. He'd left a small sum and the keys to a car, the same he had written his son about. A Chevrolet Roadster, the very model Mr. Shepherd learned to drive in Mexico, white. He kept that car ten years. I knew it well.

So, there he was. If he took any of this as a sign, it was one that said: "Drive!" He got in the automobile and he drove. The streets of Washington, D.C., were overrun with automobiles in those days, this was before the war, when the gasoline ran like water. Mr. Shepherd followed the signs pointing out of town, heading toward Mexico for want of a better direction. Twenty-four years old, with nought in this world to count as friend and no place to call his home. What he found was a Blue Ridge Parkway. He got on that and followed to its end. He thought the Blue Ridges sounded good. He had recollections, for his family had lived in the valley west of Washington in the brief time his mother and father were wed. He hoped to see blue mountains rolling away to the sky, something like the ocean in a child's eye, as he remembered it. But in this instance, he drove hundreds of miles and never saw one blue thing at all. Gray skies only, and brown mountains covered with leafless trees, and then of a sudden, no more parkway. It was a public works project, and the government ran shy of money. That is how he came here to Asheville. It would have been November. He hadn't any gumption to think what to do next. Here he stayed.

It is not a bad place to wind up, Asheville. Our town lies in the elbow of the Great Smoky Mountains, circled by high peaks and the oldest forests of the land. The Swannanoa and French Broad Rivers twine together in the valley, and that is how the city came to be put here. Mr. George Vanderbilt found it rewarding to haul trees and coal out of the mountains and float it all out on barges, or carry it off in his railroads in due time. He made himself a fortune, and a good deal of it can still be viewed in his house, the Biltmore mansion. If you want to pay fifty cents to go look at a million dollars, you can do it any day of the week except Sundays. They have paintings of countless worth, a library, forty bedrooms, and Napoleon's chess table. Later during the war, Mr. Shepherd was to have his important duties there at the mansion, but he never did go back in as a visitor.

Our city has had its pioneers and scoundrels like anywhere. When the Central Bank and Trust failed in November of 1930, the city's own funds were in it. That was bad. Those of us on the city rolls went without pay for months. I was a typist for the city clerk's office then, making little enough to begin with, yet we still came to work. For no one offered to pay us for idlement, either. Others had lost much more. Foreclosed houses stood empty in the nicest parts of town: Grove Park, Beaucatcher Mountain, even the stately homes in the woods along the Tunnel Road where it winds down from the Blue Ridge.

It was this road that brought Mr. Shepherd to town, when his parkway ended without further ado. After driving day and night through high-mountain vistas, he would have found himself in the long tunnel through Swannanoa Gap, then spit out from darkness into the valley. He stopped at one of the large houses on the Tunnel Road that had been made a boardinghouse. That was Mrs. Bittle's, a widow lady with children all grown who found herself betwixt the rock and the rail in '34, so began to take in boarders. I was her first one. She had a sign made to put out in the yard whenever she had a vacancy: "Clean To Let With Meals $10 Week, Only Good People Here." Somehow the wording of it struck Mr. Shepherd. Those words changed his course, brought his long drive to an end.

Mrs. Bittle took to him and allowed the Roadster parked in her garage for no extra. He kept that automobile under high polish for many years, though its destiny for the next while was to stay parked, it goes without saying. No new automobile could be had in the war years, nor gasoline for an old one if you had it. Chrysler set their plants to making tanks, Ford built Cyclone engines for the bombers, and they all quit making cars entirely. The railroad moved men and matériel instead of Mr. Vanderbilt's lumber, and the Asheville-Hendersonville airport was taken over by the armed forces. The nice homes that had stood empty since the crash now filled up with the families of government workers, thought to be safer here than in the capital, after the Japanese attacked the refineries at Los Angeles. The Nazis were sinking our tankers right off the Carolina coast, day in and day out. The thinking was that our marble halls might be next. For that reason, the National Gallery sent many trainloads of its national treasures to the Biltmore House, for safekeeping.

We were proud to hold on to treasure. Our city had never been asked to do anything important before. We were ready in a jig. Everything was rationed then: girdles, shoes, bobby pins, yet we did not complain. The Army Corps took over our shopping arcade downtown, and that was fine too, since there was nothing to sell in the shops. We heard they were keeping high-ranking Axis prisoners up at the Grove Park Inn. We reckoned it was Mussolini himself up there under lock and key, soaking in those grand old tubs and sitting on the Roycroft chairs, waiting with heavy heart to receive his comeuppance.

They had the USO dances at the Woodfin House, I didn't go. I turned forty the year before Pearl Harbor, too old for carrying on with soldiers. But the war made each and all feel young in a certain way. The town ripped up the trolley tracks to send off in the scrap-metal drives, and next they tore the iron cells from the old jail building! No American would commit a crime during wartime, was our thinking. Everyone went a little touched.

Mr. Shepherd did nought to call attention to himself. The question did come up in the roominghouse, as to what the arrangement might be between Mr. Shepherd and the Selective Service. The rest of us living there were women without family, or men who couldn't serve, for one reason or another. We thought Mr. Shepherd might have been found unfit for service, like so many his age. His slightly odd and solitary ways gave that impression, and his extremely slim build. He hardly had a scrap of meat on him. Many were the boys who had it so bad in the Depression, ten years later when called up for the draft, they failed the examination. Something inside them, the heart or teeth or legs, would be a little soft from so much hunger in the formative years. It was not just a few, either. It was thirty-nine percent of the young men called. I happen to know, for I was in secretarial service at the enlistment office. I saw all kinds, and for all I knew Mr. Shepherd was one of them. He was later called up to serve in the Civilian Public Service, but I will get to that.

To help pay his board at Mrs. Bittle's he cooked for the other boarders, six in all, including Mrs. Bittle. Every breakfast and supper, and noonday dinner on Sunday. That came about after the war started. He had a knack for making the ration-stamp books spread over the whole ration period. Mrs. Bittle was raised on silver spoons, hopeless at any kind of budget. She would collect the stamp books from all the boarders to get what she needed, yet by Saturday would be down to a jar of mustard and a box of Ralston cereal. She never could understand how it worked, though we tried to explain. She confused the one-point tokens with the ten-point stamps. Mr. Shepherd offered his help, and he was a whiz. He would take our A, B, and C stamps downtown on Mondays, adding everyone's meat points and so forth to get the best items first. Then sail through the week entire, with food to spare.

His trick was the fruits and vegetables. These weren't rationed, it was mainly the packaged goods, soups and canned meats and all such things they needed to send overseas. If the truth be known, Mrs. Bittle probably thought peas grew ready-frozen on the vine and cheese came from the Wej-Cut package, not a cow. But Mr. Shepherd said in Mexico every cook knew how to make from scratch. He could put a passel of red tomatoes into sauce as fast as Mrs. Bittle could have worked open a tin. In spring he planted greens, impinging on Mrs. Bittle's dahlias. She was queasy about that. The rest of us felt it a good bargain.

He looked like a scarecrow out there digging. One of the other boarders, Reg Borden, pointed out the window one time and said that. The boy was just so tall and thin, you'd have to say gaunt. And inside him, some kind of dread that went past the bashfulness. Not a workaday fear, no. He would rush in to clap a bowl over a mouse in the pantry, and once chased a sparrow from the house when it had Mrs. Bittle up on a chair. He would move a dresser any time you asked, manly in all such ways. But certain sudden things struck him dumb. He was shy of the sight of blood, and a loud sound unexpected would set his hand to trembling. A knife dropped on the floor could put such a haint over him, you would look all about for what ghost he'd seen. In summer months especially, he took spells of hardly leaving his room. Mrs. Bittle would suffer the cooking, and we all endured, saying, "Poor Mr. Shepherd has taken the grippe again." But knew very well it was no germ that had brought it on him. This is the truth, it could be anything or nothing, or just Reg Borden standing in the door with his raincoat on. There appeared to be no rhyme or reason.

Yet on most days he was like any broad-shouldered lad you'd ever known, with his manners and a sweet laugh. So fine for speaking, you asked him things just to hear what words he'd pick out in answer, for they'd be not the ones you expected. His face was pretty as a girl's, especially around the eyes. He had delicate hands despite the kitchen work, what people call "piano hands," though Mrs. Bittle had a piano and he didn't play a note.

Miss McKellar was sweet on him I believe, but all her offers to press his collars got her hands upon nothing but his shirts, so far as I know. Reg Borden was overly curious about his failure to serve. Reginald's own excuse was a glass eye. And Mr. Judd, of course too old. That poor man remained confused about which war was presently on the go. They needled Mr. Shepherd about not serving, and a foreigner in the house was something they frowned on behind his back, but Mrs. Bittle maintained he was not the bad type of foreigner, Jap or Italian. Germans she was queasy on, they ought to be bad she said, but of course they owned the hardware downtown, and no one saying you couldn't buy a ten-penny nail. In all, the men and Mrs. Bittle liked the cooking, and that swayed them.

They did press him on the lack of a fiancée, given his youth and vigor. Mr. Borden would raise this at supper, to Mr. Shepherd's mortification. I defended against the charge. I had been unwed all but one year of my life entire, and I informed the gentleman I could see the advantages. Miss McKellar had her theories: a broken heart or a girl back in Old Mexico. All we really knew of this young man was that he had a prior life in that country, and cooking was his talent, second only to making himself unseen.

To earn pocket money he taught Spanish lessons at the Asheville Teachers College, an establishment of good reputation where I also worked, up until the war. I was secretary to the administrator and recommended Mr. Shepherd to her as a person of decent character, which was all I knew. Spanish was a less fashionable language than French, so he only came to teach two days each week. He made no impression on the office staff.

His third talent was well hidden. For three years we all resided in the same house, passed in the upstairs hallway to use the bath, sat in matched parlor chairs on Monday evenings to hear *The Voice of Firestone* over NBC. And we never once saw him draw ink into a fountain pen. If he owned a typewriter I never heard it, and it's not a sound that gets past my ear. I know a Royal from a Smith-Corona from the next room. He wrote nothing in those years. This I know, for he later told me. He was dispirited of his past and stopped keeping the journals after everything was lost.

He'd brought up from Mexico a crate for a painting given him by Mrs. Kahlo, but hadn't opened it. That might seem strange to others. Not to me. He wasn't susceptible to suspense the way most are. If you gave him a package and said, Don't open that till Christmas, he wouldn't shake it. Something in his nature just did not expect good things in store. He set the crate in his wardrobe closet, leaving Mrs. Bittle to run the duster around it on her weekly rounds. There was no use in any of us having paintings. Mrs. Bittle wouldn't let us pound any nails. All pictures in the house were hers, the deceased Mr. Bittle fond of landscapes. So Mr. Shepherd's sat in the dark. I have asked him if he thought much about it. He said if ever he did, he pictured something alive in the crate, and once out, he dreaded he wouldn't have the heart to shut it back in the dark.

At the end of '43 he moved to his own house. A great event. Miss McKellar and I hung up crepe paper in the parlor and pooled our stamps to get him a set of sheets. What had happened prior, to make this possible, was that Mr. Shepherd got called up to do a war job. No, he never saw gunfire. He had the safest war job of the war, he said, which was: to oversee moving many shipments of famous pictures from the museum in Washington, D.C., to the Biltmore House. The Axis powers were having no end of amusement sinking ships and firing upon our coasts. Safety of our national treasures was the concern.

Mr. Shepherd was unsure how Uncle Sam had found him out for the task. When he'd applied at the Teachers College and was asked about previous employments, he listed "Consignment Marshal, moving art pieces to museums." He thought it more reputable than "cook" and a decent cause for traveling from Mexico. (He feared they'd think him a bandit.) Some way the word passed. The War Board knew everything about us in those days. The officers called up the galleries in New York and were surely impressed to learn his association with Mr. and Mrs. Rivera, highly famous. So Shepherd was their man. It took months to see it all through. They kept him on with the CPS for the duration but he rarely had to travel far, nor to any place more dangerous than a room of naked statues.

The job gave him means to set a payment on a two-story bungalow on Montford Avenue that had stood empty for years. It was close by the stop he took for the in-town bus to the library and he'd often taken little walks up that street, for it had a cemetery up at the end and a mental hospital with nice grounds. The empty house struck him in particular. He thought it had an aching look about it, and for that reason chose it. Up until then he'd felt underfoot in every house he ever lived in. Peace and quiet was his only wish.

Soon after moving, he pried the nails off the crate from Mrs. Kahlo to see his gift. Pandora's box you might say now, given everything that happened. The canvas itself was only some sketch she had snatched up from her bin, to carry out her plan. The gift was around the painting. There were the two crates, one inside the other, and the space between not stuffed with straw but paper, all the notebooks and typed pages taken from his room in Mexico after the murder. Hundreds of crumpled pages in all, needing to be smoothed and sorted out. But mostly all there.

Unbeknownst, Mr. Shepherd had been writing a book for years. He believed it had gone up in ash. But Mrs. Kahlo made the police not to destroy it. She was a powerful person evidently. Then hid the pages this way, not telling the author himself what he carried. Was it a trick on her friend, or did she only want to keep him safe? I can't say. But she was first to see what the world soon would, after he'd fixed it up, filled in the missing parts, written and rewritten and stewed over it until he could stew no more. In due time it came to the Stratford and Sons publishing house in New York. That was *Vassals of Majesty*. It came out in '45, before Christmas. That part is common knowledge, or ought to be.

So he was right about something alive in the crate, wanting out. Mrs. Kahlo did that for him. He'd about given up on life as a whole, going away on a train to the next world. If he didn't take one other thing, she wanted him carrying his words.

—VB

October 8, 1943
Asheville, North Carolina
Gringolandia

Dear Frida,
What you have done is a miracle. But how can any thanks be enough? Just words, brought here and heaped at your feet like a pile of cold mice with gnawed ears fetched in by a cat. You have restored a life. You will see.

This morning a white cat appeared here on the back step, and it seemed you must have sent her too. She didn't cry but stood quietly, as if waiting for a well-known outcome. The wind tugged fingers through the creature's coat, trying to un- button the shaggy garment and pull it off. Think of how you would paint this cat: with her insides exposed, the delicate rib cage curved like a ring's setting around a bloody gem of car- nivorous love. This is how she seemed. When the door opened just a crack she slipped in, curling immediately on the hearth, declaring with her eyes: "Ha, you thought I was helpless! I own you now." Of course she is Frida.

But her name will be Chispa. She is a muse, the spark you once accused me of having, now glowing quietly on this hearth. Otherwise the house is still, keeping secrets. The floors are made of the long, narrow hearts of trees brought down from mountain slopes, the chimneys are stones rolled round as biscuits in the Swannanoa River. The windows have interlaced panes like the ones in your father's house, cracked here and there but holding.

The mitered oak doorsills are like deep wooden picture frames, each holding a perfect view of the next room, where walls are touched with light, and life could be waiting. The grain of the wood tells a story of years in the mountains, all the rains and droughts leading to the beginning of my life, when these trees were felled. The house was built the same year as my birth.

So we're well-matched companions, sheltering roof and solitary soul, crouched in a domestic forest of elms and maples. The other houses along this leafy street are also bungalows with gabled roofs and trussed eaves, an architecture that is here known as Arts and Crafts. It's the opposite in every way from Diego's beloved Functionalismo, nothing modern or shocking. Probably you would both find it boring. But now your mind's eye can see your old friend where he lives: making tamales in a kitchen of his own, with shining white tiles and green-painted trim. Picture him in stocking feet padding happily through golden rooms where bookcases reside directly in the walls, and amber lamps hang on chains from the ceiling. Then, picture him upstairs with your treasure glowing before his eyes, as in a storybook when the child lifts the lid of the magical trunk.

It is a good place, Carolina, built of mountains and river valleys. Did you receive the postcard? The tall buildings you see in it are full of banks and bakeries, the usual things. But look carefully at the background of the picture: mountains. They stand behind every view, like a mother offering a blanket in which to wrap everyday life and shelter it from useless dreads. In June they are walls of white rhododendron blossom. In autumn the forests set themselves aflame with color. Even winter has its icy charms. This you will refuse to believe. But you might like the changeable nature of this place, and its people, who have the modesty of Mexican villagers. The backyards here are divided by slim wire fences like tiny farm fields, and the women tending them shout across fence lines, "hollowing" they call it, to comment on the weather. They pin dungarees to clotheslines and speak in a dialect that sounds like the plays of Shakespeare. It isn't the Gringolandia you remember. You might not find it as despicable as New York.

Congratulations on your successes there, especially the exhibition at Miss Guggenheim's. For you to be chosen among the thirty-one most important women painters in the century must make Diego proud, and you, jealous of the other thirty. The man who wrote about you in *Vogue* was an idiot—of course you don't have inferiority complexes or blood-obsession or anything like that. That man spent fifteen minutes looking at your paintings. Could you drive a car for fifteen minutes, then write a psychological analysis of Henry Ford? All right then, don't think of it any more.

Have you agreed now to be a Surrealist? Because, as it happens, the French Relief Society intends to sponsor your paintings in their program on surrealism. Do you wonder how this news reached your friend's ears? Who is the mysterious one now, and how long will he make you burn with suspense? Not very long. Here is the news: your former Shipping Shepherd now holds the same post for the Civilian Corps, a wartime position overseeing movements of art treasures and government-sponsored exhibits. The wage is forty dollars a week, every one of them welcome. So you see it's only thanks to you: this job, this house. These debts mount, all to you.

The real purpose of this letter is to acknowledge the debt most infinite: for saving my notebooks and papers. Frida, you always said the most important thing about any person is what you don't know. Likewise, then, the most important part of any story is the missing piece. What you gave me is everything. A self, the simple *yo soy*, I am. I am saved. I drowned, it seemed, and then came the light. Here I am.

I discovered it four days ago. I've only now opened the crate, for the first time. You must have wondered that I said nothing about it in the telegrams from New York. I remember mentioning the painting you gave me, thanking you in some duplicitous way. I'm sorry. You must think I had no curiosity about your gift. If you've already sent me to hell, it's fair enough, but you sent me for the wrong reasons. Disinterest in your work is not my crime; your paintings are thrilling. My faults lie elsewhere.

The truth of what you did, and what I now possess as a result (have possessed for three years without knowing) is slow to dawn. The last three mornings I've wakened to sense it arriving like a marvelous visitor coming on the train. I get dressed, I pace. I can't imagine how you bribed the police. I wonder how much of the manuscript you had time to read, and what you thought of it. But I ask for no more than what you've done already. You held faith in me as an artist. Not as a child, or servant, but as your peer. My pulse rushes, to think I will now have to earn that faith.

Here is the first step: I have got myself a typewriter. I own almost nothing else, due to the war shortages. My furniture is a few sad handprints of a foreclosed family: children's beds stripped of all but the narrow mattresses, an avuncular parlor chair with holes in its elbows. An electric stove, a wooden icebox that goes hungry for ice. (I'm told we'll get it in winter.) But my lair is the little upstairs room overlooking the street from beneath the gabled eave. My writing table is the bathroom door, taken off its hinges and set across two defunct radio cabinets I found in the alley. (Eviscerated in the last wire-and-copper drive.) And my prize: a typewriter gleaned from the rummage room at the school where I teach Spanish lessons. Probably the last such machine in the city, what with all the old ones melted down for bullets, or else urgently needed in North Africa and the Coral Sea, evidently, along with all sugar, cellulose tape, and ethyl gasoline. My relic lacks only a few of its keys, and with its help I plan to finish the book whose life you spared. It's the story we talked about, Cortés in the empire of the Azteca. The scandals of the ancients will be known.

Thank you also for the small stone figurine. I first found him lying on the bank, the day we had our picknick at Teotihuacán, while you napped. Please don't report my larceny to Dr. Gamio, or to Diego, who might be nationalistic on the subject of stolen art. (It would not bring me favor in my new employment.) This little fellow begged to be taken to a new world, after waiting two thousand years facedown in dirt. You abetted his wish. He sends his gratitude, mingled with mine, from where he now sits on my desk near the window, surveying the surprising scenery of Carolina.

Your astonished and grateful friend,

INSÓLITO

November 2, 1943

Dear Frida,
A glittering shower falls at a slant across my window. Some form of god has come to visit our dark autumn tunnel, like Zeus making himself a beam of light to impregnate Danae. In this case, it is not really glittering light but beech leaves. You've never seen anything as dramatic as these American trees, dying their thousand deaths. The giant beech next door intends to shiver off every hair of its pelt. The world strips and goes naked, the full year of arboreal effort piling on the sidewalks in flat, damp strata. The earth smells of smoke and rainstorms, calling everything to come back, lie down, submit to a quiet, moldy return to the cradle of origins. This is how we celebrate the Day of the Dead in America: by turning up our collars against the scent of earthworms calling us home.

Mexico rules my kitchen, as you know. The *pan de muerto* is rising there now, filling the house with a yellow scent, reminding me how you shaped yours like skulls sprinkled with sugar. My neighbors wouldn't care to see such things delivered on a plate. They celebrate the Day of the Dead very strangely here: they make pumpkins into heads with flaming eyes, and the children run about the neighborhood asking for cookies. But these urchins showed up two days early! Now that the cookies are made, the children seem finished with the whole thing. They have smashed the pumpkin-heads to orange gruel on the sidewalks. The cat may have to help eat the *pan de muerto*. In remembering the dead, one more this year: your father. Old Guillermo, how could he not still be there? Walking slowly around your house, blinking his huge eyes as he enters each room, not seeing the furniture but the angles of light on the floor.

Your grief is reasonable, but it's no good to hear you're a wreck from head to toe. Tuberculosis of the bones makes me shiver. It's like the season's last tomato that sat in a bowl in the kitchen this week, and when taken up to be sliced, collapsed to a limp sac of foul juice—its beautiful plump skin was hiding rot. Frida, you must feel tricked this way by your body. Even your cures sound like diseases, electricity and calcium therapy. But your doctors are good men, especially Dr. E. in San Francisco, who sounds kind. These surgeries are sure to be successful. You will have many more days like this one for remembering, and without number, *abrazos* from your friend,

SÓLI

May 21, 1944

Dear Frida,

This Sunday morning bright images of you keep nudging into my solitary confinement, urging me to write after the long silence. Here is a strange beetle, trapped inside the window near the desk. He bombs his head continually against the glass, distracting the revision of an unwieldy chapter: "The garrison stormed, heads all smashed!" This little bombardier wears a stunning uniform, emerald green with copper-colored linings to his wings, and a respectable proboscis. Words do the thing no justice. You would do better, if you saw it. You could put it in a painting.

And next: every young girl passing by on the sidewalk to catch the Haywood bus, another distraction. They're all Fridas! Since the weather turned warm they all wear peasant clothes, colorful skirts and blouses with ruffled shoulders. They don't wear their skirts long as you do because it's unlawful here, punishable by a fine. I vow it's true, fabric-conservation order. Not enough uniforms to cover all the boys at the front. The War Production Board announced also last week, no blouse may have more than one ruffle per sleeve. I thought you might like to know that, as you sit somewhere in your thousand ruffles reading this, flashing gold teeth—metal that could be used in some alloy for artillery casings, come to think of it. You can't come here, you would be confiscated.

Your despair over the war is understandable. I undertake this letter to cheer you with another view of things. The gringos are embracing the antifascist fight with whole hearts, and that surely must be good, even if it's many years late in the opinion of your friends who first went to fight fascism in Spain. But you should see the Yanks now, swearing unity with people from across borders just as you and Diego used to do, raising your glasses, singing "The Internationale" while we tried to clear the plates. I keep wondering what Lev would make of these times. He would abhor Roosevelt's friendly partnership with Marshal Stalin as our two countries lean shoulder-to-shoulder in battle. But wouldn't he agree with the president, that sacrifice must be made toward the ideal? Our GIs have genuinely rescued the Soviet State, scurrying tons of supplies across the Persian desert to save the starving Russians. And now Stalin's army returns the favor, beating back Hitler on the Eastern Front. A year ago all seemed lost, the Axis was unstoppable in Europe or the Pacific. Now some say this war could be won.

If so, then the victory will belong to housewives as well as soldiers, because every one here is part of the fight. To you the war is useless destruction, a match played out over the wireless, but here it is the organizing principle of our days. If cloth is in short supply, the girls will wear only one ruffle per sleeve, no more, and no fuss. If the Axis sank eight million tons of warships last year, so be it, these ladies will hand over what appears to be eight million tons of hairpins, let the tresses fall where they may. The neighbor children use rocks to bang old hinges from gates for the metal drives, war brides turn in their silver, grandfathers their bronze-tipped canes. Sacrifice is a sacrament. How we all cheered when Howard Hughes's new factory turned out a battleship just twenty-four days after laying its keel! This man Hughes drew my mother to her death, years ago when his stunt flight landed in Mexico City. But however I may miss her, I harbor no grudge as I watch him now, welding together the *John Fitch* from pieces of my neighborhood. All as one, with hairpins and paper clips, we vanquish Hirohito and his Mitsubishi warship factory.

The war is on every page of every magazine. Even in the advertisements, which strangely don't encourage buying now, but the opposite. Manufacturers fly the "E" flag to show their whole production is needed for war use. Buy nothing but war bonds, give your blood to the Red Cross. "Follow doctor's advice to the letter and keep appointments brief," my magazine warns, because half our doctors are in the forces, leaving the home-front men with twice as many to care for. Travel for emergencies only. After victory is won, they promise us the world: a new model of radio, automobiles with synthetic rubber tires, things yet unseen by civilian eye. But for now, don't ask even for a Dot fastener, and good luck finding butter or cheese with your ration stamps. Bacon has vanished from our land. So have new cars, not one this year for civilians, and if you already have one it wears an "A" stamp on its windscreen, for "Almost Empty"– gasoline is rationed. Horse droppings have made a bold come-back on Pack Square. One old cog on my street has roused his Stanley Steamer. He came through yesterday and a neighbor lady fainted, thinking it was an air attack. The new American motto is, "We make do with nothing new," no wristwatches, new shirts, or bedsheets, it's about the same plan as the church: endure your suffering to win a golden hereafter.

You would not believe how cheerfully the people accept this deprivation. It makes them feel brave and important. Rich or poor, the banker's wife and the secretary bring the same ration book to market and leave with the same goods. It isn't the bourgeois Gringolandia you knew, women throwing parties while homeless men starved outside. Now they all agree with your Rosa Luxemburg, "The highest idealism in the interests of the whole." Women here consent to strict rations even on food and shoes for their children. The neighbor family has seven boys, named Romulus, Virgil, and the like, running about in cloth shoes and making toys from roadside litter. Yet their mother calls out to me every day, "Mr. Shepherd, is it not a bless-ed morning?" Another neighbor brought me an "apple pie" made from crackers (she fears a bachelor will starve), and explained how we are to make up our beds: turn the bottom hem to the top every other week to distribute wear and make the sheets last. We can win the war while we sleep!

This way of thinking can be bracing. They view the future as a house they can build with hammers and planks, rather than a ripening fruit that might go rotten due to unexpected natural forces. You warned me not to let Mexican writers make my heart go cold, do you remember? In the hospital. We were speaking of *Los de Abajo*, the scene comparing the revolutionary fight to a rock rolling downhill, moved only by senseless gravity. You said, if I threw a party to cheer myself up, not to invite any writers.

But Americans crave a different story: they believe the rock could roll uphill instead of down. Probably you won't listen to this, but it's not such a bad way of thinking. A writer here could finish a whole book without wanting to drink poison. Even the story of Cortés has its invigorating theme of self-made destiny. People are much in the mood these days for soaring hearts and the clash of battle.

Here in the house of my father, as you called this country, I watch carefully, wondering if this might be a home at last. The land of the square deal and the working stiff, said my old dad. So I square up the corners of my desires, and work at pounding keys until my fingers are stiff as wooden splinters. Frida, someone here may want what I can give. See how that pronoun now stands in the lines I write, tall and square-shouldered. I strive for the stout American declarative, so entirely unaccustomed: I am.

My packet of contraband pages has nearly become a book. The old typewriter grinds its metal jaws, the battle is nearly over. Cortés took the city in the end, I'm sorry to say. I was tempted to revise history, give Mexico City back to the Azteca. But without these four hundred years of oppression, what would Diego paint on his murals? I decided to salvage, mainly for your sakes, the eventual necessity of the Mexican Revolution.

Now I ask your advice. I wonder whether you or Diego may know someone in New York who would look at this poor manuscript, once it has been wrestled to its death. It will need to go somewhere. The mess of papers can't be kept here much longer, spreading like a pox across the floors, terrifying the cat. I must exercise vigilance, or one book might even become two.

I send affection to you and Diego, and also Perpetua, if she does perpetuate. If you have any news of Natalya and Seva, it would be welcome.

Your friend,

INSÓLITO

June 30, 1944

Dear Frida,

Thank you for the name of your friend in New York. Mr. Morrison will someday regret your indiscretion, as he is sure to hear from me. Diego's miseries are worrisome; the struggle to build his rock temple-museum in the Pedregal sounds more surreal than anything in your French exhibit. Nothing he does will ever be small. Your failure to mention your own health I will take as good news, and assume the surgeries in California were successful. I'm sorry Natalya hasn't communicated, but there could be many reasons for it, given the wrecked state of everything in France, and no direct post between France and Mexico. But even so, the movement for socialist democracy seems to be rising from the ashes, with labor now on the march against Vichy in Paris, if the news of this can be trusted. Lev would find some way to be hopeful, even for poor France.

The time with Lev and Natalya seems so distant, I'm startled when any traces of it surface. In the magazine photograph enclosed, look and you'll see two of the New York boys who worked as guards for Lev. Charlie and Jake, you remember them. I practically jumped when I spotted them, right across the page from Mary Martin holding her Calox tooth powder. The picture is a peace meeting at the Carnegie Music Hall where a few hundred gathered to demand armistice. The article I haven't enclosed, but you know the kind of thing: "in attendance were Trotskyites, Teamsters, Socialist professors and old-line Quakers, the crackpot fringes of public opinion, hoping to arouse draft resistance while praying for an easy way out." In other words, the kind of thing you and your friends do on a normal Friday noon, without the praying. People here are the same as in Mexico, their passions bristle in every direction. And the presses are the same also. No reporter worth his buttons will let the facts intrude on a good story.

The newsreels that frightened you in California were of the same ilk, I'm sure. The aim is to terrify us. Not to be outdone by a giant ape climbing a skyscraper, they'll have the quiet Japanese fellow next door harboring clandestine treachery. If you saw a movie star telling about the gardener putting poison on her vegetables, it was only an entertainment set ahead of the main feature. Like Diego eating flesh. You know these howlers. You've had their noise in your ears since the day you married a famous man, and still you do as you please. Don't listen to nonsense, Frida. The idea of putting American Japanese in concentration camps is fantastical. You shouldn't worry so much.

Have faith in our Mr. Roosevelt, who has everyone bucked up. People here salute him as the flag, since most have only ever seen the one flag, or the one president. He came to office when I was only a boy at the Academy, imagine it. In those days his name was a schoolboy joke, scented with roses, but now he is our own kind of Lenin, charting the new American Revolution. Even the Communists here supported him in the last election. No one can argue against guarantees of useful work and protection from old-age hardship. Now he has even imposed a tax on businesses so they can't profit from the war, and he regulates food prices so everyone gets a fair share. We subordinate ourselves to the national good!

Your old friend,

INSÓLITO

Los Angeles Herald and Express, *June 1, 1943*

Nips Still Roam the Coast

Special to Hearst News

Former fruit-and-vegetable stands sit empty, their piles rotted away, but a contamination is not yet scoured from our city. The Dies Committee today released a report noting 40,000 dangerous persons are still at large, more than a year after Order 9066 of the Western Defense Command routed foreign- and American-born Japs to detention centers in the central states. The report contains evidence of espionage rings in which many, if not all, Japanese "fishermen" and "truck farmers" used their merchant status in our country as a cloak for approaching strategic facilities.

Military command keeps watch on more than 100,000 evacuees now residing in detention camps, where observers have noted the detainees care little whether this country or Japan wins the war. Yet the Justice Department is still considering an appeal to release certain detainees professing "loyalty" into non-war jobs. Our Western States oppose the move with a single voice. Senator Hiram Johnson vowed yesterday the

War Department will not allow resettlement of one single Jap in coastal states, pointing out that most residents here would have them shipped to Tojo after the war ends.

No Californian need be reminded of the incendiary bombs dropped on Ft. Stevens and the Pacific forests last year, or the shelling of the Goleta refinery whose flames engulfed our city in terror. The warships of Dai Nippon lurk in plain view off our coast, with pilots ready to fly on the "kamikaze wind" to meet their targets, heinously exchanging life itself for a promise of immortality. But few realize the number of such inimical persons still hiding in the Pacific states under civilian guise.

In a statement to Hearst News today, General John L. De-Witt declared, "We ignore the Dies Committee report at our peril." Describing the adversary's nefarious character he said, "Racial affinities are not severed by migration. The Japanese are an enemy race, and while many of those born on U.S. soil have become 'Americanized,' the racial strains are undiluted." In a recent conference with the Secretary of War, DeWitt cited undisclosed indications of a Nip conspiracy prepared for action. The fact that no violent outburst has yet taken place, he explained, is a confirming indication of such actions soon to be taken.

Whether of alien or American birth, Japs remain banned from our coast until the final surrender. The rightful place of all such persons is detention in the desolate interior. Responding to rumors of release, the Governor's office promised full security for our citizens. "We afford no quarter to those whose presence is inimical to the public safety. Our tolerance of their kind is revoked. Their property has been dispensed, their business contracts cancelled and bank accounts forfeited. FBI agents stand ready to conduct search and seizure raids on homes or businesses suspected of harboring aliens."

To US citizens this comes as welcome news. While Americans face death from fascist bullets overseas, the Justice Department has leaned over backward to preserve the right of free speech in wartime, opening the gates to those who would spread lies and propaganda behind the lines at home.

This report has been submitted for clearance by the Army and Navy.

The New York Times, *December 13, 1941*

2,541 Axis Aliens Now in Custody

*Biddle Says List Includes 1,370 Japanese,
1,002 Germans and 169 Italians*

Special *to* The New York Times

WASHINGTON, Dec. 12—Up to Thursday night the Justice Department had arrested 2,541 German, Japanese and Italian citizens in the roundup of dangerous aliens which got under way with the outbreak of war between Japan and the United States, Attorney General Francis Biddle said tonight. Of these 1,002 are Germans, 1,370 Japanese, and 169 Italians.

Mr. Biddle emphasized that although they were regarded as "dangerous to the peace and safety of the nation," Axis subjects under arrest "represented only a small fraction of the more than 1,100,000 Axis nationals residing in the United States."

"Arrests were limited to persons whose activities have been under investigation by the FBI for some time," said Mr. Biddle.

Aides declared that none of the prisoners would be interned throughout the war except where there is "strong reason to fear for the internal security of the United States."

The Justice Department issued a warning that any Japanese, German or Italian citizen found in possession of a camera, regardless of the use to which it was put, faced loss of his equipment and possible detention. Axis citizens already had been ordered not to make airplane flights of any kind.

26 More Aliens Taken Here

The round-up of potential saboteurs, spies and enemy aliens here brought in twenty-six more prisoners yesterday. Sixteen were German, six Japanese and five Italian. Those arrested yesterday also were taken to Ellis Island and turned over to agents of the Bureau of Immigration and Naturalization. As usual, Federal Bureau of Investigation officials refused to comment.

William H. Marshall, assistant director of emigration and naturalization, said that 553 enemy aliens have been rounded up since Sunday. The figures included those seized in places adjacent to New York City. All enemy aliens were barred by the Civil Aeronautics Authority from riding in commercial, government or private airplanes.

The State Labor Department pointed out that enemy aliens were not entitled to receive unemployment insurance, as the law provides that the payments can be made only to persons "available for work."

The large plaque in front of the Italian Building, 626 Fifth Avenue, was covered yesterday.

September 12, 1944

Dear Frida,
Thank you for sending the clippings. Forgive me for doubting you, this is terrifying news and not well known in these parts. If nothing on earth is new, these howlers are the proof. People will be made afraid at any cost.

Your Insólito remains a muddled assembly of two nations, settled for now in the house of his father, puzzling over its construction. By day we whistle "The Internationale" and reach right across the world to our comrades. My neighbor knits stockings for the orphans of Moscow. But by night the neighborhood bolts its doors and looks beneath the beds for an alien menace. Yet I stake a claim, I am here, for I must be somewhere. But only as a child it seems, struggling to understand what every wife and gentleman passing on the street seems to know by rote. Whom to love, whom to castigate.

The only certainty in my own household is: the novel is finished. I feel a peculiar sadness, like missing a lively, quarrelsome friend who has ended his long visit. These days I purse my lips at the mirror and wonder how it is that other men find first-class reasons to shave, change out of pajamas, and leave the house, practically every day.

Your friend Mr. Morrison recommended an editor who sheds a glimmer of interest in looking at the thing. His response has forced me outdoors three days in a row, blinking like an owl, in search of an envelope or packaging to carry the manuscript to New York. This effort may take longer than writing the book. Stationer's stores no longer have even enough paper for the standard sign declaring their product has gone to the front. The editor may be spared his trouble, due to the paper shortage. Probably the manuscript itself should be heaved over in the next paper drive, as ballast for a warship.

I send you two clippings in return, from earlier in the summer. Our town's newspaper is rationed to twice-weekly editions, but this article merited precious fiber—note the date, our shared birthday. You'll remember I wrote you about this beetle. The other page I tore from a respectable magazine (*Life*, how comprehensive!), enclosed mainly for its spectacular photograph. Like Cortés, I report back to my Queen on a new world wondrous strange. *Feliz cumpleaños*, my friend, from America where we make do with nothing new.

Abrazos,

SÓLI

Life Magazine, *July 17, 1944*

Japanese Beetle:
Voracious, Libidinous, Prolific

by Anthony Standen

Japanese beetles, unlike the Japanese, are without guile. There are, however, many parallels between the two. Both are small but very numerous and prolific, as well as voracious, greedy and devouring. Both have single-track minds. Both are inscrutable, the beetles particularly, for no one can say why they should be attracted by yellow when most of their food is green, nor why they rush avidly to geraniums—the smell of geraniums is used to bait the traps—when geraniums are poisonous to them. The beetles, however, are firmly settled on our middle Atlantic coast, where they chew up apples, peaches, grapes, roses, pasture grass and other useful or agreeable vegetable matter to the tune of $7,000,000 every year, and threaten to become rampant over the greater part of the entire country. Long ago we declared war on them, and though we have little chance of total victory—which would mean exterminating every single beetle on our shores—we may hope to achieve a more limited success, with the insects so harassed and persecuted that their numbers would be kept within decency's limit, although their character would never be changed.

———

The Asheville Trumpet, *July 6, 1944*

Kamikaze Peril Reaches Asheville

by Carl Nicholas

They are small, crafty, and breed unceasingly. They are driven to fly viciously into their targets, creating immense destruction. The Japanese Beetle has moved down our coast and arrived at our very door. These odd-looking green insects pose a threat to plant life and domestic tranquility alike.

"They fly all over my washing," said Mrs. Jimmy Hyder, a housewife recently sighted on Charlotte Street mounting her offensive. Sons Harold and Alter led the infantry with badminton rackets, and Mrs. Hyder followed with the pump-atomizer, dousing the battlefield with insecticide. Weekly sprayings may tip the balance against the enemy, but Mrs. Hyder complains, "They'll keep on flying into you for no good reason, down to the last one." She warned other Victory Gardeners to expect heavy losses from the enemy this year, especially in the tomatoes and runner beans.

Scientists call the greedy beast "Popillia japonica." The Agriculture Department believes they first sneaked into the country near New Jersey, some years prior to Pearl Harbor, concealed in a crate of fruit. The sly grubs hide under ground in winter, emerging famished and keen to ply their destruction in the warmer months. Their fiendish campaign has now reached the Western Carolinas, spoiling orchards worth many thousand dollars.

Wives and gardeners beware. Though badminton rackets fly on Charlotte Street, Mr. Wick Bentsen of the County Extension Service says no weapons yet devised have been found to stop this Japanese invasion.

———

Mr. Lincoln Barnes, Editor
Stratford and Sons Publishers, New York
December 11, 1944

Dear Mr. Barnes,
The sum you have proposed is overwhelmingly generous.

The changes you suggest in the story will render it much improved. However, I'm not able to consult the pages you mentioned, as the book rests entirely in your hands. You have the only copy. (The envelope also may be the sole issue of its litter.) Paper remains scarce here. Any shortages in supply lines at the

German Bulge were not due to failure of enthusiasm for the paper and scrap drives in Asheville, North Carolina. Thus, it would be useful to have the manuscript returned for corrections, at your convenience.

Your letter made reference to my secretary-typist, to whom you plan to forward more notations. Be assured, the secretary-typist will be in intimate contact with the author, the telephone receptionist, cook, and housekeeper, as we all presently inhabit the same four-dollar shoes. With clothing-ration coupons as they are, it's a useful arrangement.

Gratefully,

HARRISON W. SHEPHERD

December 21

Stalin sixty-five years old today. A panting reporter on the radio said he is the Russian Tom Paine rolled together with Paul Bunyan. Lev would now be sixty-four, but isn't. Revolutions are constantly reborn, he used to say, and men like Stalin never die.

February 1

Tonight's news: the Allies broke open the dikes along the Netherlands coast, letting in the sea and drowning thousands of German soldiers in the flood. Like the Azteca opening dikes to drown Cortés and his men on the shores of Lake Tenochtitlan. But fiction is nonsense, the war is real. Tomorrow the farmers of Walcheren will wake to see a tide standing over their crops, the floating corpses of their cattle, every tree in the land scalded dead by the salt on its roots. The glory of war is so frequently disappointing.

Too much solitude here, pent up with ghosts, and nowhere to go to escape them. The man in the street selling ice from a truck today had a pick, nearly like the one that murdered Lev. This was the month he dreaded most. Its visitations.

February 10
A better day, the manuscript set aside awhile in favor of honest work, as Lev would call it. Painted the dining room, the wainscot between the battens, war surplus paint but a decent color, flannel gray. The neighbor kindly donated an old dining table she doesn't use, and a son's Saturday help for the painting. A regular Tom Sawyer. Paid him two bits, but suspect he'd rather have had the dead rat and string to swing it with.

April 5, 1945

Dear Frida,
Your letter was welcome, even if it didn't carry much good news. It is so much better to think of you stomping down the street with skirts roiling, not in a wheelchair. This is a hateful revision. You and Diego should be marching with banners in Paseo de la Reforma this week, protesting the compromises of the Chapultepec Conference.

We are much less in the news here than Mexico City, but our headlines may entertain: Production lines at Asheville Casket Company have gone idle today (dead silent!) as workers go on strike, flouting their war duties, pending negotiations between management and the Upholsterers Union.

Next: the writer William Sidney Porter, or what is left of him, may be dug up from the cemetery in this very neighborhood, for relocation to Greensboro. The city of Asheville has leveled a protest, believing Mr. Porter to be comfortable where he is. The courts will decide. One hopes that no reupholstering will be required at this time.

Admiral Halsey came to the Grove Park for some sport-hunting: finally, a story involving no death. And fashion is alive: Lilly Daché has worked out how to make civilian Easter bonnets from 76,000 WAC hats discarded by the army in favor of the cloth overseas cap. Much on display here last Sunday. You would like gringo Easter: every woman, even the grayest little pigeon, finds the courage to be a Frida for the day.

Not much personal news. The wisteria vines that climb the sides of my house and twine from the eaves are in full purple bloom, the color of jacaranda. Do you ever hear from Van? A question asked, but truly no answer is wanted. A French instructor here at the Teachers College, a particular Miss Attwood, has lately kept up a long campaign to be taken to the movies. With all presentable men at the front, she feels that a fellow should accept his duty to take a girl to see *The Picture of Dorian Gray*. The idea of a crowded theater makes me shudder. Sometimes leaving the house at all becomes a frightful thing, I carry an inexplicable dread inside that never completely abates. But Miss Attwood would not be refused. Hurd Hatfield made a gratifying Dorian, despite his treachery toward Sibyl Vane and Gladys Hallward. Duty seems fulfilled, all quiet on the Attwood front this week.

At the end of term the Teachers College will close. Your language will cease to be maligned by the Carolina tongue. Its only advocate in Asheville will happily stay home in his vine-covered cottage, as his former pupils turn to parachute-packing and the like. These girls are so much like Mother, with their gum-cracking confidence and feral vocabularies. *Holy Joe! Oh nausea! He's oolie droolie!* But Mother would be old by now, nearly fifty. How she would wail over that, if she were still here. Probably it's a charity that she is not.

Last item: the book is to be published late this year by Stratford and Sons Publishers, New York. The editor, Mr. Barnes, confirmed it today. He wants it titled *Vassals of Majesty*, which is silly, as the characters are vassals of cupiditas and greed. The original title was meant to be *Ten Leagues from Where We Sleep*, as it's about men who find themselves always marching short of their own and everyone else's expectation, including the reader's. But Mr. Barnes says that title has too many words in it. No matter. Stratford has mailed a check for two hundred dollars, an advance payment upon royalties to be received, and if they can find the paper they mean to print up copies by the thousand. A terrifying miracle. These words were all written in dark, quiet rooms. How can they face the bright, noisy world?

You must know. You open your skin and pour yourself on a canvas. And then let the curators drape your intestines all around the halls, for the ruckus of society gossips. Can it be survived?

Your friend,

SÓLI

April 13, 1945

Roosevelt is dead. The end came out of a clear sky. Pen in his hand one moment, then dropped to the floor as his secretary watched—it must have been like seeing Lev's bright light go out. Truly, this is like the death of Lenin: a personality fused with the national purpose, struck down by a cerebral stroke, leaving his nation's purpose standing in its shirtsleeves, wondering what under heaven to do.

All last night in south Asheville a crowd stood along the tracks in the cold, hoping to see the catafalque and coffin inside the lighted car when the cortege passed through. The president could only get to Washington from Warm Springs, they thought, by passing through our valley. But no train came. The news extra this morning said the route was through Greeneville. But some still wait, mostly women with children. In a valley east of Oteen they say a hundred Negro women clearing tobacco ground have been kneeling since yesterday with hands outstretched toward the railroad track. They won't go home.

And now Harry Truman has taken the oath, in his polka-dot tie. He hardly looks the part of Man Fused with the National Purpose. He told the newsmen, "Did you ever have a bull or a load of hay fall on you? If you ever did, you know how I felt last night."

Sometimes history cleaves and for one helpless moment stands still, like the pause when the ax splits a log and the two halves rest on end, waiting to fall. Lev used to say that. So it was after Lenin died, Lev riding his train toward the Caucasus, unaware the ax had fallen on his friend. That Stalin was mounting the funeral platform to capture the panicked crowds. This may be one of those times again, when history moves toward darkness or light. Which face in the newsprint photographs now conceals treachery? Are tyrants working behind blackout shades, sending a false cable to someone on a train, conniving to keep reason at a distance while power makes its move? People are sore afraid, ready to believe anything.

May 8, 1945

The world did not end. Or if so, for the Germans only. Everyone came outside to hear the fire-siren blow at 6:01 signaling midnight in Germany, official end to the firing of weapons. Women in front yards drying their hands on aprons, telling the boys to stop shooting one another with sticks and be still. On Haywood Street the clerks and grocers closing up shop all stood perfectly still through that moment, the length of the siren, looking up at the sky. The reflected sunset blazed in the glass storefronts behind them. Some put hands over their hearts, and all of them faced east. Toward Europe.

No one knows what to do with this peace. When the horns went quiet, every person on Haywood, without a word spoken, turned to look the other way. Japan.

❋

The neighbor boy, whose name is not Tom Sawyer but the even more improbable Romulus, picked a strange flower from the Montford Hill woods and brought it here for identification. He says his mother believed it was a bad animal part that should not be touched. But the father said it's a plant, ask the fellow next door. They suspect me of having an education. We mounted a Library Expeditionary Force and struck out boldly. Victory was ours, Bartram's *Flora of the Carolinas* had full color plates of the specimen in question. It is a "Pink Lady's Slipper." Romulus was gravely disappointed to hear it.

August 20, 1945

Five years this day. Since Lev last saw sunlight. Or said the words *my son*, the only one ever to do so. His look of mischief, when handing over a newly discovered novel. The last fleeting plea over his shoulder before going in with Jacson, *Save me from this lad!* The white cuffs soaked like bandages, drops of blood falling on white paper, these images have receded, mostly gone. But then one appears, startling as a stranger standing in the corner of a room where you'd thought yourself alone. Memories do not always soften with time; some grow edges like knives. He should still be living. Murder has the weight of an unpaid debt, death as unfinished business.

No room in the house was safe today, the radio no distraction, obscenely it reported a brutal murder in the south of the city, at one of the tanneries. The teakettle screaming in the kitchen was Natalya saying his name. A sound can transform itself exactly in the brain.

The library seemed it might be a safer place, but it was not. Upstairs in the newspaper room, the curled edges of papers lay in deep layers on tables stacked with books. His desk, all those unfinished sentences. The wax cylinders that still hold his voice, somewhere. His desk calendar, if it is there, lies open to August 20, the page he last turned over, with life's full and ordinary expectation. The thought of that brought a crumpling grief, kneeling in the upstairs stacks waiting for something inside to burst and flood the maple floorboards. Blood seeping darkly between the cracks.

Hell is falling from the skies. A reporter for the *Times* rode in the plane as a witness, wondering at zero hour whether he should feel sad for "the poor devils about to die." He decided no, it was a fair exchange for Pearl Harbor. The army's plan was to drop this bomb on a different Japanese city that morning, a different set of men and dogs and schoolchildren and mothers, but the thick clouds over that city refused to part. Growing tired of circling and waiting, the bomber pilots flew southward down the channel and chose Nagasaki, thanks to its clear skies.

For want of a nail the shoe was lost, for want of a cloud, the world was lost.

Your blood for mine. If not these, then those. War is the supreme mathematics problem. It strains our skulls, yet we work out the sums, believing we have pressed the most monstrous quantities into a balanced equation.

September 2, 1945
V-J Day. If a typewriter did not have these two letters, today it would have been a useless object. The newspaper headlines could only have been larger if they'd found a way to write "JAPS SURRENDER" down the page lengthwise instead of across the top. Hallelujah, Hirohito has fallen on his knees.

During one of the many church victory picnics, a little girl drowned in the Swannanoa. Romulus came over this evening to sit on the porch swing and tell about it, for he was there: the girl in white hair ribbons gone missing, the hours of searching, then finding her on the river's sandy bottom, where the water was not very deep. He told it all and then was quiet. We could hear music of some celebration still going, all the way from Pack Square. Romulus said he couldn't tell whether it was a good day or a bad one.

MacArthur says the great tragedy has ended. We turned on the wireless, and the assured voices seemed to bring the boy back around. This man MacArthur rode horses once, cheered on by a pack of boys not much older than Romulus. Sometimes playing polo behind the academy, other times commanding bayonets into the breasts of the Bonus Marchers. "The skies no longer rain death," he said now. "Men walk upright in the sunlight and the entire world lies quietly at peace." MacArthur claimed he spoke for thousands of silent lips, forever stilled among the jungles and in the deep waters of the ocean. But how could he speak for so many silent lips lying blue beneath the water? Little fish are surely pecking at them now, nourished by worlds of misfortune.

November 19

Dear Frida,

Here is a small gift, my book, just arrived from New York. Mr. Barnes says it will begin turning up in the bookshops by Friday week, but he sent me two with a note: "A spare copy for your Mother and Dad!" The cover art is quite something, as you'll see, with the twin temples of Tlaloc and Huitzilopochtli in the distance. The flames and thinly clad women running from the conquering army should make up for any archaeological inexactness. This format, I was told, worked well for *Gone With the Wind*.

No one here knows of my impending status as a published author. The neighbor ladies find me suspiciously lacking in ambition or family. Miss Attwood still rings up; few soldiers are home yet, so she makes do with nothing new. Last week we went to a restaurant called Buck's, opened recently to wild enthusiasm, which wraps up your meal like parcel post and sends it out to the gravel car park while you wait. The idea is to picnic inside your auto, staring at other strangers with catsup on their chins and napkins draped on the steering wheels. You would bawl. It is called a drive-in. Now we can buy gasoline, food, and soon we'll have new autos too. Why not make use of all at once?

The war's end has left America with loads of get-up-and-go, and no place to send it. Also war-bond cash saved and nothing to spend it on. Unless we need hollow-lead tubing and field-combat boots, as that's what the factories are geared for making. We still use ration stamps for almost everything. Truman is trying to keep price controls on until shortages abate, but the manufacturers can smell hoarded cash. They're parading ad men through Congress to convince the lawmakers that Free Market is the way to go, and that Harry Truman is in league with Karl Marx. The neighbor ladies here are firm on the side of Harry and Karl Marx, they know price controls are the only thing standing between ourselves and the twenty-dollar steak. I confess to an unpatriotic yearning to buy a refrigerator, but if a Philco showed up in town now without its OPA ration tag, it would go to Mrs. Vanderbilt for the cost of my mortgage.

Meanwhile, the husbands concoct a black market with more plot twists than the Codex Boturini. Romulus, my young informant, reports his dad went to the car dealer's to finagle a new Ford, not yet legally for sale. He was told if he bought the salesman's dog for eight hundred dollars, they would give him a free car to drive the pup home. Romulus cheered. But he was in it for the dog.

One thing can be had without a stamp, though, and that's my book. Please feel no moral duty to read it, you've done enough. Only look for the dedication page, where you'll see a familiar name. I apologize for the title. Mr. Barnes says *Vassals of Majesty* sounds like a book people want to read, and it's his business to know. What would you do? If a museum curator said your paintings should be hung on both sides with pink organdy curtains? Oh yes, I remember, you would poke him in the eye with a paintbrush and tell him to hang organdy curtains over his dog's-ass face.

Lacking your courage, I avoid disagreements with the company that buys my bread and butter, and possibly a Philco. I am getting on fine, with no complaints at all about my new country except that it has no olives worth eating and no peppers fit for adults. This package holds the proof of my incomprehensible good fortune. Use it at the bottom of your door to stop a draft, and know that I am—
Your grateful friend,

H. W. SHEPHERD, *author*

December 5
The first snow of the season fell today on two hundred women standing in a queue on Haywood Street, after an announcement that nylon stockings would be available one-per-customer at Raye's Department Store.

One block down at the bookshop, a single copy of *Vassals of Majesty* was handled by several different customers in the course of the morning. Each conducted a close inspection of the Indian maids fleeing through flames on the dust jacket. No lines formed on the sidewalk, no Philco this year.

Book Review

by United Press

The modern reader complains that theatrics have all gone to the movies. Where is the old-fashioned barnburner to carry us away? Here is one to fit the bill. Harrison Shepherd's *Vassals of Majesty* (Stratford and Sons, $2.39) tells of a golden age when Spanish Conquistadors fought for the New World. Cortez plays out as a winning villain, lining his pockets in the name of Church and Queen while paying no heed to the trials endured by his men. The weak-minded Emperor Montezuma makes hardly a better impression, doting on his captive birds while his bloodthirsty chiefs do their worst.

The princes in this story are the common soldiers, pushed to the limits but revealing true humanity. The story's droll assertion: heroes may be less than heroic, while the common man saves the day.

"Books for Thought," by Sam Hall Mitchell

Gee, but I Want to Go Home

If you're weary of the military tribunals of Goering and Hess, their grisly details dragging on, try this one on for size: chieftains who cut out the hearts of war-prisoners while still beating! The year is 1520. The place, a glittering city on a lake where the last Aztec emperor meets his mortal enemy Cortés. The book is *Vassals of Majesty,* a plush first effort from author Harrison Shepherd. Swords clash on every page in this clever retelling of the conquest of Mexico's richest empire.

Greed and vengeance drive the action, but the novel's tender theme is a longing for home. The Spanish Royalty cry out for gold, but the young men forced into battle only wish for better shoes in a prickling desert, and something better to cook than cactus pads on a campfire. These soldiers might as well be singing the song every GI knows by heart: *The coffee that they give us, they say is mighty fine, it's good for cuts and bruises and it tastes like iodine!* While leaders plot the fate of golden cities, these soldiers worry they'll lose the wife to another fellow while they're far from home. In a nation of returning soldiers and war-weary civilians, this book will make a huge emotional mark.

The Asheville Trumpet, *February 3, 1946*

Asheville Writer Is Story of the Year

by Carl Nicholas

"Vassals of Majesty" by local wordsmith Harrison Shepherd proves nothing short of sheer fascination. It might seem only stuffed shirts and long-haired professors would clamor to read of men living hundreds of years ago. Not so! Every heart will pound as conqueror Cortez pitches battle against his foe. This book has it all: blood-curdling treachery, and even heart interest. The female pulse will race for handsome Indian prince Cuautla. With the speed of a locomotive the story hurtles to its epic conclusion. Mrs. Jack Cates, owner of Cates Bookshop, confirms she cannot keep it on the shelves.

Asheville's very own Harrison Shepherd is a young man of only thirty holding the secrets of the ages in his pen. Calls to the home confirmed he resides in Montford Hills. Young ladies take note, our sources say he's a bachelor.

The New York Weekly Review, *February 2, 1946*

Vassals of Majesty, BY HARRISON W. SHEPHERD
Stratford and Sons, New York

Never Far from Home

by Michael Reed

In the literary season of Anna's beleaguered King of Siam and Teddy Roosevelt's "Unterrified" grab of Panama, a nation at peace seems keen for tales of exotic foreign conflict. Readers will find rich fodder in this novel of shrewd ambition in the bloody Spanish conquest of Mexico.

Narrating the tale are Cuautla, an heir to the Aztec empire, and Lieutenant Remedios, who must execute the commands of notorious empire-builder Hernando Cortés. History buffs are warned, scarcely a hero in this tale survives with reputation intact. Cortés shows a weakness for Mexican liquor, and cares more about his page in history than for the men who give their lives to write it for him. And the sweet-natured, delusional Emperor Mucteczuma leaves most of the decisions to a ruthless cadre whose protocol for handling war prisoners may cause the reader a night of lost sleep.

From its snappy title onward, this is a potboiler with no real aspirations to literary importance. The exaggerated setting of blood-stained temples and battlements seems to flutter with the tags of a Hollywood film set. But the characters threaten to burst from their archetypes. The humblest have a winning way of striving for honor in duty, while the powerful fall prey to familiar political failures, revealing themselves as ordinary men all, not so different from the modern-day elected official or office clerk. The author suggests no disagreement among men is ever entirely foreign, after all.

(A sample of reviews sent by the publisher's clipping service, twelve in all, Jan.–Feb. 1946)

March 10, 1946

Dear Frida,

Thank you for the box of chiles, a spectacular surprise. I've strung them in a red *ristra* for the kitchen alongside the onions I plait and hang near the stove. The neighbor boy suspects me of "harboring spells," but Perpetua would approve of my kitchen. I will ration these *pasillas de Oaxaca* like anything, dearer than gasoline.

Our Carolina shows signs of spring: crocuses appear in front lawns, long wool underwear vanishes from clotheslines in the back. Yesterday I bought a frozen lamb shank from the butcher's and set it in the flowerbox outside the window to keep it chilled overnight. This morning it had completely thawed. Today I will rub it with garlic for an impromptu feast. The cat Chispa spreads the word of my erratic cooking extravagances around the neighborhood, and now another scoundrel has followed her home. I call him Chisme, for the gossip that brought him. Black as the devil and fond of lamb.

Soon my shanks may get to visit an authentic Philco. The publisher's accountants are preparing a royalty check for the first 50,000 copies of the book. You can't imagine what you set loose on the world, with one quick job of paper-smuggling. I have to run a gauntlet when leaving the house. Two young ladies are out there now, lollygagging on the front walk in saddle shoes and rolled-up dungarees. Reporters for a school newspaper from the look of them, or just autograph hounds, sucked in by the bizarre and rampant rumors that I am a person of interest. Even my neighbors brought over a book for autograph—it was wrapped up as if they meant to give it a state burial, or else cure it for a ham. Romulus says he spotted some girls slipping around to the back to steal my shirts off the clothesline, and chased them off by "whooping and hollowing."

I am abashed by this admiration, for it seems directed at some other person. How these girls would hoot if they saw me as I really am, cowering indoors on washdays, festooning the bathroom with my damp balbriggans so they won't be stolen or made the subject of a theme paper in Senior English. My new life. No one has said I eat human flesh in a tortilla, but I'm getting an idea how your lives have been disfigured all these years by gossip. I can't answer the telephone, for it's sure to be a newspaper man asking questions: place of birth, status of bowels. I don't know what to do with this havoc.

I learned today by mail about the publisher's check. Mr. Barnes tried all week to reach me, unaware I was hiding from the telephone. Soon I'll have to do something about the mail; the box fills daily with notes from readers. Seven proposals of marriage, so far. Such a query requires a gentle response, but I'll confess I'm flummoxed. I've had no practice in the skills of being admired. Frida, sometimes an acid panic rises in my throat; people want something, and I am not the thing at all. As I've mentioned, girls are desperate, with the fellows still over there patching up the potholes in France. Poor England and France. Their great kingdoms nothing now but fairy tales.

Did *El Diario* mention Churchill's speech last week in Missouri? The European leaders seem terrified by the new landscape, flattened at the middle with Truman still on his feet at one end, and Stalin at the other. You could see why Mr. Churchill wants to keep them from shaking hands—if Harry and Comrade Joe reach across that mess, these two could make a new empire on which the sun never sets. Mr. Churchill sounded like a child goading his parents into an argument, he was absurdly dramatic: "A shadow has fallen upon the scene. . . . Nobody knows what Soviet Russia intends to do," etcetera. Next he will probably go to Moscow and say the same about us.

How strange, that this is the wide-open moment Lev spent

his life hoping for. With America brimming with brotherly love for the Soviets, our own laborers on the march, and Russia with everything to gain, it seems the right time to support them in tossing out Stalin's bureaucrats and finishing the democratic socialist revolution as Lenin intended. Or, it could go the other way, our two nations falling apart like split kindling. Mr. Churchill seems to want that. "From the Baltic to the Adriatic, an iron curtain has descended across the Continent." He sweetened the pot later with goodwill for the valiant Russians and comrade Stalin. But the howlers went right to work as soon as they heard of this strange new curtain of metal. They are thrilled with the image. The cartoonists draw the poor Russians slamming their heads against an anvil. Probably in a fortnight they'll have forgotten it, but for now it's a sensation. Two words put together, *curtain* and *iron*, have worked alchemy on a kettle of tepid minds and anxious hearts.

The power of words is awful, Frida. Sometimes I want to bury my typewriter in a box of quilts. The radio makes everything worse, because of the knack for amplifying dull sounds. Any two words spoken in haste might become law of the land. But you never know which two. You see why I won't talk to the newsmen.

My dread is sometimes inexplicable. How do you bear up under so many eyes? And what ludicrous worries I have, compared with yours. I hope the bone-graft operation you mention will make your life worth living again. I worry for your weariness, but trust in your strength, and often see your paintings in my dreams.

Your friend,

H. W. SHEPHERD

P.S. I enclose a review, to clear up any mistaken notions you may have about my novel.

The Echo, *February 28, 1946*

This one is flying off the bookstore shelves from coast to coast: *Vassals of Majesty* by Harrison W. Shepherd, with 50,000 sold the first month after publication. Its pageant of noble heroes and dastardly villains plays out on the golden shores of ancient Rome. When you've had enough of the "heart and soul of the common man" exalted by the late FDR, here are uncommon men with derring-do, sweeping the reader into the Success Dream that drives them. Ladies and gentlemen, but definitely. Harry Shepherd cranks out a darn good read. And watch out, girls: he's single!

March 13, 1946

Dear Shepherd,

What's steamin, demon? Remember me, from civilian service? (Nobody forgets this Tom-cat.) Hope you're all the aces since last we soldiered together for Art and Country. Everywhere I go now, some guy is just home from Europe telling how he dodged the lead pill or brought in his bomber on a wing and a prayer. Does anybody want to hear a hair-raising tale of Army SNAFU in the National Gallery? You and me buddy, a couple of Civvy cream puffs, it's a void coupon ain't it? If only my old chum Shepherd were here, we could tell some war stories, sure. How you and I drank so much joe on the train, we almost dropped a marble Rodin on its head in the Asheville station.

Man, you could have had me for soup when I saw your name in the Book Review. *Is that you, or some other Harrison Shepherd? I didn't have you figured for the Shakespeare type. But who knows? If it's really you, drop a line.*

Plant you now, dig you later,

TOM CUDDY

March 29, 1946

Dear Shepherd,

Holy Joe, it's really you. Thanks for the buzz. Cat, you know how to percolate.

With everything you are currently hipped to, this will probably sound like cake and coffee, but a proposition has come up and I figure I'll give it a sock. The Department of State is getting into the art business. It's not enough that chumps like us packed off America's treasures to the Vanderbilt Mansion and back, to keep them safe from Tojo. Now the idea is to pack up a fresh load of paintings on Uncle Sam's ticket, and parade them around the museums of Europe. A special show of American painters to send overseas, to show those Parisians we're not a bunch of rubes. Somebody spilled the beans to the Department of State that the Europeans hate us. Surprise, Jean-Pierre thinks GI Joe is a slob with chocolate on his face! Between you and me, I doubt the Parisians care, as long as we keep putting the bricks back in their castles. But the Congress cares, they are convoying this ship and aim to blitz it.

Here's where you and I come in. They recruited my old boss for the job, Leroy Davidson from the Walker. He only got 50 thousand clams to work with but he's done a killer job, Leroy chose everything himself. He's fed up with the Europeans sniggering about heart-throbbing landscapes and the American Scene, so he decided to give them an eyeful. Seventy-nine paintings, mostly Modern Art: Stuart Davis, Marsden Hartley, Georgia O'Keeffe, it's a killer. Even Goodrich at the Whitney says so. We're hanging it here in New York for the summer and then it moves to the National for a few weeks. Leroy says Congress needs to see what American Art looks like, before we send it off.

That's the story, morning glory. You'd come to D.C. in October. You're already on the State Department's cleared list, Leroy says we can hire you in a tick to help with the crating and get this show ready for transatlantic. If you want, you can even come along for the ride. The war's over, pal, this time we would go first class, not steerage. No more riding on top of our wooden crates in the train car, which really was not half a bad place to lob around,

as it turned out. (Like Hope says, Thanks for the memories!) But think of it,
man, you and me in Europe. Goose-feather beds. What a gasser.

   Sounds like you might be cooking with gas already in your present
situation. But give me a buzz if you are ready to take Paris.
So long chum,

TOM CUDDY

April 3, 1946

Dear Frida,

Your letter arrived yesterday and now lies open on the desk,
a spectre, burning at its edges. This damage is not yours, you
aren't the cause. It's a normal and ordinary request, for a friend
to come and visit in New York when you are there for the bone-
graft surgery. A friend who owes you everything, and might
now smuggle *rellenos* into the hospital to speed your recovery,
who should do this. But no sleep came last night, only thoughts
in a nightlong darkness of the summer coming, a ride on the
train, the penetrating glare of strangers. Imposing on your fashionable friends in New York, these Americans who understand
everything. All of it envisioned in a cold panic.

   This is a despicable confession. But one telephone call yesterday to the train station to ask about a ticket was enough to
drag a stomach inside out, *dejado de la mano de dios*, left alone
by god, this feeling. Abandoned by reason or safety. Perched
on the side of the bathtub rocking like a child, hopeless, wishing for the invisibility of childhood. August of each year brings
thoughts of dying. But bad days come in any month. Eyes can
pierce a skull. Travel to New York is unthinkable, when even
at the corner market, a stranger's stare can paralyze. This terror
hasn't any name. This running home, feeling like a scorched
muslin curtain that blew too near the candle.

Forgive this cowardice. If you have the strength to lift your head as you travel down Fifth Avenue, look for one book in the shop windows there, standing in as a substitute for your once and future friend,

SÓLI

The Asheville Trumpet, *April 28, 1946*

Woman's Club Sponsors Book Review Night

by Edwina Boudreaux

The Asheville Woman's Club sponsored its annual Book Review Night on Thursday at 6 p.m. in the Lee H. Edwards High School Auditorium. Tickets sold for twenty-five cents each, raising $45 dollars for the Asheville Library. The theme of the evening was, "Mexico Old and New."

Mrs. Herb Lutheridge, President, opened the program with the Pledge of Allegiance and introduction of speakers. Miss Harriet Boudreaux began the festivities with her review of "The Peacock Sheds His Tail" by Alice Hobart. The book concerns the love story of a Mexican girl and American diplomat in the turbulence of unrest in modern-day Mexico City. For her presentation Miss Boudreaux wore native dress of embroidered blouse and skirt brought from the Mexican continent by her aunt, who traveled there as a bride.

The second presenter was welcomed by many excited young ladies in attendance, Mrs. Violet Brown reviewing "Vassals of Majesty" by Harrison Shepherd. The novel tells the exciting conquest of Ancient Mexico by the Spanish Army. Events came alive under Mrs. Brown's retelling, followed by a lively discussion. Numerous questions arose concerning the author, an Ashevillean residing in the Montford neighborhood, which the speaker demurred at, claiming familiarity with the book itself, not its progenitor. In her forty-five minute presentation

Mrs. Brown brought to the fore many themes that might be missed by the average reader, such as Man Against Nature and Man Against Himself.

Mrs. Alberta Blake, librarian, closed the evening by thanking the audience on behalf the Library Committee, noting all money raised would purchase several new volumes. She assured all those in attendance that duplicate copies of the two books presented will soon be on the shelves.

April 30, 1946

Mrs. Violet Brown
4145 Tunnel Road, Bittle House
Rural Free Delivery, Asheville North Carolina

Dear Mrs. Brown,

This message may startle you, please forgive a bolt from the blue. A telephone call to Mrs. Bittle yesterday confirmed that the former guild of lodgers remains intact, minus myself. (She may thus think it improved vis-à-vis her advertisement of "Only Good People Here.") And that you could therefore be reached by this address.

The purpose of this letter is to plant a request: against all odds, a man who can perform every secretarial duty himself from A to Z, including changing the typewriter ribbon, now seems to be in need of a secretary.

A startling ship of fortune has docked in this harbor on Montford Avenue, towing an unwieldy barge of correspondence, telephone calls, and attention from young ladies. It is a wonder, how others who become so blessed still manage to go forward with their lives. Mr. Sinatra receives five thousand letters a week, according to the *Echo*, and he still looks the picture of high spirits. Only a hundred or so come here each week, but they fall like mounds of autumn leaves, leaving the spirits damp and crawling with nervous beetles. What is to be done? An old friend who recently telephoned, a fellow who also worked at the National Gallery during the war, proposed: "Lace up your boots, jive cat, and requisition yourself a canary to be your stenographer." After translating this advice into my own tongue, the question remained: Where does one requisition such a canary?

Then on Sunday your name rose up boldly, Mrs. Brown, in the *Asheville Trumpet*. There you stood with my book in hand, facing down a riotous crowd at the Woman's Club gala. Applying the same calm efficiency you used for handling Mrs. Bittle and her everlasting muddles. Keeping your steady hand on the tiller, you guided the Book Night toward the deep waters of literary theme, quieting the commotion of Miss Boudreaux in her getup from the "Mexican Continent." The ladies pressed for details of the Author Himself, but you professed no knowledge of such person! Imagine the fracas, if you had revealed the truth: that you and the author had once lived under the same roof, with a landlady who sometimes mixed our laundry together.

Mrs. Brown, dear lady, your discretion is prodigious. You resisted the siren song of tattle. The seams of your character must be sewn with steel thread. If this letter delivers only my everlasting gratitude, that is a greater weight than three cents postage should allow. But it also contains an earnest query. Your conduct in the battle of Mexico Old and New has led me to think you may be just the amanuensis who could put a life to rights, and also help with typing a second book, now underway.

Naturally, you may have a different opinion. Let me sum up a few details and be finished, so you can consider the offer. Weighing in my favor, I hope: I am likely in a position to exceed your present salary. A drawback: my workplace is here where I live. Some ladies might find it awkward to work in the home of an unmarried gentleman. In this letter I have already used the terms cat and canary, not because I could ever think of a secretary in those terms, but because others do, evidently. Mrs. Brown, I have an odd impairment: the world paints its prejudices boldly across banners, and somehow I walk through them without seeing. It's a particular fault of mine, a blindness. I carry on walking down the street, dazed as a calf, with shreds of paper hanging everywhere. I hope in this case to be less naive.

A third point in my favor: I spent years as a stenographer myself, as I already hinted. In Mexico I worked for two different men, both greater than I will ever be. Oddly, the experience did not prepare me for public attention. But I understand the role of professional helpmeet, perhaps better than most men. I am not disposed to tyranny.

If anything about this request strikes you as unseemly, please ignore it and accept my high regard for our previous acquaintance. But if my suggestion holds interest for you, I would gladly schedule an interview at a date and time you suggest.

Sincerely,

HARRISON W. SHEPHERD

May 4, 1946

Dear Mr. Shepherd,

Your letter was what you said. A bolt from the blue. But not the first. At the Lending Library I saw your name on a book cover in January. My thought was, well sir, it's a coincidence there be two Harrison Shepherds in this world. Next, an article in the paper discussed the book, its author reputed to be living in Montford. The subject of Mexico I knew to be your familiar. Curiosity killed the cat for Mrs. Bittle, her niece said she'd spied on the fellow, reporting him tall as a tree and thin as a rail. Who else?

Imagine our surprise. For years we sat here like bumps on a log eating the

*cooking of a man who would shortly come to fame. Now old Mr. Judd says,
"I had no idee what that young fellow was cooking!" (You remember his
drear jokes.) Miss McKellar notes that "still waters run deep." Reg Borden
still refuses to believe it's you, but wants to read the book anyway. He's had
a long wait. The library has but one copy. I had to wait weeks myself, and
I have an "In" with Mrs. Lutheridge since I joined the Library Committee,
mainly to set the card files to rights, which were a disgrace.*

*Your book is good. This town hasn't had such a sensation since Tommy
Wolfe came out with* **Look Homeward, Angel.** *And that sensation
was not pleasing to most. Some in Asheville were disgruntled to be left out of
the story, and all others dismayed to be left in, thus the scandal was entire.
The library refused to carry it. I was already in the Woman's Club (recording
secretary), and our meeting convened the week that book came out. I doubt
if so many salts of ammonia have ever been used in our city, before or since.
You had only to open the door of the meeting hall to get a mighty dose.*

*I couldn't guess how to write a book. But here is my opinion: people love
to read of sins and errors, just not their own. You were wise to put your
characters far from here, instead of so-called "Altamont" as Mr. Wolfe did.
That "Dixieland" is his mother's boardinghouse on Spruce Street, and all
here know it. Few were spared the jabs of Wolfe's pen, even his own father
whom I myself can remember teetering into the S & W Cafeteria reeking of
spirits before noon of a Monday. Many feel there was no need to bring that
kind of thing to the lime-light, especially by a family member.*

*This all pertains to the subject of your letter. Thank you for saying I am
sewn up with steel thread, but I call it plain sense. Some writers get away
with murder, using nice words and a mannerly story to bring misery on real
folk. You did the other way, writing of murderous things but behaving as
a gentleman in the civic sense. That's how I came to speak as I did at Book
Review Night. Those girls were apoplectic to make your book into another
hometown yarn. We've had that kind of yarn here, and it got itself wound
up in a gorm of knots. Mr. Shepherd, you put your story in Mexico. Why
not keep it there? That was my thinking.*

I know you as a gentleman. Using your home as a place of employment is not unseemly. A lady in the working world all her life knows that tender manners have their place, sometimes less useful than a good cup of coffee. During the war secretaries sometimes emptied bedpans, and certain men will ask worse, even in peacetime. But knowing you as I do from Mrs. Bittle's, I've seen you show more kindness than most, even toward a hen you're fixing to put in the oven.

I will warn, I can be particular. I like a typewriter with an automatic margin and the type bar separate from the carriage. Preferably a Royal or L. C. Smith. These were used at the Selective Service office, and I got accustomed. I will come to your house for interviewing at half past six on Thursday. The neighborhood of your address is a short ride on the bus from my present employer. I'll go directly, after work.
Sincerely,

VIOLET BROWN

May 27

Mother's soul can rest: here is a woman in my life. Mrs. Brown in a pearl-gray snood, age forty-six, sensible as pancake flour. Like characters in a story, our lives were star-crossed but came together. She will rescue the hero, answer his telephone, file the mountains of mail, maybe shake a broom at the laundry thieves. And he can keep his monk's life, the holes in his underwear. Mrs. Brown doesn't care.

At the first interview she laid her failings at my feet, or would have except she hasn't any. Does not smoke cigarettes, take strong drink, go to church or gamble. Has worked for the city, the army, and most daunting of all, the Asheville Woman's Club. Thirty years a widow. She doubts being married would have been much different.

It was strange to speak forthrightly, after living at Mrs. Bittle's those years: exiting the bathroom with downcast eyes, sitting at supper while old Mr. Judd piped up with his yellowed news extras.

Now it seems we shared a kindred silence, restraining our smiles on hearing that Limburger has flown across the Atlantic. But maybe I contrive this, as lovers reconfigure the days *before*, with every glance leading ultimately to union.

In any event here she is, installed in my dining room. I hated to show her the mail, stored in bushel baskets in the empty spare bedroom. She did not flinch. Grasped each bushel by the handles, marched it downstairs, and dumped onto the maple table one mountain for each month. Bravely she dives in, even before we've found her a filing cabinet or acceptable typewriter. (Royal or L. C. Smith.) We shall put the bathroom door back on its hinges, as soon as I've cleared its surface of all piles and chapters, and found a proper desk myself. For now, when one of us needs the WC, the other steps out the back door, pretending to call the cats. This and more, she suffers with perfect composure.

Mrs. Brown is a force: small, unadorned, unapologetic. Her eyebrows arch like a pair of bridges across her wide forehead. Her blouses button to the top, she wears white cotton gloves even on warm days, and she can still any troubled waters with her austere calm and peculiar antique grammar. Each morning on arrival she taps on the front door, puts in her head and calls out, "Mr. Shepherd, where be ye?"

Her words seem scripted by Chaucer. She says "strip-ed" and "learn-ed," making an extra syllable of the past tense. A sack is a "poke." Surveying the piles of letters she declared, "Mr. Shepherd, you get mail by the *passel*." She says "nought" and "nary a one," and the garden greens she brought me were "sallets," the word Shakespeare used. She says "queasy" to mean worried, as did King Lear. When I noted this, she replied, "Well I expect he had a lot to be queasy about. He was a king, wasn't he?"

When pressed about her origins she said her people were "Mountain Whites." She seems reluctant to say more, only that it means Highlanders, people who came through the gap from England ages ago, and reckoned they ought to stay. Remaining on the spot, with idiom intact. She means "reckon" in the British sense, akin to reconnoiter, until knowing a thing for certain, which is to "ken it."

Most shocking was this pronouncement: "My family be there still, living in a cabin home in the hells." This is a kind of bush, evidently, a rhododendron. "They grow thick as can be. If you came to be lost in there, you couldn't push out with a stick. So it's called hells. Pardon if you're offended. It isn't a foul word in that sense."

No offense taken. Her past can stay where it is, lost in the hells, not my business, as my childhood hells are none of hers. We concern ourselves with the future, which we agreed should begin at once, in my dining room, as soon as she could give proper notice. And today here she is, dispatching the mess with carbon paper and a buttoned-up smile.

May 28

Mrs. Brown's advice about the schoolgirls: they won't bite. I took her word on that, and left the house for the first time in a while to wander up to the cemetery. A belated outing for Mother's birthday; it always seems important to go somewhere for her sake. But she is nowhere any longer, least of all the Riverside Cemetery. Even the writer O. Henry might have "up and gone" from here, as Mrs. Brown would say. Tom Wolfe is still in situ, though the town is evidently still put out with him. Many graves bore jars of wilting peonies today, but nary a posy for poor Tom, a man so recently gone, dramatically and in his prime, reeling from the fracas of fame. Maybe Mrs. Brown could have saved him.

A sample of one day's mail, posted forward from Stratford and Sons, received on June 6, 1946, six months after publication of *Vassals of Majesty*. (Spelling sic.) —VB

Dear Mr. Shepherd,

Your book **Vassals of Majesty** *is tops. I sobbed my heart out hundreds of times, especially at the end when the soldiers burnt up all the King's parrots in the fire. My mother has a Parakeet named Mickey Rooney. My sister never stopped razzing me because I stayed up all night, scared out of my wig on the gory parts. Then she read it, and blew her top. I think Lt. Remedios is a dream boat, but she is all for Cuautla. Which one is supposed to be the best? I am a budding author too. Please send an autograph photo and keep it coming. (My sister says, 2 please!)*
Thanks!

LINDSAY PARKS

Dear Mr. Shepherd,

I am writing about your book in regards to the War in Mexico. Usually I sit on the fence and don't argue with people or try to tell them how it is. The horror of war is part of life since recorded history. But your book showed how men really feel when they are soldiers. I served in the 12th Infantry Regiment, F Company. One of the few that made it out of Berdorf. I read your book in the Van Wyck Army Hospital. About ten other guys on my ward read your book, and most of the others couldn't hold a book or see to read one. Everything about war is bad like you said. Some of us have a bet that you were an Infantry Man yourself.
Yours truly,

GEORGE M. COOK

Dear Mr. Shepherd,

My name is Eleanor White and I reside in Springfield, Missouri. I am currently attending college at Webster Women's College. I myself am not a big reader but I must say, your book made me want to read more, more, more. Now I understand the Mexican Conquistadors through new eyes. I am recommending my History professor to read it. My hat is off to you!
Yours truly,

ELEANOR WHITE

Dear Mr. Harrison,

My name is Gary Duncan and I live in California. My girlfriend was hanging icicles all over me until I read your book Vessels of Majesty. *In a word: "Stimulating." I found your destriptions very thought provoking, even if I didn't think it is the best book ever wrote. But am I going to tell Shelley that?*

I would be tops in her book if you sent a photo. Her birthday is coming up here quick, June 14. Her name is Shelley. And the last name, same as yours, Harrison. Can you top that?

YOUR FRIEND, GARY

Dear Mr. Shepherd,

I would like to say thank you. Your writing is an inspiration to us all, or anyway that is how I feel. Your book hit me when it made me think how the boys on both sides of the war were still human whether Spanish or the Mexicans. Every person is human, even Japs, their mothers must have all cried tears just the same. That gave me something to ponder. Please continue to write more books.

Yours sincerely,

ALICE KENDALL

All correspondence answered with a short note, no photographs or inclusions. —VB

July 6, 1946

Dear Diego,

I trust Frida is still recovering from the surgery in New York. I have no address for her there, but could not let her birthday pass. I expect she is angry with me for failing to visit. Please forward my *saludos,* and tell her I never fail to bake a *rosca* in her honor on this day, whether she is present to eat it or not.

On the eve of your elections I share your thrill and dread, waiting to see what Mexico will declare for herself and her Revolution. The news is sparse, so I welcome any from you. I did read of the National Prize of Arts and Sciences, and so I congratulate you both. Your wife is a National Prize herself, as you know better than anyone.

The news from here is about what you'd expect. You wouldn't care for the food: no *empanadas dulces*, I doubt there is a tablespoon of sugar right now in all Asheville. (My cake today, with molasses and pureed apples, was a sad, dark-brown cousin of its predecessors.) But rations are lifted on nearly everything else. Prices rise like balloons, and we all jump like children under a piñata, reaching for our material passions. Americans believe in water-proof gabardine and Vimm's Vitamin Tablets. The housewives sent their butter to the Front for years, and now require their heavenly reward. To get it all manufactured on schedule, the sacrifice of laborers will have to be made permanent, it seems: they toiled like slaves for the war effort and still haven't had a single pay adjustment. You could have heard a wrench drop on Pack Square this spring, when the unions shut down everything. But Truman seized the railroad and drafted the strikers into military service, to command them back to work.

So that is the report you asked for, not entirely good. Our newsmen mostly reviled the "workers' rebellion." Politics here now resemble a pillow fight. Lacking the unifying slogan (Win the War), our opposing parties sling absurd pronouncements back and forth, which everyone pretends carry real weight. How the feathers fly. The newsmen leap on anything, though it's all on the order of, "Four out of five shoppers know this is the better dill pickle," assertions that can't be proven but sway opinion. "Dance for the crowd" is the new order, with newsmen leading the politicians like bears on the leash. Real convictions would be a hindrance. The radio is at the root of the evil, their rule is: *No silence, ever.* When anything happens, the commentator has to speak without a moment's pause for gathering wisdom. Falsehood and inanity are preferable to silence. You can't imagine the effect of this. The talkers are rising above the thinkers.

On my own advice, then, I'll close this ramble. But first I have a confession. The day I left Mexico six years ago, Frida gave me your copy of the Codex Boturini. She said it was a gift from you, and gladly I accepted. But I wonder, did she actually ask, or just tell you it was stolen? The culprit herein revealed: the cook. In this parcel I enclose it, rightfully returned. You may remember I was enthralled by this codex, which you showed me in your office one day. I understood it to be a sort of Bible for the homeless. Yet, with its little drawings of people it also resembled the eight-pagers the boys used to have at school, and I'm abashed to admit, your codex had more effect on me than the naked Sally Rand ever did. When Frida put its accordion folds in my hand, I couldn't refuse. I should have asked her whether you'd been informed of your generosity. But I wanted it badly, and took it, for this reason: in my experience, penitence is more attainable than permission.

I hope you'll be pleased to know I made good use of it. My second novel, now complete, is the story of the Mexica people's journey to their new home in the promised valley "Where the Eagle Tears the Snake" (my tentative title). Plot and dramatic interest all came directly from the codex: all those severed heads on stakes, fur-covered enemies, and eagles flying down to carry weapons to the rescue. I hardly needed to invent a thing. It was much like working as your typist: I only had to stay awake to a luminous presence, and make a good transcription.

So I'm in debt to you, not to mention the original author of the codex, attributed to Huitzilopotchli himself. I will soon send the manuscript to my publisher and receive a check for royalties-on-advance. If the Feather-Headed God expects his share, he had better get in contact right away.

With regards to all in your household,

H. SHEPHERD

July 8, 1946

The manuscript sailed off today. Mrs. Brown took it to the post office. Before going out the door she turned back and held out the bulky brown-paper package of it, resting flat on her white-gloved hands. "Look here, Mr. Shepherd, a little raft with all your hopes upon it, sailing for New York. Ye know not how light it feels in my hands."

This afternoon she discovered my birth date had just passed. She is filing old documents, the birth certificate applications and so forth, now that the flurry of typing is done. She seemed hurt. "A man turns thirty years, that's important," she scolded, "and to think I sat here and knew nought of it, all the day long."

I didn't say what Frida would have. That you can't really know the person standing before you, because always there is some missing piece: the birthday like an invisible piñata hanging great and silent over his head, as he stands in his slippers boiling the water for coffee. The scarred, shrunken leg hidden under a green silk dress. A wife and son back in France. Something you never knew. That is the heart of the story.

August 27

Murderous dreams come even in daytime, memories that occlude vision. How can a friend's blood be willed from the mind? Other men do it. They come home from a war, kiss the ground, and go forward, as easily as taking the Haywood bus to the library. Without meeting this rising panic and humiliation. Running out of the library bookless and hatless, rather than end up crumpled behind the newspaper stacks again, watching blood spread across the maple floor boards.

Last week, on the day itself, even the bedroom was too uncertain a place, its shifting walls and window's glare, letting in the clouded sky. Mrs. Brown thought it must be the grippe. She brought tea and toast upstairs on a tray.

Today, one hundred ten paces to the corner market, step by counted step. An automobile passed slowly on the street: a Buick. Two women at the newsstand professed themselves as admirers. One had just come from the market and carried a bouquet of gladiolus wrapped in a paper cone. She meant no harm at all, she was only a young wife going home to some celebration. Not Jacson Mornard stalking Frida in Paris, arms loaded with flowers, any fool could know the difference. But anyone who rises, any greatness, attracts those who would cut it down at the root. Any fool knows that also.

Every day it seems possible to walk to the door. This time, step out. But the sidewalk leads to a bridge across a precipice. There is Mother up ahead slipping off her sling-back shoes, stepping out onto the planks above the rushing ravine. Don't come. You wait here. The red-bellied spider pulls itself into a hole in the plank. Every hole could have something like that inside.

Mrs. Brown might know more than she says. Today she looked up from the table, peering over her glasses to size up her wretched, captive chief, who stands at the door looking out. "They won't bite," she said. But it isn't the girls in saddle oxfords. It is the things that have already begun, proceeding now toward their finish, the supplicant who should have been turned away, and was not. The man at the door with hat in hand and the pickax under his raincoat.

September 2

No word from Frida, still angry. Nor from Diego, not even a curse over his stolen codex, though that's also to be expected. He couldn't remember to write letters even as Chairman General of Lev's Correspondence Committee. The world is a train moving forward, with people like Diego and Frida at the fore and all the rest of us standing back, shuddering at the roar.

Of all those gone away, Frida is the most missed. Not that she ever offered real affection. Only her version of it: a game of cat-and-mouse.

September 3

Well, here is a reason for missing Frida: writing letters. Who else loved my news the way she did? A neighbor named Romulus. Now a sister named Parthenia.

"Don't trouble yourself over it, that's my sister Parthenia Goins," said Mrs. Brown today, hardly even looking up from the page she was typing. "Her husband Ottie is out there too, I see. And some of the nephews."

I'd just told her a band of gypsies had come to the end of their rope on Montford Avenue and were camped on the front yard. Very chagrined, therefore, to learn it was Mrs. Brown's family, come down into town from "the hells." A twice-yearly event, at "Eastertide and the Laboring Day," for the purchase of dry goods and a checkup on the moral progress of Sister Violet. The trip takes them the better part of a day, even though they live only a few miles up toward Mount Mitchell. But the road is "fearsome hateful."

They showed up out there at noon, in a Model T that looked older than God and more likely to drop an axle. The man in the driving seat opened the door to stretch his legs, revealing a beard that reached his belt buckle. Clumped in the back, an old-looking woman and shifting herd of oxlike boys. They sat in the car for hours, until the heat drove them out into the shade of the maple in the front yard. They showed no sign of coming to the door. Mrs. Brown said they likely meant to fetch her back to Mrs. Bittle's, and were waiting for her day's work to end.

"Shouldn't we ask them in?"

"They won't come."

"Well then, you should go."

"I'm not done here. It won't vex them any to wait."

"For *hours?*" I peered out through the curtain. "Couldn't they do some errands and come back, to save their time?"

"Mr. Shepherd, if they had any money or one precious thing, they'd be sure to save it. But time they have aplenty. They like to spend it where they be."

Realizing they might have come to investigate Sister Violet's situation, I did insist on asking them in. Elder Sister accepted, eventually, while the males remained outdoors, all of them smoking pipes. Mrs. Brown introduced us but begged a few minutes more to finish the week's work. The sister, *Parthenia*! What a strange creature, peering about this living room like Columbus among the red men of Hispaniola. She sat in a parlor chair with feet together, hands folded, a black kerchief covering her hair, a lumpish dress covering everything else down to her boots. Not even Frida could have worked this particular peasant style to much advantage. She declined my offer of tea, fiercely, as if accustomed to being poisoned by strangers. We sat facing one another across the shocking silence.

Finally: "Who mought ye all be?"

"I beg your pardon?"

"Who's yer folks?"

"My parents both passed away. I don't have any family."

She took this in slowly, like a snake digesting its catch. Then: "How old be ye?"

"Thirty."

Many other questions stood in line after these, each patiently waiting its turn, each one finally spitting, rubbing its hands, and stepping up to position.

"Violet says ye be from Mexee-co?"

"I lived there. But I was born outside Washington. My mother was Mexican, her father did business with the government here, so that's how she and my father came to meet. She was too young, the family disowned her over the marriage." *Stop*. Filling up a silence with blather, like a radio man. That cannot be what a Parthenia requires.

"Well." A pause. "What brung ye up this air way off the branch?"

A good question. Trying to steer the conversation onto her family proved difficult, but ultimately yielded Parthenia's fascinating diagnosis of Sister Violet's yen for self-improvement: "Our mother read the books. We believe it made her tubercular."

A long pause.

"Violet be the same."

Another pause.

"We was all in our family borned with sense. But Violet be the only one to vex herself on wanting to be learn-ed." *Born-ed, learn-ed*, here was the raw version of Violet's peculiar diction, without the gloss acquired from twenty years of office work. "We was afeared she would turn out like t'other one. The lady doctor that was born-ed here in the town."

"Elizabeth Blackwell?"

"That one. Violet readen a book on her. Mother was afeared of her going away to be learned for the doctoring."

"That would have been an interesting career for your sister."

"Not hardly, sir. T'would of put her in a hazard of hell's fire."

"Medical school?"

"To be learn-ed for the science, yessir. Them men casting aspersion on our Lord's hand in the Creation."

In the dining room, visible through the archway, Sister Violet's lip remained buttoned but her eyebrows nearly reached her widow's peak by the time she finished filing the day's mail. Parthenia took her away then, evidently satisfied the new employer would not threaten her sister's virtue or encourage any interest in the sciences. It explains a good deal about Mrs. Brown: her aloneness in the world, as far from home in this town as any boy from Mexico. Probably farther, given the scalding disapproval of anything "learn-ed." And yet she does carry her origins with her, revealed in the rhythms of speech, the talent for keeping counsel. The unusual respect for silence. Parthenia's silences outlasted her sentences every time, and carried greater weight. How will their tongue survive in a modern world, where the talkers rush to trample every pause?

September 14

Mr. Lincoln Barnes, my Mr. Lincoln. He means well. A second novel makes me "a novelist," says he, and therefore duty-bound to meet my editor in New York. He can't know how entirely it's out of the question. He should invite me to dance with angels on the head of a pin, I'd sooner try, if I could do it from home. But my failure will mean conceding every battle. Beginning with my title, *Where the Eagle Eats the Snake.*

"Wrong," he pronounced yesterday on the telephone. "People hate snakes."

Well then, wouldn't they be happy to see an eagle tearing one to pieces, sitting on a cactus plant? The dust-jacket art seems ready made.

He is keen to call it *Pilgrims of Chapultepec.*

Americans take "pilgrim" to mean the fellow in buckled shoes with hands folded in prayer. And the unpronounceable remainder, as dubious as Brand X soap.

Mrs. Brown suggests that for the next one I ought to turn in the manuscript with a title I despise. That way, she says, they're apt to change it to something you favor. A trick she learned while working for the U.S. Army.

September 26

The exhibit, *Advancing American Art*, is advancing at this very moment toward the National Gallery, packed up on the train with Tom Cuddy as its Shipping Shepherd. And still I have no answer for him. Tommy the golden boy, with the good looks of Van Heijenoort and a better idea how to use them—it's possible he has never been turned down before. On the telephone, he coaxes. Says I have to be there in D.C., he's desperate for backup, certain there is trouble afoot. Congress has called a special hearing to discuss the exhibit after they've had a look at it. And what Tommy said about the Hearst Press is true, Mrs. Brown brought in one of their magazine ads today, a reproduction of one of the "ugly" paintings with the caption "Your Money Bought This!" They suggest a foregone conclusion among soap-buying housewives: your money would be better spent on soap. But with Mrs. Brown their propaganda failed: she is now intently curious about the show.

Paris with Tommy, dear Lord what a vision. (He was dazzling enough in a dim boxcar.) But surely he'll understand there is too much to do here, revisions and galley proofs still ahead. He'll be less willing to understand why Washington is out of the question. To have a look at those modernists, have a drink with old Tom, help him ship out the paintings. Patiently Mrs. Brown waits to send an answer: yes or no. Probably she has already drafted both letters and only needs the word. Such is her efficiency.

We discussed it again this afternoon, or rather I talked. Justifying my absurd fear of travel and exposure, despising it all the while. My face must have been the Picture of Dorian Gray. At the end, when he goes to pieces.

She used the quiet voice she seems to draw up from a different time, the childhood in mountain hells, I suppose.

"What do ye fear will happen?"

There was no sound but the clock in the hall: *tick, tick*.

"Mr. Shepherd, ye cannot stop a bad thought from coming into your head. But ye need not pull up a chair and bide it sit down."

October 2

The matter is settled, the letter sent. Mrs. Brown provided the solution: herself. She will go along on the trip, make all arrangements, reserve the hotel rooms for both of us in names no one could recognize. No girls in short socks will gather in the halls. We will take the Roadster, she'll carry the money-purse and purchase the gasoline, no strangers need be addressed on the journey. Only Tom, once we arrive at the gallery.

Indispensable Mrs. Brown. She has known all along the problem is not the grippe. But couldn't know how her firm hand on my arm could make many things possible, including walking out the door onto that swaying bridge.

"It appeared you needed steadying," was her diagnosis.

October 12

Poor Tom. And also the forty-odd artists who will suffer from this, but somehow I worry most for Tom. He believed in *Advancing American Art*, and not just the free ride to Europe. Now he has to hang his head, call Paris and Prague, and explain the show isn't coming. They will dismantle it, sell off these treasures to the first low bid so the Department of State can recover the taxpayers' cash. The boss will make Tommy do the worst of it. The O'Keeffe already went for fifty dollars he said, salt in the wound.

Mrs. Brown and I were more than ready to put miles between ourselves and that debacle. But the journey home was long. The mountain parkway is a strange passage from city into wilderness, hundreds of miles of forest and vale without habitation. Occasionally an apple orchard, fenced by a zigzag of split rails, like a piece of green calico cut with pinking shears. Driving along high ridgetops is like being a bird on the wing, with slopes dropping steeply away from the roadsides, and views opening out to rumpled, hazy horizons. The leaves were crimson, auburn, jade, and gold, lying together in patchwork against the mountainsides. "God's hand bestoweth beauty on the advancing trial of winter," Mrs. Brown quoted. But it looked as if God had turned over the job to a Mexican muralist.

When first I made this drive, the forests were leafless. I told Mrs. Brown about it. Father unexpectedly dead, and then this endless passage into a barren wilderness. I thought I had come to a nation of the interred.

"Then you came to Mrs. Bittle's," she said, "and knew it for certain."

"Old Judd seemed mummified. True enough. But certainly not you or Miss McKellar."

Each time we stopped for gasoline she insisted we take on coffee and sandwiches as well. "Feed the car, feed the driver," was her succinct advice. The gray mass of a storm sat on the mountains to the west, waiting like a predator. In the afternoon it pounced, drenching the view and washing the brilliant leaves into matted sop in the road. The rain on the windscreen was blinding. The wiper had to be cranked every few seconds, and it made for difficult, one-handed driving. Mrs. Brown offered to help turn the wiper lever, but its location overhead above the driver makes that awkward.

"Mr. Ford should have thought to put it over here," she said, "so the passenger could help."

"He knew better. In life's dampest passages, the driver often has to go it alone."

"I ought to know that. Here knitting socks without one child of my own."

"Is *that* what you have there? I thought it was an indigo porcupine."

She had a laugh at that. She has eleven nephews and nieces, I learned, and meant to outfit the tribe on this journey, working through socks from top to toe, all from the same massive hank of blue wool. The coming holiday shall be known as "The Christmas of the Blue Socks from Aunt Violet." She worked on a little frame of four interlocked needles that poked out in every direction as she passed the yarn through its rounds.

"Aren't you afraid you'll hurt yourself with that?"

"Mr. Shepherd, if women feared knitting needles as men do, the world would go bare-naked."

What had happened in Washington was an outrage. Yet life goes forward mostly as an exchange of pleasantries on a narrow bridge that hangs above the chasm of outrage. "There's Grandfather Mountain. See, the shape of it. An old man lying down."

"Is it too cold for you? We could stop and get the lap blanket from the back."

"No. I'm warm-blooded."

"We're lucky it's cold. This Roadster overheats famously on hard inclines."

"You don't say."

Grand white clapboard hotels turned up sparsely along the route, their front porches mostly populated with empty rocking chairs. At dusk they began to be lit by the yellow glow of lamplight. Once, just as we passed an inn, a black-skinned man in a red jacket was lighting the porch lanterns one by one, leaning with difficulty around elegant men who sat idle, smoking cigars. Castes of the nation.

Mrs. Brown finally broached the void. "*Indigo Porcupine*, that could just as well be the name of one of those paintings we saw at the show."

"Yes. *Indigo Porcupine Leaping into the Void*, that might do."

"Well. I couldn't make out what all they were meant to be. Truly I've never seen the like, Mr. Shepherd. But I'm deeply obliged for it."

"I wasn't going to come until you volunteered as escort. So I'm the one obliged."

"For all, I meant. The paintings and our nation's capital. Going right straight in the hall where the Congress meets."

"Had you not been to Washington before?"

"This is my first time out of Buncombe County."

"Really?"

"Yes sir. I've read the *Geographic*s since I was a girl. My sisters could tell you, I strained for travel like a horse fresh to the bit. But never thought it would happen."

"Mrs. Brown, you make me ashamed. The whole world knocks at my door, and all I want to do is stay home."

"It's a wonder," she said tactfully, working at a tiny sock.

"Well, you're a worldlier person than most of those congressmen. They want Norman Rockwell and statues of muscular horses and nothing new under the sun."

"Even still. There was no cause to speak so rudely. What peeved them?"

"Fear, maybe. The foreign element, that's what Tom thought. They expected to go in the gallery and see old friends, but instead they met strangers. Gashes of color and surrealism. It made them uneasy."

"They didn't say 'uneasy.' They said 'un-American.' I can't see that. If an American paints it, then it's American, isn't it?"

"Not according to Mr. Rankin and the Congress."

Or Truman: *If that's art, then I'm a Hottentot.* Others said *vulgar, obscene, insane, namby-pamby pacifism.* Or *Stalinist*, a perfect irony, from these congressmen who seem as determined as Stalin to suppress creativity among artists. The show scared them out of their wits. The Special Session was a thrashing.

"We should have taken Tom out of that hearing. It was humiliating."

"Your poor friend, he'd worked so. He'll take it hard, will he not?"

"Oh, believe me. Tom Cuddy feels for those paintings about the way you do for your nieces and nephews. He'd knit socks for Winslow Homer, if he knew how. I've seen that in him ever since the civilian services. Moving paintings and sculptures to safekeeping, that was America the Beautiful, for Tom. That was patriotism."

"Bless his heart."

Bless it indeed. Now he's had to hear Congress declare the whole Western world threatened by some paint and canvas. Our finest painters, a menace. One was specifically damned for having urged Roosevelt to come to the aid of the Soviet Union and Britain, after Hitler attacked Russia. Which in fact, Roosevelt did.

The click of knitting needles, the shush of tires through leafy muck. The lozenge of space inside the automobile felt surprisingly safe, like a small home moving through a tunnel of darkness. Mrs. Brown finished off a sock before speaking again.

"Not all the pictures were hard to cipher. Some were plain. The ones with cemeteries and tenement houses got people the most riled, if you ask me. More than the ones that looked like dribble-drabble."

"The Guglielmi and those."

"Why do you think?"

"Congress has to keep up appearances. The paintings were going around the world. We can't let them know we have racial strife and tenement houses."

"My stars, Mr. Shepherd. Europe is lying in a pile. On the news they said Berlin city just dug two thousand graves for the ones that aim to starve to death before spring."

A car blazed by, two bright eyes in the dark.

"They had to dig the graves before the ground froze," she added.

"I understand."

"And London, no better. I read they're allowed nought but four ounces of knitting wool for the year and two yards of material, to cover each person in a family. They must be about naked. What's the harm in those folks seeing some of our troubles?"

"Well, five years of wartime censorship. Old habits die hard. We've gotten very good at pretending everything is shipshape here. Don't you feel that way?"

"What way?"

"That it's a little dangerous to advertise our weak points. Jerry and Tokyo Rose might be listening. Loose lips sink ships."

"They *were* listening. But the war's ended."

"True. But if it keeps the paintings pretty and all people's whining buttoned up, maybe they'll want a new war every five years."

"Mr. Shepherd, for shame. That is no subject for jest. We can't keep on forever saying the nation entire is perfect. Because between you and me, sir, it is not." The needles clicked in the dark. She must have read the pattern with her fingertips.

"Do you remember the first advice you ever gave me?"

She seemed to think it over. "The pot roast at Mrs. Bittle's?"

"Advice about writing."

"I never."

"Oh, you did. In that first letter. You said Tom Wolfe got himself in hot water exposing the scandals of Asheville, and I was wise to keep my story in Mexico. Here was your advice: people love to read about sins and errors, but not their own."

She considered this. "That's different from putting sins and errors off the map entire. How can it be un-American to paint a picture of sadness?"

"I don't know. But they did not want to see any waves on the domestic waters."

For several minutes she knitted at her sock, evidently struggling not to say any more. At length she lost the battle. "If you're standing in the manure pile, it's somebody's job to mention the stink. Those congressmen are saying we have to call it a meadow of buttercups instead of a cesspool. Even the artists have to."

"Well, but suppose the artist's job is just to keep everyone amused? Maybe get their minds off the stink, by calling it a meadow. Where's the harm?"

"Nobody will climb out of the pile. There's the harm. They'll keep where they are, deep to the knees in dung, trying to outdo each other remarking on the buttercups."

"Well, I write historical romance. I'm sorry to let you down, but any time you're looking for the meadow and buttercups, I'm your man."

"Fiddlesticks, Mr. Shepherd. Do ye think I ken ye not?"

"Do you know me? I suppose you do. Well enough."

"Well enough. You are good to children whose parents are not. You take in the straggliest cats. You are dismayed by the treatment of the Negro. You read more newspapers than Mr. Hearst himself, though it aggravates you to no end. Shiffling through all that claptrap hunting a day's one glory. The rise of the little man somewhere, or the fall of a tyrant."

"Is that everything?"

"About. I believe you stand on the side of the union of labor."

"Well done, Mrs. Brown. You can read me like a book."

Even in the full darkness I could feel her glare, the dangerous force of her. She had those needles.

"Set your photograph on the dustcover, or not, it makes no difference. You are still there, Mr. Shepherd, plain to see. Your first one was about the hatefulness of war, everyone said so. How it fills up the rich men's pockets and grieves the poor ones."

"I see."

"You needn't squirm, Mr. Shepherd. Your words are your own wee bairns. You need not leave them orphaned. You should stand up proud and say, 'Those are mine!' "

Soon we passed through the long tunnel at Little Switzerland, a deeper darkness within the night's blue darkness, like a cave in the sea. Mrs. Brown's knitting stayed in her lap, the strange blue bundle with its armature of needles, like a peculiar pet she could no longer bear to touch. When we reached Mrs. Bittle's she said good-bye, but until then we hardly spoke any more. Both driver and passenger seemed to need all our energies to find the way ahead, staring at the bleakness and the rain.

November 15

A letter from Frida after all this time, opened with trembling hands. Thrill and fear are really the same, inside a body. Her operation a partial success, good news, though she still suffers. The handsome Spaniard she met in New York seems to be good medicine, a sturdy platform from which to forgive. Her grammar was so odd though, barely coherent. The date on the letter was Lev's birthday and the day of the October Revolution, but no mention of either. No more red carnations on the table for old loves, the *viejo* and democratic social-ism. Diego has gone over completely to the side of the Stalinists now. And she, perhaps to the side of morphine.

December 24
A gift: knitted gloves of soft gray wool. What a remarkable sensation, to slide them on and feel each finger fit perfectly in its allotted space. "I noticed you have none," she said. "Or wear none. I thought maybe they didn't use them in Mexico."

"I've bought three pair since I moved here and they're all too short in the fingers. I wind up with webbed hands like a duck."

"Well, see, I wondered. Your fingers are about twice what God gave the rest of us."

I held out both gloved hands, stunned by the sight of perfection. "How did you do this? Did you measure me in my sleep?"

She grinned. "A grease stain on one of your letters. You must have leaned on the table to stand up, after eating a bacon sandwich."

"Very impressive."

"I brought in a rule and measured all the fingers."

I turned my hands over, admiring the row of slant stitches across each thumb gusset. "Not blue, though. I thought you specialized in indigo."

"Oh, those socks you mean, out of that cheap handspun. Those were for the children. This is pure merino from Belk's. I can use quality on you, because you're not planning to outgrow these in a year or run holes in them on purpose."

"I'll try not to let you down."

A memory of snow. A hill striped sideways with blue shadows

of trees. Screaming, the thrill of pursuit, some adult lobbing white balls, making the sound of a cannon blast with every volley. Cupping up hard snow that leaves pills of ice clinging to the fuzzy palms. Mittens, red with a snowflake pattern across the knuckles, made by someone. Father's mother? No contact was allowed later on, it was Mother's choice to leave everything: grandmothers, snow. All water-ice returns to the breath of the world. But those cast-off mittens might still be somewhere. Evidence of a boy's existence.

I told Mrs. Brown she'd given me my first Christmas gift in over ten years. In our many days together, she has not betrayed such emotion as that confession invoked. "Ten year! And not one soul to give you a measly giftie?"

"My family is all gone."

"But *people*. In Mexico you worked in homes, did ye not?"

"The last ones were Russian, they didn't pay Christmas any notice. Mr. Trotsky had us work through like any other day."

"He didn't hold with our Lord Jesus?"

"He was a good man. But no, he didn't. He was Jewish, his background."

"He's the one that got killed."

"Yes."

"And the ones before that, all Jews?"

"No. Mrs. Rivera was crazy for Christmas, she always organized feasts. I was the cook."

"So you had to work straight through."

"I did."

"Mr. Shepherd, it pains me to be gone away next week."

"Honestly, I'm glad you asked. You need to go see your family, and I need to be reminded what regular people do at holiday times."

"Well, regular, I wouldn't know. But you. You'll have nought here to tell you it's Christmas. What will you do?"

What will an acorn do when it has lain awhile in the ground and the rain swells its husk? Become a fig? "I have the galley proofs to finish," I said.

"Now Mr. Shepherd, that is a fib. You finished those, and I know it."

"I wanted to have one more look. And then I'll start writing something new."

The eyebrows soared. "What about?"

"I'm not sure."

She gathered up her purse and gloves, preparing to go. A light snow had been falling all day. "All work and no play, Mr. Shepherd. Makes the meat go to gristle."

"Does it? I thought it made Jack a dull boy."

"It would do that as well."

"I'll probably get nothing done at all, thanks to the pile of books you brought from the library. I'll poke up the fire and have Christmas with Mr. Hardy and Mr. Dickens. What could be better? And Tristram Shandy. The cats are hinting that I should cook a leg of lamb, so maybe I will. And I'm sure Eddie Cantor and Nora Martin will sing some carols for me on Wednesday night."

"I hate to tell you, but they're singing for their sponsor. I think it's Sal Hepatica."

"You are cruel, Mrs. Brown. Next you'll tell me all those girls on the Lucky Strike Hit Parade are crooning for Lucky Strike cigarettes, and not me."

She sat with her hands on her pocketbook, waiting.

"You want to say something. Go ahead."

"None of my business, Mr. Shepherd. But a man would have a girl usually. Or attachments. That aren't cats or books."

I took off the gloves and folded them carefully. "Now this is really a case of the skillet calling the kettle black. Thirty years is a long time to stay a widow."

"I did have a runny-go at marriage. The one time."

"Well, don't worry. I've had my runny-goes. Attachments, as you say."

"If you say so. And no Christmas present for ten years. If you get attached to something, seems like it wouldn't come all that far loose."

"No, wait, I forgot. Last Christmas Romulus brought over a jam cake from his mother. Half the cake, actually. He said they'd had enough of it."

"Blessed are the grateful, Mr. Shepherd, but that is no account as a real present. Half a jam cake showing signs of prior use."

Chispa slipped into the room, around the edge of the door and along the wall, flattened to it, as if pulled sideways by a separate order of gravity. Slowly she crossed the bottom of the bookcase in similar manner, into the inglenook by the fireplace. I unfolded the gloves. It was tempting to put them on, wear them until Whitsuntide. "I'm not the sort of person who attracts gifts."

"Mr. Shepherd, do ye think I believe it? I open the mail, with all such things in it as people can let sail. Even little embroidered things."

"Then I should say I'm not a good recipient. When people are no good at relationships, I've noticed they often blame the other people. But I don't."

"I've never heard you blame a soul for anything, Mr. Shepherd. It's one of your qualities. To the extent I sometimes wonder if your mother dropped you on your head."

"No, she probably carried me in a suitcase—she was eternally on the move. Anyone I especially liked was soon gone, household people or friends. It's been like that. Or they've left me on their own initiative. Mostly by dying."

"Well. I am not a one to argue with mortal demise."

"Well said, Mrs. Brown."

"You ought to write it down. About yourself and all those that went away."

"What, write about my life? Like poor old Tristram Shandy trying to remember his whole story helter-skelter?"

"You'd get further," she said. "You've been keeping good notes all along."

"Who would want to read such trivial stuff?"

"Well, why write it down in the first place, then? Because you do. I'm not putting my nose into anything, you do it plain in the open, Mr. Shepherd. Seems to me, if you really wanted shed of your own days, you'd not take such care to put them all down on a page. I see you go so deep in it, you forget day or night and have breakfast at supper."

"I'm just a writer. It's my way of thinking."

"It's your attachments. That's what it looks like to me. You might do as well to attach to your own self, alongside all these story people you dream up from nowhere."

"But who would want to read that?"

The light outside had gone dusky, and now the wind raised a low keen against the window. Clumps of snow fell out of the trees, shattering across the yard. "You won't want to miss your five-fifteen bus," I said.

She donned a formidable knitted hat and stood to leave, reaching to shake my hand. "I will see you on Monday week. Happy Christmas, Mr. Shepherd."

"Happy Christmas, Mrs. Brown. I thank you for the gift."

She closed the door and stepped out toward Haywood, leaving behind a house as silent as an underworld. Chisme slipped into the room, pulled by the same sidelong gravity across the bottom of the wall into the inglenook. Chispa immediately left it then, according to the inscrutable laws of attraction and indifference. The hall clock divided the scene into measured increments: *Tick, tick.*

Who would want to read all this?

Book Review

by United Press

Picture the lady walking by, a real looker, gold bangles on her arm and a tattoo on her ankle. She's headed out for some shopping, with a basket strapped on her back. For today's menu she may choose iguana roasted on the spit, or perhaps armadillo. For cash, her gal pals trade cocoa beans, or a handy gadget that's the rage with their better halves here in ancient Mexico: a double-edged throwing spear called the *atel-atel*.

That's the opening scene of *Pilgrims of Chapultepec*, a novel by Harrison Shepherd that reads like a joyride. This tribe of ancients will settle down in village life for only so long before it loses its charm to pox, invasion, or bandits—you can count on it. Then they hit the trail again, goaded on by a wild-eyed chief who claims he'll lead them to a promised land. How will they know they've found it? He claims the gods told him to look for an eagle on a cactus, snacking on snake.

Apart from its forehead-wrinkle of a title, this book aims to please: hair-rising battles, narrow escapes, and a heaping portion of adventure, in a tale of hardnosed leaders and men who suffer them.

The Evening Post, *March 8, 1947*

"Books for Thought," by Sam Hall Mitchell

The Quick and the Dead

Author Harrison Shepherd, the diffident but talented prodigy who last year brought us *Vassals of Majesty*, has another winning turn based on historical fact in ancient Mexico. In *Pilgrims of Chapultepec*, the Aztec people are driven from their ancestral home in a journey with more twists than a Chinaman's queue. By its end, the author has tackled some surprising themes, including the atom-bomb question.

These pilgrims hike for decades, pushed by a mad king who always promises happiness is just around the bend. The author's "Studs Lonigan" is an Indian youth named Poatlicue, watched by the jealous king as he hones his skill in battle. Golden boy Poatlicue was singled out by the gods at thirteen to hurl the first *atl-atl*—a razor-sharp flying weapon put in the hero's hand as he was about to die in his first battle. In a New World *Deus ex machina*, the weapon was carried to the hero by an eagle.

The ruthless king fears an upstart's power to unseat him, and offers a bargain: if Poatlicue maintains his loyalty without a hitch, he'll someday help rule the nation. But "someday" never comes, and Poatlicue grows a cynical stripe, doubting the value of following an unwise leader. On dark nights he wonders if the gods chose him for a reason: to behead the sniveling king, and rule in his place?

Poatlicue even questions the seductive power of his *atl-atl*. His tribesmen revere it as a god, rushing to make replicas of the weapon, worshipping it on an altar, believing it will grant them absolute rule. But Poatlicue notes a worrisome trend: as his tribesmen reproduce the blade's design, so do their enemies. Having perfected it, they fashion harsher weapons. With each battle the death numbers grow higher, the killing tools more precise.

Just as we've lately been warned by Bernard Baruch's somber report to Congress, these pilgrims must choose between the quick and the dead, when fate gives them a dread power without means to stop its baleful use. Baruch argues for disposal of all atom bombs, while author Shepherd only calls the reader to wonder until the final page: has the sacred weapon saved those who wield it, or doomed them?

The Asheville Trumpet, *April 8, 1947*

Asheville Writer a Mystery

by Carl Nicholas

Here where Mountain Air is clearest and Heaven is the Nearest, our most prominent writer gives a taste of faraway places in *Pilgrims of Chaltipica*, a new book flying off the shelves this month of every bookstore in the nation. Mrs. Jack Cates, owner of Cates Bookshop, tells us Harrison Shepherd knows the ropes of his trade and this book will not disappoint. "We had a hubbub the week it came in," she said. "Nobody wants to read anything but. And I'm going to warn you, it's got more bare skin in it than a hot day at Beaver Lake."

The author bases his books on his own experience growing up in Mexico, but has resided in the Montford Hills neighborhood since 1941. Calls from the *Trumpet* have not been returned. Mrs. Cates speculates he may regard his privacy, as "the most eligible bachelor in town, if not North Carolina."

At the Asheville Skating Club next door to the bookstore, 21 comely lasses partook of our survey on the subject, with fifteen saying they are "Hep to Shepherd," but definitely. Six maintained otherwise, "Spooky" and "cold cut" among the reasons given. Nine young ladies say they hold it against him for not serving in the armed forces due to a 4-F status, but the others say it was not his fault due to a perforated eardrum, the condition shared with crooner Frank Sinatra. All wondered how a well-heeled single fellow spends his time, as the author has sold nearly one million copies. As the old Asheville saying goes, Our moonshine is the meanest, our Stories are the keenest, our Sportmen are the gamest and—so it seems—our Bachelors are the Tamest!

The Echo, *April 26, 1947*

Pilgrims of Chapultepec, BY HARRISON W. SHEPHERD
$2.69, Stratford and Sons, New York

Don't look now, but a new chump named Harrison W. Shepherd is more popular than Wendell Wilkie. His *Pilgrims of Chaplutepec* is storming the nation this month and sure to be translated abroad. Don't be surprised one day if you hear they're reading Harrison Shepherd in China.

This one will be snapped up by the movies, so read it now before you see the picture. The glittering backdrop of Mexico spreads across every page, and the young hero is a heart-throb, with good looks and a secret weapon to boot. Ladies, this one will break your heart. Will this author ever give us a happy ending?

Shepherd slathers emotion on the page, yet in real life he is a shy fellow who guards against any showing of his feelings. A friend who's known him since college days revealed this mental reserve goes back to Shepherd's short-pants days, when even at his mother's funeral he remained cool as ice.

However, our source revealed, old friend Harry has one curious quirk: "He cannot look at a beautiful woman without whistling."

April 30

It was the perforated eardrum that put the pepper on Mrs. Brown. And the whistling at girls. "This friend from college days. Is that a person?"

"I don't think so. Given that I didn't go to college. The people of my past are dead and gone, Mrs. Brown, that's a fact." *Billy*

Boorzai's huge hands, both of us suffocating with laughter, trying to keep still. An officer's footsteps outside in the hall. Pounding hearts, scarlet shame.

"Who would reckon. The papers make things up out of the blue sky."

"Or, they find a little rain cloud and help it along."

She hesitated in the doorway, backlit from the upstairs hall in her square-shouldered, putty-colored suit. Platform shoes with ankle straps, oh my, and hair let out of its net today, pinned at the sides and curled at the shoulders, longer than I remembered. She looks like a tiny, earnest Jane Russell. Lately it's crossed my mind to wonder if there is some fellow. She takes a midday break for errands and a bite in one of the luncheonettes on Charlotte. She could be meeting a sailor, for all I know.

"When you see a thing like this in print, Mr. Shepherd, people think it's true. I almost think it myself, and that's me, knowing better. How can they do it?"

"Somehow they manage, every day of the year. Why be surprised, just because this time the victim is me?"

She stayed in the doorway. She doesn't like to come in the study, for fear of disturbing. "Mr. Shepherd, why are ye *not*? A shocking thing ought to shock."

A shocking thing. "The man I worked for in Mexico, I don't even know how to tell you what the newsmen did to him. One night some gunmen broke into the house and attacked him with machine guns, attacked all of us, the staff and his family. His grandson got hurt. We were terrified they'd come back. But the press said Lev had organized this attack himself to get sympathy for his cause. They reported that as fact."

"My stars."

"It didn't help us get police protection, I can tell you. And that's just one thing, a case that comes to mind. The other man I worked for reportedly ate human flesh."

"Well. That's Mexican newspapers. We want to think ours are better here. But I suppose they say the same about us."

"It was all over everywhere, about Trotsky staging the shooting attack. Europe, New York. It starts in one paper, and that's the source. The others pick it up and pass it along. Lev used to say there are two kinds of papers, the ones that lie every day, and the ones that save it for special campaigns, for greater impact."

"But a perforated eardrum. My stars. It's like you said. It starts with one and then it goes. We've not heard the end of that one."

"Like howler monkeys."

"The *Trumpet's* your own hometown. They could have asked."

"If they had called, what would you have said?"

She looked like a model standing for a portrait of misery: shoulders squared, high eyebrows knit, hands tightly folded. "I would do as you ask. Mr. Shepherd has no comment to make on that."

"Thank you."

"But."

"But?"

"When they have nothing, they fill in. If you don't stop them, they fill in more. It's like you've agreed to it. To their way of thinking, saying nothing is the same as agreeing."

"Are you saying it's my responsibility to stop another man from lying?"

"Well. No. It's his to stop himself."

"Dios habla por el que calle."

"Meaning what, Mr. Shepherd?"

"God speaks for the man who keeps quiet."

"If you say so."

" 'No comment' means 'no comment.' It does not mean, 'I hate to admit this, but yes, he has a punctured eardrum.' "

"Well, people think that. And taking the Fifth means you're guilty."

"Whatever they may think, it does not. A blank space on a form, the missing page, a void, a hole in your knowledge of someone—it's still some real *thing*. It exists. You don't get to fill it in with whatever you want. I'm staking myself on a principle, Mrs. Brown. This country promises us the presumption of innocence."

"*Presumptions* we have got, Mr. Shepherd. Coming out our ears."

"What would you have me say? Mr. Shepherd does not have a punctured eardrum, he does not have a friend from college days, he *does* look at pretty girls without whistling—oh, that's a trap. Where does it stop?"

She had no answer.

"If the *atl-atl* was meant as a symbol for the atom bomb, can't we let the reader have a chance to decide?"

"Well, I know what you're saying. The reporters would have you put in the grinder and feed you to Baby with a spoon."

"I don't think the reporters really want to know the first thing about me. They fancy themselves artists. They'd rather draw free-hand."

"They do have questions."

"I know. The one fellow wanted to ask me about Truman and the Soviet containment policy, remember? *Collier's*, I think."

"*New York Times. Collier's* said they wouldn't even run a review unless you spoke to them."

"And did they?"

"A little one. It wasn't very good."

"If I talked, I would only end up giving them more blanks to fill in. 'How do you feel about Truman's new anti-Soviet position, Mr. Shepherd?' No comment. 'That Bette Davis is quite a looker, isn't she, Mr. Shepherd?' No comment."

"So, the punctured eardrum. No comment."

"Correct."

"Next they'll be reporting you died."

"Imagine the peace and quiet."

The telephone rang, and she ran to get it. Her stockings had seams down the backs. I tried out a wolf-whistle—a feeble one, but I heard her pause on the stairs.

A sample of the mail received May 15, 1947, seventy-five letters in all. After publication of *Pilgrims of Chapultepec*, Stratford and Sons posted the mail forward in boxes once or twice weekly. —VB

Dear Mr. Shepherd,
At the youthful age of seventy here is one codger who tips my hat to you.
For years I have re-read the favorites because the new authors are not up
to snuff. But some weeks ago I ran short and went to my corner bookstore
for a suggestion. The fellow handed me two by Harrison W. Shepherd, a
name unknown to me. I read both without a pause. Of course I blush at
scenes of copulation and revelry. But you show that modern times are no
different from the old, and people the same everywhere. I was stationed
overseas in the first war and never learned to like it, but it did teach me a
thing or two. Thank you for adding spunk to my life. I look forward to your
other books.
Sincerely,

COLLIN THOMAS

Dear Mr. Shepherd,
Although we have never met I consider you a friend. You touch and inspire
me. I read **Vassals of Majesty** *twice and now the new one. Thank you*
for putting my own heart into words. I have wanted to show courage the
way your characters do. You show that men at the top don't always have
any more smarts than the rest of us. I have been thinking of telling my
boss to jump in the lake and look for better. (Secretary.) Now I just might
achieve my goal.
With admiration,

LYNNE HILL

Dear Mr. Shepherd,

I had to read your book in history at Lancaster Valley High. I don't read too many books but yours is okay. It gave me a lot to ponder about Poatlicue wanting to be a good citizen, and then ending up wanting to kill the King. Our teacher said to ask you three questions about ancient times of Mexico, for our report. My questions:

1. Is it true the Eagle gave the people their first weapon.

2. What kind of government did they have, Democracy or Dictator?

3. Did you ever really shoot a dear?

Thank you. My report is due May 12.
Yours truly,

WENDELL DIXON

One of 19 letters enclosed in a single packet from Lancaster Valley High School, California. —VB

Dear Mr. Harrison Shepherd
My heart is full of happiness, just knowing you are holding this letter in your hand. Thank you for being an author. You have gotten me through a lot of sad times, when my mother died especially. Sometimes I do everything I can just to get through the day, so I can curl up at night with my favorite book. When life is humdrum or just plain old sad I know you will take me away to the place where troubles are forgotten. When I get a letter back from you my life will be complete. Thank you, thank you.
Yours,

ROXANNE WILLS

All correspondence answered in the same week received, insofar as possible. No photographs or inclusions. —VB

June 6, 1947

Dear Frida,

Diego's telegram has terrified me not a little. He seems to believe the doctors nearly killed you, so I fear for all concerned. But for you, above all. I'm determined today to send a cheerful letter, to give you a little picknick from your worries, as you have done often for me. You'll find in this package your birthday present. Don't be too disappointed: it's only another book, which I hope will amuse you. If not, blame yourself, you should have left me a cook.

I am trying to begin a new story that will be about the Mayans, I think, and the fall of civilizations. Everyone wants a happy ending this time, so this should be just the ticket. But the writing proceeds slowly, when life is filled with such thrilling distractions. Only last week I purchased a packet of clothespins, and a new billfold. (The shopgirl informed me it has a secret pouch.) The Roadster and I "Make a Date to Lubricate" every 30 days at the garage on Coxe Avenue. A new appliance shop has opened down the street! And right now I am spying out my study window into the treetops where a gigantic bird is pecking a hole. I wish you could see the creature: its red hair stands straight up, as mine does on Mondays. Goodness, the wood chips fly, this thing is the size of an ox. And you were worried my life was dull.

I never want for company. The neighbor boy Romulus seems to prefer my house to his own, now that summer is here and he is paroled from Grade Six. With hands shoved deep in overall pockets he wanders around the house coveting things, but is not a thief. He asks. He particularly wants the little carved idol from Teotihuacán. I haven't told him it's a stolen object. Instead I gave him a fountain pen and an old fedora and he pretends to be Edward Murrow, using a Doomsday voice to interview the cats. I also offered to give him a cat, the useless black one I call Chisme, but he won't take it.

My stenographer comes Monday through Friday to answer mail and telephone, for over a year now. My wonderful amanuensis. She works at the dining room table. With each fresh day's mail piled high there, we pray: "For what we are about to receive may the Lord make us truly thankful." She is a whiz, I have known her sometimes to get through nearly a hundred letters from readers in a day, typing up a kind little note in answer to each. She hauls it all to the post office in a gigantic leather satchel she found somewhere, such as might have been used by the Pony Express: over her shoulder she slings it, and off she goes, does Violet Brown. I can't help thinking you would appreciate the irony of her name, for she is a dove-gray little bird. And something like the mother I need, commanding me to leave the house for fresh air at least once daily, if only to the corner for cigarettes. Lately she has stepped up the program: I am to undertake some level of social adventure each week. Going to the movies by myself is acceptable (Mrs. Brown is lenient), and not too bad if I slip in after the house has gone dark. The purpose of the outings is to overcome my dread of the world and all things in it. Now the magazines are saying I have a punctured eardrum, which is helpful. If the world howls too loudly, I can pretend I don't hear.

Please send word you are recovering. Diego's telegram was a shocker. He seems extremely angry, not only with your doctors but also the world and Every Damn Gringo in it, myself included. You might let him know, Truman did not consult me before committing to defeat the Communists in Greece and Turkey. Secretary of State Marshall has announced a new plan for European assistance that won't thrill your husband either. Frida, you understand men. How are these leaders different from the boys I used to watch at school, trying to make up their teams for football? Before this war we had six great players on the grass. Now only two are left standing. Naturally those two will be rivals, and try to get the rest to line up on their side. Dimes and candy will help, sure.

I struggle to understand why Diego supports Stalin now, after working so closely with Lev, and even seeing him murdered. What rational motives could cause Diego to make this change? "It's a revolutionary necessity," he said, but how am I to know what that means? Betrayal, as the means to an end? Nearly every day I wake up shocked at how little in this world I comprehend. Perhaps Diego is right, and despite all my years of serving brilliant men I am only a dumb gringo. I shall try to keep to the task I seem to know: writing stories for people who believe if you throw a rock, it could roll uphill. If your husband says I am an idiot on the subject of politics, certainly he should know. So don't ask me about the peaceful atom, or how to raise the birth rate in France.

For your amusement I enclose a newspaper review, a favorite from the last round. I take it as proof I am no literary great, but Mrs. Brown says it proves my books are about Important Things. Diego may take it as written proof that someone here besides myself opposes Truman's shocking turn against the rising proletariat. But mostly it proves nothing. You know reviewers, they are the wind in their own sails. I should like to write my books only for the dear person who lies awake reading in bed until page last, then lets the open book fall gently on her face, to touch her smile or drink her tears.

I'm not brave, as you are. However badly broken, you still stand up. In your Tehuana dresses, in your garden, with the pomegranate trees bending toward you to open their red flowers. No matter what happens, you will still be at the center of the world.
Your friend,

INSÓLITO

The New York Weekly Review, *April 26, 1947*

Author's Second Strike Hits the Mark

by Donald Brewer

Do not mistake Harrison Shepherd for a literary great. His stories are full-to-brimming with lusty, bare-chested youths. The settings are glamorous, the plots chest-heavers. You may not admit it to your friends, but somehow you can't put them down.

Pilgrims of Chapultepec (Stratford and Sons), set in Mexico before the Conquest, recounts a pilgrimage of people cast out from home, doomed to follow a neurotic leader who picks fights with his own shadow. Shepherd makes the case for those who find themselves on the ropes against bad policy, wondering what the Sam Hill their leader could be thinking. The protagonist, a boy named Poatlicue, struggles to be a model citizen but comes to view his nation's long march as a winning game for the king, and the scourge of everyone else.

Author Shepherd combines Leatherstocking action with Chaplinesque pathos, as shown in this symbolic hunting scene: Poatlicue and his friend skin a deer, grousing about the king as they hack their kill into anatomical bits. Their leader has made another outrageous edict, reversing a treaty of friendship with a neighboring clan, deciding now it can't be trusted. The tribe will have to move again, in a season when food is scarce. These youths are rankled. Poatlicue tosses a pair of testicles in the dust, calling them "the buck's last big hopes in sad little bags."

He tells his pal, "Our leader is an empty sack. You could just as well knock him over, put a head with horns on a stick, and follow that. Most of us never choose to believe in the nation, we just come up short on better ideas. It's probably a law: the public imagination may not exceed the size of the leaders' ballocks."

The author may be alluding here to the testimony of Donald Benedict, the New York theological student who refused to register for the draft during the war. "We do not contend that the American people maliciously choose the vicious instrument of war," said Benedict during trial, "but in a perplexing situation they lack the imagination and religious faith to respond in a different manner."

Does Shepherd mean to put himself in the draft-dodger's camp? One could ask many questions of this politically astute novelist, starting with his opinion of a leader who has just set the nation reeling with an abrupt foreign policy reversal, from friendly cooperation to Truman's so-called "containment" of the USSR.

We can only wonder, as Shepherd declines to be interviewed. But this week as we line up behind our man in Washington, shelling up $400 million to fight our friends of yesterday because "Every nation must choose," we might listen for a thump in the dust, and wonder whether the public's big hopes will fit in that small, sad sack.

June 11

She has raised the subject of the memoir yet again. I thought it had died a natural death, but no, she presses. If only to put to rest the perforated eardrum question, I suspect. The first chapter was very good in her opinion, and today she confessed that since the day I gave it to her, she comes to work each morning hoping I'll have the next part of it ready for her to type.

"It's been near six months now since chapter one, Mr. Shepherd. If it takes that long for each, you'll not outlive your own boyhood."

I told her I was very sorry to crush her hopes in coming to work and so forth. But there will be no next part. It was a direly mistaken idea. And anyway, even several months ago when I was entertaining the project, I'd run across a problem, the missing notebook. The very next little diary after the first one. I hadn't yet told her.

"I can't recall that year without it. I should have let you know a while ago. I just hoped you'd forget about it. The memoir fell apart before I'd even gotten started."

"What do you mean, gone?" Her eye went to the shelf. She knows where I keep them. They should all be put to the flame.

"The crucial missing piece of the manuscript. There's a word for that, historians use. A lacuna. So blame it on fate and history, if you want."

"Did you have it before? When you first took all of them out of the crate?"

This is not a set of keys gone missing, I informed her with some irritation. It just didn't come with the rest, when Frida packed up the notebooks and papers. Probably it had burned at the police station, or slipped behind a cabinet. It's small, I know exactly what it looked like—it was a little leather-bound accounts book I stole from the maid. About the size of your hand. And now it's gone. Just forget about the memoir, I'm working on something different now. I should burn up all these notebooks so you'll stop nagging me about it.

Mrs. Brown is no fool. "If you remember what the booklet looked like, you could remember well enough what was in it."

June 23

It was only one letter, but she carried it up the stairs like a sack of bricks.

"I hate to disturb. But it says they need this back by return mail."

"Who is it?"

"J. Parnell Thomas."

"Friend or foe?"

"Chairman, House Committee on Un-American Activities, formerly known as the Dies Committee."

"Rings a bell, Dies. Oh yes, I know these gentlemen." *Committee Diez*, we'd pronounced it, like "ten" in Spanish. They arranged Lev's trip to Washington, the visas all prepared and then canceled at the last minute.

"You do?" She seemed startled.

"I mean, I know what they do. They called up my former em-

ployer once, from Mexico. To testify on the treacheries of Stalin.
They're still in business?"

She held up the letter. "It's just a form. They say it's gone out to all
employees of the Department of State."

"I don't believe I'll be shipping any more art for the government."

"Present or previous, it says. They need you to sign a statement
saying you're loyal to the United States government."

"Goodness. Why wouldn't I be?"

She moved her glasses from her head to her nose, and read: "Due
to close wartime cooperation between the United States and Russia,
certain strategic areas of our government may have been opened to
Communist sympathizers. As of March 21, 1947, the President and
Congress have undertaken to secure the loyalty of all government
workers."

"Very cloak and dagger. Where do I sign?"

She approached the bench. "Are you sure you ought, Mr. Shepherd? If you aren't looking to work for the government again, maybe
there isn't need."

"Are you doubting my loyalty?"

She surrendered the letter for signature.

"Mrs. Brown, I don't hate much and I don't love much. I'm a free
man. But I love writing books for Americans. Look at those letters,
all that sky-blue goodness, this country is the berries. And Joseph
Stalin murdered my friend. He would have gotten me too, if I'd
stood in the way."

"So you've said, Mr. Shepherd. I know it sets a haint upon you,
especially of an August, and no wonder. It's no small thing to see
bloody murder."

I signed the letter and handed it back. "I'm inclined in this case to
stand out of the way. If I ever had to choose, I might just be a coward
and save my own skin."

"That's people," she said. "That's how the Good Lord made us
to be."

"No, I've known brave men. Lev saw his children murdered, and never gave in. Even young boys, like Sheldon Harte. I'm told they loved life even more than I do, it's why they became revolutionaries. And ended up bludgeoned, or dead in a lime pit."

She stood waiting. For a happier ending, I suppose.

"What we end up calling history is a kind of knife, slicing down through time. A few people are hard enough to bend its edge. But most won't even stand close to the blade. I'm one of those. We don't bend anything."

"You do, though. Look here, I've got boxes of letters downstairs, as you said yourself. People telling how you've saved their day. Do ye think that's ordinary?"

"I give them a lark. A few hours to forget about a disappointing family, or a boss who's a tyrant. But all that mess is still there, when the book ends. I don't save people."

The corners of her mouth turned down. "Mr. Shepherd, here's your trouble. You don't know your own strength."

July 3

The Pack Square Soda Shoppe could not have been decked out with more flag bunting if it were the president's train car. Romulus was dazzled, mostly by his buffalo-like ice cream sundae. Mrs. Brown was rosy-cheeked, sipping cola through a straw. "You ought be thrilled," she said. "A Hollywood movie."

"You keep saying that. I am thrilled."

"Well, ye barely look it," she said. She had on the blue Kerrybrooke beret (*wear it many ways!*), identifying this as a Social Adventure of the highest order.

"You don't," Romulus agreed.

"You pipe down. We men have to stick together. We don't wear our hearts on our sleeves the way women do."

He glanced at his shoulder, then took a whitecap of cream off his cheek with the back of a hand.

"It's not really settled yet, for one thing. Where am I going to find an agent?"

"Did Mr. Lincoln say you *have* to get one? Or just that it would be helpful? What did he say about that exactly?"

"Find someone to negotiate the contract, for the motion-picture option. He can't do it, this is between Hollywood and me. An agent is customary. Or a lawyer."

"Well, lawyers, I have known a few. Working for the city. Not that they could reckon out a motion-picture contract."

"Mr. Lincoln said brace ourselves for the press. They'll step up the pursuit."

A pea-green Cadillac hunched past like some kind of water animal, the small, split windshield like close-set eyes. They will never make another car to touch the Roadster. Mrs. Brown put us in a corner near the window so I wouldn't be spotted in the shop. But even so, I could hear a couple of girls at the counter saying "*him. It is. Isn't.*"

Mrs. Brown snapped her fingers. "I have a man! I think I have the business card in my jewelry case." For a moment she sounded so modern, a regular Gal Friday.

And she saves the day, once again. Or might have, we will see. It's a gentleman she met last year when he came to inquire about renting a vacant room. They had quite a chat in the parlor while waiting for Mrs. Bittle to return from the hairdresser's. He's from New York City, a lawyer, mostly retired. Moving to Asheville because his wife had died, and the daughter Margaret lived here. Grandchildren. He was not sure how he'd get along in Dixieland, but you can't argue with a daughter named Margaret. Even Harry Truman knows that, ha-ha. They'd had the radio on in the parlor, and Mrs. Brown happened to wonder aloud what the stars looked like. The voices give a certain impression, but the actors might be less attractive than they sound. It was *Duffy's Tavern*. The gentleman told her as a matter of fact the actress playing Duffy's daughter might sound like a girl but she is a mature woman, forty if she's a day.

Shirley Booth. And the other one, Cass Daley, has an overbite like a lizard.

How did he know? He's met them, that's how. It's his line. A radio and television lawyer.

I asked Mrs. Brown why he hadn't taken the room.

"Mrs. Bittle wouldn't let to him. She was sorry. He seemed very nice."

"I see. Only good people here. Was he a Negro?"

"No."

"Just too much of a Yankee?"

She glanced at Romulus, then back at me. "You told me in Mexico you use to work for some . . . that didn't have Christmas."

Even the word *Christmas* didn't jog a glimmer of attention from Romulus. He sat glaze-eyed as a mystic, stirring his bowl of ice-cream soup streaked with a bleeding cherry. I tried to work out the puzzle.

"Oh. This man was a Jew?"

Arthur Gold. The New York Jew in Dixie.

July 22

Poor Mrs. Brown, in trouble with the Woman's Club. She was so distracted today, she had to call Mr. Gold back twice to get instructions about mailing the motion-picture contract. She seems to think these women mean to throw her in a cauldron of bouillon. As one of three members of the Cultural Committee, she was not the lone perpetrator. But it was her idea to involve the children.

Their speaker was a girl named Surya, spending the summer with Asheville relatives, on leave from some school-term cultural exchange in Washington, D.C. It was Genevieve Kohler (neighbor to the relatives) who hatched the plot to have this girl from Russia as their Cultural Evening speaker. The ladies were in a jam; Decorating with the New Plastic Fabrics had canceled on short notice. Mrs. Brown thought of inviting local high-school girls, pointing it up as an inspirational talk. The girl had lived through war. She had overcome long odds to arrive in Carolina in time for a Rhododendron Festival.

Mrs. Brown said she looked as hale as a milkmaid, with brown eyes and dimples, and that the talk was both informative and audible. Little Surya spoke of her school in Russia, the free health program, and the Russian plan for old-age care. She contrasted the governing bodies in her country with the newly elected Communist government of Poland. She made favorable mention of the position of women in modern-day Russia, and equally favorable mention of North Carolina, and Washington, D.C. Mrs. Brown said the girl was so unsophisticated and gracious, she doubted the child would have disparaged a spider, had it walked across her face. Yet she created a sensation. The Woman's Club president, vice president, and sergeant-at-arms stood up as a block, interrupted the speaker to announce their devotion to America, and walked out. Some others followed. Mothers who had brought their girls, responding to the handbill distributed at school, left with daughters in tow, indignant at having been duped.

"We did not mislead," Mrs. Brown insists. "We put on the handbill she was here in the youth foreign exchange from the former St. Petersburg."

"Maybe they thought you meant St. Petersburg, the Republic of Florida. Just across the waters from the Mexican continent, as I recall."

"Mr. Shepherd, this is not a joking matter."

"I'm trying to lighten your mood. It's not the disaster you think."

The Asheville Trumpet, *July 23, 1947*

Crowd Takes Stand Against Reds

by Edwina Boudreaux

"Every nation must choose between alternative ways of life," according to President Truman, and the Woman's Club

Cultural Evening on Monday was no exception. Tickets sold for twenty-five cents each for a Cultural Lecture by Miss Surya Poldava of the U.S.S.R. Mrs. Herb Lutheridge, President, opened with the Pledge of Allegiance. The evening was interrupted by audience disagreement and brought to a hasty conclusion. Pastor Case Mabrey of Coxe First Baptist led the closing prayer. Mrs. Lutheridge had no knowledge of the speaker and apologizes to each and every person in attendance. "The Woman's Club opposes the suppression of personal freedoms and Communistic way of life."

Superintendent of Schools Ron Stanley called a meeting yesterday to discuss an occurrence that "shocked the school system." The nature of this assembly was repugnant to all who work with youth in Buncombe County, said Stanley, who did not attend the lecture. "It runs contrary to the philosophy of education we operate under." The Asheville D.A.R. speaking through Mrs. Talmadge Rich, President-General, not in attendance, also went on record as opposing the lecture.

The Woman's Club will review its guidelines to prevent the unfortunate occurrence in the future. The program was organized by Mrs. Glen Kohler of Haywood and Mrs. Violet Brown of Tunnel Road. Reached by telephone, Mrs. Kohler gave her occupation as housewife and apologized for the turn of events. Mrs. Brown, a secretary for a private firm, maintained the program was informative. "The world has people of all kinds, and I don't see the good of wrapping our children's heads in cotton wool." Brown, age 47, is a childless widow.

The Woman's Club will refund the ticket price to all who attended.

August 15, 1947

Harrison W. Shepherd
30 Montford Avenue
Asheville, North Carolina

Dear Mr. Shepherd,
The Federal Bureau of Investigation has been charged by the Congress of the United States with the conduct of routine investigations of all persons presently or previously employed by the federal government, in an effort to ascertain complete and unswerving loyalty to the United States. For this purpose we request that you immediately supply in writing the following information: all former places of residence and former employers, schools and colleges attended, organizations, associations and groups in which the employee has been a member.

This investigation is directed by the House Committee on Un-American Activities (formerly known as Dies Committee) and shall include reference to Civil Service Commission files, military and naval intelligence records, Dies Committee hearings of other employees when applicable, and local law-enforcement files. Any derogatory information will result in a full field investigation.

The Civil Service Commission maintains a master index covering all persons who have been subject to loyalty investigations since Sept. 1, 1939. The Loyalty Review Board of North Carolina shall be furnished the name of any individual found to have associated with such persons, or with any organization, movement, or group the Attorney General has designated as totalitarian, fascist, communist, or subversive, or advocating acts of force or violence or seeking to alter the form of government of the United States by unconstitutional means. The Review Board shall also be furnished with any evidence of sabotage, espionage, treason, sedition, or knowingly associating with spies. The McCormack Registration Act (Statute 631) requires that every person who is an agent of a foreign principal shall register with the Secretary of State. The Voorhis Act (Statute 1201) requires that every

organization subject to foreign control which engages in political activity
shall be required to register with the Attorney General.

This Bureau expects your full and prompt cooperation in this
investigation.
Sincerely,

J. EDGAR HOOVER, DIRECTOR
FEDERAL BUREAU OF INVESTIGATION

September 2

Arthur Gold in person looks like a Dashiell Hammett private eye:
white shirt, rolled-up sleeves, steel blue eyes, necktie five years out
of date. He's a regular white-haired Sam Spade, complete with the
smoky little office up a narrow flight of stairs in the Woolworth's
building on Henry Street. The ever-burning cigarette, the epic
slouch. If Violet Brown is the "do be" gal for posture, Mr. Gold is the
"don't be." His narrow body describes the shape of an S in his chair,
with a meridian running through the head, navel, and shins, with
all else slumped to the fore or the aft. It was hard at first to reconcile the slumped posture with the astute voice on the telephone. But
within minutes he established himself as the same Mr. Gold, plank-
ing out the long sentences that arrive unfailingly at their destination.
He could be formidable in court. Except midway between his subject and object, you'd become distracted by the cigarette, wondering
when that worm of ash will finally drop on his shirt.

"Congratulations on your distinguished career." He unwound
himself to stand, shake hands. "Please, call me Artie. Finally we
meet, sit down, please. It's a pleasure doing business with a man who
has made so much of himself in a relatively short amount of time in
this country, and if I may say so, on this earth. How old are you?"

"Thirty-one."

He squinted, evaluating. "Yeah, okay. You look it."

He studied the letter for only a few seconds before tossing it on his desk. "To make a long story short? You will have to answer this. If you don't, they will send you another. It's a form, they've got millions of them. Please, tell me, what is it about this particular request that worries you?"

"I'm not really worried. There's nothing on that list that applies. Honestly, treason and sedition, violent overthrow. I'm all right until they add smoking in bed."

Artie laughed, bobbing his head from the shoulders.

"I'm just wondering what's behind it, before I answer. I make mistakes sometimes. I seem to be naive about certain things."

"How so?"

"I grew up in Mexico, in the Revolution. Being a Communist was just an ordinary household thing. About like fish on Fridays."

"I grew up in a country like that also. New York in the twenties. You ever hear of Eugene V. Debs?"

"I think so."

"So. Grew up in Mexico, but you are a citizen of the United States, this much I know from working on your film contract. You were born here, moved to Mexico at the age of twelve as I recall, returning when exactly?"

"September of '40. Before that, I was here two years to attend school."

He was making notes. "Where and when?"

"Potomac Academy, Washington, D.C., '32 and '33."

"District of Columbia in '32. The summer of the Bonus Army riots."

"I know. I was in them. I was sick a few weeks from the tear gas."

He looked up. "You were in the Bonus Army riots?"

"By accident. I was trying to make a delivery from the A&P."

"Holy smokes. I will not put this in your dossier."

"I don't think my dossier is going to be problematic."

"Mr. Shepherd. Should I call you Harry?"

"No. Just Shepherd is fine. Without the Mr."

"Shepherd. In seventy-five words or less, how would you describe your dossier?"

"Empty. That's the whole truth. I spent almost all my life until now putting food on other people's plates. Eating their leftovers, if any. So you could say my sentiments lodge in the proletarian quarter. The worker control of industry strikes me as a decent idea. But I'm not a member of anything. Is that seventy-five words?"

"Or less. You are concise."

"I don't even vote. My secretary needles me about that."

"You believe in the class struggle, but you don't vote?"

"This country is a puzzle. In Mexico even the conservatives grant the power of the syndicates. But here, during the strikes, the most liberal politicians called the Mine Workers president a coal-black son of Satan. The conservatives probably just thought he was Satan père. It's a pretty watery broth. Republicans, Democrats."

"This I will not deny."

"In the war they were all friends with Stalin, but now he's also joined the Satan family line. That one I agree with. This letter they've sent me, I only want to understand it. So I won't step in something. I tend to do that, step in things."

He sat staring, the ash end of his cigarette growing long and white. "I see. This letter worries you because you're thinking you may get hit with somebody else's gas on your way to the A&P."

"This letter confounds me. I know what communism is. But a few weeks ago, my secretary was voted out of her Woman's Club because she asked a girl from Russia to give a lecture. Just a schoolgirl."

"Shepherd, my friend. This month, in certain quarters, people are burning the *Graphic Survey* magazine because it contains a picture story on life in Russia. Photographs of farms. Windmills, whatever they have on farms. Russian cows. This incites people to bonfires."

"What do you think is frightening them?"

"Hearst news. If the paper says everyone this season will be wearing a Lilly Daché hat that resembles an armadillo, they will purchase the hat. If Hearst tells them to be afraid of Russia, they will buy that too."

"If the hat is too ridiculous, not everyone buys it."

Artie finally ashed his cigarette, then paused to light a new one from the old, which he left burning in the ashtray, presumably for ambiance. He reorganized his S-shaped body into a thoughtful pose against the desk. "Do you want to know my theory?"

"Of course."

"I think it's the bomb."

"People are afraid of the bomb?"

"Yes, I believe that is the heart of the matter. When that bomb went off over Japan, when we saw that an entire city could be turned to fire and gas, it changed the psychology of this country. And when I say 'psychology,' I mean that very literally. It's the radio, you see. The radio makes everyone feel the same thing at the same time. Instead of millions of various thoughts, one big psychological fixation. The radio commands our gut response. Are you following me?"

"Yes. I've seen that."

"That bomb scared the holy Moses out of us. We became horrified in our hearts that we had used it. Okay, it ended the war, it saved American life and so on and so forth. But everyone feels guilty, deep inside. Little Japanese children turned into flaming gas, we know this. How could we not feel bad?"

"I'm sure we do."

"Okay. We used the bomb. We convince ourselves we are very special people, to get to use this weapon. Ideal scenario, we would like to think it came to us from God, meant for our own use and no one else's." He leaned in, eyes and cigarette blazing. "You wrote a book about this topic, am I right?"

"You've read my books?"

"Of course I've read your books. You're an important client, I've read your books. You of all people understand this. Suddenly we are

God's chosen, we have this bomb, and we better be pretty damn certain no one else is going to get this bomb. We must clean our house thoroughly. Can you imagine what would happen if England also had the bomb, France, Germany, Japan, and the Soviet Union all had this bomb? How could a person go to sleep at night?"

"Those countries hardly have standing armies now, they're sacked. All but the Soviet Union."

"Okay. The Soviet Union. You get it."

"I thought we had nothing to fear but fear itself."

"You see, this is what I'm saying. The radio. It creates for us a psychology. Here's what happened to fear itself. Winston Churchill said, 'iron curtain.' Did you see how they all went crazy over that?"

"Of course."

"Then Truman said, 'Every nation must decide.' You are standing on one side of that curtain, my friend, or else you are on the other. And John Edgar Hoover, my God, this man. John Edgar Hoover says this curtain is what separates us from Satan and perhaps also the disease of leprosy. Did you happen to hear his testimony to Congress?"

"I read some of it."

"'The mad march of Red fascism in America. Teaching our youth a way of life that will destroy the sanctity of the home and respect for authority. Communism is not a political party but an evil and malignant way of life'—these are his words. A disease condition. A quarantine is necessary to keep it from infecting the nation."

"I read that. But newspapers exaggerate. I couldn't quite believe he said all that."

"You have a point. Maybe he did not. And yet in this case it happens that he did. I acquired a transcript of this testimony because it pertains to certain of my clients."

"Why did he say it? I mean, what are his rational motives?"

"Rational motives are not the scope of this discussion. He is an excitable man. He heads a powerful agency. The newspapers love this kind of thing, as you say. It's a moment of history, my friend. You wonder why you've received this letter. I am attempting to draw you a picture."

"Is that really his signature?"

"No. They have a machine. I read Frank Sinatra has one also, for autographs. Maybe you need one. Okay, do you know anything at all about this Dies Committee?"

"I've heard of it. Years ago they contacted my boss to come and testify. This was in Mexico. The State Department arranged visas for us, but it never happened."

"Your Mexican boss had something to say about un-American activities?"

"He wasn't Mexican, he was in exile there, under threat of death from Stalin. So he had a lot to say about the man. This was before the war, when the U.S. was getting very friendly with Stalin. Trotsky felt the U.S. was being hoodwinked. They needed to know he was treacherous."

"Trotsky."

"Lev Trotsky. He was my boss."

The cigarette ash fell to the floor. For a moment the lawyer himself seemed poised to follow it. He straightened, shook his head slowly, and reached for the letter on the desk. "I am going to give you a piece of advice. Don't mention that you once were employed by the leader of the Bolshevik Revolution."

"I was a cook. And this was Trotsky. He hated Stalin even more than J. Edgar Hoover does. He spent his whole life trying to overthrow the Soviet politburo. The American Communist Party vilified him."

"Let me just say, these subtleties are lost on your secretary's Woman's Club, and they are lost on the Dies Committee. Most of them don't know what communism is, could not pick it out of a lineup. They only know what *anti*communism is. The two are practically unrelated."

"You're telling me anticommunism is unrelated to communism. That doesn't make sense."

"It doesn't make sense to you. You're a man of words, so you think we're speaking here of tuna fish and disliking tuna fish, but we are not. We're talking tuna fish and the Spanish influenza." He reached into the papers on his desk and drew out a pair of spectacles. "All former places of residence and former employers," he read. "Schools and colleges attended, organizations in which you have been a member."

"What should I write?"

"Tell them exactly what they already know. Mexico, they probably know very little. Military service record they know. What was your tour?"

"Civilian service. That's how this came up. I helped move federal property for the Department of State during the war."

"Civilian service, so you were 4F?"

"Something like that."

He waited. The intensity of the man's gaze is extraordinary.

"Blue slip," I said.

"Okay. Disqualified from service on account of sexual indifference to the female of the species. This one I could never figure."

"They offered to put me in a psychiatric hospital, to get me sorted out. But then suddenly my particular talents were needed elsewhere, moving art treasures out of Washington. Both coasts were under attack, so it looked very urgent."

"This was when, '42?"

"The end of summer, right after the Japanese deployed their floatplane bomber from that sub they sent up the Columbia River. It looked like a good time for the country to get our goods under cover."

"You're putting me on. If it weren't for Tojo attacking Fort Stevens . . ."

"That's right. I might be up at Highlands Hospital with Zelda

Fitzgerald. Instead, I'm living down the street from there in a house I bought with Uncle Sam's paycheck."

"Shazam," said Artie. "All's fair in love and war."

"Believe me, I know this. Better than most."

"Well, for better or worse, all this they already know about you. What else? What employment history do they have in your file at the State Department?"

"I'm not sure. I think my name must have come to them through a gallery in New York where I delivered paintings from Mexico. Or the school where I taught Spanish."

"Okay, mention those. And anything you recall listing in your employment records at those establishments. Church membership, this kind of thing, to pad out the résumé. Though you are not a joiner, you've said. So give them primary schools in Mexico, the one in D.C. The name of the painter who sent you to New York."

"Will they really go and talk to instructors at the Potomac Academy?"

"So what, they'll find out you were a schoolboy. I don't want to worry you excessively, but schoolboy shenanigans are not now your biggest concern."

September 3
Today Bull's Eye departed, and all this he took with him: schoolboy shenanigans, promises broken, dormitories and secret assignations. An invisible boy made manifest, seen for once by another's eyes, if only for a short while. A city of memories has gone up in fire and gas, and there can be no remorse.

Mrs. Brown wouldn't tolerate having the notebook burned in the fireplace. But in the end she did the job herself, outside in the barrel where she burns scrap papers. "Potomac Academy 1933" has left the world.

She was opposed at first. "You need your notebooks," she kept insisting. Without the notes she fears I'll make a mess of things, like Tristram Shandy. She still refuses to believe the memoir will not be written. I met her gaze, and leveled.

"Look, Mrs. Brown. You're a practical person. And you know me. So don't ask for impossible things. I'm working on a different book now."

"So you said."

"It was a mistaken idea, the memoir. Dragging my own entrails out for the public. And not my idea to start with, you'll recall. I told you I'd given it up when the little leather-bound diary turned up missing. Really I should get rid of all of them, just so you'll quit nagging me about it. But I'm starting with this one."

She had come a half hour early, today of all days, and caught me red-handed. The broad, canvas-bound notebook in my hand. I'd been wondering how to set that cotton duck to flame; the army tends to manufacture indestructible things. Stamped plainly across the front: "Potomac Academy." She could probably see right through to the naked figures inside, as if catching me with an eight-pager. I may have blushed.

"If you won't let me burn it now, I'll just do it after you leave this evening."

"Do as you please then. This evening." Without another word she went to the dining room, slapped out the work on her table, and said little the whole day. But at five o'clock, crept upstairs to my study door. "Mr. Shepherd, be ye free for a word?"

"All right."

"It's something to grieve you, is it? In that notebook you now want burned."

She has borne so much from her inconstant leader. The panics of the last month, for example. A better August than some, but still she takes the brunt.

"It's nothing special, Mrs. Brown. I'm just ready to be done with school days."

"Anybody would be queasy, with federal men nosing in your business."

She acknowledged the deed would already be done, if she had not by chance caught the earlier bus this morning. "Mr. Shepherd, I've got no business depriving you of your own intents and purposes. Give it over and we'll be done."

She took it out to the backyard. I watched from the upstairs window, wondering if she would have a glance inside; it's possible I was testing her. But she did not look. It was her choice to burn it in the barrel with the day's used envelopes and botched letters, rather than in the living room. "Here now, it's still the dog days," she said. "What might the neighbors think, seeing smoke from your hearth on such a warm day of September?"

She is out there now. The week's rubbish went into the tar barrel, the canvas-bound book flaring vividly in the center, its blackened leaves impossibly thin and intact, curling open before disintegrating. She stepped back from the heat of the barrel, but will remain at her post until everything is vapor. Viewed from above, she is framed by fences on both sides of the strange tableau: Mrs. Brown destroys the evidence. Her hat, a small blue plate, dampening in dark speckles as a light summer rain begins to fall.

Now the job is done.

September 8

Today the appeasement program begins. After a weekend spent drawing together a mess of notes into genuine prose, I have produced evidence of a new book. Not just some vague excuse for avoiding the memoir, but two draft chapters of the novel set in Yucatán, handed over to Mrs. Brown. The setting is giving me trouble, though, as I've never visited the Yucatán. I need to see Chichén Itzá, the stones of those temples.

Mrs. Brown's eyebrows sailed, just to hear the names spoken aloud. You could see the childhood longing still in her. The girl, hiding in some chicken coop from sister Parthenia, dreamily turning pages of the *Geographic*.

I asked her to call the Asheville-Hendersonville air-port and find out how Pennsylvania Central Airlines might connect with Mérida. Mexico City will probably be the best bet. No, not passage for one. For two.

September 22

Harrison W. Shepherd
30 Montford Ave., Asheville, North Carolina

Dear Mr. Shepherd,
Allow me to acquaint you with our services. Aware, Inc. is a private loyalty firm whose programs are independent of any government agency. Our corporation publishes the well-known directory, **Strike Back,** *used to assist hiring practices in many entertainment and service-related industries. Employers from coast to coast have learned they can rely upon our research.*

We have information we believe to be important to your current federal investigation. We have evidence suggesting your books are being read by Communists in China, and that you have opposed the use of the atom bomb. We have a news story linking you to Charles Chaplin, who is almost certainly a Communist. We do not suggest that you are in fact a Communist. In many cases, our clients find they have been painted as such via the weasel-worded gestures of someone who is, in fact, a Communist. Every day, innocents in our country become pawns in the hands of sinister manipulations for the Communist cause. The extent of their network is sadly under-estimated by most. Attorney General Clark has released to us a list of 90 organizations the Justice Department believes to be Communist Fronts. Almost anyone could have unwittingly crossed paths with a person working under the guise of one of these organizations.

For a fee of $500 we offer you the invaluable opportunity to clear your name of several charges, including those listed above. We urge you to contact us without delay to discuss this opportunity to secure our services. Sincerely yours,

LOREN MATUS, DIRECTOR

AWARE, INC.

September 23

"No soap," says Artie Gold. "You tell them that, your attorney says no soap, jump in a lake, bye-bye birdie. This letter you do not even have to answer."

Artie had agreed to an emergency meeting on the condition we invite his twelve-year-old friend Grant. Ha-ha, as he would say. Grant is a blended scotch whisky. We met downtown on Patton Avenue, but en route to the bar he had to tramp through some errands. Coleman's Man Store to pick up a shirt. ("Margaret says if I show up one more time looking like a hobo she will put me in a home. It's the husband's parents, they're snobs.") Next, Reiser's Shoe Hospital, to fetch some resuscitated wing tips that should have gone to Reiser's Crematorium, if there is one. Then Finkelstein's Pawn.

"Is this how you generally impress new clients?"

Artie had handed his ticket through the iron grille, and we were waiting for the retrieval. "Ha! Don't worry, I am not living on Skid Row just yet," he said. "Although I wish the same could be said of all my clients. That ticket was given to me in lieu of payment, a very nice camel overcoat I'm told, to be had for only ten dollars." Artie lowered his voice. "I'm going to give it back to the poor guy when cold weather hits."

The bar was Leo's, a little joint in the odd flatiron building that's wedged into the acute corner of Battery and Wall. "This okay with you? Is it adequate to the purposes of impressing a new client?"

"It's fine. I'm sorry, that was a joke."

"Okay. Not very fancy, Leo's. But a club I am allowed to join." Carefully he folded and stacked his wardrobe on the stool beside him: camel coat, shirt, shoes. The girl at the bar had reached for the bottle of Grant's when he came in the door, and came over with two little glasses hooked on her fingertips like thimbles. Artie seemed distracted, watching her fill the glasses, finishing his cigarette. "That club out at Bent Creek, you know it? I recently had a very high-profile client who moved here from Hollywood, prospective client I should say, I'm not naming names, he wanted to take me to his golf club for dinner, Bent Creek. To celebrate, get acquainted. Mr. Heston, I say to him, have you seen their promotional materials? 'We cater to the better class of gentile clientele. We reserve the right to decline service to anyone we deem to be incompatible.' *Incompatible!*"

"Charlton Heston is your client?"

"As it happens, he is not."

The waitress retreated to the other end of the bar, wiping out glasses with a red chamois cloth, but kept glancing at us. Dark lashes, cheekbones, a red ribbon around her black hair, tied on top. A tall, long-waisted girl, but still there was something of Frida about her. The way she carried those glasses on her fingers. Probably a violation of some hygiene rule, but she gets away with it. Men want their lips on her fingertips.

"Hey, how about that Jackie Robinson?" Artie asked out of nowhere. His mind moves like a train, and he pitches things out its window at an astonishing clip. "Are you a baseball fan, Shepherd?"

"I should apologize now for all the things I don't know about. You might find me as thick-skulled as Mr. Heston. Baseball is a yen one learns from a father, I gather."

He tilted his head, nodded. Though quite a talker, Artie was also a listener.

"I wasn't raised in this country. Wasn't raised, really at all."

Artie exhaled a short laugh, not unsympathetic, and tossed back the shot of Grant's. "If a person is not raised, then what? He grows from a seed?"

The whisky was both stringent and soothing, like cigar smoke. Twelve years waiting for a moment, this gullet. "No. In the scullery kitchens and probably the salt mines of this world, many a child is not so much raised as hammered into shape, Artie. To be of use. Surviving by the grace of utility alone."

"This I know to be true, you are correct. Very well said. In this case, the absence of a father notwithstanding, have you heard of Jackie Robinson?"

"I do read the news. The Negro player they've let in the white leagues."

"I saw the man play at McCormick Field this summer. I was there."

"How was that?"

"Sensational. His second or third game with the Dodgers, and they play him down here in Dixie. The Colored section was packed like the last bus out of Arnhem, and the rest of the stands, empty. Like someone had yelled they were passing out free polio germs to the white people that day. I had a good seat, let me tell you."

"I'll bet."

He unfolded the letter and flattened it on the counter. The earlier one from J. Edgar Hoover he'd barely glanced at, but this one he studied with inordinate care. Nevertheless, his verdict: No soap.

"My secretary wanted to burn it with the trash."

"Good girl. You should give her a raise."

"Well. I'm taking her to Mexico."

"Really." A wise-guy smirk.

"As my assistant, Artie. She's forty-seven, for one thing. And for another, not my type."

"Ah, yes. I recall."

"You're only about the third or fourth person to know that about me, by the way. The Selective Service, God, and you. A few others. But certainly my mother never worked it out."

"Please. Discretion is my business, and I mean that sincerely."

"Mrs. Brown is my right hand. This is a research trip, and I'll need to stay a couple of months. She called you about helping with the passport."

"Right, I recall. Well, her opinion of this letter from quote-unquote Aware Incorporated was absolutely correct."

"It's not a form," I pointed out. "These things are very specific. Charles Chaplin. My books being read by Communists in China. I have to say, I'm flabbergasted."

"That is their intention, to flabbergast. Is this a verb, can I say that?"

"I suppose."

"Their mode is the surprise attack: they flabbergast. You hand over five hundred clams."

"And then the game ends?"

"Not exactly. These publications he mentions are real. They accumulate names of alleged Reds and publish them in directories."

"Who reads them?"

"Executives. Radio producers, Hollywood studios, even grocery chains. It's handy, no muss no fuss. They can assure their advertisers they are taking every available precaution against hiring a Red."

"But before he puts me on the list, he's offering the chance to clear my name, for a fee."

Artie spread his hands wide. "God bless America."

"That's straight blackmail. The employers must know the lists are meaningless."

"So you would think. But this guy Matus has acquired for himself a certain cachet. He used to be a member of the Communist Party. Twenty years ago, when everybody including your Aunt Frances was a member of the Communist Party. Now he comes to the FBI, of-

fers to come clean. Before you know it they've got him in front of
the HUAC, the whole works. So far he's remembered hundreds of
former associates who now work in government and the media, and
for an additional fee he will remember more. Amazing, his memory.
The *New York Times* is a major employer of Communists, he says.
Time and *Life* also. This guy is a star."

"And runs his own business on the side."

"An entrepreneur."

"Nobody could take this seriously."

The girl was still watching us. Down at the opposite end, leaning backward against the bar, fiddling with the cameo on a ribbon
around her neck.

Artie sighed. "I have a client. A former president of a prestigious
southern college. Served on the War Labor Board. Currently president of the Southern Human Welfare Conference. A very celebrated
guy, consulting fees and public speaking provide most of his income.
Suddenly, he has no income. He has protestors. This antisegregation
outfit over which he presides has turned up on the attorney general's
list, one of these ninety so-called Communist front organizations."

"On whose authority? Loren Matus?"

"The HUAC in its infinite wisdom has devised what they call an
acid test for revealing an organization's true colors. You want to hear
their criteria? Any one of the following is sufficient. Number one: it
shows unswerving loyalty to the Soviet Union. Or, two: it has refused
to condemn the Soviet Union. Or three: it has gained accolades from
the Communist press. Or four: it has displayed an anti-American
bias, despite professions of love for America."

"So. If you love America, but you hate the segregation laws . . ."

"Yes. That could arguably be an anti-American bias. Let me ask
a rhetorical question. Has the American Poodle Society explicitly
condemned the Soviet Union?" He signaled to the waitress, and she
came immediately, as if pulled on a string. Refilled our glasses, her
eyes carefully down. Then the quick smile, a flash of strong teeth

with a tiny center gap. Away she went, after that, unspooling the tether.

"Let me ask you something," Artie said. "A personal question, if I may. When you look at a beautiful girl, do you see beauty?"

"A fair question. When you look at a great painting, do you see beauty? You see color and form, right? Loveliness, allure, magnificence. Maybe even arousal. So tell me, Artie. Do you want to have sex with the painting?"

"I'm sorry, my interest is not prurient. I'm just a curious man. Curiosity killed the cat, my wife used to tell me very often."

"Anyway, this letter. You're advising me to ignore it?"

"I am advising you," he said slowly, "that you are being approached by a snake. You could attempt to reason with the snake, or you could offer it a cash contribution. Most likely the snake is still going to bite."

Grant's twelve-year-old whisky is a potent anesthetic. "Luckily enough, it doesn't matter, because I'm not looking for a job right now. I have the only job I ever wanted."

"Luckily enough. You are a writer, employed by the American imagination. Your publisher does not have to answer to any sponsors, only to your readers."

"*Employed by the American imagination.* I like that very much."

"Are they really reading you in China?"

"Goodness, no. Not even in France. Some reviewer said, 'Don't be surprised if this book shows up in China.' Something like that. They also said I was Chaplinesque."

"Well, many artists are not so lucky as yourself. Mr. Chaplin among them. Film stars, directors, television scriptwriters. They all have to be produced, they require sponsors. It's becoming a lucrative industry for the likes of Aware Incorporated."

Suddenly the girl was back, unsummoned. "You're the writer, aren't you? I'm crazy about your books."

"What writer?"

"Harrison Shepherd?"

"That's so strange. You're the second person to ask me that."

"Oh. Sorry, my mistake." She floated away, an unmoored skiff, and disappeared through a door at the back.

Artie reorganized his sigmoidal curve against the bar, the better to stare at his dimwit companion. "What's wrong with you? She's a sugar pie."

"I know it. I'm grateful. To all these girls, I really am."

"So, you could sign a damn cocktail napkin. It would have made her day."

"That's what I can't see, Artie. What thrilled her was a book—she wants a hero. Not some tin whistle double-gaiter on a barstool."

"So. In a pinch, you stand in."

"Do you know how that feels to me, to pass myself off as important? Exactly like passing counterfeit money. Look at her, she's magnificent. My name, some ink on a napkin. How could that be worth the gold-brick standard of her day?"

Artie swiveled back to face the bar, fished a pack of Old Golds out of his pocket.

"So. Matus the snake has contacted me because a motion-picture option got his attention. That's what you think?"

"You know what they say. God wants to punish you, he answers your prayers."

"Artie, I didn't pray for a motion picture. It makes me uneasy. I don't like attention."

"You have a funny way of choosing your profession, in that case."

"People think that. If a person is famous, he must have wanted to be in the public eye. But to me, writing books is a way to earn a living in my pajamas."

Artie nodded thoughtfully. "I take your point. People think lawyers are a cutthroat gang, and me, I couldn't cut the throat of a fish. Margaret says I should take up fishing. And I think, an old softie like me? What would I do if I caught one? Apologize?"

October 3

Two airplane tickets purchased, air-coach to Mexico and back, at a cost of $191 each. A breathtaking sum, but all in the line of duty; Arthur Gold says it can be worked out for some reduction in the tax later on. He is helping Mrs. Brown with the passport applications. Apartment queries sent to Mérida, and fair warning to Frida, expect a visit, though Diego is sure to be out of the country. Romulus will feed the cats and mind the house, eight weeks, I will have to remember to bring back a smashing present.

Mrs. Brown stands at the ready, her suitcase already packed, though the trip is six weeks away. No price is too high for this joy. Her thrill for adventure is a thing I dearly wish I could learn by example. She makes me wish for the boy who once could swim miles underwater, looking for treasure.

Today I teased her, asking whether I needed to look out for any fellow who might be angry with me for taking her off this way. She blinked, taken aback.

"Well, it's not out of the question," I said. "I'm aware that you're an attractive woman. And I've noticed you're sprucing up, of late."

She honestly blushed. No-nonsense Mrs. Brown. She said not to worry myself, if any man she cared for took an interest, I would be first to know it.

The New York Times, *October 23, 1947*

79 in Hollywood Found Subversive, Inquiry Head Says

Evidence of Communist Spying Will Be Offered
Next Week, Thomas Declares

By Samuel A. Tower, special to the New York Times

WASHINGTON, OCT. 22—Actors, writers and others in Hollywood were named today as members of the Communist party or as Communist sympathizers. The accusations were by Robert Taylor, screen actor, and by other movie figures as the inquiry of the House Committee on Un-American Activities into the extent of Communist penetration into the film industry went into its third day.

At the same time the movie industry, reacting to a persistent committee criticism that no anti-Communist pictures were being made, charged through its counsel, Paul V. McNutt, that suggestions concerning films to be made represented "one method of censorship" and did "violence to the principle of free speech."

The committee chairman, Rep. J. Parnell Thomas, asserted that the committee would produce at coming sessions evidence that "at least 79" persons in Hollywood had been engaged in subversive activity. After a noon executive session the committee announced that it would present next week evidence of Communist espionage activities, with a surprise witness, in developing further testimony that confidential data on an Army supersonic plane had fallen into Communist hands through a Hollywood literary agent.

Mr. Taylor, arriving to appear at the afternoon session, was greeted with an audible "ah" by the spectators, mostly women, who filled the hearing chamber. Outside the chamber there was a mob scene as those unable to get in swirled and pushed against Capitol police. In his testimony he declared at one point, "I personally believe the Communist party should be outlawed. If I had my way they'd all be sent back to Russia." When this drew loud applause from the audience, Chairman Thomas reprimanded the spectators and requested no further demonstrations.

Mr. Taylor asserted that there had been "more indications" of Communist activity in Hollywood in the past four or five years, but guarded and qualified his testimony when committee interrogators sought specific data on activities and individuals. He testified that, as a member of the Screen Actors

Guild, he had come to believe that there were actors and actresses "who, if not Communists, are working awfully hard to be so" and whose philosophy and tactics seemed closely akin to the Communist party line. This group constituted what he called "a disrupting influence." The handsome actor declared that the film, "Song of Russia," was, in his view, Communist propaganda and that he had objected "strenuously" to playing in it. He added, however, that the industry at that time was producing a number of movies designed to strengthen the feeling of the American people toward Russia. Mr. Taylor asserted that he had not knowingly worked with a Communist and would not do so. After twenty-five minutes on the stand the handsome star made his departure, accompanied by applause and shouts of "Hurray for Robert Taylor" from a middle-aged woman wearing a red hat.

Members of the Committee asked M-G-M executive James K. McGuinness, who is in charge of scripts for the studio: Has the industry the will to make anti-Communist movies? Why haven't they been made? Why couldn't the studios produce such films and circulate them through schools, like the patriotic wartime pictures?

Representative Emanuel Celler, D. NY, attacked the inquiry as an act to make "all true Americans blush with shame." "If Chairman Thomas sought to strike terror into the minds of the movie magnates, he succeeded. They were white-livered. One vital aspect of these antics must be kept in mind. Today it is the motion pictures. Tomorrow it may be the newspapers or the radio. The threat to civil liberties is a real one."

October 31

I have learned from experience, make the cookies early. Children will come to the door dressed as hobgoblins. When the doorbell rang just after four o'clock, Mrs. Brown carried the plate to the door. But it was a man, clearly audible. I was in the kitchen mopping up after the afternoon's baking. Flour covered everything like an early frost.

"No, he can't," she said, in a strained voice. "Mr. Shepherd is indisposed." Her instincts for protecting her boss are unflappable.

"Are you the lady of the house?"

"I'm the stenographer."

The badge startled her, and she can't remember the name. FBI, that much she remembers. He'd come to ask Mr. Shepherd a few questions, but as he was unavailable, Mrs. Brown was duty-bound to answer them herself, insofar as she was able.

After it was all over and he left, she came in the dining room and put her head down on the table. I made a pot of coffee. Then, together, we remembered and wrote it down. To show Artie later.

"How long has he lived in this house?"

(She guessed about five years)

"No," the man said. "Mr. Shepherd purchased this house October of 1943."

"Then, my stars, why ask?"

"Has he got a mortgage?"

"If a person has a house he has got a mortgage. Evidently you have the details."

"Where did he live before?"

"He let a room from Marian Bittle at her boarding house on the Black Mountain Highway. What they call the Tunnel Road."

"And before he came to Asheville?"

"I'm sure I don't know. I don't think I can answer any more questions."

"Well, you'll have to try. Executive Order 9835."

"What's that?"

"It means you have to try. If the FBI is asking, you answer. Where did he get that car? That's a pretty pricey car. Or was, in its day."

"I believe the car belonged to his deceased father."

"I noticed an empty Remy bottle in the trash. Is Mr. Shepherd a drinker?"

"I'm sure I don't know. I think we're finished. Mr. Shepherd's lawyer might be the one to take this farther, if needs be."

"Look, lady, don't get sore. An investigation doesn't necessarily mean he's under suspicion. We're conducting a field investigation."

"Of what?"

"Just the usual."

"You can't tell me what it is you think Mr. Shepherd has done?"

"No, ma'am, we cannot."

"But if he were here, you could tell him."

"No, ma'am, we cannot tell the accused this kind of thing, for security considerations. Do you happen to know his income?"

"For goodness' sake. He's a writer. He couldn't say himself what it's going to be, month to month. Do you know what books people will buy next year?"

"Does he attend any meetings?"

"No."

"Well, the neighbors said he does. They see him take the Haywood bus every Thursday. But on other days, only to the market or the newsstand."

"Mr. Shepherd goes to the library on Thursdays."

"Why so regular?"

"He finds it comforting to keep regular habits."

"Ma'am, do you know what magazines he reads?"

"He buys about everything on the Haywood news stand. You could go down there and make a list, if you like."

"Do you happen to know if he's ever studied up on Karl Marx?"

"Go and see if they sell Karl Marx on the Haywood newsstand."

"Do you know where Mr. Shepherd stands on Abstract Art?"

"Well, if he wanted a good look, I expect he'd stand in front of it."

"Very funny. Can you tell me the name of his cat?"

"Are his cats also under suspicion?"

"The neighbors said they hear him using an obscene word to call the cat."

"I've never heard Mr. Shepherd use obscene language against any person. Certainly not his cats."

"Well, they say that he does. They say he uses a very vulgar word to call the cat. They're concerned for the youngsters. They say the boy comes over here."

"My stars. What do they think he calls his cat?"

"I apologize, ma'am, it's a very vulgar word. They said *Jism*."

"The cat's name is Chisme. It means 'gossip'."

Mérida, Yucatán Peninsula

November 1947
Notes for a novel about the end of empire.

When Cortés's men first arrived here, they asked in Spanish, "What is the name of this place?" From the native Mayans they received the same answer every time: "Yucatán!" In their language that word means: "I do not understand you."

The apartment is decently spacious, the two bedrooms and a good-sized table for working in the main room, with the window overlooking the street. The kitchen and bath are a jumble but there's no need for cooking. It's too easy to walk downstairs to the restaurant in the courtyard, morning or night. The previous residents must have shared this languor, because a long, white sprout of a bean was growing from the drain of the sink when we arrived. I offered to put it in a pot for the balcony and call it our garden.

Mrs. Brown did not smile at the joke. She submits to not one iota of domesticity here, except to make the coffee as she did at home. The inside of her room I have not seen; we simply chose doors at the beginning, and her lair remains a mystery. She emerges each morning in her gloves and Lilly Daché hat, as reliably as the little Mayan women in the market will be wearing their white embroidered blouses and lace-bottomed skirts. The gloves and Lilly Daché are Mrs. Brown's native costume.

A typewriter is installed on the writing table, delivered yesterday, a sure sign of progress. A car and driver for touring the ancient sites may soon surface as well. Mrs. Brown has gamely got her sea legs on, already going to the shops on her own to get small necessities. Each day she manages more of the arrangements, soldiering through the obstacles of a language she cannot speak. My advice (which she did not heed): in answer to any question, say "Yucatán!" *I do not understand.*

A reasonable title for the novel: *The Name of This Place.*

But for now, the name of this place is mud. Or so Mrs. Brown must think, when forced to take her life in her white-gloved hands. She grips the side-arm of the rumble seat with one, the other squashing her hat to her head, as we pummel down the peninsula over shocking roads, navigated by our fearless driver Jesús. After all the time we spent searching for this combination, vehicle and driver both together in one place, I dare not ask whether he is old enough for the job. He is just a boy, despite the authority of his Mayan nose and magnificent profile. It's a shock to realize that, not his youth really but my age, that he must regard me as a man, perhaps his mother's age more or less, not worth any real study. A series of directions to follow, and a wage at the end of the journey.

And yet he's seen something of life already, clearly. His shirt is weathered as thin as a newspaper, and the lower part of one ear is missing. It took a while to notice that. It's his left, away from the passengers' side. He calmly asserted, when asked, that it was bitten off by a jaguar. So he has the imagination, if not the experience, for labor in the service of a novelist. He can lecture on any subject without hesitation. Today en route to Chichén Itzá it was the military history of his people, the Maya: "More courageous than ten armies of Federales," he shouted above the banging axles and backfiring engine of the ramshackle Ford. Or mostly Ford; one door and the front fenders are of a different parentage. Across the land of the mestizo we ride, in a mixed-caste automobile.

"At this place, Valladolid," Jesús announced above the racket, "we view the scene of the last Mayan rebellion. One hundred years ago the Yucateca took our whole peninsula back from the ladinos. We declared independence from Mexico like your Tejas of North America, and nearly made it the nation of the Maya again." Except for Mérida, he confessed, where the Federales lodged throughout the rebellion. But fate was decided at Valladolid. A final victory over the Mexican army was at hand, but just as the Mayan warriors were poised to strike, an old shaman came with urgent news: the ancient calendar said it was time to return to their villages to plant corn. They put down their weapons and went home.

"The Gods speak to my people in their hearts," says the boy called Jesús, beating his breast with one fist as he drives, head tilted back in sloe-eyed tranquillity even as the tires hit another crater in the road and his whole body levitates. The Mayans obeyed the ancient imperatives of survival. They walked away from power, letting the federal army take back the peninsula and return it to Mexican rule.

Somewhere during the lecture he lost his way on the dirt track through jungle, and we found ourselves also called back to his home village, conveniently at lunchtime, as it happened. We were near enough to Chichén Itzá, the temples of one of its outlying towns towered above the treetops, a monument to ancient prosperity throwing its shadow across thatched roofs and the naked children who gathered to see what might emerge from this calamitous machine. We could as well have arrived by flying saucer.

The mother of Jesús, similarly sloe-eyed, bade us sit on a log while she dipped beans from a cauldron that must bubble eternally on the fire outside her hut. Her name: Maria, naturally. Her lath house, like every one in the village, had a tall, peaked roof of thatch, open at each gable end for ventilation. Inside the open doorway a knot of motionless brown limbs, presumably sleeping children, weighted a hammock into a deep V shape, the inverse of the roofline. At the side of the house a scrambled garden grew, but the front was bare dirt, furnished only with the logs on which we perched. Mrs. Brown steadied the tin plate on her knee with a gloved hand, tweed skirt pulled around her knees, eyebrows sailing high, calf leather brogues set carefully together in the dust. Flowering riotously around her were a hundred or more orchids, planted in rusted lard tins. White, pink, yellow, the paired petals hung like butterflies above roots and leaves.

My beauties, Maria called them, leaning forward to brush a speck of ash from her son's worn shirt, then gently boxing his good ear. "The only importance is beauty."

The light here at the window is good, and the view is a satisfying distraction. The street stays busy at all hours, this apartment is only a short walk from the central plaza, the markets and old stone cathedral. It must be the oldest part of Mérida, judging by its charm and conspicuous fortifications.

In the afternoon when the sun lights the stucco buildings across the street, it's possible to count a dozen different colors of paint, all fading together on the highest parts of the wall: yellow, ochre, brick, blood, cobalt, turquoise. The national color of Mexico. And the scent of Mexico is a similar blend: jasmine, dog piss, cilantro, lime. Mexico admits you through an arched stone orifice into the tree-filled courtyard of its heart, where a dog pisses against a wall and a waiter hustles through a curtain of jasmine to bring a bowl of tortilla soup, steaming with cilantro and lime. Cats stalk lizards among the clay pots around the fountain, doves settle into the flowering vines and coo their prayers, thankful for the existence of lizards. The potted plants silently exhale, outgrowing their clay pots. Like Mexico's children they stand pinched and patient in last year's too-small shoes. The pebble thrown into the canyon bumps and tumbles downhill.

Here life is strong-scented, overpowering. Even the words. Just ordering breakfast requires some word like *toronja*, triplet of muscular syllables full of lust and tears, a squirt in the eye. Nothing like the effete "grapefruit," which does not even mean what it says.

Our young lord Jesús today found the right track to Chichén Itzá. What a marvel. The Temple of Warriors, the Ball Court, the tall pyramid called the Castle. Magnificent limestone buildings glare at one another in silence across the grassy plaza. Everything is dazzling white, a timeless architecture of pale limestone. Elegant and remote. Whatever I came here looking for is hiding, holding its breath. No crime and punishment present themselves in bloodstained hallways. Unlike the grisly Azteca with their gods sticking out their tongues, the Maya seem serenely untouchable. What they've left behind is in every measure as grand and elegant as the white marble temples of the Greeks.

In the fringe of forest surrounding the plaza we found more temples crumbling quietly into themselves, sleeping under green blankets of vine. Like the ruin in the forest on Isla Pixol, beside the hole in the water, at the end of the lacuna. That one had a smiling skeleton carved on a stone. Here, footpaths through the trees led away in all directions, to different parts of a partially excavated city: the marketplace with its carved columns. The steam bath in a shady grove, its dark stone chamber like a womb, entered through a tiny triangular doorway. The vault inside was a high, inverted V shape, punctuated at each end with a round hole for venting steam. Maybe the story begins here, lit by a dim, steamy ray of light streaming through that hole: the setting for a love scene, or a murder, better yet. Political intrigue. But the place feels bloodless.

The enormous central pyramid stands high and heroic, dominating the plaza. It seems taller than the Pyramid of the Sun at Teotihuacán, though memory can play tricks in matters of heroism. We felt compelled to climb its immense stone stairs to the very top, just as it was with Frida all those years ago, dragging her miserable leg all the way. But Mrs. Brown managed the climb without sending a single soul to the devil.

Today we drove south through villages of Mayan farmers, most beginning with *X*—pronounced "ish." X-puil, X-mal, Jesús revealed the secret of the Mayan tongue: shhh. *X* does not mark the spot, it marks a hush. The Mayans speak their language everywhere in the countryside, and it sounds like whispered secrets. Women stand together in doorways, muttering: shhh, shhh. Fathers and sons walk along the roadside carrying ancient-looking hoes, quietly making a plan: shhh.

Another day driving, this time to the east. We stopped at a town and walked out an ancient stone roadbed to the mouth of a lacuna. A cenote, it's called here: a deep, round hole with limestone cliffs for its sides and blue water at the bottom. A kingfisher darted through foliage, calling: *Kill him! Kill him!* The view from above was dizzying, down the sheer rock face of the hole to the water far below. No handrail stood at the cliff's edge to prevent our falling in. Or diving in, swimming down deep to see what is there, the devil or the sea.

It is fresh water here, many kilometers from the ocean. The Mayans built their towns and civilization on these cenotes, because no sacred thing is more holy than a water source. The entire Yucatán Peninsula has not a single river or stream running on its surface, only these water caves running below, with round mouths opening here and there to the light above. *Chi-chen* means "mouth of the world," and so it is, these gasping mouths are as old as human dread. The ancients fed them as best they knew how, throwing in jade and onyx, golden goblets, human remains. Without a thought to what they might be doing to their drinking water.

Jesús claimed that many valuable artifacts had been dredged from this cenote, but all had been carried off to Harvard and the Peabody Museum. He actually named those places, so it likely could be true. Colonial ransacking in the scientific age.

On our walk back through the jungle we looked but could find no trace of the ancient farms and villages that must have been here. Thousands of ordinary people were part of this metropolis, but their homes would have been perishable wattle and thatch, stuccoed with lime and mud. Every trace of their living has returned to the earth now, except for the limestone temples of art and worship. The things made of ambition, which rise higher than daily bread.

Our automobile parked in the village had attracted a crowd. The tallest boy introduced himself (Maximiliano), and demanded pay for having guarded the vehicle during our absence. "From whom?" we asked, and Maximiliano pointed to the gang of small thugs he claimed would have damaged or even dismantled it. "They are very crafty," he said in English. His payment, a handful of coins, he instantly distributed among all the vandals, their alliance thus perfected. Even morality is a business of supply and demand.

Some older boys had lurked back, distancing themselves from piracy, but came forward then with woodcarvings to sell. Mrs. Brown took one in hand, turning it carefully. They were figures of ancient warriors in elaborate headdress, very much like my little obsidian fellow. It was striking how the wide, slant faces of the figures resembled the faces of the boys who made them. Mrs. Brown paid the sculptor his price, only a little more than the extortion had cost us. A good day for young men standing on the stone and bones of their ancestors to make their way.

In the plaza near our apartment, people come every evening to stroll around in a circle. Lovers come drifting, connected by entwined fingers. Married couples come at a clip, the children like rafts towed on ropes behind the ship. No one is alone. Even the vendors sitting on stools around the periphery work steadily at connection, nodding at potential buyers, like a sewing machine prodding its needle into the cloth.

"We used to do this in Isla Pixol," I told Mrs. Brown. "My mother always wanted to go walk the circle. As long as she had a new dress."

Mrs. Brown in the jaunty blue beret dissected her fried fish, a late supper after our day on the road. But life in the plaza was just waking up. Two men wheeled a great wooden marimba to a spot near the dining tables and uncloaked it, preparing to play.

She said, "You're home here. That's good to see. It serves ye well."

"I don't know that I'm home anywhere."

"Well, you are a queasy one, I'll grant it." she said. She used her knife to push the fish's crisp head and tail together at one side of the plate. "I always knew you came from Mexico, at Mrs. Bittle's you told us that. But see, we thought you were just bashful. We never thought of a whole country where you could call down a waiter in his language, or say, 'Look, they're going to do the hat dance,' and they would do the hat dance. Now, that sounds silly."

"No, I understand. You thought, 'foreigner,' and not of a particular place."

"I reckon that is it. All along, you have known about these folk here and I've had no inkling. I read the *Geographics*, but you can't think of the people in those stories as having life and breath, and knowing things you don't. But that sounds silly too."

"No, I think most people are the same. Until they've gone somewhere."

"I thank my lucky stars, Mr. Shepherd, and I thank you. I do. That I'm a person who went somewhere." She set her hands in her lap and drew herself fully into looking outward, as people do when settling down in a theater. Vendors had begun to work the dining crowd. You could buy anything if your supper went on long enough: roses, bicycle tires, a shellacked armadillo. A mother and daughter in long skirts and shawls moved from table to table showing their embroidery. I waved them off with a gesture so small Mrs. Brown probably didn't see. She feels obliged to look at every single thing, lest the artisans be offended.

"I have been wondering what your novel will be about," she said. "Apart from the setting."

"I wonder too. I think I want to write about the end of things. How civilizations fall, and what leads up to that. How we're connected to everything in the past."

To my shock she said, "Oh, I wouldn't."

"Mrs. Brown, I declare. That's twice you've told me how to be a writer. You apologized the first time."

"Well. I'm sorry again."

"Why would you say that?"

"I have no business. It just came out. Some of the things that happened back at home have set me to the fret."

"I do step in the pie sometimes, I know that. Go on."

"Should I?"

"Please."

"I think the readers won't like it. We don't like to see ourselves joined hard to the past. We'd as soon take the scissors and cut every ribbon of that."

"Then I am sunk. All I ever write about is history."

"People in gold arm bracelets, though. Nothing that would happen to our own kind. That's how I reckon people take to it so well."

"So I shouldn't try something new? What happened to the writer standing up for himself? Not leaving my words to be orphaned, my little bairns, as you called them."

"I still hold by that. But there's no shame in a clever disguise. To say what you believe and still keep out of trouble. Thus to now, it has done ye well."

"Oh. Then you think it wouldn't go so well if I set my stories, let's say, in a concentration camp in Texas or Georgia. One of those places where we sent our citizen Japs and Germans during the war."

She looked stricken. "No, sir, we would not like to read that. Not even about the other Japanese sinking ships and bombing our coast. That's over, and we'd just as soon be shed of it."

The marimba players struck up "La Llorona," the most cheerful rendition of a song about death. I spied the man with the shellacked armadillo for sale. It was only a matter of time, he comes every night.

"If that's so, then why did Americans make off with the historical artifacts of Mexico to put them, where did he say? In the Peabody Museum?"

"It's the same as your books, Mr. Shepherd. It's somebody else's gold pieces and bad luck. If we fill up our museums with that, we won't have to look at the dead folk lying at the bottom of our own water wells."

"And who is *we*?"

She pondered this, eyebrows lowered. "Just Americans," she said at length. "That's the only kind of person I know how to be. Not like you."

"You'd do that? Take scissors and cut off your past?"

"I did already. My family would tell you I went to the town and got above my raisings. It's what Parthenia calls 'modern.'"

"And what would you call it?"

"American. Like I said. The magazines tell us we're special, not like the ones that birthed us. Brand-new. They paint a picture of some old-country rube with a shawl on her head, and make you fear you'll be like that, unless you buy cake mix and a home freezer."

"But that sounds lonely. Walking around without any ancestors."

"I don't say it's good. It's just how we be. I hate to say it, but that rube in the shawl is my sister, and I don't want to be her. I can't help it."

A man walked among the tables working a marionette, a smiling skeleton of articulated papier-mâché bones. To the delight of a family dining nearby, he made the skeleton sneak along slowly, lifting its bony feet high, then suddenly leap on their table. The children squealed as it stamped on their plates, for the father's coins.

"And history is nothing but a cemetery," I said to Mrs. Brown. The puppeteer was behind her, she'd missed the show.

"That is exactly right. For us to visit when we have a mind, or just not go at all. Let the weeds grow up."

"Here in Mexico there's a holiday just for being with your dead. You go where your family is buried and have a great party, right on the grave."

"You have to? Plumb on top of the graves?" Wide-eyed, she looked like the girl she must have been before she was Mrs. Brown.

"People love it, as much as they love a wedding. Really it is a kind of wedding, to the people in your past. You take a vow they're all still with you. You cook a feast and bring enough food for the dead people too."

"Well, sir, that would not happen in Buncombe County. Probably the police would arrest you."

"You might be right."

She took her glass of limeade and sipped at the straw while holding eye contact. It was unsettling. The puppeteer had moved into her line of view, and her eyes left me to follow that skeleton. When she had drained her glass, she said, "You understand things like that, a wedding in the graveyard. You are from another country."

"But I want to be brand-new too. The land of weightless people and fast automobiles suits me fine. I made myself a writer there."

"You could have stayed here and done the same."

"I don't think so. I've thought about it. I had ghosts to leave behind. Mexican writers struggle with their ghosts, I think. In general. Maybe it's easier to say what you want in America, without those ancestral compromises weighing you down like stones."

"Easier to look down upon others, too."

"Do you mean to say I do that?"

"Mr. Shepherd, you do not. But some do. They look around and say, 'This here is good, and that is evil,' and it's decided. We are America, so that over there must be something else altogether."

Mrs. Brown will never cease to amaze. "That's very insightful. You think that comes of cutting our anchor to the past?"

"I do. Because if you had to go sit on a grave and think hard about it, you couldn't just say 'This is America.' Some Indian would cross your mind, some fellow that shot his arrow on that very spot. Or the man that shot the Indian, or whipped his slaves or hung up some tart woman for a witch. You'd couldn't just say it's all fine and dandy."

"Maybe readers need some of that, then. Connections to the past."

"Fairly warned is fair afeared," she said.

"I thought it was 'forearmed.' Forewarned is forearmed."

She glanced at her forearms, and never did reply.

Today was the village of Hoctún, a town the color of wheat, with a pyramid sitting at its center. It brought to mind the village with the giant stone head in the square, and Mother's shaman. Every turn in the road here runs into memory. Isla Mujeres was almost unbearable, from the ferry on. Mrs. Brown sees all, and it puts her on a fret, as she would say. I imagine her pressed against the fret-board of God's guitar, held against the slender silver bar until she wails her assigned note. She says she came here to do my worrying for me. She does much more: typing up drafted scenes, only to see me throw them away. Arranging things. She's befriended someone English-speaking at the tourist bureau, a journalist who helps her negotiate miracles. Mexico's bureaucracies do not daunt Mrs. Brown. She has worked for the United States Army.

I told her I want to study village life now, up close. We've seen enough of pyramids, I need goats and cookfires. To peer inside a hut and examine that V-shaped vault, after seeing the same architecture in stone temples. Her inspired idea: to return to the village of Maria, mother of Jesús.

❋

The eternal cauldron of beans still bubbled. Maria was animated while serving us lunch, telling about the lumbermen who passed through earlier this morning. They are clearing the forests all around, dragging out the felled giants on the same dirt track that brought us in. All she can do is stand in the road and halt each truck, insisting they let her inspect the fallen timber and pluck the living orchids from its top branches. That explains the flowers growing from tins in the yard: her rescued orphans. These orchids lived all their lives high up in the bright air, unseen by human eyes, until the firmament under their roots suddenly tumbled. It's a precarious place, up there with the howlers. Everyone wants the tallest tree to fall.

But Maria of the Orchids seemed to have no such fears, at home in the forest primeval. "The important thing is beauty," she said once more, reaching a small brown hand toward the treetops. "Even death grants us beauty."

Another visit to Chichén Itzá tomorrow, the last trip. Then we pack it all in. We will need to take the train for Mexico City on Thursday or Friday if we're to be there from Christmas until the new year, as Frida insists. Candelaria is meeting us at the station. Candelaria at the wheel of an automobile seems as probable as Jesus running a guided tour. Or Mrs. Brown in hat and gloves sitting beside the flagrant Frida, drinking tea on a bench painted with lighting bolts. Likely, all these things will come to pass.

Chichén Itzá looked completely different today, probably because of everything else we've seen since the first visit. "Elegant and remote," I jotted in my notes that time, "reluctant to reveal its human history." But today a story came up in relief from every surface, urgent and visible. Every stone was carved with some image: the snarling jaguar, the feathered serpent, a long frieze of swimming goldfish. Emperors stood life-size on stone steles jutting up from the plaza like giant teeth. The Maya carved human figures only in profile: the almond eye, the flattened forehead sloping toward the exquisite arch of nose. They needn't have worried about that profile being forgotten, it's the spitting image of Jesús and ten thousand others, automobile vandals included. Better to carve something else in stone, if you mean to be remembered: "I was cruel to my best friend and got away with it. My favorite meal was squid in ink sauce. My mother never quite liked me as I was."

Traces of paint clung to the surfaces too: red, green, violet. In their time, all these buildings were brightly painted. What a shock to realize that, and how foolish to have been tricked earlier by the serenity of white limestone. Like looking at a skeleton and saying, "How quiet this man was, and how thin." Today Chichén Itzá declared the truth of what it was: garish. Loud and bright, full of piss and jasmine, and why not? It was Mexico. Or rather, Mexico is still what this once was.

For the last time we climbed the tall pyramid, El Castillo. "We don't have to go on, you know," I told Mrs. Brown, halfway up. The day was so bright and hot it almost tasted of gunpowder, and she had left her hat in the car, where Jesús was now napping. She paused on the stone step, shading her eyes with one flat hand, her hair blowing back like the mermaid on the prow of a ship. She had removed her gloves to use both hands for the climb, the steps were that monstrous. "Of course we do," she said, sighing deeply as if to say, "Men do this." And that is a fact, men do, unable to resist the same impulse that built the thing in the first place: senseless ambition.

But the view from the top, we convinced ourselves, was worth the pain. We sat on a ledge looking down on the tourists in the plaza, pitying those little ants because they were not up here, and if they ever meant to be, they would have to pay the price. And there is the full sum of it, senseless ambition reduced to its rudiments. Civilizations are built on that, and a water hole.

"Imagine the place crawling with slaves and kings," I said.

"Ten thousand slaves to every one king, I'd imagine."

And barking dogs. And mothers, wondering if their children have fallen down the well. We stayed a good while, reconstructing the scene. She was curious about how a writer decides where to begin the story. You start with "In the beginning," I told her, but it should be as close to the end as possible. There's the trick.

"How can you know?"

"You just decide. It could be right here. In the first light of dawn, the king in maroon robes and a golden breastplate stood atop his temple, glowering down at the chaos. He understood with dismay that his empire was collapsing. You have to get right into the action, readers are impatient. If you dilly-dally, they'll go turn on the radio and listen to *Duffy's Tavern* instead, because it's all wrapped up in an hour."

"How could the king know his empire is about to collapse?"

"Because everything's in a mess."

"Fiddlesticks," she said. "Everything's always a mess, but people say 'Buck up, we just have to get through this one bad patch.'"

"True enough. But you and I know it was, because we've read about it. Chichén Itzá was the center of a vast and powerful empire, art and architecture that flourished for centuries. And then around 900 after Christ, it mysteriously vanished."

"People don't vanish," she said. "Hitler took his life, but Germany is still there. Just for example. People going to work and having their birthdays and what all."

True enough, and the Mayans who now people this forest surely do not think of themselves as a failed culture. They build their huts of ancient design, make gardens, and sing children to sleep. Rulers and generals change without their notice. In the time since Cortés, the great Spanish empire has collapsed into one small landmass of rock and vineyards, the little right paw of Europe. Its far-flung provinces have been lost, the million shackled subjugates set free. Spain outlawed slavery, built schools and hospitals, and its poets, come to think of it, are practically in a contest now to condemn the Spanish history of conquest. Did Cortés see all that roaring toward him like a steam locomotive? Did England or France? All this earnest forward motion, the marches to the mountain, the murals and outstretched hands: which part of it do we ever call failure?

"A novel needs a good collapse," I maintained. "Success and failure. People read books to escape the uncertainties of life. And they build pyramids to last forever, so we can have something to climb on top of and admire."

"You know best," she said. "But there's no use admiring a thing just because it lasted. My brother once had a boil on his bottom a whole year, and it was nothing you'd want to see in the photogravure."

"Violet Brown, the poet."

She laughed.

"I'll remind you of that boil, next time you try to stop me from burning old notebooks and letters."

She didn't like that. She pulled her thin cotton gloves from under her belt where she'd tucked them. Put them on, smoothed ruffled feathers. "Some things are worth remembering, and some are not. That's all I meant."

"And you can say which is which?"

"No, I can't. But piling rocks on top of rocks might not be the ticket. Maybe we should admire people the most for living in this jungle without leaving one mark on it."

"But how would we know about them a thousand years later?"

"In a thousand years, Mr. Shepherd, the cow can jump over the moon."

That was the end of it, because a rising storm cloud began to turn the day a menacing color, driving us down from our aerie. The heavens let loose as we reached the ground. Children who'd been hawking woodcarvings and embroidery now disappeared into the forest for shelter, while the tourists hurried back to their autos. Behind us the temples stood in the strange yellow light with rain darkening their stone pates, dissolving their limestone one particle at a time, carrying off the day's measure of history.

Asheville, North Carolina

1948–1950

(VB)

Star Week, *February 1, 1948*

Southern Star Shines on Shepherd Romance

Young men in the Land of Sky seem to prefer the taste of old wine. A decade ago in Ashville, North Carolina, young writer Thomas Wolfe rocketed to fame, fleeing Southern scandal for Manhattan's forgiving bohemian scene and the arms of a lady seventeen years his senior. The writer's family tried to squelch the match with comely theater designer Aline Bernstein—that's *Mrs.* Bernstein—and so did Mr. Bernstein, we're guessing. But Wolfe carried the torch to an early grave.

Now Harrison Shepherd is out to prove history repeats. This Ashville writer rode his pen to the heights with *Vassals of Majesty* and last year's *Pilgrims of Chaltepec*, ringing up more sales than Wolfe saw in a lifetime. Thanks to secretive habits and a well-known scorn for press correspondents, Shepherd has nudged over Wolfe as the talk of his town. In a new move plainly inspired by his tutor, Shepherd has now linked up with a lady exactly seventeen years his senior. Married? At least once, say our sources.

Little else is known about the mysterious Violet Brown, but the trim brunette must have some powerful lure for snaring this diffident bachelor and his piles of cash. You could hear the hearts crack on both sides of the Mason-Dixon last month as the couple took a pre-honeymoon tour through Mexico, Shepherd's boyhood home, where his family still resides.

Did Mamacita approve the January–May romance? Do wedding bells toll for Harrison Shepherd? Not just yet, says airport clerk Jack Curtis, who viewed the couple's passports

on their recent return to the Ashville-Hendersonville airport.
**Mr. Tall, Dark and Handsome kept a tight hand on his Shrink-
ing Violet, but as of January 26 she is on the books as "widowed." And the bachelor? Curtis reports: "still single."**

February 6

When she came in with both arms loaded and dumped the mail
and papers in a heap on the dining room table, my first thoughts
were purely selfish. Alas, this mess. The world comes in. I'd wanted
her to take more days off after our return, craving time upstairs un-
disturbed. To be in my pajamas still at suppertime, the shades still
drawn, reeling out my tale of Lord Itzá and his troubles. A story
needs a good collapse.

She began talking before she'd unbuttoned her coat, plainly out
of sorts. She is not like that, filling up a silence with idle talk, the
goings-on at Mrs. Bittle's while we were away. Then came the report
that Mr. Judd had died, on Christmas Day.

So that was it, I thought. I gave condolences.

"Well, it was his time. Even Marian Bittle thought so, and she is
not one for philosophy. She said the son came right away and took
care of everything, so she could go on with her Christmas. But this
is what floored her. Before the old man was even buried, nine people
read the obituary and came asking to let the room. Some of them had
families, can you imagine? Wanting to bring a wife and children, all
to live in the one room. There's no rooms for let anywhere. It's all the
war marriages, and now these babies nobody thought to expect. Mrs.
Bittle says a man bought a potato field outside town and is putting
up two hundred houses out there, just houses, she says, not a single
shop for them to get their goods. I suppose they'll have to come all
the way into town for that. And the houses all alike, maybe each one
is a little different shade of color, but the same house over and over,
lined up in a row."

"Goodness. It sounds like Moscow. Who would live in a place like that?"

"Well, that's the thing. The plan is for two hundred houses. But seven hundred families are already lined up to buy them."

Then she sat down at the table and began to sob. It has never happened before. The day the agent came to the door she felt faint afterward, and put her head on the table, but this was different. Her shoulders racked. She let out a thin, throbbing wail.

"Now, it can't be as bad as that." I sounded like an actor in a play. Two absurd people in this room, and I had not been introduced to either one. I was still thinking somehow her distress went back to the housing shortage.

She'd seen the first of the stories several days ago, but didn't phone, hoping to spare me embarrassment for a while. Or else, not knowing what to say. All the stories linking us romantically, she has been carrying that alone. Remarks and stares at the library and the market. I know she is often recognized.

I couldn't read much of it. It made me feel too helpless, lost in some landscape of murdered truth. Lev would have been scientific, tracking the trail of this particular prevarication, studying how the branches diverged and where the thing started. Probably in *Star Week* or the *Echo*, though the story also made the reputable papers, and of course the *Trumpet*. It always begins somewhere, one howler waking up the others. They pass it on, embellished, not through any creative drive but only a pure slothful failure to verify a fact. If the reporters made any calls, it would have been for soliciting a denial. Failing that, they run it as truth, upping the ante just enough to put their own byline on it. The lady is "demure" and then "fatally demure" and then has a "tragic past." I am evidently now locked in a battle with an "old-fashioned Mexican family" over my right to pursue the love match.

Only when I made the coffee did I see my hands were shaking.

I have had dreams of being shot, watching the blood pour out, and wondering whether it hurts.

I set a cup near her elbow, but couldn't sit down opposite her, not like a husband facing a wife across a meal. We used to do that at Mrs. Bittle's, of course, when I was the cook and she the worldly secretary. A lot of water under the bridge. I stood.

After a time she sat up, and looked at the coffee strangely, as if it had been delivered by fairies. It struck me like a draught of cold air then, about Mrs. Bittle and the housing shortage. "Is she making you move out because of this?"

"She raised my monthly rate. She said she would have to, if I meant to stay there. Due to the publicity."

"That's ridiculous. You're in a bind, and she's taking advantage. Do you want me to call her?"

"How would that look, Mr. Shepherd? You protecting me."

"I don't know."

"I'll pay it. She knows I couldn't find a single other room in town, with things the way they are."

"Is the shortage really as bad as that?" Of course it is in the papers, everywhere. It just didn't occur that everywhere was here.

"Folks read the obituaries and the homicides now, Mr. Shepherd, to find a room let open. But the police and the undertaker families get those. The rest of us had just as well reckon the next house to open up for us will be the cedar box."

"Mrs. Brown, goodness. This isn't like you." It weighed: these rooms I have, riches undeserved. For a single person who could easily live in little more than a cedar box, and frequently has.

"Anyhow, I've gone years without a hike at Mrs. Bittle's," she said. "The new man is paying twice as much. I'm lucky to have what I have."

"I'll raise your salary to compensate for it."

"You needn't."

"No, I will. If you can find another place suitable, tell me what it costs."

She went to the water closet and ran the water in there, probably washing her face. When she came out she retrieved the letter opener from the drawer where she keeps it, like the woman in a play who draws the revolver from the bureau. Instead of shooting the villain, she sat down and began to sort envelopes into piles. Not glancing up.

"Look. I'll talk to the presses about this, or send out a statement. Denying the romance business. Whatever you want me to do, to defend your name."

"I'm nobody, I don't have any name. It's your own you have to think about."

"Well, in that case there's nothing to be done. This is just more of the usual, we could have expected it. I should have thought, before I asked you to go with me."

She began slitting envelopes open. Her hair was in a net, her wool sweater buttoned to the throat; she looked ten years older than when I'd seen her last.

"At least it can't get any worse now. We're walking away from the wreck," I said. "It's just what happens."

"What happens?" she asked, in a curiously snipped tone.

"Del árbol caído todos hacen leña. From the fallen tree everybody makes firewood."

At that she looked up. "Mr. Shepherd, where did we fall?"

February 14

Dear Shep,

What's tickin? Be my valentine? Oops—you're taken! I read all about it in the papers. Well, hats off to you pal, I've thought of bagging an older pigeon for myself. She wouldn't ask for a lot in the boodle department and it throws everyone else off the scent. But the hell you yell. One of the hearts you cracked north of the Mason–Dixon was mine. Did I have to read about it in the Echo?

When are you coming to New York? The new job at the museum is steady, mostly sweetening up the top cats for cash. I've got an apartment in the Lower East Seventies now, very voot. *Kerouac was spotted in the neighborhood, and Artie Shaw plays in a joint on the corner. But forget about bebop, keep your eye out now for a potent lad named Frankie Laine. Tell him Tom-cat sent you.*

Are you the only news in Asheville these days? Howzabout that old girl Zelda, think she'd marry me? I hear she resides in one of the white-coat joints there in your fair city. Did Scott come around on visiting days, when he was still kicking? You need to cut me in on the juicy stuff. Or are you riding so high on the rocket to fame, you can't throw your old pal a saludo? From now on I'll just have to read Star Week *to find out what's oop-pop-a-da with Harrison Shepherd.*

Dig you later,

TOM CUDDY

March 11, 1948

Dear Tom,

It's strange you asked about Zelda Fitzgerald. She died in a fire two nights ago. It started in the hospital kitchen and went up the dumbwaiter shaft into her room, a freak tragedy. There's no guessing what the national presses will say, but I'm cutting you in on the scoop as you asked. I heard about the dumbwaiter from the fire marshal himself, this morning at the tobacco stand where I get the morning papers. Highland Hospital is just at the top of my street. Zelda and I have been neighbors for years, but I haven't given her much thought. Now I feel like a bum. It could have been any of us in that hospital, Tom.

The rest of my news is not such a bring-down. I am coming along very well on the new book, and have signed a motion-picture package on the last one. Most definitely, I am not married, or involved in any secret romance. Those stories are completely invented. The Violet Brown in question is my stenographer. She wears cotton gloves indoors and unless some terrible accident has deceived us, never has shared a coffee cup that touched my lips. She accompanied me on the research trip to Yucatán, so the gossip-marketers must have learned about it and fallen in love with their fantasies. Believe me, the lady is chaste. This latest run of stories has been very troubling, harder for her than for me. I'm constantly stupefied that anyone believes the nonsense that runs in the papers. And yet they do, time and again. Tommy, you ought to know I am not one for marriage, any more than I was one for the army, back when you and I were ducking bullets for the National Museum. So put your poor cracked heart back together, soldier. I didn't snub you from any wedding list.

I have no plans for New York soon, but you should visit here. Asheville has changed since the war, we are said to be a tourist destination, first rate. Out on the Tunnel Road they have a brand-new contraption that will wash and wax an auto with the driver still in it. We have instant coffee here too, and lady drivers. Are we voot? You shall have to come and see for yourself. Until then I am, as you may have heard,

Still single,

SHEP

March 22

Dear Shep,
My friends are all green that I am hep to Shep, especially when I told them
about your movie package. Holy Joe, congrats on that. Could you find a

tiny role for me? I'll be the lad in the loincloth sitting on a rock, smoking a herd of Camels during the battle scene, trying to sneak a gander at Robert Taylor. Lord and Butler, that fellow is cuter than snappers. And pointing the finger at anything pink now, I see in the papers.

Please advise: a friend here seems to be in that kind of hash. He works in radio but has the looks for television—Puerto Rican, a Latin dreamboat type. With brains, even, this boy reads, and very impressed I know you, by the way. Up until last year he was a steaming romeo. Now he can't get hired for anything. He was mixed up with the Communists ages ago, and it's a gestanko scene for those cats now, people are even getting deported. It happened to a Negro lady I knew from the museum, a writer who reviews our shows for the Harlem papers. I didn't even know she was foreign. Evidently her family came from Trinidad in the '20s when she was a tiny tot. So one day this lady is typing her story on Negro artists, then the FBI knocks on her door and she's cooling her heels on Ellis Island, next stop Trinidad. You can see why my Puerto Rican pal is worried. You're a foreigner too. He says to ask if you know some cat in the higher-ups who could help him out.

The hell you yell, Asheville has instant coffee now? I might have to come and review the action myself. The boss sends me out on the trail to beat the gums with the richie riches, so they'll loan out their Picassos for our big shows. Lately he's been scobo for the Vanderbilts. So wipe your feet on the mat, cat, I might be headed for your roost.

Later,

TOM CUDDY

April 23

Dear Mr. Shepherd,
Your news is extremely welcome. All of us at Stratford and Sons are pleased to know your novel is moving forward at a clip. I've read the chapters you sent, and find them in every way up to the standard we expect from our boy

*Shepherd. This may be your best to date. This contract explains the terms
we discussed by telephone. The late summer completion date you suggest
will be very suitable. You'll hear soon from our sales department to discuss
the title, dust jacket, and so forth. They are determined to include an author
photograph this time, so please give the request a fair consideration. I'm
afraid your title,* The Name of This Place, *does not strike us as quite
the ticket. I believe* Cataclysm of the Empire *has a good ring. But
we have time to sort that out.*

*Enclosed herein you will find two copies of the contract for your signature.
Attached to last page please note the affidavit of anti–Communism, also
for signature before a notary public. As you may know, this formality is
now requisite in all moving-picture contracts, and is expected soon to be
mandatory in publishing, so we are working to get the necessary papers on
file.*

*I send greetings from my Miss Daley, who enjoys her chats with your
Mrs. Brown. And cheers from Miss James in the mailing room who says
your letters mount up there as always, fragrant with perfume, despite
rumors of your engagement. Many will be gratified to know another of
your books will soon be available.*

Yours sincerely,

LINCOLN BARNES

May 4

Artie proposed breakfast at the Swiss Kitchen, one of his haunts. It
seemed to be a tourist place, they had a giant sign out front with a boy
in lederhosen (*Food Worth Yodeling About!*) and waitresses dressed as
milkmaids. Artie, in his ancient cuffed trousers and faint old-man
smell, was unembarrassed by any of it.

"What makes it Swiss food?" I asked, studying the menu.

"A lot of grease. Bratwurst, only here they are going to call it sau-
sage. German food with a strict doctrine of neutrality."

With Artie, irony carries the mailbag right to the door of nonchalance. Nothing seems to excite him. Short of a revelation that one has worked for Lev Trotsky. Through a haze of burning cigarettes he studied the new book contract. "These terms are basically good. I'm sorry about the anticommunism business."

"I'll sign it. I just hope they won't ask me to disavow anything more difficult."

"Such as?"

"Coffee with too much sugar. Mad irritation. Plotting murders I could never go through with. That sort of thing."

"These crimes are very difficult to prosecute. Otherwise, all of us except Eleanor Roosevelt would be in the pokey."

One of the waitresses in blond plaits was making her way toward us, a twin to the one who'd seated us at our window table. "The pokey," I repeated.

"A technical legal term, meaning the hoosegow. You're not much of one for American slang, are you? For a young man of words."

"It has never come naturally to me, no. You must hear a lot of it in your business. Actors and musicians."

"Oh yes. From those clients I hear 'Artie, where is the cabbage?' Clams, dough, moolah, many words for the one thing they don't have these days."

Our milkmaid slipped a pad and pencil from her apron pocket, then dropped the pencil. Deliberately, I could vouch. She knelt to retrieve it, all lowered lashes and ruffled décolletage, the cup runneth over. My stars, as Mrs. Brown would put it. Where do these precious creatures come from, is it Artie who draws them?

"Doll face, tell us your specials. And promise we will see your face again in thirty seconds when you return with coffee. Extra sugar for my friend." Yes, it's Artie.

"You have a manner of speaking," he said when she had gone. "The first time we spoke on the phone, I heard it. Every word is perfect, but there is an accent. Like Gary Cooper. Not quite the regular apple pie."

"They tell me the same thing in Mexico—my Spanish has a faint accent. I am the permanent foreigner."

"Well, don't cure it. Your way with words, I mean. We need the income."

"It's not my mother's fault, she was an ace at slang. Flapper first-class. Today is her birthday, by the way. I always took her to lunch."

"Happy birthday, Mrs. Shepherd. How old?"

"Forever young. She died in '38."

"Condolences. How did it happen?"

"A car accident in Mexico City. She was dating a news correspondent, they were racing to the airport to get a look at Howard Hughes."

"Now that is going out with a bang. I mean no disrespect."

"No, you're right, she was all bang. In death as in life. I miss her."

"Now, you mention plotting murders that you cannot find the heart to execute. Is this anything I ought to know about, as your legal representative?"

"Just the usual. Newspapermen. The rumors have upset my stenographer this spring. People are treating her badly. Even some of her friends have been callous."

"Now that is a subject. Freedom of the presses to destroy a person's life for no good reason." He studied the menu with the same concentration he'd given the book contract, reading all the fine print. When he'd finished he closed it.

"Congratulations on the new book, by the way. As I said, these are excellent terms. A pretty penny. Now, let me ask you something, a little personal. But I ask in a professional capacity, as the guy whose job is to look out for you and promote the general welfare."

"All right, fire away."

"I know that Mrs. Brown is not your type, categorically speaking. You once mentioned I am one of a few who knows about this. The Selective Service being another. What I am asking, and I hope the answer is yes, isn't there *somebody* else who knows?"

"Somebody. No, not for quite a while. An offer does seem to be on the table right now, but. It's not very easy to discuss this, Artie."

He held up a hand, took a sip of his coffee. "My intention is not to make you uncomfortable."

"You're concerned for my safety?"

"That you could be put at risk of, shall we say, exposure. Black-mail can arrive from unexpected quarters. I am not speaking in this case of Aware, Incorporated. I have had clients in your situation."

"Oh. Well, no, I don't think that's a worry. This particular friend would have a great deal to lose. From exposure, as you say."

"Not another Bolshevik? Never mind, pretend I didn't ask."

I laughed. "No, don't worry, this one is all stars and stripes. We worked together in Civilian Services during the war, moving paint-ings into safe storage here from the National Gallery. There were quite a few of us in that corps, you'd be amazed. The art world may never be the same."

"Really."

"He's working for a museum these days, in New York. Out of touch for years, and suddenly now he's coming to town. It's not easy to contemplate, I'll tell you the truth. I'd settled pretty well on living as a monk."

Artie waved away a cloud of smoke. "Yeah, me too. I would say, 'Since my wife died,' but under oath I would have to say since long before that. Who has the energy?"

"You might be surprised, Artie. Cocktail waitresses seem to hum around you like little bees."

"Entertainment, my friend. Sweet music. In the long run, most of us spend about fifteen minutes total in the entanglements of passion, and the rest of our days looking back on it, humming the tune. Not a bad arrangement."

"So it seems."

He carefully lit a new cigarette from the old one. "Now *love*."

"Yes. Love is another story."

"And this you have in spades, my friend. You are loved by the multitudes. Ladies and gents standing in line down the block, waiting for your every word."

Their opinion of me is approximately the same as for a talking pony. Frida said that. "Yes, I'm very lucky. Employed by the American imagination, as you put it."

"Long may it wave."

"Now I have a question for you, Artie."

"Personal?"

"No. This friend in New York tells me foreigners are being deported there, for suspicion of just about anything. Working for Negro rights and so forth. My friend is dramatic, he can exaggerate."

"Your friend in this case does not exaggerate."

"That's diabolical. To bolster support by deporting the opposition."

"Diabolical is a polite term for this behavior."

"Are they setting their caps mostly for noncitizens?"

"Mr. Hoover and Mr. Watkins at the INS are becoming very enthusiastic with their housecleaning. Some of the deportees have been living in this country since Homer was a pup. A fellow I know of, Williamson, labor secretary of the Communist Party, currently held without bond on Ellis Island. Accused of being an immigrant. He says he was born in San Francisco. Forty-five years of age, he has family, witnesses. But all the birth certificates in that city were lost in the earthquake and fire of '06."

"Goodness."

"Shepherd, you have a birth certificate, do you not?"

"I do. It was some trouble with both parents dead, but I located the hospital. I have both passports, U.S. and Mexican. I had to sort it out during the war, as you'd guess. Called up to work for the Department of State, they like to see credentials."

"Keep that U.S. passport with your guns and liquor. That is my advice."

Breakfast was biscuits and gravy, sausages, and eggs on many heavy white plates. Artie rearranged it all to make room for his ashtray, and continued smoking right through the meal. With so much grease everywhere, I wondered about spontaneous combustion.

"Mrs. Brown does her best to keep me out of trouble," I said. "She claims my ideology is transparent. But no criminal record as yet."

"Who needs crimes? The INS has a stable of witnesses, professionals. Very well paid, very talented, they can produce a testimony for any occasion. If a man is not a Communist, they'll prove he is. If he is, they can get him booked for 'creating confusion and hysteria,' to hold him until CP membership becomes illegal."

"Outlaw a political party? What kind of country does that?"

"The kind in which you reside. The party has disavowed violence, as you know. Last year they also severed all ties with the Information Bureau of the Soviet Union, to be on the safe side. Turns out, there is no safe side. A federal grand jury just declared that Communist Party membership is a threat to the civilian defense. Now Congress is working on the Mundt-Nixon bill, requiring members to enter their names in a registry. So denying CP membership will soon be a crime also. These people are damned if they do, and damned if they do not."

Outside in the parking lot under the restaurant's jolly billboard, that yodeling boy in his lederhosen, a dark-colored auto pulled in and a couple emerged from it, in the throes of a terrible argument. The plate glass window shut out any sound, but their rage was visible. The man kept circling the woman to shout at her face, and she kept turning away, her loose raincoat swinging like a bell, her flat shoes stepping side to side. A child peered from the oval of the auto's rear window, the small doomed fish in the bowl.

"Well. At least I'm no party member."

"Mr. Shepherd, you have a colorful past. Your Mexican friends, do they stay in touch?"

"Frida does. Mrs. Kahlo. Intermittently. She's just joined up again with the Communist Party, after a lapse. She says it's all going strong there."

"So it may be, and legal also, in her locale. But I suggest discretion."

"You're not saying I should simply cut off old friends, for fear of association?"

"No, I am not, and I recognize you, sir, as a man with a spinal column. But you would be amazed at the number of people who do exactly what you've just said."

"I see. My stenographer would say, 'Fairly warned is fair afeared.'"

"That is about the sum of what I can offer you, yes."

"So, keeping old letters and so forth in the house. Maybe not a good idea."

"A man with a spinal column, and a brain. Bravo. Now, what about our friend Agent X, who came calling last October. Does he also keep in touch?"

"Not another peep. He must have discovered what a lackluster stiff I am."

"Maybe. We should all be so lucky. But these men don't care who you are. Not even what you're planning to do, despite what they may say. They're like bloodhounds. What gets them baying is the whiff of where you have already been."

"Well, that can't change. I spent years around Communists, cleaning their dishes while they deliberated the transitional program and formalized party directives. You know something, Artie? They eat what people eat. They paint the dining room yellow, and love their children. I keep wondering, what have people got against Communists?"

"I told you. 'Anticommunism' is not very much concerned with 'communism.'"

"So you said. Tuna fish, and the Spanish influenza. It's hard to believe."

"Think of religion. A virgin birth. Likewise hard to believe. Yet taken by many as evidence that purveyors of indecency are every-where."

The arguing couple outside got back in their car and drove away. A stop on their journey.

"Communism? Most people have no idea what it is," Artie said. "I do not exaggerate. Look around this restaurant, ask any of these fine citizens. 'Excuse me, sir, I've been thinking of an idea, a bunch of working people owning the means of their own production. What do you make of that?' You know, he might be all for it."

"Communism is the same as Stalin, that's what he thinks."

"Correct. And baseball is nine white men and a stick. Seeing is believing. For years the president told us we had no fear. They put up signs to that effect in every post office. 'Tojo doesn't scare us.' Now we have a change of program, they're plastering up a new slogan: 'Run like hell.'"

"I see what you mean."

"According to Elmo Roper's last poll, forty percent of Americans believe the Jews have too much power in this country. Tell me, we have how many Jewish men in the Congress?"

"Not many, I shouldn't think. Maybe none at all?"

"So what is the problem? Foreign-sounding people, not Christian, and not apologetic about it. They may have their own ideas. It suggests a challenge to our hard-earned peace and bounty. Making a fuss over Negro segregation would be another example."

"I see that. The issue is not Communism per se."

He leaned forward, his blue eyes watery, feverish looking. He held up both hands as if he meant to clasp my face between them. "You know what the issue is? Do you want to know? It's what these guys have decided to call *America*. They have the audacity to say, '*There*, you sons of bitches, don't lay a finger on it. *That* is a finished product!'"

"But any country is still in the making. *Always*. That's just history, people have to see that."

He dropped his hands, sat back against the booth. "Pardon my French, but tell it to the goddamn Marines."

"My stenographer said the same thing, more or less. Minus the French."

Artie had finished his breakfast and now stacked up plates, ashtray on top, recovering himself. "Your Mrs. Brown, a very astute lady. How is she?"

"Astute, as you say. And not mine, for the record. She's all right, I think."

"Good." He ground out his cigarette, smoothed the contract on the table, and folded it into its envelope. "You can sign this. Affidavit and all, if that's what you want. I can't say yes or no. But I'm going to tell you something about history in the making. Remember you heard this first from Artie Gold, over a plate of ground hog and cackle. This is going to get serious. What these men are doing could become permanent."

"What do you mean?"

Suddenly he looked weary. "You force people to stop asking questions, and before you know it they have auctioned off the question mark, or sold it for scrap. No boldness. No good ideas for fixing what's broken in the land. Because if you happen to mention it's broken, you are automatically disqualified."

"Surely that's overstating it," I said. "America runs on extremes. The latest craze and a tank of gas will get you about anywhere. Today the Kremlin is a messianic movement and you're better dead than red. Tomorrow they'll decide the real mischief is cigarettes and sugar in your coffee. The culture is built on hyperbole." I wanted to see him smile. "Or maybe you really do think this food is worth yodeling about."

He didn't smile. "I'm an old man, I've seen a lot. But what these men are doing is putting poison on the lawn. It kills your crabgrass all right, and then you have a lot of dead stuff out there for a very long time. Maybe forever."

The Asheville Trumpet, *June 18, 1948*

City Slams Doors on Polio Menace

by Carl Nicholas

The City Health Commission this week banned all public gatherings, to stem the tide of infantile paralysis sweeping our state. The quarantine began at 1 am Monday, closing movie houses, skating parlors, swimming pools, and other public sites of infestation. All city churches except the Roman Catholic have sensibly urged their flocks to pray from the safety of home. This city of 50,000 souls is quiet as a grave, as housewives stay home from shopping and our businesses and resorts see profits stolen by the epidemic.

Dr. Ken Malusa, interviewed at the Health Department by telephone, reminded us that even the wisest of medical men can offer no chemical cure for polio. "This germ is crafty, you won't see him with the human eye or even the best microscopes. Many have given it a try, but the sneaky fellow won't show his face. Penicillin doesn't scare him, it's no use at all. My advice is, keep the kiddies away from the crowds where he travels."

That goes for men and ladies too, no one's in the clear. Seven percent of hapless victims die, says Dr. Malusa, and nearly all are crippled. The good doctor said no explanation accounts for the epidemics each year, which occur in summer only. Asheville is presently suffering the worst rate of epidemic in our nation, in a state that already this year has seen more than one thousand victims fall to the polio menace. The national total is nearly six thousand.

The town fathers have composed a letter to Bishop Vernon Reynolds in Raleigh urging him to grant permission to Roman Catholics here to remain away from their rites.

July 6

Dear Frida,

It's two in the morning, and bright as day outside. The paved street has a watery shine, with the trees lined up along both banks like the canals of Xochimilco. The moon is not quite full: perfect down the left side but a little ragged on the right, so waning. C for Cristo means it is dying away. I couldn't sleep tonight so sat up to meet our birthday. But I must have fallen into a dream for a few seconds, because you were here in my room just now, in your wheelchair, your hair all done up. Working at an easel with your back to me. I said, "Frida, look, the streets have turned to rivers. Let's take a boat somewhere." You turned to me with empty eye sockets and said, "You go on, Sóli. I have to stay."

The radio news may have put me off sleep. Stalin's blockade of Berlin is a horror, and not so difficult for us to imagine here. Asheville is also under siege, quarantined because of the polio. Today I walked downtown to put Mrs. Brown's wage in the bank, and I saw not one other living soul on the way. The school playgrounds, empty. The luncheonettes dark, their counters attended by lines of empty chrome stools. The city is a graveyard. My only compatriots today were the plaster models in the store windows, with their smug blind eyes and smart attire. Of course, the bank was closed.

I can imagine you here, Frida, limp-skipping through the streets to have a laugh at all this fear. You've already had the polio, you have your leg to show for it, your billowing woe and passion that can't be chased indoors for anything. It's a gift to survive death, isn't it? It puts us outside the fray. How strange, that I include myself, I wonder now what I mean. What was my childhood disease? Love, I suppose. I was susceptible to contracting great love, suffering the chills and delirium of that pox.

But it seems I am safe now, unlikely to contract it again. The advantages of immunity are plain. People contort themselves around the terror of being alone, making any compromise against that. It's a great freedom to give up on love, and get on with everything else.

Mainly this summer my everything-else is the new book. I believe it will be serious, Frida, and worthy. But at any rate finished soon, in autumn I hope. I proceed at a sluggish pace because I have to do all my own retyping. Mrs. Brown's efficiency has spoiled me, and now she can't come to work because her landlady is hysterical over the epidemic. She threatened the boarders that if they go out in public or ride the buses, they aren't welcome back in the house. Mrs. Brown tolerates the intolerable from that woman. Stalin himself could learn from the Siege of Mrs. Bittle.

I have wondered, Why shouldn't I let Mrs. Brown live here? We already work together, I have an empty bedroom. You see, I am dumb as a calf, trying to divine the rules about such things. In Mexico all manner of people could live in one house, half carrying hearts on their sleeves and the other half carrying sidearms, all rolled in one chalupa. But no, not here. Even a dumb calf gains a dim understanding, after enough blows to the head! We would be hung out as filthy laundry in *Echo* and *Star Week*. Children would be instructed to cross to the opposite side of the street, to pass the house.

Luckily, the mail remains under control. Mrs. Brown organized for it all to come to Mrs. Bittle's, until and unless the landlady realizes the menace of an envelope licked by a stranger. My house is as empty as the luncheonettes, Mrs. Brown's table tidy as she left it, typewriter under a dustcover, telephone standing like a black daffodil blooming from the table, its earpiece dangling. If I want company I can sift through the mail; she forwards it all here in boxes after she has answered it. Those letters continue to astonish, the flow has hardly slowed. Now the girls all beg: Please, Mr. Shepherd, give us a happy ending next time! As if I held sway over anything real, with my invented puppets. These girls have bet on a dark horse. No one should count on me for a happy outcome.

You and I are the same. Do people ask you to erase the bleeding hearts and daggers from your paintings, to make them more jolly? But Mexico is different, I know that. You're allowed your hearts and daggers there.

Our Christmas visit sustains my memories, though it's true what you said, you have become a different person. I won't agree however that you are a bag of bones. Diego is a fool, that skinny lizard Maria Félix should run up a tree and eat ants. But your health does worry me, I'll be honest. One thing that kept me sitting up tonight is the dread that I may not celebrate many more birthdays with you.

More than anything, I regret the cross words during our visit. I understand your temper, that it's a kind of poetry rather than actual truth, and that you and Mrs. Brown were not apt to get along perfectly. You and she are both important women in my life, and too many cooks will put a fire in the kitchen. If any forgiving is to be done, Mrs. Brown and I have already done it. I'm certain she would send her greetings with mine.

Abrazos to Diego, and to Candelaria, Belén, Carmen Alba, Perpetua, Alejandro, and everyone else in your house, where I seem to have more friends than in the entire city where I now live. But most of all to you, *mi querida, feliz cumpleaños.*

SÓLI

July 30

Mrs. Brown called before nine this morning, beside herself. A second letter from the scorpion at the loyalty firm. Loren Matus. An incriminating photograph, he claims, but it makes no sense at all. I made her read that part of the letter twice. "A photo of Harrison Shepherd and his wife at a Communist Party meeting in 1930." I'm to pay him a fee of five hundred dollars for the chance to examine it.

She took a letter, over the phone: Why this photograph could not be what he says. In 1930 Harrison Shepherd was fourteen years of age, attending an elementary school for the mentally damaged in Mexico City. His political leaning was to collect centipedes in a jar and set them loose under Señora Bartolome's desk during the prayers. Since that year he has discovered no reason to marry, nor has anyone signed on for the job, but it might have quite entertained him to have a wife in 1930. A lot of people might pay money to see that. Signed sincerely Harrison Shepherd. HS/VB.

August 11

"Advance the spark," says Tom Cuddy on the phone, "Square-o-lina here I come." He has museum business with the Vanderbilts, will be staying three nights at the Grove Park, proposes we meet there. "An assignation," he calls it. Oh Tom, Tom, vanity's son, expecting me to show up with hat in hand, heart pounding. Knowing, in fact, I will.

The Assignation

Long time no see, says the handsome scoundrel, looking up from his highball. The firm handshake, the chair pulled out. The terrace restaurant at the Grove Park is very grand, white cloths on the tables and candles flickering, but all other chairs were empty. Tom must have been the only guest in the hotel.

"You're brave, letting your boss send you here. Have they not heard about our quarantine, in Manhattan? Or are you all just so dashing, the plague can't catch up?"

"Who's afraid of a little polio germ?" he said. "Builds up the character."

"Tommy, that's no joke."

"What's your poison? This is a sloe gin fizz. Don't let the name throw you, it's a fast ticket. The apron back there at the bar has a heavy foot."

"All right. A ticket on the fast train, please."

Tommy signaled the waiter, who hovered constantly nearby in the dark, either at the patio entrance or over by the wall, sneaking a smoke. I have wondered if waiters will ever become invisible to me, as they seem to be for others. I wanted to help this lad out, go get the drinks myself and later help him carry the plates to the kitchen.

Tommy's cigarette end glowed, constantly in motion. "Oh, come on, look what the polio did for FDR. A gimp leg gets you the sympathy vote, you can be maudlin as anything and they all go dotty for it. *'I hate the wah, Eleanor hates the wah, our little dog Fala hates the wah. . . .'*"

The drinks appeared, followed by dinner, materializing from the dark just as Tom had, unreal as the image rising in a movie house. Cruelty is just a role he plays, like Hurd Hatfield as Dorian Gray. Tommy has seen some damage in his day. The Modern show he helped curate, ridiculed by Congress, he took that personally. And that's probably the least of it, for a boy who wants so madly to belong, and will not quite.

The truth of Tommy is slow to rise, but he is down there somewhere, underneath the shining surface. The day we first met, sitting on a crate of Rodin in the train, he dropped the clever banter along with his jaw upon hearing the name Rivera. He has studied those murals in photographs. He wanted to know everything: the mixture of plaster, the pigments. And Frida, how she laid the paint on, with brushes or knives? The warm or cool colors first? That unearthly sadness that radiates from her paintings, does she feel it herself, when she's painting? Those were his words, unearthly sadness. Tommy has handled two Kahlos already, in his time at the museum.

Later on in his room, lying on our backs smoking his herd of Camels one after another, shirtless in the dark, it could have been the Potomac Academy, or the tiny barracks at Lev's. But those places couldn't have contained him, Tom Cuddy is a one-man band. His questions don't need answers, it's hard enough just to work out what he's asking. Who would win at arm-wrestling, Frankie Laine or Perry Como? Has Christian Dior gone screwball or hopped on the genius wagon?

"Why, what's Dior done?"

"Took all the padding off the girls' shoulders and stuffed it in their brassieres."

He is thinking of leaving the gallery, the art world altogether. For advertising.

"What, to write jingles? Lucky Strike Means Fine Tobacco?"

"No, you egg. Art direction. Creating the Look of Tomorrow."

"I thought the museum was what you loved. Kandinsky and Edward Hopper. Now you want to be Llewelyn Evans in *The Hucksters*, selling Beautee Soap to unsuspecting housewives?"

"Not soap, glamour. Sex, God and the *Pa*-tri-*ah*." Tommy blew a meticulous smoke ring, watched it rise toward the ceiling. "On the seventh day Tom Cuddy made America. And Tom Cuddy said, *Cat, that is good.*"

"If I were a religious man I'd get off this bed, before lightning strikes it."

"One day you will see, Shepherd my friend. The men campaigning for president are going to hire advertisers."

"Tommy, you've lost your marbles."

"This is no fish. Do you know how many television stations there are now?"

"Six or seven, I guess."

"Twenty."

"How's your friend, by the way? The Latin Romeo with the face for television."

The question shifted Tom's mood, turning him petulant. Ramiro is gone, not to Puerto Rico but out of the city, far from the glamorous spotlight. Maybe selling brushes door to door. It was hard to avoid speculating on the clockwork of Tom Cuddy's universe: Ramiro's setting sun, the rising star of Harrison Shepherd. The long compromise against loneliness. Tom says he'll be back here in a month, and probably more times after that. To Casheville, as he calls it. Regular assignations on expense account at the Grove Park, as long as he continues to happify the Vanderbilts as planned.

"You're lucky you live here," he said.

"What, in Square-o-lina? Under a quarantine."

"Well, here, Shep, or any damned place you want. Writing what you want, with nobody watching over your shoulder. In the city we're like ants under a lens, getting scorched in the sun."

"Scorched ants. That's dramatic." I pushed myself up off the bed. It took some effort, a lot of sloe gin under the bridge, but I needed to pace the little room. Tommy's energy came off his skin like electricity. I stood by the window, a porthole into the dark.

"*I'm* dramatic," he said. "You should hear the real gory. The joes in radio and television. The producers are like those little brutes in grammar school, crowding around to watch the ant fry. Conspiracy indictments, *alien* hearings. Do you know how many New Yorkers are *from* someplace? The city's going to be as empty as this hotel."

In a rare turn of events, he seemed to have run out of words. I could hear the place breathing: the gasp of roof beams, the slow circulation of water through pipes.

Tommy lit another Camel. "They don't even have to indict you. One day you just feel the heat and you know they're up there, kneeling in the circle, watching you writhe. Your name has gone on a list. Everybody stops talking when you come into a room. You think we don't know about the plague?"

"They're only television producers, Tommy. Not heads of state, with secret police at their disposal. Just men who get up in the morning, put on Sears Roebuck suits, and go to an office to decide who gets a pie in the face today. It's hard to feature how they could be so monstrous."

"'Hard to feature.'" Tom clucked his tongue, whether at a writer's prose or his innocence, who could say. "Little shepherd boy. What am I going to do with you?"

September 2

The stars and planets are right again. Mrs. Brown is back, all this week, cheerful as anything today in a new peplum blouse. The Woman's Club has let her back on the Program Committee, mainly because she kept the club running by telephone and the post during the quarantine. Most of the good ladies were flummoxed by solitude.

We're on track to complete the novel draft by month's end. Mrs. Brown says this one is my best, and she hasn't even seen the ending yet. The title is another go-round, the publisher as usual wants crashing cymbals: *The Mighty Fallen*, or *Ashes of Empire*. I'd hoped for a pinch of metaphor. Mrs. Brown sat at her table looking thoughtful, holding a pencil alongside her cheek, and then offered: "Remember at Chichén Itzá on top of the temple, the last day? Everything looked bright, and then the storm came and put it in a different light. It was the same view, all the same things, but suddenly it went fearsome. That's what you want, isn't it? Is there a name for that?"

"Yes. J. Edgar Hoover."

She's asked permission to leave early tomorrow to see Truman on his whistle-stop for the reelection. He's coming through Asheville, speaking from a platform on the back of the Ferdinand Magellan. It's the same train the people here stood waiting for all night, when it carried Roosevelt home. But it never came.

September 15

The Grove Park is a reassuring place, all that squared-off, heavy Mission furniture with its feet firmly on the ground. The giant stone fireplaces, the carpentered grandfather clocks, even the roof, snub and rounded like the thatch of a fairy-tale cottage, with little eyebrow curves above the windows of the top-floor rooms. Tom likes those best, he feels he's an artist up in a garret. He insists Scott Fitzgerald always took a top-floor room here when he came to visit Zelda. "Just ask the bellhop, I *told* you so, and I'm right. He might have written *Gatsby* in the very room where I'm sleeping tonight."

"More likely *The Crack-Up*. If he was here in town for the reason you say."

Tommy rolled his head in a circle. "Oh, *The Crack-Up*, well done!" He moves like an actor, physically earnest, aware of his better angles. Today he had a better audience: the terrace was jammed, people out enjoying the autumn sun. The tourist trade is back, all those postponed vacations must be had before cold weather hits, it's like a rush on the bank. Tommy was playing dissect-the-guests.

"That one over there has got clocks on his socks. I'll lay a fiver on it. Go over and ask him to raise up his pants leg."

"I don't know what that means. Clocks on his socks."

"It means," he leaned forward, sotto voce, "the car he left with the valet has a *fox tail* attached to the antenna. Hubba hubba. You don't know these college boys. I can see them in the dark." Sloe gin was not fast enough for Tommy today, so we drank "Seabreezes," a concoction he'd explained to the bartender. Complicated instructions for what amounted to gin and orange juice.

"Over there, the couple. Parisians, a jasper and his zazz girl, *très* vout-o-reenee."

"Really." There was no learning Tommy's language, I'd given up on trying.

"In Paris I can always pick out the Americans like anything, *ping, ping*!" One eye closed, he feigned using a pistol. "A Frenchman's like *this*"—he pulled his shoulders toward his ears—"like someone's put ice down his collar. And a Brit's just the opposite, shoulders back. 'I say, a spot of ice down the old neck! Not a problem, by Jove.'"

"And the American?"

Tommy flung himself back in his chair, knees spread wide, hands clasped behind his golden head, vowels flat: 'Ice, what's the big idea? I take mine straight up.'"

And the Mexican: *I carried the ice here on my back, I chopped it with a machete, and probably it still isn't right.* Tommy lifted two fingers to signal the next round.

"No more for me," I said. "I'm nursing a ridiculous hope that I'm still going to get some work done this evening. Coca-Cola, please."

The waiter nodded. Every waiter in the place was dark-skinned, and all the guests white. It felt like an occupied zone after cease-fire, two distinct factions inhabiting the same place: the one tribe relaxed and garrulous, draped unguarded on the chairs in colorful clothes, while the other stood wordless in starched coats, white collars sharp against black skin. In Mexico when we served a table it was normally the guests in starched collars, the servants in floral tapestries.

Tommy informed me that Coca-Cola sells fifty million bottles a day.

"Who are you, Elmo Roper?"

"It's enough to float a battleship. I mean, literally it is, if you think about it. The French National Assembly just voted to nix Coca-Cola, no buy no sell, anywhere in their empire. What's the static?"

"Maybe they don't want it poured down their backs."

"You're going home and working *tonight*?" His eyes are so pale and clear, his whole complexion really, he seems to give off light rather than absorb it. Moths must fly into his flame and perish gladly.

"I can stay the afternoon. But I'm so near the end of the book. It's hard to think of much else."

"Oh, Jack *will* be a dull boy."

"Or my meat will go to gristle, if my stenographer is to be believed."

He leaned forward, pinched the flesh of my upper arm, clucked his tongue. Then fell back in his chair. He had a way of looking tossed around, like one half of a prizefight. "And what's the buzz on your cooper?"

I pondered this. "I give up."

"Your moving picture."

"Oh. I'm not sure. The Hollywood winds blow hot and cold."

"Listen, I could sell it. Make your picture the talk of the season."

"I thought you wanted a look at Robert Taylor. Now you're selling him?"

"Cat, you don't listen to me. I am going to be an ad man. I interviewed with a firm last week."

"I do listen. You're going to sell presidential candidates. You know what, they need you right now. All four of them."

"You said it! Four men running, and not one winner I can see. Lord and butler, spare me that cold cut Tom Dewey and his toothbrush moustache."

"You may not be spared. The newspapers say it's already over. With the Democrats split three ways, Dewey's just waiting to be confirmed. The editorial this morning said Truman's cabinet should resign now and get out of the way."

"It can't *be*. Dewey doesn't even look like a proper Republican. He looks like a magazine salesman."

"Some salesman, he's not even campaigning. 'America the Beautiful' is not exactly a platform. I suppose he doesn't want to lower himself to Truman's level, it would show lack of confidence."

Tommy put his face in his hands. "Not Tom Dewey the toothbrush moustache! *Please* not that mug in all the photos for the next four years."

"Would you rather look at Strom Thurmond for four years?"

"What a drizzle bag."

A stout woman in a scant bandeau and espadrilles minced across the terrace. In Mexico she would have been a beauty of a certain type, but not here, I gathered. Tommy's eyes tracked her too dramatically, like Charlie Chaplin in *The Gold Rush*.

"Maybe Scarlett O'Hara will come out and stump for Strom," I suggested. "And Rhett Butler, whistling Dixiecrat to call out the segregationists."

Tom looked up, eyes wide. "Now *that* is a campaign image. You've got the gift! And on the other team, Henry Wallace as the Pied Piper, with the liberals skipping off behind him."

"Poor Truman, he's got nobody left. I read he's asked a dozen men to run as his vice president, and they all turned him down. Do you think that's true?"

"He can't get reelected, why should they waste the time?"

A young couple slid into the next table, inciting Tom to announce: "Hardware and headlights, call the nabs." The fellow was an Adonis, more or less Tommy in a younger model. The girl wore a tennis dress and diamond bracelets.

"My stenographer went out to see Truman at his whistle stop here, just a couple of weeks ago. She's League of Women Voters. So there's one he can count on."

"Oh, gee. Little man with high voice makes barnyard jokes from back of train."

"She said he turned out quite a crowd."

"Natch. The first thing he's accomplished in the last two years."

"That's not fair. The Republicans kill every one of his bills in Congress. They can't be bothered with the minimum wage or housing starts, they're all crowding into the communism hearings to see Alger Hiss charged with espionage."

Tommy vamped a few bars of "I'm Just Wild About Harry," with jazz hands.

"It's true, Tommy. If you read something besides the *Echo*, you'd know that."

"Fine, down with it. Harry Truman gets *two* votes."

"I don't vote. I never have."

"*Really?* Conk me. I had you down for a Henry Wallace type. The rise of the common man and all that. All the reviewers say so."

"Politics in this country are never quite what they seem. I don't quite feel . . . what? Entitled."

He looked genuinely amazed. "*Entitled.* Cat, this is *America*, they let anybody vote. Crooks, wigs, even cookies like us. Dogs and cats, probably. Don't take Fido to the polls, he might cancel you out."

"Well, that's the thing, it's all too much. Too fast. I need to brood on things."

He cocked his head in a sympathetic pout. "Sad stranger in the happy land."

The New York Times, *September 26, 1948*

Truman Is Linked by Scott to Reds

Special to The New York Times

BOSTON, MASS., SEPT. 25—Hugh D. Scott Jr., chairman of the Republican National Committee, told Massachusetts Republicans today that the Communist party endorsed Mr. Truman for Vice President in 1944, with the result that the President now shows "indifference to Communist penetration at home." Delivering the keynote address at the party's state convention, Mr. Scott assailed the President's reference to spy investigations as a "red herring" and said the explanation for this attitude could be found in history.

"The New York *Daily Worker*, the official Communist organ in the United States, endorsed Mr. Truman cordially in the issue of Aug. 12, 1944," he said. "The endorsement was signed by Eugene Dennis, secretary of the Communist party, who recently was cited for contempt of the House of Representatives for refusing to testify concerning his subversive activities in this country."

Mr. Scott quoted Mr. Dennis as writing, in connection with the Democratic Party's 1944 candidates: "It is a ticket representative not only of the Democratic Party but of important and wider sections of the camp of national unity."

Another link between the President and *The Daily Worker* was claimed by Mr. Scott. This is a letter written on Senate stationery and signed by Harry S. Truman, August 14, 1944. This communication to Samuel Barron, public relations director of *The Daily Worker*, expresses thanks for the copy of an article that appeared in the paper.

Calling for an all-out drive on subversives in Government, Mr. Scott said: "Once the Dewey-Warren administration takes over we will see the greatest housecleaning in Washington since St. Patrick cleaned the snakes out of Ireland."

Senator Henry Cabot Lodge Jr. was chairman of the convention, which adopted a platform making no mention of controversial state referenda on birth control and labor unions.

November 1

This strange day. Early snow, and a visit from the FBI.

The snow fell in huge, leisurely flakes, piling itself carefully on everything, even twigs and telephone wires. Putting white caps on the hydrants, covering the mud puddles and buckled sidewalks. A Benediction for the Day of the Dead. Or perhaps last rites, this weary world with all its faults consenting to lie down with a sigh and be covered up with a sheet. "Holy is the day"—I had just thought those words when he came tramping tiredly up the walk, leaving behind a trail, the impressions of his leather shoes. At the curb he'd hesitated, turning this way and that before coming up my walk. It looked like an Arthur Murray dance diagram.

Myers is the name. I made sure to get it this time, Melvin C. Myers, special agent from the Federal Bureau of Investigation. Not the same man who was here before, right away I knew it was a different voice. This Myers is a man of rank, evidently, but he seemed almost apologetic. Too old for a fight, sorry that life has come to this.

I could hardly let him stand out there getting a snowdrift on his hat. I had a fire on the hearth and coffee made, prepared for a solitary day. Mrs. Brown is kept home by the weather, her bus line canceled. So I brought Myers his coffee on the sofa and poked up the fire, to all appearances entertaining a guest. We joked about the elections coming up, how Truman will soon be looking for a new job. Three magazines lay on the coffee table, the week's editions I'd purchased from the newsstand, all of them with President Dewey on their covers, his bold new plan for the nation outlined inside. Chisme and Chispa weren't fooled by the friendly patter, they rose from their pool of warmth by the hearth, hissed inaudibly, and slunk away. I should have done the same.

He believes I have a very large problem, does Mr. Myers. Things really do not look good regarding my position with the State Department. I'm about to be in the same boat with Truman, he said. Hunting a new job.

"Oh, well, it's too bad. A lot of it going around." I decided to play it contrite, to satisfy this fellow. No need to tell him I hadn't worked for the State Department in years, and had no intention of ever doing so again.

"Except for us gumshoes," he said with a chuckle. "Our job security is A-okay."

"I've heard that. Snakes out of Ireland, and so forth."

He was eager to show me his portfolio of evidence against me, and I was curious, especially about the photograph. Harrison Shepherd and wife, Communist party meeting 1930. It was a puzzling disappointment, not one thing in the picture I could recognize. No person I'd ever known, no place I had been.

"Is this the noose around my neck? I can't even guess which one of those men is supposed to be me. I was fourteen that year, living in Mexico." I handed back the photograph, and he took a great deal of care to put it inside a folder and settle it in the correct compartment of his briefcase.

Then said, "That photograph is a piece of garbage. I realize that."

The man was so shabby and earnest, I almost hated to let him down. Probably people habitually responded this way—shop clerks slipped back his change, the butcher put an extra ounce of chuck on the scales. Probably I'd let him in the door because of some vague sense he was a man of Artie's ilk. A short, bald, gentile Arthur Gold. A widower, judging from his clothes, and the long, scant hair combed over his bald head, no one to tell him that was a bad idea. He had none of Artie's cleverness but seemed to carry the same torch. Searching for an honest man and fed up with the whole shmear.

"I know that you were in Mexico," he said. "We have this information. You worked for a painter in Mexico City, a very well-known Red. I can't recall his name, but it's in the files. I came here today to question you about this. In all of this mess, this kind of weather, in North Carolina. I don't even have chains on the tires." He sighed.

"To question me about working for a painter in Mexico?"

"That's about the extent of it. You could deny it, most of them deny. To begin with. But I'll be honest with you, it doesn't usually help."

"Why would I deny it?"

"This information alone is reason for dismissing you from your government post. That's what happens now, if you choose not to deny the associations. In time there may be more. I think you're probably going to get a McFarland letter."

"Who is McFarland?"

"McFarland is nobody. But this letter is bad news, it would contain the actual charges. The higher-ups have intimated they are accumulating some pretty shocking evidence against you."

"I see. Who is supplying this shocking evidence?"

"Mr. Shepherd, be reasonable. You know we can't tell you that. If we allowed all the accused to confront their accusers, we would have no informants left. It would infringe on our ability to investigate."

"Your ability to investigate. That's the important thing."

"Correct. In this day and age, we have a duty to protect the citizen. It's a precarious business. People have no idea, they should be very grateful. You should be grateful, Mr. Shepherd."

"It's a difficult point you make, Mr. Myers. I felt pretty cozy here today, before you came knocking." I got up to put more wood on the fire, a piece of cedar shingle that sent a little shower of sparks onto the floor. I dusted up the ash, no harm done. But I seemed to have gotten up the dander of Myers, as far as it went.

"The mental world of the Communist is secretive," he said. "The Soviet Fatherland has to be preserved at any cost, and its enemies confounded." He seemed to be quoting a handbook, speaking in the general direction of the bookcase. Maybe he was trying to read titles: *Dickens, Dostoyevsky, Dreiser*, the suspect will alphabetize his books at any cost. Mrs. Brown, largely to blame.

"I wouldn't know," I said. I stayed where I was, feet to the fire. This was some sort of Jacson Mornard who'd arrived at my door, hat in hand, blade beneath the coat. I had let him in, brought the coffee. As Lev always said, you won't see it coming.

He shifted himself around to face me. "The thinking of the Communist is that no one who opposes him can possibly have any merit whatsoever. It's a psychological illness. The Communist cannot adjust himself to logic."

"That's a point of view. But I was thinking of what you said about confronting my accuser. I thought the Constitution gave me the right to know the charges against me. And who was bringing them."

Myers drained his coffee cup and leaned forward with a little grunt to set the cup on the table. We were nearly finished, I could tell.

"Whenever I hear this kind of thing," he said, "a person speaking about constitutional rights, free speech, and so forth, I think, 'How can he be such a sap? Now I can be *sure* that man is a Red.' A word to the wise, Mr. Shepherd. We just do not hear a real American speaking in that manner."

November 2

Mrs. Brown left early to go to the polls. She says the Elementary down the block would be my voting place, if I could be troubled to use it. I have promised her I'll get my voting card before the next go-round. Meanwhile the neighborhood children are having the day off, out fighting their snow wars, building forts and goggle-eyed men. The one in the next yard looks like Agent Myers, rotund and slump-shouldered, a potato for his nose, peering at my window wearing the old fedora I gave Romulus.

November 3

She came in at nine with the mail and daily papers, all claiming Dewey had won the presidency, in the largest typeface imaginable. Poor Tommy: that toothbrush moustache does loom large, above the fold. But Mrs. Brown's eyes were ablaze. She did a little dance stomp-ing the snow off her boots in the doorway, unwinding her scarf. I haven't seen such fire in her since Mexico.

"You look like you've had the canary for breakfast."

"Here it is, Mr. Shepherd. Dewey hasn't won it. Turn on the radio."

At first the news was about airlifts into Berlin, those desperate people now six months under siege. The American flyers are get-ting in more food than ever, thousands of tons, and now also coal so the Berliners won't freeze. The interview was an air force man who said next month they plan to drop candy and toys from the planes, with little parachutes. "Those German kiddies will have Santa Claus, whether Joe Stalin wants them to or not," he vowed.

"Mr. Shepherd, how be ye?" she asked suddenly. I must have looked unwell.

I blew my nose to preserve dignity. I'd been close to tears, for the most ridiculous reason. "I was thinking of my old boss, Lev Trotsky," I confessed. "He would have loved that report. The triumph of com-passion over Stalin's iron fist. The people prevail, with candy and parachutes."

"It's our boys helping them do it," she said, and I said yes, it is, and wanted to dance with Mrs. Brown, stomp my feet at the doorsill. My country 'tis of thee.

At half past, the election news came back. Truman had been awakened and rolled out of bed in Missouri, informed he might not be on vacation yet. He didn't stay up last night to listen to the returns; the Democratic campaign had not rented a suite or organized any party for that. They saw no need. While Dewey's men popped the champagne in New York, Harry put on his pajamas, ate a ham sandwich, and went to bed early.

Now the race was neck and neck, with many states still counting. By mid-morning it was Harry ahead by a nose. We didn't move from the radio.

Shortly before noon they called it. Harry Truman won.

"Oh, Mr. Shepherd, it's a day to remember. Those news men could not make a thing true just by saying so. It's only living makes life."

I knew what she meant. The cold spell on us is deep, but however bitter the day might appear, winter will pass. I made a fire for us in the living room. A neighbor across the way has torn down his old carriage house and piled the scrap wood by the street.

Mrs. Brown rolled up the *Washington Post* like a log and waved it high, her eyes alight with mischief. "Here's something to fuel the flames," she suggested. Before long we'd cast in every one, the magazines too, warming our hands over those trumpeting false prophecies. The magazines with color in them curled in a blue-green blaze. By afternoon the house was so warm Mrs. Brown took off her gloves.

"You can't give up," she kept repeating. "You think you know it's all hopeless but you do not, Mr. Shepherd. You know not."

December 10

The United Nations have adopted the Universal Declaration of Human Rights. It was all on the radio today, and even the howlers achieved a tone of deference. Eighteen articles, establishing every person on earth to be born free and equal, endowed with conscience to act toward every other in a spirit of brotherhood. Maybe Mrs. Brown is right, and we know not where a little raft of hope could carry us.

Article 18 states: All persons have the right to freedom of thought, conscience and religion or belief.

Mr. Harrison W. Shepherd
30 Montford Ave.
Asheville, North Carolina

Date: December 13, 1948

Dear Mr. Shepherd,

The evidence indicates that at certain times since   1930   *you have been a close associate of*   Mr. Deigo Riveira   *a person or persons who displayed active and sympathetic interest in the Communist Party. We also have evidence that your name has appeared in* Life Magazine, Look Magazine, Echo, Star Week, New York Post, Kingsport News, New York Times, Weekly Review, Chicago Times Book Review, Washington Post, National Review, Kansas City Star, Memphis Star, Raleigh Spectator, Library Review, The Daily Worker, Hollywood Week, Asheville Trumpet *making statements to the effect that you believe in the overthrow of the United States government.*

The foregoing information indicates that you have been and are a member, close affiliate, or sympathetic associate of the Communist Party, and are therefore permanently dismissed from active employment by the federal government. All pension monies and any portion of salaries unpaid as yet, if any, are hereby claimed as property of the U.S. government. Sincerely,

J. EDGAR HOOVER, DIRECTOR
FEDERAL BUREAU OF INVESTIGATION

The Raleigh Spectator, *December 16, 1948*

Communist Writer Fired for Misdeeds

The Associated Press

WASHINGTON, D.C.—Writer Harrison Shepherd, nationally known author of books on the topic of Mexico, was fired this week from federal employment for reasons of un-Americanism. The Asheville man had worked for the Department of State since 1943. His role there remains unclear, but Melvin C. Myers, chief investigator on the case, confirmed it could well have given access to sensitive information. The misdeeds came to light through the massive loyalty investigation of federal employees initiated last year, which has so far identified hundreds of cases of un-Americanism but no espionage. Myers cited this as proof the campaign is working to drive out potential spies that may be hidden in government ranks.

December 18

They seem so thrilled to pounce, these press men. Not before, when I was nobody of consequence, only now. Mrs. Brown says envy plays into it. "There are some who'd hardly lift a finger for kindness, but they would haul up a load of rock to dump on some soul they think's been too lucky. They take it as duty, to equal out life's misery."

"They think I've been too *lucky*?"

She sighed. "Mr. Shepherd, it's what you've said a hundred times, they don't know a person's whole story. They think you just sit in your little room making up tales and getting bags of money for it, while they have to go out rain or shine and talk to Mrs. Smith on Charlotte Street about a pie contest. They're put out with you for having an easier life."

"Mrs. Brown, who in this world has an easier life?"

"I wonder that too."

January 26, 1949

An assignation. First of the new year. Tommy's attention seems to be wearing thin. Lying on his back blowing smoke rings, his eyes kept going to the window like a bird trapped indoors, wanting out. Rather than gazing upon the spectacle of me, sitting in the Morris chair all bundled up in my long knitted scarf. Mrs. Brown's Christmas present. If I can keep her long enough I shall be warm as a lamb, head to toe. I thought of getting out last year's gloves and putting those on too; the little room was freezing.

Maybe I'm only imagining Tommy has gone cool. What do I know of hearts in winter? He's tired, I know that much. And disappointed. No job in advertising yet, still a traveling salesman for Art, in Washington all last week before coming here. Something at the National Gallery.

"It must have been a hubbub in D.C., with the inauguration."

"*Hubbub*," he said. "Cat, what language do you speak? My *grandmother* said 'hubbub.' Harry Truman says 'hubbub.' I believe it was the theme of his inaugural speech. 'My fellow Americans, we face a great hubbub.'"

"Actually his theme was the false philosophy of communism. We will roll up our sleeves and defeat it."

"That sounds like a variety of hubbub."

"It's not all that funny, Tommy. Not to me. I was hoping for a new theme."

"Oh, cheer up. You'll never get to move Winslow Homers for the Department again, poor you. Maybe this solid gold little writing hobby will pan out instead."

"Because I still have money, I have no problems. Is that what you think?"

"It will get you through times with no friends, my friend."

"So they say."

Tommy was carefully studying the palm of his hand, for some reason.

"My motion-picture agreement is off, by the way. No reason given. They're getting ever so touchy out there about the color red."

"Stark! There goes my chance to meet Robert Taylor."

"You could probably arrange it. If you wanted to help him testify against someone. The money's fantastic, I hear."

Cold was literally leaking into the room. I could feel it pour in like water around the edges of the window. I had a strange vision of the whole hotel sunk like a ship beneath the sea, entering the world of the fishes.

"Do you know what, Tommy? Next month we should get together at my house. Honestly, it would be nice. I'll make a *lomo adobado*. You've never seen my house."

He raised his eyebrows. "Oh, but what will the neighbors think."

"They'll think I have a friend. One person knocking on my door who's not in the pay of myself or the FBI. You hear about it all the time."

He didn't answer. Finished with the hand inspection, he wound his watch.

"Aren't you sick of hotels?"

"Fed up to the blinkers, if you want to know. Let's go down to the bar."

"We should get dinner. Some nice oxtail soup and Horlick's, that's what you need. You've let yourself get run down."

"Oxtail soup and Horlick's. Cat, you are off the cob."

"Corny, that would mean. Sorry. I guess I'll go."

He rolled himself upright, facing me, black socks on the floor. "Sorry me, chum, I'm just whammed. Sick of hotels, you said it. What is this furniture, all these bars on everything? It gives me the heebies, like I'm in the pen."

"It's a style. Mission."

"*Mission.* Do they send up a preacher with the room service?" He lay back down on the bed, reached overhead to grasp the upright slats on the headboard, and briefly rattled them like a prisoner. "The hotel in D.C. had a lousy bar, the place was gestanko in general. Did I tell you there was a big scene?"

"No."

"Last night. No, night before. I get back to my hotel after a whole day of meetings with the drizzle bags, I'm beat to the socks, and I can't even get to the elevator. There's a scene in the lobby. This huge colored cat, he's got on a nice overcoat, hat, briefcase, everything, but he's flailing. Football with the bellhops. I mean he's down on the floor, they tackled him when he came in I guess. He's a Negro, see. The hotel doesn't have Negro guests."

"What happened?"

"Well, dig this. It turns out he's an ambassador from some African country. Ethiopia, I want to say. They got it sorted out. It's all right because he was foreign, not an American Negro. What do you make of that?"

"Good God. I hate to contemplate. That foreigners aren't even worth the full measure of American contempt?"

"Could be. But he seemed decent. A nice accent, like a Brit. We rode the elevator together, he was on my floor. He said he hoped I didn't mind. He's stayed there loads of times before, and they still make the same mistake."

"Mind what? You said he hoped you didn't mind."

"I'm sure I don't know."

"How did you feel, Tommy?"

He rolled over onto one elbow, narrowing his eyes. *"Feel?"*

"In the elevator, with that poor man."

He fell back again, staring at the ceiling. "I felt I was going up."

February 11

"There was a poke on your mailbox," Mrs. Brown announced this morning as she came in the door. After these years it still takes me by surprise, though I should have known, she stood there holding it. A poke is a sack. A mesh bag in this case, the type the neighbor uses for carrying home her groceries. Today it contained sundry fountain pens, a fedora, things I've given Romulus over several years. Including the rubber *atl-atl* brought from Mexico, his reward for feeding the cats.

"Here's a note," Mrs. Brown said, puzzling over it. "Romulus isn't to visit here any more." *Please keep away from my boy* was the nature of her explanation. Agent Myers had advised her they should not keep any objects given him by a Communist.

"Take a letter, Mrs. Brown. Tell the lady she needs to get in touch with General Eisenhower right away, because he too is in possession of a Communist Object."

Mrs. Brown sat at the typewriter, hands poised, waiting for the cue that my words were going to make some kind of sense. Sometimes she waits all day.

"What did they call it? Oh, yes!" I said, snapping my fingers. My memory is fine, thank you. "The Order of Victory. It was in *Life Magazine* years ago, they had a full-page photo. A platinum star set with diamonds. Stalin gave it to him at Yalta. Tell her the next time Agent Myers comes around, she'd better tell him to go see Eisenhower. Make sure the general puts that thing in a poke and sends it right back to Stalin."

March 4

I grew cross with Mrs. Brown today. It shouldn't have happened, she is as good as gold. She did the shopping for me, I'm losing the nerve for going out, and it's only March. She tolerates, as usual. Returned with change and receipts, plus cheerful news of spring, crocuses in the yards on Montford, tennis shoes on sale. A 12-pack of pencils is now 29 cents. The Zippo lighter went up to $6, so she went against orders and bought matches, more economical. I scolded her for it, telling her matches don't work worth a damn in the bathtub. I've never sworn at her before. It made her go pale and sit down, like a telegram bearing bad news. It took her half an hour to respond.

"You shouldn't be smoking in the bath, Mr. Shepherd."

"Why, because I'll burn down the house?"

This afternoon she brought letters up to my study for signature, and I noticed her nails looked ragged. She is on edge too; we both jump when the telephone rings, like schoolgirls, waiting for Lincoln Barnes to ring up. It's been months that they've had the manuscript, and now the corrected galleys. A title, jacket art, everything you might want to have on hand for a publication. Except a publication date.

"Your stories are all about Mexico," Mrs. Brown posed today, with forceful cheer. "Have you ever thought about writing them for Mexicans?"

"Where in the world did that come from?"

"I only ask."

"I don't write in Spanish. I write in English, about Mexicans. If I wrote in Spanish, I suppose I'd have to write about Americans."

"I know you speak Spanish perfectly well. I've heard you."

"Ordering a plate of fish is not writing a novel. I don't even dream in Spanish. I can't seem to invent anything in that language. Don't expect me to explain."

She should have said *Yes sir*, and turned on her Kerrybrooke heels. That's how Gal Friday does it in the movies. Yet there she stood, wearing that look: Hell or High Water. "You might could learn," she said. "If you stayed there awhile longer."

"Living there from the '20s until 1940 wasn't enough? You think a few more decades of practice might do the trick?"

"I mean living there as a man. A writer. You'd get used to it."

"Is this a suggestion?"

She didn't answer. I laid down my book and glared.

"Look, I don't have the temperament. Mexican writers are all depressives."

She has been hiding mail. Filing it in the boxes for the attic without letting me see it all first, as is the custom. I caught her out and made her show what she'd been holding back. She insists nearly all the mail is the same as ever, it's only a handful that are "not very nice."

"We say onions to H. W. Shepherd!" is the general sentiment. Shepherd the squealing pathetic traitorous free speecher, the Communist.

"You have to forgive hateful people, for what a man hates, he knows not."

"Who said that, Jesus Christ?"

"Mr. Shepherd, there's still a good deal of nice mail here, and some hateful. The good are from people who've read a book of yours or more, and glad of it. And the hateful ones are from people who know nothing of you. That's all I'm saying. Look if you're going to look. See if they mention a word you ever wrote."

She was right, they didn't. They addressed a creature they had learned about through some other means. The news, presumably.

"I can see how you'd get your feelings hurt," she said. "As a man. But not as a writer, for they've not read your books. From the look of it, I'd say they've read nary a book at all."

Still, it was hard to put the things down. Like a gruesome potboiler. You know how it will finish, you know it will turn your stomach, you go on reading. There were a dozen or more. "Your treacherous behavior in the Department of State is nothing but slings and arrows aimed at Old Glory. It is hard for us Americans to know how self-hating Communists can live with your grotesque deeds."

"If the majority felt as you do, we would all be in chains. Freedom is what our country is based on. If you won't stand up for our country, you deserve no freedom."

"I and my friends will certainly do all we can to spread the word about your disgusting hatred for our country, and make you even more a footnote of litery history than already."

"It sickens me to think you and your old haggard wife might raise another America-hating child. I hope she is barren."

"Go back to your own filthy country. When we need Mexican's opinion of America we'll ask."

"I'm proud to say I don't own your book, if I did it would go in the fireplace."

Well, naturally I felt a twinge at that one. After our newspaper-burning party. But Mrs. Brown said fiddlesticks, it's usual to start the fire with a newspaper when it's no longer of any use. "This is something different. It's not civilized. Imagine saying any such things to a human person."

"No, you're right. They're an angry bunch."

She took the pages out of my hands. "Angry is not the word for it. These folk don't even ken you to be a real man. They give you no benefit of a doubt. I expect they'd be kinder to a neighbor's dog that bit them."

"Well, that's true. My neighbor here at least sent a note about Romulus. She said 'please,' and sent the gifts back. I'll give her that."

"They are just so happy to see the mighty fallen," was her verdict. She tore the letters to pieces and threw them in the bin, then sat down to the day's typing. Even from upstairs, her Royal sounded like a Browning machine gun.

April 7

Infuriating telephone conversation with Lincoln Barnes.

Say, did you ever think of doing short pieces? The kind of thing they run in the Popular Fiction Group?

Pulp stories. I asked him why.

"Oh, just wondering."

My opinion of those stories, which I shared with Lincoln Barnes, is that they are all written by one person using a hundred different pseudonyms. Her real name might be Harriet Wheeler. She eats nothing but chocolates and lives in one of the upstairs rooms at the Grove Park.

It should have been a good day. With Tommy coming tomorrow. Not on the Vandy-wagon either, he just wants to visit. Passing through on his way to see some sculpture in Chattanooga. He'll stay here, he wants to see my cave he says, the pork roast is already marinating. Mrs. Brown left early, I was boiling chiles and garlic in water to mix with the vinegar and oregano when the phone rang. Months without a call, waiting for Tommy and for Lincoln Barnes, and now they both turn up.

Barnes didn't want to talk to me directly, I could tell. He'd hoped to leave a message with Mrs. Brown. I usually don't answer in the afternoons. What he seems to be saying is they are uncertain about publishing the book. At all. With the Communist Business starting to tie their hands.

"I could see that, if I were a Communist. Luckily for you, I am not."

"Look, I know you're not a Communist. Everybody here knows that. We know you're loyal to the U.S. Your name doesn't even sound all that Mexican."

I had to go in the kitchen and turn off the pot, it was boiling over.

"What you are," he said when I came back, "is controversial. The fellows running the show here are not very keen on controversial, because it stirs people up. For most readers out there, controversial means exactly the same thing as anti-American."

"Barnes. You're a man of words, they matter to you. Why would you say this? You don't like controversy because it stirs people up. Controversy *means* stirring up."

He didn't respond.

"You could say you don't like an eggshell, because it has egg in it. Why not go ahead and say you don't like eggs?"

He sighed into the phone. "I'm on your side, Shepherd. Believe me. I didn't call you up to play games. The suggestion that has been made here is that we publish the book under a pseudonym."

Good idea. How about Harriet Wheeler? This is madness. The

novel is set in Mexico, written in the same style as two previous books, which have been read by practically everyone in the nation, schoolchildren included. Does he think they'll believe this is some other writer's work?

He said every publisher in New York is now scrambling to publish books set in ancient Mexico.

"Are you serious?"

"Oh, yes. You're going to have fifty imitators soon. Why not get in line? You could be among the first."

The thing was boggling. He mentioned other possibilities. Using a ghostwriter. Not exactly that, but a real person, I would pay him a fee to use his name. In case I am worried about the press uncovering that the book was actually written by me.

Uncovering. My words, me, how could there be any difference?

"You're an editor, Mr. Barnes. Your stock-in-trade is the handiwork of other people. So this could be Stanback Powders we're discussing, or fine leather shoes, as far as you're concerned. I don't know, I'm only guessing. But for me it is different. I am the tongue of the shoe. If you pull me out of it, the whole thing falls apart."

April 8

A day could be perfect. You could forget fear altogether. Or fear might no longer make any difference, because it is the whole ocean and you're in it. You hold your breath, swim for light.

Tommy found it hilarious that Barnes had to be talked into putting my name on my book. Or that he would at least "pitch that idea to marketing." A freaking gasser. Somehow I was persuaded to agree. Tommy is persuasive.

"Oh my *God*, pitch that to marketing. Author's name on the author's book, *what next?*"

God has no better card to play than an April day, a well-tuned car, a world with nothing so wrong in it really, if a *lomo adobado* could still be cooked to such perfection, consumed to excess, distributed thereafter between a working Philco refrigerator and two happy, useless cats. And all of it left behind, dishes still in the sink. The mountain parkway is open to the west now, a skyline viaduct to the Great Smokies, they finished it just for us. Tommy and me. We were quite sure of that. The tunnels are no longer blind, they all go somewhere. You arrive at the other side.

"Mr. Barnes seemed to think he was taking a terrible risk on me. I'm a regular Moriarty, my menace looms large. He said, 'I just hope I won't be sorry about this.'"

"Oh, you devil," Tommy said. "Wanting your name on your book. Next thing you know they'll be calling a spade a spade."

"Calling a rake a rake," I proposed, opening the Roadster full throttle on the parkway, letting the curves pull us, feeling their outbound gravity. The world blurred, the April trees lit up with pale green flames, scenes flashed by, falling water, swinging bridges strung across rocky ravines. Windows wide open, the full breath of spring of dirt of new life stirring in the breast of whatever was left for dead, all that rushed at us now. Tommy's hair shuddered golden in the wind. He is a rake, a rake, the blinding shine of him reflected in the windscreen, Tommy's glint and glory. Tommy's hand laid here and there as if it hardly mattered, making me want to wreck the car. To find speed, drive myself deep into it.

"You and me, cat, this is the life," he said, and with Tommy that's as near as it gets to the terms of affection. "This is the life and you know it."

Loose pages, Montford

June 1949–January 1950

(VB)

When the FBI called on Mrs. Brown, that was the alarm bell gone off. That was the waking up. How stupid I have been. I'd failed to expect it, the FBI going to see her at Mrs. Bittle's. So I knew then, burn everything. It was May 10 or 11, the burning. They'd come on the evening of May 4, she said, not a forgettable date, and she went a week without telling me. I didn't expect that either. It wasn't Myers but two other men, looking for anything she could think of. Not only during our acquaintance, they told her, but anything she might know about my past. Tax avoidance, girlfriend troubles.

Well, I hope you told them. I have the worst trouble finding any girl-friends.

She would not let me make it into a joke. They offered to give her money if she thought of something. They mentioned five thousand dollars. She asked if I had any idea what kind of money that is. I said, "Do you think I don't?" We were sitting at the green table in the kitchen, it was after we'd taken to eating lunch there together because she doesn't like going to the luncheonettes now. I fixed her a pork sandwich that day. It was raining. No, not raining, because later she would be out in the back, that fire roaring.

What I remember plainly is how she bit the sandwich, set it down, chewed, bit again. Nearly choking, the whole time. I was sorry I'd made the sandwich, she was obviously not hungry but now would feel obligated to eat. In Mexico she looked at every piece of embroidery that any barefoot mother held up to her. Not just pretending, really examining the stitches with full appreciation. She can't dissemble to save her life.

That is why, when I asked why she wasn't hungry, she told me the reason. She really had not wanted to bother me about the FBI men who came to see her at Mrs. Bittle's. Not to worry me. *Five thousand dollars.* For the first time I began to understand what a danger I pose to her. I have been so thick, so naive.

She said she felt covered with dirt with those two men there. Mrs. Bittle dusting every sill in the parlor, trying to hear. I could picture that, and Mrs. Brown telling them I was a fine citizen, standing up for me, which I told her she should not do anymore. The less said to those men, the better.

"Maybe you're wrong," she said. "Maybe we need to give them what for."

"Why? What does it matter if I go on their list as a Communist?"

"For one thing, it proves their so-called informing man was reliable. Whoever is making things up about you. Now these agents will look on their Communist list and see you're on it. Then they'll look to see who accused you, and they'll say, 'Well, good, that fellow was reliable. We'll use him again.'"

That is true. She was right. Her acuity humbled me.

She had more to say, about using gossip as its own evidence. The Woman's Club now has a committee to check the schoolbooks for Americanism. In Mrs. Brown's opinion things have gone too far, it's time somebody showed some intestinal fortitude. Her words. She was holding back tears. What I held back, that would be harder to name. Chispa strolled in with her tail high, indifferent to the crisis. Checked the half-filled food dish next to the Philco, snubbed it, left the kitchen. Life proceeds, it enrages. The untouched ones spend their luck without a thought, believing they deserve it.

I told Mrs. Brown she should consider looking for a different job. Her eyes flew wide, the sandwich in both hands. She looked like an advertisement.

"You firing me, Mr. Shepherd? For what I just said?"

I told her that wasn't it. That I was very worried about causing her more trouble than I already had. She drank half a glass of water and went to look for a handkerchief in the other room. I heard her rummaging in the big leather mail pouch. I cleared the plates, put that sandwich out of sight so it wouldn't be the end of her. Some waterworks in the dining room, I think. All dried up when she returned, but the eyes were puffy.

"Mr. Shepherd, don't you read the papers? They've already had me as your secret wife, the whore of Babylon, crime partner, and I don't know what. Your bee keeper, for all I know. Who else would have me now? My stars, I might yet learn to keep bees."

That is what she said, bee keeper. I wanted to give her a bear hug. It would have involved lifting her off her feet, she's so small, I really could see the whole thing. Probably we both did, facing one another in a white-tiled kitchen, hands open at our sides, the embrace playing out between us like a motion-picture scene that makes you whistle and throw popcorn. We elected just to stand and watch it.

We made the agreement then. I would keep her hired, on certain conditions. A lot of things had to be taken care of: all the rest of the old notebooks. All those names and dates. I have done nothing wrong, she knows this and I know it, and still we both understand the position she is in. They could get a warrant, use something in those notebooks as evidence and make her a party to it.

I told her it's time, I kept saying that. It is time. I'd been piddling at it, trying for more than a year since we pitched Billy Boorzai into the flames. Better dead than read, I told her. Expecting a fight, but strangely, no fight came. Not even from Violet the defiant, who always insists, *Those are your words so claim them, leave your bairns not to be orphaned, you wrote those.* She too is defeated. She wanted to do the job herself. Stood at the door watching while I cleared the whole shelf, all the way back to the beginning. She seemed as eager as I was to get it over with, taking our medicine.

She went downstairs with the first armload, and I ransacked my desk drawers. Sometimes I'll type up a day and forget to file it with the others. And letters. I'd long since done away with Frida's—they were hardly mine to begin with—but the carbons of my own were harder to part with. I scooped up all that now, and odd little clippings I'd kept, oh, I was on a tear. By the time she had the fire going in the tar bucket outdoors, I was making a mad sack of the house to see if there were any notebooks I'd missed, hidden from myself like a drunk's gin bottle tucked in the chandelier. It feels that way sometimes, that desperate.

I went a day. Spent that evening standing at the window lighting one cigarette off the last, after she'd gone, to keep myself from sitting and writing out the scene as freshly recalled. One week, thirty packs of cigarettes. Weeks. Without spooling out more of a tale, creating more to burn, knitting away at the front of the long knotted scarf that will have to be unraveled at the back. How helpless I feel before this flood of words, how ridiculous. A hundred times trying to shut off the flow. Under orders from Mother. From Frida and Diego, arms crossed, feet tapping, stop it. In the name of the law. Stop writing down everything, it makes me nervous. And something inside the boy cries out, *Those are the only two choices: read, or dead.*

This only feels like madness; really now it's just the usual thing, summer and polio. Going mad inside a house. The wisteria vines have blocked up the windows. No matter where I try to look out, it's those palmate leaves, green hands shoved against my eyes. The neighbor used to bring over his pruners and do the job as a favor, but Myers likely advised him against pruning Communist vines. He hasn't done his own either, I notice. The house looks like it's cowering behind its own shrubbery. Every bungalow on the block is the same, curtained, folded shut. Quarantine. The siege of Berlin ended May 12, the barricades finally came down. But here they seem high as ever.

Tommy can't risk the plague—Keep cool, he says. Nor can Mrs. Brown, but she would if she could, I'm sure of that.

Lincoln Barnes says, Don't get excited. Arthur Gold has informed him that breach of contract can be costly, and they would be wise to release this book on the schedule previously agreed upon by all parties. He must have been persuasive. Barnes said if we don't make any waves they'll put the book out quietly, buried in their list of summer reading.

America has had a change of management. It's as plain as anything in the magazine advertisements. All the July issues came this week, and where are the square-shouldered gals pouring Ovaltine for their children, the mother who knows what's best? Who smiles ruefully and shakes her finger at that husband who used the wrong hair tonic? She's fired. They've got scientists in now, white laboratory coats and reports showing that the ordinary doesn't measure up to our brand. Goodness, they can prove anything: skin softness, quicker relief. I miss the mothers. If you didn't like the taste of Ovaltine, you might have wheedled. With these new authorities, you've got no chance.

"Summer Reading" is upon us, but so far not one review of *The Unforetold*. Sales nil, reports Barnes; the bookstores have not really picked it up so much as others on the list. A whisper campaign, he was afraid of that. *I just hope we won't be sorry about this.*

He needs to hire some of those scientists. Our studies show Harrison Shepherd provides a happier reader, 14 percent faster to achieve the racing pulse. This morning I found an advertisement for a condensed-book series: regular books with all the unnecessary parts cut out, to get it over faster. "Dr. George Gallup recently revealed in his polls, an astonishingly high percentage of the nation's university graduates *no longer read books*. The reason is obvious: because of their educational advantages, they occupy positions where they are busy, busy, busy always!"

I'll tell Barnes that must be it. Not a whisper campaign, no Communist longhairs or fairies about, everyone's just too busy.

❊

The library has opened two days a week now. Evidently the polio germ takes a rest on Mondays and Fridays. Well, three cheers for the brave ladies who volunteered to preside over the crypt. Not a soul in the place, the perfect opportunity to walk about openly carrying *Look Homeward, Angel* and *Tropic of Cancer* without raising an eyebrow. All of Henry Miller in fact, I'll take the whole pile, and Kinsey too.

How extraordinary he is, the good Dr. Kinsey. Another man in a white coat, with proof. Everything we ever dared think about men and sex turns out to be true. One hundred percent of men are homosexual for 4 percent of their lives (the Billy Boorzais), and 4 percent are homosexual for 100 percent of their lives (the Tommy Cuddys). Strangest of all, Dr. Kinsey's book has not been checked out of the library before. Not even once: the slip in the jacket hasn't a single name on it. Yet the spine was well cracked, every page of the book dog-eared and bent.

The news all looks the same now. The National Educators Association routs communism at its national convention in Boston. "The Communist is not suitable as a teacher." Nor as butcher, baker, candlestick maker, beggar man, or thief, as far as that goes. The Negro singer Paul Robeson they have taken to calling the Black Stalin.

Has the world stopped on its axis? It doesn't seem to be so, as the wheels of Mexico creak forward on their slow revolution. Europe raises herself from the ash and holds out a hand to her poor and damaged. But if Truman calls for any change, education improvements, or Social Security, a chorus shouts him down: welfare state, collectivism, conspiracy. What an extraordinary state of things, we are the finished product. A rock thrown in the canyon rolls neither uphill or down, it's frozen in place.

August 5

Nationalist China falls to Mao's armies. Or fell already. Acheson disclosed the collapse. The chorus is now at full howl, Truman presides

over the Party of Treason, he and his Democrat cronies have thrown
China into the mouth of the Communist dogs, didn't everyone say he
should send more gunpowder to help Chiang Kai-shek? *I just hope
we won't be sorry about this, and now we are, now you pay.*

September 23
Russia has the bomb. Every evening radio program was stopped for
this: the crooners in front of microphones quietly folded their sheet
music, the wise guys laughing it up at Duffy's Tavern set their steins
slowly on the counter, their jaws dropped, they gaped. The fine fabric
of our nation, ripped open to reveal a naked vulnerability. An atomic
explosion has occurred in the USSR. Truman said the thing in as few
words as possible. Two nations now have the bomb.

A man is shot dead this morning in Oteen. A panic on this land, the
crowds toting pitchforks. Someone gave the Russians that bomb, they
didn't make it on their own, they don't have the brains the drive the
science, it had to be Alger Hiss but it could have been any of them,
Paul Robeson, Harrison Shepherd, they all stick together it's what
they do.

It feels out of the question to go outdoors, to walk about in the
open. With anger running this high, it finds targets. The man in
Oteen was killed by someone living right on the same street, a warehouse security guard. At the end of a brooding night shift, instead of
going home he walked through an unlatched screen door, screaming,
"Dirty Russians!" and shot a neighbor in his undershirt. The wife
and children watching.

They are Slavs, judging from the name, probably emigrated to escape Stalin. The gunman knew of the family through his son. The
children go to school together.

The terrible concert in Peekskill, that was Robeson. Working-
man's songs and Negro spirituals and concertgoers beaten bloody afterward. Just one road leading out of the place—how trapped those

families must have felt, with throngs of armed police and citizens waiting at the roadsides to hurl rocks at their buses. Hands pressed flat against the windows, automobiles overturned, families dragged out and beaten, no matter their color. It's here in *Life Magazine*, photo and caption: *"In scheduling the concert the party-liners had hoped for just such a chance to become propaganda martyrs, so there was a tendency to conclude that 'they asked for it.' The Communists got more help from the hoodlums who stoned the buses than they did from their own fellow travelers."*

It's the same as the Mexican press after we were attacked at Lev's. We asked for those blazing guns and fire bombs and screaming panic and Seva shot, Trotsky organized it all himself. We are doing this to ourselves.

The Evening Post, *October 6, 1949*

"Books for Thought," by Sam Hall Mitchell

An End Foretold

Harrison W. Shepherd is that twentieth-century phenomenon—the international Communist. He has vehemently shunned publicity, but thanks to a persistent campaign of public exposure his ties with Mexican Communists have lately come to light. His life has been obscure but hardly small, as thousands of Americans were drawn into his message, particularly the young and impressionable as his writings pressed their way even into children's schoolrooms.

Now his latest arrives as the most insidious of the lot. *The Unforetold* is the story of an ancient empire crumbling through its final days, while those in power remain insensible to their nation's impending collapse. This book takes a dismal view of humanity indeed, leaving no room for wise leadership or energetic patriotism. We should expect nothing else from Harrison Shepherd, who was quoted two years ago in the *New York Weekly Review* (March '47) as follows: "Our leader is an empty sack. You could just as well knock him over, put a head with horns on a stick, and follow that. Most of us never choose to believe in the nation, we just come up short on better ideas."

Earlier this year Shepherd was dismissed from a government position for Communist activity. The public cannot now be blamed for wishing to second the motion with a single mind, dismissing the rogue scribe from our libraries, bookstores and homes.

Mrs. Brown is on a war path. "Mr. Shepherd, it's a character in your book that said that. Would they hang Charles Dickens for a thief because he made up the old fellow Fagin that told boys to go pick pockets?" Given the current climate, I told her, Charles Dickens is wise to be dead already. Which did not please her.

Intestinal fortitude, Mrs. Brown has got. Marching in here to work despite Mrs. Bittle's ban, the concern no longer being polio but other contaminations. Mrs. Brown says if the lady evicts her, she will go live with a niece. One of Parthenia's daughters "up and married a towner" and they get on well, the niece and aunt. The couple's house is small as a pin, but she could sleep on a chaise, care for the baby, and try to be a help.

We waited for the telephone to ring off its handle. Other newspapers are sure to pick this up, as it's too thrilling to keep under a hat. She stood near the telephone, arms crossed, ready to knock me cold if I tried to overrule her. "You can go on about your business now and leave me be, Mr. Shepherd, any man who calls here to confirm that quote will have me to talk to, and he shall hear what's what."

I agreed, we seem to have no choice this time. We can set the record straight: these are words spoken by a character in a novel, Poatlicue by name, disgruntled with a deranged Aztec king.

We looked it up, to verify the passage. It's from *Pilgrims of Chapultepec*, we both recognized that—a scene about midway through, the fourth forced exodus, the two boys talking while they skin out the deer. Sure enough, he's got it word for word, this Sam Hall Mitchell, but why that line, attributed to an interview? Mrs. Brown looked through the files and found he did take it from the *Review*, as he says, a piece about the book that quoted that excerpt. She had several copies in the files, and I may have sent one to Frida—we'd liked this reviewer. He was thoughtful on many subjects, including Soviet containment, a new doctrine at that time. Poor man, they'll now be after him too. The last line he'd quoted from my book, Mr. Mitchell has dropped in his exposé, for better or for worse. Wherein Poatlicue says, "It's probably a law: the public imagination may not exceed the size of the leaders' ballocks."

Not a call came about it. A strange, quiet day, the telephone did not ring once.

October 19

Of all things unexpected, this is the largest. Harrison Shepherd fires the shot heard 'round the world. That quote has gone everywhere, even overseas to the armed services, they've run it in *Stars and Stripes*. *Here's what one spineless fellow thinks back home, and you can bet Harrison Shepherd did not serve active duty: "Our leader is an empty sack, let's knock him over, put some horns on a stick and follow that. Most of us never choose to believe in our country, we just come up short on better ideas."*

Republic Digest, "Words from the Nation's Most Dangerous." Harrison Shepherd has gone to the top of their list, above Alger Hiss and the Hollywood Ten. The clip service at the publisher's counted sixty-one newspapers and magazines running the quote so far, and the monthlies are yet to come. These words seem to be driving some form of madness that gets in the head like a nursery rhyme. Leader is an empty sack, empty sack, empty sack! Head with horns upon a stick, follow that!

It's hard to guess why the publisher needed to call Mrs. Brown with that stunning figure from the clip service. Can it be they are pleased? Because they are rid of me now? The receptionists at Stratford's are star-eyed at the measure of my infamy; they have no capacity to resist it. The reach of the quote has gone far beyond any readership of mine, by a hundredfold, bringing joy to people with no prior knowledge of my prowess. It's bracing in these times. A man you can love to despise.

Mrs. Brown is so distracted she can't type a letter. Most of the morning she sat in a chair near the front window, knitting a baby shawl. She keeps dropping stitches, finding mistakes, tearing it all out to begin again. Her eyes go out to the street. I've never seen her so frightened. More dangerous than Alger Hiss. Who is well on his way now to conviction for treason.

Most of us never choose to believe in our country, we just come up short on better ideas. The most widely printed words ever written by Harrison Shepherd.

The Echo, *October 21, 1949*

Spy Secrets Between Hard Covers

Author Harrison Shepherd has covered a long career of Communist tricks under the guise of mild-mannered writer, producing facile novels that appeal mainly to intellectuals and longhairs. But he has thrown off his cover with the latest round of arrogance, declaring openly in print, "Our leader is an empty sack. You could just as well knock him over, put a head with horns on a stick and follow that."

Threatening violent overthrow is a matter for public outrage. What's at the bottom of this twisted mind? His family life tells it all. Born in Lychgate, Virginia, Shepherd was a child of divorce. The father worked as an accountant in the Hoover administration, while the mother was an impecunious Mata Hari, changing her name repeatedly to get close to men in government on both sides of the Mexico border. New York psychiatrist Nathan Leonard, asked to weigh in on the disturbing case, said, "The shattering psychological effects of a maternal example like this cannot be escaped."

The son dropped out of school to become a Communist sympathizer, working in the households of leading Stalinist functionaries in Mexico City. From there he moved on to a life of such intrigue it would confound most men: art smuggler, womanizer, State Department courier, using at least two pseudonyms on two continents. All this he accomplished despite a physical appearance so repellent, photographers have shunned him for a lifetime. Such remarkable feats of philandering and espionage carried out by a homely man may arouse false hopes in the Walter Mittys among us. But Harrison Shepherd is not cut from the ordinary cloth.

Among the latest charges: he supplied secrets to the Communist Chinese revolt against Chiang Kai-shek. Like all enemies of America, he adheres to the plan of giving aid and comfort to our enemies. A year ago he told the *Evening Post* he agreed with Bernard Baruch that our atomic bombs should all be thrown in the drink. Now he's found a better way to throw us on the mercy of the Communists: experts confirm a copy of his book has been found with certain passages underlined, possibly a coded blueprint for the atom bomb. Fortunately this country has a cure for such troubled minds. It is known as the electric chair.

According to the United Press, the Committee on Un-American Activities has already documented countless plans to smuggle bomb secrets to Russia and China. In a 384-page report released last week after five years of investigation, the committee detailed techniques used by American Communists for sending coded secrets to Moscow. "Devices for concealing such messages include necklaces, boxes containing matches cut at various lengths, dental plates, a notching of postage stamps, engraved cigarette cases, embroidered handkerchiefs, special book-bindings and tiny compartments in phonograph records." A copy of George Bernard Shaw's *Devil's Disciple*, the report disclosed, was found to carry a Russian code message by means of having certain of its words underlined in invisible ink.

Now another Devil's Disciple, in the guise of writer Harrison Shepherd, has released his latest tome, *The Unforetold*. To such a chilling title we need only add a small footnote: buyer beware.

November 7

Mrs. Brown went to the bookstore to have a look. She did not want to go, and did not want to tell me about it when she came back. So help me God, I pressed her into spying for me. They've made a "Ban Harrison Shepherd" window display. I'm not alone; they've found a pile of other books written by Communists.

The sign asks, "Would you buy a book if you knew your money was going to the Communist Party?" Under the question were two boxes marked "Yes" and "No," with a cup of pencils handy for the plebiscite.

What more can they take from me? I asked Mrs. Brown, what do they want? About what anyone wants, was her best guess: safety. That and grace. They know not what they do. Probably they were all aimed at heaven at one time, and lost their way.

What is that, *grace*?

She says, believing you are special and saved from harm. Kissed by God.

Well, that's how thick I am, I never knew how to want what everyone wants. I only thought to look for a home, some place to be taken in. Handing over a crumpled heart, seeing it dropped in the wastepaper basket every time. Here, though. Americans sent love letters in return.

December 22, 1949

Dear Shepherd,

All right pal, keep your hair on. Probably this is not going to be the salutations you've been waiting for. Merry Xmas and all that. Things have changed here, it can't be helped. I collared a job in ads. No fish! Me myself, in an office full of neck ties, and let me tell you, these cats are steaming. I don't want to be the jerk that can't keep up.

Listen, I sure was hung up to see what you wrote about our country. Sorry you feel that way, I guess I never really knew you so well. Cats joke around, but I for one still believe in the Patria and I'm just sorry you can't say the same. I guess coming from another country, you have your reasons.

Don't be a dog about this, right? Nice knowing you but things change. Best for both of us if we shove off and no more correspondence. No one in my present situ knows of our acquaintance.

So long,

TOM CUDDY

1950, January

The newspapers slump under the weight of their end-of-the-world headlines. ALGER HISS VERDICT: SPY AND LIAR. Larger type even than used for V-J Day; evidently the new enemies are worse than the Japanese. Phony liberals who sell their souls along with the secrets that safeguard our nation. Stalinist tuning forks. Slobbering on the shoes of their Muscovite masters. Henry Wallace is under fire now too, testifying before the Un-American Committee. Henry Wallace, vice president under Roosevelt, the Liberal Democrat candidate in the last election, now faces Trial by Headline. WALLACE DENIES SENDING URANIUM TO RUSSIANS. May God protect him, today he lashed out against the press: "King Solomon should add to his list of things beyond the wisdom of men: why the newspapers print what they do!"

Mrs. Brown noted that Wallace has been reading aloud from his diary in the hearings, as evidence of what was said in the uranium meetings now under scrutiny. "Good thing he kept that diary," she says, standing in my doorway in a red-and-white-checked tailored shirt. With her, there's no knowing, it could be the latest fashion or something she made from a tablecloth—or both. Mrs. Brown proves stylish gals can still be thrifty in 'fifty.

She believes I'm taking things too personally. She brings the articles on Wallace, Robeson, Trumbo, those Hollywood writers, the union men, teachers, accountants, office workers, the butcher, the baker, and in the end neither of us is consoled. It's not just you, she says. People driven out of work, children taunted at school. The children whose father was shot, over in Oteen. What can any child be learning now, she asks, but to fear the wide world and all that's in it?

"Mr. Shepherd, they have to grow up in this. How will they all be?"

The Asheville Trumpet, *February 12, 1950*

Asheville Writer Faces Tough Questions

by Carl Nicholas

In a letter received this week from Federal Investigator Melvin C. Myers, the *Asheville Trumpet* has learned local writer Harrison Shepherd faces numerous charges related to his Communism. Foremost among them is misrepresentation of qualifications in signing an affidavit that he had never been a Communist. He is further charged with falsifying qualifications to serve as an educator. The press release from Myers stated a subpoena will soon be sent to Shepherd with arrangements to follow regarding a hearing before the House Un-American Activities Committee in Washington, D.C.

Fellow citizens of Asheville cannot say we wish him well. It is no source of pride that our town is called home by one of the many Communists now known to have infiltrated government, as revealed this week by Senator Joseph McCarthy at a meeting of the Ohio County Woman's Club of Wheeling, West Virginia.

Mrs. Herb Lutheridge, President, Asheville Woman's Club, confirms the Senator's speech was intended here when the freshman Senator first contacted the Program Committee, hoping to make our city the first stop on his re-election campaign crusade through the South and West. Mrs. Lutheridge says honorarium discussion was under way when the Senator's office notified her of plans to kick off the tour instead in W. Virginia. Mrs. Lutheridge regrets the mixup but stated, "The main thing is, we are proud of this young man going to Washington to ferret out all those with Soviet leanings."

The information release concerning Shepherd states that House Un-American Activities Committee has full authority to subpoena a suspect and ask questions based on substantive researches, for the public record. If the hearing warrants, criminal charges will follow. The subcommittee is charged to investigate communism in many guises including "education," which pertains to Harrison Shepherd as many schoolchildren read his books about the Mexican civilizations. In closing, the letter states, "Through a simple exercise of question and answer, the witness may prove his innocence or be seen to hide behind the Fifth Amendment."

The *New York Times* reported this month that Communist parties worldwide now have a record membership of 26 million persons.

The Wheeling Intelligencer, *February 10, 1950*

M'Carthy Charges Reds Hold U.S. Jobs

Wisconsin Senator Tells Lincoln Fete Here 'Chips Down'

by Frank Desmond of the Intelligencer *Staff*

Joseph McCarthy, junior U.S. Senator from Wisconsin, was given a rousing ovation last night when, as guest of the Ohio County Republican Women's Club, he declared bluntly that the fate of the world rests with the clash between the atheism of Moscow and the Christian spirit throughout other parts of the world.

More than 275 representative Republican men and women were on hand to attend the colorful Lincoln Day dinner of the valley women which was held in the Collonnade room of the McLure hotel.

Disdaining any oratorical fireworks, McCarthy's talk was of an intimate, homey nature, punctuated at times with humor. But on the serious side, he launched many barbs at the present setup of the State Department, at President Truman's reluctance to press investigation of "traitors from within," and other pertinent matters. . . . However, he added: "The morals of our people have not been destroyed. They still exist and this cloak of numbness and apathy needs only a spark to rekindle them."

Referring directly to the State Department, he declared: "While I cannot take the time to name all of the men in the State Department who have been named as members of the Communist Party and members of a spy ring, I have here in my hand a list of 205 that were known to the Secretary of State as being members of the Communist Party and who, nevertheless, are still working and shaping the policy in the State Department."

The speaker dwelt at length on the Alger Hiss case and mentioned the names of several others who, during the not so many years, were found to entertain subversive ideas but were still given positions of high trust in the government. "As you hear of this story of high treason," he said, "I know that you are saying to yourself well, why doesn't Congress do something about it?

"Actually, ladies and gentlemen, the reason for the graft, the corruption, the disloyalty, the treason in high government positions, the reason this continues is because of a lack of moral uprising on the part of the 140 million American people. In the light of history, however, this is not hard to explain. It is the result of an emotional hangover and a temporary moral lapse which follows every war. It is the apathy to evil which people who have been subjected to the tremendous evils of war feel.

"As the people of the world see mass murder, the destruction of defenseless and innocent people and all of the crime and lack of morals which go with war, they become numb and apathetic. It has always been thus after war."

At another time, he declared: "Today, we are engaged in a final all-out battle between Communistic atheism and Christianity. The modern champions of Communism have selected this as the time and, ladies and gentlemen, the chips are down they are truly down."

In an informal quiz with his audience, the Senator answered a number of questions dealing mostly with the plan of Secretary of Agriculture Brannan to destroy millions of tons of potatoes, eggs, butter, and fruits; he gave forthright views on the old age and social security problems and a number of other topics. . . .

Mrs. A. E. Eberhard, president of the Women's Group, presided. State Senator William Hannig led the group singing. The invocation was delivered by the Rev. Philip Goertz, pastor of the Second Presbyterian church, and the benediction was pronounced by the Rev. W. Carroll Thorn, of St. Luke's Episcopal Church.

(undated page, HWS journal)

Universal declaration of rights of the howlers:
Article 1. All human beings are endowed with the god-given right
to make firewood from the fallen tree. Article 2. Any tree will do.
If it is tall, it should be cut down. The quality of wood is no matter, the tree asked for it by growing tall. A decent public will cheer
to see it toppled. Article 3. Rules of normal kindness do not extend
to the celebrated person. Article 4. All persons may hope to become
celebrated. Article 5. It is more important to speak than to think. The
only danger is silence. Article 6. A howler must choose one course or
the other: lie routinely, or do so only on important occasions, to be
more convincing. (The Trotsky tenet.)

HEARINGS REGARDING COMMUNIST INFILTRATION OF THE
UNITED STATES GOVERNMENT AND EDUCATIONAL INSTITUTIONS

UNITED STATES HOUSE OF REPRESENTATIVES,
SPECIAL SUBCOMMITTEE OF THE COMMITTEE
ON UN-AMERICAN ACTIVITIES
PUBLIC HEARING, TUESDAY, MARCH 7, 1950

TRANSCRIPT: UNITED STATES GOVERNMENT PRINTING OFFICE

COMMITTEE ON UN-AMERICAN ACTIVITIES,
UNITED STATES HOUSE OF REPRESENTATIVES:
JOHN S. WOOD, *Georgia, Chairman*;
FRANCIS E. WALTER, *Pennsylvania*; RICHARD M. NIXON,
California; BURR P. HARRISON, *Virginia*; FRANCIS CASE, *South
Dakota*; JOHN MCSWEENEY, *Ohio*; HAROLD H. VELDE, *Illinois*;
MORGAN M. MOULDER, *Missouri*; BERNARD W. KEARNEY, *New York*

FRANK L. RAVENNER, COUNSEL
MELVIN C. MYERS, SENIOR INVESTIGATOR

The subcommittee of the Committee on Un-American Activities met in a public session, pursuant to notice, at 9:35 a.m. in room 226, Old House Office Building, Hon. John S. Wood (chairman) presiding. Committee members present: Representatives John S. Wood (chairman), Francis E. Walter, John McSweeney, Richard M. Nixon (arriving as indicated) and Harold H. Velde. Staff members present: Frank L. Ravenner, counsel; Melvin C. Myers, chief investigator.

MR. WOOD: The record will show this is the Committee on Un-American Activities sitting now in the city of Washington, District of Columbia. Those present in addition to Committee and Staff members are the recording secretary and visitors from the press corps in the back gallery of the room. Mr. Harrison Shepherd sits here before us accompanied by two persons. The committee will be in order.

   Mr. Shepherd, will you hold up your right hand, please, and take the oath. Do you solemnly swear the testimony you shall give this committee will be the truth, the whole truth and nothing but the truth, so help you God?

MR. SHEPHERD: Yes.

MR. WOOD: Will you state your full name?

MR. SHEPHERD: Harrison William Shepherd.

MR. WOOD: When and where were you born?

MR. SHEPHERD: Lychgate, Virginia, July 6, 1916.

MR. WOOD: Have you any objection to the photographers making pictures?

MR. SHEPHERD: I would be happier if they didn't.

MR. WOOD: Well, gentlemen, you've heard him. Follow your conscience as usual.

(Murmuring and laughter from the gallery and photographs flashed.)

MR. RAVENNER: Honorable Chairman, before we begin questioning, may I ask to have Mr. Shepherd's friends or counsel identified?

MR. SHEPHERD: This is Mr. Arthur Gold, who is a lawyer, and Mrs. Violet Brown, who is my stenographer.

MR. WOOD: Mr. Shepherd, the committee retains a recording secretary to make a very thorough transcript of these proceedings. Mrs. Ward, would you please identify yourself.

(So identified.)

MR. SHEPHERD: Sir, Mrs. Brown and Mr. Gold are here in the capacity of friends.

MR. RAVENNER: Fine, then. Mr. Shepherd, the purpose of this meeting is for the Committee to determine the truth or falsity of certain statements you have made, regarding membership or association with the Communist Party. Do you understand?

MR. SHEPHERD: Yes.

MR. RAVENNER: All right. This will not take all day, gentlemen, we should be out of here in time for lunch. Mr. Shepherd, would you please tell us where you now reside, and your present occupation.

MR. SHEPHERD: I live in Asheville, North Carolina, and am an author of books.

MR. RAVENNER: How long have you lived there, and what employment have you held in that time?

MR. SHEPHERD: Since 1940. I haven't had very much work in Asheville, other than the writing. During the war I taught some Spanish lessons at a Teachers College.

MR. RAVENNER: While teaching foreign languages at the College, did you ever succeed in recruiting students to a Communist way of thinking?

MR. SHEPHERD: Goodness, I doubt it. I couldn't recruit them to put their bubble gum in the wastepaper basket before standing up to do conjugations. Sometimes it fell out of their mouths on the third-person plurals.

(Laughter in the gallery.)

MR. RAVENNER: Now will you answer the question? Did any of your students join up with the Communist Party?

MR. SHEPHERD: I honestly don't know what they did after the class.

MR. RAVENNER: Were you also in the Armed Services during those years, as a young man obviously fit for service?

MR. SHEPHERD: Unfortunately I was not found fit for service. I was called up instead for special work with the National Gallery of Art in Washington, D.C.

MR. RAVENNER: You were found unfit for service on what grounds, Mr. Shepherd?

MR. SHEPHERD: Psychological grounds.

MR. RAVENNER: You were determined unfit for reasons of mental and sexual deviance, is that correct?

MR. SHEPHERD: I was found only sane enough for the Civilian Services, sir. My mental capacities were deemed adequate for handling the country's most important national treasures. That was the determination of the Selective Service board.

(Mr. Nixon here entered the hearing and was seated near Mr. Velde. Brief discussion between Mr. Nixon and Mr. Velde.)

MR. RAVENNER: Did you or did you not at that time believe membership in the Communist Party was inimical to the interests of the United States?

MR. SHEPHERD: To be honest, sir, I didn't think one way or another about it. I never met any Communist Party members in this country.

MR. RAVENNER: Can you give me an answer 'Yes' or 'No'?

MR. SHEPHERD: Does a citizen have a right to be uncertain until further informed?

MR. RAVENNER: Let me inform you. A member of the Communist Party is a person who seeks the overthrow of the government of the United States by force and violence in this country. Is that something you approve of?

MR. SHEPHERD: I've never sought to overthrow the United States. Is that an answer?

MR. RAVENNER: It is a form of answer. Now, I understand that you were born in the United States, but chose to spend most of your life in another country. Is that correct?

MR. SHEPHERD: My mother was Mexican. We moved back there when I was twelve. She threatened to leave me by the tracks if I put up a fuss. So yes sir, I chose to go.

MR. RAVENNER: And after many years, what made you want to live here again?

MR. SHEPHERD: That's a complicated question you ask. It would take me a good while to answer, and you said you wanted to get this over quickly.

MR. RAVENNER: Well, then, let me ask an easier question. Did you associate with Communists while living in Mexico?

(A long hesitation from the witness, prior to answering.)

MR. SHEPHERD: That is not an easier question. Again, it could take some explanation.

MR. RAVENNER: Then let me make it easier still. We have papers here that show you were granted travel documents to come here in November 1939, as a travel companion and assistant to a man called to testify before this same committee. The Dies Committee, as it was called then. Our documents say a Harrison Shepherd, born 1916 in Lychgate, Virginia, was a member of the party that was granted a travel visa. Are you that person?

MR. SHEPHERD: I am.

MR. RAVENNER: Then we may assume these documents refer to you. That you were then living in the Mexican headquarters of the well-known Communist leader of Stalin's Bolshevik revolution, Leonadovich Trotsky.

MR. SHEPHERD: I beg your pardon?

MR. RAVENNER: Answer the question.

MR. SHEPHERD: I only want to clarify. Do you mean Lev Davidovich Trotsky, who led a worldwide movement to oppose Stalin? He was called by your Committee as a friendly witness, sir.

MR. RAVENNER: Just answer the question. Did you work for this Trotsky?

MR. SHEPHERD: Yes.

MR. RAVENNER: In what capacity?

MR. SHEPHERD: As his cook, his secretary-typist, and some-times cleaner of rabbit cages. But usually the Commissar preferred handling the manure himself.

MR. WOOD: Here, I'll have order!

MR. RAVENNER: You say you were his secretary. Do you mean to say you helped prepare documents whose purpose was to arouse a Communist insurrection?

(The witness did not answer.)

MR. VELDE: Mr. Shepherd, you may take the Fifth Amend-ment if you wish.

MR. SHEPHERD: I don't know how to answer, when you say 'helped prepare documents.' I was a typist. Sometimes I could hardly understand the words in those documents. I don't have any expertise in politics.

MR. NIXON: Is the welder of a bomb casing innocent of the destruction it causes, just because he doesn't understand physics?

MR. SHEPHERD: It's a very good question. Our munitions plants make arms we sell to almost every country. Are we now on both sides of all the wars?

MR. RAVENNER: Mr. Shepherd, you are instructed to answer 'yes' or 'no' to all further questions. One more outburst will land you in contempt of Congress. Did you help pre-pare Communist documents for this Trotsky, a leader of the Bolshevik revolution?

MR. SHEPHERD: Yes.

MR. RAVENNER: And are you still in contact with Comrade Trotsky?

(Very long pause.)

MR. SHEPHERD: No.

MR. RAVENNER: Did you come to the United States directly from his employ?

(Pause.)

MR. RAVENNER: Yes or no?

MR. SHEPHERD: Sorry. Could you clarify the question?

MR. RAVENNER: Yes or no. Your last place of residence, prior to entering the United States in September, 1940, was the Trotskyite World Revolutionary Headquarters on Morelos Street, Coyoacán, outside of Mexico City.

MR. SHEPHERD: Yes.

MR. RAVENNER: Is it true that in that same place, several extreme acts of espionage and violence were committed, all directly linked with the Secret Police of Joseph Stalin?

MR. SHEPHERD: Yes. Committed against us.

MR. RAVENNER: You say you have no head for politics, so try to focus your powers, if you will, on one simple question. From that headquarters, did you come here on a program of overthrowing the United States government, however poorly you may have understood it? I want to hear one word, sir. Yes, or no.

MR. SHEPHERD: No.

MR. RAVENNER:: For what purpose, then, did you come to the United States?

MR. SHEPHERD: (Pause.) Yes or no?

MR. RAVENNER: You may elaborate in this instance.

MR. SHEPHERD: I came to deliver paintings to museums in New York City.

MR. NIXON: Well, that's some delivery job if he's still here after ten years. Even Sears Roebuck doesn't generally take that long.

(Laughter in the gallery.)

MR. RAVENNER: Tell me, what was the nature of these paintings?

MR. SHEPHERD: Oil-based paint applied to canvas.

(Laughter in the gallery.)

MR. WOOD: Mr. Shepherd, we are not fools. We can see you're attempting to mock this hearing. This is the last time I will warn you to answer the question as directly as you can. What sort of paintings did you smuggle into the United States?

MR. SHEPHERD: Surrealist. All transported with legal customs documents. The papers are still on file at the museums, I expect.

MR. RAVENNER: And were these paintings by the Mexican painter Diego Rivera, who is well known as a dangerous Communist agitator?

MR. SHEPHERD: No.

MR. RAVENNER: No?

MR. WOOD: Remember, Mr. Shepherd, that you have sworn an oath.

MR. SHEPHERD: Not Mr. Rivera's paintings, no.

(Congressmen Wood and Verne spent some moments conferring with Mr. Ravenner and looking through documents.)

MR. RAVENNER: Were these paintings from the household of Diego Rivera, or his possessions? Answer the question fully.

MR. SHEPHERD: They were painted by his wife, the artist Frida Kahlo.

MR. RAVENNER: Then you admit, you knowingly associated with the Communist militants, Mr. and Mrs. Diego Rivera?

MR. SHEPHERD: Yes.

MR. RAVENNER:: For what purpose?

MR. SHEPHERD: In the instance you mention, to oversee the transport of her paintings to galleries in New York.

MR. RAVENNER: They hired you to carry crates across the border into the United States. Where you have now remained nearly ten years. My documents say there were eight crates altogether, some of them too large for a man to lift by himself.

MR. SHEPHERD: That's right. We used hand trucks to get them off the trains.

MR. RAVENNER: Did you know precisely what you were transporting? Did you pack these crates yourself?

MR. SHEPHERD: No. I had a roster with the names of the paintings.

MR. RAVENNER: You smuggled large crates of unknown content into this country? From the headquarters of some of the most dangerous Communists in any country touching our borders. Is that correct?

(The defendant conferred briefly with the identified friend, Arthur Gold.)

MR. SHEPHERD: Congressmen, nothing exploded.

MR. WOOD: What say?

MR. SHEPHERD: I delivered artworks. You're hinting at a crime that was not committed.

MR. WOOD: Mr. Shepherd, I will put to you then a different question. Could this so-called artwork also be called Communist propaganda?

MR. SHEPHERD: In my opinion, sir? Art takes its meaning in the eye of the beholder.

MR. RAVENNER: Could you state an answer in plain English? What was the purpose of the concealed objects you transported into this country?

MR. SHEPHERD: May I answer freely?

MR. RAVENNER: In your own words, yes. All right.

MR. SHEPHERD: The purpose of art is to elevate the spirit, or pay a surgeon's bill. Or both, really. It can help a person remember or forget. If your house doesn't have many windows in it, you can hang up a painting and have a view. Of a whole different country, if you want. If your spouse is homely, you can gaze at a lovely face and not get in trouble for it.

(Laughter in the gallery.)

It can be painted on a public wall or locked in a mansion. The first paintings Mrs. Kahlo ever sold went to one of your famous film stars, Edward G. Robinson. Art is one thing I do know about. A book has all the same uses I mentioned, especially for the house without enough windows. Art by itself is nothing, until it comes into that house. People here wanted Mrs. Kahlo's art, and I carried it.

(Silence in the gallery.)

You asked me why I've stayed here so long. I can try to say. People have a lot of color and songs in Mexico, more art than they have hopes, it often seemed to me. Here, I found people bursting with hope but not many songs. They didn't sing, they turned on the radio. They wanted stories, like anything. So I decided to try my hand at making art for the hopeful. Because I wasn't any good at the other thing, manufacturing hopes for the artful. America was the most hopeful place I'd ever imagined. My neighbors were giving over their hairpins and door hinges to melt down for building the good ship America. I wanted to give her things too. So I stayed here.

(Quiet in the gallery for some time. Of an unusual kind, the type to hear a pin drop.)

MR. RAVENNER: You say that Edward G. Robinson is an associate of Communists?

MR. SHEPHERD: I'm sorry, I might have made a mistake. It was a long time ago. It might have been J. Edgar Hoover who bought the paintings.

(Considerable laughter in the gallery.)

MR. WOOD: Order!

MR. RAVENNER: Now see here, if you continue to mock this hearing we will hold you in contempt of Congress. I am going to ask you a series of questions to which you will answer Yes or No. One word beyond that will get you removed to the jail house. Do you understand me?

MR. SHEPHERD: Yes.

MR. RAVENNER: Do you now, or did you ever, work for Communists in Mexico?

MR. SHEPHERD: Yes.

MR. RAVENNER: Have you yourself written works about foreign people, men disloyal to their leaders, with the intention of distributing these tracts widely in the United States?

(Pause.)

MR. SHEPHERD: Yes.

MR. RAVENNER: Have you been in contact with Communist revolutionaries since coming to the United States?

MR. SHEPHERD: Yes.

MR. RAVENNER: I have here a good deal of evidence, *in print*, news articles and so forth, to the effect your books are being read in Communist China. That you opposed the use of the atomic bomb. I have evidence you made the following statement. I want you to listen carefully, and then confirm or deny it. And here I quote Mr. Shepherd: "Our leader is an empty sack. You could just as well knock him over, put a head with horns on a stick, and follow that. Most of us never choose to believe in the nation, we just come up short on better ideas." Mr. Shepherd, are these your words?

MR. SHEPHERD: A few among many, yes. In a story.

MR. RAVENNER: Mr. Shepherd, I am asking a simple question. Did you write these words? You are asked only to confirm or deny.

MR. SHEPHERD: Yes. Those are my words.

MR. RAVENNER: Mr. Wood, gentlemen, that is all I have. This hearing is finished.

Afterward, 1959

by Violet Brown

The Asheville Trumpet, *July 16, 1951*

Obituary

Harrison Shepherd, 34, perished June 29 while swimming in the ocean near Mexico City. A resident of Asheville, the deceased had traveled to Mexico under an assumed name while under investigation for crimes including dismissal from the Department of State for treasonous actions, misrepresentation of qualifications and fraud. He wrote two books, had no record of military service and was well known as a Communist. Authorities cite no evidence of foul play and believe he took his life. Reared in a broken home, Shepherd leaves no survivors. No services are planned.

The most important part of a story is the piece of it you don't know. He said that plenty. It would be no surprise if he asks for that put on his gravestone, if there is to be one. There you see. Hangs the tale, and still yet more to find out.

You believe a thing is hopeless. You believe a book burned, yet the words persist. In this case twice, first in Mexico, his notes and drafts all taken by police after the murder, meant for destruction but precariously rescued. Then later on given to me for burning, and not burned. You believe a life ended, but the newsmen can't make that true by saying so, even saying it many times. It's dying makes a death, and living makes life.

The salvation of all, the life or the tale either one, I'll come to directly. First the notebooks. For you see I hadn't burned them, the day I was asked. He said I could only stay on working with him if we disposed of every word, his life entire if you asked me. I saw what he meant to do that day, and why. He took those writings to be evidence for his hanging. But I believed it could be otherwise, evidence for the good in him. I had no idea what his notes contained, but I knew the man.

I took what he pulled off his shelves that day, and while he was upstairs looking for more, I stuffed it all in the big leather mail pouch. My heart cantered, I have no nerve for crime. But that day, found some. By the time he was watching me out the upstairs window, I was half done. You should see what all I threw in that tar barrel: wastepaper, advertising supplements, the whole trash basket under my table, and more. Quite a few ugly letters I'd set aside. Things that deserved to be gone.

His notebooks went home with me to Mrs. Bittle's, and there they stayed in a box in my wardrobe, hidden under some knitting wool. Let those men come and search the place, was my thought, for they'd not have a second look at a box of knitting wool and needles. Most will run from the sight. I thought I would only keep it there until Mr. Shepherd changed his mind. Or until such time as needed, to prove he'd done no wrong. No such time came, as far as I could see, though I still had no idea what he'd written in a natural lifetime of little books. A nerve for that sort of crime I did not have, to poke my nose in a living man's diary.

I didn't do that until coming back from Mexico. At first, a glance was all I could endure, looking for certain dates and such, to make a proper obituary. But of course that did not come to pass, they ran their own little useless piece, so my researching wasn't any excuse for long. But still I went on glancing, a page here and thither. Time and again I took up his notebooks knowing they were not meant for my eyes, yet my eyes went on looking, many were the reasons. Some of them plain by now, I surely think.

Going to Mexico, that had been my idea. I didn't like to say so afterward, due to events. But at the time I proposed it, things had come to a point. After the hearing he'd stopped writing, for good he said. Instead he bought a television set and let its nonsense rule his days. *Mook the Moon Man* comes on at four, and so on. I still came to his house twice a week, but the mail was not worth answering. My concern wasn't to take his money, I'd found another job. I could have left him alone, but feared to do it.

One day he sat staring at the advertisements and declared he hated what America looked like now. Sofas and chairs with little pointy legs. Like a woman in high heels, he said, walking around smiling with a bad backache. And those metal funnel-hat lamps on poles, they look like they want to electrocute you. He missed beauty.

I asked him, why not go to Mexico then, I reckon it is prettier there. He said he couldn't unless I went with him. Thinking that would be that. But I said, "All right, I will call the air-port right now." What possessed me? I can't say.

He was so changed by then, even his looks. Whatever used to show up for its workaday there inside him, it had shut off the lights and gone on home. He was fagged out in the chair as usual, in his old gray flannels, smoking, never taking his eyes off the set. *Captain Video* was on, some underwater band of thieves fighting. They had Al Hodge by the neck, fixing to drown him. I asked him whether we ought to go back to Mérida, because he'd seemed to like it there. He said no, let's go to Isla Pixol so he could dive in the ocean, because that was all that made him happy as a boy. That was a grave moment, I see that now. Full of all that was to come, and me with no inkling. But I believe he did. Have an inkling.

That was in April, a year and some past the hearing. A Monday or Thursday, for those were the afternoons I still came. A joyful month if there ever was one, you'd think. Even a feather duster will lay an egg in April. But such generous feeling had gone from the land. No real work remained for me at Mr. Shepherd's after the hearing, and I'd commenced looking for another income, disliking to be any burden. I was floored to find the city wouldn't hire me. Not at the clerk's office, though I'd once kept that whole place afloat. Not at the library where I'd volunteered. I can't be a government employee due to previous association with the wrong element, they told me, it is all in print, and nothing to be done about it. It was the same at the Teachers College. After some months of asking, a hateful thing in itself, an acquaintance from the Woman's Club consented to recommend me as a book-keeper at Raye's Department Store. It was a low position, mornings only, and I had to work in a basement office. They could take no chance on a customer seeing my face.

Hard times are nothing new to me. My father used to say a man can get used to anything except hanging by the neck. I believe that. But Mr. Shepherd could not. He had a well of hopelessness inside him, and it bubbled out to flood his days and his sights for the future if any. He said if readers found him so despicable, he wouldn't trouble them with more books. It was hard to argue, as the trinkle of mail that still came was dreadful. Why does a person spend money on a stamp, to spout bile at a stranger? "Now our boys are going to Korea to be killed and mutilated by the Communists. So if one of them named Harrison Shepherd is starving, that delights me immeasurably."

He'd been called names before, and borne it. But when a man's words are taken from him and poisoned, it's the same as poisoning the man. He could not speak, for how his own tongue would be fouled. Words were his all. I felt I'd witnessed a murder, just as he'd seen his friend murdered in Mexico. Only this time they left the body living.

His books weren't banned anymore, just gone. They said he'd defrauded the publisher with the loyalty affidavit, so the advance money had to be returned and the book dropped. Not many options remained to Harrison Shepherd, watching a Moon Man in his living room being one of the few. He said Artie Gold had predicted it. That sometimes you really can see the empire is falling, and Mr. Gold saw it coming, all the green grass of our land killed for good. I said fiddlesticks, grass will grow right up through a sidewalk and the Lord loves what He cannot kill.

But that was false cheer, I knew better. Nothing was coming up by then, no gumption rising anywhere without a resolution promptly passed to cut it down. The Woman's Club had become a drear business, their sole concern to oppose waywardness: a City Council man or a school history book. Harriet Tubman and Frederick Douglass no good for children, they set a bad example. It's the same everywhere now, look at faces. In the luncheonettes on Charlotte you'll see people lined up with a haint upon them, sore afraid of not being as American as the next one. What's the matter, sir, you look as though you've seen a Communist! The word itself could get a child's mouth washed with soap. It used to be in the *Geographics*, I learned the word as a child, "Every-Day Life in the Ukraine" and so forth. But the newspapers and magazines have had their mouths washed with soap too. Even today, years after Mr. Shepherd's hearing. It would still proceed just about as it did then. People have no more vinegar in them. You can resign from the Woman's Club, but the world is all, you can't just stop attending.

Around the first part of May, then, after we'd discussed it, I went and had a talk with Arthur Gold about going to Mexico. Mr. Gold encouraged it. He said the drives were stepping up. Now that they had what they called evidence on Mr. Shepherd from the hearing, it was paperwork and only that, before criminal charges came. With an indictment the federal men would take his passport. Really Mr. Gold was unsure why they hadn't done so already. He said Mr. Shepherd should go now, while he still could.

I hated to ask it, but inquired whether it would be wise for him just to go on down to Mexico and stay put. Mr. Gold allowed that he and Mr. Shepherd had discussed this already, some time ago. It wouldn't do any good. The federal investigators can pull him right back here, once they have indicted. Mr. Gold said there were many examples. A man escaped from Ellis Island by stowing away on a ship, and they tracked him down all the way to France. They'll go to the ends of the earth to haul back people they've declared unfit to be Americans. It makes no sense. Like hateful letters from people declaring they'll never read Mr. Shepherd's books. Why not leave the book where it is and get on with the day? I didn't see how they could take another pound of flesh from this poor man, when all he'd done in life was work at making others content. Mr. Gold said with due respect, a lot of men without one mean bone in them are currently sitting in Sing Sing prison. And now the Congress was voting to make treason laws bind in cold war as they do in a shooting war. Meaning, some would hang.

Well, that lit a fire under me. I went on and booked the tickets and made the plans. Mr. Gold advised reserving the tickets under a different name, the film stars do that regularly. Then simply give the right name when you show up. I chose Ben Franklin and Betsy Ross. Mr. Shepherd was tickled with that. He began to take interest. He stopped smoking all the time and went outside more. They opened the swimming pool in Montford after two summers closed for the polio, and he started to go there often. He'd loved swimming as a boy. I would walk to the pool with him sometimes just to sit and watch, for he was changed in the water, shiny as soap, and could hold his breath like I don't know what. I want to say a fish, but that isn't right. He'd go the whole pool, one end to the other not coming up. I asked him about it, and he said his childhood was that exciting: he learned to hold his breath for entertainment.

The flight was on the Compañia Mexicana de Aviación. In Mexico City, on the way to the train station, we got caught up in an awful traffic jam. Suitcases between us in the taxicab and the sweat rolling down, for we had to keep the windows closed, the city entire smelled of tear gas. The driver told Mr. Shepherd a riot had been going for days, working men, and police trying to break it up. Mr. Shepherd said good, they've still got fight in them here, and while we sat stuck there he told a story of long ago, his school years in Washington. The homeless veterans making a riot for their war pay. He said it smelled like this. The army used gas and guns against people living in tents, Americans. And those folks still yet bold enough to give it heck, fight back or die trying.

We took the train to Veracruz, then a bus, and a ferry. Like the sailors with Columbus, I felt we'd soon come to the edge and plop off. Mr. Shepherd said his mother used to complain Isla Pixol was so far from anything, you had to yell three times before Jesus would hear you. That I believed. The hotel in town was old as Moses, its elevator nothing but a cage on a chain. The boy that carried our suitcases into it claimed it was the oldest in all the New World, and I believed that too.

First off, Mr. Shepherd hired a car to take us out to the old hacienda where he had lived. The old place lay in ruins, but he didn't seem disappointed. He went back many more times, often alone. I found my way around the little town and shopped for trinkets to bring my niece and the babies. One day Mr. Shepherd came back with a man who had supper with us, the two of them slapping one another's shoulders, saying "brother" and "the devil." Each unable to believe the other was still alive. Leandro was his name. There were others in the village, evidently, who remembered the boy with no inkling he now walked the earth as a man of repute, or even as a man.

All Mr. Shepherd wanted to do was dive in the water. I wanted no part of that, but to hear him tell it, the ocean was heaven and all the fish angels. He had a diving mask he'd bought in town, and needed nothing else, he'd stay out the day entire and come back sunburned. I thought he would grow some gills. More and more he returned to the fishes, leaving the world of people, it seemed. One evening he came to dinner with a calendar and showed me a day he'd circled, some two weeks off. He wanted to stay until then. Well, that meant changing our return, no small thing. I wasn't very pleased. I'd begged time off unpaid from Raye's, and they would be happy to replace me. I asked if he meant to change it again after that. Like a child putting off the bedtime. He said no, that was the day, after the full moon. That meant something to him.

On our last day, he got himself set to go out to his beach and wanted me to come. I didn't mind sitting on the shore with a book. I'd done so before. But once there, he began to act peculiar. A slew of little boys came by, and he told them in Spanish he'd pay them money to come watch him dive, just to see how long he could stay under. These fellows looked like they'd take his coin to watch him whistle Dixie if that's what he wanted, so off we all did troop down a path through the bushes.

The place he meant to go diving was a little cove with cliffs behind it and a strip of shore growing smaller by the minute, as the tide came up. The morning was getting on, and he seemed impatient to go in the water. The tide was still low but coming in right fast, eating up that little beach as it came. I wondered how long he'd expect me to stay there. I don't know what he said before wading in. I paid no heed. Probably I was a little put out with him. I had my book. But after a while I looked out at the water and didn't see him. I waited. Then counted to fifty, then one hundred. I didn't see any way he could have left the cove. And it struck me: he's drowned. Those little boys knew it too, standing in their group, for they were not looking at the water anymore, but at me. They seemed to think it was up to me now, to fix what had gone wrong.

Did I scream? That isn't my way, so I don't think so. I'm sure I stood up, threw down the book, and moved about. I remember thinking I couldn't go in the water because it would wreck my shoes. So it hadn't soaked in yet, that life had set down here before me a far worse thing than wrecked shoes. Or anything else I'd thus far known. It's true I lost a husband in the flood of the French Broad River in '16, Freddy Brown, and that broke a young girl's heart. But this was worse. My heart had grown older, with more in it to break. I can't put words to that afternoon. He would know words for the feelings I bore, but I only knew the feelings.

I told those boys as best I could, to run get some kind of help. A group of men came out from the village and searched the cove. One was the friend, Leandro. Later the police came along too. By nightfall a hundred people must have been in that cove as the tide went out, every hour giving back more beach for the crowd that came to stand on it. It never really went dark, for the moon rose big and full, just as the sun went down. Most of those people were merely curious to see a body, I expect. Yet all went away that night without satisfaction, there was no body. He was just gone.

I remember parts of that day, not all. I can't say how I came back to the hotel. Police had to search his room for some clue or a note, thinking Mr. Shepherd might have done away with himself on purpose. I knew better, and yet I really didn't. I stood at the door while they turned out suitcases and drawers, and me thinking, "Here it is again, the police ransacking for evidence, and the man they will not find." I spied one peculiar thing—the little stone man he liked to carry in his pocket. He'd left his room tidy, every last thing put away, but that little man was out on the table grinning at me! Or rather it howled, that round mouth open like a hole in the head. It made me want to howl too, and not much does. I could tell it had been set there for a reason, and I was the reason. But what he meant to tell me, I knew not.

Once back home, I took care of things as best I knew how, which was not very well. I could only think one thing at a time, starting with: get up. Arthur Gold was a great help, also torn up about it, but less surprised. He had done the will, you see. Mr. Shepherd left all to me, his house and proceeds from the books, if any. The cats. The money was no fortune, but more than a widow's mite. Curiously, he had wired some money to a bank in Mexico City, addressed to Mrs. Kahlo. He did that shortly before our trip. He hadn't mentioned it, but I decided it was no great surprise. That lady was ever in need of cash.

With his legal testament was a letter he'd written to me. It

THE LACUNA ❋ 503

contained certain instructions about his books, and personal things, appreciation for the years. Most of it need not be told here. But he said two things that shocked: first, that we'd had a great love. So he said, in those words. No one had been more important to him. And he said not to grieve. His sole regret was the stain his life and ways had put upon mine, and he wanted me to be shed of all such worry. He said this is the happy ending everyone wanted. Well, I was furious at that. For him to quit on life, and call that happiness.

I moved into his house, farewell to Mrs. Bittle at last, I won't dwell on that. The part-time at Raye's gave me afternoons free for setting things to rights in his house and answering what mail still came. My first chore was an obituary for the Asheville paper. I can't begin to tell what care I took, keening over each word and many unwritten. I delivered it to the office and spoke with a man, and was barely out the door I expect when he threw it in his ashcan. They ran their own little piece instead. They had no wish to tell what a man has done with his life. That would require honest witness. The simpler thing is to state what he has been called.

In 1954 came the death of his friend, Mrs. Kahlo. The family must have gone through some upheaval, the usual business of sorting the clutter of the deceased, for they sent a trunk of Mr. Shepherd's things. A young man's clothes many years out of date, a few photographs, and not much else to speak of. But inside the trunk was a letter from Mrs. Kahlo, addressed to me. I thought that very strange. We'd only met the once. But there was my name, so this trunk was not some mere forgotten thing, she'd meant to have it sent to me. She planned that before she died.

The letter was so peculiar. A drawing of a pyramid sketched out in drab purple and brown, and on its top a yellow eye with lines like rays from the sun. Across the eye she'd written "soli" to mean the sun, I gathered. And scribbled at the top of the page in a hand like a child's: "Violet Brown, Your American friend is dead. Someone else is here." It was in English. But I could no more understand it than the man in the moon.

The photographs I put away, and the clothes I meant to give the Salvation Army, for who knows what a person will wear if he's cold enough. They would have to be washed first, and it sat for some weeks before I could get around to that. It was only by luck I went through the trouser pockets. That makes my heart race now, for how easily this could have gone another way. But it happened as it did. I found the little notebook.

I knew what it was. I'll say that. I opened the little leather booklet and saw a penciled hand, the boy with his laments about Mother and so forth. Oh, I cried. I felt I'd found my own lost child. I sat and read it through on the bedroom floor where I'd been sorting the clothes. My heart pounding, because of that cave he found under the water. And his business with the moon, learning to wait for a day the tide would help push him through to the other side, without his drowning first. That was him all over. That patient study.

I read all of it. The happy ending, as he called it. Because that is what he did, right under my nose while I sat reading on the beach. He swam in that cave, to rest with the bones or else come out the other side, and walk himself into life as some other man who is not dead.

Fight or die was his choice. I know which it was. Mrs. Kahlo would have hidden him when he got that far, and helped him make a new start. She thrived on that kind of thing. He had wired the money. "Someone else is here," she'd written, plain as daylight, and also the name she used to call him, long forgotten. It was his idea to make her send a message, to put me at rest. I feel I know that too.

I had to get out all his notebooks then, and look again. Three years earlier I'd read most of it through eyes half-shut with grief, then packed it away, forgetting what all I could. Now, out came the box. Papers covered the dining table, a mess like times of yore. With that one little booklet put back in place, it came as a different story. Because of that burrow through rock and water— lacuna, he called it. This time I read with a different heart, understanding the hero would still be standing at journey's end. Or at least, live or die, he'd known of a chance and aimed to take it. What you don't know can't hurt you, they say. Yet it can. So much hangs upon it.

What I have done with these writings he could have done himself. Set down his life as he chose, for others to read. He began the one chapter, then stopped, claiming he couldn't go forward for want of the booklet that was lost. I could say, "Now it is found, so Mr. Shepherd would want to go on with his story." Which is fiddlesticks, and I know it. He wanted to put his boyhood away and keep still about it. God speaks for the silent man, oh, that I have heard. I've struggled with my conscience, it has cost me dear. It does so still.

Yet one day I decided to go on with it. I was here in Montford, for he gave me the place and only could have meant for me to live in it. I use a different bedroom to sleep in, of course, and his study room under the gable eave is a place I don't go. But it had to be his own bathroom mirror I faced each morning, the very place where he shaved and answered his Lord and conscience. Now it was a lady looking back from the glass, and one bright morn I told her: Listen here. If God speaks for the man who keeps quiet, then Violet Brown may be His instrument.

I don't say it was swift or sure. It took considering. Typing up a manuscript, that I can do. His hand was legible, and errors were few. Putting all in order was no easy trick, but no worse than some card files I've seen at the Asheville library. I left nothing out but the things that had no business, a market list or telephone numbers, certain letters. Of his story I have told all, even when it pained me to do it, or passed my understanding. But the question stood everlasting at my shoulder: Was it mine to tell?

This day the telephone could ring and my heart would squeeze, for the thought it might be him, and the answer no. Even as I am a person of the world, and eight years now gone by since I saw him in it. Years do not erase a bereavement. Mr. Shepherd, where be ye? I could still ask. And here is an answer: in those little books. I always could find him there. So this might be nothing very different from the pining girls singing for lost love on the radio. Maybe I turned to typing it for the pleasure of being his daily helpmeet again. Even if that's so, in the middle of all, the story worked itself ahead of the man. I will say Mr. Shepherd persuaded me, against his own will.

Not in so many words. I did hope for that, some instruction in his text to guide my hand. Well, my stars, the thing was like the Bible—look hard enough in its pages, and you'll find what you seek. Love your neighbor, or slay him with the jawbone of an ass.

It's the same herein. He plainly said, Burn these words. He said a mute people will leave behind good stout architecture, and not their squalid lives of trial. Those who come after will be struck by the majesty. He meant to leave behind only the monuments of his books. As he lived and breathed, I saw his wish and I held to that. And then saw the monuments tumble. In this strange, cold time that has settled on us, people did what they could to bury the man and throw everything he'd ever made into the hole they'd dug for him. Like a mummy in Egypt.

His life was a marvel, whether he knew that or didn't. His way of seeing a cat in a cold wind, or skeletons pressed flat in the dust. A dead fish thrown in the kitchen slop pail. He could cry for about anything and give it a decent burial. He was so afraid of living, yet live he did. That's a monument. He wrote about those who came before, giving flesh to their cares. He was driven to it.

Now I do the same for him. Even knowing, as I do, how everyone makes firewood from the fallen tree. The professors like to hunt out some sin of Shakespeare himself, and pass that off as the golden store of the learned. I couldn't bear this to touch Mr. Shepherd, or his loved ones or even children, if such a thing has now come to pass. I want time for him. All the paint washed off, bare limestone revealed.

That is my reason for having it locked up and held. Mr. Gold knew how to fix that up. People at a bank do this very thing, holding documents for a set number of years before hauling it out of the vault for the newspapers or what have you. I told him fifty. I had to choose, and that is a sturdy number. Long enough to be sure we are gone. Yet not so long that I couldn't imagine people still walking about in shoes, rather than flying on clouds. People who might want to look back on those who labored and birthed the times they have inherited. But maybe that's wrong, and already we'll be a graveyard of weeds they won't want to visit. You, I mean to say. The times you have inherited. I wonder that: Who be ye?

I dread to do what I do now, commending a man's life into the bleak passage to some other place, be it filled with light or darkness. This is my small raft. I know not what waits on the other side.

ABOUT THE AUTHOR

Barbara Kingsolver is the author of seven works of fiction, including the novels *The Poisonwood Bible*, *Animal Dreams*, and *The Bean Trees*, as well as books of poetry, essays, and creative nonfiction. Her most recent book is the enormously influential bestseller *Animal, Vegetable, Miracle: A Year of Food Life*. Kingsolver's work has been translated into more than twenty languages and has earned literary awards and a devoted readership at home and abroad. In 2000, she was awarded the National Humanities Medal, our country's highest honor for service through the arts. She lives with her family on a farm in southern Appalachia.

"More than any book I've read, *The Endgame* captures impressive historical detail to illuminate the major themes and issues that were woven through our war in Iraq. Gordon and Trainor avoid the temptation to oversimplify what was a complex experience, yet relate the story with amazing clarity. The definitive work to date."
—General Stanley McChrystal, U.S. Army, Retired Commander, Joint Special Operations Command, 2003–2008

"An exhaustively researched chronicle of the war's final years. It captures the ineptitude and duplicity of U.S. and Iraqi officials but also the heroism of many soldiers and anonymous government bureaucrats as they struggled to bring Iraq and its people back from the brink."
—Andrew Exum, Senior Fellow, Center for a New American Security

"Ultimately, *The Endgame* invites the question whether President Obama threw his support behind the wrong war." —*Newsweek/The Daily Beast*

"A fantastic book . . . highly anticipated and a must-read on this subject."
—Joe Scarborough, MSNBC's "Morning Joe"

"An epic piece of work."   —Andrea Mitchell, MSNBC

"What Michael Gordon has written is correct."
—Iraqi Foreign Minister Hoshyar Zebari

"If you want to know about this painful and critical episode of American history, you have to read these books."   —James Rosen, Fox News

Michael R. Gordon and
General Bernard E. Trainor

THE ENDGAME

MICHAEL R. GORDON is the chief military correspondent for *The New York Times*, where he has worked since 1985. He is the coauthor, with Lieutenant General Bernard E. Trainor, of *The Generals' War* and *Cobra II*. He has covered the Iraq and Afghan wars, the Kosovo conflict, the Russian war in Chechnya, the 1991 Persian Gulf War, and the American invasion of Panama.

BERNARD E. TRAINOR, a retired Marine Corps lieutenant general, was a military correspondent for *The New York Times* from 1986 to 1990. He was director of the National Security Program at Harvard University's John F. Kennedy School of Government from 1990 to 1996 and was a military analyst for NBC during the Iraq War.

www.michaelrgordon.com

THE ENDGAME

ALSO BY MICHAEL R. GORDON
AND GENERAL BERNARD E. TRAINOR

The Generals' War
Cobra II

THE ENDGAME

THE INSIDE STORY OF THE STRUGGLE FOR IRAQ, FROM GEORGE W. BUSH TO BARACK OBAMA

Michael R. Gordon and General Bernard E. Trainor

VINTAGE BOOKS
A DIVISION OF RANDOM HOUSE, INC.
NEW YORK

FIRST VINTAGE BOOKS EDITION, MARCH 2013

The Library of Congress has cataloged the Pantheon edition as follows:

Gordon, Michael R., [date]
The endgame : the inside story of the struggle for Iraq,
from George W. Bush to Barack Obama /
Michael R. Gordon and General Bernard E. Trainor.
p. cm.
Includes bibliographical references and index.
1. Iraq War, 2003–2011.   2. Insurgency—Iraq.   3. Iraq—Politics and government—
21st century.   4. Iraq War, 2003–2011—Political aspects—United States.
5. United States—Armed Forces—Iraq—History.   6. Iraq—Ethnic relations.
7. Iraq—Relations—United States.   8. United States—Relations—Iraq.
I. Trainor, Bernard E., [date]   II. Title.
DS79.76.G672 2012   956.7044'3—dc23   2012024746

Vintage ISBN: 978-0-307-38894-0

Book design by M. Kristen Bearse

www.vintagebooks.com

Printed in the United States of America
10 9 8 7 6 5 4 3 2 1

To the Iraqis who risked their lives
to try to build a democratic Iraq

Authors' Note

Wesley Morgan, a 2011 graduate of Princeton University, was integral to the research and writing of this book. He conducted interviews in the United States, Iraq, and Afghanistan, drafted chapters, and contributed reported material and fresh ideas throughout. His encyclopedic knowledge of the American military and its wars, along with his dogged reporting, added substantially to the work.

Contents

PART 3 *New Dawn*
Obama, Maliki, and Beyond, 2008–2012

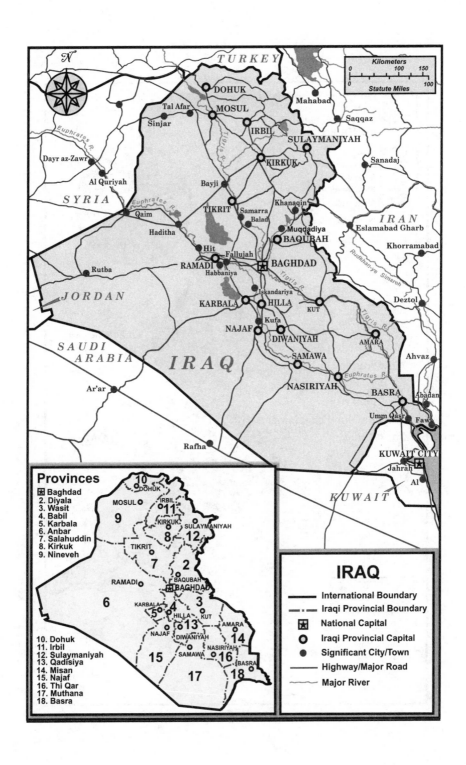

N

TURKEY

DOHUK

Tal Afar · MOSUL

Sinjar · IRBIL

SULAYMANIYAH

Mahabad

Saqqaz

Sanadaj

KIRKUK

Euphrates R.

Dayr az-Zawr

Al Quriyah

SYRIA

Bayji

Euphrates R.

Qaim

TIKRIT · Samarra

Balad

Khanaqin

Muqqadiya

BAQUBAH

Eslamabad Gharb

IRAN

Haditha

Hit

Fallujah

RAMADI · BAGHDAD

Habbaniya

Rutba

JORDAN

Iskandariya

KARBALA · HILLA

Kufa · KUT

NAJAF · DIWANIYAH

SAUDI
ARABIA

IRAQ

Ar'ar

SAMAWA

AMARA

Khorramabad

Deztol

Ahvaz

Abadan

NASIRIYAH · BASRA

Umm Qasr · Faw

Rafha

KUWAIT CITY

Jahrah

Al

KUWAIT

Kilometers
0   100   150
0   100
Statute Miles

Provinces

- ⊞ Baghdad
- 2. Diyala
- 3. Wasit
- 4. Babil
- 5. Karbala
- 6. Anbar
- 7. Salahuddin
- 8. Kirkuk
- 9. Nineveh

10. Dohuk
11. Irbil
12. Sulaymaniyah
13. Qadisiya
14. Misan
15. Najaf
16. Thi Qar
17. Muthana
18. Basra

10 — DOHUK

MOSUL — IRBIL

9 — 11

KIRKUK

8 — 12

SULAYMANIYAH

TIKRIT

7 — 2

RAMADI

BAQUBAH

⊞ BAGHDAD

6

KARBALA — 3

5 — 4 — HILLA — KUT

NAJAF — 13 — AMARA

DIWANIYAH — 14

15 — 16

SAMAWA — BASRA

17 — 18

IRAQ

- ——— International Boundary
- —·—·— Iraqi Provincial Boundary
- ⊞ National Capital
- ○ Iraqi Provincial Capital
- ● Significant City/Town
- ——— Highway/Major Road
- ——— Major River

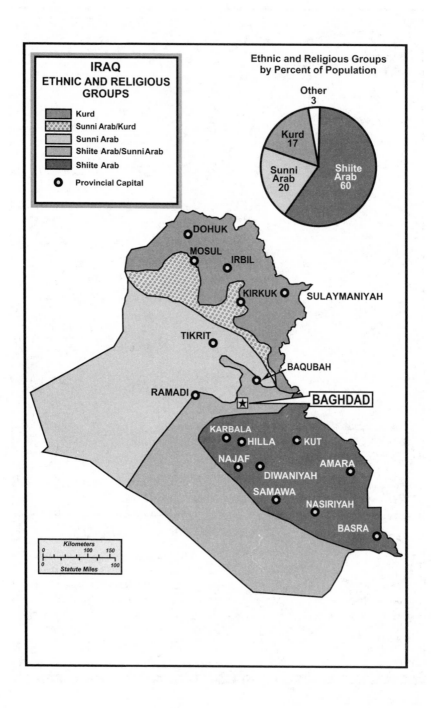

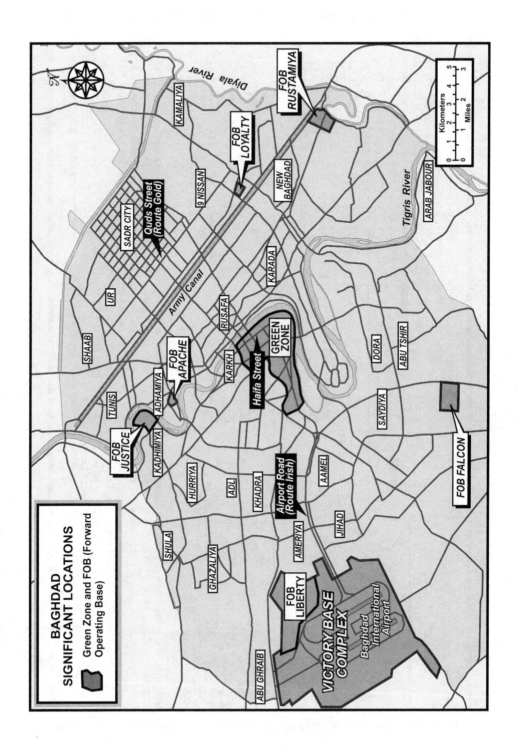

BAGHDAD
SIGNIFICANT LOCATIONS

Green Zone and FOB (Forward Operating Base)

FOB RUSTAMIYA

FOB LOYALTY

Diyala River

KAMALIYA

NEW BAGHDAD

Quds Street (Route Gold)

SADR CITY

9 NISSAN

KARADA

Tigris River

ARAB JABOUR

UR

Army Canal

RUSAFA

GREEN ZONE

DORA

ABU TSHIR

SHAAB

FOB APACHE

KARKH

Haifa Street

SAYDIYA

TUNIS

ADHAMIYA

FOB JUSTICE

KADHIMIYA

HURRIYA

ADL

KHADRA

Airport Road (Route Irish)

AAMEL

FOB FALCON

SHULA

GHAZALIYA

AMERIYA

JIHAD

FOB LIBERTY

VICTORY BASE COMPLEX

Baghdad International Airport

ABU GHRAIB

Kilometers
0 1 2 3 4 5
0 1 2 3
Miles

Organization of Coalition Forces in Iraq

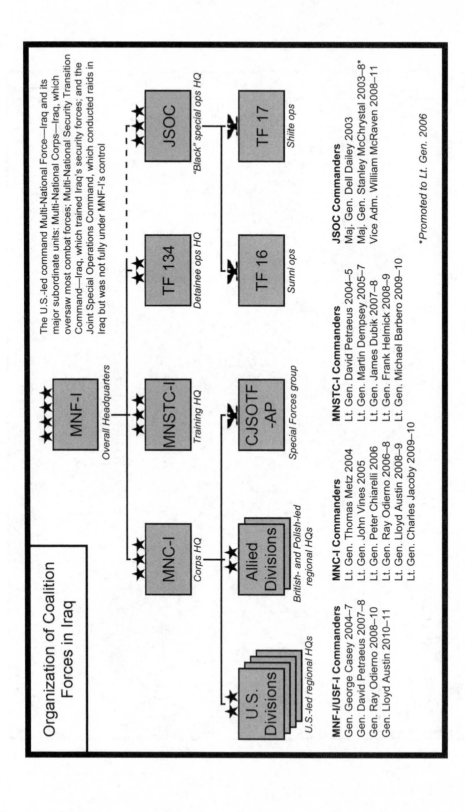

The U.S.-led command Multi-National Force—Iraq and its major subordinate units: Multi-National Corps—Iraq, which oversaw most combat forces; Multi-National Security Transition Command—Iraq, which trained Iraq's security forces; and the Joint Special Operations Command, which conducted raids in Iraq but was not fully under MNF-I's control

MNF-I
Overall Headquarters

MNSTC-I
Training HQ

TF 134
Detainee ops HQ

JSOC
"Black" special ops HQ

CJSOTF-AP
Special Forces group

TF 16
Sunni ops

TF 17
Shiite ops

MNC-I
Corps HQ

Allied Divisions
British- and Polish-led regional HQs

U.S. Divisions
U.S.-led regional HQs

MNF-I/USF-I Commanders
Gen. George Casey 2004–7
Gen. David Petraeus 2007–8
Gen. Ray Odierno 2008–10
Gen. Lloyd Austin 2010–11

MNC-I Commanders
Lt. Gen. Thomas Metz 2004
Lt. Gen. John Vines 2005
Lt. Gen. Peter Chiarelli 2006
Lt. Gen. Ray Odierno 2006–8
Lt. Gen. Lloyd Austin 2008–9
Lt. Gen. Charles Jacoby 2009–10

MNSTC-I Commanders
Lt. Gen. David Petraeus 2004–5
Lt. Gen. Martin Dempsey 2005–7
Lt. Gen. James Dubik 2007–8
Lt. Gen. Frank Helmick 2008–9
Lt. Gen. Michael Barbero 2009–10

JSOC Commanders
Maj. Gen. Dell Dailey 2003
Maj. Gen. Stanley McChrystal 2003–8*
Vice Adm. William McRaven 2008–11

Promoted to Lt. Gen. 2006

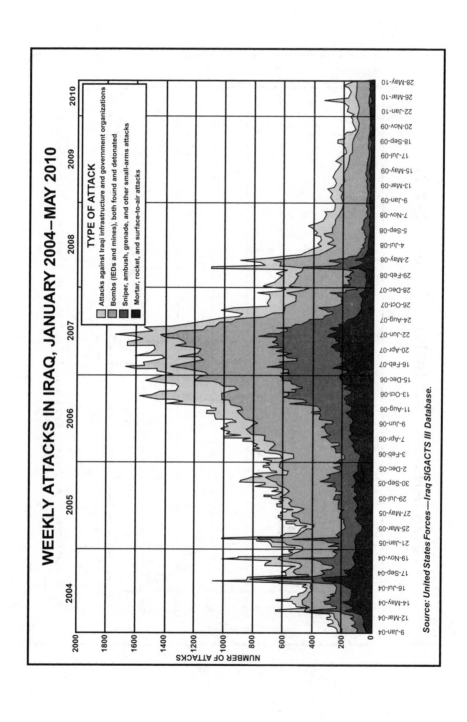

WEEKLY ATTACKS IN IRAQ, JANUARY 2004–MAY 2010

TYPE OF ATTACK

Attacks against Iraqi infrastructure and government organizations
Bombs (IEDs and mines), both found and detonated
Sniper, ambush, grenade, and other small-arms attacks
Mortar, rocket, and surface-to-air attacks

NUMBER OF ATTACKS

Source: United States Forces—Iraq SIGACTS III Database.

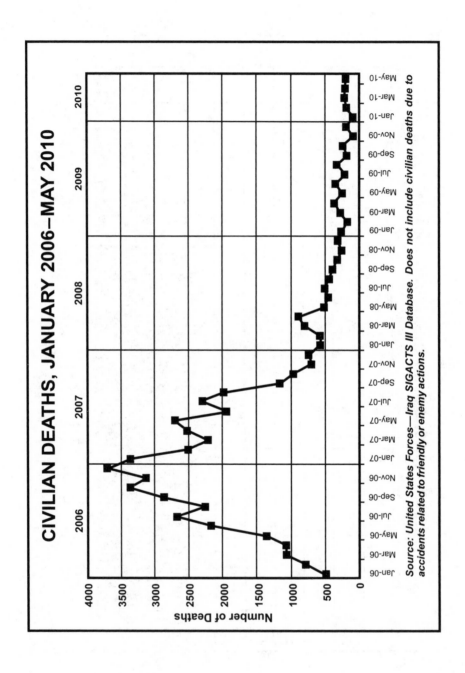

CIVILIAN DEATHS, JANUARY 2006–MAY 2010

Number of Deaths

Source: United States Forces—Iraq SIGACTS III Database. Does not include civilian deaths due to accidents related to friendly or enemy actions.

Prologue

No one book can capture an event as complex as a war, especially a nine-year war in a distant nation that from its outset was permeated by tribal, religious, ethnic, local, and regional politics. Nonetheless, this volume seeks to provide the most comprehensive account to date of the United States' involvement in Iraq.

From the start, our goal was to cover Iraq's halting political development as well as the military battles. We gave attention to decisions in Baghdad as well as Washington. And we covered the clashes and political maneuvering from the early days of the American-led occupation, through the descent into sectarian violence, the surge that pulled Iraq back from the brink of civil war, and the vexing aftermath.

This was an ambitious project, but we have been covering the Iraq War from the start. Through two American presidents, a succession of Iraqi prime ministers, and a variety of United States commanders, we tracked events on the ground in Iraq and in Washington. We were present for many of the ferocious battles in Anbar, Diyala, Mosul, and Sadr City, and we covered the nation's political development. We saw American and Iraqi blood spilled, and we interacted with the generals, diplomats, and politicians on whose shoulders the decisions of the war rested.

Too many American accounts of the war in Iraq have left out the Iraqis, or cast them as little more than a backdrop for dramas that were played out in Washington or among American commanders in Baghdad. But they are essential actors in their own nation's drama. For this reason, Prime Minister Nuri al-Maliki and rivals like Ayad Allawi, Massoud Barzani, and Adil Abd al-Mahdi share the list of the hundreds of interviews we conducted along with Iraqi generals, police commanders, tribal sheikhs, and student protesters. We also interviewed myriad American and British generals, as well as officers and enlisted troops down to the platoon level.

The objective was to weave together battles fought by the troops with closed-door Green Zone and White House meetings from the conflict's earlier days through the military withdrawal in December 2011. More than that, we have sought to explain not just what happened when and where, but why.

We have been aided in our task by unprecedented access to classified documents that chronicle the war as it was seen from the American embassy in Baghdad, from the White House, from military headquarters across Iraq, and from the command posts of special operations and intelligence units. The troves of secret documents on which we were able to draw shed light on corners of the Iraq story that would otherwise have remained dark for years.

Internal military and State Department reports have provided glimpses of roads not taken and opportunities missed. Firsthand after-action reports and cumulative briefings chart and bring to life the nighttime campaign waged in Iraq by the Joint Special Operations Command, the headquarters overseeing America's most elite and secretive commando units, both against Sunni insurgents and later against Shiite militias and even the Quds Force, Iran's operations and intelligence arm in Iraq. Still-classified oral histories show the war as commanders recounted it. CIA and other intelligence reports helped complete the mosaic.

In painting a picture of America's complicated struggle with Iran in Iraq, for instance, we have been able to draw on General David Petraeus's classified updates to Defense Secretary Robert Gates, an unauthorized disclosure that opens a window into the inner workings of the war and describes Petraeus's own third-party interactions with the leader of that force, Qasim Suleimani.

Other documents provide rare glimpses of the war through the eyes of those who fought against the United States and the Iraqi government. Detailed reports on the interrogations of Qais and Laith al-Khazali, two Iraqi Shiite militants captured by the British Special Air Service in 2007, offer an inside view of Iraq's Sadrist political movement and militias and its ties to Iran. Transcripts of the interrogations of Sunni insurgents captured by American troops, along with internal reports by insurgent commanders recovered from hard drives and flash drives, have helped us understand the activities of Al-Qaeda in Iraq, the local franchise of the global terrorist group that was the United States' main antagonist for much of the war.

Heavily classified embassy cables, internal Red Team analyses organized by the American military command, notes of critical meetings in Washington and Baghdad, and classified assessments and war plans commissioned by the generals who prosecuted the war round out our account. We have protected the intelligence community's sources and methods. By combining extensive interviews with this documentary history, we have sought to convey a full and rich history of a tumultuous period that has put its stamp on the American military, has decisively altered the history of Iraq, and will influence events in the broader Middle East for decades to come.

PART 1

Iraqi Freedom

The Occupation and Its Discontents, 2003–2006

CHAPTER 1

Desert Crossing

On a stone gray December morning in 2011, Nuri Kamal al-Maliki arrived at the White House for a meeting with President Barack Obama. The Iraqi prime minister had maintained his grip on power atop a government that was more an ongoing collision of ambitions than a well-oiled machine. The furious sectarian bloodletting in Baghdad that had come close to pushing the country into civil war; the belated American military surge that had tamped down the violence; the Iranian-sponsored attacks; uprisings by rival Shiite parties; the Al-Qaeda bombings: Maliki had maneuvered through it all.

But now the Iraqi prime minister and the American president were about to enter uncharted waters, more than eight years after the American invasion and occupation of Iraq. To shore up Iraq's still-shaky military and maintain a modicum of stability, American diplomats had spent much of the summer pursuing an agreement that would have enabled the United States to keep several thousand American troops in the country to train Iraq's armed forces, protect its skies, and conduct joint counterterrorism operations, only to have the negotiations sputter to a halt. The collapsed talks had been a casualty of rising Iraqi nationalism, backroom machinations by Iraqi politicians, and a deep ambivalence about continued American military involvement in Iraq on the part of President Obama and his inner circle as they approached the election season at home.

The result was that for the first time since the March 2003 invasion Iraq would be without U.S. troops. The departure of the last of them was just days away. While American and Iraqi military officers nervously eyed the risks ahead, both leaders had pronounced themselves to be satisfied with the outcome. Maliki's visit to Washington, in fact, had been cast by the

White House as a celebration of the new normal: a sovereign Iraq that was putatively on the path to democracy and capable of providing for itself.

After a brief photo op in the Oval Office, which Obama appeared to enjoy and Maliki to endure, the two sides engaged in a closed-door discussion about the way ahead. The president urged the prime minister not to release a notorious Hezbollah militant whom the Americans had captured in Iraq and handed over to Iraq's wobbly judicial system. The question of how to respond to the violent crackdown in Syria was a point of contention, but the two leaders affirmed Iraq's plan to proceed with a multibillion-dollar purchase of American F-16s.[1]

After the discussions were done, Maliki and Obama jointly faced the press. Maliki led Iraq's most inclusive government, Obama asserted. His country's economy was projected to grow faster than China's and the violence that had once wracked the country was at a record low. In an event that would symbolize Iraq's reemergence in the club of Middle East nations, Baghdad, for the first time in two decades, would host a summit of the Arab League in March. "People throughout the region will see a new Iraq that's determining its own destiny—a country in which people from different religious sects and ethnicities can resolve their differences peacefully through the democratic process," Obama added. "A new day is upon us."[2]

Within a week, Iraqi tanks were parked near the residences of the nation's leading Sunni politicians, the government's lone Sunni vice president had dodged arrest by taking refuge in Kurdistan, and American officials were working overtime to try to head off more detentions, the collapse of the cross-sectarian coalition, and perhaps even another bloody round of sectarian strife. Was this just another bump in the road, a political uproar that could be contained, if not defused, with a few high-level phone calls from Washington? Or was it the start of a new chapter of authoritarian rule that the United States had inadvertently put into place?

The United States had stormed into Iraq in 2003 with extravagant hopes but little understanding. Four years later, it had pulled Iraq back from the precipice of civil war at enormous cost. Generals had been fired and hired. The American military had rediscovered counterinsurgency. Struggling to decipher the labyrinth of sect, religion, and tribe, American commanders and diplomats had cut deals with an assortment of politicians, clerics, militia leaders, and even insurgents. But after the loss of nearly 4,500 American troops and many more Iraqi lives, and the expenditure of more than $800 billion, just what sort of Iraq was the United States military leaving behind?

In the United States' tangled involvement in the Middle East, Iraq had morphed from an expedient partner to an adversary, and, finally, a titanic project to establish a democratic beachhead in Mesopotamia.

Seized with the mission of containing the new theocracy in Tehran, President Ronald Reagan had seen Iraq primarily as a means of containing Iranian power, so much so that during the Iran-Iraq War, he dispatched an envoy—Donald Rumsfeld—to nurture ties with Saddam Hussein, a partnership which eventually included sharing American intelligence on Iranian military positions. Reagan's successor as president, George H. W. Bush, had expanded the policy, calculating that an Iraq weary from eight years of war with Iran would see enough advantage in a pragmatic relationship with Washington to temper its regional ambitions. Even when its strategy collapsed ignominiously with Saddam's invasion of Kuwait, the White House had envisioned nothing so bold as the democratization of Iraq. The goal of the Gulf War, the president confided to Turkey's ambassador in a declassified transcript, was to loosen Saddam's grip on power in the hope that the Sunni-dominated Baath Party and the Iraqi military would topple the Iraqi dictator. The empowerment of Iraq's Shiite majority, an impoverished and long-suppressed group about whom the American government knew little, was decidedly not part of the plan.[3]

Bill Clinton's election had signaled more of the same. In early 1993, Clinton suggested that he was prepared for a fresh start with Baghdad, expounding famously that even a dictator like Saddam was capable of a "deathbed conversion." Under pressure from the right and following an intelligence assessment that Saddam's regime had conspired to assassinate his predecessor, however, Clinton stiffened his stance. On October 31, 1998, as a weakened Bill Clinton faced the threat of impeachment as a result of the Monica Lewinsky scandal, he signed the Iraq Liberation Act, a Republican-inspired piece of legislation that formally committed the United States to a policy of regime change and the emergence of a democratic government in Iraq, a measure the White House saw no profit in vetoing but had little intention of fully implementing.[4]

One of the most telling explorations of the challenges involved in remaking Iraq was carried out during Clinton's tenure by the Central Command, or CENTCOM, the United States military headquarters that had responsibility for the Middle East. After Saddam rescinded his fitful cooperation with United Nations weapons inspectors in December 1998, Clinton ordered four days of air strikes on suspected weapons of mass destruction sites. (Only after the 2003 invasion did a CIA-sponsored investigation establish that Iraq's chemical, biological, and nuclear programs had been shelved by late 1998, making the raid the first major American military operation conducted against Iraq on the basis of erroneous intelligence. The intelligence failure would be repeated in gargantuan proportions by Clinton's Republican successor more than four years later.)[5]

After picking up reports through the Polish embassy in Baghdad that the strikes might have shaken Saddam's regime, General Anthony Zinni, who led CENTCOM, began to worry what he would do if the despot's government collapsed and he was saddled with the mission of occupying the country and advancing the Liberation Act's democratic agenda. Zinni did not think there would be much left to work with if the United States military had to go in. Saddam's regime and the governmental apparatus it controlled, Zinni confided to Laurence Pope, his foreign policy adviser, would likely fall apart like a cheap suit.[6]

To examine the problem, Zinni convened a classified exercise in the McLean, Virginia, office of Booz Allen, a Pentagon contractor. The war game, which was held in June 1999, involved more than seventy officials from the National Security Council, the Defense Department, the CIA, and other agencies. Saddam had often employed the metaphor of a river crossing to extol Iraq's supposed march toward a better future and to celebrate his own revolutionary exploits, which, lore had it, included a dramatic swim across the Tigris. So the command's intelligence experts recommended that the war game be dubbed "Desert Crossing," calculating somewhat naively that the name would unnerve Saddam if news of the secret exercise somehow leaked.

But it was the Desert Crossing participants themselves who were unnerved by the magnitude of the task before them. The refashioning of Iraq presented daunting challenges at every turn. If a new group of Iraqis grabbed power—the exercise described this as the "inside-out" approach—policymakers in Washington would be confronted with the fact that they might know precious little about the new leadership, let alone how the United States might attempt to influence it. American officials knew some of the exiles who had taken up residence in London but hardly the Iranian-based or Syrian-based contingents. And any new government that was likely to rise out of the ashes was bound to include Iraqis who had endured Saddam's rule as well. When it came to the welter of Iraq's tribes, underground parties, and mid-level bureaucrats the country was a virtual black hole. The "inside-out" strategy would relieve the United States of the burden of trying to secure and reorganize Iraq, but Washington could not be sure just which Iraqis would push their way to the top of the heap.

If on the other hand the American military moved in and occupied Iraq—the "outside-in" approach, modeled after the American experience administering postwar Japan under General Douglas MacArthur—the United States could determine what political institutions should be established, who should run them, and arrange for elections to be held, according to democratic principles imported from Washington. But the price would be the deployment of hundreds of thousands of troops, the commitment of billions of dollars, and, perhaps more importantly, the will to see the project through some difficult days. "A change in regime does not guarantee stability," the after-action report of the exercise dryly noted.

Nor would the establishment of a democracy necessarily bring stability to the region. There would be threats galore—to the east, theocratic Iran; to the south, the Saudi kingdom and other autocratic Arab states, not to mention Islamist terrorist groups—who would be eager to snuff out the democratic experiment before the contagion spread. "The presence of a government that may be more representative (i.e. democratic) in its decision-making functions than any of its neighbors may invite the conduct of subversive activities in Iraq," the report added. "Neighboring regimes will also be concerned with all catalyzing effect on their own pro-democracy movements. In a sense, a western-style democracy may not engender long-term stability without considerable stabilization, preparation, and long-term sustainment."[7]

Since the end of the 1991 Persian Gulf War, the American desideratum had, implicitly or explicitly, been regime change. Yet if the moment finally came, Washington would face a choice between a speedy process the United States would be at pains to control and an externally imposed solution that would require extraordinary patience and resources, and which even then would not be assured of success. The removal of Saddam would surely open the door to political change in Iraq, but with unprotected borders, the possibility of looting, sectarian strife, and bare-knuckled power struggles, Iraq might also become a veritable Pandora's box. If push came to shove, Martin Indyk, the assistant secretary of state for Near East affairs during the Clinton administration and a participant in the Desert Crossing exercise, concluded that the wisest approach would be to opt for minimal American commitment in a region of the world that appeared to offer more peril than promise. "We had very little intelligence on what exactly was going on in Iraq," he recalled. "So the idea was to take what you had in there and build on it, the inside-out model. There was no discussion about democratization or elections. That was simply not on the agenda. We were not democratic crusaders in the Clinton administration, especially when it came to the Middle East."[8]

George W. Bush saw things differently. While his predecessors considered the occupation of Iraq to be a debilitating snare, Bush viewed it as a strategic opportunity and even a moral crusade. The president and his aides had been caught short by the September 11 terrorist attacks. Missile defense, military competition with China, the pursuit of high-tech weaponry, and the nation's defense overall—these had been the pressing security issues in the early months of his administration.

But after the terrorist strikes in New York and Washington and the administration's improvised campaign in Afghanistan to topple the Taliban for their role in harboring Al-Qaeda, Bush had searched for a doctrine that would confer a larger meaning on the fight against terrorists. Iraq would be the second phase in the administration's self-described "War on Terror." Washington would resolve, once and for all, its anxiety over Iraq's suspected WMD programs and frustration with Saddam's persistent efforts to punch a hole in the economic sanctions. The demonstration of American power would strengthen the United States' position in the Middle East, recruit a new Iraqi ally in the fight against extremism, and send a message to Iran, Syria, and other miscreants in the region about the risks of pursuing WMD.

Reflecting a new "freedom agenda," the United States would join the ideological struggle for the hearts and minds of the Muslim world by implanting a democracy in the heart of the Middle East. The bold vision was outlined in August 2002 in a classified document that Bush had signed before the invasion. Blandly titled "Iraq: Goals, Objectives and Strategy," the document proclaimed that the United States would midwife a new Iraq whose society would be "based on moderation, pluralism, and democracy."[9] With his reversal of Iraq's invasion of Kuwait, the president's father had vowed to preserve international norms against the forces of chaos; this new president would upset the established order to spread the gospel of freedom.

The philosophical differences between the two Bush administrations emerged when Condoleezza Rice, the younger Bush's national security adviser, sat down with Brent Scowcroft, her former mentor and counterpart in the administration of the elder Bush. Over dinner at 1789, a swank Georgetown restaurant, Rice revealed her goal of bringing democracy to Saddam Hussein's Iraq. "I said, 'Condi, it's just not going to happen,'" Scowcroft recalled. "'You can't build democracy that way.' She said, 'Oh yes you can.'"[10]

As the clock ticked down on the invasion of Iraq in the spring of 2003, Deputy National Security Adviser Stephen J. Hadley convened a meeting of the Deputies Committee, a panel of sub-cabinet-level officials, to ponder the vexing question of how the United States might respond if a band of Iraqi generals took matters into their own hands. "The question came up: What if a group of generals sent us a message that they were willing to topple Saddam if we promised to support them?" recalled Hadley. "Would it be sufficient if they said they would not do anything that troubled the U.S.?" The answer the officials settled on, and which Hadley dutifully reported to his boss, was that the United States would be content to let the generals do the dirty work of disposing of Saddam on two conditions: the United States would be allowed to retrieve the presumed stocks of WMD and the United Nations would be allowed to supervise elections and the transition to a democratic government. Absent those steps American forces would still march in.[11]

Zinni, who had conducted the Desert Crossing exercise and had retired from the military in 2000, publicly opposed the invasion. But, concluding that the war was all but inevitable, Zinni was prepared to fly to Tampa to advise his successor at CENTCOM, Tommy Franks, about the need to face up to the challenges of dealing with the failed state that might well follow the American invasion. That plan was thwarted when the Pentagon blocked the trip.[12] The Bush administration never studied Desert Crossing. Yet more than any other president, Bush keenly experienced the vicissitudes of the "inside-out" and "outside-in" options.

"There were two conflicting concepts at play for some time for what we would do after liberation," recalled Zalmay Khalilzad, the Afghan-born senior NSC staff member for Iraq and the highest-ranking Muslim in the Bush administration. "One idea was that we could form a government very quickly, à la Afghanistan. The competing narrative was 'No, we will govern ourselves for a while and transition ministries to the Iraqis as they get ready to take over responsibility. The Iraqi political exiles and some from inside will be appointed as advisers to us.'"

Khalilzad was very much in the first camp, as was, initially, the president himself. Bush had campaigned for the White House as a skeptic of the sort of nation-building the Clinton administration had undertaken in the Balkans, and the Bush administration's early months in Afghanistan had reinforced its belief that regime change could be carried out without a major commitment to reconstruction or lingering deployments. "He repeatedly said in meetings, 'We need to give this to the Iraqis as quickly as possible to form a government,'" said Khalilzad, who was responsible for taking the official notes of the president's meetings on Iraq. Rice, Bush's loyal national security adviser, was also fully on board.[13]

The American-led invasion force would pry Saddam's followers from the levers of power, snap enlightened technocrats into place, and quickly hand over responsibility to the new Iraqi authorities, who would be made up of exiles and internal players recruited after Saddam's fall. The changes in Iraq (and eventually the broader Middle East) that followed would be more like the sweeping transformation of Eastern Europe in 1989 than the prolonged and costly rebuilding of Germany after the Second World War. An oppressive, authoritarian regime would be removed, the liberated masses would breathe a sigh of relief, and new officials would grab hold of the levers of power and administer the new state.

Khalilzad, who had played an important behind-the-scenes role in the deliberations that elevated Hamid Karzai to power in Afghanistan after the Taliban were toppled, served as Bush's envoy to the Iraqi opposition. With one regime change already under his belt, Khalilzad would oversee the caucusing over the sort of government that should take over after Saddam was ousted, which began in London before the dictator was toppled.[14]

The closest Khalilzad would come to fulfilling his vision involved a helter-skelter episode during the early days of the American-led invasion in 2003, when American troops, to their surprise, encountered stiff opposition from the Fedayeen Saddam and the dictator's other paramilitary forces. The White House had dispatched Khalilzad to Ankara to keep the pressure on the Turks not to intervene in northern Iraq. Late one night, as he was holed up in a hotel in Ankara, he was woken up by a phone call from an agitated John Abizaid, the deputy head of CENTCOM, who wanted Khalilzad to slam his political plan into fast-forward.

Abizaid, an American general of Lebanese descent, had been convinced from the start that American troops would be an "antibody" in Iraqi society and had been looking for a way to put an Iraqi face on the American military campaign since its inception. Barking instructions, Abizaid told Khalilzad that he needed to round up the Iraqi exiles and bring them straightaway to Umm Qasr, the ramshackle port city at the southern tip of Iraq, so they could immediately stand up a new government. The Iraqi resistance to the American liberators was greater than anticipated and Abizaid was convinced that it was because they did not want to surrender to the Americans.

Khalilzad said that he needed to be sure the new government included not only exiles but also Iraqis in the country, and he was uncertain as to whom among them to invite. Abizaid brushed this consideration aside. "Those are goddamn details," the general bellowed. "It's about American lives. Today, this morning, it was discussed at an NSC meeting. The president has asked me to tell you this." Several days later, the American military juggernaut resumed its advance to Baghdad and White House interest in an Umm Qasr–based government vanished as quickly as it had materialized. Still, Khalilzad believed his strategy to quickly stand up a new Iraqi authority was on track and convened meetings with Iraqi exiles, sheikhs, and other leaders near Nasiriyah and, after Saddam was toppled, in Baghdad.[15]

Khalilzad's partner in those early meetings was Jay Garner, a retired three-star Army general with a background in air defense whose formative experience in Iraq was a humanitarian effort to help the Kurds in the wake of the 1991 Persian Gulf War. As the head of the Office for Reconstruction and Humanitarian Assistance (ORHA), Garner expected mainly more of the same. The mission was to cope with the expected flood of refugees and the oil field fires the Americans feared Saddam's henchmen would set, avert famine, and, in general, deal with the short-term dislocations that would be endured by what was presumed to be a largely grateful population. In keeping with his mandate, Garner planned to administer the country by assigning advisers to the government's ministries, which he projected would be intact; remove only senior members of the Baath Party; and quickly recall the Iraqi Army, which had dispersed in the face of the American-led onslaught, to help rebuild and secure the country—an approach endorsed by Bush himself in a March 12 National Security Council meeting and energetically supported by David McKiernan, the three-star general who led the land war command that oversaw the invasion.

Soon after American forces reached Baghdad, there were intimations that the White House thought the hardest part of the mission had been accomplished. During the first weeks of the occupation, Richard Armitage, the powerfully built deputy secretary of state and confidant of Secretary of State Colin Powell, received a call on the Red Phone that connected him to the White House. Stephen Hadley, Bush's assiduous deputy national security adviser who was known for always being prepared for anything the president might ask of him, wanted to know how the Pentagon had organized the victory parade for American forces following the 1991 Desert Storm campaign to evict Iraqi forces from Kuwait. Armitage discussed the call with Powell, who thought the question was odd and never got back to the White House.[16]

The civilians were not alone in thinking the main fight was over. On April 16, just a week after Baghdad fell, General Tommy Franks, the CENTCOM commander, told his subordinates that some form of Iraqi government would be functioning in thirty to sixty days. Franks's position was evident a few days later when General Richard Myers, the chairman of the Joint Chiefs of Staff, called Franks at his forward headquarters in Qatar, to let him know that he might need to defer his retirement from the military while the Pentagon sorted out some important personnel decisions, including who would serve as the next head of the Army and who would look after Iraq. "More than out of the question," Franks shouted, according to notes of the conversation taken by a military aide. "Not going home? Buttfuck me." It was not necessary, Franks added, to have the CENTCOM chief "doing three-star work." As far as Franks was concerned, the heavy lifting had been done. When it came to finding a new Army chief of staff, Franks said that the only way he would consider such a post was if Rumsfeld promoted him to five stars and made him General of the Army, a rank that had not existed since Omar Bradley. Myers rode out the outburst—he would later observe that Franks had "taken his pack off"—and by early July, John Abizaid had taken the reins from Franks at CENTCOM.[17]

It had always been envisaged that a former governor or ambassador would assume the lead role for the American mission in Iraq after Garner's ORHA had several months to address the country's humanitarian problems. But Iraq's infrastructure was in shambles after years of mismanagement and United Nations sanctions. Much of the middle class was gone. With the looting of Baghdad's ministries and the collapse of the fragile electrical grid after the toppling of the regime, the once seemingly all-powerful state had, much as Zinni forecast, fallen apart like a cheap suit. Seeking to bring order to the chaos of the occupation, the Bush administration decided to expedite the transition. On April 30, just two weeks after he arrived in Baghdad, Garner learned that he and his team were to be supplanted. L. Paul "Jerry" Bremer III was to take over the civilian mission.

Bremer had an impressive set of Washington credentials. During the span of his State Department career, he had worked for Henry Kissinger, led the department's counterterrorism bureau, and lately overseen a blue-ribbon commission on fighting terrorism. He was an amateur chef, a serious jogger, a faithful convert to Roman Catholicism, and looked a decade younger than his sixty-two years, but he had never served in the Middle East. For a White House wary of old Middle East hands—shades of Desert Crossing—who saw nothing but difficulties in carrying out Bush's project to bring democracy to Mesopotamia, that was not a minus. When Bremer was first interviewed by Bush for his Iraq post, he passed on a message from his wife, Francine, her favorite passage from the president's State of the Union address: "The liberty we prize is not America's gift to the world. It is God's gift to mankind."[18] Bush smiled and shook Bremer's hand, convinced that he had the right man.

In preparation for his post, Bremer pored over a RAND Corporation study of classic nation-building efforts, including those in Japan and Germany. The report had been given to him by his friend James Dobbins, a former State Department troubleshooter in Afghanistan, the Balkans, and other failed states. It encouraged Bremer's view that Iraq needed a dramatic reassertion of the American role and a substantial increase in American troops.[19] Before Bremer's selection was formally announced, Bush invited him to a one-on-one lunch at the White House. Bremer knew that Bush was a fitness buff, so, employing a sports metaphor, he told the president that Iraq was not going to be a hundred-yard sprint but a marathon, and alluded to the RAND report. Putting his trust in his newly appointed envoy, Bush told Bremer to take whatever time he needed. "We'll stay until the job is done," the president said, an assurance Bremer intended to take literally. As for more troops, the president was noncommittal but noted that his aides were soliciting troop contributions from allied nations.[20]

Khalilzad had planned to go to Baghdad with Bremer to introduce him to the Iraqi leaders with whom he had been meeting and to attend a conference he had already arranged for May 15 to form the new interim Iraqi government. But Bremer had no use for Khalilzad's conference or for Khalilzad himself. The intricate wheeling and dealing that Khalilzad had done in London, Kurdistan, Nasiriyah, and Baghdad to quickly stand up a new Iraqi authority was over. Bremer was not interested in presiding over the Iraqi equivalent of an Afghan Loya Jirga. Instead, like General MacArthur in Japan, Bremer would run Iraq as the head of an occupation authority while nurturing a Western-style government. So Bremer used his lunch with the president to stake out his position: the new Coalition Provisional Authority (CPA), as it was to be called, needed clean lines of authority with a single master. Khalilzad was not needed. Less than an hour before the White House announcement of Bremer's appointment, Khalilzad learned to his amazement that he would not be joining Bremer in Baghdad.

At the State Department, Colin Powell was just as taken aback. Before Bremer was picked, Powell had met with him in his seventh-floor office at the State Department and come away with the impression that he merely intended to be a more dynamic and articulate steward of the American project than the rumpled Garner. There was nothing in Bremer's presentation that suggested to the secretary of state that he was planning a radical departure from Khalilzad's mission or was planning to make himself the de facto, if provisional, government of Iraq. Powell called Rice and told her it was a mistake to exclude Khalilzad, one of the few American officials who knew the Iraqi players. But Rice responded that Bremer had set this as a condition for taking the job.[21] This was more than a personnel matter. A new phase in Iraq's governance had begun: the pendulum had radically swung to "outside-in."

Few diplomats had been given an opportunity to shape history on so grand a scale. Bremer's office in the Republican Palace, his new headquarters, featured a carved wooden sign: "Success Has a Thousand Fathers." But the organizational chart of his CPA was steeply vertical. Stomping around Iraq in a business suit and hiking boots, he was consumed by a sense of mission. There was an enormous amount to do, and those who challenged first principles were either sidestepped or rebuffed.

In an effort to raze the old political structures and clear the ground for the new state he was determined to erect, Bremer issued a decree just ten days after arriving in Iraq that barred officials who served in the top four ranks of the Baath Party from serving in the new Iraqi government. To the consternation of Abizaid and American commanders in Iraq, he followed that up with an edict to formally disband the Iraqi military and methodically build a new and considerably smaller force from scratch. Only three divisions, or some forty thousand troops, were to be recruited and trained during the first two years of the occupation, and they were to focus only on defending the nation from external enemies, not on putting down troublemakers at home.

Operating on the assumption that he had Bush's full support for an "outside-in" approach, Bremer also elaborated a seven-step, 540-day strategy to organize the drafting of a new Iraqi constitution, conduct a referendum on the final text, arrange for the Iraqis to lay down an election law, and, ultimately, hold national, regional, and local elections to seat a sovereign Iraqi government. The goal was nothing less than a representative and democratic state that would feature political parties, an independent media, an active civil society, including women's organizations, an impartial judicial system, and respect for human rights.[22]

In his first report to the White House, the CPA chief wrote that he had "re-launched" a political dialogue with Iraqi politicians, but on a new basis: there could be no hasty handover. "My message is that full sovereignty under an Iraqi government can come after democratic elections, which themselves must be based on a constitution agreed by all the people," Bremer wrote the president. "This process will take time."

"You have my full support and confidence," Bush wrote back. "We will fend off the impatient."[23] At the start, Bush gave Bremer enormous latitude to pursue his vision—so much so that neither the president nor his closest aides balked when Bremer told the president and his National Security Council in a videoconference that he was on the verge of issuing the decree to formally disband the army and security ministries, a move that stood the president's initial decision to vet and retain much of Iraq's armed forces on its head and that all but shut the door on the original scheme to quickly hand over control to the Iraqis. "I talked to Rice and said, 'Condi, what happened?'" recalled Powell, who was attending an international meeting in Paris when the May 22 NSC meeting was held. "And her reaction was: 'I was surprised, too, but it is a decision that has been made and the president is standing behind Jerry's decision. Jerry is the guy on the ground.' And there was no further debate about it."[24]

Some of the United States' closest allies, however, were concerned by the unyielding nature of Bremer's vision and the inflexibility of his tactics. Jeremy Greenstock, who as the British ambassador to the United Nations had helped the Bush administration shepherd the Iraq issue through the Security Council, got a taste of that when he arrived in Iraq in September to serve as Britain's top representative. Greenstock had met Bremer three decades before when Bremer was an aide to Kissinger and Greenstock was the private secretary of the British ambassador in Washington. But in Baghdad, Greenstock later told the official British government inquiry on the war, he found a changed man: an American envoy who was more conservative politically, more religious, less humorous, and more impatient.[25]

There were some early indications that the lengthy nation-building exercise Bremer intended might meet resistance from some of the Iraqis. A new Governing Council was being established to give the Iraqis a voice, but not a veto, in the decision making. In July, Bremer's chief of staff, Pat Kennedy, grabbed a rail-thin, newly arrived young American staffer from Houston named Ali Khedery and drove him to a compound that had previously been home to Saddam's vaunted Ministry of Military Industrialization in the Green Zone, the fortified international enclave that housed the CPA and the Iraqi government. Khedery, who was of Iraqi descent and was one of the handful of CPA aides who spoke fluent Arabic, was given two weeks to evict a U.S. Army colonel and his troops from the building, remove the dozens of murals of the omnipresent Saddam, have a twenty-five-person conference table custom-built, landscape the ruined grounds, and locate and install a generator in time for the first televised Governing Council meeting—all while Baghdad was wracked by looting, an emerging insurgency, and had no electricity.[26]

Over the coming year, the relations between Bremer's occupation authority and the Governing Council would prove tumultuous. While Khedery and his colleagues furnished Iraqi council members with offices, weapons, villas, cars, cell phones, and the highly prized Green Zone access badges, the Iraqis grew resentful of the foreigners' authority. On July 13, the day of the Governing Council's inaugural session, Ahmed Chalabi, the Iraqi exile who had helped beat the drums for war and had emerged as a major political player in postwar Iraq, was nearly prevented from attending the session by Kennedy, who insisted that there was no room inside the new compound for Chalabi's twenty-car convoy. More importantly, for some senior Iraqi politicians, providing advice to an American proconsul was not the sort of relationship they were looking for. "When he came he asked all of us, the political leaders, to see him in Baghdad," Massoud Barzani said of his first meeting with Bremer. As Barzani, who would later emerge as the president of the Kurdistan region of Iraq, recalled the encounter, Bremer told the Iraqis that he had come with the full support of the U.N. Security Council, was the legitimate authority in Iraq in the eyes of the international community under the law of occupation, and was considering uniting them in a consultative committee. As much as they did not like the concept of occupation, they should try to accept it. "We were all looking at each other like, 'What is he saying?'" Barzani said. "And then afterwards, I told him, 'I will be going back to [Kurdistan], I have nothing to do here. This is where my headquarters is, I am not based in Baghdad. If you need me, I'm there.'" With that, the Kurdish leader gathered up his retinue and left in a convoy of SUVs.[27]

Bremer flew north a few weeks later to coax the Kurdish leader back.

Upon arriving at Barzani's guesthouse, which had been the site of numerous plots to topple Saddam during the 1990s, Bremer asked Barzani, "Who is that guy in the painting?" Barzani remained silent and there was an awkward pause until an aide blurted out: "That's the late Mullah Mustafa Barzani, Massoud's father and the founding father of modern Iraqi Kurdistan. The U.S. government worked with him for decades."[28]

Grand Ayatollah Ali al-Husseini al-Sistani, the preeminent Shiite cleric in Iraq, was also concerned about the new governing arrangements. In July, Sergio Vieira de Mello, the Brazilian diplomat and veteran United Nations official who was dispatched to run the first U.N. mission in Iraq, and his deputy, Jamal Benomar, met with Sistani. Vieira de Mello began the meeting by talking about the advisory body Bremer had established to give the Iraqis a voice in the CPA's decisions, which following the U.N. envoy's recommendation, had been given an important-sounding name, the "Governing Council." Sistani, however, was focused on a much more fundamental issue. He did not trust the Americans and their anointed representatives to draft the nation's constitution, a central provision of Bremer's plan, and insisted that only Iraqis who were elected could play that role. Bremer would need to back away from that element of his plan, Sistani suggested, and if he did not, the cleric implied he might issue a fatwa against it.

Sistani's arguments were conveyed to Bremer, who thought he would find a way to mollify the ayatollah. But they made more of an impression on Greenstock, who had previously served in Saudi Arabia and Dubai and was more inclined to give weight to the views of prominent clerics. When Powell visited Baghdad in September and met with Bremer and Greenstock, the British diplomat used the occasion to argue that the seven-step plan the CPA had hatched should not be considered sacrosanct. "Bremer brought up, under Powell's questioning, the political process, and I said, because I wanted to get the point across to Powell, we must also think about how we handle Iraqi resistance to this, particularly with Sistani, we may need some alternative approaches," Greenstock told the British inquiry. "And Bremer shouted at me in front of Powell, '[T]he President has decided on the seven steps. This is our approach. Either you give me loyalty—I don't want to hear talk about alternative approaches—or we find some other way of working together,' and Powell changed the subject. He was quite surprised."[29]

Powell, indeed, was struck by the session. He found it distasteful that Bremer had dressed down a diplomat from the United States' most loyal ally and compounded the indignity by doing so in front of a visiting secretary of state. It was not just the substance of the issue that bothered Powell. The tone suggested that the mission was not under control.

The switch from the strategy of a speedy transition to a prolonged and intensive rebuilding of the Iraqi state caught the commanders in the field by surprise and laid the groundwork for persistent friction between the military and Bremer's CPA. Major General Ricardo "Rick" Sanchez had entered Iraq as commander of the last-arriving division, but after Rumsfeld soured on overall ground commander Lieutenant General Dave McKiernan, Sanchez was promoted to three-star rank and took the helm of a new Iraq headquarters, Combined Joint Task Force 7. The most junior three-star general in the Army was now running its largest combat operation. Abizaid advised Sanchez to stand "shoulder-to-shoulder" with the hard-charging Bremer. But it took months for Sanchez's military command to figure out that their vision and Bremer's differed profoundly.

In July, Sanchez's aides put together a six-month plan, which was more of a series of PowerPoint slides than a detailed counterinsurgency campaign. The United States was to "defeat internal armed threats," disarm the militias running around Iraq, and find the supposed caches of WMD that military and intelligence experts still thought might exist. By February 2004, the main responsibility for securing the country was to be transferred to the Iraqis. Sanchez figured that he would probably leave Iraq by then. The word was that he would be tapped to serve as the first Hispanic head of SOUTHCOM, the four-star command that oversaw South and Central America. In effect, the military command's policy remained "inside-out" even as the civilian viceroy's had changed to "outside-in."[30]

"[Sanchez] was supposedly going to be a caretaker commander," Lieutenant Colonel Bjarne "Mike" Iverson, Sanchez's political-military adviser, later told a military historian in a classified interview. "When we did those plans in July of '03, they were thinking that six months later, things would be back to normal and we would be moving out of there," he added. "How they thought that the Iraqis would be ready to take over those institutions, all of their ministries, and the defense and security of the country, when we had just disbanded the very apparatus that had been running it for the past thirty-five years is beyond me, but that's what we did."[31]

CHAPTER 2

Politics of the Gun

The first few weeks of the occupation in the spring of 2003 had been deceptively quiet. Looters had picked the ministries clean down to the electrical wiring and even ransacked decades of weather records. Many Iraqis, however, had been too stunned by the sudden appearance of American tanks in their streets to know how to respond and were sitting on the fence waiting to see what their liberators had in mind. By June, that started to change.

The first inkling Mike Iverson had that American forces were contending with something more than the usual postwar mayhem came as he was driving with his sergeant major on Baghdad's traffic-clogged streets. Coming upon a tangled mass of metal, Iverson found two dead Americans, one of whose brains were splattered across the highway. "It was a pretty brutal scene," Iverson recalled. "We went in and picked up what we could and put the parts in MRE bags."[1] It was only later that Iverson learned the destruction had been caused by a weapon that had not been seen before in his part of Baghdad: an improvised explosive device, or IED. Before long these homemade bombs would become the war's signature weapon and the greatest killer of American troops.

As the insurgency grew in strength, Abizaid asked his staff to determine just whom the American-led coalition was fighting. As they grappled with the question, one senior analyst was advised that the Defense Department did not welcome references to "the resistance," a term that some Pentagon officials appeared to think gave the insurgents some sort of legitimacy.[2] Abizaid avoided the terminological minefield but made headlines nonetheless when he declared at a press conference shortly after taking over from Tommy Franks in July that the United States was confronted with a "classical guerrilla-type campaign" and cautioned that year-long troop deployments were possible.[3] It was a far cry from the "pockets of dead-enders" Rumsfeld had described just one month prior.[4]

In Baghdad, much of the burden of figuring out what was going on with the budding insurgency fell on Colonel Derek Harvey. Mild-mannered but fiercely independent, Harvey had served as an intelligence officer for Dave McKiernan during the invasion and stayed on to help Sanchez, who had assumed the command of Combined Joint Task Force 7 with a handful of trusted aides, no interpreter, and few of the resources that would be needed to run a major military operation for an extended occupation.

Installed as the head of the intelligence cell that was to decipher the enemy threat, Harvey was given a double-width trailer at the sprawling American military base near the airport, a small staff, and several vehicles. At times, Harvey seemed to have the weight of Iraq on his shoulders. An American embassy official later noted in his memoir that Harvey seemed to be "so worried about what was going on in Iraq that it was hard to look at him."[5]

Digging through the classified data, Harvey discovered that the situation was even worse than it seemed. In a classified assessment he prepared in early 2004, Harvey examined the official number of attacks Sanchez's command had recorded—"significant activities" or SIGACTS in the argot of the military—and concluded they represented a substantial undercount. A fair number of insurgent attacks on Iraqi forces—what the military called "Red-on-Green"—and even some terrorist strikes had been left out of the count for the simple reason that United States troops had not been around to witness them. Harvey offered some vivid examples: an explosion that demolished a police station in Suwayra, which killed four police officers, and the bombing of the Sheraton Hotel in Baghdad. It was as if the American command believed that if a tree fell in the forest and nobody was around to hear it a sound had not been made.

Harvey's analysis as to just who was unleashing these attacks was even more disconcerting. Debriefs of Saddam and his inner circle after their capture, as well as a treasure trove of captured records, also made it clear that the Iraqi leader had not anticipated the Bush administration's decision to march on Baghdad. First and foremost, Saddam was worried about the sort of Shiite and Kurdish uprisings that erupted in 1991 when an American-led coalition reversed his invasion of Kuwait. As for external threats, the Iraqi dictator had considered Iran his primary adversary, which accounted for his reluctance to be completely transparent about the dormant state of his once-thriving WMD programs.

Taking steps to avoid another insurrection, Saddam expanded paramilitary organizations like the Fedayeen Saddam and the Baath Party militia. Networks of safe houses and arms caches for the paramilitary forces, including materials for making improvised explosives, were also established throughout the country. If the Shiites or Kurds mounted another rebellion, the regime's paramilitary forces would hold its enemies at bay until the Iraqi Army and Air Force could be brought in to establish order. It was, in effect, a counterinsurgency strategy to fend off what Saddam saw as the most serious threats to his rule.

But the preparations Saddam had made to put down a Shiite or Kurdish insurrection also had an unintended effect that haunted the Americans during the early months of their occupation: weapons, explosives, safe houses, and paramilitary fighters were distributed throughout Iraq. The force Saddam had established to conduct counterinsurgency against his internal foes had morphed into an insurgency all its own. In fashioning its initial Iraq strategy, Bush administration officials had hoped to piggyback on Iraq's institutions and bureaucracy to build a new Iraq. That hope had vanished in the chaotic first weeks of the occupation: now, it was the insurgents who were using the instruments of the collapsed state to take on the Americans.

Taping sheets of butcher-block paper to the walls of his trailer, Harvey and his team began to trace the complex interrelationships among the former denizens of Saddam's regime, the jihadists sneaking into the country, the tribes who were sympathetic to the brewing insurgency, and Al-Qaeda's affiliate in Iraq, a group called Tawhid wal-Jihad. The results were included in a classified assessment entitled "Sunni Arab Resistance: Politics of the Gun."[6] The very title suggested that the insurgency had legitimacy in the eyes of many Sunnis and roots in the Sunni community. Harvey reported that when Saddam was toppled, there were 65,000 to 95,000 Special Republican Guard officers, Iraqi Intelligence Service officers, Fedayeen Saddam paramilitary forces, Baath Party militia, and the like who had gone to ground in and around Baghdad.

Even the front companies Saddam had set up to evade the United Nations provided some handy relationships, as did the organized crime tolerated by the regime. The family of Izzat Ibrahim al-Duri—Saddam's vice president, one of the handful of plotters who had brought the Baath Party to power in Iraq, and the King of Clubs in the famous deck of cards the Americans had distributed in their hunt for remnants of the regime—had operated a stolen car ring during Saddam's years in power that smuggled vehicles from Europe through the Jordanian port of Aqaba. Now that very car theft network, complete with auto body shops, had been pressed into service to supply vehicles for car bombs and suicide attacks.

Other Saddam survival mechanisms had also become valuable tools for the insurgents, Harvey concluded. Saddam's intelligence agents had infiltrated the mosques, the better to keep tabs on the fundamentalist Islamic movements that the secular Iraqi dictator had tried to mollify with small gestures—"God is Great," in Saddam's handwriting, had been added to the Iraqi flag in 1991—and that he feared might pose a danger to his rule. Now they were using that network to funnel suicide drivers into Iraq from Yemen, Saudi Arabia, Sudan, North Africa, and Syria.[7] The practice had been documented in October when insurgents carried out suicide car bomb attacks on five police stations in Baghdad. One attacker had survived when the bomb he was carrying failed to detonate, and American intelligence had traced his movements to a house in Ramadi, which was controlled by Sulayman al-Khalafawi, a brigadier general in Saddam's military who had penetrated the religious institutions in Anbar Province.

Saddam's security services had also established relationships with terrorist groups to monitor their activities and pursue some of the regime's enemies. According to Harvey's analysis, one member of Saddam's Special Republican Guard who was involved in the terrorist training was Muhammad Khairi al-Barhawi, who, captured documents indicated, had been training the Egyptian Islamic Jihad, the Palestinian Jihad, and Algerian groups before the American invasion. Barhawi had been installed as the police chief in Mosul during the early part of the American occupation but later played a role in helping the Sunni insurgency operate in northern Iraq, Harvey assessed. This assertion, which was never publicly disclosed, was one of Harvey's most controversial conclusions. During his year in Mosul as commander of the 101st Airborne Division, Major General David Petraeus had worked closely with Barhawi and was adamant that the police chief had initially worked with the Americans in good faith until he came under pressure from the insurgents to shift to the dark side.[8]

Iraq's tribes also figured heavily in Saddam's strategy to stifle challenges to his rule. Saddam and his aides decided that it would be asking too much to try to disarm the tribes and that they should instead be allowed to keep weapons as long as they worked with the regime. The tribes provided a potential pool of manpower for the insurgents as well.[9]

Two of the insurgency's major brains, Harvey argued, were Izzat Ibrahim al-Duri and Muhammad Yunis al-Ahmed, ranking Baathists who had been given refuge in Damascus and were trying to guide the insurgency from there. Harvey did not argue that the insurgency had a monolithic and hierarchical structure, but he did see the sanctuary former Baathists enjoyed in Syria as important.

Not everybody in the intelligence community accepted Harvey's points. The CIA held to the view that the insurgency was largely an indigenous reaction against the American occupation and tended to denigrate the "Syrian brain theory," as some analysts called it.[10] Major General Stan McChrystal, the commander of Joint Special Operations Command (JSOC), gave much more weight to the efforts of Abu Musab al-Zarqawi, a thirty-seven-year-old Jordanian terrorist leader his troops were hunting in Anbar.[11] Zarqawi had begun his career as a militant in Afghanistan, but had been turned away by Ansar al-Islam, the Al-Qaeda-linked terrorist group in northern Iraq, when he entered the country in 2002 and sought to play a dominant role in the organization. Now he had struck out on his own as the leader of Tawhid wal-Jihad, which sought to become Iraq's franchise of Al-Qaeda; the group had been responsible for some of the earliest suicide bombings against civilian targets in Baghdad.

Still, there was no question that Iraq's overmilitarized society and a plethora of paramilitary and intelligence organizations Saddam had established provided the foundation for a well-trained and disciplined insurgency. Some of the insurgents, Harvey established, had even been involved in the former regime's "Gafiki project" to develop IEDs and small backpack-size bombs, skills that had a diabolical utility in the campaign against the occupiers.

Beyond the order of battle, there was every reason to think that the insurgency would not be easily defeated. After more than fifty years of rule, the Sunnis were angry that they had been displaced from the top strata of Iraqi society and were fearful that they would be marginalized politically. The Sunnis comprised no more than 20 percent of Iraq's population but, Harvey noted, were "concentrated in the geostrategic heartland of Iraq," which enabled them to pose a powerful challenge to a new Iraqi state. Mao Zedong had famously observed that guerrillas needed to move among the people the way fish swim in the ocean. By 2004, the Sunni insurgents who were making war on the American-led coalition and the Iraqi government appeared increasingly to be maneuvering in a warm and inviting sea.

Nobody in the military command, Harvey concluded, seemed to have a good handle on just how many Sunni insurgents the American-led coalition might be fighting. The initial estimate during the summer of 2003 was that the insurgents were some three thousand strong, but the United States had detained more than ten thousand in Abu Ghraib, the massive prison where allegations of abuse would soon arise, and killed many others. "It is like mowing the grass," Harvey noted in his brief. "When we take down operations and cells the capability tends to return to an area over time." Numbers aside, the insurgents had been extraordinarily adaptive. They had started out with primitive roadside bombs and moved to ones with remote-control detonators, antitampering devices, and multiple charges.

It did not take long before they had the American command center itself in their sights: a captured insurgent map provided a detailed lay-down of Camp Victory, the American headquarters by Baghdad Airport, with notes about when the soldiers gathered for meals at the dining hall. As the Americans sought to stiffen their defense, the insurgents shifted to softer targets, including Iraqi forces. The campaign of intimidation had forced the resignation of the mayor and police chief in Haditha. Indeed, the violence directed at Iraqis was far worse than anything the Americans had to contend with. More Iraqis had been killed in the month of February than Americans in the war to date, Harvey noted.

The American military's inability to establish security was an enormous burden for Bremer, since it jeopardized the United States' efforts to restore electricity and rebuild the economy, and even made it difficult for CPA civilians to get around the country. During the early months of the occupation, the military and the CPA were involved in a dialogue of the deaf. The civilians complained there was only so much they could do unless a modicum of security was established.

The military, for its part, argued that the civilians' failure to jump-start the economy, and put a dent in Iraq's soaring unemployment, provided legions of potential recruits for the metastasizing insurgency. From the lowliest captain to the generals in the field, most military officials believed that Bremer's decision to dismantle the Iraqi security forces and methodically build a new three-division army from scratch over a two-year period was little more than a self-inflicted wound, and that the Iraqi soldiers who had gone AWOL could have been recalled.

The military's frustrations came to a head in a closed-door meeting of American commanders, which was convened by General Abizaid during a September 2003 trip to Iraq. According to confidential records of the meeting, Major General Martin Dempsey, the commander of the 1st Armored Division in Baghdad, who would later be picked by Barack Obama to serve as chairman of the Joint Chiefs, said that he had thought that many of the insurgents his soldiers were confronting were foreign jihadists but the detainees they had captured during Operation Longstreet, a series of raids in and around Baghdad, had shaken that assumption. Of the 550 insurgents the division had captured, only 9 were foreigners, an ominous indication that much of the problem was a budding native insurgency among the Sunni Arab minority that had been unseated from power. Some of the insurgents, Dempsey added, had become so confident that they had begun to keep meticulous records of their attacks, calculating that they would be rewarded when the Americans were routed and Saddam was back in power.

Colonel David Teeples, whose 3rd Armored Cavalry Regiment had been saddled with a huge swath of territory that the invasion force had bypassed in the Sunni province of Anbar, complained that the CPA had failed to provide the radios, weapons, vehicles, and even uniforms it had promised to the local police that his soldiers were trying hard to stand up. The regiment kept ordering supplies from the CPA to no avail. Unless the province had police, the Iraqis would not be able to protect themselves or help the Americans secure their supply lines. More importantly, the CPA's lapses, Teeples said, were undermining his unit's credibility with the Iraqis.

David Petraeus, whose 101st Airborne Division was in Nineveh Province and who would later emerge as Obama's choice to run the CIA, had some problems of his own. Taking advantage of his distance from CPA headquarters in Baghdad and his recent experience in Bosnia, Petraeus had made a push to get the local government up and running, picked a police chief, opened a trade route to Syria, and, in general, mounted his own brand of nation-building. Petraeus had preached that the money commanders were authorized to spend for civil projects was ammunition. The slowness in getting those funds replenished—Petraeus called them "reloads"—was killing the credibility of his soldiers with the Iraqis. Nor was Petraeus happy with the performance of Bremer's representative in the region, noting that the head of the CPA office in the north had identified ten or so projects to improve the supply of electricity and gone on leave without taking any action. It seemed to take a crisis, Petraeus complained, to get any action by the CPA. Already, there was a three-month backlog in pay for teachers. When it came time to replace his unit, the Pentagon needed to dispatch more soldiers who could do "engagement work," such as civil affairs units. It was an implicit criticism that the Pentagon did not have the right doctrine and had not sent the right mix of troops.

Major General Ray Odierno, the towering two-star commander of the 4th Infantry Division and future chief of staff of the Army, who was head-quartered in Saddam's old stomping ground in Tikrit north of Baghdad, expressed frustration with the CPA's rigid de-Baathification policies, its decision to abolish the Iraqi military, and its big-ticket approach to recon-struction, which steered projects to large foreign corporations but failed to generate many jobs for the Iraqis. Odierno told Abizaid that he had been in touch with a Sunni former general who was looking for a way to be part of the solution. Some way, he cautioned, had to be found to bring the Sun-nis into the political process. Most of the Iraqis in his area were sitting on the fence and could throw their support behind either side if progress was not made. Odierno would later be criticized for some of the heavy-handed tactics his division employed as it struggled to contend with a brewing insurgency. But he was also anxious to give the Sunnis, including former Baathists, some sort of stake in the new Iraq. "If they can't get jobs, they will turn on us," Odierno warned, according to the notes of a participant. "If we are not going to solve it by paying them we might as well arrest them right now," he added with exasperation.[12]

In Odierno'a area, Army Special Forces troops had seen an opportunity to work with former Baathists come and go. Along with CIA officers and more than four dozen other Special Forces troops, Major Mark Grdovic had snuck into northern Iraq from Turkey before the invasion to link up with Kurdish forces. (In two cases, the Special Forces troops found them-selves in firefights well before the war officially began.) After the fall of the northern city of Kirkuk in April, Grdovic spent hours on the phone talking to Iraqi generals in Tikrit. The Special Forces drafted a formal letter and sent it to a number of Iraqi generals offering them a place in the new Iraq. Many were open to the idea, calling Grdovic and other Special Forces offi-cers to ask for assurances that they and their men would not be harmed. But when higher echelons decided that the Special Forces could not make such arrangements, the deals fell through, and the CPA order disbanding the old army put the nail in the coffin. Grdovic was convinced that some of his contacts joined the insurgency when the offer was pulled away. "They would say, 'All right my friend, this is the last time we will speak, and I wish you luck in the hard times to come,' and hang up," he recalled.[13]

As Bremer sought to realize his master plan, however, one of his immedi-ate challenges was not in Iraq but in Washington, where opposition was already beginning to build within the Bush administration over his ambitious and time-consuming version of the "outside-in" approach. Before returning to Washington to testify to Congress on the billions of dollars of new reconstruction money the Bush administration planned to spend on Iraq, Bremer published on September 8 an op-ed in the *Washington Post*—"Iraq's Path to Sovereignty"—outlining his seven-step plan.[14]

Bremer had stated the intricacies of his plan in internal cables and discussions, but with casualties on the rise and the American involvement in Iraq growing increasingly complex and deeper by the day, what Bremer considered a mere account of his position in the article seemed to strike the Defense Department like a thunderclap. Bremer had not proposed the quick in-and-out war that the Pentagon had hoped for, but an occupation plan that some Defense Department officials feared would take two or even three years. It was less akin to the post–Soviet Union awakening in 1989, in which the newly liberated populations of Eastern Europe willingly took over the machinery of their states, and more like the laborious postwar nation-building exercise that the United States had carried out in Japan and Germany after World War II. Bremer had told Bush the process would be a marathon; now not everybody wanted to join the race.

At the White House, Condoleezza Rice was becoming uneasy. As national security adviser, she had been more of a coordinator than an architect and had to contend with men with outsized egos—Rumsfeld, Vice President Dick Cheney, Powell—each of whom had thought at one time that he should be president. But Rice understood Bush and was doing her best to advance his vision. While she was an apostle of the president's "freedom agenda," Bremer's grand plan appeared to portend more of a financial, military, and political burden than the Bush administration had bargained for, and was ill-suited to the Pentagon's wish to keep the occupying force to a bare minimum. Broad swaths of Iraqi territory, including Anbar, were only thinly occupied. Violence was on the rise and the Iraqis who were supposed to begin the much-ballyhooed constitutional drafting effort were falling behind schedule. Bush had told Bremer he could have the time he needed, and over the long, hot summer of 2003 the CPA chief had heard nothing to indicate that the president was unhappy with his schedule. But now, Rice confided to her aides, the White House had come to the conclusion that it had signed on to a wrong timeline.[15]

On September 13 Rumsfeld called Bremer with an idea: the United States should immediately confer sovereignty on the Iraqis. In effect, the secretary of defense was reviving Khalilzad's "inside-out" position to which Bush himself had initially adhered, by advocating a quick handover to Iraqi rule. Bremer, however, was not about to surrender his vision and sought to head off the defense secretary's brainstorm with a memo entitled "No Quick Fix on Sovereignty."[16] Handing over control to Iraqi Governing Council members who had been brought in to advise the occupation authority but who had "no popular support" would be a blunder, Bremer argued. The CPA chief thought Rumsfeld had accepted the point, but when Bremer traveled to Washington in late September to testify to Congress and consult with the administration, Rumsfeld invited him to his house for a Sunday night chat and reargued the issue.[17]

In early October, Rice moved to grab back a measure of control from Bremer by establishing a "stabilization group" to coordinate the administration's Iraq policy and arranged for Robert Blackwill, a colleague from the George H. W. Bush administration who had served as George W. Bush's ambassador to India, to be named as the White House point man on Iraq. Richard Armitage and Colin Powell had cautioned against the move. Blackwill was smart and savvy, no doubt, and had enjoyed an impressive academic career at Harvard, but he had a volcanic temper and had browbeaten the embassy staff in New Delhi so hard that the State Department had mounted an internal investigation and even dispatched a psychiatrist to inquire about the emotional health of the New Delhi diplomatic team. For Rice, Blackwill had the confidence and bureaucratic wiles to deal with Bremer and she was firm regarding her choice. Bremer learned of the move when his son called to say he had just read about it in the newspaper.[18]

Bremer was scheduled to return to Washington again in October and Rice convened her senior aides on October 15 to discuss the next steps. "We already know that we are on a schedule that won't work," said Rice, according to notes of a participant. Blackwill, Rice said, needed to plant the notion with Bremer so that he would think that any changes to the plan were his idea. It was imperative, she stressed, to "camouflage Plan B."[19]

In the meantime, Rice said, the White House planned to press George Tenet, the CIA director, to step up his efforts to find out what was happening on the ground. Colonel Marty Sullivan, a Marine assigned to the NSC, and Frank Miller, the staff member in charge of defense issues, were reading through the tactical reports that the units were filing in Iraq and were convinced that Bremer and Rumsfeld had not been giving the White House the entire story. Rice encouraged them to press their contacts for information and to report their findings to her. She also instituted a nightly report for Bush—the POTUS Iraq note—which Harriet Miers, the White House counsel, stipulated be no longer than four pages long. The document was intended to provide the president with the most reliable and up-to-date reporting and was in great demand during the 2004 presidential campaign as White House officials worried about the political reaction to the rising casualty count.[20]

The White House's determination to modify Bremer's prolonged timeline for achieving a sovereign government in Iraq set the stage for a high-stakes, behind-the-scenes debate. Less than four months before, Rumsfeld had played the central role in supporting Bremer for his post, and had arranged for the CPA chief to report to the president though the Pentagon. But now the two strong-willed executives were at odds over the most fundamental goals of the American occupation.

The CPA chief was coming around to the view that Rumsfeld and the hard-liners in the Defense Department had sold Bush a bill of goods: an Iraq invasion that would be quick and easy with all the hard problems shifted to a fledgling Iraqi government, including Ahmed Chalabi, that was hardly up to the task. The military, Bremer worried, was also beginning to back Rumsfeld's stance, if only to alleviate the burden on its overstretched forces. To maintain substantial force levels, the military was looking at a twelve-brigade rotation in the spring of 2004, which would need to include a substantial number of National Guard units—no small political or military risk for an administration heading toward a presidential election.

Rumsfeld and his deputies had their own suspicions. Bremer, they complained privately, had hijacked the Iraq mission and was expanding its political goals far beyond what the president and most of his team had ever anticipated. The hard-charging CPA administration was no longer an instrument of Pentagon policy and was acting with extraordinary autonomy and publishing op-eds without Defense Department sanction. Bremer, in effect, had become his own Rumsfeld.[21]

As soon as he returned to Washington on October 27, Bremer plunged into two days of meetings at the Pentagon, the details of which he chronicled in letters to his wife. Paul Wolfowitz, the deputy defense secretary who was one of the foremost advocates of regime change in Iraq and Bush's freedom agenda, had prepared a paper arguing for handing over sovereignty to the Iraqis on April 9, 2004—the one-year anniversary of the toppling of the statue of Saddam in Firdos Square and the capture of Baghdad by the American-led coalition, and Rumsfeld used the sessions to throw his weight behind the proposal. Operating within the strictures of the Wolfowitz plan, there would be an interim prime minister and, Rumsfeld also insisted, an interim national assembly, which the defense secretary argued would broaden the political base of the government and make it possible for the Sunnis to be more involved. But there was no time to organize and conduct elections before handing over sovereignty. The prime minister and assembly would need to either be appointed by Bremer or be named by the Governing Council, the panel of Iraqis who had themselves been appointed by the Americans. Pluralism, not direct democracy, would be the initial goal. The main point would be to take the sting out of the occupation for the Iraqis by committing the United States to a fast track to sovereignty, which the defense secretary calculated would allow the American military to shrink its footprint in Iraq, reduce American casualties, and find a way out of the morass.

Bremer was hardly persuaded. As soon as the Americans conferred sovereignty on the Iraqis, he argued, they would lose control of the political process. It was the same dilemma that had been identified in the Desert Crossing war game. How was the CPA supposed to fulfill Bush's vision of a democratic Iraq if the reins were turned over to the Iraqis before they had a post-Saddam constitution and the legal and political framework were established? Nor did Bremer see how proclaiming that Iraq was sovereign would stop the insurgency. The insurgents would simply make the new Iraqi government their target.

Frustrated by Rumsfeld's attempts at political engineering, Bremer asked what powers the unelected legislature that the defense secretary proposed to establish was supposed to have. "Whatever you say they should be," Rumsfeld shot back. Bremer said that since he thought the Pentagon plan was a poor idea, he had no clue as to what the legislature's powers should be. The defense secretary responded tartly by encouraging Bremer to be creative and think of some. Attempting to meet Rumsfeld partway, Bremer argued that he could speed up his plan and wrap up the CPA's mission by December 2004, but insisted there was no point in discussing the Wolfowitz plan in detail, as he could not support its assumptions.

Having agreed to disagree at the Pentagon, Bremer took his case the next day to the Principals Committee, a cabinet-level body that included the most senior policymakers in the government, excepting the president. As the meeting got under way, Vice President Cheney asked the crucial question: how would speeding up the handover to the Iraqis lead to a reduction of attacks by the insurgents? The insurgents were not concerned with such legal niceties as whether the United States was formally an occupying power; they wanted to frustrate the broader American project in Iraq.

Then the discussion got down to specifics as Bremer presented the two options from the Pentagon debate, identifying them only as "Option A," which entailed sticking with Bremer's program through December 2004, and "Option B," which was the Wolfowitz plan. Powell was quick to note one drawback of "Option B": it was similar to the plan to end the American occupation and hand over authority to the Governing Council that the French had pitched at the United Nations and that the United States had managed to block just the week before. In his determination to put an end to the occupation, Wolfowitz had inadvertently found himself aligned with the French foreign minister, an odd pairing given France's opposition to the American invasion. For her part, Rice zeroed in on the need to adjust Bremer's schedule so as to end as soon as possible the status of American troops as "occupiers." After the principals staked out their positions, Bremer gave his recommendation, arguing that "Option A," extending the CPA mission through December 2004, was the most likely to fulfill Bush's vision.

The issue was put on the docket of the National Security Council for October 29, which meant that Bush himself would preside. The president was well informed on the debate and, after hearing the options, suggested a compromise. "Perhaps there is something between 'Option A' and 'Option B,'" he said. Then seeking to rally his team, lest anybody conclude that the White House was backing away from its vision, Bush said that he was determined to do the right thing. The United States would succeed in Iraq and its success there would change the world. Nobody should doubt it. The United States might not be able to demonstrate success by the time of the next presidential election in the United States, but so be it. The president insisted that he did not care what the media said and was prepared to live with the political consequences.

After the NSC meeting broke up, Rice met privately with Bremer in her office, which, sports fan that she was, was festooned with helmets and other football paraphernalia. The Pentagon, she told Bremer, appeared to be panicked by the long road it saw ahead in Iraq and was looking for a way out. Rice said that she also wanted to get out of the occupation phase as quickly as possible but understood that this was difficult. Then hammering the president's point home, Rice asked if Bremer could work on the compromise plan Bush alluded to, which she called "Option A Prime." In her discussions with Blackwill, Rice had dubbed the fallback scheme she was prodding Bremer to devise "camouflaged Plan B." But now that she was alone with the CPA chief she was trying to put the best face on the option to secure his support.

Bremer capped off the day by accepting Bush's invitation to come by the Oval Office so they could hit the White House gym and continue the conversation. After the workout, Bremer shared his apprehensions about the Pentagon. The military, he complained, had the tendency to treat Iraqi policemen as if they were as competent as American soldiers when it chronicled the number of boots on the ground in Iraq. The numbers game seemed designed to strengthen the case for withdrawing U.S. forces, but it was grossly misleading. There was no way a fresh Iraqi recruit with a few weeks of training was the equal of a trooper in the 101st Airborne. Warming to his subject, Bremer continued his lament. Abizaid had expressed the hope during the NSC meeting that the coalition would deal a body blow to the insurgents over three months, but Bremer said that, too, appeared calculated to minimize the need for another American troop rotation. The problem, Bremer insisted, was not the CPA's policies, but the fact that the military was not finding and killing enough bad guys. Too much of the intelligence effort, he added, was still devoted to finding out what happened to the supposed WMD. In public, Bremer seemed determined and even stoic. But alone with the commander in chief, he confessed that he was afraid that he was being set up by the Pentagon as the fall guy: the one who stubbornly refused to end a difficult occupation and, thus, prolonged an increasingly unpopular war.

Bush said he had not thought of that possibility and told him not to worry. The president had his back, and the United States was not going to fail in Iraq. But Bremer was not off the hook. When it came to the project of building democracy in Iraq, there would need to be an "Option A Prime."[22]

In early November, Blackwill traveled to Iraq to take the pulse of the country and the American effort there. The weeks around his visit would be marked by a dismaying series of firsts. November 7 saw the first reported use of a remotely controlled IED, in an attack on an American military convoy in Baghdad. Five days later, in the first successful attack against a coalition base, a dozen Italian soldiers were killed in Nasiriyah when a truck breached the perimeter of their compound, enabling a car packed with explosives to slip through the gap.[23] Car and truck bombs like this would become so common that they were given their own military acronym: VBIEDs, for vehicle-borne IEDs. The violence was not limited to the ground. During the first six months of the occupation, six helicopters were lost, mainly in the Taji, Yusifiyah, and Fallujah areas surrounding

Baghdad; in a two-week period in October and November, three helicopters were downed by shoulder-fired SA-16 missiles, including a Chinook crash that killed sixteen troops. Cargo planes taking off from Baghdad International Airport came under fire as well, although without success: on November 22, a civilian A-300 transport was hit on the wing by an SA-7 shoulder-fired missile, and two weeks later one of the military's huge gray C-17s was damaged by a more advanced SA-14.[24]

When Blackwill returned to the White House to brief the NSC, on the security front he reported that the situation was "very grim." In Baghdad, the insurgents appeared to be operating around every corner. The CPA was "an embattled island in a hostile city," and Bremer's personal security precautions were so stringent they resembled those of the president.[25] The Americans sorely lacked intelligence about what was going on in the country, and the best intelligence officers and generals in the Iraqi armed forces had fled the country fearing reprisal. The buzz on the street was that the United States would soon withdraw as well. In a disturbing allusion to Vietnam, Blackwill quoted John McNaughton, the Pentagon aide to Robert McNamara, who once observed that he had "signed up on the wrong side—the side that's going to lose this war."[26] The parallels to Vietnam continued: Blackwill noted that porous borders were allowing a highly motivated and organized enemy to enter the country with the goal of attacking the United States' political will. As for Bremer's CPA, all decisions had to be personally approved by him. The plan to write a new constitution had ground to a halt. Sistani's concerns had registered with the Governing Council, which had no desire for a confrontation with the cleric in Najaf. Effectively, Blackwill observed, Sistani was dictating the constitutional process.

There was little Bremer could do to address security concerns. His task was to develop "Option A Prime." Bremer's governance team had already determined that a fallback plan to hand over sovereignty might be needed and had drafted ideas to shift the strategy. Based on his conversations in Washington, he now told them that he needed a plan that would let the occupation wind down by the end of June—six months before Bremer's most optimistic deadline. Yielding to Rumsfeld's demand, Bremer agreed that a transitional national assembly would be established, which in turn would settle on a transitional prime minister. The rest of Bremer's democracy-building program, including the all-important national elections, would need to come later. The Iraqi leaders' agreement to draft an interim constitution gave Bremer the confidence to move forward.

But, not all the members of Bremer's inner circle were happy with "Option A Prime." Meghan O'Sullivan, a young former academic and policy aide at the State Department who had emerged as one of Bremer's closest advisers on Iraqi governance, had agreed that there needed to be a quicker route to Iraqi sovereignty. But she was not pleased with the way Washington had gone about it. Distressed by the postponement of elections, she fired off a memo to her boss warning that the Bush administration's enterprise in Iraq was at risk. An unelected government would lack legitimacy. Iraqis would interpret the new policy as a sign that the United States was not willing to trust Iraqi voters to pick their own leaders.[27]

On November 9, Bremer hopped a flight out of Iraq on a C-141 filled with wounded soldiers. Meeting with Bush the next day, he outlined two alternatives: the CPA could try to organize elections before the scheduled transfer of sovereignty in June and accept a delay if the election arrangements required more time; or the CPA could rely on a system of caucuses to pick the members of the national assembly, which would ensure that the deadline would be met, but would at first turn Iraqi politics into an insiders' game. Bush opted for caucuses.

The end result became known as the November 15 Agreement. For the better part of a year, the American political strategy for Iraq had been like a car hurtling down the road with many hands on the steering wheel as the vehicle fishtailed back and forth. "Inside-out" had yielded to "outside-in" as the Bush administration's agenda in Iraq expanded from the minimalist goal of regime change to the lofty ideal of democracy promotion. Now a complicated hybrid plan was in the works. The one saving grace from the White House's point of view was that the details of the plan were too arcane to be grasped by the American electorate, which would likely be more impressed by the symbolism of conferring sovereignty on the Iraqis, assuming some way was found to tamp down the escalating violence and limit American casualties.

Having overhauled his seven-step plan and won the approval of Washington, Bremer's next step was to get the Iraqis on board. But even meeting with them was becoming tricky: in early November, the Governing Council's oldest member, Muhammad Bahr al-Ulum, had a near miss as he approached the Green Zone—not at the hands of insurgents but at the hands of trigger-happy American troops. As Bahr al-Ulum's car approached one of the Green Zone checkpoints, its American guards signaled for it to stop; when the driver failed to do so, the troops opened fire, missing the senior council member by inches. In response, the entire Governing Council had decided to boycott the CPA's Green Zone facilities. Bremer would need to present the new plan at the Baghdad residential compound of Jalal Talabani, the Kurdish political leader and council member.[28]

When Bremer presented the November 15 Agreement to the Governing Council, the room erupted in protest. Many of the Governing Council members, especially Chalabi, wanted more control over the political process that would lead to the new government. There were rumblings that the clerics in Najaf might not accept the transfer of sovereignty to an unelected body. Bremer chalked up the dissension to Shiite machinations to control the political process that would lead to the new government. The CPA chief told the council that if they did not sign the document, he would hold a press conference to announce exactly that: that the CPA had tried to hand sovereignty to Iraq's leaders and they had rejected the idea. The American ultimatum worked, and the council members signed the document.[29]

The new American plan represented a balance of bureaucratic forces in Washington. The president had not abandoned his vision of a democratic Iraq, but had insisted on a shortcut as he sought to realign ends and means. The question was whether the amended approach would work.

While Bremer was adjusting deadlines in both Washington and Baghdad, the officers in the military's intelligence cell were developing an idea to blunt the insurgency: reaching out to tribes, just as Saddam had done and the insurgents were doing.

As the team saw it, the reasons for the insurgency were deep-seated and would not be fully addressed by the scheduling of elections, the drafting of a constitution, or the formal transfer of sovereignty. If the United States was going to defeat the insurgency, or even blunt it, it needed to reach deep into the fabric of Iraqi society and find allies where it could. Strikingly, there were indications that some Sunni tribal leaders wanted a better relationship with the Americans.

Harvey's team raised the issue in the fall with the Iraq hands on the Joint Staff, the team of military officers who worked for the chairman of the Joint Chiefs, hoping that the Pentagon would spur Bremer's occupation authority to reach out to the Anbar tribes. The Joint Staff team drafted a classified two-page memo in October. Entitled "Sunni Outreach to the Governing Council and Coalition Provisional Authority," it was stamped "NOFORN," meaning not for sharing with allied officials, and approved by Major General Ronald Burgess, the director for intelligence on the Joint

Staff. General Myers, the JCS chairman, scribbled his endorsement in the margin: "Good paper. Pls ensure CPA and CJTF-7 see this."[30]

The October memo summed up the problem. Sunni tribal leaders in Anbar did not need to be persuaded to work with the American-led coalition. They were already offering to do that but complained they had been rebuffed. Coming on top of the CPA's de-Baathification decree, which had already hit some of the tribes hard, tribal leaders were increasingly worried that they were becoming marginalized. The leader of the Albu Nimr, among other sheikhs, had offered to organize a tribal force to provide border security as part of a "Coalition venture." There would be a cost if the CPA ignored such offers. "Leaders of these tribes—many of whom still occupy key positions of local authority—appear to be increasingly willing to cooperate with the Coalition in order to restore or maintain their influence in post-Saddam Iraq," the memo noted. "If they perceive a failure, they may take other actions, to include creating alternate governing and security institutions, working with anti-Coalition forces, or engaging in criminal activity to ensure the prosperity and security of their tribes."

For all that, getting the CPA's attention was not easy. After Harvey returned to Washington in the fall, his successor, Colonel Carol Stewart, the head of the intelligence plans section at CENTCOM, worked doggedly on the issue. One of Stewart's aides, Stan Silverman, had come to know Russell Khatib, an interpreter for the CPA and an American of Arab descent. Khatib explained that he had been in touch with several sheikhs from Anbar, who reported that Fallujah was "broiling." Silverman, who was a Vietnam veteran, saw the potential to work with the locals and urged Stewart to press ahead.

Meeting with a group of Anbari sheikhs—with scant attention from the authorities in Baghdad—Stewart developed a plan to bring them into the fold. The sheikhs said that they needed help evicting insurgents and could keep the roads clear of IEDs if the Americans would allow their tribes to be armed. In a classified paper, Stewart outlined what each side would do.

The strife-ridden Ramadi and Fallujah areas would become a tribal security zone. Eighteen sheikhs would participate at the start, with perhaps more to come. Tribal leaders would be asked to police their own areas and given vehicles, ammunition, and money to pay their men, who would be dubbed the "Anbar Rangers." The entire program would cost less than $3 million from the end of January through June, a tiny sliver of the multibillion-dollar reconstruction budget the Bush administration would later propose for Iraq.

Along with American and British intelligence officials, Stewart went to brief the plan to all of the division chiefs at Bremer's CPA and Sanchez's command. Stewart received some positive feedback, but when she briefed Meghan O'Sullivan and Catherine Dale, Sanchez's political adviser, O'Sullivan gave the party line: the CPA did not intend to plan to make the tribes a formal part of Iraq's security or political structure.[31]

Leaving the meeting, Stewart muttered in frustration, "If the United States is not going to be working with the tribes in the new Iraq, where is this new Iraq going to be? On Mars?"

Undeterred, Stewart continued to press her case. Encountering Bremer in the hallway of the Republican Palace, she quickly pitched her plan. Bremer wanted a detailed financial plan and formal approval from all of the American divisions in Iraq, which Stewart secured. The final roadblock was money. Bremer said that he did not have the $3 million to spare and that the funds would need to come from the emergency response funds that Sanchez controlled. The British deputy to Sanchez, Major General Freddie Viggers, was no more accommodating. He declined to provide the money.

The occupation authority later established an office of tribal affairs, but it fell well short of the sort of military and political alliance with the tribes that some in the American military had in mind. Although not all of the Sunnis in Anbar were ready to work hand and glove with the Americans at this point, some notable tribal leaders, including those of the Albu Nimr, clearly were.

There was a parallel with the relative lack of regard Bremer's governance advisers expressed for Sistani. The CPA had a plan for building a political system, and to the occupiers, some of Iraq's most time-honored traditions were merely timeworn. Tribes and clerics could coexist with Bremer's team, but unlike the Iraqis on the Governing Council they were not to get a favored place at the table.[32]

Recalling the episode in a still-classified interview with an Army historian, Harvey concluded that the conditions for a tribal awakening were better three years later, after Anbar's Sunnis had gone through the stages of denial of their reduced status in Iraqi society, anger at the Americans for being the agent of change, and, finally, acceptance and a desire to forge a place for themselves in the new order. Still, Harvey asserted, the United States might have mitigated many of the problems in Iraq by working with the tribes sooner. There was a glaring need, he argued, for an initiative to reach out to the Sunnis and try to bring them into the fold. Instead, the CPA and the White House were focused on elections that were likely to cement the Shiites' advantage.

"We said, look, the fabric of society is gone. We've done de-

Baathification. You don't have the competent cadres. The technocrats and the military have been pushed aside. There is insecurity. The normalcy of life has been ripped asunder, the people are falling back on two things: the mosque and their family, which was the clan, the tribe," Harvey told the Army historian. "We didn't have to keep travelling down this dead end."

"Bremer never understood the art of the possible here," Harvey added. "Never did. He never understood the issue of time in relation to all this, and he was too enamored of process, just as the administration was too enamored of process, of making benchmarks, and having a transfer from the CPA to the Interim Iraqi administration and apportionment by sectarianism, and then building a constitution, and a referendum, and an election, and at the end, the process will achieve the goal. Those benchmarks and timelines replaced fundamental issues."[33]

As 2003 drew toward a close, there was a military breakthrough that led Bremer to think the United States might finally be turning the corner. While conventional troops grappled with the Sunni insurgency taking shape around them, the military's most secretive branch, the Joint Special Operations Command or JSOC, had kept up the hunt for Saddam Hussein and his Baathist henchmen. Led since October by Major General Stan McChrystal, JSOC's small, elite force was split between Iraq, Afghanistan, and the continental United States, and it relied heavily on conventional troops to help with its raids, most of which were focused on trying to pick up Saddam's trail. (While Army Special Forces and most Navy SEAL teams in Iraq fell under the conventional chain of command, McChrystal's JSOC task force worked independently.)

A series of raids during the fall led JSOC's teams to a site in Baghdad where, on December 12, they captured Muhammad Ibrahim Omar al-Musslit, one of two men the military judged likely to know where Saddam was hiding. In an interrogation, Musslit described a rural area near the town of Dawr, across the Tigris from Tikrit, and the next day he was flown to an American base in the area along with a Delta Force squadron. That night, December 13, the Delta squadron and more than six hundred soldiers from one of Odierno's conventional brigades in Tikrit descended on the area Musslit had described, bringing him with them. The cavalry and artillery troops manned a double-layered cordon while AH-64 Apaches, AH-6 and MH-6 Little Birds, and an AC-130 Spectre gunship all circled overhead.

After the force spent fifteen minutes fruitlessly searching the area's buildings and orchards, Musslit led the Delta Force team on the ground to a patch of dirt next to a flowerbed, under which was a Styrofoam block— the hatch to a tiny underground hiding site inside which the commandos found a disheveled, bearded man, a Glock handgun, a rug, a fan, a pair of flip-flops, and, somewhat incongruously, a poster depicting the biblical scene of Noah's Ark. The soldiers dragged the man out and, through an Iraqi-American translator, asked who he was. "I am Saddam Hussein, the duly elected president of Iraq, and I am willing to negotiate," he answered. "Well, President Bush sends his regards," quipped one of the Delta Force soldiers.[34]

As one of the Little Birds landed and picked up the captured dictator, the Delta Force squadron commander and Colonel Jim Hickey, the brigade commander, informed Odierno and the JSOC chain of command. The next morning, Bremer broke the news at a press conference: "Ladies and gentlemen, we got him."[35]

But Saddam's capture did not stem the growing tide of attacks. Just twelve hours after Hussein was captured, a massive car bomb exploded outside the Iraqi police station in Khalidiya, a town sixty miles west of Baghdad in Anbar Province. Seventeen policemen were killed and thirty-three were wounded; the attackers had waited until the policemen were changing shifts in order to maximize the toll.[36] The attack was a grim indicator that Saddam's capture would not be as decisive as the Americans thought. The dictator's legacy—the decentralized Sunni insurgency that he had unwittingly enabled and equipped—had metastasized during the seven months of American waffling on what course to pursue. By January, McChrystal's commandos were focused on Anbar, the site of the abortive tribal outreach efforts, where escalating violence around the cities of Fallujah and Ramadi suggested that there was much more to the threat than "former regime elements."

CHAPTER 3

"Sovereignty with Limits"

One person the White House had not heavily factored into its decisions concerning the November 15 Agreement was the senior Shiite cleric in Iraq, Grand Ayatollah Ali al-Husseini al-Sistani. Born in Mashhad, Iran, in 1930, Sistani came from a long line of Shiite religious scholars and spoke classical Arabic with a Persian accent. Residing in the Shiite holy city of Najaf, Sistani had been jailed for a time during Saddam's reign, and like other Shiite clerics, had been carefully monitored by the regime's intelligence services. For all that, Sistani belonged to the "quietist" school of Shiite theology, whose clerics eschewed the kind of domineering political role that underpinned the Iranian theocratic model.

For Sistani, politics was a vulgar game that clerics ought to hold at bay unless the very existence of the faith was in danger. Civil institutions, not religious ones, should run the country. Sistani made his views on political life clear a year later when he met with Haydar al-Khoei, the son of a venerated Shiite cleric who was murdered by supporters of Muqtada al-Sadr in April 2003. When Haydar told the ayatollah that he had switched his university major to political science, Sistani solemnly shook his head. Politics had killed his father, Sistani observed tartly, and it would kill him, too.[1]

But while Sistani refused to meet with American officials and studiously avoided endorsing political parties or candidates, he grasped that the machinery of democracy the United States had pledged to introduce would empower the long-suffering Shiite majority, whom he saw as the rightful stewards of the Iraqi state. Adil Abd al-Mahdi, the Shiite political leader, once confessed to the U.N. team in Iraq that the Shiites were bound to love democracy since they had numbers on their side. Sistani's logic was much the same.[2] History had deprived the Shiites of their chance to be in control in 1920 when the British imposed a Sunni monarchy on Iraq; they were not about to squander another opportunity. As opposition groups returned from exile, the lines of the postwar Shiite political structure had begun to emerge: Muqtada al-Sadr's populist movement and the Iranian-backed Supreme Council for the Islamic Revolution in Iraq, or SCIRI, had the greatest sway among Shiites, but smaller parties, like Dawa and Fadhila, were carving out places for themselves, too.

For all of his disdain for politics, Sistani followed it closely and even received regular reports on the work of the Governing Council. Sistani had been unhappy with the notion that an unelected group of Iraqis anointed by the Americans would draft the nation's interim constitution, and he liked the plan to have the national assembly chosen through a system of caucuses even less. Iraq, it seemed, had powerful advocates of direct democracy, just not ones that the Americans had expected to encounter or who were willing to acquiesce to Bremer's latest plan.

Soon after the November 15 Agreement was settled in Washington, several Shiite members of the Governing Council, worried about the aspect of the plan calling for caucuses to choose the transitional parliament, took their concerns to the Grand Ayatollah. Sistani issued a legal clarification: if there was to be a parliament, it must express the will of Iraqi voters; an unelected assembly would not do. The intervention by the reclusive cleric in Najaf was enormously frustrating to Bremer's team, who saw it as a challenge to their strategy for building the new Iraqi state.

In a memo to Bremer, Meghan O'Sullivan complained that the American-led occupation should not "allow Iraqi clerics to overrule and/or nullify decisions made by Iraq's political authorities."[3] Rarely had a memo so succinctly captured the misconceptions that marked the first year of the occupation. None of the decrees the CPA could issue or the billions of dollars the United States was prepared to spend could replicate the moral authority of the Shiite cleric, who with a single fatwa could mobilize support or opposition for the American vision. In Washington, Richard Armitage, the deputy secretary of state, recognized the problem. At a December 2 Deputies Committee meeting of subcabinet officials, Armitage attacked the issue head-on. "Are we going to fight Sistani?" Armitage asked before answering his own question. "I think that would be a mistake."

Ahmed Chalabi, who had secured an important position on the Governing Council but had no real party apparatus to drum up popular support, continued to champion the idea of handing power over to the Governing Council, insisting that Sistani might yet be won over and elections avoided.

But other members of the Governing Council knew that Sistani's demands could not be so easily ignored. Ayad Allawi, one of the more secular Shiites, who also had ties to the Sunni community, summed up the political realities this way: when the Governing Council held its deliberations, "Sistani is in the room."[4]

With the Americans insisting that there was no way to organize elections before sovereignty was conferred in June 2004 and Sistani ruling that Iraq's voters had to go to the polls, Abd al-Aziz al-Hakim, the leader of the Supreme Council for the Islamic Revolution in Iraq, decided to take the issue to the United Nations. Hakim's SCIRI party was closely tied to the Iranian patrons who had sheltered it in exile—hence the "Islamic Revolution" in its name—but it was one of the largest Shiite parties in Iraq, and Hakim was the rotating head of the Governing Council for the month of December. To the consternation of the Americans, on December 28 he sent a letter to U.N. secretary-general Kofi Annan seeking his views on the matter. Annan responded by inviting the Governing Council delegation to meet with him in mid-January in New York.

The White House's attitude toward the United Nations had been conflicted from the start. Bush, counseled by Colin Powell and urged on by British prime minister Tony Blair, had taken the allegations about Iraq's WMD programs to the United Nations in 2002. But the president was prepared to proceed with the invasion even if, as it turned out, the Security Council was gridlocked and unable to approve military action. Even so, Powell had pushed to keep the United Nations in the picture after the invasion, calculating that sooner or later—and he hoped it would be sooner—the administration would want to hand over at least some of the problems following the invasion to the world body.

The United Nations' initial foray in Iraq had ended abysmally in August 2003 when its poorly secured headquarters in Baghdad's Canal Hotel was destroyed by a car bomb, killing Sergio Vieira de Mello and twenty members of the United Nations staff. After the attack, there was fierce debate at the United Nations headquarters about the wisdom of associating the international organization with Bush's Iraq agenda and about the terms of its reengagement in Iraq. As part of its push to enhance the legitimacy of the American project in Iraq, the Bush administration had supported a Security Council resolution in October authorizing Bremer's CPA, had appealed for multinational troops to assist the overextended American military, and had called on the United Nations to play a role in assisting in the political transition in Iraq. Jamal Benomar, who had been jailed for years in his native Morocco for his human rights activities before emerging as a U.N. expert on post-conflict issues and who had escaped the Canal Hotel disaster by sheer luck, argued that the United Nations should not wash its hands of Iraq. There were still ways the U.N. could influence the political process there, he insisted. To replace Vieira de Mello's conspicuous head-quarters and undefined mission, Benomar proposed sending a small U.N. team to address election issues, with a view toward quickening the transition to Iraqi sovereignty.[5]

In December, Larry Diamond, a political science professor at Stanford who was tapped for a stint on Bremer's staff, stopped by the U.N. head-quarters to consult with Benomar. During the course of their conversation, they discussed what it would take for the Bush administration to grant the U.N. a decisive role in Iraq. Their consensus was the involvement of Lakhdar Brahimi, the former Algerian foreign minister who, as a U.N. official, had played a critical role in the Bonn conference that propelled Hamid Karzai to power in Afghanistan. Diamond, who knew National Security Adviser Rice from her days as the provost of Stanford, broached the idea with her and Bob Blackwill at a White House meeting on December 12. Brahimi might conceivably be able to overcome Sistani's objections, Diamond argued, which could facilitate the administration's sprint to hand over sovereignty to Iraq by the end of June.[6]

As eager as it was for help in winning Sistani over, the White House was wary of any unscripted meeting between U.N. officials and the Iraqis. On December 30, two days after Hakim sent his letter to the secretary-general of the U.N. seeking his views on electoral matters, Bush's most senior aides gathered to discuss how to respond. Bremer, who had returned to Washington for the Christmas holiday, described the problem as he saw it: the head of the Governing Council had dared to appeal to the U.N. without coordinating his action with the CPA, Bremer complained, according to confidential notes of the meeting. Bremer had little control of the world outside the Green Zone, riddled as it was with violence. But he and his staff believed they guided the political processes in Iraq, and the viceroy was miffed. The Bush administration, it seemed, was eager to confer at least a symbolic sovereignty on the Iraqis, but it was not always happy at their flashes of independence.

Trying to make the best of the situation, Paul Wolfowitz wondered if the move might not represent an opportunity. If the White House could persuade the United Nations that elections were indeed not feasible before sovereignty was granted, perhaps Sistani would listen. Kofi Annan might carry more sway in Baghdad than Bremer, and the United States could use that to its advantage. "If the U.N. could be steered in the right direction, could Sistani climb down?" Wolfowitz asked.

"Yes, but we can't let Kofi get cross-threaded with us," responded Bremer. If the U.N. secretary-general came up with yet another new set of political options, it would call into question the American strategy. Bremer added that John Negroponte, the United States ambassador to the United Nations, "must head this off."

Colin Powell offered to take on the matter himself. There was a lot at stake, and Powell knew how to work the U.N. "Send me the letter," Powell said, referring to Hakim's communication. "I'll talk to Kofi."

Bremer was still concerned that the January meeting might lead to a scenario beyond the Bush administration's control. "What the Governing Council asks for might not satisfy Sistani," he said. "We must stand by the November 15 Agreement."

Rice gave the marching orders. Powell, she said, would contact the secretary-general "to freeze Kofi in place." The administration, meanwhile, needed to have a fuller discussion to prepare for Hakim's visit.[7]

Having discussed the latest twists and turns in Iraq's tangled politics, the participants turned to security in Iraq and in the region. As Vice President Cheney saw it, the United States was on a collision course with Muqtada al-Sadr, the fiery anti-American Shiite cleric, and would have to face that fact sooner or later.

For Cheney and the NSC, Sadr was yet another Iraqi enigma. Descended from a distinguished line of Shiite clerics, his father, Grand Ayatollah Muhammad Sadiq al-Sadr, had run afoul of Saddam and was murdered by the regime's security services in 1999. Although Muqtada enjoyed a certain amount of residual popularity thanks to his martyred father, he lacked the religious qualifications of an ayatollah like Sistani. Nevertheless, after the fall of Baghdad, Sadr's angry sermons against the occupation endeared him to Baghdad's impoverished Shiite population; soon thereafter, he began recruiting his followers into a militia called Jaish al-Mahdi—known by most American troops as JAM or the Mahdi Army—while simultaneously establishing a political wing, the Office of the Martyr Sadr.

By the summer of 2003, Sadr controlled a nascent organization similar to Hezbollah in Lebanon—a quasi-political, quasi-militia group with ties to Iran, led by a revolutionary figure with a strong cult of personality. Like Hezbollah, the Sadrist Trend, as it was called, was the de facto authority in certain neighborhoods and had engaged in violence against both coalition forces and its domestic political rivals.

In August, the Iraqi Central Court that Bremer stood up had implicated Sadr and seven others in the murder of Abd al-Majid al-Khoei, a potential clerical rival of Sadr and Haydar al-Khoei's father. An Iraqi judge had issued a secret warrant for Sadr's arrest. While Bremer wanted to act, the plan was shelved after Rumsfeld began second-guessing the idea, fearing that it would further entangle the United States in Iraq and interfere with the quick turnover he still hoped for. But the tensions between American forces and Sadr's Mahdi Army militia had continued. Marty Dempsey's 1st Armored Division intelligence staff had stood up a group called the "Sadr Fusion Cell" to monitor developments on the Sadrist front, and the NSA began to covertly eavesdrop on the cleric's inner circle.

Now, Cheney wanted to put the arrest option back on the table: Muqtada al-Sadr and his organization were quickly becoming problems that directly challenged the Bush administration's vision for Iraq. "We made a decision to get Sadr," observed Cheney. "Long term we are likely to be better off getting him now. We need to decide one way or another next week."

"I agree completely," Rumsfeld added enthusiastically, making no mention of his earlier reluctance to take on Sadr. Rice instructed Bremer's CPA and Sanchez's CJTF-7 to produce an assessment of the implications of going after Sadr so the Bush administration could decide the matter.

Rice then raised her concerns about Mujahideen e-Kalk, an Iranian opposition group that had made common cause with Saddam, earned a place on the State Department terrorism list, but which had forsworn opposition to the United States and was seeking Bush administration support. Confined to a camp north of Baghdad, denizens of the compound were no longer undertaking any operations in Iran, limiting their activity to radio transmission of anti-Iranian propaganda. Abizaid wanted time to "condition" the MEK to the new realities in Iraq before pressing the dissident group to shut down its radio, Wolfowitz reported.

Rice had little patience for that. She was trying to persuade the Iranians to detain Al-Qaeda operatives who were seeking refuge or transiting their territory. To be sure, Bush had put Iran in the "Axis of Evil" in his 2002 State of the Union address, but Rice saw an opportunity to mollify the Iranians to achieve a goal of the Bush administration: "It is important to shut it [MEK radio transmission] down," she said. "Don't let it slide. We need to get this done to make sure the Iranians get the Al-Qaeda in Iran. Make sure that Abizaid understands the urgency to shut down the radio."

The enormous earthquake that rocked Iran in December and devastated the southern city of Bam, killing more than 26,000 people, also presented an opportunity for a diplomatic opening toward a nation that the Bush administration had publicly deemed to be implacably hostile. Rice wondered if it was possible to organize a "large-scale private effort sparked by the president" to provide humanitarian assistance. The White House could get a figurehead to launch the effort, such as former Secretary of State George Shultz or a member of the Bush family. Powell suggested Elizabeth Dole, the Republican senator from North Carolina and former head of the American Red Cross. Bush, Rice added, might even arrange to waive sanctions imposed on Iran for its suspected nuclear program and support of terrorism for a short period so as not to interfere with the aid effort. Its public denunciations of Iran aside, the Bush administration had its hands full in Iraq and was prepared to engage with Tehran. Such was counterterrorism realpolitik.

On January 19, 2004, representatives of the Governing Council of Iraq arrived at the United Nations headquarters in New York for a meeting with Kofi Annan. Annan agreed to send Brahimi to assess the feasibility of elections before the handover of sovereignty at the end of June, and to determine how else the world organization might help. The next day, Bush delivered his State of the Union address, his first since the invasion of Iraq, and used the occasion to talk about his "forward strategy" of spreading freedom in Iraq and the broader Middle East. "As long as the Middle East remains a place of tyranny, despair, and anger, it will continue to produce men and movements that threaten the safety of America and our friends," he said. America was dealing with that threat by building democracy in Iraq.[8]

Adnan Pachachi, who served as the rotating head of the Governing Council in January and was also a senior statesman in the Sunni camp, was seated in the Senate gallery as an official guest of Laura Bush along with Hoshyar Zebari, Iraq's interim foreign minister. Still, the machinations of Iraqi politics once again confounded the Americans. Ahmed Chalabi had managed to attach himself to Pachachi's delegation as a representative of the Shiites and to the surprise of Bush turned up in the row with Laura Bush as well. The morning after the speech Bush convened an NSC meeting. After his aides congratulated him on his address the president turned to Richard Armitage, who as deputy secretary of state was sitting in for Powell. How, the president wanted to know, had Chalabi managed his way into the chamber and found himself seated in the same box as Laura? Armitage replied that he had no idea; no one else knew either.[9]

Brahimi brought some unique qualities to his U.N. assignment. He was an Arab nationalist, a Sunni, and, thanks to his experience contending with a fundamentalist Muslim rebellion in Algeria, had little empathy for Islamic parties or Iranian-based groups. He was a generation older than most of the Iraqis who were in the Governing Council: he had known Gamal Abd al-Nasser of Egypt. He had also opposed the Bush administration's decision to go to war and had even argued against sending Vieira de Mello to Iraq. The Bush administration, Brahimi argued at the time, seemed determined to run Iraq by itself and would come crawling to the United Nations only when it discovered that the task was more onerous than it had imagined. But now that the Americans were prepared to fast-track Iraq toward sovereignty, both Brahimi and Annan believed that it was time for the U.N. to get back into the thick of things despite the risks to life and limb.

The United Nations had a dubious reputation among many Iraqis. The sanctions that had been imposed by the Security Council as a result of Saddam's resistance to United Nations inspections had taken a toll on the Iraqi economy, and the Oil-for-Food Program that was intended to alleviate the hardship had fostered official corruption. The Iraqis were well aware that Brahimi had not favored regime change. But if there was a bias on the part of the United Nations it was in favor of empowering the Iraqis and ending the American occupation as soon as possible. On this point, at least, the U.N. was in agreement with Sistani and most of the country's politicians.

After arriving in Baghdad in February, Brahimi made his way to Najaf for his audience with the Grand Ayatollah. Seated on the floor in a spare room, Brahimi told Sistani that it was critical that security be in place for the elections, that there was no way this could be done before June, and that a six-month postponement of the elections was not the end of the world. Sistani's son, who insisted on the need for early elections, sought to intervene but Brahimi asked him to be quiet. He had come to talk to the Ayatollah, and only to the Ayatollah.

As the NSC was informed, Sistani and Brahimi had agreed on five key points. National elections were essential. They would be held near the end of the year. The United Nations would stay through that process. The newly elected legislature would select the government ministers, including the prime minister. The new legislature would write the new constitution.

Those points were incorporated into the broader American and U.N. strategy. Sovereignty would be transferred by the end of June; the Americans would make their deadline. An assembly of Iraqis would be convened during the summer, including Governing Council members and Iraqis who were not represented in the body. They would select members of an interim parliament. By the end of January 2005, the elections Sistani so badly wanted would be held. There would be an unelected interim Iraqi government but it would not be in power long before Iraqis went to the polls and Sistani's conditions were met.

On February 13, Bush convened an NSC meeting to take stock of the situation. According to notes of the session, Bremer reported that Brahimi had acquitted himself well with Sistani and that the CPA was still anticipating handing over sovereignty at the end of June. Rumsfeld was worried that the United States would lose leverage as the Iraqis began to assume more control. In the fall, the defense secretary had been pressing Bremer to hand over sovereignty as soon as possible. Now he was worried that the June deadline might undermine the Bush administration's ability to shape events in Iraq. If Iraqi politicians understood they would be taking over, what incentive did they have to be guided by Washington? "We shouldn't be supplicants. We will work with them to gain what is agreeable to us. We have leverage, right?" Rumsfeld asked. "We can be flexible on the date of sovereignty, to make sure that we are not disadvantaged?"

Bush was skeptical about missing the date. The administration could try quietly to negotiate a delay but the perception would be that the United States had been unable to make good on its promises to grant sovereignty. "We can negotiate that in private, but the public view will be that we failed," he said. Powell sought to redirect the discussion toward the critical issue at hand. The important thing was that the post-CPA government that took over in June could handle its responsibilities. "We can't have a collapse after 30 June," he observed.

The president summed up the discussion. It was all well and good for the Iraqis to declare Iraq sovereign but the country would not be ready to stand on its own feet yet. The United States would still need to have a role in securing the country and guiding the politics behind the scenes. "We have to have sovereignty with limits," Bush observed. "We need to calibrate this." As for security, Abizaid took the floor and said that American commanders were beginning to see a shift on the battleground in Iraq. The major threat was no longer coming from former members of Saddam's regime, he insisted, but from hard-core Sunni terrorists affiliated with Al-Qaeda, like Ansar al-Islam in northern Iraq and Abu Musab al-Zarqawi's Tawhid wal-Jihad in Anbar. The enemy seemed intent on attacking Iraq's fledgling forces as soon as they were stood up, to undermine the new super-structure of security before it could be built. "Zarqawi looks at this as a race," Abizaid added. The "ISF is on edge," Abizaid said, using the mili-tary acronym for Iraq's security forces. "But more folks are trying to hold Iraq together than are pulling it apart," he concluded optimistically.

Given that the United States was in a race with Zarqawi, Bush won-dered about the problems the Americans had encountered in training the Iraqi Army and police. Did the United States need to step up training? "We need a report on police problems," the president added. "Get it on my desk." The hope had long been that the Iraqi police would take the lead for securing Iraq's cities once the insurgency had been blunted; they did not appear remotely ready.

Bush pointed out that new information gained from the capture of Has-san Ghul, a Zarqawi courier detained by the Kurds the previous month, "gives us a propaganda advantage." A lengthy letter that American intel-ligence believed had been written by Zarqawi himself had been found on a computer disc Ghul was carrying, and it called for suicide car bombs and other attacks to spark a civil war between Sunnis and Shiites. "Let's use it," Bush added.

Bremer said the letter had already been shared with the Governing Coun-cil. "Is the message sinking in?" Bush asked. Bremer said he would report on this the following week. What Bush did not know at that time was that Ghul's capture would lead to much more than a propaganda coup. During his years in CIA custody Ghul divulged the name "al-Kuwaiti" as an alias for one of Osama bin Laden's couriers who was still at large. That piece of information helped the CIA pick up bin Laden's trail in late 2010, and cul-minated in the raid on the Abbottabad compound in Pakistan that finally killed the Al-Qaeda leader on May 2, 2011.[10]

Are we getting good intelligence from normal Iraqis? Rice asked. "Yes," Abizaid responded. The average "person on the street is cooperating," he added before expressing his belief that "Ansar al-Islam is almost extinct" in Iraq. Abizaid's upbeat assessment contrasted starkly with Harvey's ear-lier analysis of developments on the ground and Blackwill's grim report from his November trip to Iraq. Bremer had warned the White House that the military might oversell its accomplishments in order to justify drawing down, but Abizaid was the most senior military officer in the chain of command. His words carried weight with the NSC.[11]

Cheney had raised the question of what to do about Sadr. In February 2004, as Paul Wolfowitz swung through Iraq, he was briefed on a highly classified plan to snatch Sadr, dubbed "Operation Stuart."[12] The National Security Agency was "currently monitoring [communications] between women of Sadr's household," Wolfowitz was told. The CIA and British intelligence did not have the ability to routinely track Sadr's whereabouts but had reliable sources who could provide "intermittent notification of potential early movement."[13]

The plan outlined a number of options. The first sought to put an Iraqi face on the effort by stipulating that the Baghdad police's nascent Special Crimes Unit, backed up by a U.S. military police platoon on the ground and helicopters above, would intercept Sadr the next time intelligence came up that he was moving between Najaf and Karbala; upon arrest, he would be flown to Badush Prison in the north, well away from his political base in Baghdad and the Shiite south. A second option called for raids by elite American troops on various houses in Najaf, and left open the possibility that Sadr could be killed instead of arrested: one of Stan McChrystal's JSOC strike forces, Army Special Forces troops, and a tank company would "conduct simultaneous operations to Kill/Capture Moqtada al Sadr and key lieutenants [Mustafa al-]Yacoubi and [Riyadh al-]Nuri." The commandos, the briefing noted, had already surveyed the houses in Najaf where Sadr was known to stay and rehearsed the mission. The third and most drastic option involved the movement of a large U.S. conventional force—two full battalions—into the city, with Latin American coalition forces, Iraqi police, and the nascent Iraqi 36th Commando Battalion supporting them. The force would deliver a "verbal demarche" to Sadr, and if he did not respond, the 36th Battalion and its American Special Forces advisers would launch the actual raid against him.

All of the plans carried risks, identified in the briefing as "Unintended Consequences." The paradox was that the more the Americans relied on Iraqi forces to carry out the politically sensitive mission, the less assured it was of success. An Iraqi police raid was assessed as being the least risky option politically but also likely to be less effective in catching Sadr than an American commando raid. Conversely, a U.S. raid would likely succeed when it came to capturing Sadr, but there was a real risk that the arrest would be a Pyrrhic victory if it also sparked an uprising in Iraq's Shiite community. The conventional assault would almost certainly run into heavy resistance. A major problem, the briefing noted, was that Rumsfeld kept such tight control of politically sensitive operations in Iraq that he had to approve the operation at least forty-eight hours in advance, a requirement that needed to be relaxed, the briefing noted, if the military planned to pounce on as elusive a quarry as Sadr.

Each time, however, that it looked like Operation Stuart, or some version of it, might be implemented, the Bush administration backed off, fearing that moving on Sadr would stir up more political trouble than it would resolve. In one instance in February, the Baghdad police unit was actually sent down to Najaf in preparation for launching the operation, but with policemen calling home on their cell phones, the unit's presence leaked and the mission was scrubbed.

In early March, the NSC's Principals Committee met again and struggled to flesh out how the United States could confer sovereignty on the Iraqis in June while maintaining the legal latitude to conduct military operations in Iraq. The plan was to write a provision to this effect into the Transitional Administrative Law (TAL), the legal mechanism that would be adopted prior to the handover of sovereignty, which in deference to Sistani would not have the status of a formal constitution. The measure would make clear that the United States military would have a free hand militarily under the terms of previous U.N. Security Council resolutions. Colin Powell was unclear how the provision would be fulfilled. The TAL language was referred to as the "self-limiting clause," the idea being that when it came to security, the Iraqis would agree to limit their own sovereignty in exchange for the coalition's continued assistance. "How does the self-limiting clause become enacted?" Powell asked. Via an annex that has yet "to be written," Blackwill responded. "Brahimi's mission is to get concurrence on that annex," he added.

"If they are self-limited, who gets the option to exercise the constrained rights?" Powell asked again, a little confused by the quasi-sovereign democracy the administration was proposing for Iraq. There was precedent for this, noted Rice, who had coauthored a book on the reunification of Germany. After the Second World War, West Germany had political sovereignty but the Allied occupation forces were empowered to carry out collective security.

As to how the interim government should be fielded pending elections,

Brahimi, Blackwill reported, favored a government run by technocrats rather than Iraq's ambitious and scheming politicians. As to the structure of the interim government the Americans planned to hand off, Blackwill stressed that it was important that its character be more executive than legislative. The bigger the government got, Blackwill cautioned, the more it would look and act like a legislature and the less it would get done. Bremer added that checks and balances—a judicial system—were needed to protect against Iraqi abuse of power.

Bremer also insisted that, even though the Governing Council would be phased out after a new government was formed, he wanted now to expand it. Many Sunnis were unhappy with their modest representation in the body, and if Sunnis were added to the council Shiites would need to be added as well so as to remain a majority. The problem of the Sunnis' alienation from the new nation Bremer was building, underscored by both Harvey and the Defense Intelligence Agency, was finally receiving high-level attention at the CPA and Bremer was trying to find his own way to address it. Cheney countered that there was an argument to be made for only minimal changes to Iraq's governing structure at this juncture so as to create the smallest number of "perturbations" before conferring sovereignty. Powell supported Cheney's line. This was no time for "exotic governments." The United States had to have something in place by June. This urgency had to be conveyed to Brahimi.

This time the arrangements for Brahimi's trip to Iraq were far more problematic than those for his first. The Algerian diplomat had irritated much of the Governing Council by reaching an understanding on the political way forward with Sistani behind their backs. Nor had he hidden his disdain for Chalabi and other politicians he deemed too friendly toward Iran. (Brahimi had initially been reluctant to even meet with Chalabi until prodded by Benomar.) Given his interest in technocrats, Brahimi did not see the Governing Council as the nucleus of the new Iraqi government. That portended problems, since Ibrahim al-Jaafari, the leader of the Shiite Dawa Party, and other members of the council had been constantly jockeying for the prime minister post since the day the Governing Council was formed.

As Brahimi prepared to fly to Baghdad, word from the Governing Council was that the Iraqis had had their fill of the self-confident U.N. envoy and did not want him back. Rice was adamant that a way had to be found for Brahimi to continue his work. As the national security adviser saw it, the U.N. was instrumental in fielding a politically credible government. "Brahimi must come," she said in a March 8 White House meeting.

American diplomats scurried to make the case that Brahimi's role was essential by translating the issues in dollars and cents: without the U.N. imprimatur the World Bank and other international financial institutions would find it difficult to provide assistance to Iraq. Acting on Rice's request, Bremer called Brahimi, who was in Abu Dhabi, and urged him to come. The CPA chief acknowledged that there were some on the Governing Council that did not welcome the U.N.'s active role, but insisted he was trying to lay the groundwork for a successful trip. Brahimi said that he did not want to come to Iraq only to be "sniped at" but finally agreed. The Bush administration had gone from restricting the role of the United Nations in Iraq to trying to open the door for the secretary-general's envoy; so important had the deadline for handing over sovereignty become.

Two days later, Blackwill offered more observations at a meeting with Rice and a handful of aides that further complicated the situation. "The U.N. doesn't like the Transitional Authority Law. The U.N. doesn't even want to be in Iraq, except for Brahimi, and it thinks the CPA and Governing Council are colluding to keep it out." Blackwill added: "We must reduce expectations of a pure Iraqi government. It has a culture of corruption."[14]

In struggling to shape events in Iraq, Bush regularly consulted with Tony Blair. On March 15, Bush discussed the planning to stand up a sovereign Iraqi government with the British prime minister. There were a lot of members on the Governing Council, but Bush had clearly had his fill of some, particularly Chalabi. It was the Americans who had established the panel to rid the government of senior Baathists, but Chalabi had grabbed hold of the Council's de-Baathification portfolio with a vengeance and was using it, the Americans thought, to pursue a sectarian agenda.

"What's Chalabi up to?" Blair asked.

"No good," Bush responded.

If Iraq was to have "sovereignty with limits" by the end of June the United States would need to open an embassy in Baghdad—its first since the one April Glaspie headed was shut down soon after Saddam's 1990 invasion of Kuwait. John Negroponte, the Bush administration's ambassador to the United Nations, called Powell to volunteer for the job.[15]

The polyglot son of a Greek shipping executive, Negroponte prided himself on his challenging assignments. Inspired by John Kennedy's clarion call to explore the New Frontier and roll back communist insurgencies in the Third World, Negroponte had withdrawn from Harvard Law School to join the Foreign Service, where he became friends with another intrepid young diplomat: Richard Holbrooke. In a few short years, he had made enough of a name for himself as a young diplomat in Vietnam that he was plucked from the field and made an aide to Henry Kissinger, President Richard Nixon's domineering national security adviser.

It was a heady assignment for a precocious foreign policy hand but not one that Negroponte was prepared to cling to at the expense of his convictions. After concluding that Kissinger was negotiating behind the backs of the South Vietnamese, Negroponte broke with his boss. The move endeared him to conservatives, as did the discretion with which he had carried it out. There had been no angry blasts to the papers, just a quiet transfer to Latin America, where he served as an economic officer in Ecuador. After Ronald Reagan became president, Negroponte's discreet protest led him to return to the world of counterinsurgencies. Appointed as ambassador to Honduras, he played a supporting role in the secret war against the Sandinistas in neighboring Nicaragua before going to prestigious ambassadorships in Mexico and the Philippines and posts at the State Department. Significantly, he had also worked as a deputy to Colin Powell when the general was called back to Washington in the wake of the Iran-contra scandal to serve as Reagan's national security adviser.

When the Clinton administration did not offer him a high-level post he followed the trajectory of many well-connected foreign policy hands and secured a lucrative position in the corporate sector. Summoned back to the world of diplomacy, Negroponte was named as the American envoy to the United Nations, taking up his post just days after the September 11 terrorist attacks. For all of his conservative credentials, Negroponte had not been among those who stumped for regime change in Iraq. When the administration decided to detail its claims that Saddam was concealing programs to make chemical, biological, and even nuclear arms, he had even advised against making the presentation at the United Nations Security Council. Despite the mountain of allegations emanating from Washington, he did not think the threat was so dire that it amounted to an Adlai Stevenson moment.

But like most administration officials, Negroponte figured that Saddam was up to no good. When the president decided to bring the Iraq issue to the Security Council, Negroponte labored loyally to build support for the resolution that found Iraq in "material breach" of its disarmament obligations, the charge that became the formal casus belli of the 2003 war. When Powell appeared before the Security Council a month before the invasion to argue that Iraq had failed to disarm, Negroponte sat behind him, paired with George Tenet, the director of Central Intelligence.

One conclusion Negroponte had drawn from the debacle in Southeast Asia was that the process of helping the South Vietnamese military and government to stand on their own—what President Nixon dubbed "Vietnamization"—had begun too late. As ambassador in Baghdad, he would have a chance to apply that lesson while the war still hung in the balance. To the NSC staff, the transition to the embassy could not come too soon. Blackwill had praised the work ethic of the CPA hands during the fall of 2003, but during the March deliberations with the NSC staff he unburdened himself. The organization, he complained, was stovepiped, undisciplined, and, apart from the small number of CPA experts in the field, disconnected from the Iraqi populace. "They think they know more than the military," he added.

For all that, Negroponte's appointment was hardly assured. Rice, for one, was wary. The *Washington Post* had published an article that portrayed Negroponte as the voice of caution on invading Iraq, and the national security adviser was concerned that the veteran diplomat might not share the president's vision. Powell went to bat for Negroponte, and eventually it was agreed that he would get an audience with the president. Negroponte knew the Bush family well. He had been in the same Yale fraternity as the president's uncle, and worked for his father. Still, the president would need to be persuaded.

On March 30 Negroponte strode into the Oval Office for his interview with the president. As he settled into an overstuffed chair, Negroponte figured that Bush would ask him about his tours in crisis zones or thoughts about the monumental problems that lay ahead. But the president had just one question: "What I want to know about you, John, is whether you think democracy is possible in Iraq."

Surprised by the president's query, Negroponte muttered a response: "It is not beyond the wit of man." Negroponte got the job.[16]

CHAPTER 4

Vigilant Resolve

The day after Negroponte's meeting at the White House, four armed contractors from the American company Blackwater drove into the Sunni city of Fallujah with an Iraqi military escort to pick up some kitchen equipment. Ambushed in broad daylight, they were abandoned by their Iraqi military escort and killed. Two of the bodies were hung, upside down, on a railroad bridge that spanned the Euphrates, a grisly warning of what would happen to any Americans who dared to venture into the city.

At Camp Blue Diamond in nearby Ramadi, the staff of the 1st Marine Division watched the grisly episode on a video feed from a small, remotely piloted drone. The division, led by Major General Jim Mattis, had just arrived in Anbar Province two weeks before. It was already too late to help the contractors, and the Marine commander decided that the best thing to do was to let the riot play out and go after the culprits later. It would be dangerous and counterproductive to react emotionally or with too much force.

The next day, Brigadier General John Kelly, the assistant commander of the Marine division, sent a memo to the division explaining the command's thinking. "We are convinced that this act was spontaneous mob action. Under the wrong circumstances this could have taken place in any city in Iraq. We must avoid the temptation to strike out in retribution," Kelly wrote. "Going overly kinetic at this juncture plays into the hands of the opposition in exactly the way they assume we will." The Marines' strategy was to work with the population as much as possible, and they had every intention of sticking to the plan.[1]

Fallujah had been a problem since day one. The Euphrates valley running through Anbar, a province of 1.2 million Sunni Arabs, was scattered with former military bases and the homes and retirement communities of officers loyal to the Baath Party. In late 2002, Saddam had relocated the headquarters of his intelligence service from Baghdad to Karma, to keep it out of the way of the looming American bombing campaign. With a porous border with Syria that was easily infiltrated by foreign fighters, it was a natural petri dish for the various strains that would become the Sunni insurgency to organize and regroup.

Despite its potential to serve as an escape valve for the remnants of Saddam's security forces, Anbar had been treated as a virtual afterthought. The American military juggernaut that bulled its way to Baghdad had barely touched Anbar. David McKiernan, the three-star general who led the land campaign, had planned to send the Army's 1st Cavalry Division to the area near Fallujah and Ramadi, the provincial capital, so it could control the western approach to Baghdad and provide additional combat power for what was expected to be a tough fight to seize the capital. But when the battle for Baghdad turned out to be easier than expected, Rumsfeld pressed Tommy Franks to "off-ramp" the division, to McKiernan's disappointment. The result was that only a thin American presence had been allocated to control Anbar following the fall of Baghdad. It was not for nothing that when it was time to flee the city Saddam Hussein and his sons Uday and Qusay had headed west, first to Ramadi and then to the palm groves outside Hit, where they split up, the better to elude coalition forces.[2]

The speed with which Army units had rotated through Fallujah and Ramadi had also made it all the more difficult for the military to forge ties with the locals. The Anbar occupation had started out on a sour footing in April 2003 when soldiers from a battalion of the 82nd Airborne Division, who had made camp in a schoolhouse inside Fallujah, killed seventeen Iraqis and wounded more than seventy after coming under fire from some militants in the crowd. After the soldiers from the 82nd left in May, the 3rd Armored Cavalry Regiment worked briefly in Fallujah until Colonel David Perkins's 2nd brigade from the 3rd Infantry Division, which had carried out the famous "Thunder Run" through Baghdad on April 5, 2003, arrived.[3]

By the end of the summer, it was time for the 3rd Infantry Division to leave Iraq and plans were made for another 82nd unit to come back again. The Iraqis' experience with the 82nd had been so fraught that Buford Blount, the 3rd ID commander, offered to extend his unit's tour of duty in Fallujah so that paratroopers wearing the 82nd patch would not need to come back. But Rick Sanchez, who was determined to make the troop rotations work according to schedule, turned down the recommendation. By fall, Anbar was the domain of Major General Charles Swannack, the 82nd Airborne commander, who oversaw a hodgepodge of units: one of his brigades was in Fallujah, a brigade from the 1st Infantry Division was stationed in Ramadi, and the 3rd ACR was responsible for the far west.

Under Swannack, the city grew into even more of a hotspot. On November 2, insurgents downed a CH-47 Chinook south of the city with a shoulder-fired missile, the first of several helicopter shoot-downs that would occur in the area over the fall and winter. In response, Sanchez ordered the 82nd to plan for a four-battalion assault on the city, but Abizaid and the battalion commander in Fallujah objected and the attack never went forward. Abizaid visited the city in the fall to remonstrate with tribal leaders and see why violence was escalating.[4] The helicopter downings continued, though, in Sunni cities elsewhere in Iraq like Tikrit and others closer to Fallujah. During the first two weeks of January 2004 alone, three Army helicopters—an OH-58 Kiowa, an AH-64 Apache, and a UH-60 Black Hawk medevac aircraft—were brought down by insurgent fire near Fallujah. On February 14, insurgents in Iraqi National Guard uniforms staged a mass prison break from the city police station.

When the Marines took over from the 82nd, Jim Mattis—who had led the 1st Marine Division during the invasion a year before and went by the call sign "Chaos"—knew that Anbar would not be easy. In a message to his division before it deployed, he stressed the stakes of the campaign the unit was heading back to. "We are going back into the brawl," he wrote. "This is our test—our Guadalcanal, our Chosin Reservoir, our Hue City."

Even so, Mattis and his superior, Lieutenant General James Conway, the Marine commander who would oversee all forces in the province, were convinced they could manage the area better than the Army by being more discriminate about the use of force and building relationships with local residents. To reduce the risk of collateral damage, the military's anodyne term for the inadvertent killing of civilians, the Marines vowed not to fire artillery based on nothing more than radar projections of enemy mortar positions, drop bombs with abandon, or rely heavily on their M1 tanks. To show respect, they would take off their sunglasses and look the Iraqis in the eye when speaking to them. When it came to military operations, the Iraqi police and military—the Marines hoped to create an Iraqi marine battalion or brigade—would be the first line of defense, backed up by a Marine quick reaction force. The measure of success would be the number of tips about insurgent hideouts by an indulgent, if not grateful, population, not the number of enemy killed or captured. Inside the velvet glove would be a mailed fist, but the Marines would first seek to restore a degree of civility. The Marines would take things slowly, build civil capacity and the Iraqi security forces—all while pursuing any insurgents who took up arms—without alienating the population. "The enemy will try to manipulate you into hating all Iraqis," Mattis advised his Marines. "Do not allow the enemy that victory."[5]

Taking control of Anbar in the last week of March 2004, the Marines had just enough forces to cover the province and an adjoining area south of Baghdad with no battalions as a reserve. The Marines' Regimental Combat Team 1 took over the east of the province, including Fallujah, Regimental Combat Team 7 took over the west, and an Army brigade, with Marine attachments, stayed in Ramadi. That same week, Fallujah began to present itself as the Marines' most difficult problem. On March 25, three days before RCT-1 formally took the reins in Fallujah, a special operations patrol was ambushed in the city, wounding two commandos. The very next day, the Marine battalion that had encamped itself just east of Fallujah sent two companies into the northern part of the city to feel out the situation, got into a gunfight, and pulled back at the request of the Fallujah city council.

Ominously, the insurgent threat was made up of more than resentful Baathists. By March 2004, Stan McChrystal's task force of elite JSOC commandos was venturing frequently into Fallujah and Ramadi in pursuit of suspected leaders of Tawhid wal-Jihad, the radical Sunni terrorist group led by Abu Musab al-Zarqawi that was seeking to establish itself as Iraq's affiliate of Al-Qaeda. Both volunteers from neighboring Arab countries and larger numbers of religiously conservative Anbaris were joining the group in Fallujah and Ramadi. "In 2004 Al-Qaeda began to appear," an Anbari sheikh later told a Marine historian. "We warned General Swannack at the time."[6]

Even with the killings of the Blackwater contractors, Mattis's plan did not require rushing into anything. But that approach did not stand for long. Rumsfeld, then traveling in Europe, Abizaid at CENTCOM, and Bremer in Baghdad all agreed that what was needed was quick and decisive military action. On April 3, Sanchez's command sent Conway a written order directing him to take away the insurgents' sanctuary in Fallujah and apprehend the men who killed the contractors. Wearing a pistol on his hip,

Brigadier General Mark Kimmitt, the command's spokesman, vowed there would be an overwhelming response to "pacify that city." Though Marine commanders believed the timing was wrong and the mission ill advised, orders were orders. They dubbed the operation "Vigilant Resolve."

The Marine forces already in the vicinity of Fallujah—two infantry battalions and a reconnaissance battalion—cordoned off as much of the city as they could on April 5 while Navy engineers constructed a berm to limit access to the south side of town. That first day, one infantry company found itself in a heavy gunfight in Jolan, a neighborhood in Fallujah's northwest corner whose narrow, curving streets were difficult for Humvees to traverse. On day two, a third Marine infantry battalion arrived, pulled from duty south of Baghdad, and for two days the three battalions pushed slowly into the edges of the city—one from the east, one blocking the south. On the fourth day, one more battalion joined the fight after making the long move from western Anbar.

Thanks to Bremer's decision to dismantle the Iraqi military, few Iraqi units were available to join the Marines. Two battalions of the Iraqi Civil Defense Corps, a regional militia that CENTCOM had promoted as a stopgap until a new army was raised, were ordered to help secure the periphery of Fallujah, but only one actually showed up. The Marines' experience with the Iraqi Army was even worse. Only a handful of Iraqi Army battalions existed. One, which was training at Taji north of Baghdad, was tapped for Fallujah. It was a delicate mission, which Major General Paul Eaton, who was in charge of training the Iraqi military, sought to smooth over. Eaton assured the Sunni commander that his soldiers would not be roaming Fallujah's mean streets with the Marines or engaging in house-to-house fighting. Their job was to maintain a few checkpoints outside the city and patrol some of the major supply lines. Still, it was not an easy sell. In building a new Iraqi military, Eaton recalled, Iraqi recruits had been told that their role would be to protect the nation against external threats. Nothing had been said to the recruits about pursuing enemies, the vast majority of them Iraqi insurgents, inside Iraq. Officially, the battalion numbered about seven hundred, but in practice there were no more than 450 due to desertions and leaves.

Heading out for their first combat test, the Iraqi soldiers loaded up in a convoy of trucks and began the long drive to Anbar only to run into angry crowds and a few sniper rounds, which wounded one of their American military advisers. That was enough to create mayhem with the battalion and the convoy turned back. Hoping to sidestep the problem, U.S. Army officers arranged for the Iraqis to be flown by helicopter to Anbar. But the Iraqi soldiers had never trained with helicopters and were anxious about what might be in store for them: more than seventy of the Iraqi soldiers refused to budge and the battalion's mission had to be scrubbed. Eaton took full responsibility for the setback, which said as much about the Americans' efforts to build a new Iraqi military after the old one had been dismissed as it did about the soldiers themselves. For his part, Mattis was bitter about the Iraqis' reluctance to join the fight. The Iraqi security forces, he told his Marines in frustration, were "little more than a jobs program."[7] Now that the Marines were asking the Iraqi troops to stand up beside them, "it would seem many are either voting with their feet—or their allegiance."

One Iraqi unit pushed alongside them into Jolan, though, and performed well for the first few days of the fight: the 36th Commando Battalion, the unit tapped for Operation Stuart. Formed from recruits from the five major political parties in post-Saddam Iraq, including an ample number of Kurdish Peshmerga, the unit had been trained in less than a month by American Special Forces advisers, seventeen of whom accompanied the commandos to Fallujah.

As the four Marine battalions pressed the attack, echelons far above them began to have second thoughts. From afar, and filtered through the lens of Al-Jazeera, the battle did not look like it was nearing success, as Mattis and his regimental commander in Fallujah believed despite the problems with Iraqi troops. Reports—some of them put out by doctors who were pressed into service as medics to the insurgency—were circulating that hundreds of civilians had been killed in indiscriminate attacks, forcing Fallujans to turn two soccer fields into makeshift cemeteries. The leading Sunni member of the Governing Council, Adnan Pachachi, denounced the operation as a wanton form of collective punishment.[8]

Brahimi was also concerned and made his unhappiness known, even threatening to resign: the Americans had brought in the U.N. to find a way out of the political logjam only to find itself in the middle of a swirling dispute over an escalating battle that was being chronicled exhaustively and often one-sidedly in the Arab media. For the first time, the initiative to bring in the United Nations and the mission to pursue insurgents had collided. Nor were some of the White House's allies pleased: the British let Bremer's occupation authority and Sanchez's command know that what was happening in Fallujah did not look like any kind of counterinsurgency with which they wanted to be associated.

As the political squabbling escalated, Abizaid, Bremer, and Sanchez met in Baghdad and agreed that the advance into Fallujah had to stop. The final call, Bremer recalled, was made by Bush after Bremer advised him that continuing the fight might lead to the fracturing of the Governing Council, the failure of Brahimi's mission, and, ultimately, a delay in the projected June date for transferring sovereignty.

On April 9, Abizaid flew to the Marine base outside Fallujah and, over Conway's objections, ordered a halt to the attack. But though the Marines on Fallujah's edges could no longer advance, they had not been called entirely off, either. They settled in for a siege until an order came to resume the advance—a call that Conway and Mattis expected would eventually come after the Bush administration soothed the concerns of the Governing Council.

Figuring that he was dealing with a pause, Mattis sought to beef up his forces near the embattled city. The rural areas around Fallujah had become insurgent staging areas, and on April 6 violence had also exploded in Ramadi. After submitting a request for more forces, which took months to trickle in, the Marine commanders stripped western Anbar of troops and sent them toward Fallujah, a move that left the west secured by no more than two infantry battalions and a task force scrounged up from an amalgam of small support units: a riverine boat company, engineers, Reservists, and Azerbaijani troops. The Marines continued to lose men in skirmishing on the edges of Fallujah, and three special operations troops were wounded mid-month when an RPG downed their MH-53 Pave Low helicopter outside the city. But the insurgents were taking losses, too, and the Marines were convinced they had the upper hand. "As late as the 25th, we thought we were going to reattack the city," Conway said.[9]

In Washington, the episode had come as a shock. One week into the fight, Hadley convened a restricted session of the Deputies Committee and talked about his disappointment with the Iraqi forces and the generals who had been reporting their progress. "It's been a rough seven days," Hadley said, according to notes of the meeting.

The poor performance of the Iraqis had "changed our assessment of the ISF [Iraqi security forces]," Hadley confessed. CENTCOM and CJTF-7, he complained, had been passing "overly optimistic reports" about the training and equipping of the Iraqi forces. Something needed to be done. The administration needed to consider stepping up its funding of the program to train and equip the Iraqis. Hadley also wanted an assessment of the reliability of the Iraqi forces and a plan on how they could be improved. "A rejuvenation entails more information on what we will do with spending and training," Hadley noted. "What does the Secretary of Defense want to do, and what has the relevant violence done to cripple the ISF and cause the loss of weapons?"

Shifting to the foreign fighters that had crossed the porous Syria-Iraq border to fortify the insurgency in Anbar, Hadley noted that the Bush administration would make a quiet diplomatic push to reach out to Bashar al-Assad, the Syrian leader, and persuade him to clamp down on the militants. Rich Armitage, the deputy secretary of state, would be visiting Damascus and bringing a demarche from Secretary of State Powell. A separate demarche was being sent by the Central Intelligence Agency director, George Tenet, through intelligence channels. Hadley instructed the State Department to devise economic sanctions that could be imposed if the Syrians refused to cooperate. It was the beginning of years of fruitless efforts to enlist Syria's cooperation.[10]

Once it became apparent that the pause in offensive operations was indefinite, the Marines went to their Plan B. Negotiations in the middle of the month among Governing Council, CPA, and Marine representatives had not been promising; when the Marines agreed to establish locations for Fallujah residents to turn in heavy weapons ahead of a possible cease-fire, no weapons materialized. Conway had already been discussing another solution with General Muhammad Abdullah al-Shawani, a Sunni hero of the Iran-Iraq War who had been installed as the head of Iraq's newly formed intelligence service with the CIA's blessing and support. If the Iraqis on the Governing Council could not abide a Marine solution, then perhaps the Marines could pull back entirely and put together an Iraqi unit of some kind to take care of Fallujah. Shawani liked the idea and said that he would find some Iraqi generals in the area, officers who had been shunned since the disbandment of the Iraqi Army the previous year. In a meeting at the Presidential Palace in the Green Zone, Bremer and Sanchez discussed the idea of a "Fallujah Brigade" with Mowaffak al-Rubaie, a prominent member on the Governing Council, and other Iraqi officials. As Rubaie remembered it, he was opposed to the idea, warning Bremer and Sanchez that arming the unit in Fallujah would work out just as well as arming the mujahideen in Afghanistan had, a comparison that infuriated Bremer.

On April 25, Conway and Mattis met with the retired generals and discussed forming the Fallujah Brigade, a motley collection of former soldiers that included more than twenty out-of-work generals. Abizaid and Sanchez gave the Marines the go-ahead to proceed with the idea. Despite the objections, the Fallujah Brigade began to assemble outside the city on April 28. Two days later, as the Marine battalions inside Fallujah retreated from their battle positions, the Fallujah Brigade's commander and five hundred of his men met with Conway at the cloverleaf just east of the city, and soon after they began to move in. The battle later known as First Fallujah was over. It had cost twenty-seven American lives and ninety more wounded. Two Recon Marines and two Delta Force soldiers would be awarded the nation's second-highest valor medal for their actions in the battle. All this had resulted in a solution that inspired little confidence: the deployment of a largely unvetted brigade of Sunni military veterans that melted away within weeks.

While the Fallujah fight was under way, a smaller but equally fierce battle had been unfolding just up the Euphrates in Ramadi, Anbar's capital. Lieutenant Colonel Paul Kennedy's battalion, 2/4 Marines, which had missed the invasion the previous spring, had set up shop there alongside an Army mechanized battalion that had been there since the summer.

On the morning of April 6 a platoon from the battalion's Golf Company was moving west through Ramadi's downtown Government Center when it was ambushed. As the platoon waited for relief, a Marine who had already been wounded was shot in the head and killed. Outside the city, a team of four snipers could hear the gunfire a few miles away when they, too, came under heavy attack. A lieutenant from Echo Company piled a squad into a Humvee and came to the team's aid but, as they fought off the attackers, two Marines were shot and killed. Later in the day, another relief column from Echo Company was ambushed. The fighting lasted until a nearby Army mechanized battalion massed its forces and swept into the city on a wide front. In all, thirteen Marines had been killed and twenty-five wounded: excepting helicopter crashes, the one-day toll remains among the highest for any firefight in the Iraq and Afghanistan wars.

The next morning it started up again, and by April 10 the battalion had lost another four Marines and, along with the Army unit, had killed an estimated 250 insurgents. "Within the blink of an eye, the situation went from relatively calm to a raging storm," Kennedy, the battalion commander, wrote to his Marines' families. "Where did this organization come from?" Echo Company's commander, Captain Kelly Royer, asked. "Were they always here? Did they come from outside Ramadi?"[11] Mattis, whose division headquarters was just across the Euphrates from Ramadi's densely packed streets, was surprised at the ferocity of the fighting, too. "I thought I had a pretty good idea what was in Ramadi," he recalled, until Kennedy's unit "kicked over a real hornet's nest."[12]

Largely out of the media's glare, the battalion's fight in Ramadi continued into the summer; eventually the battalion would lose thirty men, including a team of scouts and snipers that was overrun by insurgents in June. When the battalion did not have enough troops to man all the guard posts at their positions—which was often, especially until additional Army troops arrived in Ramadi from Korea in July—the Marines put uniforms on cardboard cutouts.[13] It was a desperate measure to cope with a chronic insufficiency of forces. Finally, the fierce fighting devolved into something of a stalemate. Kennedy agreed to requests from local leaders to keep his troops out of their neighborhoods so as not to inflame violence, and the battalion mostly confined itself to trying to keep the main road through Ramadi, Route Michigan, clear of IEDs as insurgents became more and more entrenched in the city.

In the far west portion of Anbar, the fight was escalating, too. The insurgents' grip on the area was so firm that they had begun to enforce their own curfews in the border town of Husaybah to set up their attacks before the Americans' curfews took hold, according to intelligence reports trickling back to Sanchez's command. They also penetrated the local security forces. A classified Marine history of the Anbar insurgency noted matter-of-factly that the Marines "clashed with the entire pro-insurgent Husaybah police department."[14]

Led by Lieutenant Colonel Matt Lopez, 3/7 Marines was tasked with securing Qaim and several other towns on the Syrian border. On April 14, Lopez's convoy came under attack in Husaybah, and a bullet lanced through the colonel's Humvee, striking him in the back. Hearing that their commander had been wounded, a fourteen-man patrol from the battalion's Kilo Company jumped in their Humvees and raced toward the scene, where they began searching cars for weapons. As Kilo Company searched a white Toyota Land Cruiser, its driver assaulted Lance Corporal Jason Dunham, who wrestled the assailant to the ground. As a grenade rolled free from the enemy's hand, Dunham slammed his helmet over the device and rolled onto it to keep it in place.

Dunham was wounded badly, with shrapnel lodging in his brain. The assailant was hurt but tried to run away, only to be cut down by two dozen bullets. The insurgent and the Marine who had tackled him were evacuated together by Army helicopter. Between the April 14 incident and the fighting that continued for the rest of the spring, the battalion lost ten Marines killed and twenty-seven wounded. One of the dead was Dunham. He had survived treatment at Al-Asad Air Base, in Baghdad, and in Germany, and brain surgeries at Bethesda National Naval Medical Center. But Dunham was never going to recover and soon after the Marine commandant pinned a Purple Heart on his pillow, doctors removed his ventilator at his parents' decision. Nearly three years later, in January 2007, President Bush presented Dunham's parents with the Medal of Honor—he was the first Marine to be given the award for actions since Vietnam.[15] The heroic episode was worthy of all the attention that was bestowed on it, but it distracted from an uncomfortable fact: much of Anbar was little more than what the military called an "economy of force" operation, a place where the armed forces had too few resources and had to do the best with what it had. The troops on the ground were paying the price, and the momentum that American forces had achieved with the fall of Baghdad had been lost.

At the White House, the hope was that the push toward sovereignty would soothe the Iraqis' grievances over the occupation and take the steam out of the insurgency. Politics, in effect, was to enable the military strategy. Abizaid had encouraged this thinking by suggesting that the United States was winning the race with Zarqawi and building up Iraq's security forces before Al-Qaeda could take them down or spark a civil war that would make Iraq unmanageable. But the developments in Anbar had raised questions on both counts. The talk of a June handover to an unelected Iraqi government appeared to have had no effect on the insurgents in Anbar, who were foes of all of the new authorities—American and Iraqi alike. In Fallujah and Ramadi, the insurgents and the military seemed to be settling in for a long and difficult fight.

The Fallujah battle in particular had been a textbook example of how not to go to war. There could not have been a greater misnomer than Vigilant Resolve. The Marines had been ordered to attack against their better judgment by superiors who failed to secure the necessary backing from the Governing Council or the U.N. and then stopped the attack in its tracks just as they were making progress. There had been a yawning disconnect between the battlefield and the Bush administration's political strategy. The White House had wanted to put the Sunni insurgents in their place without upsetting the timetable for conferring sovereignty, and the result was that the enemy was allowed to survive to fight another day. But the Marines had miscalculated, too. As much as the Marines had hoped to win over the population, the situation in Fallujah they had inherited had deteriorated so much, and the insurgents were so entrenched that a major fight seemed unavoidable. At best, the day of reckoning had been deferred.

As the battles of Fallujah and Ramadi raged in the west, Rick Sanchez's command had another rebellion on its hands in April, this one closer at hand and larger in scope: an uprising across Baghdad and southern Iraq by Muqtada al-Sadr's Mahdi Army. On March 28, three days before the Blackwater killings in Fallujah, Bremer had ordered *Al-Hawza*, a newspaper the Sadrist Trend put out, shuttered for inciting violence against allied troops. American military policemen padlocked the newspaper's offices. Sadr was furious. Ali Khedery, the young Iraqi-American CPA staffer, was sitting in his office in the Republican Palace when he got a call from Abd al-Karim al-Muhammadawi, a Governing Council member from Maysan Province who was nicknamed "Prince of the Marshes." Muhammadawi was sitting with Sadr in Kufa, a suburb of Najaf, and the two had just received the news about *Al-Hawza*.

"I'm going to make this very simple," Muhammadawi told Khedery after asking if he could relay a message to Bremer. "We have a message, and you need to listen to it carefully. Either the newspaper is reopened or there will be hell to pay." Khedery passed the message to the CPA chief. The Mahdi Army, Bremer responded derisively, was not an army at all but a militia. He would not reopen the newspaper.[16]

On April 2, Sadr's weekly Friday sermon was a bitter invective against the United States, denouncing the Americans and even praising the September 11 attacks. In his movement's main Baghdad stronghold, Sadr City, members of his Mahdi Army marched menacingly in the streets, dressed in their distinctive black uniforms and marching under green banners. At the CPA, the general counsel sent Bremer a legal opinion that the diatribe was a clear violation of the transitional law the Americans had established against incitement to violence and could, once again, subject Sadr to arrest. The next day, the American military arrested one of Sadr's top advisers and fellow targets of Operation Stuart, Mustafa al-Yaqubi, who had been accused of serving as an accomplice in the murder of Khoei. The Sadrist discontent that had been brewing since the previous summer exploded into violence—and into a second, southern front for the American military.

Like Anbar, Baghdad was in the throes of a major troop rotation when the rebellion struck. Marty Dempsey's 1st Armored Division troops were on their way home, with replacements from Major General Peter Chiarelli's 1st Cavalry Division beginning to take over their duties. Like the Marines, Chiarelli was determined that his division's year in Iraq would be marked not by excessive force but by efforts to win over Baghdad's popula-tion. Before deploying, he had arranged for his commanders and staff to observe how the city of Austin, Texas, delivered electrical power and orga-nized trash collection, and he had sent some officers to Britain, where they huddled with the ostensible masters of counterinsurgency, and to Jordan to learn about Arab customs and traditions.

On instructions from on high, Chiarelli had also left behind the majority of his division's Abrams tanks and Bradleys, tracked armored vehicles with a 25mm gun that could hold several "dismounts." Originally, he had been directed to leave them all behind by superiors who appeared to believe that the days of tanks rolling through Baghdad's streets were over. But after considerable importuning, he had managed to bring fourteen tanks per brigade, a single company's worth, and twice that many Bradleys. Even as Chiarelli hoped to minimize the fighting, he was unhappy with the decision to abandon his armor. There had been too many unforeseen twists and turns. If tanks and Bradleys were not needed, Chiarelli would park them in the motor pool, but he wanted to have them at hand.[17]

Like many other commands, the 1st Cavalry Division was forced to use its tankers and field artillerymen as infantrymen. Indeed, the division used its entire artillery section that way. To Chiarelli, it seemed unfair that only infantrymen and Special Forces qualified for the Army's Combat Infantry-man Badge when so many other troops were performing the same mis-sions. So over the course of the deployment he would push the Army to adopt a new variant of the award, the Combat Action Badge, for which any soldier who took part in combat could qualify.

On Sunday, April 4, one of Chiarelli's battalions was in the process of relieving an outgoing unit in Sadr City when one of its patrols was ambushed in the late afternoon. In the seven-hour gun battle that followed, seven soldiers from the incoming unit and one from the outgoing unit were killed, and the newly arrived brigade commander, Colonel Robert Abrams, saw just how weak the new Iraqi security forces at his disposal were. On the first day of the fighting, 80 percent of one Iraqi National Guard bat-talion deserted, as did 70 percent of another.[18] The next morning, Chiarelli was touring the battlefield with Dempsey and Lieutenant Colonel Gary Volesky, the Sadr City battalion commander, when a soldier asked him why the division had left so much armor at home. It was the only ques-tion Chiarelli was ever asked by a trooper that he was unable to answer. Returning to his headquarters at Camp Victory near the airport, Chiarelli began to lobby furiously for the rest of his tanks. With no time to send the armor by ships the M1s had to be flown by "strategic airlift," C-17 Globemaster transports, which were capable of hauling only one Abrams tank per plane.[19]

The Sadr City uprising taught Chiarelli another equally important lesson about the Sadrist enemy he was up against. During the first few days of their revolt in Sadr City, the Mahdi Army took over all of the district's power stations, and instead of rationing the electricity in accordance with the CPA plan kept it going around the clock. The move would be unsustainable in the long run since it would merely drain power from other parts of the Iraqi electrical grid. But it sent a powerful, if misleading, message to the impoverished Iraqis who lived in Sadr City: if Sadr was in charge instead of the Americans or the Iraqis they had appointed, they would have electricity all the time. It was a shrewd move by the Sadrists and a portent of more to come.

In a pattern that would emerge over and over again in the years ahead, when the Mahdi Army took to the streets in Sadr City, it also did so in cities across southern Iraq, throwing the area into chaos. The spiraling violence meant that Sanchez's command was fighting on multiple fronts. It also exposed one of the command's conceits: its multinational character. In an effort to foster the impression that the American intervention had international backing and ease the strain on the American military, south-central Iraq had been placed under a multinational force, whose members operated under separate and often restrictive rules of engagement. The international troops had been deployed in the south precisely because the American command considered the region to be one of the most benign in Iraq. Most had come to Iraq expecting to do little more than occupy checkpoints and conduct patrols. But while the Bush administration had touted the "coalition of the willing" it had assembled for the invasion of Iraq, much of that coalition was not that willing or that able.

Across the south, allied forces came under attack, and each national contingent responded differently. In and around Karbala, where two Polish battalions and a Bulgarian battalion were based, the Poles managed to hang on to city hall, but other sites were quickly taken over by the militia. In Kut, the Ukrainian commander kept most of his troops at their rural base, leaving the British-led CPA team, two dozen Ukrainian soldiers, and a handful of armed contractors to fend for themselves downtown, where they quickly ran out of ammunition and then received orders from Baghdad to withdraw. And the Italian governor of Nasiriyah, Barbara Contini, made a deal with the Mahdi Army that her troops would stay on their base across the river from the city, infuriating Bremer.[20]

In Najaf, the Shiite city of a half million that boasted the Imam Ali

Shrine, one of the two holiest sites in Shiite Islam, Mahdi Army fighters besieged the CPA compound. When the small contingent of military and Blackwater guards there took casualties and ran low on ammunition, it was a Blackwater Little Bird helicopter that arrived first to resupply them. Two CPA men, a retired Vietnam veteran named Jim Steele and a colonel named Jim Coffman on temporary duty from the Pentagon, pushed ammunition to the defenders on the roof of the compound before Special Forces and eventually Sanchez himself arrived to survey the situation.[21]

Robert Ford, the American diplomat who would later become renowned for his outspoken opposition to Bashar al-Assad's repression as the United States ambassador in Damascus, also had seen some of the problems with the coalition in Najaf in the months before the battle. A career diplomat, Ford had been serving in Bahrain when Powell sent out the call for all able-bodied Arabic-speaking foreign service officers to go to Iraq. Ford had been assigned to Najaf, where he served as the one-man branch office of Bremer's CPA.

At that time, U.S. Marines had handed over responsibility for securing Najaf, Karbala, and south-central Iraq to Spanish, Honduran, Salvadoran, and other multinational forces, which shared the zone with a small force of U.S. Army military police. In an effort to maintain a modicum of control, Ford had encouraged the Badr Corps, the armed wing of SCIRI, to keep its militia off the streets and arranged for the U.S. Army's military police to run the Najaf checkpoints, though they were careful to keep their distance from the Imam Ali Mosque in the old part of the city. His effort to deliver the message had been a memorable one as he and a Marine lieutenant colonel in civilian dress were briefly detained at gunpoint by Badr Corps militiamen while their interpreter was beaten, but the policy stuck. That is, until Spanish commanders gave the Badr fighters carte blanche to set up their own checkpoints. The Badr militia threw its weight around to the point that it and the Army MPs were almost at the point of firefights. With no reliable phone communications with Bremer's headquarters, Ford sent an urgent email message appealing for the CPA to countermand the decision.[22]

It had not been the only disconnect between the Americans and their Spanish-speaking allies. After the Iraqi Central Court issued a secret warrant for Sadr's arrest, Ford was shocked to learn that a Honduran checkpoint had stopped Sadr in October only to release him. The Hondurans explained that nobody had ever instructed them to apprehend Sadr or even to contact Bremer's man in Najaf if Sadr was found. The episode, never publicly disclosed, was one of the major "what-ifs?" that haunted the war. From his Iranian exile and during his time in his hometown of Kufa, Sadr would continue to vex the coalition for years.[23]

At first, Bremer's authority sought to put the best face on the situation. After the CPA reported that its representative in Kut and other bases in the south were pulling back, Dick Jones, a top deputy to Bremer and a former ambassador, insisted in an April 6 teleconference with the White House that the coalition was gaining ground in restoring security. The Iraqis in the south were not rallying to Sadr, and the success of the American-led coalition in bringing Sadr's Mahdi Army to heel would have a salutary effect by encouraging other militias to put down their arms and join the CPA program to be integrated into the Iraqi security forces. As Jones gave his presentation, an aide on the NSC made a note to himself: "overly optimistic."[24]

Sanchez's command treated the events with less equanimity. Scrambling to respond, Sanchez froze the departure of the units Chiarelli was supposed to replace: Dempsey's 1st Armored Division and the 2nd Armored Cavalry Regiment, which was attached to Dempsey's unit. On April 9, Dempsey announced to his troops that they had been extended and began moving soldiers, tanks, Bradleys, helicopters, and other equipment back from Kuwait and in some cases even from Germany. The division became Sanchez's on-the-fly reserve, and pieces of it began to be parceled out across the south immediately.

Dempsey's division's first blow fell in Kut. The division's 2nd Brigade commander, Colonel Ralph Baker, led a reinforced battalion to the Ukrainian camp outside Kut on April 8 and, barely pausing to refuel, moved into the city from two directions. While Apache helicopters and an AC-130 gunship demolished the Sadrist political headquarters, Baker's troops retook the bridges and the CPA compound and occupied them until reinforcements from the 2nd Armored Cavalry Regiment arrived the next day, allowing the assault force to return to Baghdad and prepare for the next hotspot.

Things were not so easy in two other cities where the Mahdi Army had a firmer grip, Najaf and Karbala. Even getting forces to the outskirts of the cities where they could assess how to proceed was difficult. Central Iraq's highways were under siege by Sunni insurgents. Resupply convoys were coming under ferocious attack. On April 14, five bridges were destroyed along Route Tampa, the main artery from south to north, leading the occupation authority to declare the highway off-limits to civilian traffic. In effect, Iraq's major roads had become another front. It was another sign that the resistance had the ability to coordinate, even, it seemed, across sectarian divisions: Sadr, according to an American intelligence report, dispatched weapons and supplies in mid-April to the Sunnis fighting in Fallujah, veiling it as "humanitarian assistance" for the trapped residents of the cities.[25]

To regain control of Najaf, American battalions and companies were pulled from Baqubah, Tuz, and Mosul and assembled into an ad hoc brigade, Task Force Duke. The unit lost its first soldier before it got to Najaf during the forty-hour, hundred-mile road march to get there. Once the task force got to Najaf it spread out around the outskirts of the city, but Sanchez balked at actually sending them in, fearful that doing so would only inflame the revolt further. For ten days, the unit contained the city before being pulled back and replaced by a smaller force around April 20.

In the meantime, the small CPA compound at the edge of the militia-controlled city remained under a kind of siege, outside the protective sphere of Task Force Duke, which had been ordered not to go that close to the city unless the post was on the brink of being overrun. Ron Neumann, an American diplomat who had been an infantry officer in Vietnam and who was working at the CPA, flew down to see if the precariously situated compound could be held a few days after it was first attacked. He went with the two men who had been tossing ammunition boxes from the Blackwater helicopter on day one, Steele and Coffman. "Everyone was holed up in the main CPA building because their trailers were getting riddled with shrapnel every night," recalled Neumann. "They would stay there every night, watch war movies, and then go up on the roof and have a gun battle."[26]

Unlike Najaf, U.S. troops did push into the cities of Karbala and Diwaniyah. In Karbala, Polish troops defended some government buildings, but the Mahdi Army controlled most of the inner Old City where they turned the Mukhayem Mosque into a headquarters and arms depot. The job of taking Karbala back fell to the 1st Armored Division's 1st Brigade, under Colonel Pete Mansoor. In the second week of May, Mansoor's main battalion, 1-37 Armor, joined the nascent Iraqi Counterterrorism Task Force and its Special Forces advisers in attacking the Mukhayem Mosque just outside the Old City, one of the few significant contributions that the Iraqi forces made to righting the situation.

Now all that was left was the Old City, where the militia was entrenched everywhere except the Hussein and Abbas shrines, which guards loyal to the Badr Corps still held. The brigade rehearsed its final assault, but on the evening of May 20 word came that it, like the assault on Fallujah a month earlier, had been called off. The brigade managed to push the militia out anyway, though. The same night, Mansoor sent a tank company to run along the edges of the Old City, daring the militia to fire, from their headquarters next to the Hussein Shrine. The militia took the bait, firing an RPG at a passing tank, and an AC-130 demolished the headquarters. The Mahdi Army pulled out of the Old City, and two days later American troops moved in without resistance. It was another demonstration that even in an urban setting, tanks had their uses after all.

After several more weeks of fighting in the south and in Sadr City, the bloodied Mahdi Army would stand down on Sadr's orders. The cleric's June cease-fire was the first of many he would issue throughout the war in order to preserve the militia after it took heavy losses.

On May 5, after the dust had mostly settled in Anbar but with fighting still continuing in the south, Bush convened an NSC meeting to review the military situation in Iraq. John Abizaid, the CENTCOM commander, expressed confidence that the situation was getting under control.

"There is a better mood in the Sunni community," Abizaid said regarding Fallujah. Abizaid said that he had been in touch with the head of the Fallujah Brigade, and pressed him on the need to restore order. "We have been aggressive and on the 10th of May, the Marines are scheduled to conduct joint patrols."

Bush wanted to be sure the Iraqi forces did not sit on their checkpoints and were aggressive. "Are we dealing with the sitting duck syndrome?" the president asked. "We need offensive operations and publicity—these oil infrastructure attacks are not isolated."

"We are going to squeeze Sadr," Abizaid stated, promising that the Americans and the Iraqis would also be aggressive on their second front. The president seemed encouraged by the move but advised that the military needed to "anticipate another enemy surge."[27]

CHAPTER 5

A Lost Cause?

With the June 30 transfer of sovereignty fast approaching, the White House turned its attention to messaging. There would need to be a presidential speech in anticipation of the event, one that would make clear how the transfer of sovereignty complied with the president's larger strategy of spreading freedom throughout the Middle East, but a speech that avoided any imitation of the blunder Bush had committed when he landed under the "mission accomplished" banner on the USS *Abraham Lincoln* aircraft carrier soon after Saddam fell.

On May 6, the Deputies Committee met to focus on strategic communications. Jim Wilkinson, the NSC media man who had overseen the million-dollar press center Tommy Franks had used in Qatar during the invasion, was tasked by Hadley to handle "the optics of the transfer" of power. Hadley wanted his media team to come back with a storyboard depicting the visuals the administration would present, in addition to a script.[1] A few days later, Hadley returned to the point. "We need to find a way to describe our strategy between today and June 30 and then beyond the 30th because the events that occur between now and the transition will serve as evidence that the strategy is happening," he said.

On May 13, Hadley met again with top aides to discuss Bush's role. As for the presidential address to the nation, each point, Steve Hadley said, would need to contribute substantially to explaining how the Bush administration was going about achieving its strategy in Iraq. The address, Hadley continued, should take note of three to five scenarios that were challenging and for which the United States needed to be prepared. Dan Bartlett, the White House counselor, heartily agreed. "We don't want others to frame the debate," he said. The president needed to "give a little to gain a lot." The administration would have no credibility if it did not acknowledge the mounting difficulties the United States was facing in Iraq. That meant, in part, owning up to the insufficiency of Iraqi security forces while stressing that Dave Petraeus was being sent back to Iraq to train the Iraqi military and police. The message would be that Bush was "steadfast on ultimate goals but can be flexible and agile when faced with challenges about the realities on the ground."[2]

Behind closed doors, it was clear there were challenges aplenty, including in the northern city of Mosul that Petraeus had more or less managed to stabilize earlier in the year. While Bremer's CPA was generally upbeat on the situation in Mosul, the CIA told the White House on May 17 that the occupation authority had painted a picture that was "far too rosy." The fractious political scene made Mosul very dangerous, the agency reported. Too, there were vexing issues having to do with the transition itself. In a May 20 White House meeting, Hadley put one impolitic question on the table: what if the newly sovereign Iraqi government asked the United States to cease its occupation and leave? "We don't want that question to be asked," Hadley mused. "They could ask us to leave despite the UNSCR language, but hopefully they will not."[3]

UNSCR referred to a Security Council resolution that was to be passed supporting the transfer of sovereignty. There was some unfinished business there as well. The White House wanted the resolution to stipulate that the Iraqi forces would be "in" the multinational command the Americans led in Baghdad. This was meant to codify the Bush administration's expectation that burgeoning Iraqi forces would be overseen by American commanders with the power to veto their operations—at least for a good while. The British and other members of the Security Council, Hadley reported, preferred "with," which left open the possibility that the Iraqi forces would be directed by their newly sovereign government. It appeared that this position would hold sway. It was a small matter, but one that reflected the administration's concern that it somehow retain a measure of control even as it formally transferred sovereignty.

Armitage raised another issue: how to measure the progress, or lack thereof, that the American-led coalition and the Iraqis were having against the insurgency. "We are having a hard time getting a metric," he said. Harriet Miers, a Bush favorite whom the president would later unsuccessfully nominate for a seat on the Supreme Court, stressed the importance of measuring and publicizing what progress had been made. "How good we do is limited by how well we can communicate our success," she said.

On May 24 Bush was to deliver his address to the nation. With opposition to the war growing, the White House had taken to arranging the president's major speeches at military bases, the better to ensure an appreciative audience and a patriotic backdrop. Bush flew by helicopter to the Army War College in Carlisle, Pennsylvania—the first visit by a sitting president to the college since George Washington's. In a gymnasium festooned with flags, Bush outlined the plan for a sovereign Iraq firmly on the path of elections and constitutional governance. To ensure that insurgents or militias could not derail the plan, the troop withdrawals the Pentagon had hoped for and even advertised would be temporarily suspended. The stubborn insurgency that had reared its head in April and the inevitability of brutal fighting to come—the very factors that critics had cited as a reason to withdraw—had made it all the more imperative in Bush's mind to triumph in a titanic struggle between good and evil. The American goal was not merely to beat back the Sunni insurgents, quell the Shiite militias, and stop Syrian and Iranian meddling. It was to build a stable and democratic Iraq in a land that had never known representative government. "The rise of a free and self-governing Iraq will deny terrorists a base of operation, discredit their narrow ideology and give momentum to reformers across the region," Bush vowed.[4]

Brahimi, Bush explained, was working on the composition of the new Iraqi government. American civilians would do their part rebuilding Iraq's dilapidated infrastructure, and one of the United States' most experienced diplomatic hands—John Negroponte—would be there to make sure that the political-military strategy worked. The speech was everything Hadley and Bartlett had imagined: one that acknowledged the hard days ahead but that expressed unyielding confidence. It closed with a full-throated declaration of Bush's doctrine of freedom. "Our actions, too, are guided by a vision. We believe that freedom can advance and change lives in the greater Middle East, as it has advanced and changed lives in Asia, and Latin America, and Eastern Europe, and Africa," Bush said. "And when that day comes, the bitterness and burning hatreds that feed terrorism will fade and die away. America and all the world will be safer when hope has returned to the Middle East."

As the White House worried about the transition, Brahimi and Blackwill were putting the final pieces of the new Iraqi government in place. As Blackwill had told the White House, the U.N. envoy had championed a government of technocrats. When it came to picking a prime minister, Brahimi thought he had found just the man: Hussein al-Shahristani, a nuclear physicist turned Iraqi official. Born in Karbala, Shahristani had received a doctorate in chemical engineering in Canada and had married a Canadian woman. He had returned to Saddam's Iraq, where he was made the chief scientific adviser to the Iraqi Atomic Energy Commission. Accused of "religious activities"—Shahristani later told an interviewer that he provoked Saddam's ire by refusing to work on Iraq's nuclear weapons program—he was arrested in December 1979, interrogated, and imprisoned for eleven years in Abu Ghraib, much of which time he spent in solitary confinement. Deprived of books, newspapers, or a radio, he kept himself busy by inventing mathematical problems and trying to solve them, in addition to reciting the Koran from memory. One night when Baghdad was blacked out and under attack by the Americans during the 1991 Persian Gulf War, Shahristani escaped with the help of a sympathetic guard, linked up with his family, and headed north to Kurdistan and eventual exile in Iran, among other places.

Shahristani's name as well as others—Ibrahim al-Jaafari, Adil Abd al-Mahdi, and Mahdi al-Hafidh—were floated to Grand Ayatollah Sistani in phone conversations with his son. The Shiite cleric made clear that he had no problem with the appointment of any of them, but made no mention of Hafidh, a former Iraqi diplomat to the United Nations and deputy to Pachachi. Hafidh was soon excluded from consideration simply because Sistani had not acknowledged the name.[5]

At one point, Shahristani's appointment as prime minister seemed so assured that the U.N. team began to look for office space for him. Bremer himself had voiced no objections to him. But as the Americans began digging into his background they were unable to account for his entire stay in Iran, a U.N. official recalled, and the apprehension about appointing a figure they were not intimately familiar with got the better of them. Nor did it help that rivals complained that he was too close to Tehran. So the search for an interim prime minister began anew.

Ayad Allawi was not on the initial short list for prime minister. Allawi was the scion of a prosperous Iraqi family—his father was a doctor and parliamentarian while his mother hailed from a prominent Lebanese Shiite family. He came of age in Baghdad before Saddam's rise to power, a cosmopolitan capital of coffee shops and cinemas, no doubt more fondly remembered through the prism of nostalgia. Allawi attended Baghdad College, a preparatory school for boys that was housed on a twenty-five-acre campus on the east bank of the Tigris. Founded and run by a group of American Jesuits—the school was sometimes known as "B.C. on the Tigris"—the academy accepted Muslims as well as Christians and, before they were expelled from Iraq, Jews. As the school grew in prominence it supplanted Alexandria, Egypt, as the place for the sons of Baghdad's elite, including Adil Abd al-Mahdi, who would rise to prominence with the Iranian-based Supreme Council for the Islamic Revolution in Iraq, and Laith Kubba, who would serve as a government spokesman.[6]

The Baghdad of Allawi's privileged youth did not stay peaceful for long. The Hashemite monarchy, which had been installed by the British, was overthrown in 1958, and Abd al-Karim Kasim, a nationalist Iraqi Army officer, grabbed power and set out to improve ties with Moscow. The Iraqi Communist Party appeared to be getting strong, and a nationalist pan-Arab movement, the Baathists, began to push back. The burly Allawi cast his fate with the Baathists, and managed to insert himself in the thick of things. Years later, Allawi recalled, he had been drawn to the Baath Party by its opposition to communism, its anticolonial ideology, and its embrace of pan-Arabism. After Kasim was toppled by another coup, the Baathists came to power, only to be swiftly deposed nine months later by military officers who sought to unify Iraq with Egypt and Syria. For five years, Colonel Abd al-Salaam Arif governed the country, and the Baath Party was forced underground; Baghdad was convulsed by a round of brutal and often lethal infighting. However, in 1968 the Baathists managed to infiltrate the military and took power in a bloodless coup, which culminated in the ascension of a ruthless party member from a small town near Tikrit, Saddam Hussein.

Allawi and Ahmed Chalabi had crossed paths as youths in Baghdad. Chalabi also hailed from a prominent and prosperous family and attended Baghdad College before his family left the turmoil in Baghdad and moved to Lebanon. Though the Allawis and Chalabis were related, the two boys were never close. "He was not an athletic person and did not have any political inclinations like me and Adil Abd al-Mahdi," Allawi sniffed almost half a century later. Over the years, their rivalry deepened. Though he came late to politics Chalabi became a formidable organizer and proselytizer for the opposition. After graduating from the Massachusetts Institute of Technology and then getting a Ph.D. in mathematics from the University of Chicago, Chalabi taught mathematics at the American University in Beirut for several years and then founded Petra Bank in Jordan, before allegations of fraud prompted him to flee the country.

The differences between Allawi and Chalabi went far beyond personality and extended to the most fundamental questions of how to build a post-Saddam regime in Iraq. Allawi was a living example that an anti-Saddam alliance could include converts from the old Baath Party and military order. His American backers included the CIA, which was also operationally inclined to influence, bribe, and otherwise win over local forces. Chalabi wanted to remove the old power structure root and branch. By the time Zalmay Khalilzad gathered together the Saddam opposition in London in December 2002, Chalabi was already committed to a stringent form of de-Baathification—the term "de-Baathification," Chalabi proudly recalled later, was coined by his daughter Tamara—and to a purge of the Iraqi Army, an approach that, not coincidentally, would have enabled him to strike at Allawi's base of support inside Iraq and clear a path to power for himself.[7]

"We thought that the best way for change is from inside Iraq by the establishment itself," Allawi recalled. "The differences between me and Chalabi grew wider. He was in support of de-Baathification. This was before the downfall of Saddam, before the war."[8]

After a run-in with Saddam and a wave of arrests of party members, Allawi determined that it might be better to live abroad. He decamped for Lebanon and, finally, London, where he pursued his studies in medicine. To what extent Allawi kept up his Baathist affiliations during the early years of exile is a matter of contention. What is clear is that he eventually became a target for the Baghdad regime. After Saddam's henchmen tried to murder Allawi and his wife in England, Allawi founded the Iraqi National Accord, a movement that sought to elicit support from Iraqi Army officers, diplomats, and high-ranking officials in Baghdad who harbored grievances against Saddam. Traveling throughout the Middle East, he pursued the backing of Turkey, Egypt, and Saudi Arabia, who he hoped would not only back his movement—Hosni Mubarak allowed him to broadcast anti-Saddam messages from Cairo—but also encourage the Americans to do so as well. Along the way, Allawi developed ties with British intelligence and with the CIA.

The Americans figured that Allawi's long-standing ties with American and British intelligence would make him unacceptable to Brahimi, so they began promoting him to serve as minister of defense. "I said, 'What is the authority of the minister of defense?' By then the army was dismantled," recalled Allawi, who said he turned down entreaties by Bremer, Blackwill, and Brahimi. "Who is going to be prime minister, and who are the rest of the Council of Ministers? They said that the prime minister they are think-ing of is al-Shahristani."[9]

After rebuffing the offer, Allawi was told that an important visitor carrying a personal message from President Bush wanted to meet him in Amman. "So I went to Jordan, and the guy who came to see me was George Tenet," said Allawi. The CIA director—a somewhat ironic envoy, given that the main rap against Allawi was that he was too close to West-ern intelligence—again pressed him to take the defense minister post, and again he turned down the job.[10] Not for the last time Allawi made it clear that he would not play second fiddle to anyone. After returning to Bagh-dad, Allawi argued that the Iraqis on the Governing Council should decide who should be prime minister, not Brahimi or Bremer. In the end, he man-aged to line up enough support for himself and, with the blessing of the United States, the Governing Council announced on May 29 that he would get the job.

Iraq's new government still needed a president, a largely ceremonial post. But symbolism was important: with a Shiite prime minister, the job ought to go to a Sunni. Ghazi Mashal Ajil al-Yawar, a Mosul-born Iraqi who got his master's degree from George Washington University, worked as a businessman in the Persian Gulf, and whose uncle was head of the Sham-mar tribe, badly wanted the post. During a term as the rotating head of the Governing Council, Yawar had effusively thanked Bush for overthrowing Saddam, which had forever put him in the president's good graces. Yawar stood in stark contrast with Pachachi, who had condemned the Marines' offensive in Fallujah to the Americans' chagrin.

Still, Brahimi believed that the eighty-year-old Pachachi was a man of greater stature and experience and the better choice. When Yawar was told by Brahimi that he had been passed over, he startled the U.N. team by burst-ing into tears.[11] Over the ensuing weeks, Yawar continued to display his sen-sitivity to slights real and perceived. On a helicopter flight with Bremer from Mosul to Baghdad, an American crewman, with a lamentable lack of fore-sight, placed Yawar in a Black Hawk helicopter's "hurricane seat"—when Black Hawks flew with their doors open, as they often did in 120-degree Iraqi heat, the right-rear passenger seat became a kind of vortex for the rotor wash, uncomfortably buffeting and contorting whoever was in it. Back in the capital, Yawar called Ali Khedery. "Why do you do this to us?" he asked in exasperation. "We are your friends—don't insult us like this!"[12]

But Yawar would have a second chance. After some of Pachachi's critics among the Shiites mounted a campaign against him in the press and misgivings on the part of some Governing Council members became evident, Pachachi decided to pass on the post. The way was clear for Yawar to serve as president.

One important piece of business remained. If elections for a democratically elected government were to be held no later than January, some basic decisions regarding the electoral process had to be taken. In theory, one option would have been to allocate seats in the prospective parliament to each of Iraq's eighteen provinces based on estimates of their population and then allow people in each province to vote on a slate of local candidates who would represent them. Concluding that there was no way to organize a vote along those lines and still hold elections by January 2005, as the White House wanted and Sistani was insisting, the U.N. with Bremer's support opted for another: all of Iraq would be considered a single electoral district. This would have enormous implications. The electorate would cast their vote for a national slate, not an individual, and the party bosses would determine who was on their lists. No representative would be accountable to their local constituency. This system gave the well-funded religiously based parties a huge advantage, solidified the role of the party leaders, and magnified the consequences of even a partial election boycott. But it was the simplest way to organize the vote in the time available, so the plan was agreed upon without much discussion or debate.[13]

The impending transition was enormously important to the State Department. At Rumsfeld's insistence, the Defense Department had been given the lead for postwar planning, and Jerry Bremer was a power unto himself, at least until Rice and Blackwill brought him to heel and made him rework his plan. With Iraq moving toward sovereignty, however, the United States would finally have an embassy, an ambassador who was a close colleague of Colin Powell, and normal reporting arrangements.

The State Department's intelligence analysts saw nothing but problems. Foggy Bottom had its own intelligence shop—the Bureau of Intelligence and Research, whose leading Iraq expert, Wayne White, had been decidedly skeptical about the triumphalism within the administration during the invasion. His analysis of the situation since the opening shots of the war made him even more skeptical about the prospects for tamping down the Sunni insurgency and building an inclusive government in

Iraq. The White House seemed to think that its new plan to expedite sovereignty for Iraq would take the sting out of the occupation and undercut the insurgents. But why, White asked, would the Sunnis welcome the hastening of a government dominated by Shiite exiles? Thomas Fingar, a former Stanford University academic who ran INR, as the bureau was known, felt that any despairing assessment would be rejected by much of the administration, especially since Department of State intelligence experts had a reputation for being contrarian. He urged White to canvass analysts throughout the government to arrive at a broader summary of the thinking in the intelligence community. White did as much, but the result was no sunnier.

The highly classified memorandum—which had been completed on April 7, in the middle of the Fallujah battle, and was provocatively entitled "Iraq, Falluja, and the Sunni Arab Heartland—A Lost Cause?"—was marked "SECRET//NOFORN": not to be shared with allied intelligence services. It noted that the more than a dozen agencies that made up the American intelligence community had convened the previous week to begin work on an updated NIE, or National Intelligence Estimate, on Iraq. At the session, the memo noted, the INR representative had asked whether any of the analysts thought Iraq's Sunni heartland was "irretrievably lost, both politically and militarily." About half of the intelligence analysts present said yes.[14]

There were grave reasons for concern. The number of insurgent attacks was up in Sunni areas. Punitive coalition military operations in Fallujah would likely "boomerang" and generate more unrest in other Sunni areas with tribal links to Fallujah. Nor would Fallujah stay quiet after an American operation against insurgents who had taken refuge there; it would revert to its previous "unruly, hostile posture." Providing a list of "poor fundamentals" that bedeviled the administration's project in Iraq, the memo virtually guaranteed continued armed resistance. Even Ahmed Chalabi, the memo noted, had acknowledged to Blackwill that he had no answer to the "perennial problem" of Iraq's Sunnis. The memo listed eight factors:

- "A large number of Sunni Arabs still believe they have no stake in the Coalition vision for Iraq: many believe that, with U.S. backing, Shia and Kurds are taking over much of the government Arab Sunnis once dominated, leaving them out in the cold and vulnerable to retribution."

- "Because so many Sunni Arabs held jobs in the Ba'ath Party, the security services or a bloated military—none of which will be reconstituted anytime soon—unemployment is far worse in Iraq's Sunni heartland and is likely to remain so for a long time."

- "Sunni Arabs were intensely proud of their previous status in Iraqi society and appear to be less tolerant than other Iraqis toward 'occupation.' Residual pan-Arab Ba'athist ideology makes them more susceptible to comparisons with the Israeli occupation of Arab territories to the West. It is no coincidence that the most significant outburst of anger in Iraq following the assassination of Shaikh Yasin in Gaza occurred in the Sunni Arab city of Ramadi."

- "The image of the Coalition among all too many Arab Sunnis continues to be shaped by largely hostile regional Arab media, with Coalition public relations efforts drowned out by far more prolific Arab sources of anti-U.S. commentary, false conspiracy theories, and negative spin regarding ongoing developments."

- "Violence has reduced the ability of contractors to function in Sunni Arab areas, impeding reconstruction and feeding conspiracy theories that the Coalition unduly favors Kurds and Shia in this respect."

- "Foreign fighters appear more active in Sunni Arab areas of the country, compounding the security challenges there."

- "In the face of the aforementioned challenges, local Sunni Arab police and other security elements are the least loyal and effective in the country, often presenting little more than a speed bump in the face of a determined anti-Coalition insurgency or, worse, are assisting those engaged in armed resistance."

- "Those tired of violence and who might cut a deal with the Coalition—primarily some tribal sheikhs—probably have little sway over the militant Sunni Arab 'street.' In addition, many who wish to cooperate with the Coalition in Sunni Arab areas have avoided doing so for fear of violent local retaliation."

It would be difficult to imagine a more dispiriting analysis. Bush's confident Army War College speech suggested that Ambassador Negroponte would be advancing a well-conceived program of political reconciliation and nation-building, an elaboration of Bremer's efforts. White's classified assessment, however, suggested the impossibility of the mission. The memo was even more pessimistic than Derek Harvey's earlier assessments. Like Harvey, it argued that giving the Sunnis a stake in the new Iraq was more important than organizing elections. Unlike Harvey, it did not see a way forward and discounted the prospect for working with Sunni tribes. Fingar sent the memo to Powell, who in turn circulated it to Vice President Cheney, Defense Secretary Rumsfeld, White House chief of staff Andy Card, and CIA director Tenet. With some understatement Powell scribbled a terse cover letter: "Another perspective. CP." A copy of the memorandum was also made available to General Richard Myers, the chairman of the Joint Chiefs of Staff, who had it faxed to General John Abizaid, the head of CENTCOM. "John, this analysis seems about right to me," wrote Myers. "As you have said, the political dimension of this situation is fundamental to the way forward."

In late June, Negroponte set off for Jordan to acclimate himself to the Middle East for a few days before flying to Baghdad to assume his ambassadorship on June 30, even as Bremer would be heading out. Bremer was engaged in intensive consultations with the White House about the last-minute logistics of the transfer of his authority and his departure. There had been a steady stream of intelligence reports asserting that the insurgents were planning a devastating series of attacks—"The Greatest Battle of Baghdad"—to rock the ministries in the Green Zone, bloody the coalition, and frustrate the much anticipated handover of power to the new Iraqi government. Insurgents were reported to be making their way to Baghdad from their strongholds outside the city. If the intelligence panned out, Bremer and his team might find themselves under attack as they made their way to the airport. The scene would be reminiscent of the American withdrawal from Saigon. Rice raised the issue with Bush, who suggested a preemptive gambit: the Americans would foil the insurgents by handing over sovereignty early. Bremer mentioned the ploy to Allawi, who thought it was a good idea. Bremer was also on board, on condition that his departure would be in the wake of relative quiet so it would not appear that the CPA was being chased out.[15]

Bush and his national security team were at a NATO meeting in Istanbul on Sunday, June 27, when Bremer called Rice and said that the number of attacks had been sufficiently low to render Monday a "go." On Monday morning, Bremer and Rice reconfirmed the decision. Hoshyar Zebari, who had been picked to serve as the foreign minister of the interim Iraqi government and was also at the NATO meeting, had heard that Bremer's departure might be pushed forward for security reasons. A British official even told him that the handover of sovereignty would be timed to coincide with the NATO summit. Zebari figured that if the news was going to come out it should come from an Iraqi. So he announced the impending event to the media, upsetting the White House's laboriously crafted strategic communications plan. "I said that Iraq is sovereign and that we would declare our sovereignty sooner than what had been planned," Zebari recalled. "This was my first experience breaking a story. They didn't expect it, and I personally feel that they didn't like it."[16]

As the minutes ticked down on the Baghdad handover, Barham Salih, a Kurd who was to serve as deputy prime minister in the new government, met with Allawi. The Americans, Allawi told Salih, had decided to hand over sovereignty that morning. The prime minister in waiting was apprehensive about the next steps. "Can you imagine," he told Salih. "I am the prime minister of Iraq, and I do not even have a battalion." At 10:26 a.m. Bremer handed over a blue binder of documents to Iraq's chief justice, Medhat al-Mahmoud, who was accompanied by Shiite interim prime minister Allawi, Kurdish deputy prime minister Salih, and Sunni president Yawar. Hope that Shiites, Sunnis, and Kurds might work together was in the air. A red Koran was presented and Allawi took the oath of office. "You have said, and we agreed, that you are ready for sovereignty. I will leave Iraq confident in its future," Bremer told the assembled dignitaries. "There is no way to turn back now," Yawar declared.[17]

In Istanbul, Rice passed Bush a memo noting that Bremer had handed over the paperwork that officially conferred sovereignty on the Iraqis. "Iraq is sovereign," Rice's note read. "Letter was passed from Bremer at 10:26 a.m., Iraq time." Bush leaned over to give the news to Blair, the British prime minister and Bush's closest ally in his project of liberation. Before he did so, the president grabbed a black felt marker and scrawled "Let Freedom Reign!"

As an additional security precaution to foil the potential surface-to-air missile threat, Bremer had made arrangements to engage in a last bit of political theater. He would get onto a C-130, exit surreptitiously, then fly out of Iraq on a CIA turboprop plane. Salih escorted Bremer to the airport and walked with him to the C-130. "I said to him, 'What are your parting thoughts on Iraq?'" Salih recalled. "He said, 'You are a tough people.'" Salih was not sure if Bremer meant hardy or obstinate but suspected that he might have intended the latter.[18]

Not everyone got the heads-up that Bremer was leaving early. In Jordan, Negroponte was in the middle of his morning swim at the embassy when an aide notified him to his surprise that the CPA had already closed shop. Negroponte got out of the pool, dried himself off, and made preparations to leave. Negroponte would be flying to Baghdad on the same CIA turbo-prop plane on which Bremer would be arriving.[19]

There was another notable consequence of the early transfer. Some of Bremer's own aides had been caught by surprise. Ron Neumann, the intrepid Foreign Service officer who had survived the siege of the CPA compound in Najaf and would stay on to run the political-military section of the embassy, had worked to set up a foundation in Kirkuk with a British CPA officer named Emma Sky. They thought if the Arab, Turkmen, and Kurdish communities in the city had a program to administer jointly, it might help them to reconcile as well as rebuild the city. One hundred million dollars had been earmarked for the venture with the money coming from the proceeds from Iraqi oil exports that the United Nations had handled during the Oil-for-Food Program under Saddam's rule. Ghazi al-Yawar and Bremer had gone to Kirkuk to announce the project, and Neumann and Sky worked extensively to lay the groundwork: a board of local notables had been established to oversee it; and arrangements to transfer the $100 million had been made with a bank in New York. But with the deliberations over the transfer shrouded in secrecy, Neumann was left in the dark. Now that Iraq was officially sovereign, the U.N. and the CPA no longer had the authority to transfer the $100 million. They had missed the deadline by four hours. The money was never transferred; the foundation never came into being.[20]

When Negroponte arrived in Baghdad and presented his diplomatic credentials to the IIG, as the Iraqi Interim Government was known, the Iraqis indicated that a harsh crackdown was in the works to quell the chaos. The CPA had suspended the death penalty, Zebari said in a meeting with Negroponte and Neumann, implying that newly sovereign Iraq planned to restore it. Arab societies, he continued, were accustomed to seeing justice rendered directly, including the use of televised confessions, a practice Iraq would later return to, but which had been forbidden by Bremer's occupation authority, Zebari added disapprovingly. Zebari was championing the rule of law as imagined by Iraqis. The implication was clear: the Americans should expect to see some tough measures enforced. There was even talk that Allawi might impose a state of emergency.[21]

Three days after arriving in Baghdad, Negroponte sent a blunt cable to

Washington, which his deputy James Jeffrey helped draft. Jeffrey, a Boston native who had attended Northeastern University, had served in the Army in Vietnam and Germany. He knew the military and was no stranger to security issues, having served as a diplomat in the Balkans, Turkey, and Kuwait. With his military background he was skeptical of the glass-half-full assessments emanating from Rumsfeld's Pentagon and Sanchez's head-quarters. There would be a temptation for the military to declare the situation greatly improved and ready for a drawdown of American troops. The Pentagon's plan to cope with Iraq, he declared at a Deputies Commit-tee meeting to discuss the transition from the CPA to an embassy, was to change the color-coded boxes that it used to measure progress in Iraq in its PowerPoint presentations "from red to green."[22] Now that the embassy was stood up and he could submit his own assessment, Jeffrey again did not mince words.

"The IIG is fighting for its life, literally in the case of security forces and officials," the classified cable noted. "The IIG knows that it has to consult with us on constructing a state of emergency law since its enforce-ment could involve coalition forces. An emergency law used to stifle politi-cal development obviously would not be helpful. An emergency law that restores public confidence on security while also allowing free political debate and competition would be a positive development."[23]

CHAPTER 6

Our Man in Baghdad

The man tasked with securing Iraq was General George W. Casey, the four-star Army vice chief of staff who had been named to take over the military command in Iraq. Like Negroponte, Casey had been given only a glimpse of the president's vision. At a White House dinner on May 31 to honor Negroponte and Casey, Bush told a story about how his father had once met the Japanese premier and reflected on how he had flown planes against Japan three decades before. Bush had related the tale to Ghazi Mashal Ajil al-Yawar, the future Iraqi president, during his recent visit to the United States, the moral being that an American president would one day sit down with the head of a free and democratic Iraq. It was the most explicit guidance Casey received from the White House before heading to Baghdad.[1]

Casey, who hailed from an Irish family in Boston, had grown up with the Army. His father was a general, and as a student at Georgetown University during the Vietnam War years, Casey had signed up for ROTC, hoping to become an armor officer before heading off to law school. These were politically tumultuous and divisive days and Casey's familial ties pulled him in the direction of the military. Casey's father, before heading to Vietnam to assume command of the 1st Cavalry Division, had given his family an admonition: if anything happened to him, they were not to talk to the media. Tragically, he was killed in a helicopter crash, making him one of the highest-ranking American officers to perish in the conflict. Casey was at Dover, Delaware, when his father's casket arrived.

Casey had not been the obvious choice to take over the military command in Baghdad. As an Army officer, he had accumulated little combat experience and had never logged a real combat command. He had flirted with joining Delta Force, but backed out fearing it would disrupt his family life. After rising through the ranks, Casey had done a stint in Bosnia in 1996 when the 1st Armored Division was deployed for peacekeeping duties and was later assigned to run the division's rear command post in Croatia. As the division's commander in 2000, he had overseen the deployment of troops to Kosovo.

It was as a staff officer at the Pentagon that Casey made his mark. Casey had served as the chief planning officer for the Joint Chiefs after the September 11 attacks and then succeeded Abizaid as director of the Joint Staff during the lead-up to the Iraq War. The job required steady nerves and long hours but provided invaluable career-building face time with the defense secretary and other top civilian officials.[2] Rumsfeld had initially favored Lieutenant General John Craddock, his senior military assistant, for the Iraq post, but, with the Senate growing increasingly uneasy about the war, Craddock's association with Rumsfeld suggested that his confirmation would be a contentious affair.

Paul Wolfowitz, the deputy secretary of defense, also had some ideas of his own. As Wolfowitz mulled over the appointment, he solicited nominations from David Petraeus, who already had a reputation as a forward thinker for his efforts in Mosul. Petraeus suggested his mentor: Jack Keane, the towering former commander of the 101st Airborne with a no-nonsense New York style. But Keane had already left the Army and Wolfowitz wondered whether the Pentagon would be sending a message that the current brass was not up to the job by calling a general out of retirement. For all that, Wolfowitz sought out Keane for his views on the matter. Keane told Wolfowitz that it was vital to elevate the command in Baghdad to four stars and install a top-notch staff. Wolfowitz asked if Keane would consider the job. Keane, whose wife's battle with Parkinson's disease had prompted him to retire, declined and suggested Petraeus, who at the time was just a two-star general.[3] His recommendation, though a nonstarter, would prove revealing: the close relationship between Petraeus and Keane would play a fateful role in the strategy deliberations yet to come.

As the Pentagon searched for a commander, Pete Schoomaker, the Army chief of staff, instructed Casey to draw up a list of candidates. Reviewing the choices on the porch at Quarters 1, his official residence, Schoomaker observed that Casey's name was not on the list. "You could do this," Schoomaker said. Casey shot back, "I know I can do it." The list was whittled down to three names and sent to the White House. Soon after, John Abizaid, the head of Central Command, called to say that Casey had the job.[4]

Casey and Rumsfeld looked at Iraq through similar prisms. Casey's Balkan service had taught him that, by assuming too heavy a burden for security and national reconstruction, the American military had merely delayed the day when host nation forces took responsibility for themselves. He shared Rumsfeld's jaundiced view of nation-building, which the defense secretary had publicly expressed in a speech a month before the war in spring 2003. The major lesson Rumsfeld imparted to the general was his attitude that American soldiers will try and do too much, recalled Casey, who hardly needed convincing.[5] In his memoir, Rumsfeld argued that he never turned down a troop request from any of his generals. But this missed a more fundamental point: there was little need to countermand your generals if you were careful about how you picked them. The defense secretary did have two specific tasks for the new Iraq commander: he wanted a status report thirty days after his arrival in Iraq and an assessment of the Iraqi military. Nearly a year after Bremer had disbanded the Iraqi Army, the goal of replacing it with a three-division force, largely oriented toward defending the country from external threat, had not been revised.

Abizaid, who held the view that the American military was an "antibody" in Iraqi society and who saw nothing but trouble in a lengthy and extensive occupation, provided Casey with more concrete guidance.[6] In a June entry in Casey's personal journal, Casey listed twenty-eight specific instructions from the CENTCOM commander. In sum, Casey had to stay resolute, finish off Al-Qaeda-linked insurgents in Iraq, and safeguard Iraq's borders. The goal should be to have Iraqi troops participate in every coalition patrol so that operating with Iraqi forces would become the norm. What is more, "Iraqis must take the lead in capturing or killing former regime elements."[7]

Casey's command was headquartered in Al-Faw Palace on what the American military called Victory Base Complex, surrounding Baghdad International Airport. Saddam had built the huge and lavish complex for the use of the elite of his regime, in spite of sanctions imposed by the United Nations. More than two thousand workers had been devoted to the project, including craftsmen from Morocco, Egypt, and Sudan as well as Iraqi convicts, who supplied much of the manual labor. The palace had been named after the 1988 battle in which the Iraqi Army had fired artillery barrages and used chemical weapons to reclaim the Al-Faw peninsula near Basra during Saddam's calamitous war with Iran. Surrounded by a large moat and luxurious villas, it had sixty-two rooms, twenty-nine gilded bathrooms, and an enormous chandelier with 256 lights. The lush area surrounding the palace had been stocked with game, catfish, and carp and used as a hunting and fishing preserve. Saddam had anticipated that his palaces would be bombed in the 2003 war with the Americans and had stored furniture in a nondescript Baghdad building for safekeeping and precisely labeled it for ease of return to its proper place. The Iraqi leader had assumed a limited war that would leave his regime intact, though an F-16 had dropped a satellite-guided bomb on the palace as a "show of force."

Looking for a location to plant his command post, Dave McKiernan, the land war commander, had moved into the abandoned palace in April 2003. By that time, it had lost much of its luster and had become a refuge for some stray goats. Only later did the Americans discover that the Iraqi prison labor that erected the palace had used the nearby salt-laden sand to mix the cement, which had the unfortunate result of eroding some of the metal structure and causing the marble slabs that were affixed to the exterior to fall off. Over time, however, the palace had been transformed into a high-tech command center, complete with a tiered auditorium that was dominated by large screens for PowerPoint presentations and video feeds. The vast palace compound itself was dubbed Camp Victory, a name that was taken from the Army's V Corps. The Al-Az villa, which Casey and his successors used as their official residence, had been built for Saddam's mother.

The rituals of military life at the Victory Base Complex began each morning with the Battlefield Update Assessment or "boo-ah," as it was known by the troops. Casey would preside as briefers covered every facet of the deployment—the latest intelligence, operations, casualties, political gossip, and troop movements. In PowerPoint representations of Iraq, towns were color-coded red (under hostile control like Fallujah), yellow (semipermissive for coalition troops), or green (under coalition and Iraqi government control). The high-tech American military had sophisticated weapons systems to attack the enemy with devastating effect. But if a commander was not careful, his technology could ensnare him and his staff in a virtual reality in the auditorium. The iconography of the presentations implied a fine understanding of the chaos that was Iraq and an orderly mechanism for influencing events that bore little resemblance to the volatile reality outside.[8]

The technology also tethered the command to Washington. The annals of military history are replete with accounts of the loneliness of command.

Casey—with 140,000 American forces overseen by his headquarters and an escalating insurgency in Iraq—was not immune. But the world of the modern-day general is informed by ceaseless communication: emails; classified videoconferences with White House and Pentagon officials; phone calls over secure lines. Casey had his first videoconference with President Bush on June 30, the day after he arrived, and by his own account talked to Abizaid almost as often as he did to his wife. The connectivity was an opportunity to solicit guidance from the home office, but also an open door for kibitzing and second-guessing from on high.[9]

In the ceremony heralding his assumption of command on July 1, Casey lavishly praised Sanchez for his vision and leadership. Those were qualities Sanchez's Army peers rarely associated with his tenure in Iraq. Sanchez's three-star headquarters had had the deck stacked against it from the start. Starved of resources, it had taken on a mission that would later be carried out by a larger four-star headquarters and two subordinate three-star ones. Nor had Sanchez come to Iraq with the expectation that he would be elevated to the command of the entire Iraq military mission. But the Army's most junior lieutenant general, who had earlier demonstrated his proficiency at tactics on the battlefield, had not proved adept at the kind of political and military skills that the Iraq command required. "Even if Sanchez had been the best three-star in the Army, he was not set up for success," was how one colonel later put it. The implication was that he was not the best three-star in the Army. Casey graciously overlooked the difficulties his predecessor had endured and vowed to pursue a strategy that would enable the Iraqis to progressively take over their own security.

Officially titled Multi-National Force—Iraq, or MNF-I, Casey's command oversaw a vast organization: 162,000 American and allied troops spread out across bases around the country. Three three-star generals answered to Casey. One was a British officer who served as his deputy—an important symbol in a "Multi-National Force." The British military had a reputation, deserved or not, for being good counterinsurgents and "thinkers." When a quarterly progress review was held at Casey's headquarters, it was always chaired by a British colonel, habitually nicknamed the "gloomy Brit."

The second was Lieutenant General Thomas Metz, the commander of Multi-National Corps—Iraq. Metz's headquarters oversaw most allied combat troops in the country, including all Army and Marine infantry units and an Army Special Forces group to which some Navy SEALs were attached. (Although based at Balad Air Base north of Baghdad, Stan

McChrystal's JSOC task force had a separate mandate, operating in Iraq, Afghanistan, and the Horn of Africa and working directly for CENTCOM.) Ironically, given Canada's opposition to the Iraq war and unwillingness to contribute troops to the coalition, Metz's deputy commander was a Canadian one-star, who was there as part of a longstanding exchange program between his Texas-based corps and the Canadian military.

The third three-star who reported to Casey was Dave Petraeus, who took on the job of building and training Iraqi military and paramilitary forces—although his command's tongue-twisting title, Multi-National Security Transition Command—Iraq, or MNSTC-I (pronounced "Min-Sticky"), had "training" nowhere in it. Petraeus had been widely lauded at home for his work in Mosul with the 101st Airborne, and the return of the media-friendly general did not fail to cause a splash. *Newsweek* put Petraeus on its cover with the headline "Can This Man Save Iraq?" almost as soon as he arrived.[10] Jack Keane had argued that with so much going wrong in the war the American public needed a hero. But the Pentagon was riddled with critics who thought Petraeus was grandstanding and getting in the way of the administration's line that the Iraqis were taking charge of their own country. Myers, the Joint Chiefs chairman, was decidedly of the view that Petraeus should be neither seen nor heard and conveyed the message in a phone call to Casey, who dutifully wrote down his instructions: "No US in View" and "Petraeus—Off Net."[11]

Even behind closed doors, there were tensions. Where Casey was deliberative, the younger man was decisive. Military headquarters are rife with nicknames, and Casey had one for Petraeus, one that alluded to his job of allocating large sums of money to different ministries: "General Sugar," as in Sugar Daddy. Though that was an unavoidable facet of Petraeus's job and Casey jokingly called him by the moniker (or a rough Arabic translation of it, "Abu Flus") in his presence, to some it seemed there was an edge to it.[12]

Three days after assuming command, Casey sent Myers and Abizaid an email indicating that the rapid standing up of Iraqi forces would pose special challenges. A group of American soldiers had observed Iraqi forces roughing up prisoners near the Ministry of Interior, intervened to stop it, and taken photos of the battered and bruised prisoners, which Casey had reviewed. "Have shared with the ambassador and his staff has taken lead to raise with the MOI," Casey wrote in his email message. "We will likely suggest that the Iraqis announce that they are aware and are investigating, but I am not sure how they will take it." Casey signed off with a jocular reference to the July 4 holiday: "May your fireworks be great and mine small!!!!"[13]

Nine days later, Casey was buoyed by a series of classified memos from the Pentagon that indicated that the United States might receive help from Muslim nations. Prince Bandar bin Sultan, the long-serving Saudi ambassador in Washington who had urged George H. W. Bush to do what he could to get rid of Saddam, had met with George W. Bush on July 13 to propose a plan that would maximize Saudi influence in post-Saddam Iraq and, he said, help the United States draw down its forces. The Saudis would put together a thirty-thousand-strong Muslim force for duty in the troubled country. The offer was deemed sufficiently serious that Peter Rodman and another Rumsfeld aide met the next day with Rihab Massoud, the deputy chief of mission at the Saudi Washington embassy, to flesh the idea out, according to a memo from Rodman to Casey. The troops were to come from Tunisia, Indonesia, Malaysia, Senegal, Bangladesh, Pakistan, and Niger, among other African and Asian countries. No soldiers from Saudi Arabia or other states bordering Iraq would be involved, but the Saudis would provide political and religious cover and hoped to arrange a separate Arab command for these troops. Rodman reported that the Pentagon liked the idea, providing that "U.N. cover" could be arranged, the United States would not assume the cost of dispatching and sustaining the troops, and Casey's headquarters would retain overall command.

Excited about the prospect, Casey's staff developed plans to have the Muslim troops protect polling stations, safeguard United Nations compounds, guard the borders, escort convoys, and even conduct joint patrols with the Iraqis in lieu of American forces. But the idea of deploying Sunni troops in a nation with a Shiite majority government had little appeal for the new Iraq authorities; moreover, the true extent of Saudi enthusiasm for the proposal was unclear. In a late July meeting at the White House, Elliott Abrams, the Middle East hand on the NSC staff, questioned whether the Saudis were doing all they could to persuade Pervez Musharraf, the Pakistan leader, to contribute forces. "We have no indications that the Saudis have pushed hard on this," Abrams said. "They have not offered to pay, but if they did it would help Musharraf." "Would it be helpful to have Allawi talk to Musharraf?" Bob Blackwill asked. Aides at the NSC resolved to make another push, but the idea of bringing in Muslim troops, which was kept under wraps, gradually faded. Petraeus, for his part, never took the idea seriously.[14]

The specter of Vietnam had haunted the American military for so long that it was hard to imagine that anything good might have come out of the war. During Negroponte's years in Vietnam as a young diplomat he had observed that Ellsworth Bunker, the American ambassador in Saigon, chaired a Mission Council that included the embassy's political officers as well as the military staff. It was an arrangement that Negroponte thought was well worth emulating. Casey, too, wanted to synchronize military and civilian planning. Soon after arriving in Baghdad the commander—famous for jotting down barely legible notes on small index cards, which military historians later had to strain to decipher—scribbled that it was time to bring the bickering between the military and civilians to an end: there would be "one team" with "one mission."

To forge a common vision, Negroponte and Casey established the "Red Cell," whose ranks included embassy officials, military officers, and intelligence experts, as well as a few British officers and diplomats. The Bush administration's goal was to guide Iraq toward full and lasting sovereignty by holding elections no later than January 2005. The Red Cell was to generate a big-picture report that, Casey later observed, aimed thoroughly to assess "what's the nature of the enemy and the nature of the war we are fighting."

Robert Earle, a retired Foreign Service officer, who had worked for Negroponte in Mexico and written a novel along the way, was summoned for Baghdad duty at the ambassador's request. Earle bore much of the responsibility for drafting the assessment. Earle had arrived in Baghdad with a box of books, intending to do research for a new novel about ancient Palestine. Instead he was given a desk and told to work nonstop in preparing an assessment, which only officials with access to classified information would read. His military counterpart was Major General Hank Stratman, a deputy chief of staff to Casey. Derek Harvey, who had been analyzing the insurgency full-time since the first days of the invasion, provided the intelligence analysis for the team.[15]

As the cell saw it, the main challenge did not come from the Shiites—notwithstanding that a major rebellion by a Shiite militia, the Mahdi Army, had derailed planned troop withdrawals just weeks before. Since the Shiites made up a majority they could consolidate control through the ballot box and had no interest in thwarting the elections. Besides, the Red Cell had little interest in picking a fight with the Shiite establishment that was bound to control the new Iraqi government. These were just the political facts of life. Stratman told Earle that the coalition did not have enough forces to take on both the Sunnis and the Shiites.

But there were problems galore. The big reconstruction programs were in trouble. They were being stymied by the insurgency and were not employing many Iraqis anyway. The promise that the $18.4 billion the White House had earmarked for reconstruction would erase unemployment had not been fulfilled and, as the program was structured, would probably never be. That money needed to be reprogrammed and directed toward smaller job-creating projects and improving security. Despite Iraq's symbolic sovereignty the insurgency was more active than ever. The Fallujah Brigade that Jim Mattis had assembled to keep order had fallen apart and, as far as the Marines were concerned, was little different from the insurgency it was meant to contain—so much so that on June 19 American air strikes on targets in the city had resumed.

After several weeks of discussion, the team met with Negroponte and Casey to present its initial findings. The United States, the team members argued, had not come to terms with the character of the conflict or the lack of coordination of its response. Harvey and Earle talked about the importance of working with the Sunni tribes. (Earle had heard from the CIA station chief that the agency had also tried to work with the tribes but that Bremer had not supported it.)[16] The principal danger came from the Sunni tribes, who needed to be lured into the political system before they fully bonded with the insurgents. When the idea of forging an alliance with the tribes was briefed to Negroponte and Casey, they dismissed it. Like Bremer, Negroponte saw his mission as building a new Iraqi state and had little interest in strengthening an age-old Arab order. The idea of reaching out to the tribes would be shelved for now.

The cell's final assessment did not pull any punches. There were eight thousand to twelve thousand Sunni insurgents and fewer than one thousand Islamist terrorists. The former were seeking to restore their place in Iraqi politics and society; the latter wanted to bring down the pillars of the state. Still, both were sufficiently flexible to make common cause at times against the occupiers and the new Iraqi authorities.

"The insurgency is much stronger than it was nine months ago and could deny the Interim Iraqi Government (IIG) legitimacy over the next nine months. In response, the coalition must find ways to strengthen the IIG in all dimensions of national power (political/economic/security) and facilitate political reconciliation. Otherwise, the insurgency will grow more violent and the election and constitutional process will be endangered," the Red Cell stated in its report. "The Interim Iraqi Government (IIG) shares our mission but is in the early stages of consolidating the aspects of national power that, combined with public consent, underpin any nation's legitimacy and enable it to defend the people's sovereignty. Our aim is to bolster the IIG's legitimacy in perception and in fact. This is a major challenge," another document based on the report noted.[17]

Like the State Department's intelligence assessment, the Red Cell saw a plethora of difficulties in Iraq. The diplomats and military officers in Baghdad did not have the luxury of pronouncing the mission a lost cause. They had been charged with defining a way forward and finding a way to make the mission work. That entailed making sure the January elections took place as planned, supporting national reconciliation, stopping external support for the insurgents, building Iraqi forces, protecting the United Nations presence in Iraq, and helping the Iraqi government provide jobs and services. Signaling their agreement, Casey and Negroponte each signed the Joint Mission Statement outlining this program, which was sent to Bush on August 17.[18] The chasm between the military and civilian efforts in Iraq, which had characterized relations between Bremer and Sanchez, had been narrowed. For the first time, there was a unified vision.

With the Joint Mission Statement as a framework Casey and his team drafted a detailed campaign plan for future military operations. The plan covered an eighteen-month period and was entitled "Operation Iraqi Freedom (Partnership: From Occupation to Constitutional Elections)." The plan began, somewhat incongruously, with a Japanese proverb: "Vision without action is a daydream, but action without vision is a nightmare." The vision was clear: an "Iraq at peace with its neighbors, with a representative government that respects the human rights of all Iraqis, and security force sufficient to maintain domestic order and to deny Iraq as a safe haven to terrorists." As ambitious as that was, the White House later proposed one more desideratum: "an ally in the War on Terror." Casey obligingly added it to his formulation.[19]

While there were many armed groups and factions in Iraq, "the preeminent threat," the plan asserted, was Sunni insurgents and former members of Saddam's regime—the plan referred to them as "Sunni Arab Rejectionists" and "Former Regime Elements"—who were supported by Iraqi Baathists who had taken refuge in Syria. The long-term goal was not to defeat the insurgents—that was deemed to be too lengthy and costly a mission—but to "reduce the insurgency to levels that can be contained by ISF, and that progressively allow Iraqis to take charge of their own security."

The assumption was that the period leading up to the January 2005 vote would be one of maximum vulnerability, but that if the election were held, the main danger would pass. The machinery of democracy would yield an elected parliament, which would pick a prime minister, and via a national referendum in October 2005, approve a new constitution that would enfranchise the Iraqis, bring the Sunnis into the process, and take the steam out of the insurgency. It fell to the American-led coalition to "create and sustain irreversible momentum toward a freely elected Iraqi government" and the subsequent "Iraqi Self-Reliance Phase."[20]

The Iraqis had only a few battalions of army troops, although less formal "pop-up" units were beginning to be seen in some parts of the country. Their so-called Civil Defense Corps, a workaround Abizaid pushed for after Bremer dismantled the Iraqi armed forces, was composed chiefly of locals hired and given a few weeks of training. So the main burden of securing the way to the January election would fall on American troops, who would have to eliminate the insurgents' safe havens, particularly in cities in the Sunni Triangle so that voters could go to the polls there. Sixty percent of Iraq's population lived in fifteen cities. Of these, seven were the focus of American military operations.

In Washington, Steve Hadley's Deputies Committee was kept apprised of the strategy. As Casey's plan was being hammered out, Lieutenant General Walter "Skip" Sharp, the director of planning on the Joint Staff, noted that the plan provided for monthly assessments of the situation in the cities. In Baghdad, Lieutenant General Thomas Metz, who as Casey's corps commander oversaw day-to-day military operations, suggested one important change. The military had a phrase—"center of gravity"—which denoted the principal objective of a military campaign. Metz suggested in a classified memo that the plan explicitly treat the support of the American public as a "center of gravity." The war had taken a difficult turn and would be all but impossible to wage if voters at home opposed it. "As of today we most certainly do not have the support of the international community nor that of the people of Iraq," Metz wrote. "At best, we have only the most grudging support of the Iraqi people, who are waiting to see if we can bring them security and some measure of economic development. Beyond that, most of them want us to leave as soon as possible."[21]

The notion that the campaign plan should aim to win over the American public was controversial: it raised the possibility of accusations that the command might exaggerate its accomplishments to secure backing at home. Stratman was unhappy about Metz's recommendation and asked Earle if he could get Negroponte's help to knock it down. But Metz's idea was carried over into the plan, which defined the strategic center of gravity as "coalition public opinion." It noted that the operational center of gravity was the "legitimacy of the transitional Iraqi government," which the Americans and Iraqi politicians would need to work hard to establish.

A more problematic goal outlined in the plan was to "change the Iraqis' perceptions of Coalition Forces," who, because of early mistakes, were no longer seen by many Iraqis as benevolent liberators. Casey had a Commander's Initiative Group, brainy officers who were supposed to advise him on strategy and operations. They analyzed reams of polling data collected by the American occupiers, accounting for challenges ahead: 50 percent of those surveyed did not feel safe in their neighborhoods and only 23 percent felt that the presence of the coalition contributed to their safety. The Iraqis' confidence in the new Iraqi government was no more impressive. Confidence in Prime Minister Allawi's ability to improve the situation had declined from 74 percent to 62 percent since July 2004. Few had heard of the National Conference in Baghdad, which was held in August, and the National Assembly, which was convened in September, had been eclipsed by the standoff in Najaf. When Iraqis were asked to name the most trusted leaders, "none" was the most common pick and "don't know" was a close second. The most revered leader in Iraq was Sistani, the Shiite cleric who insisted on keeping his distance from politics, even as he repeatedly refused to meet with the Americans.

Casey's campaign plan had not even been formally issued when Robert Ford received a call from the Iraqi governor in Najaf. Convinced that, during his 2003 tour in Najaf, his messages to Bremer's CPA were not making their way to Washington, Ford had used his Hotmail account to send reports to Ronald Neumann, his former boss in Bahrain.[22] Accounts of Ford's role in Iraq had come to the attention of Negroponte, who asked him to return to Baghdad, this time as the director of the embassy's political section. Now, almost a year after his time in the holy Shiite city, events had run full circle.

A tenuous cease-fire had broken down. The immediate reason for the crisis was the July 31 detention in Karbala of Sheikh Mithal al-Hasnawi, a Sadrist lieutenant, which the militia responded to by kidnapping a group of policemen in Najaf before attacking a U.S. patrol there on August 2. The Mahdi Army was in the streets. Muqtada al-Sadr was reported to have taken up residence in Najaf. The governor was holed up in his office with a small and not particularly proficient group of police. He wanted American help, he told Ford, and fast.

The campaign plan had portrayed "Sunni rejectionists" as the main obstacle to a stable Iraq. Indeed, the main thrust of Casey's campaign plan was to reclaim Fallujah, Samarra, and other cities that were under the sway of Sunni insurgents so that the January election could proceed on schedule. But the trouble was again coming from the Shiites, namely Muqtada al-Sadr and his Mahdi Army militia. The events in Najaf were an object lesson in how Iraq could upset the planning of even the most expert officials.

When Ford heard that another battle had broken out in the holy city, he went looking for Negroponte. He found the ambassador having lunch in the embassy cafeteria with Ron Neumann, who was now running the embassy's political-military section. Negroponte said that this was a crisis the Iraqis should be capable of handling on their own. It was clear to Ford and Neumann—who had had a harrowing time of his own in Najaf when the CPA office there was besieged in April—that the Iraqi forces lacked the capability to do that. Neumann gently noted that Ford had experience in Najaf, and it would make sense for him to head there to report on the situation. Ford caught a helicopter to Najaf later that night.

As always, turmoil in one Sadrist stronghold spread instantly to others, threatening to open up the same second front—a Shiite one—that had strained the military in April and that the Red Cell had discounted. A British base in Maysan Province took four hundred rockets and mortars, and in Kut, Ukrainian troops ran low on ammunition fighting Sadr's militia. In Sadr City, "Abe" Abrams's brigade once again faced street battles. According to a secret cable from Robert Ford, the Baghdad slum's police chief even ordered his men to stand down instead of helping American troops to quell the violence. When an American helicopter was shot down on August 7, the police colonel was seen leading his men in celebratory fire.[23]

Sadr was young—just thirty-one at the time of the Najaf battle—relatively inexperienced, and lacked the religious qualifications that his father, an ayatollah, had enjoyed; he was, for instance, not qualified to issue fatwas. Indeed, his father's true ideological successor was widely considered not to be Sadr himself, but a cleric based in the Iranian holy city of Qom who had close ties to the Iranian regime and the Dawa Party, Grand Ayatollah Kadhim al-Husseini al-Haeri. Sadr's lack of worldly sophistication was evidenced when he met with Sergio Vieira de Mello, the U.N. envoy, and his deputy, Jamal Benomar. In contrast to Grand Ayatollah Ali al-Sistani, who was well read in Iraqi politics and international affairs, Sadr had trouble understanding the very concept of the United Nations. After Vieira de Mello told Sadr about the 191-nation body and its desire to help in Iraq, Sadr told the puzzled U.N. envoy that he had no problems with "Christian organizations."[24]

The looming battle in Najaf would put on display Sadr's complex and evolving relationship with Iran. Much of the young cleric's appeal stemmed from the fact that, like his martyred father, he had stayed in Iraq throughout the Saddam years rather than fleeing to Iran and Syria as had many of the leaders of the Dawa Party and SCIRI.[25] But since the fall of Baghdad, Sadr's tone toward Iran had changed. As a junior cleric he needed the endorsement of the Iran-based Grand Ayatollah Haeri. After Haeri gave Sadr this endorsement, in May 2003, the young cleric had made his first trip to Iran.

According to one of Sadr's closest aides at the time, Qais al-Khazali, who was later captured by British commandos, on the visit Sadr met not only with Haeri but also with Brigadier General Qasim Suleimani, commander of Iran's Quds Force, and Abdul Reza Shahlai, another Quds Force officer (who years later would be linked by the Obama administration to the alleged assassination plot against Saudi Arabia's ambassador to the United States). The Quds Force was the arm of Iran's Revolutionary Guard charged with intelligence collection, back-channel diplomacy, and covert operations in Iraq, and the trip was the beginning of a long and rocky association between the force and the Sadrist Trend, which had long taken pride in its independence from Iran.

By the time the battle of Najaf kicked off, Iran was keeping a close eye on its new Iraqi ally. Embedded with Sadr and his forces in the holy city was an Iranian Quds Force operative named Sheikh Ansari—"most likely Hossein Ansari," according to an American intelligence report. Ansari worked for Department 1000, the Quds Force branch that was responsible for special operations in Iraq. Acting as an adviser to Sadr and the Mahdi Army, his role included "taking part in combat operations with JAM Sheikh Adnan (aka Abu Muhammad)," a Mahdi Army commander. Sadr had previously led an uprising against the American military, but this would be his first against a post-Saddam Iraqi government.[26] The cleric's fateful decisions to use the Imam Ali Shrine as a military headquarters and seek assistance from Iran ensured that the politics of confronting Sadr—no easy task to begin with—would be even more complicated this time around.

To fill the void left by the departure of Dempsey's 1st Armored Division, CENTCOM had reached deep into its pockets for two Marine expeditionary units, each of which was based around one infantry battalion. Collectively, the Marine force was smaller than the Army unit they were replacing. The main coalition force in Najaf, the 11th Marine Expeditionary [U]nit, which reported to a Polish general, had only just arrived in late July and had been CENTCOM's reserve for the entire Middle East theater.

The newly arrived Marines quickly found themselves drawn into combat with Sadr's militia, especially in the Valley of Peace Cemetery abutting the Old City. A six-square-kilometer expanse of tombs the size of small buildings where a large number of Iraq's Shiites choose to be buried, the cemetery made for a ghoulish, quasi-urban battlefield. As the fighting worsened, Casey, Metz, and Conway, the senior Marine in Iraq, visited Najaf and rushed more forces to the fray. Two of Chiarelli's battalions came south from Baghdad, with one of them joining the Marines in the cemetery fight and the other pushing into the city to establish a cordon around the shrine where Sadr and his commanders were holed up. The Americans had sought to whittle down the Sunni resistance and prepare for the next stage of the fight in Fallujah, which was deemed to be all but inevitable, but now they were headed for a Shiite slugfest. The military made sure that a handful of newly built Iraqi units were also present for the battle, the Iraqi Interim Government's first. One, the 36th Commando Battalion—the sole unit that had acquitted itself well in Fallujah—performed well. Others, crippled by limited training and almost no resources, did not.[27]

By the middle of August American troops were inflicting punishing losses on the Mahdi Army in Najaf, forcing its lines to collapse ever closer to the Imam Ali Shrine. The shrine itself, though, had to be dealt with using the utmost care, as it was among Shiite Islam's most sacred sites, despite the fact that Sadr had elected to use it as a military command post. The politics and optics of moving on Sadr's cohorts in the shrine were riddled with complication, as became apparent when the generals and diplomats began to dig into the details of the operation. If the United States wanted to put an Iraqi face on the assault, as it would have to, it would have to rely on the 36th Commando Battalion. The Americans had about seventy Special Forces soldiers disguised to look like the Iraqi commandos and would accompany them if the operation took place. But the subterfuge could be carried only so far. To push their way through Najaf's embattled streets, the force would need to use Amtracs, large personnel carriers the Marines used. More important, there were reports that Sadr had more than five hundred fighters around the shrine.

As the Americans pondered the difficulties of the situation, a potential solution emerged from an unexpected source: Mowaffak al-Rubaie, Allawi's national security adviser. At the very beginning of the battle, Rubaie had received a phone call from Grand Ayatollah Sistani's son. The ayatollah was ill and needed a visa to see a heart specialist in London. Complicating the request, his and his son's passports had been issued by Iran. The ayatollah had never bothered to secure an Iraqi passport, having seen no need for it. After a few hours, the British approved the request for the visas, and Sistani, his son, and their personal physician drove from Najaf to Baghdad in an undercover car. A private jet was hired to take Sistani to London. American Humvees escorted the unusual convoy to Baghdad International Airport, the stipulation being that no vehicle could be closer than fifty yards to Sistani's at his insistence. The cleric had made it a practice to keep his distance from American officials, and his stance toward the occupiers was not about to change now. With Sistani out of the country, the United States had lost a voice of moderation and restraint in Najaf. But Sistani's departure also opened up a window for action, if the Americans and Allawi wanted to move against Sadr.

When Hadley's Deputies Committee met on August 17, it appeared that an operation would go forward. The American military was actively planning to go into the Najaf shrine to "dig out Sadr," reported Frank Miller, the senior NSC staff member for defense issues who had just returned from a trip to Iraq. The Iraqi government, he added, was trying to put out the word that Sadr was defiling the mosque. "Ambassador Negroponte thinks Sadr's death will create violence, but that it can be handled," Miller added.[28]

Eight days later, Bob Blackwill pulled aside a few aides to help him prepare for a trip to Baghdad. One of the issues they discussed was the political implications of clearing out the mosque by force and what Sistani's response would be. The best-case scenario, Blackwill said, would be if "Sistani awakens after they have freed the mosque." The worst case, he added, would be if "Sistani wakes up, the mosque has been damaged and fighting has not abated."[29]

With the crisis building, Rubaie received an unusual visitor: Abu Mahdi al-Muhandis. An Iraqi who had spent long years in Iran,[30] Muhandis was close to Qasim Suleimani, commander of Iran's Quds Force, so close, in fact, that Iraq's Interior Ministry privately told Iraqi Foreign Ministry officials that they considered Muhandis to have been an actual member of the Quds Force, according to a classified American report.[31] Muhandis had been close to the most extreme elements of Badr, the military wing of SCIRI that Iran had backed against Saddam, and was believed to be linked to the 1983 bombing of the American embassy in Kuwait. In appearance, Muhandis was unassuming, almost slovenly, and wore sandals. It was clear that he had his own connections: Muhandis made it into the Green Zone without an escort to meet with Rubaie.[32]

A peaceful solution to the situation could be had, Muhandis explained, as Rubaie in turn would tell Allawi and Casey: it might be possible to negotiate a way out with Sadr. Iran had an interest in bringing the battle to an early close. Even though its Quds Force had at least one military adviser embedded with Sadr, Iran was also backing an array of Shiite politicians in the upcoming January elections. The Islamic Republic had as much reason as the Americans to ensure that the violence in Najaf would not prevent the elections from taking place. Rubaie and Muhandis flew by helicopter to Najaf with Brigadier General Dennis Hejlik, who was commanding the Marine effort there; they then drove with him in a Humvee to the governor's office. It was unusual for the United States to be transporting an ally of Suleimani's Quds Force, but Rubaie did not advertise Muhandis's Iranian ties, simply insisting all the while that he was a channel to Sadr.

Rubaie came close to meeting personally with Sadr, but their session was aborted when the rebel cleric grew suspicious that the encounter was a setup and failed to show. For years, Rubaie harbored suspicions that his own whereabouts were being tracked as a means of pinpointing Sadr. An American official involved in the efforts told a slightly different story. Specialists from the NSA, the United States' electronic eavesdropping agency, were monitoring Sadr so that the American special operations forces could detain him if the go-ahead was given, when to their surprise, Rubaie entered the picture.[33]

Working through Muhandis, Rubaie came back to Allawi with the draft of a settlement that the prime minister felt gave in too much to Sadr's demands. Rubaie was relieved of his negotiating responsibilities. As the standoff continued, word came that Sistani had recuperated from his heart treatments and was returning to Iraq. Allawi wanted the Americans to close Iraqi airspace but he did not prevail. "I wanted him to stay in London, to finish this," Allawi recalled. "We wanted to get Sadr out of the shrine." As his frustrations grew, Allawi became so agitated that he slammed his fist on his desk and broke his right hand.[34]

As the Americans had hoped, Sistani's return offered the best hope to ease the confrontation. Sistani flew to Kuwait and drove to Basra. He led a widely publicized march from Basra to Najaf. On August 26, Sistani arrived in Najaf in a convoy of thirty vehicles, with many more of his followers trailing behind. Under the protection of a cease-fire that Allawi had declared, Sistani and Sadr met in the Imam Ali Shrine and agreed on the terms of a truce. The next day, Sadr and his men left the shrine, handing the keys over to Sistani. With the fight for the holy city over and American troops pulling back, Colin Powell reminded reporters that the warrant for Sadr's arrest in connection with the murder of Khoei was still valid—"right now we are not pursuing it."

Putting a halt to the fighting before it reached the Imam Ali Shrine suited the purposes of both the United States and Allawi's government. Sadr had rebelled, and his forces had taken a serious beating. But for the second time, he had ended the rebellion in an agreement that would allow him to gradually repair the losses his Mahdi Army had taken. In Sadr City, meanwhile, his forces kept fighting. Only after another month of pressure from the tanks and Bradleys that had now joined Chiarelli's troops—backed up by AC-130 Spectre gunships, whose nighttime whir would be familiar to Sadr City residents for years to come—would the Mahdi Army finally stand down in the slum.

On August 31, the CIA informed the NSC of its postmortem analysis of the Najaf episode. The agency concluded that Sistani's stature had been enhanced.[35] Sadr had only marginally been diminished by the outcome, for the Mahdi Army had not been disbanded and Sadr's statements about joining the political process were hardly credible. Allawi's government, whose credibility the Americans had hoped to shore up through their new strategy, had benefited least.[36]

CHAPTER 7

New Dawn

The events in Najaf drove one point home to Ayad Allawi: his supposedly lofty post did not confer on him the wherewithal to cope with the violence in Iraq. George Casey and John Negroponte had cobbled together a plan to lead Iraq to elections but Allawi was afraid that Iraq's enemies were multiplying faster than the Iraqi government's ability to deal with them. The issue seemed all the more pressing because Fallujah had fallen into the hands of an assortment of Baathist and Islamist insurgents led by Abu Musab al-Zarqawi.

In a confidential letter to Bush, Allawi decided to go over the heads of the generals and diplomats. "The situation on the ground in Iraq is grossly unstable. The threat is now much greater than it was a year ago and it is continuing to escalate," Allawi wrote on August 19 to the president. "Our friends in the USA promised and delivered us their help and assistance before and during liberation, however now it seems that the authority to do so does not exist."[1]

The Iraqi prime minister had never been in favor of the deep de-Baathification Bremer had pursued or his decision to build a new military from scratch. In his London exile, Allawi had wanted to reach out to the disgruntled members of the Baath Party and the military and enlist them in the campaign against Saddam. But now his problem was more of a practical one. As prime minister, Allawi controlled few real levers of power.

Alarmed by the slow progress in building a new Iraqi Army, Allawi implored the president to reverse—at least partially—Bremer's decree to disband the Iraqi Army. "We need to immediately beef up our forces in Iraq by calling back 2 of the mechanized divisions in the old Iraqi army," he wrote.

The Iraqi prime minister was planning a trip to New York to speak, along with other world leaders, to the United Nations General Assembly and wanted to use the opportunity to huddle with Bush and discuss the steps ahead. "The points that I have outlined above are simply just a few of the barriers that I face in order to proceed with the progress that we have so far together accomplished," Allawi added. "I would like to once more reiterate my sincere gratitude for your heroic deeds to this date and I look forward to visiting you in New York on the 21st of next month so that I can present you and your people with this gratitude in person."

Allawi's appeal put the White House on the spot. Since the invasion it had been accustomed to telling the Iraqis what needed to be done by way of security. Now, its partner had his own ideas and was demanding more of a say. Determining how best to support Allawi had not, in fact, been an easy question for the Bush administration. At the Pentagon, Donald Rumsfeld had been so concerned with shrinking the American military footprint in Iraq that he had complained in a White House meeting in July that 240 SEALs were "consumed" in efforts to protect what the military called Tier 1 officials: Allawi and the top Iraqi politicians that governed the country. "It is not a good optic to have the U.S. protecting them," Rumsfeld argued. "The U.N. must get with contractors or train the Iraqis themselves."[2]

Condoleezza Rice was not persuaded. "We can't let Allawi down." The assassination of Iraqi leaders could throw the country into a tailspin, and the Americans were best poised to prevent that. That ended the debate for a while, but it was a point Rumsfeld would stubbornly return to.

The United States, in fact, was not the only country Allawi had approached to speed the development of a dependable Iraqi military. Egypt's Hosni Mubarak had sent fifty military vehicles. The United Arab Emirates had provided speedboats and a few helicopters. King Abdullah of Jordan had offered eighty wheeled armored vehicles. Worried about where the vehicles might end up, American troops insisted that the machine guns that were mounted on them be removed when they crossed the border. That did not deter Allawi. "I told the Ministry of Defense: 'go and find the black market.'"[3] But only the Americans had the capability to fund and properly equip a new Iraqi Army, and Allawi was keeping up the pressure. After writing to Bush, Allawi called Tony Blair and asked him to use his influence with the president.

Still, Rice was concerned that Allawi, who was courageous but famously disorganized and often given to conferring with foreign leaders on the sly, was not as effective as the administration needed him to be. "Allawi is a one-man band. Some things are falling through the cracks," Rice said. "Are we getting him help on staffing?" Allawi and the Bush administration, it seemed, were hardly hearing each other: Allawi wanted Iraqi forces he could command and control; the Americans wanted to bolster his effectiveness by helping him to manage affairs of state better.

As Allawi's visit approached, the reports out of Iraq were not encouraging. September 7 marked a grim milestone: the number of American soldiers killed in Iraq since the invasion hit one thousand. With just two months to the presidential election in the United States, there was enormous concern at the White House that the statistic would assume outsized importance in the debate over the war and the president who had decided to wage it. Hadley met with the White House press team to help formulate a communication plan and draft a speech for the president to acknowledge the great sacrifice of U.S. service members. He also wondered if there was a different strategy the military might employ to hold down its losses—at least for a while.

"Blackwill says that Allawi is buying some time," said Hadley, who questioned whether that was enough. "Do we need to change our strategy? What do we do if we are in a 60–90 day hold? How many engagements are they conducting against us? How many are we conducting against them? Do we hunker down?"

"What do we generate to determine how we're doing in Iraq?" Hadley continued. If the measure was the casualty count the verdict would be a harsh one. Having raised the question, Hadley moved toward a solution. The metrics could include a list of countries that were cooperating with America in Iraq, the strength of the coalition, recruitment rates in the American military, tribes won over to the side of the Iraqi government, employment statistics, the number of Iraqis registered to vote, and assassinations. Hadley proposed a rating system, perhaps color-coded to help "tell us what is going on and what adjustments must be made."

When it came to Iraq, Bush, too, was hands-on and had his own ideas for how to help the Iraqis. One week before Allawi's visit, Bush chaired an NSC meeting and suggested how Allawi might persuade the Sunnis to throw their support to the new government. "Get Allawi on TV in Iraq," Bush interjected. The president's own political instincts were shaping his advice. "We need him to say things on TV. Let him show the will to succeed. He must address what is going on." When John Abizaid, the CENT-

COM commander, reported that Jordan's King Abdullah believed that the Iraqi Sunnis were ready and willing to work with Allawi, Bush proposed: "Abdullah ought to be taking the lead on TV."

As the meeting continued, the president wanted to know if there was a sense that Iraqis were getting tired of Zarqawi. "Why aren't they coughing him up?" Bush asked. "They are getting fed up," Negroponte reassured the president. At that point, Dick Cheney observed that opinion polls indicated that the number of people who felt the country was on the right track is "better in Iraq than in the U.S."

When the conversation drifted back to Allawi, Rice raised another concern. Now that Iraq was officially sovereign, Allawi's travels through-out the Middle East in search of political support or arms were a poten-tial problem. Big decisions were looming on Fallujah and other military operations and Allawi could not always be found. "Are we worried that Allawi is spending ten to eleven days [a month] outside the country?" she asked. Negroponte explained that when Allawi was gone the United States worked with the deputy prime minister. "We deal with Barham Salih," said Negroponte. "He's good."

Richard Myers, the Air Force general who served as chairman of the Joint Chiefs, was not reassured and reinforced Rice's point. Myers said that he was worried about command and control issues. There might be major decisions to make on operations in Iraq and getting decisions made by the new authorities in Baghdad might prove difficult when the prime minister was on the road.

"Do we have an understanding and a communications plan to work with Allawi while he is out of town?" Bush asked. If the United States could not persuade the itinerant Allawi to spend more time in Baghdad, it had better develop the means to communicate with him on a secure line when sensitive decisions came up. Negroponte and Casey promised to work on the matter.[4]

On September 23, Allawi called on the White House. He opened the meeting, the notes from the session show, by emphasizing Iraq's need for reconstruction funding and investment before he addressed security issues. As expected, the prime minister repeated his appeal for two Iraqi mecha-nized divisions and a rapid deployment division, which he said were "vital" for Iraq. Petraeus's effort to train the new Iraqi Army was critical, but it was taking too long. "The arming of units is not taking place," asserted Allawi, who predicted that the insurgency would only escalate in October and November.

Hoshyar Zebari, the Iraqi foreign minister, who joined the prime minister at the session, chimed in to support Allawi's point. "The perception is that the U.S. isn't serious about building an army," Zebari said. "We must build an army quickly and Iraqis must confront the insurgency. But we can't build the Iraqi Army without APCs [armored personnel carriers] from Jordan. Timing is important." Rice countered that the United States had studied Iraq's military needs and already had in place a good plan, which the indefatigable Petraeus was running. Though Rice did not say so, the Pentagon had argued that operating two mechanized divisions would be too great a logistical challenge for the new Iraqi military and wondered if Allawi just wanted to have a lot of tanks on hand for show. "There is a difference between what we're doing and what you want," Rice put it diplomatically, adding that recalling mechanized divisions was "outside our plan."

Would you accept less fully manned and equipped Iraqi Army units just to have them in place? Rice asked. It soon emerged that Allawi was more concerned with how soon he would have operational divisions than with buying a lot of tanks and armored vehicles.

As to Fallujah, where a mix of Sunni insurgents and a hard-core band of militants led by Zarqawi held sway, Rice wondered: "Can we wait out the insurgents?" Allawi was full of bravado. "Go sooner," he said, stressing that the operation against Zarqawi should be spearheaded by the Iraqi security forces and that the support of tribes should be solicited. "Hit them hard and maintain pressure," he added. "Fallujah is the prime target."

"What about Baghdad?" Rice asked. "The insurgents are scared," Allawi insisted. "They saw Najaf and Samarra. That is why they hit the ISF, exposing their desperation. They are feeling the squeeze in Sadr City." Zebari was more cautious: "We lack intelligence and must apply Iraqi solutions to Fallujah," he said. "Even Saddam could not control it. In Baghdad we must crack down on criminals."

"How about the political atmosphere," Rice inquired, "what is the mood of the populace?" "Iranian intervention is a problem," Allawi said. We must "ensure a decrease in Iranian intervention and increase Sunni participation. We are working hard on the Sunni problem and must go ahead with national reconciliation." "Syrian and Iranian influence will keep some from participating in the upcoming elections," Zebari added. "The UN has a plan that I consider to be workable. The one district approach will prevent the rise of Islamist radical groups." Secretary Rice closed the meeting by reaffirming American support: "Iraq will succeed. We will stand by you."[5]

The next day Bush gave British prime minister Tony Blair a report on Allawi's visit in a 7:20 a.m. phone call. The two leaders had made common cause to take on Saddam and had been hurt politically by the failure to uncover WMD. The Bush administration and the Blair government had been besieged by critics. The two leaders often discussed the raw politics of the war—at home and abroad—and sought to reassure each other that for all of their difficulties they were on the right track.

We are "down the stretch," Bush said in reference to the upcoming presidential election contest with John Kerry, who had criticized Bush's management of the war but had not gone so far as to declare the decision to invade Iraq a mistake. "The best thing Kerry has is Zarqawi, but the Allawi visit helped."

"Same here," Blair responded. "We've got to deal with the argument that 'You got us into this and made a mess of it.' We need to say this is part of a worldwide struggle" against terrorists. Bush agreed. "If Saddam was still there, he would have emboldened them," the president said.

"Iraq is the battleground; stay and see it through," Blair added. Like the White House team, Blair had some concerns about Allawi's management style. The American elections were not the only thing on his mind. He wanted to see Allawi prevail as well. "He needs a professional staff," Blair continued. "He also needs a proper political strategy and a proper strategic communications strategy. He needs an organization with a chief of staff. We need to I.D. the correct Iraqis. The January elections are critical."

"He thinks he can win," Bush said of Allawi. Allawi "must get the Kurds and moderate Shia" to participate, Blair observed. Sistani needed to stay involved. "It's an organizational task, but Negroponte and our U.K. ambassador are doing a good job. You gave a good speech to the U.N. and Congress."

"Zapatero is a weak fish," Bush said of Spain's prime minister. The Socialist politician had campaigned on a platform of pulling Spain's brigade out of Iraq, and won.

"Most of these folks want the U.S. to fail," Blair said. "What about reconstruction problems? What is the story?"

"We moved money to quick reaction projects, but the security situation precludes spending the money," Bush responded. "What about Iran?"

"We just need to toughen up," Blair said.

The conversation then shifted back to American politics and the presidential debates in the United States. "The electoral map looks good for us," Bush said. "We're in good shape."

"Kerry has gone full out on attack," Blair said.

"He says he can do the Bush plan better," Bush allowed. "Kerry doesn't know what he believes." For his part, Bush did not lack confidence in his convictions or in the "freedom agenda" to spread democracy. Bush saw Iraq and the Middle East as the setting of a Manichaean struggle between the proponents of democracy and the forces of evil. The terrorists, Bush continued, want to "get Iraq, get Kuwait, topple Saudi Arabia, control the oil assets and drive up prices. We can't let a future President or Prime Minister be faced with that."

After the September 11 terrorist attacks, Blair responded, there were two views about how to deal with terrorists: you could go after them root and branch or merely increase security measures. "You and I," the British prime minister said, "believe that we must go after them root and branch."[6]

There was no mistaking what the root-and-branch approach meant in Iraq. With the battles of Najaf and Sadr City over, in October the attention and resources of the American command shifted west again, to Fallujah, which had to be dealt with before the January elections. The elections could not go forward, in Allawi's and his American partners' view, if Iraqi cities were in enemy hands.

The first step was to regain control of Samarra, a mostly Sunni city north of Baghdad that seemed to be going the way of Fallujah until a brigade of the 1st Infantry Division cleared it in Operation Baton Rouge. The Samarra battle was the first test for a new Iraqi force. In mid-September, word reached American forces that Major General Adnan Thabit, a relative of the interior minister, had assembled a group of commandos from contacts in Saddam's old special operations forces. The first officials to visit this "pop-up unit," dubbed the Special Police Commandos, were a British brigadier and Matt Sherman, a lawyer from New Jersey who was a senior civilian adviser to the Interior Ministry. At a ramshackle site at the edge of the Green Zone, Thabit showed off his troops. The only thing their mismatched uniforms had in common was a red patch with the image of a wolf on it, but they seemed motivated. Barely two weeks later, the commandos deployed to Samarra, where they showed discipline and aggressiveness, a welcome change after so many Iraqi units had collapsed during the spring fighting.

Fallujah remained a far greater challenge: with Zarqawi's influence on the rise, the prospects of a negotiated solution that would allow Iraqi government forces to enter the city seemed remote. At first, senior officials from the chairman of the Joint Chiefs to the commandant of the Marine Corps had thought that the Fallujah Brigade the Marines had organized might last. But by the time Mattis left Iraq over the summer, it had collapsed into the insurgency. The military had begun launching air strikes into the city again in June, and on July 7 Casey briefed Bush that 70 percent of the Fallujah Brigade's officers were "part of the resistance." According to a report the CIA presented to the White House on September 2, there had never been more than 580 members of the brigade to begin with. A briefing to Abizaid called Fallujah "a safe haven for the best organized, most effective terror network in Iraq."[7] As Mattis said that summer: "There's only one way to disarm the Fallujah Brigade. Kill it."[8]

The insurgents were a diverse lot, and, as the battle approached, American intelligence sought to identify its foes. One faction of the insurgency was led by members of the old regime, including Izzat Ibrahim al-Duri, the last surviving leader of the 1968 coup that brought the Baathists to power. In 2003 Duri had quickly become an influential figure; he and his subordinates viewed Anbar and Salahuddin provinces as good, quiet areas to regroup and organize. They had access to substantial funds and to a large pool of unemployed members of the security forces whose only other options to support themselves were farming and the black market, and many Baathists quickly learned that it was in their interest to cooperate with other fledgling insurgent groups that were of a more religious bent, like Abu Musab al-Zarqawi's Tawhid wal-Jihad.

With the dissolution of the Fallujah Brigade into the insurgency in May, Zarqawi's group and smaller ones like it used their secure position inside the city to stage operations in nearby rural areas, on the highways, and even in Baghdad. Insurgents assembled and dispatched car bombs, and they began to use one of their main financial and propaganda tools: hostages. When Nicholas Berg, an American citizen, was kidnapped and killed on video by the group, the CIA believed that the execution took place in a safe house in the Jolan neighborhood, Tawhid wal-Jihad's base, and that Zarqawi himself slit Berg's throat.[9] In July, around the same time that Casey made his first visit to Anbar to consult with Mattis on the problems posed by Ramadi and especially Fallujah, Zarqawi's fighters kidnapped the sons of the governor of Anbar in Ramadi and forced him to resign his position. Then in August, the group stormed the compounds of the 505th and 506th Battalions of the Iraqi National Guard outside Fallujah, capturing both battalion commanders, torturing and executing one, and turning the 505th's compound into a command post for Zarqawi's Iraqi deputy, Omar Hadid.

In the view of Casey's command, it was the "former regime elements" or FREs that were the main problem in Fallujah. Stan McChrystal's JSOC task force, based at Balad Air Base north of Baghdad, saw it differently. Tawhid wal-Jihad, JSOC believed, had been bolstered hugely by the role it played in the spring battle and was now the most dangerous part of the Sunni insurgency. Prohibited by Casey's headquarters from sending its commandos on the ground or on helicopter raids into Fallujah, JSOC did its best to attack insurgent leaders from the air. "We proposed a number of raids to get in there, but we couldn't physically get in and get on the ground," McChrystal said of his plans to send Delta Force operators on raids into the city. "They were afraid we were going to start a big gunfight, which we might have." Instead, JSOC used a lone Predator drone orbit to track cars moving in and out of Fallujah and call in nighttime air strikes from jets on target houses, a campaign approved by Abizaid.[10]

Reports to Casey's headquarters corroborated that the Predator-guided air strikes were taking a toll on Zarqawi's people in Fallujah during the summer and fall months when operations elsewhere in Iraq forced the Marines to sit on their hands outside the city. A September 2004 monthly assessment for Casey said that the strikes had killed "six of fourteen major operators in Fallujah." One of the dead was a radical cleric who had served as Zarqawi's spiritual adviser.[11]

Though the strikes kept the pressure on Zarqawi's organization, they hardly crippled the group. Nor did a failed September attempt by an Anbari tribe, the Albu Issa, to capture Omar Hadid, who had offended many local residents by taking control of much of the city. In fact, in October, bolstered by six months of perceived success in staring down a coalition that had retreated from confrontation mid-fight, Zarqawi made a pronouncement beamed online to jihadist groups across Iraq and around the world: he ceremoniously swore fealty to Osama bin Laden, and he changed his group's name from Tawhid wal-Jihad to Tanzim al-Qaeda al-Jihad fi Bilad al-Rafidayn, or Al-Qaeda in the Land of Two Rivers, often referred to by the Americans as Al-Qaeda in Mesopotamia or, more commonly, Al-Qaeda in Iraq. In effect, Zarqawi had surpassed the more established Al-Qaeda affiliate, Ansar al-Sunna, as the primary franchise of the Al-Qaeda brand in Iraq.[12]

In late October, after the Samarra operation and as JSOC-guided precision bombs exploded, lighting up Fallujah's night sky, the buildup for the second assault on the city began. While Recon Marines and Navy SEALs pushed close to the city to scout out assault positions, Casey and the new

Marine commander, Lieutenant General John Sattler, met with Allawi. After showing him overhead footage of JSOC air strikes in Fallujah, they extracted a promise from him that once the assault into the city began, he would not voice second thoughts. The military did not want a replay of the spring offensive, when Iraqi government officials had condemned the attack and stopped it in its tracks.

This time the Marines would be going in with much greater force. Two regiments—RCT-1 and RCT-7—were to push through the city, while several more battalions blocked and screened the exits. To mass that large a force, the Marines both stripped combat power from elsewhere in Anbar and looked to the Army, which supplied two battalions of tanks and Bradleys, one from Diyala Province under Lieutenant Colonel Peter Newell, who would earn a Silver Star in the battle, and another from Baghdad. The Army also provided a brigade headquarters and several battalions to run the blocking and screening operations. A British battalion came north from Basra to free up Marines who had been in the rural areas south of Baghdad, a move that caused controversy in Britain but that fell well short of what Casey's command hoped the British in the south would be able to contribute.[13]

As during the spring, the Marines also brought a regiment from the western Euphrates river valley to join the Fallujah fight. This time, a Marine expeditionary unit came up from Kuwait to take over the territory the regiment would be leaving behind, but it was still woefully short-handed. In Haditha, the departure of the Marines for Fallujah left the Iraqi police they were working with exposed. In a grisly episode, Al-Qaeda moved in, corralled the police, and executed them on the town's soccer field, an event that would stifle efforts to field a police force in the region for years.

The attack was set to begin the Sunday after President Bush's reelection. Just as Bush had feared, Allawi was out of the country during the week leading up to the attack and the United States had no secure communications with him. Metz and Ron Neumann flew to Amman so that on Allawi's return flight to Baghdad on a British C-130 they could brief the prime minister on the assault plan and receive his permission. First announced as Operation Phantom Fury, the assault's name was revised by the next day to Operation al-Fajr, or New Dawn, after the Iraqi government raised objections to the American nomenclature with the Marine command.[14]

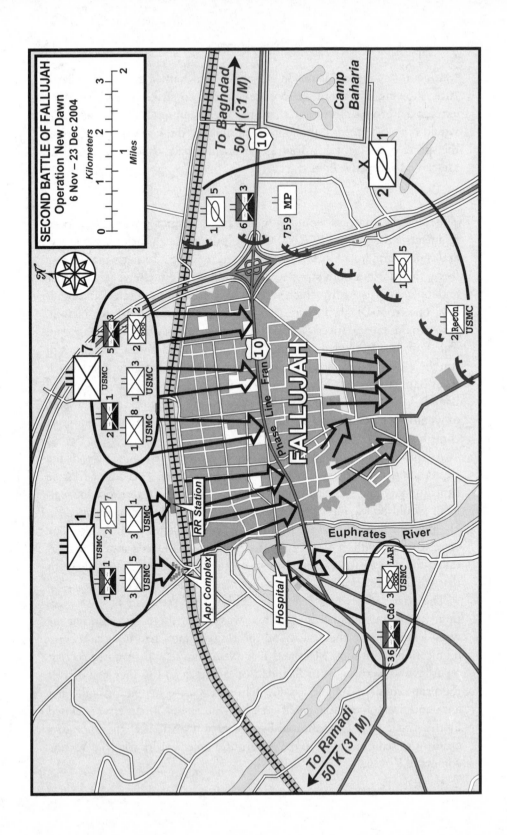

In all, ten battalions of U.S. soldiers and Marines had moved into position around the city. To the south and east—the direction many insurgents expected the attack to come from, based on the areas they fortified with bunkers, firing positions, and IEDs—a diverse force of three Army and Marine battalions was spread out under the control of an Army brigade from Baghdad. Their job would be to stay put and keep insurgent fighters from escaping the city when the real blow came from the opposite direction. To the north of the city, RCT-1 and RCT-7 staged on the opposite side of the train tracks just beyond the outskirts of the urban area. Each of the two regiments comprised two 1,000-man Marine infantry battalions, an Army battalion equipped with Abrams tanks and Bradleys, a four-hundred-man Iraqi battalion, and such support troops as engineers. The command in Baghdad also ensured that Fallujah would have extra air support: the size of the Marine Harrier attack plane force was doubled, and each of the two assault regiments was assigned a dedicated AC-130 gunship, a weapon that had proved invaluable on nighttime urban battlefields during the spring and summer.

At 10 p.m. on November 7, a Marine light armored reconnaissance task force kicked off the operation in coordination with the 36th Commando Battalion, the Iraqi unit that had fought alongside the Marines during the first Fallujah battle in April and then again in Najaf in August. While the Iraqi commandos and their Special Forces advisers seized a hospital on the peninsula to the west of the city, the Marine task force took control of the two bridges over the Euphrates connecting the peninsula to the city. That night, American warplanes struck nine targets in the city, and the first two Marines to perish in the battle lost their lives when their bulldozer slid into the rain-swollen Euphrates.

A pause followed as the Marine units made final preparations for their advance across the railroad tracks and parallel earth berm. Late the next morning, November 8, one of RCT-1's battalions, 3/5 Marines, made a quick advance to take control of an apartment complex just outside the Jolan neighborhood, where much of the April fighting had taken place and where Tawhid wal-Jihad and then its rebranded descendant, Al-Qaeda in Iraq, had been based. In the afternoon, F/A-18 Hornet jets, including one flown by Major General Keith Stalder, dropped two-thousand-pound bombs on the railroad tracks, blowing breaches in them. After sunset, engineers cut electrical power to the city, and then during the night the Marine infantry battalions finally crossed the tracks into the city with the Army tanks and Bradleys forming strongpoints along the way to back them up—

RCT-1 pushing south through the northwestern part of the city, and RCT-7 through the northeast. As 3/1 Marines crossed, loudspeakers on some of their Humvees blared Wagner's "Ride of the Valkyries." Some Marine units were accompanied by Iraqi scouts they dubbed the "Shawanis," after Iraqi intelligence director Muhammad Abdullah al-Shawani, who played a role in assembling them just as he had with the ill-conceived Fallujah Brigade. One of the first casualties was the sergeant major of one of the U.S. Army battalions, who was fatally shot just after he walked through the breach into the city. By dawn, 3/5 Marines in the northwest had cleared the cemetery abutting Jolan and pushed into the neighborhood itself. In the northeast, the elite troops of the Iraqi Counterterrorism Task Force took a mosque along the axis of advance.

For the next two days, the six U.S. battalions advanced methodically through the northern half of Fallujah before stopping at Highway 10, the road that bisected the city east to west. November 10, the third day that the troops were inside the city, was the Marine Corps's birthday, and one psychological operations company played the Marines' Hymn over loudspeakers. The insurgents used loudspeakers, too, blaring orders from mosques' minarets; Al-Qaeda in Iraq cells communicated with black-and-green signal flags, and cells led by officials and officers of the old security services used coded instructions on Baath Party letterhead. In Jolan, the area that 3/5 had cleared, the Marines made grim discoveries, including an insurgent safe house that contained the flag of Zarqawi's organization and a detailed schedule for the performance and filming of beheadings. In another part of the neighborhood, near a long-abandoned Ferris wheel, muffled screams drew them to a house in which they found two Iraqi men whose legs had been sawed off by their captors, one dead and one alive.

The fighting was some of the fiercest of the war, closer to the scale of Hue City than to Mogadishu. Marine, Navy, and Air Force jets circled overhead, ready to drop their bombs, as did Marine and some Army attack helicopters; the AC-130 gunships went to work at night, orbiting the fixed points onto which they unloaded their ordnance, and Marine artillery fired at all hours. Marine platoons called in artillery shells, bombs, rockets, and missiles on buildings they suspected of containing insurgents with little restriction from rules of engagement. Houses and mosques alike were destroyed if fire came from them.

"You sometimes wonder what the appropriate use of force is, but Fallujah was just a joke as far as the amount of force we could use," recalled one Army lieutenant who employed his tanks' main guns to quiet snipers.

"There seemed to be no limit on main gun or .50-cal [ammunition], so we were hitting every house we were taking contact from with main gun rounds. Why show them mercy, you know what I mean?"[15] Despite all the high-tech firepower that was brought to bear, communication between Army and Marine units was sometimes primitive: leaders from one organization would often have to run over to their counterparts in another to talk face-to-face, since the two services could communicate only at higher echelons. (Some Marine units used a Microsoft chat program to share intelligence within and even between headquarters, something the Army did not do.)

Compared to the division's plan, the advance went quickly, and by November 12, the bulk of RCT-1 and RCT-7 had crossed Highway 10 into the southern half of the city. In the southeastern industrial areas, RCT-7 encountered heavily defended pockets manned by fighters who either would not or could not flee. The Nazal and Shuhada neighborhoods were the most heavily seeded with prepared bunkers and spider holes. In one such corner on November 13, a group of Marines came under heavy fire in what became called the "Hell House." With Marines pinned down and wounded, Bradley Kasal, a rifle company first sergeant, entered the house. Shielding a wounded Marine from attack, he was shot seven times with rifle rounds and absorbed more than forty pieces of grenade shrapnel. By the time he was finally carried out of the house, still clutching an M9 pistol— a moment captured by an embedded photographer—Kasal had lost half the blood in his body, but he lived.

As the units advanced, they uncovered more and more eerie evidence of the insurgency. There were hints of foreign fighters, like a GPS device programmed with waypoints leading back into Syria that turned up at one of the eleven IED-assembly houses the troops discovered. Other finds included two "torture houses," in addition to the one found by 3/5 Marines in Jolan, and a car bomb factory. A platoon from 3/1 Marines found a basement complex in the southern half of the city that contained bloody handprints and vials and syringes of amphetamines.[16] 1/3 Marines found another Al-Qaeda flag, which they would bring home to Hawaii and showcase in their headquarters. Zarqawi was nowhere to be found, though.

By the end of the first week, the American force and the Iraqis who came in behind them had swept from one end of the city to the other and had begun to sweep back to clear areas they had missed. The violence of the fighting—and of the U.S. approach to it—was demonstrated by the scale of the destruction. During the two weeks of the heaviest fighting, Marine artillery units around Fallujah fired an average of 379 high-explosive 155mm shells per day; jets flying above the city dropped a total of 318 bombs; and together jets and helicopters fired 391 rockets and missiles. The attack helicopters watching over the ground troops were not immune to danger; two Marine Super Cobras were shot down over the city, and four Army Apaches were damaged.

Publicly, Allawi's office claimed that only two hundred buildings in Fallujah had been destroyed or heavily damaged. But the Marines estimated that out of about fifty thousand residences in the city, their operations had destroyed between seven thousand and ten thousand, as well as sixty mosques. The city had already been nearly empty before the assault; some estimates for the year put the number of residents "displaced" by the two battles of Fallujah and the siege in between as high as 200,000, out of a total of somewhere between 250,000 and 300,000. Despite this massive use of American firepower, American casualties were high, even higher than they had been in April. In all, the Marine command reported that it lost seventy men killed and slightly more than 650 wounded, including over 250 who had to be evacuated to Germany and the United States. Early casualty estimates were low; it turned out that 75 or more Marines concealed their wounds to avoid being evacuated from their units. The battalion that took the worst hit was 3/1 Marines, with 22 killed and 206 wounded. The losses of the smaller and heavily armored Army battalions were lighter.[17]

The scene in the city after the battle was grisly. Days of rain complicated the task of collecting and burying the hundreds of slain insurgents in the streets and in buildings. "Almost as soon as these insurgents were dead, the dogs started gnawing on their bones," an officer from 1/3 Marines recalled.[18] When Interior Ministry adviser Matt Sherman visited, he was struck by the stench of the corpses. According to a year-end report from Casey's headquarters, American troops had killed an estimated 8,400 insurgents in 2004, and of those, a full quarter, 2,175, had been in Second Fallujah.[19]

The November assault on Fallujah resulted in the receipt of nine Navy Crosses by Marines, the valor award second only to the Medal of Honor—far more than in any other battle in the wars in Iraq and Afghanistan. Of the nine, three were posthumous. No Medals of Honor were awarded, a fact that remains controversial in the military. But in at least two cases that top honor was considered: that of Bradley Kasal, the company first sergeant shot seven times on November 13; and that of Rafael Peralta, a Mexican-born sergeant. During a house clearance on November 15, Peralta was shot several times, including in the head; he fell to the floor. A live grenade appeared. Lying severely wounded, he scooped it under his body, absorbing the blast. He chose to die in battle to save his teammates, by their account, and so was put up for the Medal of Honor. In one of the many reviews conducted before the award packet reached the Pentagon, an examining pathologist raised the possibility that, with a fatal head wound and brain damage, Peralta's "scooping/grabbing" of the grenade could have resulted from "involuntary muscle spasms." Major General Richard Natonski, the division commander, resubmitted the nomination, citing the findings of three different neurosurgical investigators, but a shadow of doubt haunted Peralta's case: in 2008, Defense Secretary Robert Gates ruled that Peralta's Navy Cross would remain a Navy Cross.[20]

Another posthumous cross went to Lance Corporal Christopher Adlesperger, who survived the heroics for which he was nominated, only to die later. As a private first class with 3/5 Marines, Adlesperger, despite being wounded by shrapnel, led his unit to storm a machine gun nest in Jolan on the second day of the battle. Nearly a month later, on December 2, he was killed as the battalion continued to clear enemy fighters from the city. Adlesperger's case showed that the fighting in Fallujah was not over for good—in some areas, it continued fiercely well after the assault units had begun to disperse. By mid-November, a week in, the six battalions inside the city had achieved all their objectives. But then came a laborious process of reclearing, as platoons came under attack from buildings and blocks that they had missed or where insurgents had snuck back in. During the third week, while the reclearing continued, the huge American force began to shrink as the two Army battalions left with their tanks and Bradleys, returning to Baghdad and Diyala. The cavalry brigade headquarters followed in mid-December. Sharp fights continued to pop up through December, especially on the eastern side of the city; sometimes they involved tanks and air strikes.

Of those who had participated in the attack on Fallujah, not everyone was pleased with how quickly the force was split up, fearing that the city was now vulnerable to falling back into insurgent hands. RCT-1's operations officer, Lieutenant Colonel Jeffrey Chessani, raised the issue with his commander in a memo. "Why would higher headquarters want to cre-

ate a vacuum like this after successfully crushing an insurgency that has
been a thorn for more than a year?" Chessani asked. Higher echelons "are
going to walk away thinking they did their part and the smoldering heap of
rubble that is Fallujah is going to start sparking again because higher headquarters failed to follow through with the resources we need to smother the
embers. Then they are going to ask us why we let the embers become a fire
again."[21] (Chessani would, a year later, lead 3/1 Marines—the battalion
hit hardest in Fallujah—back to Anbar for the deployment in which some
Marines in the battalion killed two dozen civilians near Haditha in one of
the war's most notorious incidents.)

Rebuilding and resettling were slow. U.S. troops allowed returnees into
only one neighborhood at a time starting in late December, but by the January elections only a small proportion of the 200,000-plus Fallujans had
returned. Fewer than 7,800 people voted, which the Marines estimated
comprised a third to one-half of eligible returnees. By the end of March,
the count had risen only to 30 percent of the pre–April 2004 population.

The second battle of Fallujah took a toll on the enemy but did not
break the back of the Sunni insurgency in Iraq. Instead, it scattered Sunni
militants of all sorts into other cities and other provinces, with insurgent
groups planting the flag—sometimes literally the green and black banners
of groups like Al-Qaeda in Iraq—in places where their presence had been
less conspicuous before.

Some fighters and their leaders had fled Fallujah as the fighting began,
sneaking through the cordon the military threw around the city. Zarqawi
himself, the Marines believed, had left on November 8, the first full day
of fighting, probably heading toward Mosul, leaving his lieutenant Omar
Hadid behind to be martyred. (In December, Al-Qaeda in Iraq publicly
claimed that Hadid was not dead, only wounded, but the next month the
group held a memorial service for him in the rural area south of Fallujah.)

Other groups of fighters had left well before the Marine assault. Their
leaders had seen the writing on the wall and decided to limit casualties.
Although Hadid himself had stayed, in October he had sent a large portion
of his fighters—perhaps as many as half, according to Marine intelligence—
away, ordering them to disperse into the villages and smaller towns on the
road to Ramadi in the west and to the south of Baghdad, in the Zaidon,
Yusifiyah, Mahmudiyah, Lutifiyah, Hawr Rajab, and Arab Jabour areas—
the region that would come to be known as the "Triangle of Death" as
Al-Qaeda established rural strongholds among its canals and palm groves.
In December, as they finished their work in Fallujah, McChrystal's JSOC

commandos turned their attention to the area, beginning a campaign that would last several years.

Inside Baghdad, both the October Samarra operation and the displacement from Fallujah had pushed Islamist insurgents, including those of Al-Qaeda, to establish new footholds in predominantly Sunni neighborhoods. Four areas where Sunni militants began to put down roots were the Adhamiya neighborhood of East Baghdad, Ameriya on the western edge of the city just outside Camp Victory, Dora just south of the Tigris, and Haifa Street, which ran north out of the Green Zone's Assassins' Gate. Haifa Street, lined with high-rise apartments that housed Sunnis who had felt Saddam's largesse before the war, had become an insurgent enclave over the summer. When a Bradley was disabled there in September, insurgents had hung a black Tawhid wal-Jihad flag on its 25mm gun, and the battalion tasked with controlling the place, from the 1st Cavalry Division, began calling Haifa "Little Fallujah" and "Purple Heart Boulevard," after the medal that would be awarded to 160 of the unit's 800 soldiers by the time they went home in early 2005. In Dora, another 1st Cavalry battalion began to see new graffiti as Second Fallujah inflamed the Sunni population and the January election loomed: "No, No, Allawi, Yes, Yes, Zarqawi."[22]

The most dramatic spread of the Sunni insurgency while American forces were committed to Second Fallujah occurred in Mosul, the huge northern city of 1.8 million Kurds and Sunni Arabs where Dave Petraeus's 101st Airborne Division had kept the peace in 2003. Petraeus—now back in Iraq to train Iraqi forces after just a few months stateside—took great pride in what his troops had accomplished in Mosul. Spreading out into dozens of small outposts, the 101st had stood up a local government and lobbied for exceptions to the de-Baathification decree in order to hire university professors, creating one of the few apparent victories of the first year of the occupation. Petraeus's troops had commanded the operation that killed Uday and Qusay Hussein, and on their watch Nineveh had not appeared to be spawning the kind of Sunni insurgency that other units' areas were.

Since the 101st had left at the beginning of the year, things had changed. As the Army's first brigade of Stryker armored vehicles, the unit that replaced the 101st in Mosul had every high-tech advantage available, including new sniper rifles and new uniforms called ACUs. But it was much smaller—fewer than half as many combat troops—and when Nineveh had stayed calm during the April uprising, more troops had been pulled out of the city to guard the embattled highways in central Iraq, a job to which the fast, eight-wheeled Stryker was well suited.

Over the summer, cracks began to show in the Mosul success story. Some of them had already been noticed. Derek Harvey, the intelligence officer who had written the "Politics of the Gun" report on the Sunni insurgency, believed that Muhammad Khairi al-Barhawi, the Baath brigadier general whom Petraeus had backed as Mosul police chief, had developed ties to insurgent leaders. A May CIA assessment agreed that the quiet in Mosul was not what it seemed, and might not last much longer. Then at the end of June, on the eve of the transition to Iraqi sovereignty, insurgents assassinated Nineveh's governor. In mid-August, McChrystal's JSOC task force briefed Casey that Mosul was becoming a new safe haven for Zarqawi.

When a new Stryker brigade arrived in Mosul in September, it found a deteriorating situation. In October, the CIA's station in Mosul was attacked, an event that was briefed to Bush. When the fight in Fallujah flushed the insurgents north, Mosul was ready to explode. On the morning of November 11, the fourth full day of the Fallujah battle, Zarqawi had just arrived in Nineveh. So had Lieutenant Colonel Ed McKee. The commander of an aviation battalion from the South Carolina National Guard, McKee had taken heat from the Army for painting his battalion's fourteen AH-64 Apache attack helicopters an experimental shade of blue-gray to make them less visible to insurgents on the ground. After being put on the spot to explain his decision in Kuwait by General Richard Cody, the Army's vice chief of staff, McKee, along with his gray Apaches, had arrived in Mosul late on November 10. They planned to begin operations gradually, taking time to learn the ropes from the OH-58 Kiowa pilots they were replacing.

But on the 11th, before any of his helicopters had flown over the city, McKee got a call from Brigadier General Carter Ham, the commander overseeing Mosul, who years later, as head of Africa Command, would play an important role in the fight against Libya's Muammar al-Qaddafi. "I get a call from General Ham, and he says, 'I need your Apaches over Mosul, now,'" McKee recalled. "We're getting our classes done, air recon maps, receiving all the briefs. He said, 'Ed, you don't understand. I'm within a couple hours of calling General Casey to let him know I've lost control of Mosul.'"[23]

From above, the pilots of the gray Apaches, on their first missions in Iraq, could see a city spiraling out of control. Insurgents had seized the five bridges across the Tigris in the middle of the city, and had captured one police station and burned two more to the ground. "Smoke columns were just part of the landscape," McKee said. The Stryker battalion responsible for West Mosul, led by Lieutenant Colonel Erik Kurilla, was fighting hard, but the police force and Iraqi Army units that existed in the city had evaporated completely. The next day, November 12, flames engulfed another police station and insurgents occupied eight more. In East Mosul, the compound of a Kurdish political party, the PUK, defended itself with heavy machine guns. Soon only one police station, called 1-West, remained, along with a handful of American bases.

Mosul had fallen, and with the battle of Fallujah under way, there were precious few American forces available to take it back—the Stryker brigade itself had one battalion down in Fallujah as part of the cordon. The job of taking back the city would fall on three groups: the two Stryker battalions left in the city; the aviators above them, whose blue-gray Apaches insurgents came to call the "Blue Dragons"; and one of Adnan Thabit's new self-made Special Police Commando battalions, trucked north from Baghdad on short notice.

Two Americans accompanied the commandos, Jim Coffman and his colleague Jim Steele, who had turned up for the fight in Najaf. Both were older than most generals. Coffman had enlisted soon after the Vietnam War and gone on to a career in Special Forces and civil affairs units before joining Steele as an augmentee to the CPA and then as an adviser in Petraeus's new training command. After the Blackwater killings in Fallujah on March 31, Coffman and Steele had gone into the city in civilian clothes to recover the last corpse, and during the April battle, Coffman, who looked more like a professor than a soldier, had visited the city with Petraeus, walking with him to the Marine front line.

Coffman and Steele had been accompanying the police commandos from one hot spot to another, including the October clearance of Samarra, when word came that they were needed in Mosul. On the morning of November 14, the general in charge of the police commandos gave his men a speech, and then they headed out into the city in four columns of unarmored trucks—each was to retake a police station in one of the four corners of Mosul. Around 10 a.m., a call came in: the column that had planted the flag in northwestern Mosul, at the 4-West station near Yarmuk Traffic Circle, was under heavy attack, and needed help.

Coffman and eighty Iraqi commandos piled into Dodge Ram pickups and headed into the city. Just after they crossed the Tigris into the city's west side, they were ambushed—first by a small insurgent force in a eucalyptus grove, then by a much larger group. Under withering RPG, rifle, and machine gun fire, the column stopped in its tracks and began to suffer casualties. As Coffman hopped out of his pickup, the Iraqi commando next to him was shot. Running toward the head of the halted convoy, Coffman found the Iraqi commanders holed up in a building, one of them shot through both arms and the other apparently overwhelmed. For the next three hours, Coffman led a dozen commandos in a desperate defense of their position, alternately calling for help on a satellite phone that eventually died, tying tourniquets on wounded Iraqis, distributing ammunition, and picking off insurgents, who were close enough that he could see them dashing from one firing position to another.

By about 1 p.m., the group was running low on ammunition, and Coffman's M4 carbine had been hit, forcing him to use a discarded AK-47, when he was shot through the hand. Upon the arrival of a Stryker quick reaction force, Coffman was down to four rounds in his last AK-47 magazine, and all but one of the Iraqis at his position were dead or wounded. Before heading back to base with what was left of his force, Coffman accompanied the relief column to 4-West, the police station that had originally called for help. Of the eighty commandos who had set out from 1-West, fourteen were killed—including an injured major who fled the fight only to be beheaded by Al-Qaeda fighters who tracked him to a hospital—and nearly fifty were wounded.

Coffman managed to avoid being evacuated to Germany, and then, IV bag in hand and in desert fatigues still caked with blood, snuck out of the Mosul combat hospital and returned to Baghdad on a series of flights. In the Green Zone, a bemused Petraeus told him to give his briefing on what had happened and then report to the hospital for surgery. Petraeus then put Coffman in for the Distinguished Service Cross, the Army's second-highest valor award—not one often given to fifty-year-old colonels.[24]

Two days after Coffman's fight by the Yarmuk Traffic Circle, the immediate crisis in Mosul passed, as insurgents withdrew from the ten police stations they still controlled and Stryker units pushed back into most areas of the city. The battalions in Mosul still had their work cut out for them, though. As they pushed back in, American troops found the bodies of seventy-six Iraqi security personnel who had been executed by insurgents, and on the west side of the city they came across a high-rise apartment building whose entire fifth floor had been taken over by Al-Qaeda for use as a command post and media lab for producing propaganda videos.

The insurgency was not gone from Mosul—far from it. As the January elections loomed, in fact, Al-Qaeda kept up a steady drumbeat of attacks in the city in an effort to frustrate the voting.

CHAPTER 8

The Long Telegram

As the White House saw it, victory in Fallujah had put the United States back on track. George Casey's plan had been to fight to the January elections in the expectation that the Iraqis would elect a parliament, stand up a new government, and pave the way beyond notional to political and military sovereignty. Some leading Sunni politicians, however, were apprehensive about the timing of the elections. The Shiite parties appeared to be very organized and poised to elect the preponderance of the 275 members of a transitional assembly that would also pick the prime minister. Security was also a worry. Zarqawi had suffered a blow, but he was hardly out of the fray and was demanding that the Sunnis boycott the vote. If Al-Qaeda's campaign of intimidation was effective and Sunni Arab turnout was low they would be woefully underrepresented in the new government, all of which could have profound implications. The new parliament would have a decisive role in drafting the new constitution. Without sufficient participation, the Sunnis would find themselves not only marginalized in the legislature but on the sidelines when it came to determining the very shape of the new state. The United States would have achieved a Pyrrhic victory: there would be elections without reconciliation.

After the Fallujah battle, Adnan Pachachi, the venerable Sunni politician, and Hamid Majid Mousa, a former Governing Council member and former head of Iraq's Communist Party, paid a visit to Negroponte and questioned the election timetable. "This is only November," Negroponte said reassuringly. "By January, we will have the violence better under control. You'll see. We need to go forward with the planning." Even as the meeting was taking place, there was a huge explosion: a rocket had struck the Republican Palace, where the embassy was housed. "See, it didn't hit a polling station," Negroponte said, trying to ease the tension. The ambassador continued to explain how the Americans would be imposing new security measures to facilitate the vote when there was yet another enormous explosion, resulting in stone silence, as paint chips from the ceiling drifted to the floor.[1]

Sunnis were not the only ones nervous about going ahead with the vote: the Iraqi prime minister had his concerns as well. After being rebuffed by Jerry Bremer, Zalmay Khalilzad had been appointed as the American ambassador to Afghanistan, but it did not seem that he would be in Kabul for long. There was discussion that Khalilzad was likely to succeed Negroponte, and he was doing his best to stay in the loop on Iraq. In a meeting with Lakhdar Brahimi, the U.N. official confided to Khalilzad that Allawi was apprehensive about going ahead with the January vote. A secular Shiite who had some support among the military and former Baathists, the Iraqi prime minister thought more time was needed to bring the Sunni Arabs on board. If the election was held without significant Sunni participation, it could backfire and strengthen the insurgency and, though he did not stress the point publicly, eat into part of his potential political base and deprive him of his chance to keep the prime ministership.

Khalilzad suggested that Brahimi pass Allawi a message: if the prime minister really thought that holding the elections in January was a bad move, he needed to take his concerns directly to Bush. The president was interested, first and foremost, in success, and Allawi had been a good partner. Brahimi related his conversation with Khalilzad by phone to Kofi Annan, the United Nations secretary-general. The call was picked up by the National Security Agency, which monitored international communications, and when the intelligence report made its way to Steve Hadley, the deputy national security adviser intervened. Khalilzad already had a reputation as a diplomatic freelancer and his most recent involvement was seen as a sign that the envoy was encouraging the Iraqi prime minister to oppose the president's policy.

The shoe dropped when Khalilzad was passing through Dubai on his way back to Kabul: he got an urgent message instructing him to go immediately to the United States consulate for a call on a secure line from the White House. The usually unflappable Hadley was concerned about the reports of the envoy's presumed impertinence. Khalilzad did his best to give his version of events, hoping to persuade the White House that he was not countermanding official policy and keep alive the idea of having him replace Negroponte in Baghdad.[2]

At the United Nations, Brahimi, Jamal Benomar, and Kieran Prendergast, the British diplomat who served as the undersecretary general for political affairs, shared Allawi's misgivings about the timing of the election. The message the U.N. team was getting from Allawi was that he wanted the elections delayed but was hoping the United Nations would deliver the message to the Americans. Benomar pressed the issue with Meghan O'Sullivan, formerly with the CPA and now on the NSC staff, but she told him that the president was firm on the date. "Jamal, let me tell you something, he's religious about the date of the elections," said O'Sullivan. "That's my advice to you."

The difficulty of pressing ahead with the elections was not to be underestimated. Sistani had thrown down the gauntlet, insisting that polling take place in January, and if security was insufficient in the wake of the Fallujah operation it seemed unlikely that it would improve substantially in the months ahead. Without elections and the creation of a strong Iraqi state the United States had no exit strategy. All the same, at the heart of the White House plan was the principle that the new government be representative and inclusive.

To beef up security for the vote, Casey arranged for a temporary surge of ten thousand extra troops. Ever since the twin spring uprisings, the American force in Iraq had been much larger than planners had originally projected for 2004. With the elections coming up, the commander found a way to swell the forces some more. Two Army brigades—one that had formed the cordon around Fallujah, and one in Kirkuk—had their deployments extended to overlap with those of the National Guard brigades that were replacing them. Casey also prolonged the stay of the Marine expeditionary unit that had come for the battle of Fallujah—the CENTCOM reserve for the entire Middle East—and he was given two infantry battalions from the 82nd Airborne Division, the Army's reserve for worldwide contingencies. In December 2004 and January 2005, the American force in Iraq grew to more than 150,000.

The area that was most reinforced was Mosul, where the insurgency remained strong. Stryker units had spread out into a net of outposts across the city and a December gun battle at one of them—Combat Outpost Tampa—resulted in the award of six Silver Stars. The gray Apaches of the South Carolina National Guard fired Hellfire missiles in support of ground troops every other day, and rockets and cannon rounds several times a day. In the weeks before the elections, troops raided an insurgent hideout and found not just weapons, but also election banners that had been stolen in

Baghdad and snuck north for the purpose of setting up fake polling sites to which voters could be lured and killed. As part of the election preparations, the number of American battalions climbed from two to six, and Abrams tanks rumbled through the city.

As hard as he had toiled to ensure that voting occurred on schedule, Negroponte was not going to be on hand for the important work of forming the new government. The White House had tapped the ambassador to serve as the first Director of National Intelligence, the office established to respond to the intelligence shortfalls that had preceded the September 11 attacks. Negroponte was convinced that the election would be just one more milestone in a long road and not the beginning of the end of the American mission in Iraq, as the Pentagon seemed to hope.

So much of the American experience in Iraq appeared to be based on sanguine assumptions. Before Negroponte left for his Baghdad post, Admiral David Nash, who managed the $18.4 billion reconstruction budget, had boasted to the new ambassador that so many jobs would be created by the program that laborers would be flocking to Iraq from throughout the Middle East. In fact, hampered by the insurgency, few of the large infrastructure projects had gotten very far or generated much by way of employment. As the violence grew, Negroponte ordered a major shift. To speed the buildup of Iraqi forces and combat the spread of the insurgency, several billion dollars' worth of reconstruction funds were redirected toward Petraeus's budget for training the Iraqi Army and police and for smaller-scale projects that could more quickly produce jobs. Soon after he arrived to take over from Nash, William Taylor, a former Army officer and State Department expert on assistance programs, went to see Iraq's minister of water resources to break the news: the ambitious budget that was to have gone for building wastewater treatment plants was being put to other uses. Whatever planning the Bush administration did following the elections needed to be infused with a sober realism about the mountain the Iraqis and their American patrons still had to climb.[3]

In an effort to point the way forward in Iraq, Negroponte called in Bob Earle, the aide who had worked with Derek Harvey to draft the common Joint Mission Statement with Casey, and gave him a new assignment. Even at this late stage, Negroponte feared, the White House was underestimating the extent of the challenge. So Earle was to draft a confidential memo on the severe difficulties of Iraq that Negroponte would sign and send directly to Bush. The aide was given a desk in a pink hallway to pull together the seminal assessment. With a novelist's flair, he taped a sign to his cubicle: "The Pink Motel." As he sifted through the intelligence, Earle intended to write a comprehensive forty-page paper he took to calling "The Long Telegram," an allusion to George Kennan's famous 1946 diplomatic cable setting the stage for decades of containing Soviet power. Worried that Bush might not read something so long, he boiled it down to nine pages and entitled it "A Plan for Dealing with the Next Government of Iraq."

Negroponte sent the confidential memo to Washington on December 2. Addressing the question Bush had put to Negroponte in his March Oval Office meeting, the cable affirmed that Bush's vision was still possible even though the quick handover to the Iraqis he still hoped for was not. "Democracy remains possible in Iraq, but Iraq is a post-conflict failed state." In terms of infrastructure, the challenges were monumental. "Every key sector—from health to education to transportation to water, electricity, and oil—is run down and dilapidated."[4]

Efforts to rebuild the country had been severely hampered by the resilient insurgency, which had been blunted at great cost in Fallujah and Mosul, but was hardly defeated. "This insurgency and foreign terrorism, strengthened by Zarqawi's alliance with al-Qaeda, will remain an enemy of freedom and democracy in Iraq well beyond next January's elections, the subsequent constitutional debate, and the election of another Iraqi government under that constitution. At a minimum, we need to make a comprehensive, five-year commitment that will give us the time, resources, and manifestation of political will to crush it," the cable continued.

A major problem was the growing resentment of the liberated Iraqis. "We are in a deep hole with the Iraqi people. They hold us accountable for not delivering better services, more security, and a swifter reduction of forces. This is a bitter harvest for Americans who have sacrificed so much in Iraq's behalf," the cable stated. But if the United States was honest with the Iraqis and the American people about the scope of the challenges—and if it fashioned a long-term plan to deal with them—it was still possible to summon sufficient support from the Iraqi public.

When Negroponte met with Bush in Washington that month and fleshed out his position that five years or more would be needed to build the new Iraq, Bush was not pleased. "We don't have that much time," Bush said without further elaboration. The president had great hopes for Iraq and was determined to succeed, but he had never bargained for such a lengthy and intensive commitment.[5]

As hard as Negroponte's cable was for the president to swallow, the verdict of the intelligence community was even harsher. As his deployment in Iraq drew to a close, Derek Harvey was initially assigned to be the inspector general for the Intelligence and Security Command at Fort Belvoir, only to find himself restored to Iraq duty at the Defense Intelligence Agency headquarters after Abizaid and Casey interceded. Working out of Washington, Harvey continued to refine his sobering analysis—and to present it to any senior officials who would listen.

After Harvey briefed the Defense Policy Board, a panel of former officials who advised the Pentagon, one of the more notable members of the panel, Henry Kissinger, said that this was an assessment that should go to Rumsfeld and the president. Jack Keane, the retired Army vice chief, a member of the board, arranged for Harvey to see Rumsfeld. Dick Myers, Marine vice chairman Peter Pace, and a cluster of aides from the staff of the Joint Chiefs crowded into Rumsfeld's third-floor office for Harvey's presentation. The analyst went through his assessment that the insurgency the United States was facing was well trained and linked by family, tribal, and professional ties. It was stronger than most other insurgencies in history because it was exploiting the remnants of the collapsed state and had both leadership and direction. The Sunni resistance was an indigenous and determined affair, a foe fighting for its place in the new Iraq and for future generations; its stomping ground comprised provinces in and around Baghdad. Simply holding elections and empowering a Shiite-dominated government would not change the dynamics. The insurgency, Harvey argued, was also likely to get stronger unless the United States changed its strategy.

Harvey's analysis was a direct challenge to Rumsfeld's assumption that the enemy fight was being led by some die-hard fanatics and "dead-enders." The cantankerous defense secretary pushed back while the rest of the attendees sat quietly. At the end of the session, Rumsfeld indicated that while he did not agree with much in Harvey's brief it needed to be shared "across the river" at the White House.[6]

Before seeing the president, Harvey met with Rice and Hadley. Harvey gave a thorough presentation. Rice, who looked very tired, was silent for much of the time. It was not the first time she had heard that there were problems. Frank Miller and Colonel Marty Sullivan had been funneling some of the troubling information from their contacts to Rice and Hadley. During the Fallujah battle, Rice had pulled Sullivan aside in the driveway between the White House and the Old Executive Office Building, where the NSC staff was housed, and asked the Marine officer if he thought the United States needed more troops in Iraq. Sullivan told her that two additional divisions needed to be deployed to the Sunni Triangle and Baghdad, not only to win the Fallujah fight but to expand the coalition's control afterward. Rice said nothing to suggest she disagreed.

Hadley probed Harvey's analysis and noted the more positive assessment the NSC was receiving from Abizaid, Casey, and the Pentagon. Pulling out binders of memoranda, Hadley pointed to the programs in Iraq, the money that had been allocated and spent. It was not clear if Hadley disagreed with what the Army colonel was reporting or was pressing Harvey as the lawyer he was. But Harvey stood his ground. The money was going to those regions of Iraq where there was the least resistance, not places like Anbar or Diyala where money was badly needed. The political process in Iraq, Harvey insisted, was not addressing the core issues forcing the Sunnis to take up arms.

When it was time for Harvey to brief the president in the White House Situation Room, his presentation was listed on the agenda as the "Col. Derek Harvey Brief," implying that it was a lone view and not the collective assessment of the DIA Iraq task force. Bush pressed Harvey on what qualifications he had to offer such a vexing assessment, one that was not consistent with what Casey and the embassy were reporting. Harvey cited troubling information about insurgent leaders and their networks but the president did not appear to be persuaded.

The CIA was counseling caution as well. The agency had been profoundly skeptical of claims of progress in Iraq. Charlie Allen, the assistant director for collection who had a long and storied career as an iconoclastic analyst fearless in speaking truth to power, had traveled twice to Baghdad and prepared an assessment that reinforced already alarming reports prepared by the agency's station chief. Allen thought Iraq was slipping into a civil war that the American military was not prepared to handle and was pessimistic that elections could even be held. Iran's Quds Force had extensive intelligence and operations networks in Iraq, and the United States was not pushing back hard enough. Oil pipelines and the electrical grid were being sabotaged and the economy was terrible. When he visited Baghdad in late 2004, Allen had been given a VIP trailer near Landing Zone Washington, the helicopter pad in the Green Zone. All night long, the helicopters flew in carrying the wounded to the combat support hospital. Meanwhile, most of the diplomats and even some of the CIA personnel seemed to be trapped in their fortified Green Zone sanctuary.

Returning to Washington, Allen wrote a searing evaluation for Porter Goss, the CIA director, and marked it "Eyes Only."[7] The intelligence chief no sooner read the report than he ignored the "Eyes Only" directive and circulated it to Condoleezza Rice, who passed it on to Abizaid, Casey, Negroponte, and the other major participants in her classified videoconference. Allen heard through the grapevine that Abizaid was steamed, and Negroponte was convinced Allen was unduly negative. Casey thought that the CIA had failed to grasp the logic behind his strategy. The commander told the acting CIA station chief in Baghdad, Allen later heard, that he planned to keep a copy of Allen's analysis so he could "stuff it down his throat when he returns."[8]

Despite his reputation as an iconoclast, Allen was hardly the only questioning voice at the agency headquarters. In a classified report, "Near Term Regional Implications of Successful Iraqi Elections," the CIA concluded that even if the elections could somehow be held they would not necessarily yield all the benefits that Bush's "freedom agenda" envisioned. While a democratic Iraq, the agency concluded in its assessment, would reduce the potential for unrest it would likely spur the authoritarian Sunni regimes in Saudi Arabia, Egypt, and the Gulf states to crack down at home, including against a Shiite minority that wanted to assert its rights. "Rather than moving more quickly toward reform in response to the Iraqi example these Sunni regimes, particularly Saudi Arabia and Egypt, are likely to shift even further toward survival strategies that extend and consolidate their authoritarian and nationalist policies and characterize local reformers as enemies to be suppressed," the October 29 CIA assessment noted. They would even "seek ways to offset the presumably Shia makeup of the new Iraqi Government."[9]

As the president sought to steer events in Iraq, the future appeared fraught with complications. His loyal ambassador was urging the Bush administration to gird itself for an enervating five-year slog. Two of his most experienced intelligence analysts were warning that the insurgency was likely to intensify unless Washington changed its strategy. The CIA acknowledged that a democratic Iraq would demonstrate to the Arab world that there was a middle path between authoritarian rule and radical Islam, as Bush hoped. But at the same time it was warning that the autocratic regimes would not give up without a fight and that they were prepared to use their money and contacts to intervene in the politics of Iraq and strangle the democratic experiment in its crib.

The president had put his bet on the election, and in the weeks that followed his team discussed how to encourage a large turnout and maximize Sunni participation. In a January 3 Deputies Committee meeting, O'Sullivan threw out a number of ideas, including Internet voting and mobile polling units. Marc Grossman, the undersecretary of state for political affairs, who was later appointed by the Obama administration to serve as the point person on Afghanistan and Pakistan, suggested taking the polls directly to the voters much like the Turks conducted their census. Participating from Baghdad, Jim Jeffrey sought to inject some realism into the discussion about how to arrange elections in a war zone. Mobile polling stations, which would require military escorts and would quickly become targets for insurgents, "won't work in Iraq," Jeffrey said, "but we still can't have business as usual." The United States needed an "airtight" security plan.[10]

With American forces protecting polling stations, the CIA's worst fears were not realized: the vote took place on January 30, 2005.[11] The White House hailed the results and Bush called Allawi to congratulate him: the 58 percent of eligible Iraqis who had dipped their fingers in purple ink and voted in spite of the day's three hundred insurgent attacks had taken the first step toward building a new democracy. But the election had come at a price. The American military suffered its largest one-day casualty toll of the war when a CH-53 Super Stallion helicopter, which was carrying thirty-one Marines and a sailor to a polling site near Rutbah, 220 miles west of Baghdad, crashed, killing all aboard. A State Department officer in Fallujah had insisted that the remote voting station be secured, and the chopper had run into a sandstorm.

As Allawi had feared, however, the election hardened the sectarian divides. The United Iraqi Alliance, a coalition of most of the Shiite religious parties besides the Sadrists, came in first with the most seats. The Kurdish parties came in second. Allawi's coalition won only twenty-five seats. Many of the Sunnis boycotted the polls outright or were too afraid to vote. In Anbar, where the Marines on the Super Stallion perished, the Sunni turnout was just 2 percent.

The Iraqi parliamentary system had been constructed in the shadow of the old regime. To guard against the rise of a new tyrant, a super-majority was required to pick a new prime minister. At its best, it was a system with checks and balances that emphasized consensus. But with a multitude of parties and sectarian groupings it was also a prescription for deadlock. To the consternation of the Bush administration, the much ballyhooed election had simply set the stage for seemingly endless backroom wheeling and dealing as parties formed ad hoc alliances to reach the required number of seats to nominate a prime minister. The delays in forming a new government were aggravating an already difficult situation. The Iraqi public was impatient. The Sunnis were fractured and worried: those willing to work, or at least converse, with the government had nobody to work with. With public passions running high, Abd al-Aziz al-Hakim, the leader of the Iranian-supported SCIRI party, had given a troubling speech, referring to a "timetable" for an American withdrawal. In short, the house was on fire and its residents were quarreling over who should get the master bedroom.

Two days after the vote, Rice and other officials on the NSC discussed how to help the Iraqis form their new government. In a telling example of the tendency to interpret the vote in American terms, Rice suggested that a push be made to develop "a package of initiatives to give the new government a road map for the first 100 days." The Americans would not be picking winners, but still needed to convey their concerns.

A few days later, Hadley's Deputies Committee met to discuss a possible role for the United Nations in helping the Iraqis bridge their differences. Jeffrey had argued that the United Nations might be a vehicle to give the Sunnis a role in writing the new constitution despite their boycott of the polls. But there was general agreement among the Bush team that Brahimi had worn out his welcome with most of the Shiite politicians in Iraq and that his role was more trouble than it was worth. An alternative was Ashraf Qazi, a Pakistani diplomat now formally serving as the U.N. envoy in Iraq. "Brahimi is damaged goods in Iraq," Wolfowitz observed. "We should reinforce Qazi or other U.N. officials." Victoria Nuland, an aide to Vice President Cheney who would become the State Department spokesman for Hillary Clinton, seconded the thought. "We don't want an aggressive U.N. political outreach," she said, adding that Brahimi should be kept out of the government formation process." Despite all the anti-Brahimi talk, Meghan O'Sullivan posed an important question at the end of the meeting: "Who do we have to reach out to the Sunnis if not Brahimi?"[12]

On February 5, Robert Ford pondered the problem in a videoconference with members of the NSC staff. "The election was sobering for the Sunnis," Ford said, because now "they are really on the outside looking in." Ford said he was "re-encouraging Sunnis to talk to the Shia and Kurds," and said he expected that the Sunnis will "respond if approached." He also described the de-Baathification process as "very poisonous, particularly in Baghdad."

Allawi had recently given a speech on national unity, and Frank Miller, the senior NSC aide for defense programs, asked Ford if he had been able to gauge the Iraqi reaction on the street. Ford, at some personal risk, had gotten around Iraq in the past, but the diplomats were now hunkered down behind concrete blast walls. "No," he said matter-of-factly. "We are trapped in the Green Zone."[13]

At Casey's headquarters at Camp Victory, the American command was focused on the silver lining of the gathering dark clouds. Even as the Iraqis wrangled among themselves and the formation of the government was delayed, Casey optimistically laid the foundation for the next phase of his strategy to hand the fight to the Iraqis. As he saw it, his plan for 2004 had gotten the country through the January 30 elections. The inability of Al-Qaeda to prevent the vote—Casey overlooked the Sunni boycott—indicated that there was little popular support, he argued, for the enemy.

Casey bravely called his strategy for 2005 the "transition to self-reliance." Capitalizing on the "momentum" of the election, the United States would "diminish" the insurgency and prepare the nascent Iraqi forces "to begin to accept the counterinsurgency lead," Casey's strategy documents asserted. The assumption was that the insurgency would stay at the same level in Sunni areas but weaken in the rest of the country. When it came to security, key cities would be given priority: Baghdad, Mosul, North Babil, Baqubah, Samarra, Fallujah, and Najaf. They would need to be under firm Iraqi control for the next round of elections.[14]

To lay the groundwork for the next phase of his strategy, Casey flew to Fort Bragg, North Carolina, to meet with Lieutenant General John Vines, the commander of XVIII Airborne Corps, who was slated to replace Tom Metz as the corps commander in Iraq. Vines's preparation for Iraq was somewhat unorthodox. With the American military stretched thin, his headquarters had been the only one available to participate in the annual major exercise in South Korea: Ulchi Focus Lens. After returning to Fort Bragg, Vines was focusing again on Iraq when Casey came calling. The Americans were going to do their best to push the Iraqis to the fore. The number of American advisers to the Iraqi forces would be increased. By the middle of 2005, the Iraqi military would be largely trained and equipped. "The strategic guidance changed about the time we hit the ground to transition, transition to the Iraqis in the lead," Vines told a military historian. "So there was an enormous push to, one, put transition teams with Iraqi units, develop capacity with Iraqi units, and to put Iraqis in the lead in the operational and tactical formations."

From a logistical standpoint, the plan made sense. There would be fewer installations to supply and defend, and the military could reap the economy of scale. "There was a recognition that a good deal of the forward operating bases were expensive to operate and so OSD essentially was continually pressing General Casey and me to reduce the footprint and draw it down," recalled Vines, referring to Rumsfeld's Office of the Secretary of Defense. "The guidance was pretty clear, 'Hand this thing over to the Iraqi Government.' That was the guidance from the national level."[15]

But the plan was essentially a bet that the insurgency would be weakened as the Iraqi forces stepped forward. If the insurgents continued to grow stronger, as Harvey predicted, or the Iraqi security forces took time to mature, the enemy would have more space in which to operate. The measure of success for the American military appeared to be how much battle space it could put under the control of the Iraqi military and how many provinces could be designated as being under the writ of Iraqi political authorities. This was at best a mechanistic bet on the outcome. The military strategy did not set the conditions for political progress; it counted on it.

In a briefing to Abizaid, Casey spelled out his plan. Casey was in command of 160,000 American and foreign troops in Iraq, including seventeen American combat brigades spread out across 109 bases. By the end of the year, Casey wanted to bring the number of bases down to 86, and then early in 2006 begin a year-long reduction to 91,000 Western troops, built around 10 American brigades and more than 250 small adviser teams, all on just 41 bases. "Smaller footprint increases risk," the briefing to Abizaid noted; so did "Iraq's historical and social, political and economic situation."

In an early March email to diplomats Negroponte and Ron Neumann, Casey again made his case. "The Iraqis now have the capacity in the military and special police to begin taking on a larger role in the counterinsurgency—with our help." But there were risks, which he laid out as bullet points:

- "New government does not pursue inclusive outreach that brings Sunni into political process—insurgency intensifies"
- "New government does not support strategy and disrupts recent gains by leadership changes in the military, police and intelligence leadership"
- "New government politicizes security ministries and military and police forces—heightening Sunni anxieties"

- "Iraqi leaders fail"
- "Coalition lets process be driven by fixed dates rather than subjective evaluation of Iraqi combat capacity, pushes too fast and sets up Iraqi forces for failure undermining morale and setting back the program"[16]

On March 21, almost two months after the vote, Bush chaired a meeting of his National Security Council to discuss the continued political gridlock in Baghdad. Jim Jeffrey, the chargé d'affaires in Baghdad who was running the embassy after Negroponte's ascension to his intelligence post, painted a frustrating picture. Jalal Talabani, a Kurdish political leader, was pressing for a government under Ibrahim al-Jaafari, the leader of the Dawa Party. Talabani had a strong personal stake in the arrangement: he was to serve as president under the Shiite prime minister. But the deal was hardly sealed. Kurdish officials were still negotiating with the Shiites over the distribution of numerous secondary posts. Allawi, meanwhile, appeared to be doing his best to encourage a prolonged negotiation in the hope that the Shiite-Kurdish talks would collapse and he could make a renewed bid to remain prime minister, Jeffrey reported. There were reports that Ahmed Chalabi and even the Kurds who did not anticipate benefiting from Talabani's largesse might be plotting with Allawi. But according to Jeffrey's calculations, there was no way that Allawi could obtain the necessary majority to become prime minister.

Casey and Negroponte had liked working with Allawi, despite some of his surreptitious maneuvers and propensity to disappear. Allawi was action-oriented and eager to cooperate with the United States. But Allawi had not managed to secure much support in the elections. The only way he could engineer a comeback was to prolong the deadlock. "Our sense is that the time has come to tell Allawi that we will not countenance violations to keep him in power," Jeffrey said in a presentation to the NSC. "We and the British believe that there would be an extraordinarily negative reaction in the Shia south if delay continues—or if Allawi remained in power despite the Shia list's victory in the elections." The foot-dragging had to stop, Jeffrey argued. The United States had to convince the Iraqis that they needed to form their government in days, not weeks. Along with Massoud Barzani, Talabani's Kurdish rival, and possibly Muqtada al-Sadr, Allawi could delay the government's formation. On the other hand, the Iraqi government would have a broader base if Allawi threw his support to the new government, Jeffrey advised. Rumsfeld said that he hoped that Allawi could be talked into taking a post as defense or interior minister or perhaps national security adviser.[17]

Jaafari emerged as prime minister on April 7, even as Allawi pointedly declined to serve the new government in any capacity whatsoever. He was a man accustomed to giving orders, not taking them, and would spend most of the next several years traveling outside Iraq, plotting a comeback.

The machinations over which party would supply the prime minister were matched by a scramble to control the government's most important ministries, like Defense, Interior, and Finance. Control of a ministry allowed a party to hand out jobs and services to its loyalists. In the case of the Interior Ministry, it meant much more.

The outgoing Sunni minister, Falah Naqib, and his hard-charging uncle, Adnan Thabit, had spent late 2004 building the Special Police Commandos and another paramilitary force, the Public Order brigades, into a large and effective fighting organization, armed and equipped by the United States but more independent than the new army. Control of that force was now up for grabs. Quietly, the Shiite powerhouse party SCIRI made it known that it would make big sacrifices in exchange for the top spot in the Interior Ministry.

The prospect of the ministry and its sixteen thousand troops falling under control of a Shiite party whose very name promoted the same Islamic Revolution as Iran did not sit well with Naqib, a secular Sunni. He was convinced that SCIRI would invite thousands of Badr militiamen into the ministry's forces, hijacking them. "Either we have a state of Iraq or a state of militias," Naqib told an American official in mid-March. But the writing was on the wall—SCIRI would run the Interior Ministry.

Like many Iraqi political factions, SCIRI had several faces: the face it showed its Western partners, and a private face. At the top of the organization, Americans dealt with Adil Abd al-Mahdi and Abd al-Aziz al-Hakim. At the next level down, the Americans dealt with the smooth-talking Bayan Jabr, while the Iranians dealt with Hadi al-Amari, who as Badr Organization chief had well-known ties with Quds Force figures like Qasim Suleimani and was generally a much rougher and tougher man. When SCIRI put forward Amari's name as their candidate for interior minister, the United States embassy swiftly vetoed it. So the party fell back on Bayan Jabr.

In his last days in office, outgoing minister Falah Naqib loudly expressed his worry over the fate of the Interior Ministry to American officials. On April 4 he met with American diplomat Robert Ford and British Lieutenant General John Kiszely. In the southern provinces of Basra, Najaf, Wasit, and Maysan, Naqib said, newly elected SCIRI governors and newly empowered SCIRI provincial councils were dismissing police chiefs he had appointed over the past year in favor of Badr Corps members, who often brought with them their own retinues of militiamen. Ford felt for Naqib and told him that he should continue to voice his concerns. "Clearly disappointed at this response, Naqib said it would be impossible to be in the opposition in Iraq because SCIRI and Badr would assassinate their opponents," Ford wrote in a cable. "If SCIRI gains the Minister of Interior portfolio, it will likely trigger worries among many more Sunni Arabs than just Felah Naqib," Ford concluded. The next day Naqib voiced his fears to Casey directly. SCIRI did not have Iraq's best interests at heart, he said—it wanted to create an autonomous southern region tied more closely to Iran than to the United States. A civil war, Naqib gloomily predicted, was coming. "We either stop them or give Iraq to Iran. That's it," Naqib asserted, opening his arms wide.[18]

The next month Casey had his first meeting with Jabr. Like SCIRI's other new cabinet ministers, Jabr told Casey, he had been preparing for the job for a year and a half, since receiving orders to do so from Ayatollah Muhammad Baqir al-Hakim, the late brother of Abd al-Aziz al-Hakim, who had been assassinated in 2003. In what the Americans took as a reassuring sign, Jabr told Casey that he would be keeping Adnan Thabit on as chief of the ministry's paramilitary troops.

In fact, Jabr planned not to change the top leadership of the Interior Ministry forces, but to change the forces themselves, with an influx of new recruits and mid-level commanders from the Badr Organization, the paramilitary group that had begun its life as an arm of the Iranian Revolutionary Guard against Saddam and evolved more recently into the officially sanctioned militia of SCIRI.[19] He quickly moved to sideline Thabit and change the face of the Special Police Commandos and Public Order battalions by authorizing an influx of new Shiite recruits. By mid-June, Jabr had broached the idea with American advisers of creating three new battalions purely of Shiite recruits. To undercut Thabit, he hired a Badr Corps veteran, Major General Muhammad Ne'emeh, as the ministry's director of operations. When a Turkmen deputy minister resigned in protest, another Turkmen found to replace him, Ali Ghaleb, was a Shiite, not a Sunni, and he began to fire Sunni police officials. A renewed de-Baathification effort championed by Jabr allowed him to fire more Sunni officials in the ministry and replace them with SCIRI and Badr hands.

The Jaafari government was off to an inauspicious start.

CHAPTER 9

Papa Jaafari

Iraq's new prime minister was unlike Allawi in just about every respect. Born in the Shiite holy city of Karbala, Ibrahim al-Jaafari's revolutionary pedigree was beyond challenge. Jaafari's great-grandfather had led the 1876 al-Ushaiqir revolt against the Ottoman Empire. Jaafari had been in medical school in Mosul when in 1966 he was invited to join the Dawa Party, the secretive and conspiratorial anti-Saddam group whose senior leaders were hunted and in many cases executed by Saddam. Like many other Dawa members, Jaafari fled the wave of executions and arrests Saddam had ordered and went into exile in Iran, where he remained throughout the Iran-Iraq War, before relocating to London where he served as a Dawa spokesman.[1]

But while Allawi was deeply suspicious of Iran, American intelligence reports indicated that Jaafari, who visited Tehran in the run-up to the 2005 vote, received millions of dollars in political funding from Iran.

Allawi had been backed by the United States because he was deemed to be decisive enough to cope with worsening security. Jaafari, in contrast, was a consensus candidate among the Shiite religious factions who was chosen precisely because, unlike SCIRI or the Sadrists, his party lacked mass appeal and did not have its own militias. Jealous of their prerogatives and reluctant to cede power to a strong national figure, Iraq's quarreling politicians had settled on a prime minister who posed little threat to their authority, but who also showed little evidence of wielding the strong hand that would be needed to govern a failed state. In Iraq, weakness could be strength—at least when it came to climbing the political ladder.

Whereas Allawi was an impulsive man of action, Jaafari was cerebral, given to writing poetry and peppering his discussions with Western officials with references to Samuel Huntington, Francis Fukuyama, and Noam Chomsky. In a typically discursive meeting with Phebe Marr, the renowned Iraq historian, he explained his vision of humanity by drawing a diamond. Pointing to the bottom point of the diamond, he explained that the people start out as one. Tracing with his finger the widest part of the diamond, he continued, they grow apart over time. "But in the future we will form the rest of the diamond. The lines will begin to converge again—to a small point where people will be together again," he added confidently.[2] Years later, he showed a visitor a dog-eared copy of an Arabic-language biography of Michelle Obama, with notes in the margins.

Acting on his belief that the family was the cornerstone of society, Jaafari preferred not to discuss work over meals or in the evenings. Indeed, he once put aside his duties for two hours one evening to give marital advice to an American diplomat making the rounds in the Green Zone to say her goodbyes at the end of her tour. Sitting in the garden of his official residence—a walled compound in the heart of Baghdad with a fetid pond, geese, and a volleyball net (Jaafari was an avid player)—the prime minister counseled the diplomat to choose wisely in picking a mate. Physical beauty will decline, he observed, but if one's spouse had "moral beauty" he or she would grow even more beautiful through the years.

David Satterfield, a senior diplomat at the embassy, later sent Washington a cable on the episode entitled "Garden Chats with Papa Ja'fari and Crew."[3] The same Satterfield cable quoted the prime minister's former chief of staff as saying that Jaafari's office was hopelessly disorganized and mired in detail. Jaafari had surrounded himself with loyalists with no management experience and was reluctant to delegate even minor decisions because he believed that they, too, would reflect on him. The prime minister's penchant to meander off topic in the midst of important engagements was evident when Jaafari flew to Washington in 2005 for a private meeting with George Bush and his top advisers.

The July trip—which was to take the new prime minister through Washington, Brussels, London, and Kuwait City—did not begin in the most felicitous manner. Jaafari and his entourage began the odyssey on an Iraqi Airways Boeing 707; over Budapest, a loud thud resounded through the cockpit—the windshield had cracked. The pilot was unflustered but upon landing in London, an American civilian aboard called the defense attaché there to arrange repairs. After inspecting the plane, though, U.S. Air Force personnel found another problem—the 707 did not belong to Iraq. It belonged to a Syrian company registered in Sierra Leone that was under

United States sanctions, and hence could not be repaired. For the next leg of the trip, Jaafari's party flew commercial, and then they went from Brussels to Washington on a KC-135 tanker jet.

When he made it to his meeting with Bush, Jaafari talked at length about one of his favorite themes: Thomas Jefferson, Abraham Lincoln, and the great American presidents. Bush shot his aides a quizzical glance as if to say "What gives?" The Iraqi leader's interest in American history was commendable but the upheaval in Iraq had barely been discussed.[4]

Bush later rewarded Jaafari for his erudition, presenting him with a leather-bound 1826 edition of the *Federalist Papers,* a gift that was also a symbol of the democratic Iraq the president wanted to build. For all that, Jaafari was stunningly ill-equipped to deal with the escalating crisis in Iraq. Indeed, one of the Americans' greatest frustrations was that Jaafari did not perceive the country to be in crisis. He was hardly the leader the Bush administration had hoped for when it first contemplated invading Iraq. But Jaafari had been elevated by an electoral system the Americans had helped to create and the Bush administration had no choice but to work with him.

Relations between the Iraqi leadership and the military command remained under strain. Casey was not enthralled by Jaafari's references to poetry and the intricacies of European history. The new prime minister, captivated by the historical figures he studied so closely, did not find the American general to be particularly impressive. "Casey likes to appear to be doing more than he actually is," recalled Jaafari. "He speaks more than his actions." Jaafari made an effort to study Casey's "facial expressions" rather than actually listen to him.

As Jaafari settled into his job, the American military began to pursue the two goals of its strategy: shrinking its footprint in Iraq and standing up the Iraqi forces. At the end of February 2005, the 3rd Infantry Division took over in Baghdad from Chiarelli's 1st Cavalry Division. Led by Major General William "Fuzzy" Webster, the division had spearheaded the 2003 invasion and was now the first Army division to return for a second tour. With American force levels in Iraq dropping from their election peak, smaller American units occupied larger expanses of terrain. Webster's new 4th Brigade took over for two of Chiarelli's brigades, assuming control not just of the Green Zone and surrounding areas but also of southern Baghdad's touchy Rashid District.

In other parts of Baghdad, the new American command pushed Iraqis to the fore. Less than a week before Chiarelli handed over Baghdad to Webster, on February 21, the 40th Iraqi National Guard Brigade took formal control of sixteen square kilometers of northern Baghdad spanning both sides of the Tigris and including two Sunni areas where the 1st Cavalry had encountered fierce fighting—Haifa Street and the Adhamiya District. On Haifa Street, the commander of the Iraqi 303rd Battalion, General Muhammad al-Samarrai, set up his headquarters in an abandoned palace and confidently proclaimed that his men had turned the tide.

The 40th Brigade's takeover in central Baghdad was supposed to lead the way for many more, as Iraq's security forces expanded during 2005 under Petraeus's training command. By the end of 2005 the strength of the Iraqi security forces was to rise, from 100,000 in late fall 2004, to 210,000. On the cover of his briefings about the dramatic expansion of the Iraqi forces, Petraeus took to featuring a famous quotation by T. E. Lawrence: "Do not try to do too much with your own hands. Better the Arabs do it tolerably than that you do it perfectly. It is their war, and you are to help them, not win it for them." The message reflected Casey's emphasis on transition, but it was a philosophy that Petraeus would later reverse.[5]

To advise these units once they were in the field, the American military turned to twelve-man "transition teams." Before the 2003 invasion, the elite Special Forces had borne the responsibility of advising foreign armies, but now a much larger cadre of advisers was needed in Iraq. During 2004, some American units, like Chiarelli's 1st Cavalry, had created adviser teams "out of hide"—that is, pulling advisers from within their own units and assigning them to work with the Iraqis. As he left Iraq, Chiarelli strongly recommended this approach, figuring that American commanders in the field would be motivated to assign some of their best people to the mission. The Army, however, rejected Chiarelli's advice as a long-term solution; it chose instead to rely on stateside units to provide advisers. As it turned out, many of these advisory teams were not top-of-the-line or were resourced so thinly that they never had a chance to be effective.

In the fall of 2004, Petraeus's understaffed command's ranks swelled with the arrival of hundreds of officers and senior sergeants from the Army Reserve's 98th Training Division, devoted to training other Reserve and National Guard units during their two-weeks-a-year sessions or whenever they were activated. Drill instructors found themselves on paltry teams embedded with Iraqi troops in the harshest of conditions, with little oversight or support. The following year the 75th Training Division's transition teams were larger, but not much better prepared for the rigors of advising

Iraqi troops in combat. For most of 2005, for instance, just 113 soldiers from the 75th Division's 2nd Brigade were responsible for advising the Interior Ministry's Special Police Commandos in combat, a job for which Special Forces, active-duty infantrymen, or military police troops would have been better qualified.

In the Americans' haste to grow the Iraqi forces some of the Iraqi units were little more than militias that had been issued uniforms and new unit names. Much of the Iraqi Army's 2nd Division came from Kurdish Pesh-merga militia, who fought well but often inflamed Sunni Arab populations in the areas of northern Iraq for which they were responsible.

Worse, with Bayan Jabr in charge of the Interior Ministry, many of their units incorporated members of Shiite militias like the Badr Organization and the Mahdi Army with little or no screening process. An adviser assigned to the ministry's 2nd Public Order Brigade in East Baghdad recalled a day when his team visited an Iraqi base and found more than three hundred unfamiliar young men there in "various forms of military dress." The ministry had hired them en masse the day before, many of them straight from the militia. Throughout that brigade, which was almost exclusively Shiite, there was much evidence of Sadrist loyalty. "They had Muqtada al-Sadr posters on everything, like on the trucks, on the gun shields, in the barracks, and on the walls of the FOB [forward operating base], and we were constantly ripping that stuff off and it was constantly reappear-ing," the adviser recalled.[6] In West Baghdad's Dora neighborhood, which was largely Sunni and Christian, the 4th Public Order Brigade displayed similar tendencies. "On the day of the election, they would drive through this Sunni market playing Shia songs," said Colonel Ed Cardon, a brigade commander in the 3rd Infantry Division who later rose to command the 2nd Infantry Division.[7]

As the new Iraqi units were thrown, often with little American over-sight, into the fight against Al-Qaeda's widening car bomb offensive, a number of them, particularly those from the Interior Ministry, acquired reputations for using brutal tactics against Sunni suspects and civilians. Many of the atrocities were carried out by individuals or groups in Interior Ministry units at night, rather than during official unit operations, mak-ing them difficult to verify, especially for undermanned adviser teams. In Dora, Cardon suspected the 4th Public Order Brigade of this but could not prove it. The ministry's Special Police Commandos—or *maghawir,* as Iraqis knew them—were widely feared by Sunnis, especially the 2nd Com-mando Brigade, or "Wolf Brigade," which had a heavy Badr tinge among its leaders and troops. The brigade "did a lot of bad things," said an American battalion commander who worked alongside it, Lieutenant Colonel Jim Blackburn. "But you never saw them do anything. You just saw the aftermath the day after."[8]

A confidential cable sent on June 16 by American diplomats in Mosul chronicled the abuses committed there by the Wolf Brigade. An Iraqi human rights organization had investigated twenty-five cases of torture and abuse, including six deaths, at the hands of the Wolf Brigade, noted that report, which concluded that the allegations were "credible." The torture, according to the cable, involved shooting prisoners with stun guns, hanging them from their wrists, confining them in basements full of human waste, beating them, and threatening "detainees with demeaning acts against their wives and sisters." Some of the prisoners had been ordered released but that judicial ruling had been ignored.[9]

In the highest echelons of the new Iraqi government, Jaafari sometimes seemed oblivious to the sectarianism bedeviling much of his security apparatus, and some American officials suspected that his professorial demeanor hid a deeper complicity. Over the spring and summer of 2005 Jaafari rarely called meetings of the Ministerial Committee for National Security, or MCNS, the Iraqi equivalent of the National Security Council, preferring to rely on a set of personal advisers.

Petraeus visited Bayan Jabr's office on July 10 to show him photos of the prisoners abused by the Wolf Brigade. "It is a large group of people," the general told the minister, although to soften the criticism, he noted, in an apparent reference to the Abu Ghraib prison scandal, "we have also made our share of mistakes." The Wolf Brigade, he said, should not be doing unilateral operations without American troops—a big change from a year before, when Petraeus had greeted the independent stand-up and operations of Adnan Thabit's commandos with enthusiasm. Jabr dismissed Petraeus's suggestion that the brigade's new Shiite recruits were acting with a sectarian bent and downplayed the seriousness of the alleged crimes, chalking them up to cultural differences. "This isn't a Sunni-Shia problem, it is all of us against the terrorists," he told the American general. "Let me be clear: They were trained under the culture of Saddam."

The very same day, men wearing the uniforms of the Interior Ministry commandos and the now-defunct Iraqi National Guard kidnapped eleven Sunni men from the main Sunni district in East Baghdad, Adhamiya, according to an American diplomatic cable on the incident; two days later, the eleven victims' bodies showed up in nearby Sadr City, the epicenter of

Mahdi Army activity in Baghdad, bearing signs of torture. In another case in late August, the bodies of thirty-six men were found in Wasit, a largely Shiite province southeast of Baghdad. The day before, thirty-six Sunni men had been rounded up in Hurriya, a mixed district in West Baghdad, by men in commando uniforms driving police trucks. "The bodies were found partially clothed, handcuffed, with bullet wounds to the head," explained a State Department cable.[10]

Some senior Americans were slow to acknowledge the problem, too. In the fall, Petraeus rotated home from the top training job and was replaced by Lieutenant General Marty Dempsey, who had commanded the 1st Armored Division in Baghdad in 2003–2004. One of the first major Iraqi offensives on Dempsey's watch was Operation Knockout in November, in which seven battalions of Interior Ministry troops deployed from Baghdad to Baqubah to attack Sunni insurgents there. In a report to Casey, Dempsey wrote glowingly, "The operation will serve as a model for future special police operations."

The American brigade commander in Baqubah, Colonel Steve Salazar, saw Operation Knockout differently. His brigade was responsible for a province where American troop levels would soon be cut, and where 2005 had already seen tensions between Sunnis and Shiites running high. In August, after a suicide bombing at an American base killed several government officials, Diyala's Shiite governor had called the Interior Ministry and requested the deployment of the Special Police Commandos. Salazar talked the governor out of it, believing that the arrival of the Shiite-dominated force would only inflame Sunni insurgents more, but after the appointment of a new Diyala police chief from the Badr Organization, he got an email from a friend in Baghdad telling him that Interior Ministry troops would be coming to Diyala after all, for Operation Knockout. "I wrote back, copy to all, something to the effect of, 'That would be a disaster of biblical proportions and that is the worst possible thing that could happen in Baqubah,'" Salazar recalled, but it happened anyway. With Salazar's troops shadowing every move the Interior Ministry forces made in Operation Knockout, there was no suspicious violence, but the seven battalions rounded up between three hundred and four hundred detainees, most of them Sunni, and also tried to detain Baqubah's Sunni mayor until Salazar refused to allow it. "I think the [provincial] government was compromised by Operation Knockout," Salazar said.

Some of the conventional American units had their deficiencies, too. Nor was all of the American force as capable as the one that had marched to Baghdad during the heady days of the invasion and toppled Saddam. By early 2005 the Army was running very low on fresh combat units to send to Iraq. To fill the gaps, the Army turned to the National Guard. During the invasion two years before, National Guard units had been called up only in small numbers and mainly for support roles like guarding supply bases and headquarters. In early 2004 that had begun to change, with the deployment of brigades from the Washington, North Carolina, and Arkansas National Guards for full-blown combat duty.

In 2005, the Army marked a dubious first when it called on the Guard to send as many combat brigades to Iraq as the active Army. The division responsible for the volatile area in north-central Iraq consisted of a New York Guard headquarters, two active-duty brigades, and two Guard brigades from Idaho and Tennessee. Louisiana Guard units operated in West Baghdad, and over the winter and spring other Guard units took responsibility for South Baghdad, Babil, Karbala, and Najaf. For much of the year, seven of the seventeen combat brigades in Iraq would be from the Guard, and after a Pennsylvania brigade arrived in the explosive city of Ramadi over the summer, the number briefly rose to eight.

Guard units had advantages—their "weekend warriors" were on average older, and often had experience that was relevant in Iraq, such as jobs as law enforcement officers or municipal officials. But their disadvantages were profound enough to discourage the Army from using National Guard brigades for full combat roles for years afterward. Commanders and junior soldiers alike had less training and less experience than their active counterparts, and they were often last in line for new equipment.[11]

The rush to expand the Iraqi forces meant that officers with a sectarian agenda were willy-nilly absorbed into the military and especially the Interior Ministry's forces. The policy of consolidating American bases and shrinking America's footprint meant that a growing burden fell on Iraqi troops rarely well equipped to handle it. The deployment of U.S. National Guard units also meant that the American forces in Iraq, although similar in number to the first rotation of Operation Iraqi Freedom, were less capable of taking the fight to the insurgents. A critical assumption underpinning Casey's strategy had been that the insurgent threat would not increase. But Casey's headquarters had underestimated the foe and its strategy had given the enemy more room to maneuver.

There was little question but that the Sunni insurgency was developing strength in early 2005. During late winter and spring, Al-Qaeda unleashed a deadly wave of car and truck bomb attacks, many against Iraqi security forces and against Shiite markets and other public spaces. In January there was roughly one suicide bombing per day in Iraq, many targeting Iraqi police and military or paramilitary troops at checkpoints, recruiting drives, and so on. As the winter progressed the attacks grew deadlier. On February 18 and 19, suicide bombers attacked Shiite civilians gathered near the Kadhimiya Shrine, the holiest Shiite mosque in Baghdad; the second day's attack included multiple bombers. On February 28, a particularly lethal suicide truck bomb—a VBIED, or vehicle-borne IED—killed more than 120 people in the Shiite city of Hilla south of Baghdad, many of them young men who had assembled to apply for slots in the security forces. Ten days later forty-seven people were killed in an attack at a funeral in Mosul, most of them members of the city's small Shiite minority. Attacks on May 7 and June 14, one in Baghdad's Tahrir Square and one in Kirkuk, each killed about two dozen people (including in the Baghdad bombing two American security contractors). And on July 16, ninety people died when a fuel truck rigged with explosives blew up at a Shiite mosque in the Euphrates River town of Musayyib, near Karbala.

One purpose of Al-Qaeda's car and truck bomb attacks was to prompt an overreaction by the Shiite militias and Shiite-dominated Iraqi security forces so that Sunni insurgents would assume the role of defenders of the Sunni community. In July, Al-Qaeda leader Zarqawi made this aim explicit when he announced the creation of what he called the Omar Brigade, after the early Muslim caliph who conquered Persia in the seventh century and whose name had Sunni connotations. Zarqawi framed the organization as one that would combat Iranian influence and protect Sunnis. He described it as a foe to the Badr Organization—still the Badr Corps to most regular Iraqis—which he derided as the Ghadr Corps, a play on words suggesting the organization's presumed treachery and duplicity. As Zarqawi understood, among Iraq's Sunnis, many of whom stubbornly believed themselves to be a majority in the country, the "Persian" threat was a worry.

For all of the emphasis that Casey put on tamping down the Sunni insurgency, for American troops in East Baghdad, as for the British in Basra, Muqtada al-Sadr's Mahdi Army remained the main enemy. And Sadr's fighters were increasingly using a new and sophisticated roadside bomb. Colonel Joe DiSalvo's 2nd Brigade, 3rd Infantry Division—the unit that had conducted the first "Thunder Run" into Baghdad in 2003—had returned and was given a vast area to patrol in East Baghdad, including

Sadr City, where DiSalvo put one of his battalions at the northeast corner. To the east, Lieutenant Colonel Kevin Farrell's battalion, 1-64 Armor, was responsible for 9 Nisan, a large and at one time mixed sectarian district.

In an effort to change the sectarian balance of the neighborhood, the Sadrist political movement had been financing the construction of low-cost homes and filling them with poor Shiites relocated from southern Iraq. The satellite imagery of the area that the American military accessed showed that what had been empty lots and fields on the edges of 9 Nisan in 2003 were now filled with new construction. The Interior Ministry forces with whom Farrell's battalion worked, called Public Order battalions, did not inspire confidence: some of their Chevy pickup trucks were adorned with placards featuring the figure of Muqtada al-Sadr against a backdrop of burning Humvees.

In March, one of Farrell's Abrams tanks was hit by an IED while traveling on Route Predators, a highway running through East Baghdad. Though none of the crew was killed, the attack was unsettling, because the tank—the most heavily armored vehicle in the American inventory, and supposedly invulnerable to roadside bombs—was put out of commission. The bomb that accomplished this feat looked like a large coffee can with a wide and precisely milled copper disc at one end. When activated by a passive infrared sensor, explosives in the can went off, propelling the disc forward and turning it into a slug of molten copper that lanced through heavy armor with ease. Sometimes several cans would be linked together.

Some Mahdi Army fighters called the new bombs *kafa* ("jumpers"), while others called them "Persian bombs" or "Nasrallahs," alluding to a connection between the weapons and Iran. As the number of new bombs rose, the military started calling them explosively formed penetrators, or EFPs. Though they were classified as a type of improvised explosive device they were, in fact, a sophisticated and carefully machined weapon of war. Often encased in concrete or in Styrofoam disguised as concrete, they were particularly prevalent on highways. The weapons were lethal and those soldiers that survived the attacks often had gruesome injuries. By summer Farrell was so concerned that he declared Route Predators "black," or off-limits. "The only thing that really worried us were the EFPs, because they could take out just about anything we had," Farrell said. "For a long while we couldn't get division to recognize the EFP as a different type of IED, and they wouldn't categorize it as anything else."[12]

The first EFPs had been used in Iraq two years earlier. In August 2003, in what may have been the first EFP attack of the war, an Abrams tank patrolling a Shiite neighborhood in Baghdad had been penetrated by a copper slug that puzzled investigators at the time. During July, August, and September 2004, there was an average of about one EFP attack per week, although the actual number may have been somewhat higher because American units did not know what they were running into. Many of the attacks occurred around the periphery of Sadr City. By the end of 2004, according to a CIA estimate, there had been about fifty EFP attacks.[13]

In 2005, the numbers increased. Task Force Troy, the military unit responsible for gathering intelligence on IEDs and deploying countermeasures against them, counted fifty EFP attacks in the first half of 2005, and in the period from September 2005 through January 2006 another seventy-five.[14] Although the attack numbers remained very small in comparison to the enormity of the overall IED problem in Iraq, the EFPs proved especially deadly and the perfect weapon for use in urban environments. The bombs Al-Qaeda emplaced were hugely destructive but often required huge amounts of explosives, which meant militants needed time and privacy to dig deep holes in roads to bury their devices. By contrast, EFP components could be smuggled easily, even in bulk. Moreover, the weapons could be precisely targeted. The fact that American convoys insisted that Iraqi vehicles keep their distance, a precaution against suicide car bomb attacks, meant that occupiers could be singled out for EFP attacks.

The rising number of EFP devastations eventually drew the interest of the American intelligence community. Back in the United States, the National Ground Intelligence Center tried to reverse-engineer EFPs. They found that manufacturing the copper discs that turned into the bombs' lethal slugs required a forty-ton press with a high degree of precision. With this information, the 3rd Infantry Division commander, Fuzzy Webster, launched a sweep of all of East Baghdad's industrial areas to find any presses that could be doing the job. "Operation Traffic Stop was part of our overall campaign to try to find places where EFPs could be produced inside Iraq," Webster recalled. "We produced pictures and descriptions of machine tools that would be used to produce the copper face of the devices that would create the shaped charge, the slug; we were looking for copper material; and we were looking for machine shops in general and their supply lines."[15] Nothing turned up.

The intelligence community concluded that the EFPs' key components were being manufactured in Iran and then brought into Iraq via the same covert arms distribution network that the Quds Force had relied on before 2003 against Saddam, only now the arms were going to units of the Mahdi

Army and other Iran-backed militias rather than to the force's old proxy the Badr Corps. A GPS device recovered during a raid on a cache of EFP components years later and turned over to Task Force Troy showed the smuggler had checked a series of waypoints that led back to Iran.

The methods for concealing EFP components were ingenious. One story that often cropped up was that components of the weapons—the copper discs and can-like housings for the explosive—came across the border inside deep-freezers on tractor trailers; one report claimed the parts were actually frozen in ice, while another had them in "propane bottles and air conditioner Freon bottles." Other Iranian-built weapons systems like rockets and mortar shells had their Farsi manufacturing markings scrubbed off before they were pushed across the border into Iraq. "Where Farsi markings have existed, attempts have been made to remove them," a report by British military intelligence noted. "In some cases this has been only partially effective and identification has still been possible. This process, known as 'sanitisation,' has no purpose other than to prevent identification."[16]

The Iranian role was not a surprise. Soon after the American invasion, Iran's two intelligence arms, the Ministry of Intelligence and National Security, or MOIS, and the Revolutionary Guard's shadowy Quds Force, had stepped up their intelligence gathering in Iraq, taking advantage of the two decades they had spent developing networks of sources and fostering opposition groups. In December 2003, the Quds Force moved a section of its headquarters from its usual compound on the grounds of the old American embassy in Tehran to the border city of Mehran, where its Iraq-focused Ramazan Corps was based, according to American intelligence reports.[17] In February 2004, American forces seized a MOIS document asking operatives in northern Iraq to gather information about American aircraft and installations, singling out the 101st Airborne for mention, and also for any hints of an Israeli presence.

Iran, in effect, was employing the same sort of strategy the United States had used to counter the Soviet invasion of Afghanistan. During that conflict, the Reagan administration had funneled Stinger antiaircraft missiles to the mujahideen, which the fighters used with devastating effect to shoot down Soviet helicopters and constrain the Soviet military's mobility. By sending EFPs to the Shiite militias, the Iranians were helping their proxies contest the ability of the United States coalition to maneuver its armored vehicles around the country.

The Israeli military had known about Iranian-supplied EFPs for some time and provided their findings to the Pentagon. Israeli troops operating in Hezbollah territory in southern Lebanon had first encountered one of the bombs in October 1998, according to a detailed technical assessment the Israelis shared with the Americans. Between then and 2002, there had been fifteen EFP attacks in Lebanon, sometimes against soft-skinned Israeli trucks that filled a Humvee-like role and sometimes against armored vehicles. Often, the bombs had been convincingly disguised with fiberglass and Styrofoam as rocks, as in East Baghdad.[18]

American intelligence turned up some documents from the days of Saddam's regime suggesting that Iran was smuggling other kinds of bombs into Iraq at the time that the Israelis were facing EFPs in Lebanon. A document from July 2001 described how Badr Corps operative Abu Mustafa al-Sheibani had been smuggling "conically shaped bombs filled with TNT, weighing 5–6 kg and using a locally made metal base" from Iran into the Diyala-Baghdad area.[19] At the time, Sheibani, an Iraqi national who would later serve as the Badr Corps's intelligence chief, was in charge of what the organization called Axis 3 of its arms smuggling network. In 2004, Sheibani was performing the same role; the old Badr Corps smuggling "axes" closely matched the three regional commands of the Quds Force's Ramazan Corps. The Iranian special operations groups were using the same Iraqi proxies to distribute weapons to new allies.

Over time American intelligence pieced together a better picture of the EFP distribution network. The EFPs, rockets, and other weapons making their way into central Iraq from Iran were coming through border crossings in Diyala and Wasit, in the area for which the Quds Force's Zafr Command based at Mehran was responsible. One military intelligence report alleged that it was at a petroleum factory in Mehran that many of the EFP components were manufactured. Sheibani seemed to run the key smuggling network there. According to a member of his network whom American troops detained, a group of Sheibani's people had traveled to a military base inside Iran in July 2004, where Lebanese Hezbollah instructors put them through a course on the use of EFPs and their passive infrared sensors, and after that the Sheibani network started running the bombs into Iraq.

In southern Iraq, across the border from the Quds Force's Fajr Command's bases in Khorramshahr and Ahvaz, another smuggling group was run by a former Mahdi Army commander, Abu Sajjad al-Gharawi. Gharawi's group was particularly active in the border province of Maysan north of Basra, where on May 29 and July 16 British troops were attacked with EFPs. Gharawi had ties to a senior Quds Force commander based in Iran, Abdul Reza Shahlai; Western intelligence got ahold of messages between the two in November 2004 and January 2005 discussing the bombs in code, according to a CIA report.[20] Another arms smuggler in the south was Ahmed al-Fartusi, a Mahdi Army commander who, according to the British intelligence service, had lived in Lebanon for five years before coming back to Iraq and had worked with Lebanese Hezbollah there. British forces detained Fartusi in September 2005 after he was linked to three EFP attacks in Basra in one week.[21]

Two other figures who popped up in American intelligence archives regarding EFPs were Mahmud Farhadi and Abu Mahdi al-Muhandis. Farhadi, a Quds Force lieutenant colonel, was believed in mid-2005 to be one of the chief Iranian officers responsible for financing Sheibani and others and helping them get bomb components into central Iraq. The Iraqi-born Muhandis was a senior Badr Corps operative who in 2002 left that organization to work directly for the Quds Force in its weapons-smuggling networks and had accompanied Rubaie in 2004 from the Green Zone to Najaf on an American helicopter. In December 2005, he would be elected to the Iraqi parliament.

The British, operating in southern Iraq, suffered EFP attacks as well; so, too, did a Japanese convoy near Samawa. The question of how hard to press the Iranians had long bedeviled the Americans. Soon after the United States invaded Iraq, American intelligence determined that Iran's chief diplomat in Baghdad, General Ali Reza Hassan Kazemi-Qomi, was a veteran Quds Force officer with experience in Lebanon and a previous stint as an assistant to Supreme Leader Ayatollah Ali Khamenei. Determined to push back, the Americans decided in 2004 to declare the diplomat and several Iranian embassy personnel persona non grata because of their Quds Force connections and tried to kick him and some of his deputies out of Iraq. "We knew that getting rid of him would not entirely shut down their operation," recalled diplomat Ron Neumann. "But we were looking at things that would make their life more difficult."

Washington and London agreed. Neumann drafted a letter to Hoshyar Zebari, Iraq's foreign minister, asking him to formally expel the Iranian envoy. But the British, who unlike the Americans retained formal diplomatic relations with Iran, had reservations about the demarche. They feared that the Iranians would retaliate in some way against the British embassy in Tehran. Knowing of the British unhappiness, Neumann delivered the letter to Zebari anyway, hoping the diplomats could be expelled before London changed its mind. Within an hour of delivering the letter,

Neumann got fresh instructions to abort the move. He called Zebari and told him that he needed the letter back.[22]

As the toll from the EFPs began to mount the United States and Britain each lodged formal complaints. Through Swiss intermediaries, the United States submitted their formal protest to the Iranian government, blandly titled "Message from the United States to the Government of Iran." Taking note of an earlier British protest to Tehran, the American complaint cited a May 29, 2005, EFP attack near Amara that killed a twenty-one-year-old British lance corporal, Alan Brackenbury. "We will continue to judge Iran by its actions in Iraq," the protest insisted.[23]

Two diplomatic cables sent to the State Department by the American embassy in Baghdad within twenty-four hours of the demarche described the embassy's impressions of Iran's role in Iraq. One recounted a recent conversation between American diplomats and the Iraqi national security adviser. "Rubaie stated that he was aware of IRGC's introduction of advanced IED technology into Iraq," the cable stated, using the American acronym for the Revolutionary Guard.[24] The other cable, entitled "Building a House on Shifting Sands: Iran's Influence in Iraq's Center-South," noted the number of casualties caused by EFPs. It was "speculated," the cable went on, that the Quds Force was "cultivating" the arms-smuggling networks "to maintain a latent capability to direct highly lethal attacks on Coalition Forces when required."[25]

The same cable, classified by David Satterfield, also described Iran's role more generally. Underneath a "calm, benign surface, exists a dark undercurrent of aggressive IRGC activity detrimental to U.S. interests," it explained. It noted that the Jaafari government "is now reported to be exploring close, cooperative relationships with the MOIS," the acronym for Iranian intelligence, hoping to pattern its State Ministry of National Security Affairs after it and "supplant" the CIA-sponsored intelligence agency, the Iraqi National Intelligence Service, or INIS. On the financial side, SCIRI in 2005 had so far accepted $100 million from Iran, much of it from the Quds Force and $45 million of it allocated to Badr: "Unchecked IRGC-QF and other Iranian patronage ensures that the Shia political spectrum is conclusively dominated by political parties that are at least sympathetic, if not entirely beholden, to their financial benefactors."[26]

On intelligence matters in particular, Jaafari was deeply suspicious of institutions that he saw as dominated by Sunnis and Baathists, like the INIS. In June 2005 National Security Adviser Rubaie, a Shiite, told American diplomats that Shawani, the INIS's director, was effectively shut out of the government despite repeated efforts to reach out to Jaafari and make himself and his agency useful. The next month, an embassy cable reported that Jaafari's government was attempting to bypass the INIS altogether and establish a new, parallel, and unofficial intelligence arm, "possibly headed by State Minister of National Security Abdul Kareem al-Anzi, the primary advocate for intelligence sharing with Iran."[27] The initiative had the backing of Ahmed Chalabi, who had his own close ties to Iran. At the very least, this attitude of suspicion and sectarianism clouded and colored the information reaching Jaafari and other top government leaders about the rising sectarian tensions just outside the walls of the Green Zone.

Jaafari never acknowledged any sympathy for Tehran, but he did not disguise his interest in good relations with the Iranians. "I personally look at Iran as part of the geographical entourage of Iraq and a friendly state which stood by Iraq's side in a time of crisis," he said. "It harbored Iraqis"—including Jaafari himself—"when Saddam Hussein killed, displaced, and harmed many of them."[28]

CHAPTER 10

The Red Team

On July 24, 2005, Zalmay Khalilzad hopped a C-17 flight to Baghdad to fill the long-empty ambassadorial post that Negroponte had left behind over the winter to become the first Director of National Intelligence.

Khalilzad was the product of two worlds. Born in the city of Mazar-e-Sharif in northern Afghanistan, he was the son of a civil servant and an Afghan woman who lacked a formal education. He became a star student at his high school in Kabul before spending a year as an exchange student at an American high school near Modesto, California. It was a pivotal experience for Khalilzad, whose decision to make the United States his adopted country was cemented after the Soviet invasion of Afghanistan.

After a doctorate at the University of Chicago and a stint as an assistant professor at Columbia University, Khalilzad was awarded a fellowship to work for the Reagan administration on nuclear issues. He never went back to academia. Khalilzad embarked on a long career in the foreign policy world, where he made a name for himself in conservative circles.[1] After Bremer's intervention prevented him from continuing his work in Iraq as a political envoy, he was appointed ambassador to Afghanistan.

The Iraqis impressed Khalilzad as even more difficult to deal with than the Afghans. But nothing, he thought, could happen without fixing security in the country. Khalilzad had spent a few years in the Pentagon when Dick Cheney was defense secretary and had his own contacts in the think tanks, including Andrew Krepinevich, who had written a book about the Army's experience in Vietnam and who had become a proponent of a renewed counterinsurgency effort in Iraq. Before leaving for Iraq, Khalilzad had outlined his views to the Senate Foreign Relations Committee. In addition to political reconciliation, it was imperative to "break the back" of the insurgency. The diplomat said that it was important to study the lessons of other counterinsurgencies like Malaya: "Concepts that produce results in those areas; I am very much open to that," he said during his Senate confirmation hearings.

After hearing Khalilzad's statement, Joe Biden, the ranking Democrat on the Foreign Relations Committee, complained that the military effort was under-resourced, making the sort of arguments that John McCain would continue to press during the next presidential campaign. "They don't have enough troops now," Biden said. While Petraeus was doing a "first rate job" building a new Iraqi Army, Biden continued, the American training effort was two years behind the curve. The junior senator from Illinois, Barack Obama, asked for and received an assurance that the United States was not seeking permanent bases in Iraq but he was not yet pressing for a troop withdrawal. Obama asked whether it would take ten or twenty years to defeat the insurgents. "It could take much less than that," Khalilzad responded reassuringly.[2]

After arriving in Baghdad, Khalilzad held his first "country team" meeting at the embassy the next day and announced that security was his main concern. Casey had arranged a series of briefings for Khalilzad, the title of which, "Securing Strategic Success," implied that there was not much need for change. The objectives were to train and equip the Iraqi Army while "bringing the insurgency and foreign terrorists to a level that can be contained by the ISF," the briefing said, using the military acronym for the Iraqi security forces. Behind closed doors, defeating the insurgency was not the goal. Rather, the goal was to whittle it down to manageable proportions so that the Iraqi forces could handle the fight for a protracted period. In the meantime, the American-led coalition would "secure" Baghdad and the Sunni Triangle around the capital, "sustain" the areas to the north and south, and "block" infiltration by militants across Iraq's long borders. The year 2006 would see even more progress, Casey's briefing suggested. There would be a "transformed coalition" that was no longer carrying out the main fight but supporting "Capable Iraqi Security Forces," which would be protecting a constitutionally elected and representative government.[3]

As he had hinted during his Senate hearings Khalilzad wanted to conduct a review that would look at the alternatives. Casey had joined forces with Negroponte to draft a common Joint Mission Statement, and he was prepared to work with Khalilzad—at least, up to a point. A civilian and military Red Team was formed to devise an alternative plan. Major General Rick Lynch, who was overseeing the effort to reach out to the Sunnis while also serving as Casey's spokesman, picked Colonel Bruce Reider, an Army strategist who was working on governance issues for Casey's command, to cochair the review on behalf of the military. Marin Strmecki, a conservative defense consultant who was recruited by Khalilzad for the effort, would cochair the review for the embassy. The team was to assess Casey's strategy and its prospects for success in light of previous counterinsurgency campaigns, evaluate the quality of the intelligence the Americans had on their enemy, analyze how the enemy viewed the coalition's strategy, and develop a plan to "break the back" of the insurgency in one year and defeat it in three. The primary emphasis would be on designing a course of action for the next twelve months, but the strategy review also needed to consider the next twenty-four to thirty-six months. The guidance was to keep the team small; in addition to Reider and Strmecki there would be only a handful of other experts, including British and Australian officers and an analyst from the CIA. The entire review was to be completed within thirty days.

The team's diagnosis of American accomplishments thus far was troubling. The effort to disrupt the insurgents' planning had not been decisive. The enemy was able to retain freedom of movement and conduct operations. The perception of many Iraqis is that their government, and by implication, the coalition has failed the Iraqi people. Iraq's security forces had been stood up at great speed, but lacked qualified leaders. The development of the police was a year behind the Army's estimates, and there was little to demonstrate that the Iraqi government had the will to establish apolitical security ministries. Understanding the tribal culture was critical. Time was running out.

In a December 2004 review Casey had overseen on the progress being made in the campaign, the command had concluded that its strategy was sound and its plan "broadly on track," an assessment the command had reiterated when it conducted another review in June 2005. But the Red Team affirmed that Casey's strategy was badly off course and had almost no prospect of success. Because little headway was being made against the insurgents and Iraqi forces were still a work in progress, Casey's timetable for handing power over to the Iraqis simply set them up for failure. If the American military had its hands full coping with the insurgents, how were the Iraqi Army and police to do better? Casey, it seemed, had a plan for taking American troops out of Iraq but not for leaving a stable and democratic country in their wake.

"The current plan does not envision the defeat of the insurgency before the completion of transition to Iraqi self-reliance, only its suppression to levels the ISF can handle on its own," the Red Team report noted. "The insurgency is resilient and capable of regenerating itself. The Coalition and the Iraqi government have not been able to suppress the insurgency in an enduring way. The planned size of the ISF is likely to prove insufficient, based on historical cases, to defeat the current insurgency. The ISF, still an immature force, will be taking on the burden of security in 2006 and 2007 with inadequate funding and less experience, training and equipment than MNF-I. This creates the possibility that after transition to self-reliance the ISF could lose ground to the insurgency in central and western Iraq and perhaps be unable to control Baghdad." The eventual result, the report suggested grimly, might be "civil war along the lines of the one in Afghanistan in the 1990s."

Spelling out the implications, the report noted that fears of abandonment by the United States might lead the Iraqis to hedge their future by developing greater reliance on Iran. Insurgents, who believed that disengagement and not victory was the American goal, would be less likely to cut the political deals that would be needed to shore up the new Iraq: "The perception that disengagement, not victory over the insurgency, is the objective could encourage the insurgents to believe that they have broken the coalition's will." The fragmentation of the country would increase. The American public might question whether a muddled outcome in Iraq had been worth the cost. "If the war on terror is the central conflict of our times and if the conflict in Iraq is the central front in that war, it would be confusing to Americans (both in Iraq and at home) why victory was not the campaign plan's goal," the study noted. "Confusion in this regard could lead to disaffection."[4]

As the team worked through the problem it determined that breaking the back of the insurgency required that the insurgents be physically isolated from the population in key areas. It argued that the "ink spot" approach Krepinevich had touted, in which an area was secured and developed politically and economically until a patchwork of safe zones was extended across the country, should be adopted as the basic strategy. It was a troop-intensive recommendation, one that was incompatible with Casey's emphasis on consolidating the American footprint in Iraq, reducing the number of bases, and withdrawing forces.

The team had been told its plans should assume that the only American forces available were the ones that were already on hand, and there was no way to blanket the country. So it proposed concentrating the forces in specific areas to effect a mini-surge. Beginning during the October referendum and December election, when some extra forces were on hand, it recommended creating the first of several ink spots, either in Tikrit, Mosul, Baqubah, or the Fallujah-Ramadi corridor. Then as 2006 began, more ink spots would be created in the Euphrates and Tigris valleys, and the corps headquarters would oversee the effort to expand and link them. This ambitious "Two Rivers Campaign" was a far cry from the focus on transition that Casey saw in store for 2006.

For all its incisiveness, the Red Team report revealed a deeper problem: a basic disagreement between the command and the new ambassador on the military goals in Iraq. "There is a fundamental issue over what we are trying to achieve," Reider wrote in his diary. "Gen. Casey believes we are trying to develop ISF so we can hand over the COIN [counterinsurgency] fight to the Iraqis. The ambassador believes we are here to defeat the insurgency. This explains the intelligence disconnect over who is the greatest threat: the foreign fighters and terrorists or the Iraqi rejectionists."[5]

Casey had not taken well to Charlie Allen's critical assessment in 2004 and he was not happy about the Red Team critique either. When it came time for Reider and Strmecki to present their interim conclusions, a meeting was called on August 23 in Khalilzad's office, which included the commander and the British ambassador. Casey took the floor and began to question the rationale for a Red Team assessment. The subject dominated the discussion, and the Red Team's PowerPoint slides were never presented.

On September 7, Lynch approached Reider. Casey, Lynch reported, had heard that the Red Team was not in agreement and had been coerced to go along with the ink spot approach, implying that Strmecki had been the culprit.[6] Reider told Lynch that the notion the team had been pressured to go along was false. Lieutenant Colonel John DeJarnette, who was a member of Casey's initiatives group and had participated in the effort, had been skeptical of some points but had not fought the report, Reider explained.

As the senior diplomat in Baghdad, Khalilzad was not prepared to challenge Casey's military strategy, but the ambassador took a copy of the Red Team analysis with him to Washington that month and told Hadley about it. The national security adviser encouraged Khalilzad to find a way for the generals in Baghdad to submit it through military channels so it might stimulate some new thinking within the Pentagon. Hadley was a stickler for procedure and was concerned that if there was to be a change of military strategy it be something that the generals themselves could embrace.

A member of the British team slipped a copy to London, where it made its way to Prime Minister Tony Blair. He was struck by the analysis and raised it with Bush in a secure videoconference after which the report all but vanished from the war deliberations.

An opportunity to change the strategy by making counterinsurgency the core of the military's approach had passed. It would take another sixteen months before Casey's strategy of handing off to the Iraqis was formally rejected and for the concepts in the ink spot approach to return in the guise of the surge.

Casey and John Abizaid were scheduled to visit Washington in October to testify to Congress and consult with the administration. As their visit approached, Rumsfeld sent them a classified note advising them on how to manage their appearances before the media. Complaints about the war were reaching a crescendo and Rumsfeld wanted to do everything possible to tamp down the critics. Rumsfeld, who was famous for his micromanagement, wanted Casey and Abizaid to split up for greater effectiveness and had some specific ideas about which media they should talk to. "I have reviewed your inputs for your visit and they look fine with a few minor exceptions," Rumsfeld wrote in a September 26 note. "We need you to do the Sunday talk shows, separately, so that between the two of you, all five talk shows have an appearance by one of you. George will do Larry King and John will do the Fox Special Report. Finally, George, your time with the Washington Post Editorial Board might be better spent doing radio interviews."[7] For the defense secretary, conservative talk radio was a friendlier conduit than the editorial writers of the capital's newspaper.

Casey and Abizaid were still convinced they were on track and had no reluctance to deliver that message. "I do still believe that we can make coalition reductions in '06," Casey said. "They will be progressive as the Iraqi security forces come forward."

Even as Casey was telling the world his plan was on track, he needed to find a way to weaken the Sunni insurgency and stem the flow of car and truck bombs into Baghdad. The solution the commander came up with was to make a new push to strengthen control over Iraq's border with Syria. If some way could be found to intercept foreign fighters crossing into Iraq—those who drove the suicide car bombs, carried out the spectacular attacks against the Shiites, and stoked the flames of civil war—the hardcore component of the insurgency might be weakened. As Casey figured it, he needed to enfeeble, not defeat, the insurgents in order to shift the burden of security to the Iraqis. Diluting the flow of foreign fighters on the Syrian border, Casey calculated, was a way to cut Al-Qaeda in Iraq down to size.[8]

Not everyone agreed with Casey's emphasis. Lieutenant General John Vines, whose XVIII Airborne Corps was in charge of most of Casey's combat forces, also believed that the foreign suicide bombers were a problem, but shifting forces to the borders and their suspected transit routes seemed a luxury: already American forces were having a hard time controlling Baghdad and the key cities of central Iraq, like Ramadi, Baqubah, and Samarra. As American intelligence would later establish, much of Al-Qaeda's campaign relied on a network of safe houses in the belts around Baghdad where the car bombs were assembled. Moving forces away from central Iraq to the borders put at risk the very areas where they might have the greatest impact on Al-Qaeda's car bomb campaign.

"Well, there was an area of healthy tension between the MNF-I and MNC-I headquarters about what the nature of the threat was and what to do about it," Vines later told a military historian. "At the MNF-I level, a decision was made, probably with national guidance, that we wanted to reestablish control of Iraq's borders; but that was going to be expensive," he added. "There was an argument about whether it was to be part of our main effort, center of gravity, or a decisive point because there were a lot of resources that were going to have to be committed."[9]

The summer–fall 2005 border campaign was to have two prongs: one on Al-Qaeda's northern infiltration route, in western Nineveh Province around the towns of Tal Afar and Sinjar, and one on the southern route, the western Euphrates river valley in Anbar. For the southern prong, Stan McChrystal's JSOC task force would surge new forces into theater: of Delta Force's three squadrons, one would be brought west from Baghdad, and a second would fly in from Fort Bragg. For the northern prong, Casey and Vines plucked a unit from the periphery of Baghdad: the 3rd Armored Cavalry Regiment.

The 3rd ACR was led by Colonel Herbert "H.R." McMaster, who before deploying to Iraq had put the regiment through an unusually intensive course of Iraq-specific training, including language and cultural instruction. Before earning a Silver Star as a captain in the 1991 battle of 73 Easting, McMaster had been somewhat of a prankster at West Point, once marching a group of first-year cadets to the academy mess hall from the comfort of his bedroom window instead of the drill field. ("It was poor judgment and I was duly punished," McMaster said of the incident.) In the years since Desert Storm, McMaster had authored a trenchant dissertation, later published as a popular book, criticizing the performance of American generals during Vietnam, and had then served at CENTCOM as an adviser to Abizaid during the first year of America's involvement in Iraq. The colonel had never entirely fit into the Army culture of conformity, and in the eyes of Abizaid and Petraeus he was one of the Army's most promising field-grade officers.

Like Chiarelli's 1st Cavalry Division, which was sent without all of its tanks, the 3rd ACR ran into a series of supply problems, forcing it to fight the same bureaucratic battle over again. McMaster insisted on bringing a full complement of armor but had to do battle with a logistics officer to secure the sniper rifles he knew his regiment would need. "I thought that getting M24 sniper rifles, because we are the United States Army and not the Ecuadorian Army, would not be a big deal," he quipped.[10]

Almost as soon as 3rd ACR arrived in February 2005, it received orders to leave behind one of its cavalry squadrons and go north toward the Syrian border in Nineveh Province and secure the town of Tal Afar. The city, in effect, had become a training base for the foreign fighters that were recruited by Al-Qaeda before they deployed throughout Iraq, and to protect that training base the city was heavily defended. The mixture of Al-Qaeda, Ansar al-Sunna, and Baathist fighters inside Tal Afar formed four groups, each with subordinate cells responsible for ground attacks, mortar firing, sniping, kidnapping, and videography and propaganda. Many of the city's Sunni Turkmen had served in Saddam's army, among them warrant officers and others with precious technical skills; as a result, the cells specializing in mortar fire were particularly strong, using 120mm tubes they had dug into preselected firing points in the hills.

McMaster's 2nd Squadron, under Lieutenant Colonel Chris Hickey, got to Tal Afar in March, well ahead of the rest of the regiment. The first element of the squadron to arrive hit six IEDs on the road surrounding the city, and within a few days Hickey's troops were engaging in long gunfights with coordinated groups of insurgents as they pushed into the outskirts of the city and took key terrain like the hospital.

The rest of the regiment arrived in late May. While one squadron pushed west to retake the desert towns of Rabiya, Biaj, and Sinjar, an attached Stryker cavalry squadron, reinforced by an air cavalry troop, pushed south to reconnoiter the huge desert beyond which lay Anbar. Meanwhile, Hickey's squadron settled in on the outskirts of Tal Afar to keep the pressure on the insurgency there and win the support, or at least the acceptance, of both Sunni and Shiite tribal leaders.

Besides being a waypoint along the northern of the two Al-Qaeda ratlines from Syria, Tal Afar was also incubating the virus that would soon threaten much of Iraq: sectarian violence between Sunni and Shiite communities, with Al-Qaeda on the side of the former and government forces on the side of the latter. The previous fall, in September 2004, Tal Afar had flared up as Sunni insurgents attacked city police stations and the police force had vanished, an offensive that served as a dress rehearsal for the larger one that linked insurgent groups would launch in nearby Mosul in November. An American Stryker unit had pushed into the city briefly, leaving a single cavalry squadron to secure all of western Nineveh Province, and by early 2005 Al-Qaeda had the Sunni Turkmen majority in Tal Afar under its thumb and the Shiite Turkmen minority under siege. Only a small police force defended the Shiite community in the east of the city, based in an Ottoman-vintage fort; American officers viewed the police as somewhere between ineffective and a "Shiite death squad."

3rd ACR did its research on Tal Afar. McMaster had been in Mosul the previous November when the city had fallen to insurgents, so he knew the stakes and he knew something of Nineveh Province. His intelligence staff dug back into the secure Internet files that the 101st brigade Petraeus had assigned to the area in 2003 had amassed, and Petraeus visited to share his views on Nineveh. McMaster also flew in a West Point instructor, Major Dan Barnard, who had written a doctoral dissertation about tribal resistance to the British occupation in Tal Afar and surrounding areas. Barnard helped map out which tribal leaders McMaster and his squadron commanders should be talking to, which ones made their money from smuggling, and which ones fed recruits to the insurgency.[11]

As McMaster's troops sealed the city off—attached engineer personnel were even building an eight-foot berm around Tal Afar's perimeter—it was obvious that an assault was coming. Inside the city, the insurgents hunkered down, especially in the Sarai District, which they fortified with machine gun and RPG fighting positions, defensive IEDs, and houses rigged for demolition. A delegation of Shiite sheikhs traveled to Baghdad to discuss with the Interior Ministry what was coming in July. "That very much scared the Sunnis," McMaster remembered, and at the end of the month a Sunni delegation went to Baghdad as well, in secret, trying to avert an offensive that they feared would be a repeat of Fallujah.

In fact, the clearance operation that McMaster and Hickey were planning would not resemble Fallujah at all—no one had the stomach for that kind of urban destruction, the propaganda value it gave the enemy, or the exhaustive reconstruction effort that would be required afterward. The plan, instead, would be to ring the city off, evacuate as many civilians as possible, and then push in with as little destruction as possible—Najem al-Jabouri, the new police chief and soon-to-be mayor, insisted that the use of air strikes by fixed-wing aircraft be kept to a minimum.

The plan was for the push into Tal Afar to take place in September or October. In the meantime, the force outside the city was bolstered with extra Iraqi units, amounting to nine battalions, including Kurdish troops, a special operations unit, and a police commando brigade from the Interior Ministry. Each Iraqi battalion was assigned a Special Forces adviser team. McMaster wanted more American troops, too; his regiment, although large, was light on infantry, so in early July he sent a request to Baghdad for an infantry battalion. The request was denied. Then as the fall operation loomed, Casey came to visit. Briefed on the plan, he pointed out that it seemed like it could use more infantry. Yes it could, McMaster agreed. McMaster again requested a battalion, and Casey granted the wish. By that time, though, Prime Minister Jaafari was pushing for the operation to go forward as soon as possible, in early September, before he left for the United Nations, so the battalion from the 82nd Airborne that Casey released did not arrive in time to participate in major offensive operations.

On September 2 the attack, Operation Restoring Rights, began, with one squadron pushing into each side of the city after an evacuation of thousands of civilians through Iraqi police and army checkpoints in the surrounding berm. Tanks led the way, while AC-130 gunships, attack helicopters, and artillery pounded known insurgent positions. Apache attack craft fired eighty-four Hellfire missiles. A contingent of Navy SEALs helped with countersniper work, and the battle saw one of the first uses of the military's new Guided Multiple Launch Rocket System, or GMLRS (pronounced "Gimlers"). In the first five days, the attacking force killed 118 insurgents. Outside the city, the regiment's chemical company acted as military police, running a temporary detention facility that swelled to nine hundred occupants. By the time Sarai District, the main Al-Qaeda stronghold in Tal Afar, had fallen, only four American soldiers had been killed in the fighting—three of them before the actual entry into the city.

In contrast to Fallujah the previous fall, the Tal Afar assault went off with little collateral damage. Fallujah had been a ghost town by the time the second battle began; Tal Afar, a city of 250,000, saw an exodus of only about 50,000, about half of whom left during a carefully managed evacuation just before the attack began. Though some seven hundred suspected

insurgents were detained, a consequence of the publicly announced evacuation before the assault was that many fighters managed to sneak out with
the tide of civilians.[12] Others escaped via a tunnel system that troops found
along with abandoned command posts, media labs, and sites of torture and
execution. Among all the insurgent bodies and detainees, only two could
be positively identified as foreign fighters. A month later, reports were coming in that fighters who had escaped from Tal Afar had set up camp on
the edge of Lake Tharthar, in a remote area with no U.S. troops near the
border between Salahuddin and Anbar provinces.

To hold the ground they had taken in Tal Afar, Hickey's troops—along
with the battalion from the 82nd Airborne, which had just arrived—built
a net of platoon-sized outposts across the city. "We would typically go
in with an American platoon and an Iraqi platoon, set up in an empty
house, put barriers around the house to keep the car bombs away, and
then we would patrol that neighborhood," McMaster explained. "Every
time we established a patrol base, about six hours later there was a suicide
bomber." They took to moving in at 1 a.m., so that concrete barriers would
be in place by morning. Eventually, the two American battalions in the city
would establish twenty-nine such outposts.[13]

Building outposts was not new—some Marine battalions had done the
same in Anbar, and when Stryker troops had wrested Mosul back from
insurgent control in the past year, they had spread out into urban patrol
bases as well. McMaster had learned from that example as well as from
other units that had embraced counterinsurgency tactics: Jim Hickey's brigade in Tikrit in 2003, part of Ray Odierno's 4th Infantry Division, Mark
Milley's brigade of the 10th Mountain Division in West Baghdad. In little
Tal Afar, though, 3rd ACR's outposts were so dense that a platoon in one
strongpoint could often see the next platoon over. There was little dead
space for insurgents to reinfiltrate the city. And the outposts stayed for
weeks and then months, convincing locals that McMaster's cavalry and
paratroopers would not be pulling out anytime soon.

Not everything went smoothly. Insurgents continued to attack the new
American positions, hoping to dislodge them, and the Shiite-dominated
Interior Ministry brigade that had taken part in the attack soon came
under a cloud of allegations of abuse of Sunni residents. The brigade "was
withdrawn at the earliest possible time to improve the situation and lower
tensions," according to a State Department cable, and was not immediately
replaced by Public Order battalions "for the same reason."[14]

At the urging of David Satterfield, the American embassy's political officer, and Robin Brims, Casey's British deputy, a Sunni Arab official was put in charge of the reconstruction effort over the Iraqi government's initial choice, Barham Salih, a Kurd who had held a succession of senior posts in the Iraqi government. "The Americans worked as a safety valve inside the city," said Najem al-Jabouri, the mayor, who years later was given asylum in the United States to protect him against terrorist reprisals.[15] Violence did not disappear, but it dropped off steeply, and Tal Afar began to ship men off to recruitment training centers to build up a new police force. The regiment had been successful because it had used time-tested counterinsurgency tactics. But its approach was the exception to the rule. The sort of counterinsurgency tactics McMaster employed were accepted by Casey as a means to deal with the foreign fighters along Al-Qaeda's northern infiltration route but were not seen as a core principle of the campaign plan. The overarching strategy was still to shrink the American military footprint and hand over to the Iraqi forces.

The southern prong of Casey's border strategy was in the western Euphrates river valley, or the WERV, as the Marines in Anbar called it. There, too, Casey gave tactical commanders more leeway than he did commanders in central Iraq, allowing them to open bases instead of closing them and to pursue just the kind of counterinsurgency tactics that he had rejected when the Red Team recommended they form the foundation of a new American approach in Iraq.

During 2004, the Marine force in Anbar had neglected the string of western towns along the Euphrates—Husaybah, Qaim, Rawa, Haditha, Hit—in favor of Fallujah and Ramadi, where things had been spiraling out of control. During both Fallujah operations, Marine units had been stripped away from the west, leaving behind skeletal commands often with ill-prepared units. By early 2005, the Marine presence in the west consisted of a handful of infantry battalions, mostly confined to a few bases and with little understanding of the complex network of tribes that populated the area for which they were responsible.

One side effect of the low priority that the Marines gave to the west in 2004 was that their commanding general, Mattis, gave an Army Special Forces company under Major Adam Such free hand to try new approaches in the area. One of the company's teams, Operational Detachment Alpha 555—which had been among the first to infiltrate Afghanistan in 2001— was based at Al-Asad, the big Marine air base in the west, and with Mattis's blessing it began to investigate the complex tribal dynamics of the west and make use of them. Asked years later about the genesis of the American cooperation with Anbari tribes that would later become the "Anbar Awakening," Mattis said: "It starts with Adam Such."[16]

What ODA 555 briefly tapped into was the deep complexity of the tribally dominated culture in Anbar. There were tribal groups that aligned with Al-Qaeda or aligned with the Americans, often for profit or as a result of intimidation, but there were also groups that wanted nothing to do with either.[17] After insurgents killed a sheikh of the Albu Nimr tribe, which was already fed up with foreign extremists' stern rules, abusive behavior, and restrictions on profitable smuggling, the Special Forces built a company of tribal irregulars to patrol the roads near Hit.

Without a continued American push, however, ODA 555's gains began to evaporate. Al-Qaeda was fighting for the area, too. Zarqawi declared Qaim his capital and just across the border in Syria lay a network run by an Al-Qaeda figure named Abu Ghadiya, whose job was to bring foreign recruits into Damascus International Airport and then smuggle them east into Iraq.

McChrystal moved his focus to western Anbar in May. After pitching the move to Abizaid and Casey, he began shifting his troops to the WERV for a summer JSOC offensive. There was plenty of reason to think it would be a tough fight, McChrystal warned his bosses. A Marine operation in Qaim early in the month had run up against insurgents wearing helmets and body armor.

In late May Delta Force began launching raids in the west, based at ODA 555's old Al-Asad team house. The operations were the most difficult that JSOC had conducted since the early days of the war. In Baghdad, Delta Force had gotten used to operating out of specially outfitted Pandur armored vehicles that protected them from IEDs; in western Anbar, they would have to rely more on support from long-range special operations helicopters like MH-47 Chinooks and MH-53 Pave Lows. Right away, on May 31, a Delta operator was killed in the Qaim area, followed by two more on June 17. So JSOC reinforced, "surging" its limited forces: in June it brought in a second of the three Delta Force squadrons from Fort Bragg along with extra Rangers and helicopters, one of the most substantial troop commitments McChrystal's command would make to Iraq.[18]

All summer, the fighting in western Anbar was fierce, both for the JSOC commandos and for the Marine battalions supporting them. On August 1, two scout-sniper teams from 3/25 Marines, a battalion of Reservists charged with patrolling Haditha, Hit, and everything in between, were overrun and all six team members killed. Two days later, during the response operation, the battalion lost fifteen more Marines when one of its armored tractors hit a huge IED; in all, the battalion would lose forty-eight men on its deployment, a casualty toll worse than that suffered by any unit that fought in Fallujah. Then in late August, three Delta operators and a Ranger were killed in Husaybah, with more losses in the fall. At one point, an MH-53 Pave Low helicopter crashed about a hundred meters from the Syrian border while supporting a JSOC raid.

The losses McChrystal's troops took were small compared to many conventional units, but they had a deep impact in the small JSOC world—each Delta Force squadron contained only about eighty commandos.[19]

In one raid in Haditha, troops captured eleven insurgents along with $56,000 in American bills, thirty-two assault rifles, four body armor vests, and two computers. Putting together the results of that raid and others in which American cash had turned up, a joint report by the CIA and DIA reached a troubling conclusion. "Iraqi companies working for the US military are a major, though often indirect, source of insurgent funding. Coalition cash seizures frequently include sequential $100 bills, many of which entered Iraq via US military payments to contractors," it noted. "Two-thirds of cash seizures in Iraq included US dollars, and the largest source of these US dollars was the US military."[20]

In the fall, Casey sent conventional forces to the west to support McChrystal's efforts there. Extra Army battalions, a Sunni-led brigade from the 1st Iraqi Army Division, and a pair of Marine expeditionary units joined fresh Marine battalions in Qaim and Haditha. Special Forces teams returned to the area, too.[21]

Beginning in September, the Marines took control of Qaim and its satellite insurgent strongholds—Husaybah, Karabilah, Sadah, and Ubaydi. Early in the month, CENTCOM permitted the Marines to destroy several bridges in the area that they believed eased Al-Qaeda mobility, bombing them first with concrete dummy bombs, then with real bombs when that failed, and finally with GMLRS, the rocket system making its debut there and in Tal Afar. Then, starting on September 11, 3/6 Marines moved into one town after another.

The battalion's commander, Lieutenant Colonel Dale Alford, had already led the same unit through an Afghanistan deployment, and was well known in the Marine Corps as an aggressive commander. First he attacked with two companies in Qaim, the biggest of the five towns in Al-

Qaeda's western Euphrates "emirate," and then in October into Sadah and Karabilah. At the beginning of November, his battalion was the centerpiece of a larger operation into Husaybah and Ubaydi, called Steel Curtain, that involved Iraqi troops, a Marine expeditionary unit, and, as in Tal Afar, a battalion from the 82nd Airborne. The Marines found police stations and government buildings in all the towns in ruins.

Once inside the towns, Alford's Marines built outposts, like the ones McMaster's troops were constructing at the same time inside Tal Afar. To achieve their fortification faster, the Marines used partially prefabricated structures called "FOBs-in-a-box"—shipping containers that held all of the equipment and materials necessary to establish an austere operating base. By winter, 3/6 Marines and two Iraqi Army battalions had spread out into more than two dozen such bases in and around the five towns.

Working closely with a Special Forces team, Alford's Marines also made overtures to the tribal leaders in the newly liberated towns. The Albu Mahals, whose Hamza Battalion had been fighting Al-Qaeda all spring and summer before being defeated in August, had already supplied the Marines with a small irregular force for Operation Steel Curtain. After the operation, four other local tribes joined, each supplying a company's worth of recruits. With the blessing of the Defense Ministry and American head-quarters in Baghdad, the recruits were shipped to Camp Fallujah, where Special Forces and Navy SEALs put them through a basic training course, and then back to Qaim.

The tribal recruits formed a battalion-sized, un-uniformed force called the "Desert Protectors." There had been some outposts in the area already, left over from earlier Marine operations, but they were mostly in the desert, faced toward the border, not in the towns. The Marines and Special Forces used these as bases for further training of the Desert Protectors. The irregular force helped provide security for the parliamentary elections, and by early 2006 violence in Qaim had dropped steeply.[22]

Pushed into a life-or-death situation by the Al-Qaeda occupation of their five towns, the Albu Mahals and other tribes in Qaim had done what the Special Forces had hoped the Albu Nimrs would do in Hit the previous year before they were pulled out: chosen sides, and, reassured by the presence of Alford's outposts, fought alongside the Americans in appreciable numbers. Qaim's mayor later boasted, "I will tell you regarding the Sahwa that the sun rose from the west, not from the east, in this country," meaning that the Awakening had first emerged in Qaim, rather than Ramadi.[23]

Casey took a personal interest in Qaim, which, along with Tal Afar, was a centerpiece of his border strategy. During the seven months 3/6 Marines

Secretary of Defense Donald Rumsfeld (left) and CPA chief L. Paul Bremer at a 2003 press conference. Although Rumsfeld initially supported Bremer, the two men later held very different philosophies on how to handle the occupation of Iraq. (ROBERT D. WARD/DEPARTMENT OF DEFENSE)

Prime Minister Ayad Allawi announces the formation of his cabinet on June 1, 2004. President Ghazi al-Yawar stands in the background. (STAFF SERGEANT ASHLEY S. BROKOP/U.S. AIR FORCE)

L. Paul Bremer and Interim Deputy Prime Minister Barham Salih walk on the tarmac at Baghdad International Airport as Bremer prepares to leave the country on June 28, 2004. Before departing, Bremer told Salih, "You are a tough people." (STAFF SERGEANT D. MYLES CULLEN/U.S. AIR FORCE)

(Left to right) Lieutenant General Ricardo Sanchez, General John Abizaid, and General George W. Casey salute during a change-of-command ceremony at Camp Victory in Baghdad on July 1, 2004. Sanchez transferred the Iraq command to Casey under the supervision of Abizaid, the CENTCOM commander. (MNF-I PUBLIC AFFAIRS OFFICE)

A member of Muqtada al-Sadr's Mahdi Army raises his weapon while standing on a burning American tank during the 2004 uprising in Sadr City. (JOÃO SILVA)

A Mahdi Army sniper takes aim at U.S. soldiers during the August 2004 battle of Najaf. (JOÃO SILVA)

Mahdi Army fighters in Sadr City fire a mortar at U.S. positions. (JOÃO SILVA)

A partially torn poster of anti-American cleric Muqtada al-Sadr, leader of the Sadrist Trend and Mahdi Army. (BEN LOWY)

Muqtada al-Sadr with his followers. (BEN LOWY)

Marines from Bravo Company, 1/8 Marines, conduct a patrol during Operation New Dawn, the November 2004 second battle of Fallujah. (STAFF SERGEANT JONATHAN KNAUTH/U.S. MARINE CORPS)

Colonel H.R. McMaster, commander of the 3rd Armored Cavalry Regiment, and Major General Ahmed al-Jabouri, commander of the 3rd Iraqi Army Division, near the town of Tal Afar in 2005. (MASTER SERGEANT DONALD SPARKS/3RD ACR)

Colonel H.R. McMaster (second from left) walks with Najem Abdullah al-Jabouri, mayor of Tal Afar during the surge. In 2005, McMaster and Najem had led a successful counterinsurgency operation in the town. (COURTESY OMAR ABDULLAH AL-JABOURI)

Condoleezza Rice holds a press conference with Interim Prime Minister Ibrahim al-Jaafari on May 15, 2005, during her first visit to Iraq as secretary of state. Her primary military adviser, Lieutenant General Ray Odierno, and the embassy's chargé d'affaires James Jeffrey appear in the background. (SERGEANT FERDINAND THOMAS/DEPARTMENT OF DEFENSE)

An Iraqi Army Humvee burns after being hit by an improvised explosive device (IED) near the town of Baghdadi in Anbar Province. (JIM WILSON/ *New York Times*)

Colonel Dave Sutherland, commander of the 1st Cavalry Division's 3rd Brigade, pays his respects at a memorial ceremony for a fallen soldier in Diyala Province. (EROS HOAGLAND)

Ambassador Zalmay Khalilzad (right) holds a joint press conference with General George W. Casey in January 2007. Khalilzad had long been involved in Iraq policy: in late 2002 and early 2003, he organized a series of conferences for Iraqi expatriates who would join locals to form the core of the new Iraqi government.

Secretary of Defense Robert Gates responds to a question during a press conference in Baghdad on December 22, 2006. Chairman of the Joint Chiefs of Staff Peter Pace (left) and General George W. Casey accompany him. Soon after this trip, Casey and Gates proposed a two-brigade surge. (CHERIE A. THURLBY/DEPARTMENT OF DEFENSE)

spent in the area, Casey visited the battalion five times, encouraged the Desert Protector program, and even had Alford visit the MNF-I "counter-insurgency academy" at Taji to share his approach with new commanders. When an opportunity arose at the end of 2005 for an alliance with Anbari insurgents on a much bigger scale than the Desert Protectors, though, Casey was unwilling to commit extra forces to exploit it.

When Colonel Blake Crowe, the commander of Regimental Combat Team 7 and the son of William Crowe, the admiral who served as the former chairman of the Joint Chiefs, arrived in Anbar in January 2006, he was intent on building on the success Alford had enjoyed in Qaim and expanding the sort of alliance the Americans had achieved to the east. To do that, Crowe needed more American forces. If there was to be a partnership between the U.S. military and the tribes, there needed to be troops the Iraqis could partner with.

Taking a required course at the counterinsurgency academy Casey established for incoming commanders, Crowe approached the four-star general. Crowe recommended that an additional Army brigade be deployed in his area, which would allow him to consolidate his gains in Qaim and make inroads against the insurgency around Haditha and Hit.

A week later, when Casey flew to Camp Al-Qaim, an old train repair facility, Crowe again briefed his plan. He could extend the Qaim model into the western Euphrates river valley but needed more troops. As Crowe saw it, he was twenty-seven Marine rifle companies short of what he needed. Instead of sending Army troops back to the United States as planned, he wanted a brigade's worth of Army troops to help him secure the WERV. General Casey had applauded the progress at Qaim, just as he did H.R. McMaster's operation in Tal Afar, but the main thrust of his strategy was to consolidate the number of American bases and hand over to the Iraqis. Partnering with Iraqi tribes across Anbar was a troop-intensive strategy and would have required expanding the American footprint just at the moment that the general was committed to shrinking it. The request was denied.[24]

Crowe was not the only officer who thought the failure to send more troops to work with the tribes in Anbar was a lost opportunity. In some larger Anbari towns, farther from the border, a struggle was under way within the Sunni insurgency. On one side were all the groups and fighters who were staunchly opposed to dealing with Iraq's new government, let alone the American military, most prominently Al-Qaeda in Iraq. On the other were fighters and leaders who were worried that without reaching out to the government and perhaps the Americans to see what they had to offer, Anbar's Sunnis would be left without a place at the table after the coming December elections, which Al-Qaeda planned to disrupt with rockets and car bombs wherever it could.

At the middle of the mostly invisible tug-of-war within Anbar's insurgency was Dr. Muhammad Mahmud Latif, an insurgent leader whom Army and Marine troops had been hunting for over a year. In 2004, Latif had run a council in Ramadi that coordinated anti-American attacks by various nationalist Sunni groups. But the minuscule voter turnout among Anbaris in January 2005 had disturbed Latif, who saw it as evidence that Al-Qaeda in Iraq's violent stance against the new Iraqi government was depriving Sunnis of representation and influence in that government. Marine intelligence believed that he was mulling a run for a seat in the new Iraqi parliament. By fall, he had pulled together an underground alliance of Ramadi-area sheikhs who shared his view that the new government offered a better future for Anbar than Al-Qaeda did.

The American military was unsure what to make of Latif and the Anbar People's Committee, as his pro-government alliance was known. To the Army brigade fighting for its life in Ramadi, Latif was never anything but a high-value target, one responsible for the deaths of American troops. Major Alfred Connable, an intelligence officer in Marine headquarters, had dealt with one of Latif's lieutenants, Nasr al-Fahadawi, in 2004. He "would stare daggers into me and told me in no uncertain terms that he wanted me to leave and wanted the rest of us to leave," Connable remembered.

Early in the summer, though, as JSOC was beginning its western offensive, Major General Richard Huck, the Marine ground commander in Anbar, met secretly with Latif, as did Defense Minister Sadoun al-Dulaimi. The discussions grew into a quiet agreement: to prove its good faith, the Anbar People's Committee would provide armed men during the upcoming December national elections to patrol some neighborhoods in Ramadi and protect voters, and then encourage its followers to join the police and army. Because it was the Iraqi government that the Anbar People's Committee seemed inclined to support, not the American military, Marine officers stressed to its representatives that America was going, not coming. When Marine Brigadier General James Williams met with sheikhs from the council in November, he stressed that if they held up their end of the bargain, his soldiers and Marines would soon be a much less visible presence in Anbar's cities. At the urging of Khalilzad, Casey even met with representatives of the Sunni insurgency himself in December, but based on his time in the Balkans he did so very warily. Marine intelligence later learned that Latif and the Anbar People's Committee held a general meeting to discuss their way ahead, post-election, and agreed to encourage the young men of their tribes to join the police. The Army National Guard brigade in Ramadi was about to stage a police recruiting drive at a glass factory in the city, and the committee decided to throw its support behind the drive.

As it turned out, the glass factory recruiting drive would be the high-water mark of the Anbar People's Committee. On the first day of the drive, encouraged by their sheikhs, two hundred recruits showed up to the Ramadi factory; on the second day four hundred and on the third six hundred. The numbers were far higher than anything the National Guard officer charged with dealing with Ramadi's sheikhs, Lieutenant Colonel Michael McLaughlin, had ever seen, and on the fourth and final day the turnout was higher still. But on that day, an Al-Qaeda suicide bomber snuck into the crowd of recruits and detonated an explosive vest, killing between fifty and sixty Iraqis and two Americans—including McLaughlin.

In the days after the bombing, Al-Qaeda fighters made a concerted effort to destroy the Anbar People's Committee, described in detail on a thumbdrive that American troops captured after it was all over. For three weeks, they killed one committee sheikh after another, including Nasr al-Fahadawi, and forced Latif to flee the region.

American military intervention might have saved the Anbar People's Committee, but none came. To Major Ben Connable, the Marine intelligence officer, the failure to deploy extra troops to save the Anbar People's Committee or to reinforce the Desert Protectors, as Blake Crowe wanted, was an embarrassing failure, one that prolonged the war in Iraq's bloodiest province. At the beginning of 2006, Anbar was "almost like a blank canvas, where we could have repainted the whole program," Connable later told Marine historians. "And instead of taking advantage of this, we flubbed it."[25]

While the Red Team report had no influence in Washington, the State Department began to search for a new strategy. After being appointed secretary of state, Condoleezza Rice and Philip Zelikow, her counselor at the State Department, became concerned that the strategy was drifting and began to lobby for a course correction. Zelikow, a brainy and punctilious history professor at the University of Virginia, had come to know Rice when they worked on the NSC together during the administration of George H. W. Bush, an association that later led to their coauthoring a book on the reunification of Germany. After George W. Bush became president, Zelikow took a leave from his academic post to serve as the principal drafter of the 9/11 Commission report, before being installed on the seventh floor of the State Department as an aide to Rice.

It seemed clear to Zelikow that the fight was not going well and that the State Department was barely relevant to the war. Zelikow dived into the literature on Vietnam hoping to figure out how his agency could make more of a contribution and elevate State's standing with a president who saw Iraq as his administration's top priority. Zelikow became a proponent of "provincial reconstruction teams," a civilian-led effort that was roughly modeled on the CORDS concept during the Vietnam War. CORDS stood for "Civil Operations and Rural Development Support." It was a joint civilian and military effort that enlisted State Department officials, the foreign aid bureaucracy, the CIA, and military officers to build hospitals and schools, and generally try to win over the hearts and minds of the Vietnamese. Both the United States and NATO had set up provincial reconstruction teams in Afghanistan, and Zelikow wanted to introduce them in Iraq.[26]

That was not the only Vietnam lesson Zelikow sought to apply. In reading Lewis Sorley's controversial revisionist history of Vietnam's final years, *A Better War,* Zelikow was struck by Sorley's claim that the United States had—too late in the historian's estimation—adopted a strategy to "clear and hold." During a trip around Iraq, Zelikow insisted on talking to H.R. McMaster during the heat of his battle in Tal Afar. When he got back to Washington, Zelikow also concluded that the strategy was broken—or "astrategic," as he put it. Casey believed he was holding the line until the Iraqi security forces were mature enough to take over the main fight, but it looked like he was presiding passively over an increasingly bloody stalemate. In contrast, Zelikow was impressed by McMaster's campaign.

As Rice prepared to testify to Congress, Zelikow injected a phrase into her prepared testimony that would have sounded familiar to many Vietnam-era officers but which had yet to be rediscovered: "clear, hold, and build." He first tried it out on a three-star general on the Joint Staff who had some Iraq experience and had accompanied the secretary of state on her foreign trips—Ray Odierno—and he thought it had merit. The State Department had no responsibility for military strategy, but if the secretary of state and White House officials used the terminology often though, it might prompt some changes at the Pentagon. Saying it enough just might make it so, especially if it caught on at the White House.

Given Rumsfeld's stubborn commitment to the transition strategy, Zelikow saw no merit in discussing the concept with Rumsfeld or his civilian aides. Rumsfeld was sent an advance copy of the testimony while he was traveling but he did not focus on it. As Zelikow saw it, sharing his project with Casey was equally problematic. The State Department could hardly expect him to hold something as fundamental as this back from a secretary of defense who managed his talk show appearances.

What Rice outlined to Congress came as a surprise to Rumsfeld, and an unwelcome one at that. Casey was also taken aback. He had facilitated Zelikow's trip around Iraq and had never heard anything about the "clear, hold, and build" strategy the United States was supposedly pursuing. When Zelikow made his next trip to Iraq, Casey pulled him aside. "This is personal," he said. Zelikow protested that he had told Odierno, which merely drew Casey's ire and was not a very convincing response. Odierno was not in the chain of command.[27]

Rice's efforts to overhaul the strategy had been stymied but Peter Feaver found some utility in her testimony. Feaver was an academic, a protégé of political scientist Samuel Huntington. He had done research on public opinion in wartime and the effect of casualties, and it showed that the number of corpses coming through Dover Air Force Base was not as key as was commonly thought. The public would accept casualties if it thought the United States could and should win. Feaver had interviewed for a number of positions when Bush was elected, including at the State Department. By 2005, when Hadley was interested in hiring somebody to run a strategic planning cell that would take a long-term look at security issues and draft the annual National Security Strategy, Feaver got the job on the NSC.

It was not a good time for the White House. Polls showed that support for the war was waning; Cindy Sheehan, an antiwar activist whose son had been killed in Sadr City on the first day of the Mahdi Army uprising in 2004, was making headlines by holding vigils near Bush's Crawford, Texas, ranch. Bush was starting to lose control of the debate. Meghan O'Sullivan, who had taken over the Iraq portfolio from Robert Blackwill, was talking about pulling together a White Paper. The White House counselor and main political operative, Dan Bartlett, liked the idea. Feaver, too, thought it had merit. He had gone to a strategy session at the Aspen Institute and for days heard all manner of criticism that the Bush administration did not have an Iraq plan. But the administration had a plan—a phased withdrawal—that was similar to what most of the critics wanted to see: handing control over to the Iraqis and easing its way out of Iraq.

Feaver drew on two documents to write his White Paper: "The National Strategy for Supporting Iraq," an internal interagency product, and Casey's campaign plan. The idea was to be candid about what had gone wrong and to provide clear benchmarks for the public to measure progress, like the growth of Iraqi forces and tips from Iraqi citizens about insurgents. The goal would remain the same: a democratic Iraq that was an ally in the War on Terror—Bush insisted on the latter provision. But the day when this would become a reality was well into the future. To pacify the public there would be intermediate stages: the public would be shown that the United States was making headway, deflating the pressure for immediate withdrawal. The United States would hand over a war that the Iraqis would eventually win. The White House would not come up with a new strategy, but would do a better job of describing the strategy already in place.

Feaver liked Rice's "clear, hold, and build" phrase. The United States would not merely be handing the war over to the Iraqis but committing itself to securing and holding contested areas. But Rumsfeld was wary, suspecting it was a way for the State Department to shift the burden onto the Defense Department and concerned that the phrase would acquire greater meaning if it were to be codified in a presidential document.

To make the phrase more palatable to Rumsfeld and sidestep the debate over what to name the strategy, Feaver came up with three proposals: The military would clear, hold, and build. American diplomats would work to isolate insurgents, engage the Sunnis, and build. The civilians and the international community would work to help restore, reform, and build the Iraqi economy. However hackneyed this formulation was—everybody was doing some kind of building—it made clear that the American military would not be shouldering the entire burden of the strategy. Feaver thought the goal of the Iraq policy should be "success." But Bartlett thought "victory" had a more winning ring to it and insisted on the substitution. The result was "The National Strategy for Victory in Iraq." Trying to summon support for the war, Bush gave a speech soon thereafter. He held up Tal Afar as an example of American success in Iraq.

The strategy was criticized in the press for its repeated incantation of the notion of achieving victory in a conflict that seemed murkier than ever.

But Bush's speech, informed by aggressive White House public relations, moved public opinion five points. Casey, again, was not consulted on the PR offensive. But by now he had become accustomed to Bush officials in Washington taking it upon themselves to explain the strategy he was supposedly pursuing. The mantra of clear, hold, and build was an elaborate bumper sticker for the White House and, in the final analysis, an egregious bit of deceptive advertising, since the hope-inspiring military effort it highlighted—Tal Afar—was the exception rather than the rule when it came to the American strategy in Iraq. When Casey visited Washington in early January 2006, no one insisted that he change course.[28] The general was asked to extend his tour as commander for more than another year, until the spring of 2007, and he agreed.

CHAPTER 11

The Year of Living Dangerously

When he arrived in Baghdad at the end of 2005 to command Multi-National Corps—Iraq, Lieutenant General Pete Chiarelli thought he had a plan to turn the situation around. Apart from a few farsighted military commanders, the Army had often paid only lip service to the "nonkinetic" side of its operations: those activities like civil affairs that were intended to win over, or at least reassure, a wary occupied population.

Despite his struggles with the Mahdi Army during his 2004 tour in Baghdad as the commander of the 1st Cavalry Division, Chiarelli thought the approach was as valid as ever. After the uprising, Chiarelli's intelligence officer approached him with an analysis showing that the areas that were the most heavily contested were also the ones with the greatest deficiencies of clean water, sewerage, and electricity. There was, Chiarelli reasoned, a correlation between the neediness of the population and the violence they were prepared to tolerate or even abet. Nor did he think the American project in Iraq was hopeless. Chiarelli had been heartened by the January 2005 elections. The inked purple finger, he later enthused, had been "a symbol of defiance and hope."[1] He intended to bring that attitude to his new job as corps commander.

Chiarelli had proselytized on behalf of his version of counterinsurgency, coauthoring an article with one of his officers for the Army's premier professional journal, *Military Review,* which bore the optimistic title "Winning the Peace." "The people just will not support a resumption of large-scale violence in the face of clear signs of progress," he argued. "Will Muqtada Al Sadr or his lieutenants attack again? Probably. But the support for the attacks will be waning at best and will not last if infrastructure improvements continue."[2] However one interpreted the lessons of the 2004 fight in

Sadr City, Chiarelli had identified one of the important principles of counterinsurgency. Military operations against the insurgents were necessary but not sufficient. It was impossible to kill your way out of a fight.

Chiarelli's preparations for his return as corps commander were hampered by one of the bizarre administrative issues that often made it hard to believe the Army's stateside bureaucracy was fully engaged in the wars its deployed troops were fighting. Lore had it that the 1st Cav's shoulder patch had been designed by the wife of a cavalryman, who made it large and yellow, emblazoned with the black profile of a horse's head, which faced forward, so she could see her husband riding across the desert. All troops in the division wore the patch on their left sleeve, but once they had been in combat with the "First Team," they were authorized to wear it on their right sleeve as well, as a "combat patch." As with a number of other divisions' patches, though, this presented a curious dilemma. Worn on the right, the patch had the horse facing backward. It looked strange, and to some cavalrymen, including Chiarelli, it seemed wrong for the horse to look as though it were retreating. That kind of heraldic logic sometimes flew in the Army: the American flag patch that soldiers also wore on their right shoulder was printed in reverse for the same reason, so that it would not appear to be in retreat.

After taking the 1st Cav to Baghdad, Chiarelli had proposed a new patch reversing the horse's profile and submitted the change to the Institute of Heraldry, the division of the Army that serves as the guardian of military tradition. When Heraldry was slow to respond, Chiarelli went ahead and ordered a shipment of new patches using $60,000 of his division's funds. Since the soldiers would be issued new uniforms called ACUs when they returned to the United States anyway, if the Army chose not to continue the innovation the patches would go the way of the old uniforms. No harm, no foul, or so Chiarelli thought. The new patches were issued as part of the July 4, 2004, Independence Day festivities in Baghdad. The issue was long forgotten when, near the end of 1st Cav's deployment in early 2005, Chiarelli received a phone call from a friend, Lieutenant General Stan Green, who served as the Army's inspector general in Washington. Chiarelli figured that the colleague wanted to congratulate him on his division's role in securing the January election, which had just taken place.

"Peter," Green said, "I need to read you your rights." Chiarelli was apparently being investigated for violating the Antideficiency Act, which prohibits wrongful government expenditures—in this case, the purchase of a nonstandard patch. With that cloud hanging over his head, Chiarelli could not officially be promoted. And when he was named to lead V Corps, which was headed back to Iraq, Chiarelli could not formally take charge of the unit or train with the soldiers he had been selected to command. The result was that Rick Sanchez, who had left Iraq after a rocky year in which he presided over the Abu Ghraib scandal, still remained in charge of V Corps. Due to Chiarelli's minor infraction, the Army had left the training of the V Corps to a general in whom few knowledgeable superiors retained confidence and who was not expected to deploy with the corps.

With the V Corps deployment just weeks away the Army belatedly decided that the flap over the patch should not be a barrier to Chiarelli's promotion. Two days before Thanksgiving, Chiarelli was cleared. Shortly before Christmas, Chiarelli arrived in Baghdad to scout the situation before his unit arrived several weeks later. The city had changed immensely since Chiarelli was last there with the 1st Cav in early 2005—and not for the better. Many of the projects he had struggled to launch had disappeared. Chiarelli had taken pride in the rehabilitation of Abu Nawas Street, a grassy stretch of fish restaurants along the Tigris. Now it appeared to be an abandoned war zone.

Even more disturbing was the guidance Chiarelli received from the outgoing corps commander, Lieutenant General John Vines. "I spent all the time with Vines, I went to all his meetings, all his boards that he had, and in every one of them it was clear that it was totally focused on drawdown," Chiarelli recalled. "When I visited brigade commanders, it was drawdown. This is how we're going to move out of here. Everything was that way."[3] Casey's strategy of pulling back and withdrawing American troops to try to prod Iraqi politicians and generals to step up was in full swing. When Chiarelli assumed control the American-led coalition had 112 forward operating bases. By the time he left a year later the number was supposed to shrink to 50.

Even so, Chiarelli's new post made him the day-to-day commander of coalition forces and the second-ranking American military man in Iraq. Implementing the lessons Chiarelli had learned about winning the Iraqi people over would not be easy given that the American military footprint was slated to shrink. Still, Chiarelli intended to do his best to put his strategy to work in all of Iraq. His success would depend on two critical factors: having the right Iraqi partner and establishing sufficient security throughout the country to justify handing over increasing responsibilities to the Iraqi government. But who that partner would be, and how he would structure his government, was up for grabs.

As Iraqis went to the polls on December 15 to vote for a new parliament, and potentially a new prime minister, it was clear that ensuring a serious role in the government for the Sunnis would be a challenge. In the fall of 2005, Casey and David Satterfield, a political officer at the embassy, had gone to see Ghazi al-Yawar, who was serving as the Sunni vice president under Jaafari. After complaining that Jaafari was cutting him out of key decisions, Yawar succumbed to frustration and, as he had done in front of Brahimi years before, began crying, an extraordinary display of emotion for a proud Arab politician.

Compared to the January election eleven months earlier, the December vote went off with little violence—only one-third as many insurgent attacks. In addition to stepping up election day security and pressing Al-Qaeda in Iraq's car bomb networks with commando raids, the American military had also done its best to secure the election from the Internet. In a rare and highly classified move over the summer, the Joint Chiefs had ordered General James Cartwright, commander of STRATCOM, a stateside headquarters that had a cyber-operations unit at the National Security Agency's electronic eavesdropping and hacking nexus in Fort Meade, Maryland, to take action to prevent insurgents and militants from taking to the Internet to disrupt the elections. The undisclosed operation was carried out during both the October referendum and the December elections, and would not cease until March 2006.[4]

For all of the high-technology efforts that were made to ensure the elections went ahead there was an important step that was not taken. The decision to treat all of Iraq as a single electoral district played to the strengths of well-resourced Shiite Islamist and Kurdish political parties. That advantage, in the case of the Shiite religious parties, was enhanced by covert funding from Iran. Moderate Shiites and Sunnis, in contrast, had yet to develop well-organized political parties of their own. To level the playing field, Tom Warrick, a State Department official and Arabist, advocated an overt program of financial and material assistance to Iraq's emerging political groups. The funds would be channeled to those parties that adhered to democratic principles. Despite years of lobbying for the proposal, the idea was never carried out. Resistance on the part of some State Department and even White House officials to intervening in Iraq's electoral process stymied the effort, an inhibition that was not shared by Iran or Iraq's other neighbors.

Despite all that, Iraq's Sunnis appeared ready to put aside their boycott and vote this time. To encourage their participation, Casey had met with leading Sunni politicians to effect an informal cease-fire: if they could influence the insurgents not to attack, the coalition would hold off major military operations in the lead-up to the vote. It was the first time that Casey had acknowledged that the Sunni leadership not only had contacts among the insurgents, but held some degree of sway over some of them. While the election was another important step in the American plan to build a democratic Iraq, the prime minister, however, would not be chosen directly by the electorate. In accordance with the new Iraqi constitution, the largest bloc of political parties in parliament would nominate a candidate for prime minister, around whom the government would be formed. The country's next leader would be chosen in true Iraqi fashion—with politicians jockeying for the top job in quasi-conspiratorial backroom negotiations.

The goal, Zalmay Khalilzad insisted, should be to form a "national unity government" that included Sunni Arabs, Kurds, other minorities, and the Shiite majority. To ensure that the Americans had sufficient leverage to press for such a broad-based government, Khalilzad urged the Kurds to agree to withhold their support from any government that the two sides did not agree was sufficiently inclusive. Without the Kurds, the Shiites would be unable to achieve the two-thirds majority needed to elect the prime minister. Khalilzad then urged the Sunnis and Kurds to form a bloc with Allawi in order to begin talks with the Shiites from a position of strength. It was vital, Khalilzad argued, that the Sunni Arab politicians be included as "core partners" and not offered mere crumbs after a deal between Shiites and Kurds. The ambassador advised the parties that the choice for prime minister should be based on a consensus and that the choices for the security ministries also should be consensus choices with no links to militias.

As for the choice of a prime minister, it was clear to the Americans and British, and not just the Sunnis, that Ibrahim al-Jaafari was no longer the man for the job. The coalition saw a vivid demonstration of Jaafari's sectarianism in late September when he called a surprise meeting of the Ministerial Committee on National Security, along with Khalilzad and British ambassador William Patey, to complain about an American raid in Sadr City. Soon, the conversation had turned to the issue of sectarianism in general.

Sadoun al-Dulaimi, the Sunni defense minister, found the issue worrisome. "If sectarian feelings start infiltrating the MOI or MOD, it would be the beginning of a civil war," he said, referring to the Ministries of Interior and Defense, and adding later that he viewed the resurgence of the Mahdi Army under cover of the 2004 cease-fire in places like Sadr City as one of the toughest problems facing the government. "Jaafari strongly disagreed," a cable from Khalilzad recounted. "He said that JAM [the Mahdi Army] is part of the government, with three ministers and 23 assembly members."[5]

A broader problem was the human rights abuses on an institutional scale that had occurred under Jaafari. Earlier in October, Casey sent a letter to Interior Minister Bayan Jabr. Soldiers from the 3rd Armored Cavalry Regiment patrolling the rural Arab Jabour area just south of Baghdad "observed soldiers of the 1st Battalion of the Wolf Brigade burning cars, attempting to light houses on fire, and slapping and repeatedly striking detainees," Casey wrote.[6] Adding to the problem, the Americans had received numerous reports that Badr members had infiltrated the police and were carrying out police duties. Kidnappings were also a concern. There were reports that Sunnis were being abducted and hauled to the sixth and seventh floors of the Interior Ministry headquarters for interrogation, or worse. The report was hardly far-fetched. Jabr worked out of his house, rarely visiting the ministry's main office building, either out of fear for his physical safety or out of a desire to maintain distance and plausible deniability from what was going on there. The ministry headquarters was a battleground in its own right; while SCIRI ran the ministry, other mostly Shiite political parties, like Dawa and the Sadrists, ruled its different floors like fiefdoms. Fearing for their safety, some senior officials avoided the elevators, and American advisers went to the latrine in pairs.

The most shocking revelation was not at the ministry but at a bomb-hardened facility south of the Green Zone called Jadriya Bunker, where an official who went by the name of Engineer Ahmed was running an off-the-books operation. Ahmed, whose real name was Bashir Nasr al-Wandi, was not the kind of SCIRI official who spoke English, wore suits, and chatted frequently with Americans; he was the other kind, hard-nosed and working mostly in the shadows. National Security Adviser Mowaffak al-Rubaie put it simply to an American officer: "Engineer Ahmed is a man of action." Before the war he had been a senior intelligence officer in the Iran-based Badr Corps, working closely with the Quds Force and with other Badr intelligence veterans who had stayed on in Iranian service.

When Jabr became interior minister, he installed Engineer Ahmed in the ministry's intelligence section to counterbalance the Kurdish deputy minister in charge of the portfolio. Ahmed took over the Jadriya Bunker, and ran a group called the Special Interrogations Unit out of it. When American advisers went to visit him, they sometimes found handcuffed detainees on the floor outside his office, apparently waiting for him to personally interrogate them.

In November, one of the American brigade commanders in Baghdad approached Brigadier General Karl Horst, a deputy commander of the 3rd Infantry Division. A well-to-do Sunni couple from Adhamiya—a doctor and professor—had come to him for help looking for their teenage son, who, they said, had been kidnapped by the Mahdi Army. Word quickly got out within the ministry that Horst was asking questions about the missing boy, and during a meeting on November 13, an Iraqi colonel surreptitiously slipped Horst a piece of paper. The missing boy, the note said, could be found at the Jadriya Bunker.[7]

When Horst and his soldiers arrived at the bunker later that same day, November 13, they were denied entry, so Horst put the site's commandant on the phone with Jabr. Reluctantly, the commandant let Horst in. As he wandered around the facility he discovered a large locked room, which housed 12 blindfolded prisoners. The men said they had been held for months and urged Horst to look in two adjacent rooms where he found 168 detainees lined up in cramped rows and blindfolded. The stench in the rooms was overwhelming; without access to latrines, the prisoners had been forced to urinate in water bottles and defecate wherever they could. Horst had the Iraqi guards leave the rooms, and as soon as they were gone the prisoners began lifting up their shirts to show the marks of beating and torture, which many said had occurred in that very room. According to a State Department cable written about a month later, more than a hundred prisoners bore signs of abuse.[8]

Shocked, Horst instructed the site commandant to order all his men into their barracks, and then he called for backup. While American troops swarmed over the bunker, locking it down and preventing its staff from leaving, military lawyers and detention officials began combing through the files on the detainees, nearly all of whom were Sunnis. Fourteen prisoners had been so badly beaten that the Americans immediately evacuated them to the military hospital in the Green Zone. The missing boy had not been found, but Horst had uncovered abuses that went beyond anything wayward Americans had done at Abu Ghraib.

In a press conference, Jabr, who never visited the Jadriya Bunker to see what the Americans had found, downplayed the allegations and claimed that the prisoners held in the bunker were only "the most criminal terrorists." "No one was beheaded, no one was killed," he said.

Disturbingly, some of the prisoners in the Jadriya Bunker had something in common besides being Sunni. Many were either former pilots or the relatives of former pilots. Engineer Ahmed, some American officers came to believe but could never prove, was using the ministry to settle old scores, either those of SCIRI or of Badr—who blamed Saddam's air force for strikes on Shiite insurgents during their 1991 rebellion against Saddam's regime—or those of Iran. Jaafari had not directed the torture, but he had presided over a government that had tolerated it.

On December 30, Patey expressed the British objection to Jaafari to Qasim Daoud, a British-educated Shiite parliamentarian. In Khalilzad's own meeting with Daoud, the politician opened a window on the political maneuvering among the Shiites. Grand Ayatollah Ali al-Sistani, Daoud disclosed, was also concerned about the prime minister's performance but had been told by Jaafari that he still had the backing of the United States. Daoud had told Sistani this was not the case. The American-led coalition, Daoud said, needed to make crystal clear to Jaafari that he did not have its support, a message that needed to be broadcast to others in his Dawa Party like Ali al-Adeeb and Nuri al-Maliki. Otherwise, Jaafari would try to manipulate the process just as he had sought to do with Sistani.

"Jaafari believes he has a religious responsibility to be prime minister," Daoud said somewhat mockingly. "This language is reminiscent of Saddam." As for who should succeed Jaafari, Daoud advocated for Adil Abd al-Mahdi, a senior politician with SCIRI, the Hakims' Shiite party. Daoud acknowledged that he had some reservations about Abd al-Mahdi, fearing that he was too prone to make concessions to the Kurds and a bit too close to the Iranians. Still, Abd al-Mahdi was, Daoud insisted, one of the few genuine statesmen in Iraqi politics. As for Khalilzad's desire to find some sort of role for Allawi, the former prime minister who Khalilzad hoped could reach out to the Sunnis, Daoud was skeptical that Allawi would accept anything other than the post of prime minister. If Allawi participated in the government at all, Daoud advised, it would only be indirectly through the Iraqiya Party he had recently established.[9]

By January, the embassy's Shiite contacts were reporting a fierce competition between Jaafari and Abd al-Mahdi. One mid-level Dawa official, Nuri Kamal al-Maliki, told the Americans in early January that the Shiites did not yet have an understanding of how they would go about picking a new prime minister, whether by consensus or majority vote. Many Shiites, Maliki also told the Americans, would like to see the Kurdish leader Jalal Talabani displaced from the post of president. As for the Sunnis, if they were too demanding in negotiating a role for themselves in a coalition government, Maliki added, the Shiites would try to make a separate deal with the Kurds. Maliki insisted that the Shiites agreed the security ministries should not be in the grips of the militia. And, as he saw it, there were still too many Baathists holding office in the government.

Iran's influence on the negotiations was an open secret in Baghdad. On January 9, Khalilzad had a meeting with the foreign minister, Hoshyar Zebari, in which they discussed prospective nominees for prime minister, including whom the Shiite bloc, formally known as the United Iraqi Alliance, would nominate. "Zebari believes that ultimately the Iranian Revolutionary Guard Corps intelligence chief Soleimani and Sistani will decide the UIA PM nominee," Khalilzad's cable on the meeting reported, referring to Qasim Suleimani, the commander of Iran's Quds Force, and to Iraq's senior ayatollah.[10]

The American embassy did not intend to let the Iranians call the shots. In a classified February 10 cable, entitled "No Perfect Candidate," Khalilzad summed up the choices. None of the candidates were ideal and the United States would need to guide whoever was picked to deal with the deep problems bedeviling Iraq.[11]

Abd al-Mahdi, a former minister of finance, had the best executive skills and had worked closely with the embassy's economic experts, an important plus given the economic challenges facing Iraq.[12] A number of American officials, including Meghan O'Sullivan—the Iraq hand on the NSC staff—thought that Abd al-Mahdi, a fluent speaker of English and technocrat, was the best candidate. But Khalilzad had his concerns. He had, Khalilzad asserted, regularly deferred to the SCIRI leader Abd al-Aziz al-Hakim, who had argued for setting up a Shiite federal region in the south, and was, the Americans feared, too close to Iran. Allawi had made it clear that he would not serve under Abd al-Mahdi. Jaafari had a golden tongue, but a leaden hand. He had been unready to take on the Shiite militias and unwilling to make hard decisions. Jaafari had been unable to unify the political parties "except in their opposition to him," Khalilzad noted. His inability to manage his own government had been clear when six ministers disobeyed his direct order and left with Talabani to attend the United Nations General Assembly. Lastly, he was indebted to the Sadrists, who were likely to secure control of prominent ministries in another Jaafari government.

Nadim al-Jabiri, the head of the small Shiite Fadhila Party, had cross-sectarian appeal. Allawi and Barzani each supported him. But he was a dark-horse candidate who lacked broad support on the national scene. A political science professor at Baghdad University during Saddam's rule, Jabiri did not go into exile in London or Tehran, which was a point of pride. "He says the right things about containing the sectarian conflict, but we are not sure about his ability to deliver," Khalilzad wrote. Hussein al-Shahristani, Brahimi's original choice for prime minister, a nuclear scientist and the deputy speaker of the parliament, was the weakest candidate, Khalilzad wrote. A hard-liner on security issues, Shahristani had criticized the United States for not giving the Ministry of Interior a freer hand.

Another long shot was Dawa's Nuri al-Maliki (also known as Abu Esraa, after his daughter), who, Khalilzad said, might emerge victorious if opposition hardened against Abd al-Mahdi and Jaafari did not prevail. As the chairman of the parliament's security committee and a spokesman for the Shiite alliance, Maliki was one of the government's "most tireless operators." Maliki, Khalilzad concluded, had deep concerns about Iranian influence. He was a hard-liner on de-Baathification, which meant he often clashed with Sunni Arabs. "His deep unease about the Iranian intervention is matched only by his unease about the possibility of another Baathist coup," Khalilzad wrote, adding that Maliki "claims to have stopped several efforts to install Baathists into leading positions." Maliki, Khalilzad cautioned, also advocated a tough policy against the Sunni insurgency "even at the expense of human rights violations." But he had, Khalilzad revealed, cooperated with American diplomats to head off a Sadrist move to create a Sovereignty Committee in the parliament that would have called for an imminent American withdrawal.

None of the candidates would ease "Iraq's political dysfunction," Khalilzad concluded. "Would benefits of Abd al-Mahdi's presumed effectiveness outweigh the disadvantages of a PM perceived as linked to Badr Corps and Iran? Could Abd al-Mahdi be prevailed upon to take a tough stand against his own party's militia? Would the unquestionable cost of Jaafari remaining in office, with his well known track record of ineffectiveness, be greater than the risks of the comparatively unknown Jabiri? Would the right mix of competent ministers, representing all sectarian/ethnic groups, be able to manage around Jaafari in his second term?"

Amidst the wheeling and dealing, the American military sought to keep Al-Qaeda from interfering while also beginning to draw down its troop levels significantly for the first time in two years. After the vote, in the early weeks of 2006, Casey made the decision to off-ramp two brigades that were getting ready to deploy, in effect cutting the force by that amount. One of the brigades preparing to head to Iraq, from the 1st Infantry Division, had its deployment canceled entirely, instead drawing the mission of training and fielding adviser teams in both Iraq and Afghanistan. The other, the 1st Armored Division's 2nd Brigade, went as far as Kuwait, where it became CENTCOM's reserve force, on call to move into Iraq in full or in part if needed. By March, the American force amounted to 135,000 troops, including fifteen combat brigades.[13]

Casey's decision had the greatest effect in Diyala, the ethnically mixed province to Baghdad's northeast. For two years, a pair of brigades had split responsibility for Diyala, with one brigade focusing on the populous area around the provincial capital, Baqubah, and the other spread out along the province's long border with Iran. The off-ramp decision meant that for 2006 a single brigade would be in charge of Diyala. The outgoing brigade commander in Diyala, Colonel Steve Salazar, warned before he went home that forces in the province were spread too thin. One brigade could handle Diyala, so long as it was sufficiently large, he thought, but that was not the case. Instead, all that was left was a brigade with two battalions. Salazar's worries were driven in part by the fact that while Diyala had been calm for the first half of 2005, since summer there had been one sign after another of increasing tensions between Sunnis and Shiites in the province, often called a "microcosm of Iraq" because of its ethno-sectarian makeup. "I shared with General Casey and [division commander] General Turner, 'I never signed up for two battalions, I had always said four was the minimum,'" Salazar told an Army historian.[14] With recent abuses by Shiite Interior Ministry forces inflaming local Sunnis and creating a perfect opening for Al-Qaeda in Iraq, one assessment by the corps headquarters agreed. The "most likely course of action" following the off-ramp, the briefing said bluntly, was this one: "AIF use eastern Diyala as base."[15] (AIF was the military's euphemistic and unhelpful abbreviation for Anti-Iraqi Forces, or insurgents of all stripes.)

The decreased size of the American force in Iraq also had important consequences in Baghdad. In early January 2006, J. D. Thurman's 4th Infantry Division replaced Fuzzy Webster's 3rd Infantry Division as the main American force in the capital. The incoming division was smaller than the outgoing one, in part due to what the Army termed "modularization"— brigades were being revamped both to increase the number of them and to add high-tech tools like drones to their arsenal, but in the process the brigades themselves were losing infantrymen and engineers. By the time

Webster left, out of six Iraqi brigades in Baghdad, four were operating independently in their own sectors, in some cases with very little American oversight. Despite the wide array of Interior Ministry troops deployed throughout the capital, the 3rd Infantry Division had had only two small "Special Police Transition Teams" dedicated to the task of advising them.

In East Baghdad, an epicenter of worrisome activity by the Mahdi Army and by Badr-infiltrated Interior Ministry units largely ignored by the overall American strategy, Joe DiSalvo's 2nd Brigade, 3rd Infantry Division, was replaced by the 4th Brigade, 101st Airborne, and the incoming unit chose to scale back. The 101st Airborne unit became the first brigade not to devote a battalion to Sadr City, choosing to replace both 3-15 Infantry and the battalion operating in the large neighboring district of 9 Nisan with a single battalion. FOB Hope, the base on the outskirts of Sadr City, was left with an Iraqi Army unit and its adviser team of twenty-six Americans who lacked even secure Internet access. With the American battalion dedicated to overseeing Sadr City gone, the Iraqi units in the area fell deeper and deeper under the sway of the Mahdi Army. The chief American adviser at FOB Hope believed that the second in command of the Iraqi battalion there was in league with militia leaders or at least in regular communication with them—so much so that when the American military formally transferred control of FOB Hope to the Iraqis the Mahdi Army commander for Sadr City was invited to, but did not, attend the ceremony.

The Shiite militias were a major problem, but not one that senior commanders wanted to confront unless absolutely necessary. This policy was reflected in the guidance given to the 2nd Brigade, 4th Infantry Division, which in January 2006 took charge in a large, mostly Shiite area south of Baghdad that included the cities of Najaf and Karbala, both centers of Sadrist influence. "We were told, basically, to leave the Jaish al-Mahdi alone and to not start a fight with the Jaish al-Mahdi," said the brigade's commander, Colonel John Tully. "MNC-I and MNF-I had their hands full just trying to deal with the Sunni insurgency; so we were told, 'Don't pick a fight with the Shia militia folks.'"[16]

In early 2006, Al-Qaeda in Iraq was stronger than it had ever been. Its leader, Abu Musab al-Zarqawi, had evaded a two-year-long manhunt run by Stan McChrystal's JSOC task force, and in cities like Ramadi and Baqubah and rural expanses like the ring of towns around Baghdad, the group controlled its own scattered fiefdoms. The 2005 elections had drawn some moderate Sunnis out of the insurgency, increasing the relative strength of the Al-Qaeda brand name, which was now drawing fighters and even whole cells and units from other Sunni insurgent groups into its fold. Beyond the group's core of trained terrorists and one-way turnstile of foreign suicide bombers, more and more local Sunni fighters were renouncing mantles like the 1920 Revolution Brigades and Jaish al-Islami in order to benefit from Al-Qaeda's name recognition and resources. To manage independent groups that were joining his cause and to put an Iraqi face on it, Zarqawi announced in January the creation of the Mujahideen Shura Council, a governing body to coordinate the groups.

Zarqawi's strategy was to spark a civil war between Iraq's Sunnis and Shiites. The October referendum and December 2005 elections had seen fewer attacks by car bombs—Al-Qaeda's signature weapon—than the January one, a reduction that Casey's command credited in part to the previous fall's operations to close the Syrian border. But in February Al-Qaeda operatives struck back with their biggest coup yet. Just before 7 a.m. on February 22, a series of explosions collapsed the famous golden dome of Al-Askari Mosque in Samarra. Built in A.D. 944, the mosque was the burial site of two of the twelve imams, or rightful successors of the Prophet, and recognized by most Shiite Muslims as a holy shrine of the same order of importance as those in Najaf, Karbala, and Kadhimiya. The shrine had been remodeled in 1868 and its dome, said to have been covered by 72,000 gold pieces, was added in 1905.

One American intelligence report said that four Al-Qaeda operatives in Interior Ministry uniforms had entered the mosque beforehand and had spent several hours inside planting the explosives, likely with the collusion of the Interior Ministry personnel assigned to guard the mosque.[17] The Samarra mosque bombing neither killed nor injured anyone, but because of the sensitivity of its target American leaders were concerned that it would unleash a wave of retaliatory violence between Shiites and Sunnis.

After hearing about the bombing, Khalilzad and Casey went to see Jaafari. The Americans were afraid that Shiite militias would take to the streets. Khalilzad told Jaafari that the United States had information that there would be a lot of bloodletting, including attacks on Sunni mosques. It was imperative that Jaafari impose martial law. Jaafari did not appear perturbed. The people, he said, needed to let off some steam. Khalilzad was incredulous. The prime minister's constituents would be appalled, Khalilzad argued, were they to know that Jaafari was prepared to sanction several nights of massacres. "Mr. Ambassador, you have been here how many months?" Jaafari asked. "You know Iraq better than I do?" The Americans made clear that they could not stand by and watch the attacks happen. If the Iraqi government did not act, the coalition would.

Two days later, Casey issued a classified memo to his senior officers. With the country in the middle of a political transition, the goal for the next thirty to sixty days was to "help the Iraqis project calm, confident and unifying leadership." It was vital, Casey added, to prevent the Iraqi security forces from fracturing along sectarian lines. The Al-Qaeda attack was just one in a series of bombings, and the United States needed to help the Iraqis defend other strategic sites to deprive the militants of a chance for another provocation.[18]

Even in the middle of the crisis, however, Casey was reluctant to abandon the central tenet of his strategy: shifting responsibility to the nascent Iraqi forces. "We must do this in a manner which puts the Iraqis in the lead and bolsters the confidence of all Iraqis in their government, the Iraqi Security Forces, and the Coalition," he wrote. "The resolution of this crisis should advance our campaign objective of keeping Iraq on the path to self reliance."

Implementing the guidance was easier said than done, since some of the Iraqi forces, particularly the National Police and its Wolf Brigade, had a well-earned reputation for abusing the Sunni community. The two forces that had gained the worst reputations, the Interior Ministry's Special Police Commandos and Public Order brigades, had been combined in early 2006 into a single force of two divisions, the National Police. The new name did not fool anyone who dealt with the Wolf Brigade, which retained its moniker despite being officially renamed the 2nd Brigade, 1st National Police Division. In many areas of Baghdad, the National Police's green camouflage uniforms—the same pattern worn until recently by stateside American troops—were soon a sight to be feared.

On the day of the Samarra bombing, Lieutenant Colonel Gian Gentile, a cavalry squadron commander in West Baghdad, was meeting with Sunni tribal leaders on the outskirts of the capital, trying to convince them to accept the deployment of an Interior Ministry battalion to their rural district. The response of local tribal leaders was eye-opening for Gentile. "Of course, when I started telling the Ghartani tribe sheikhs that, they started freaking out," he recalled. "They said, 'You can't bring National Police down here,' and I said, 'Why?' And they said, 'Because you're bringing the devil into our homes.'"[19]

Even with the additional vigilance, the sectarian violence was prompting

Sunnis to pick up and leave. On March 6, an Iraqi nongovernmental organization provided the American embassy with a report, which the Americans considered credible, on population displacement since the bombing. The report estimated that more than three hundred Shiite families—some 1,800 people—had fled from Sunni-dominated towns outside Baghdad like Abu Ghraib, Yusifiyah, Taji, Saab al-Bor, and Tarmiya, and from West Baghdad's Bayaa and Ghazaliya neighborhoods, to Shula, a Shiite slum in the city's northwest corner. Four hundred more Shiite families—about 2,400 people—had left the southern and western outskirts of Baghdad and its southern neighborhood of Dora for Sadr City, Shula's larger equivalent in East Baghdad. The Iraqi organization also reported smaller numbers of Shiite families displacing from the Baghdad area entirely, to Najaf.[20]

As it became clear that more American forces would be required, Lieutenant Colonel Jim Danna received an alert on March 11. The battalion he led, 2-6 Infantry, had never made it to Iraq but had been kept in Kuwait as a standby force. Now he was told to head to Baghdad the next day for a combined Iraqi-American operation, Operation Scales of Justice, to prevent reprisals against the Sunnis. It was a piecemeal response to a yawning security problem, but Casey looked at the operation as a stopgap that would only briefly interrupt the American troop drawdown.

Danna was told the mission would last only thirty days; his battalion was broken up into companies and parceled out to different units. Other units that were dispatched to the Iraqi capital for Scales of Justice included a Marine battalion that was sent to Abu Ghraib and a battalion of the 101st, which was based out of Taji and worked the northern part of the city. On the Iraqi side, the operation saw the introduction of Shiite-dominated Interior Ministry troops. There were dual chains of command, and the Interior Ministry could veto any orders that the Americans gave to the Iraqi forces. Most of the Iraqis were tethered to checkpoints, some 130 in all.[21]

A March 29 intelligence assessment provided a snapshot. Tensions were still running high and civilians were continuing to leave the area, and the Mahdi Army, which maintained illegal checkpoints, was engaged in "extrajudicial detention." In the previous two weeks, 1,272 Sunni families had moved out of Baghdad, as had 425 Shiite families. The performance of the Iraqi security forces was uneven. There were "extremely porous ingress/egress routes" into Baghdad and a permissive environment within the city. The number of ethno-sectarian incidents was on the rise. Executions were going up now that Mahdi Army members had returned from the Arbaeen pilgrimage.

In both the Green Zone and the United States, the weeks after the Samarra mosque bombing saw a strange public debate: had the bombing sparked a civil war? Casey's command argued that there was no civil war. The general still held that position years later, arguing that since all the government's forces were all fighting on the same side, the conflict did not fit the bill—a dubious distinction since plenty of uniformed Iraqi troops were essentially allied with groups like the Mahdi Army that were taking the fight to the Sunni minority. Some in the Bush administration argued that the United States had had an effective strategy until the diabolical Zarqawi lit the fuse of sectarian war by orchestrating the attack on the Samarra mosque. The evidence did not support that view either. Looking back on the months of Al-Qaeda car bombings, abuses by Shiite government troops, and Mahdi Army murders that both preceded and followed the February 22 bombing, it seems clear that Samarra merely accelerated a Sunni-Shiite conflict that had already been under way in 2005. The terminological debate over whether it was a civil war, an "ethno-sectarian conflict," or simply "communal violence" distracted from the larger point: the problem had been going on for months before February 2006, and as the spring wore on it worsened.

After the first thirty days of its deployment were up, and the security problems persisted, the Baghdad mission of Danna's battalion was extended. The troops that had been dispersed throughout the city, minus a tank company, were put under Danna's command, and sent to West Rashid, a mixed Sunni-Shiite district where things looked very much like civil war indeed.

As the attacks and revenge killings continued to spiral, the Americans struggled to pull together a new Iraqi government. In early February, Abd al-Mahdi thought he had enough support to win endorsement from the Shiite bloc but lost by one vote, prompting Khalilzad to refer to him somewhat playfully as "the man who cannot count." Recalling the event, Abd al-Mahdi insisted that he, in fact, had an accurate count, but was done in by Sadrist pressure. "Saturday we had the majority," he said, adding that the Sadrists and Dawa Party responded by delaying the vote. The next day, he had lost the majority and the vote by 64–63. "It was badly played," said Abd al-Mahdi. We were too confident that we would win. And he played it not so good," he added, referring to Khalilzad. "Khalilzad acted here as an Iraqi, the way we do things here in Iraq. He was promising people they could be P.M." Khalilzad did not wait long before moving to broker a solution. Upon learning that Abd al-Mahdi had lost, Khalilzad rushed out of a lunch with Talabani and Barham Salih. "The game just began," he exclaimed. Soon, he and William Patey, his British counterpart, were discussing alternatives, including another Dawa member. As a small party without a militia, Dawa posed the least threat to SCIRI or the Sadrist Trend.

In Iraqi politics, that was not necessarily a disadvantage. The next leader of Iraq needed, in effect, to be a consensus choice among the Shiites and not too objectionable to the Kurds, the Sunnis, or the Americans, who would not relent on their talk of a "unity government." The power of the prime minister was to be limited in any event as the understanding was that the major ministries and deputy positions would be parceled out among the parliamentary factions based on their political strength.[22]

The notion of installing a Fadhila representative had failed and the Iraqis had also thwarted the effort to give Allawi the security portfolio. So Khalilzad was prepared to look within Dawa's ranks as well. A leading contender was Ali al-Adeeb. Born into a lower-middle-class family in Karbala, where his father was a school principal, Adeeb had earned his college degree in education and went to work at a teachers institute before joining Dawa. By the 1970s he had been thrown into jail for agitating on behalf of the movement. (His brother was sentenced to life imprisonment.)

Adeeb moved to the United Arab Emirates to pursue his anti-Saddam activities as a journalist and, like many in the opposition, drifted to Iran. For years Adeeb had shuttled between Iran and Syria, returning to Baghdad only after Saddam was ousted. When he interacted with the Americans, Adeeb sought to play down his links with Iran, casting himself as an Iraqi nationalist uneasy with the relationship that Abd al-Karim Kasim, the Iraqi Army officer who seized power in 1958, had had with the Soviet Union. In a meeting with the Iraq historian Phebe Marr, Adeeb declined to discuss any of his activities in Iran.[23]

The British were prepared to back Adeeb but his suspected Iranian ties made him a dubious choice for Khalilzad: word was that Adeeb still held an Iranian passport. The candidate Khalilzad had his eye on was a minor party figure who had served as Dawa spokesman in Syria and had done serviceable work on the parliament's security committee. Khalilzad had read through his CIA dossier and there were no red flags or reports of egregious abuses or corruption. One report asserted that he had left Iran for Syria after the Iranians asked him to swear allegiance to Ayatollah Khomeini, the leader of Iran's Islamic revolution. So Khalilzad invited Nuri Kamal al-Maliki to meet with him and Patey.

Before the session, Khalilzad checked with the Kurds. He called Massoud Barzani, the president of the Kurdish region, whom Khalilzad knew from his days of working with the anti-Saddam resistance. Barzani indicated that Maliki was acceptable to the Kurds. He had lived in the mountains with them during the Saddam years. They were prepared to work with him. The other major Kurdish figure, Jalal Talabani, signed off on Maliki as well, as did Tariq al-Hashimi, a leading Sunni politician. It seemed the votes might be there to move forward.

Maliki was well aware that the Americans were determined to thwart Jaafari's bid to remain as prime minister and he assumed that they had it in for him as well. Khalilzad got right down to business, asking Maliki if he had ever considered making a run for the prime minister post. Maliki was taken aback. He told Khalilzad that he had been informed that the American ambassador had vetoed his candidacy. Everybody knew, Maliki said, that Khalilzad did not like him. Khalilzad assuaged Maliki's concerns, saying that he had been reading about Maliki's background and was impressed. Patey was not happy with how the conversation was going and made his displeasure known. As far as he was concerned, Ali al-Adeeb was the better and more experienced candidate. Khalilzad suggested that Patey leave the room so he could talk to Maliki alone. For all of the United States' special relationship with Britain, it was not about to involve its closest ally in the picking of the next Iraqi leader. The United States military had nearly twenty times more troops than Britain in Iraq and was clearly the senior partner. Khalilzad intended to handle the matter on his own.

After Patey departed, Khalilzad turned to Maliki. There was a basis for an understanding. As prime minister, Maliki could bring more Sunnis into the fold and establish a genuine unity government. He could work for a national compact. Because of his long-standing anti-Baathist credentials, he was in a position to reform the de-Baathification procedures and make them less stringent. Khalilzad would have no problem with such a program. Khalilzad could not anoint the next prime minister; the Iraqi political process would decide that. But as far as the United States government was concerned, Maliki was fine.

"Are you serious?" Maliki asked. Maliki ventured that his party wanted him to seek the post, but he had thought the Americans would not accept him. Khalilzad said he was absolutely serious. Maliki and Khalilzad would meet for dinner and discuss it further that night.[24]

"Khalilzad spoke with me and said 'We are ready to support you in case you accept the post,'" Maliki recalled in an interview five years later. "And the British ambassador, William, indeed he was in disagreement with

Khalilzad. And I told them I don't care about either Khalilzad's support or William's objection."

After the meeting, Maliki said, he conferred with Jaafari and related that the American ambassador wanted him to serve as the next prime minister. The Sunnis and Kurds were supportive, and Jaafari decided to withdraw his candidacy. "I was not yet ready for the post," Maliki said, later. "The situation in Iraq was very difficult at that time. I became prime minister shortly after the bombing of the Samarra shrine and the emergence of sectarian violence. Only an insane person would accept the position at that time."[25]

Khalilzad's role in selecting the Iraqi prime minister remained a secret. The notion that he was the American choice would do Maliki no good, and the Bush administration was interested in fostering the belief that the compromise choice was purely the product of the Iraqis' deliberations.

As Maliki negotiated with the different factions, Khalilzad lobbied to shape the new unity government. He told Hakim and others that the Ministry of Interior, which was run by Bayan Jabr of Hakim's SCIRI, had been infiltrated by militias. Jabr had to go. Ashraf Qazi, the Pakistani diplomat who had replaced Brahimi as the United Nations representative to Iraq, was surprised and initially somewhat skeptical of Maliki's appointment. While Maliki was far more decisive than Jaafari, he had been a strong advocate of Shiite views. Maliki's leadership, Qazi told Khalilzad, would be tested, but it was important to be optimistic.

The Americans had big hopes for the Maliki government. Before leaving for Iraq, Chiarelli had recruited a State Department official and former CPA aide, Celeste Ward, to serve as his political adviser. After arriving in Iraq, Ward drafted a confidential memo on a hundred-day program that would give the United States a partner in winning over the Iraqis and confirm the credibility of the fledgling Iraqi government. Ward's memo noted the programs that Franklin Roosevelt, Ronald Reagan, and, to be politically correct, George W. Bush had put in place during their initial one hundred days and provided some suggestions on how the Iraqis might do the same. (Bush's hundred-day accomplishments included the rejection of the Kyoto Treaty, the blocking of U.S. funds to international family planning groups, a $1.6 trillion tax cut plan, and efforts to meet with seemingly every leader in the Western Hemisphere except Fidel Castro.)

The plan had five main planks. To generate jobs, a Civilian Conservation Corps would be established to help repair Iraq's fraying electrical and oil infrastructure and bridges, clear the streets of garbage, and undertake other public works. To build up the Iraqi government's credibility on security, an agreement between it and the United States would be announced that would have the government gradually assume responsibility for safeguarding the country. "This would allow the Iraqi government to get a quick win with the public, demonstrating that they have a firm hand on the tiller in securing their own nation," Ward wrote. "It could enhance the IG's [Iraqi government's] credibility and show the Iraqi people that their own forces have stepped up to the challenges."

The third step was economic and called for opening state-run factories that had been closed down by the CPA after Saddam was deposed, including the Hateen Tractor Factory south of Baghdad, the phosphate factory in Anbar, and a meatpacking plant in Baghdad. Legislation would be prepared to encourage foreign investment. The hours when electrical power was available in Baghdad would be published, no small matter since the electricity seemed to go on and off at whim. Anticorruption efforts would be announced. And there would be a review of the draconian de-Baathification procedures so that Sunni technocrats could be hired.

The fourth step was political. The new prime minister would address the parliament and outline his program. Among his long-term goals: Iraq would have the highest literacy in the Arab world by 2016; 90 percent of Iraqis would have access to clean water and electricity within a decade; and the unemployment rate would be cut in half by 2011. In addition, the prime minister and key cabinet members would conduct town hall meetings in each of Iraq's eighteen provinces and thus "provide average Iraqis with the opportunity to have their voice heard." To rally the public around a common cause, the Iraqi soccer team would go on a national peace tour and then play friendly matches in Europe. Lastly, the government would invite Middle Eastern, European, and other foreign leaders to visit Baghdad.

Ward's plan reflected an idealized vision of how the government might work. But the Iraqis had their own ideas about their government, informed as it was by backroom deals among rival politicians and shifting coalitions. As Maliki sought to line up his coalition, Casey had a telephone conversation with Rumsfeld and General Pete Pace, the chairman of the JCS, over the changing political scene in Baghdad. Maliki, Casey reported, had an agreement that the Ministries of Interior, Defense, Electricity, and Finance would not be overseen by political party leaders. General Abd al-Qadir al-

Obeidi was the front-runner to serve as minister of defense. Casey reported that Abd al-Qadir was "fairly competent," was acceptable to Maliki, and would work with the United States. Casey had suggested that Allawi be appointed as the minister of interior, but Maliki had rejected that, as did some of the Kurds.

Surveying security, Casey noted that the police in Ramadi had abandoned their posts and let insurgents overrun much of the town. As for Basra, the British had lost a helicopter to a missile they had traced to Iran. In Baghdad, the Iraqis were still short 2,400 police. Rumsfeld had a concern of his own. Casey needed to get the Iraqis to affirm that their army and police would total no more than 325,000. The Iraqis wanted a larger force, but the Americans were concerned that they could not pay for it and did not intend to subsidize their wish. The Pentagon was trying to wring maximum efficiency from its Iraq operation. With regard to American and Iraqi forces it wanted no excess inventory. The forces should be large enough to cope with the insurgency and no larger. Like other decisions during this period, this one, too, would prove to be profoundly shortsighted.

Casey's initial campaign plan focused on securing the country through the first set of elections. On April 28, he issued a new campaign plan, entitled "Transition to Iraqi Self-Reliance," which concluded that the strategy had been generally accepted and that the planned downsizing of American forces should continue. "We will succeed by increasingly putting Iraqis in charge across all lines of operations," it noted. "As we transition responsibility to the ISF, the Coalition footprint and levels of support provided should reduce commensurately if we are to make progress towards Campaign End State. Acceptance of appropriate and calculated risk, both with ISF and with Transition Teams, will be an inevitable component of this process."[26]

With Maliki and his cabinet scheduled to be sworn in on May 20, Iraq had passed a milestone. Within the American military, though, tensions were bubbling in the relationship between Casey's and Chiarelli's commands, not least over a spate of abuses committed by American troops and how best to respond to them.

Over the winter, less than a month after taking command in Baghdad, Chiarelli had learned that *Time* magazine was looking into allegations that twenty-four civilians had been massacred by Marines the previous November in Haditha. Chiarelli had an investigator look into the matter and learned that, indeed, on November 19 a Marine patrol had killed two dozen Iraqis in Haditha after an IED blew up one of their Humvees, killing a Marine. A Marine press release the next day had falsely claimed that most of the twenty-four Iraqis had been killed by an IED and the others had been insurgents, and the Marine headquarters had not alerted the corps to anything out of the ordinary. But in fact many of the dead were women and children killed in their houses—in one house, the Marines had killed a four-year-old and a seventy-six-year-old, and in another house children aged one, three, five, eight, and ten—and photographs demonstrating this had been circulating among Marines in the unit for weeks. The incident promised to be a worse public relations disaster than the Abu Ghraib detainee abuse scandal two years earlier.

In March, Chiarelli alerted the Naval Criminal Investigation Service that it should examine the November 19 killings for criminal conduct, and he started a broader investigation into whether the Marines in Haditha had violated the standing rules of engagement and whether there had been a cover-up. To run the investigation, he appointed one of the most respected officers in the Army: Major General Eldon Bargewell, who in a forty-year career had earned a Distinguished Service Cross and four Purple Hearts as a sergeant in MACV-SOG, the legendary Vietnam War forerunner of JSOC, before leading Delta Force squadrons in the 1989 invasion of Panama and the 1991 hunt for Scud missiles in Anbar.

Bargewell spent three months on his investigation. Marines he interviewed in the battalion, its parent regiment, and the division headquarters repeatedly cited the brutal fighting in Anbar as a rationale for why reports of a dozen or more civilians killed in a house had raised no red flags. On June 15, he submitted his report, concluding that while 3/1 Marines had been adequately trained on the rules of engagement, the squad responsible for most of the killings had concocted a false version of the events, and then the company and the battalion commander, Lieutenant Colonel Jeffrey Chessani, had passed only a partial accounting upward. Regimental and division commanders Colonel Stephen Davis and Major General Richard Huck, for their parts, had failed to show any interest in further investigating what had happened on November 19, even after allegations of a massacre had been brought to their attention.[27]

Chiarelli did not disagree with Bargewell's findings, but he felt that with additional time the investigation could have raised more questions on how the episode had been handled by the chain of command. After Bargewell wrapped up his report to meet his deadline, for instance, the Marines had made available the video feeds from a ScanEagle drone that had recorded from overhead much of what happened that day. To incorporate this new material and review the 3,300 other pages of evidence attached to Bargewell's 104-page report, Chiarelli and a team from his staff sequestered themselves for days in late June and early July, and on July 7 forwarded both Bargewell's investigation and some additional findings to Casey. "I find that many units in Iraq are very comfortable with kinetic operations, but less so with the complexities of counterinsurgency operations, in which support of the population is essential to success," Chiarelli wrote in the cover letter accompanying the report.[28]

In the two-hour July meeting at which Chiarelli presented his and Bargewell's findings, Casey seemed less than enthusiastic about digging into how the Marine command had handled itself in a brutal war. "The problem is that other people just aren't as good as you are," Casey said to Chiarelli sarcastically. Later in the year, four Marines from the battalion would be charged with murder, and four more with covering up the nature of the killings, including Chessani. But not until the next year, after Casey had left Iraq, would the Marine Corps reprimand Davis and Huck.

Those were not the only abuses that bothered Chiarelli. In his report, Chiarelli had noted, "Any criticisms made here do not apply uniquely to the Marines." Indeed, by the time of the contentious meeting with Casey over Haditha, the corps was also investigating two Army units, both from the 101st Airborne Division, for unlawful killings. One was the division's 3rd Brigade, whose commander, Colonel Mike Steele, clashed over the winter with the corps over how a counterinsurgency should be fought. "Let's do projects. Projects will turn the population toward our favor," was how Steele sarcastically characterized the corps's strategy later to an Army historian. "[W]e can satiate the enemy's desire for contact because the reason he is fighting is because he is disenfranchised and he is impoverished and we need to give him a job."[29] After troops from one of Steele's units killed eight unarmed men, including three blindfolded detainees, in a botched May raid near Lake Tharthar, a corps investigation found partial fault with Steele for relying on byzantine and aggressive interpretations of the rules of engagement. Though Chiarelli considered pushing for Steele's relief, he settled for a letter of reprimand.[30]

While Chiarelli's headquarters was already deep into the Haditha and Tharthar investigations, in June, a private in another 101st Airborne unit, 1-502 Infantry, told a mental health counselor about a third recent atrocity, in the rural Yusifiyah area south of Baghdad. Three months before, in March, Army investigators learned, five soldiers from the battalion had snuck away from their six-man checkpoint in civilian clothes to a nearby house, where they raped a fourteen-year-old girl, killed her and three of her family members, and set the house on fire. The incident came to light after Al-Qaeda fighters kidnapped and executed three soldiers from the same platoon two months later; in a video of the mutilated bodies, the terrorist group would later claim the killings were revenge for the rape and murders nearby.

The three atrocities were a dark stain on the American record in Iraq and indicated that at least some in the military were having difficulty coping with the stress of war. To the average Iraqi Sunni, the Iraqi security forces were much more of a persistent threat though, particularly because of systemic collusion between some elements and the Mahdi Army. After the Jadriya Bunker raid in November, American troops had begun inspecting other Interior Ministry detention facilities in Baghdad. At one, called Site 4, inspections in December and February noted overcrowding, disease, and some signs of physical abuse among the 1,400 detainees. When inspectors visited again in May, what they found, after initially being denied access by guards, was much worse: evidence of widespread beatings and rape and an attitude among the staff that there was nothing wrong with it.

"Forty-one detainees interviewed at Site 4 had bruising and lash-marks consistent with violent physical abuse," a cable said, as well as thirty-seven juvenile detainees, held there illegally, who alleged "that MOI interrogators had used threats and acts of anal rape to induce confessions and had forced juveniles to fellate them during interrogations. These allegations were also raised independently with inspectors by adult detainees who claimed knowledge of juvenile rapes." Many detainees, the cable went on, "claimed to have been hung by handcuffs from a hook in the ceiling and beaten on the soles of their feet and their buttocks. A hook was discovered on the ceiling of an empty room at the facility; attached was a chain-and-pulley system ordinarily used for lifting vehicles. Apparent bloodspots stained the floor underneath."

The inspectors confiscated the pulley systems and military advisers began to visit Site 4 every day. On June 5, Khalilzad briefed Maliki on the conditions at the facility, and the prime minister created a committee to investigate it. But the problems at Site 4 seemed to run very deep. One National Police colonel at the site told American inspectors that "detainees guilty of some crimes deserve to be beaten," and right away the inspectors saw signs that the ministry was making efforts to whitewash the incident. Perhaps the grimmest sign of how far the Interior Ministry had fallen was that one of the chief whitewashers was Adnan Thabit—the Sunni general who had raised the Special Police Commandos to fight alongside the Americans in Samarra and Mosul.[31]

Together Forward

At Balad Air Base, Stan McChrystal was involved in a manhunt. A sprawling camp forty miles north of Baghdad, Balad was home to American F-16s, served as a massive logistics hub, and was also home of the secretive Joint Special Operations Command. During the early years of the war, insurgents had lobbed so many rounds at the base that the soldiers and airmen took to calling it "Mortaritaville."

By the summer of 2006, McChrystal, now a lieutenant general, had already logged two years in Iraq. The product of a military family—his father had been a two-star general, and all of his siblings had either served in the armed forces or married somebody who did—McChrystal had graduated from West Point in 1976, a legendary class whose members also included Ray Odierno and a host of other wartime generals. "Competitiveness, dedication and desire made 'Mac' the friend we know and respect," noted his yearbook entry, which also acknowledged his rakish side. In his "infamous Grant Hall raid," McChrystal borrowed several old Thompson machine guns from the school's museum, made fake grenades, and along with fellow cadets assaulted one of the academy's office buildings. Unlike other top generals such as Casey, Chiarelli, and Petraeus, McChrystal had not sat out Desert Storm, deploying to a secret base in Saudi Arabia as JSOC's operations officer for its Scud hunt.[1]

Famous for his spartan and almost ascetic ways, McChrystal used to run ten miles each day to the New York office of the Council on Foreign Relations when he did a fellowship there. His zeal and dedication paid off in 2003 when he was put in charge of JSOC, whose forces included the Army's Delta Force and Ranger Regiment and the Navy's SEAL Team Six, and also oversaw a squadron of Britain's Special Air Service, Task Force

Knight. After spending much of 2005 focused on Iraq's border with Syria, McChrystal's command had shifted its attention to central Iraq, where Al-Qaeda was fomenting sectarian violence with an escalating campaign of car and truck bombs against Shiite targets.

McChrystal's JSOC was a different organization from the one that had helped kick off the war with Ranger and Delta Force raids in western Iraq and captured Saddam Hussein. Over the past two years, the intelligence infrastructure that worked behind the scenes to give McChrystal's skilled assault teams their targets had expanded hugely. Under McChrystal's leadership, the JSOC headquarters at Balad had drawn in hundreds of personnel from the NSA, CIA, DIA, FBI, and other agencies, and the command had built up its own contingent of armed drones and other surveillance tools called the "Confederate Air Force." The buildup changed the way the commando task force did things. At the beginning of the war, JSOC had amassed intelligence for days and weeks in order to guide meticulously planned raids. Now, the command launched far more raids with far less preparation, using the raids to amass intelligence. Strike forces in the field supported the work of interrogators and analysts back at Balad, instead of the reverse. The numbers of special operations raids reflected the change: in August 2004, during the Fallujah fighting, McChrystal's command launched just eighteen raids during a month of intense combat across Iraq. By the spring of 2006, the monthly numbers had increased almost tenfold, to between thirty and fifty night raids each week.

JSOC's focus in the spring of 2006 was split between two insurgent hotbeds: Anbar in the west, and the rural expanse south of Baghdad around the towns of Yusifiyah and Mahmudiyah, the Triangle of Death or the "southern belt." The triangle was an important support zone for Al-Qaeda: a rural region where the American military presence was limited and where both the terrorist group's senior leaders and the workshops needed to build car and truck bombs could exist in relative safety. The area had been largely neglected in 2004 and 2005, the victim of the "rotating door" phenomenon where units never stayed long enough to do much good; H.R. McMaster's 3rd ACR had barely settled into the area in early 2005 when it was called north to Tal Afar. In 2006 a conventional unit, the 101st Airborne Division's 2nd Brigade, was deployed in the region, but it was up against an enemy that had had time to dig in, both in the terrain and in the area's tribal structure. The fighting was so tough that one area on the banks of the

Euphrates, featuring a Russian-built thermal power plant that Al-Qaeda used as a command post, waypoint for foreign fighters, jail, and car bomb workshop, was declared off-limits to American aircraft, even medevacs.

The trail of Al-Qaeda in Iraq's leader, Abu Musab al-Zarqawi, had gone cold since a near miss in Anbar in February 2005, forcing the command to try to take out the enemy by going after mid-level operatives and staff. In the late spring 2006, the strategy began to pay off. In April and May the JSOC unit that focused on central Iraq, which incorporated Delta Force and Ranger elements as well as the British SAS's Task Force Knight, launched a flurry of raids in the rural belt south of Baghdad. On April 16 in a predawn raid on a house, Objective Larchwood IV, five commandos were wounded when a suspect detonated his suicide vest. But several militants were brought in alive, among them a detainee who turned out to be Al-Qaeda's administrator for the Abu Ghraib area, a good mid-level catch. Among documents at the site was an unedited version of a propaganda video that featured Zarqawi mishandling a light machine gun. While interrogation of the detainees proceeded at Balad, Zarqawi released the edited version of his propaganda tape, the bloopers excised. It was an intriguing indicator that the commanders were getting closer to their quarry.

Meanwhile, the raids continued. One strike, on May 14 near Yusifiyah, went badly: an AH-6 Little Bird helicopter supporting the raid force was shot down, killing both crewmen. By mid-May, the captured Al-Qaeda administrator and another detainee who was seized at a place code-named Objective Mayer had described in detail Al-Qaeda's command structure in the rural belts around Baghdad and fingered someone called Abd al-Rahman as Zarqawi's religious adviser. By early June, a detainee had provided interrogators with new details on the elaborate routine that Abd al-Rahman used to arrange a meeting with Zarqawi and then link up with other operatives who would drive him to Zarqawi's location. The long-awaited breakthrough had finally occurred: by monitoring Rahman the Americans could find Zarqawi.

On June 7, a JSOC drone watched Abd al-Rahman enter a car and then tracked the car to a house in Hibhib, a well-to-do rural area northeast of Baghdad near Baqubah. Zarqawi was practically on McChrystal's doorstep: Hibhib was just twelve miles from Balad. At their Balad headquarters, JSOC officers watched the live video in their command post as the car drove up a driveway to the house and was greeted by a figure in black. There was no way to know for sure if it was Zarqawi, but the figure fit the profile.

The order went out for a Delta Force assault team to climb into their helicopters and take off for Objective Arcadia, as the target was code-named. McChrystal and the colonel in charge of his Iraq task force, the deputy commander of Delta Force, had to decide whether to wait for the helicopter force to arrive and assault the target or to cut things short and bomb the house. The lay of the landscape made the officers watching the drone feed nervous: the only place the helicopters could deposit the assault team was on a nearby road, linked to the house by a long driveway. On the other side of the house was a grove of tall palm trees. Watching the video provided by the drone, the officers in Balad knew that it would not be practical to seal off the palm grove, and that in the time it would take the commandos to run up the driveway, Zarqawi might be able to slip out into the grove and escape. Worse, since it was daylight, the people in the house might see or hear the helicopters coming. With the helicopters twenty minutes out, the Delta Force colonel told McChrystal that he thought the risk of waiting and using the raid team was too high; it would be better to flatten the house.

Ensconced in his headquarters at Camp Victory, George Casey was in a videoconference with a class of military officers at Fort Leavenworth when he was handed a note that McChrystal needed to speak with him right away. The JSOC commander said he had Zarqawi in his sights and wanted Casey's permission to take him out. There were women and children in the house with Zarqawi, and the odds of collateral damage were high. Casey wanted to know if McChrystal was sure the target was Zarqawi. The JSOC commander said he was confident and Casey gave him the go-ahead. "You know you didn't need my approval for this," Casey added. Zarqawi was such an important and fleeting target that the Americans were prepared to take some risks. "I know," McChrystal said, "but I feel better."

Two Air Force F-16 fighter-bombers were orbiting high overhead waiting if needed. But when the order came one of them was refueling from an aerial tanker. At 6:12 p.m. the available jet dropped a five-hundred-pound laser-guided bomb on the Hibhib house and followed up with a satellite-guided bomb. According to the official account, Iraqi forces were the first on the scene of the strike, followed by a team of American advisers. Zarqawi was still breathing and even tried to crawl off the litter, but died just as JSOC commandos arrived on the scene.

That night, Casey was having dinner with Eric Edelman, the third-ranking civilian official at the Pentagon, when McChrystal called again. The commandos had retrieved Zarqawi's body and flown it to Balad. McChrystal had personally inspected his corpse and was convinced he had gotten his man. "I have never been so sure of anything in my life," he told Casey. Casey decided to pass the word to Rumsfeld, who was on an official trip in Asia. Rumsfeld was surprised to get a call from Casey and was uneasy. He had been getting reports from Iraq and few of them had been good. Informed that Zarqawi had been killed the defense secretary breathed a sigh of relief: "Jesus Christ, I was saying to myself, 'What else could have gone wrong in that place?'" he said to Casey. That night President Bush called McChrystal to congratulate him.[2]

Despite the destruction caused by the two bombs, the Hibhib blast site yielded a substantial amount of intelligence that drove further raids. The same night, June 7, commando teams ran seventeen missions in the Baghdad area, between one-third and one-half the number JSOC usually ran in a week. One document recovered from the site was a handwritten Al-Qaeda campaign plan that laid out the group's organization and strategy in Baghdad and the rural belts around it; in a validation of the combined efforts of JSOC and the brigade of the 101st the commandos had worked closely with south of Baghdad, the document said that the Americans were winning the battle for the Triangle of Death and that the area was no longer a suitable safe haven for senior Al-Qaeda leaders.

While Al-Qaeda settled on its new leader, the American military reveled in its two-pronged victory: a new government had been seated, and now the terrorist leader it had been hunting for over two years was dead. There would be difficult days ahead, Casey knew, but with Maliki and his cabinet in office and Zarqawi out of the picture, the general was convinced that his strategy was on track—and that it was time to begin the withdrawal of the next few brigades of American troops.

At the behest of NSC aides and State Department officials who were getting nervous about Casey's strategy, the White House had arranged for a two-day top-level review in mid-June. To avoid the media glare, the president and his team were to repair to Camp David. To stimulate discussion, several experts outside government were brought in: Fred Kagan, a conservative analyst who favored an expanded military effort; Eliot Cohen, the author of *Supreme Command,* which argued that it was the responsibility of the civilians to question the generals; Michael Vickers, an expert on special operations forces; and Robert Kaplan, an author who had written a book on the Balkans and other failed states. Nobody within the administration was prepared to directly challenge Rumsfeld or Casey in front of the president, so the outsiders were expected to stir up the debate. Casey, who would be participating by videoconference, understood that it was an important meeting and had been preparing for it along with his staff for weeks.

Much of the analysis that buttressed Casey's position was prepared by Major General Richard Zahner, who headed the military's intelligence shop in Baghdad. Zahner had impressive credentials. After obtaining a BA in history from Cornell, he had risen through the Army's ranks as an intelligence officer in Germany, South Korea, and the Pentagon. Schooled in the classified systems the United States uses to collect signals intelligence, he was intimately familiar with the American military bureaucracy that sought to make sense of it all, having completed a stint at the NSA and having worked with the Special Operations Command. What he lacked was the kind of extensive on-the-ground experience in Iraq that Derek Harvey and other lower-ranking intelligence officers had gained during the early stages of the war.

Zahner's officers had aggregated and crunched the data. The suicide bombings, IED detonations, and sniper attacks had been turned into SIGACTS—significant actions—all of which, Zahner's team insisted, showed that the insurgents were literally losing ground. Plotting the incidents on a map, Zahner argued that the enemy's footprint had shrunk. Eighty percent of the attacks were concentrated in four of Iraq's eighteen provinces. Twelve provinces, which contained more than 50 percent of Iraq's population, experienced only 6 percent of the attacks. Nor was the spike in attacks during the spring a cause for alarm, the analysis asserted. The data, he suggested, had been distorted by a spasm of Iraqi-on-Iraqi mayhem following the Samarra mosque bombing and did not mean that the enemy had become more active.

Congress had mandated that the Pentagon give quarterly assessments of security and political trends in Iraq and the analysis from Casey's command provided the core of the May report. At DIA headquarters, however, Zahner's analysis had not gone unchallenged. In a May 2 memo to Lieutenant General Michael Maples, the head of the DIA, Derek Harvey questioned the optimistic conclusions emanating from Camp Victory. The fact that the insurgents' attacks were concentrated in and around Baghdad, Harvey argued, did not mean they were being defeated in the rest of the country. Rather, it was a sign that they were stepping up their efforts to undermine the Iraqi government. Zahner, in effect, had misinterpreted strength as weakness. The insurgents were pouring it on in the area where it mattered most and Zahner was taking that as a sign that the insurgency was losing steam. "It's as if you're saying all of Arizona is fine, except Phoenix and Tucson," he wrote.

Reprising the point he had made about SIGACTS in early 2004, Harvey also asserted that the Baghdad intelligence staff was understating the number of attacks. IEDs that were found before they detonated were routinely excluded from the command's attack data even though they were a measure of enemy activity. An enemy RPG that missed its target was still an attack, Harvey reasoned, and IEDs that were found and cleared should be treated much the same. Far from being in the last throes, the insurgency had the wherewithal to carry out the fight through the following year. The Iraqis seemed to understand the situation better than Casey's team. Polling data analyzed by DIA noted dwindling confidence in the Iraqi security forces among Sunni Arabs and growing support for the "armed resistance."

When Harvey made these points to Casey's command, he wrote, he encountered some "push-back." But events in Iraq, he insisted, were raising more questions than answers. Intelligence analysis had estimated that the United States was fighting 5,000 to 7,000 insurgents at a time when there were nearly 30 attacks a day. But now there were more than 100 attacks daily. Did that mean the coalition was facing 17,000 to 24,000 insurgents? Beyond that, how many attacks a day do the insurgents need to carry out to achieve their political goals? Could even "unsuccessful" attacks enable the insurgents to intimidate and coerce their foes? Could the absence of attacks also imply that the insurgency had triumphed in certain areas, or that U.S. troops were simply no longer there to report on enemy activity? Finally, were the milestones that seemed so important to Casey and his aides also critical for the insurgents? These were good questions, but the debate among the intelligence analysts was not on the Camp David docket. In Casey's estimation, the war was progressing on schedule and that was the message he provided the president.

As it turned out, it was Bush who cut short the two-day review. The United States' principal nemesis in Iraq had been eliminated even as the Maliki government finally appeared ready to get down to business. The fundamental problems had not changed, but a recent flurry of events was welcome news to a war-weary White House. After telling officials he planned to turn in early, Bush slipped out of Camp David for a secret flight to Baghdad with a handful of aides and his first face-to-face meeting with Maliki. To mask Bush's movements the White House issued a press release about the president's upcoming activities at Camp David. The Iraqi prime minister learned Bush would be in Iraq just minutes before he arrived.

"I've come to not only look you in the eye, I've also come to tell you that when America gives its word, it will keep its word," Bush declared at his June 13 press conference with Maliki. "I have expressed our country's desire to work with you, but I appreciate you recognizing the fact that the future of this country is in your hands."

"God willing, all the suffering will be over and all the soldiers will return to their countries," Maliki said.

The episode spoke volumes about Bush and his stewardship of Iraq. The president saw his role as demonstrating his support of Maliki and giving him the confidence to make the tough decisions. The White House had waited a long time for a prime minister it could work with. Bush had curtailed his own brainstorming session so he could forge a personal relationship with his Iraqi partner.

Less than two weeks later, Casey left Baghdad to give a series of closed-door briefings to the Joint Chiefs and the president on the latest iteration of his transition plan. The United States now had fourteen combat brigades in Iraq, the lowest number in over two years, and in a May 5 videoconference, Casey had broached the idea of bringing the number down to thirteen early in the summer by off-ramping the unit set to replace Colonel Jeff Snow's 1st Brigade, 10th Mountain Division, when its tour in West Baghdad ended in late June. Pete Chiarelli and 4th Infantry Division commander J. D. Thurman made it clear to Casey that losing Snow's brigade would make it harder for them to control West Baghdad. But Casey put them on the spot by asking them if the departure of the brigade would be such a grave blow that it would risk the "strategic" failure of the American mission in Iraq. Casey's can-do subordinates were not ready to make such a draconian assessment, and as unhappy as they were about losing forces in Abu Ghraib, they did their best to soldier on. By the time of Casey's visit to Washington, the brigade was beginning to depart, leaving behind just a handful of American battalions inside Baghdad—six battalions of infantry and armor, plus some repurposed field artillery troops.

As significant as this troop reduction was, Casey was projecting even steeper ones for the months ahead. After returning to Baghdad from Washington, he gathered his commanders and announced that he had decided to off-ramp three more brigades starting at the end of the summer, so that by the end of the year only ten would be left in Iraq, on just sixty-nine bases. He hoped that over the course of 2007 that number could be brought down to seven brigades at eleven bases. Casey later explained the idea to

Bush, who was growing increasingly nervous about the security trends in Iraq: the United States had to draw down to win. His command had its own metrics for determining progress and many of them, it seemed, had to do with real estate. Success depended on how much battlespace could be handed off to the Iraqi military, how many regions could be formally transferred to "Provincial Iraqi Control," and how quickly the United States could shrink its own network of bases.

On June 14, Maliki announced a new offensive to quell sectarian violence in Baghdad. Operation Together Forward was a response to an increase in murders that followed Operation Scales of Justice. The new operation did not differ significantly from the previous one except that it relied on fewer American and more Iraqi battalions—two counts against it from the start. In interviews, many commanders could barely remember where one operation ended and the other began—it was just more units pushing out into more checkpoints, aiming to restrict the movements of both Sunni and Shiite insurgents, but with a focus, insofar as the small force allowed for a focus at all, on West Baghdad.

On June 16, almost as soon as Together Forward began, J. D. Thurman's division was distracted by a crisis outside the city. In an attack partly motivated by revenge for the earlier rape of an Iraqi girl in the area and the killing of her family, an atrocity that would not be publicly disclosed for months, insurgents ambushed a patrol from 1-502 Infantry, killing one soldier and kidnapping two others. Like all DUSTWUN, or missing soldier, incidents, this one triggered a massive response, with the division directing precious aviation, surveillance, and ground combat resources to the area of the attack—and away from Baghdad proper—in the hope of finding the two missing soldiers alive. Three days later the "severely traumatized" bodies of the two soldiers were found near the Russian-built thermal power plant on the banks of the Euphrates.

Having been disrupted by the search for the missing soldiers and the departure of Jeff Snow's brigade, Together Forward all but started over again in early July, as a new "Phase One" kicked off on July 9. The few American battalions left in the capital were now responsible for vast areas. No unit better exemplified this problem than 8-10 Cavalry, commanded by Lieutenant Colonel Gian Gentile. In June the small squadron of cavalrymen and field artillerymen had become nominally responsible for almost the entire northwestern quadrant of Baghdad, but unsurprisingly it was only able to actively patrol a small part of it, the Ameriya neighborhood just outside the Victory Base Complex. On July 9, Gentile was escorting division commander Thurman in one part of his sector when a large car bomb went off on the other side of the Airport Road, in the Jihad neighborhood. In the aftermath of the attack, gunmen arrived and killed as many of the survivors as they could before security forces reached the scene. The next day, Gentile went home on leave, and when he came back two weeks later, in late July, "everything had changed—Baghdad was imploding."[3]

An intelligence report described how the sectarian war was playing out in Ameriya. Residents got much of their food from a government warehouse in nearby Iskan, but the Mahdi Army prevented Sunni residents from going to the warehouse and killed truck drivers whose job was to deliver food to Ameriya. Propane for Ameriya came from Hurriya, and as a result from November to the end of December the price of that commodity in Ameriya doubled. The government also closed the Ameriya branch of the Rafidain Bank, a move that forced residents to travel to other neighborhoods where they could be in greater danger. "This denial of essential services forces many Sunni to relocate without the need for violence on the part of JAM," the report commented. "The resources that JAM can draw upon as legitimate members of the GOI puts them in a position of power and enables them to use government resources for their sectarian agenda."[4] Mahdi Army members were neither hesitant to exploit the upper hand nor subtle about their agenda: when John Abizaid visited Ameriya in August, he stopped by a National Police station there whose walls were plastered with Shiite religious flags and posters of Muqtada al-Sadr, an experience he described in a videoconference to Casey and Rumsfeld.

Another report, written in the fall, described the next stage of the Mahdi Army offensive as it played out in Ghazaliya, sandwiched between Sunni Ameriya and the Shiite stronghold of Shula:

Jaysh al Mahdi (JAM) members in Ghazaliyah were systematically killing Sunnis using police checkpoints. Operations ran 24 hours per day in four shifts of six hours each. The procedure was to use two uniformed police officers and position an officially marked police vehicle on each side of the road. The police stopped all vehicles and inspected the passengers' national identification cards to determine their sect by their name and neighborhood. If they were Sunni, the police would use their radios to communicate with a JAM member on an adjacent street who was not a policeman, but wore a uniform and drove an officially marked vehicle. The police would identify the person to JAM as Sunni. The police would inform the stopped individual that his paperwork needed to be inspected at the police station. Another officer would enter the vehicle and accompany the driver to a location where the JAM member would be positioned who would either execute the Sunni, or take them to the nearby Office of the Martyr Sadr (OMS) in al Shu'la to be killed. The checkpoints were set-up at different points on al Daghad Street. In the Ghazaliyah police station, the entire police force was involved in JAM activity.[5]

Ameriya became a Sunni bastion against Shiite encroachment, and a diverse array of Sunni insurgent groups infiltrated the neighborhood to defend the residents from the Mahdi Army and the security forces they viewed as being in league with the militia—and to strengthen their own position in the Sunni community. "During the early summer months of 2006, reporting indicates that AQI, Ansar al-Sunna, the 1920s Revolutionary Brigade, Mujahadeen Army and Islamic Army joined together to push the Shi'a out of the area through a combination of violent measures," an intelligence assessment noted. Sunni fighters killed Shiite residents suspected of collaboration with the militia and left their bodies in the street. The same groups also used the neighborhood and other Sunni-controlled positions as staging areas for car bomb attacks in other parts of the capital; Ameriya, Ghazaliya, and Dora in particular all bordered the rural areas outside Baghdad where Al-Qaeda built many of its car and truck bombs, and both Ameriya and Ghazaliya stood astride the highway that linked Baghdad to Sunni insurgent base areas in Anbar.

The story was the same throughout much of Baghdad: security in May and June had been bad, but during the Together Forward offensive in July it worsened considerably. "Atmospherics from each of the Operation Together Forward (OTF) areas illustrate a picture that the security situation is worsening," noted one 4th Infantry Division assessment. Another added bleakly, "People have no confidence in the ability of the IP or IA to provide security," referring to the Iraqi police and army. "People have lost all hope in receiving any security from ISF. JAM controls the streets in Sadr City."[6] Although between mid-June and mid-July overall attacks dropped in seven of the capital's ten districts by the division's count, in those three remaining districts, violence became intense. The signs of sectarian murder were evident, marks from electrical burns and power drills on many of the bodies that showed up every morning in vacant lots, canals, and the Tigris.

In Adhamiya, the main Sunni stronghold in East Baghdad, such bodies began to pile up, and local leaders transformed a soccer field near the Abu

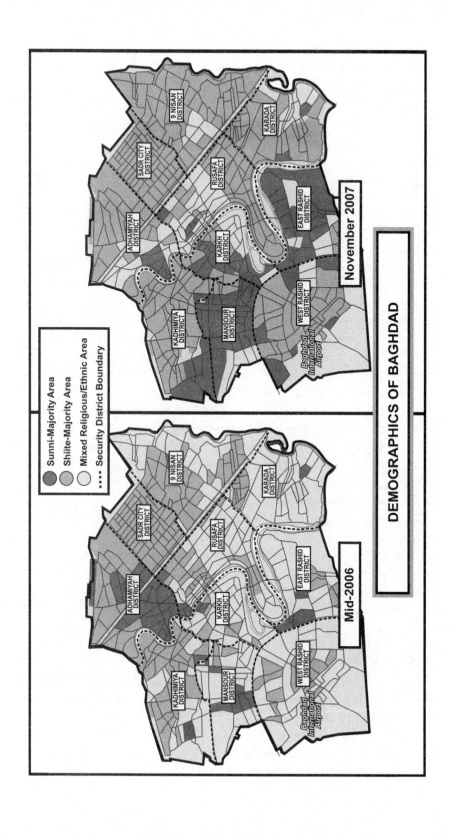

DEMOGRAPHICS OF BAGHDAD

Legend:
- Sunni-Majority Area
- Shiite-Majority Area
- Mixed Religious/Ethnic Area
- Security District Boundary

Mid-2006

November 2007

Districts labeled (both maps): 9 NISAN DISTRICT, SADR CITY DISTRICT, ADHAMIYAH DISTRICT, KADHIMIYA DISTRICT, MANSOUR DISTRICT, KARKH DISTRICT, RUSAFA DISTRICT, KARADA DISTRICT, EAST RASHID DISTRICT, WEST RASHID DISTRICT, Baghdad International Airport

Hanifa Mosque into a new "martyrs' cemetery," for the Sunni victims of sectarian violence. On some days, gravediggers buried as many as thirty or forty bodies. By the end of the year at least three thousand people would be interred in the new cemetery.

In early July, Bush asked Casey to extend his command tour for yet another year, and after accepting, the general went home on leave, thinking Baghdad was more or less under control and leaving Chiarelli to run the war. But as Chiarelli saw it, the violence on Baghdad's mean streets was just part of the problem. Despite Maliki's proud announcement of Together Forward, and the fact that Iraqi forces were to make up the majority of the security force in Baghdad, Chiarelli felt that the Iraqi government was acquiescing in the Shiite attacks—or at least not doing enough to stop them. With J. D. Thurman in tow, Chiarelli went to see Casey's British deputy, Lieutenant General Rob Fry, and proposed that they go to see Maliki. Perhaps the prime minister was isolated in the Green Zone and did not understand how bad the situation had become. A meeting would drive the point home and prompt the Iraqi government to step up its game.

When the day of the meeting came Thurman pulled out a map to illustrate the latest spasm of sectarian bloodletting. When they got in to see Maliki, Thurman showed the prime minister the map, indicating where bodies had been found in the previous twenty-four hours. "This is Baghdad. These are the bodies we found just last night," Thurman explained. "It was much worse under Saddam," Maliki responded.[7]

The encounter shook Chiarelli and made him wonder whether the Iraqi government and the American command shared the same goals for Iraq. Chiarelli and his fellow generals kept the exchange to themselves, but Chiarelli did offer some skeptical asides about the Iraqi government performance during the morning Battlefield Update Assessments, the briefings that were widely attended. When Casey returned to Baghdad from his leave he was not happy to hear from his aides that his corps commander seemed to harbor doubts about the strategy of handing full responsibility for Iraq over to the Maliki government.

At a dinner at his villa at Camp Victory, Casey confronted his subordinate. "You're being negative," he said. Chiarelli endured the criticism, but he was not the only senior officer to express doubts. Thurman later vented his frustration in a newspaper interview: "Part of our problem is that we want this more than they do. We need to get people to stop worrying about self and start worrying about Iraq," he said.[8]

Convinced that the United States needed to do more to secure the capital, Chiarelli and his aides had checked the flow chart: now that Snow's brigade was gone, another brigade was not scheduled to deploy to Baghdad until December, a four-month wait. A lot could happen in four months, and it seemed much of it would not be good. By mid-July Casey realized that he had erred by sending Snow's brigade home without replacement. Operation Together Forward was failing because it relied too heavily on Iraqi forces that were in many cases part of the problem, and its sequel, Operation Together Forward II, set to begin in early August, would fail, too, if more American troops were not brought back into the capital. On July 18, the general sent a secure email to Rumsfeld, John Abizaid, and Joint Chiefs chairman Pete Pace, explaining that in the short term he needed to bring the CENTCOM theater reserve brigade north from Kuwait and in the long term he wanted to cancel the fall's projected drawdown to ten American brigades.[9]

Reluctantly, Rumsfeld approved the decision. But Pete Chiarelli felt that bringing the theater reserve brigade up and canceling further cuts did not go far enough—the brigade in Kuwait was really not a brigade at all, just a headquarters and some engineers and artillerymen, since all three of its armor and infantry battalions had already been parceled out to Baghdad and Anbar. So Chiarelli approached Casey with a proposal. Colonel Mike Shields's 172nd Stryker Brigade could be brought down from Mosul. Stryker vehicles had rarely been used in Baghdad. Compared to units that relied on Bradley fighting vehicles and Humvees for transport, Stryker units could bring along more infantrymen per patrol—while a Bradley could hold a maximum of six "dismounts" and a Humvee three, a Stryker could carry nine. The Stryker vehicles had a sophisticated targeting system, and were better protected than Humvees (especially with add-on slat armor known as the "RPG cage," which could stop RPG rounds). They were also faster and quieter than the tracked Bradleys. These qualities had served Stryker units well during nearly three years of operations in Mosul and made Strykers a favorite of JSOC units like the Ranger battalions. (Before the 172nd was extended, in fact, JSOC had been hoping to inherit some of their Strykers.) In short, the brigade could bring lots of troops and firepower to the neighborhood—and fast. Some of the Stryker battalions could be assigned to specific districts while others could serve as mobile strike forces.

There was one problem. The brigade was on the verge of being redeployed to its home base in Alaska. Stryker vehicles had already been loaded onto the heavy equipment transporters that would lug them out of the country. Several hundred of the brigade's soldiers were already back in Alaska or in Kuwait preparing to fly to the United States. Moving the 172nd to Baghdad for several months would mean extending its tour of duty to sixteen months, a long stretch even by Army standards and a step the military had not taken since the 2004 Mahdi Army uprising. Nevertheless, Chiarelli was convinced it was a move the Army had to make and was able to persuade Casey. The senior general broke the news to Rumsfeld, who was not happy. "You've got to get better at looking around corners," the defense secretary complained to Casey.[10]

To extend the tour of duty of the 172nd meant that the brigade's soldiers, who had already returned to Alaska, as well as those in Kuwait awaiting redeployment in the United States, would need to be recalled to Iraq—a public relations nightmare. In an August 31 videoconference with Casey and Abizaid, Rumsfeld described a contentious visit he had recently paid to the 172nd's Alaska home station, where he had tried to explain to the soldiers' wives why their husbands' deployments were being extended. Fearful of how their families and the media might react, the Army quietly kept track of how many of those soldiers who returned to Iraq became casualties. Some did.

With some additional forces in hand, the command was ready for yet another try to fix the mess that was Baghdad; after the fashion of a Hollywood sequel, Operation Together Forward II was conceived. The plan was straightforward: American troops would cordon off a neighborhood, search the houses for weapons, and hand it over to the Iraqi forces, who would secure the neighborhood while the United States troops moved on to clear another section of the city. Meanwhile, the Iraqi government would provide jobs and services to zones that it now controlled.

Operation Together Forward II kicked off on August 7, focusing on five areas where murders were very high: in West Baghdad, the neighborhoods of Dora, Aamel, Ameriya, and Ghazaliya; and in East Baghdad, the neighborhood of Adhamiya, all Sunni areas facing ever closer Shiite militia encroachment. Though the offensive employed more forces than the two Baghdad operations that had gone before, it shared some of the same flaws. With so much ground to cover American forces were not able to stay in the areas they cleared for very long, and when they left they were handing them off to some of the same Iraqi units that had joined in the sectarian violence or had turned a blind eye to it. By the end of August, civilian deaths in Baghdad had not dropped—at about 1,500 they were at roughly the same level as in July.

On August 17, 2006, President Bush discussed via a videoconference with Casey the status of the operation. Casey said he had enough U.S. troops but said he was not sure the Iraqis could "deliver" on securing the neighborhoods. Bush stressed that more American troops were available if the commander needed them. "We must succeed. We will commit the resources. If they can't, we will. If the bicycle teeters, put our hand back on it," Bush added. "I support you guys 100 percent, but I need to ask you tough questions. Different times call for different kinds of questions."

CHAPTER 13

The Perfect Storm

To secure broad support from the Shiites, Prime Minister Maliki had reached out to an array of political factions, but the results had not been everything the Bush administration might have wished for. As Baghdad became one battlefield in the civil war, Iraq's ministries became another, with different Shiite parties struggling to carve out their own fiefdoms of resources and power within the government, so they could provide services to their constituents and deny them to their foes.

The Sadrists established themselves in the ministries of Transportation and Health, which enabled them to control the distribution of government services, employ "soft power" to their own advantage, and use the government apparatus as a source of patronage. By the fall, American intelligence was worried that the Mahdi Army, the Sadrists' militia arm, had also ensconced themselves in the ministries and were using them to advance their military ends. It was bad enough that the Mahdi Army was the dominant security force in Sadr City and other Shiite neighborhoods in Baghdad. Now it had captured the very instruments of the state.

Sadrist control of the Transportation Ministry—and, by extension, Baghdad International Airport, which it oversaw—was one of American intelligence's deepest secrets. The American military did not want the Sadrists to know how much the United States had figured out about their operations until they were prepared to move against them, which in 2006 the Americans were not.

The problem was evident at the very top. During his term as prime minister, Ibrahim al-Jaafari had moved to create a new intelligence arm he could control, the Ministry of State for National Security Affairs, which quickly became a rival to the CIA-backed Iraqi National Intelligence Service. Shirwan al-Waeli, a figure who was well known to American intelligence, was installed as the head of the new organization; under Maliki, he had his power expanded when he took on the duties of acting transportation minister as well.

According to a highly classified American intelligence report, Waeli had shared the movements of American forces with the Sadrists as well as plans for American operations against their militia. Waeli understood that his actions were being scrutinized by the occupiers, and during a trip to Tehran he had been instructed by Iranian officials on how to counter American electronic eavesdropping, American intelligence reported.

Under Waeli's tenure the Sadrists took over the nation's transportation infrastructure in more direct ways. The director general of Iraq's seaports was reporting to the Mahdi Army, American intelligence observed. He had come over to their side after he was physically assaulted. As for air travel, the Sadrists appeared to control every facet. Within the Transportation Ministry, the Sadrists controlled the civil aviation department. The director general of Iraqi Airlines, Iraq's national carrier, had accompanied Waeli on his trip to Tehran, where he had interacted with Qasim Suleimani, the head of the Quds Force.

Baghdad International Airport was the real prize. Construction on Saddam International Airport was completed in the early 1980s. From the start, the facility was intended to accommodate military as well as civilian traffic, and the names of the passenger terminals originally recalled ancient eras of Iraqi glory: Babylon, Samarra, and Nineveh. Even before their invasion began, the American military had given it a new and more politically correct name, Baghdad International Airport. Its position on the doorstep of Camp Victory and other American bases on the outskirts of Baghdad meant that those who ran the facility would be operating virtually under the nose of the American command and its major combat units.[1]

As American intelligence began to unravel the airport operations, it discovered that Sadrists had penetrated every aspect of the facility. Airport Village—a settlement where personnel lived so they did not need to travel back and forth each day on the perilous airport road—was used as a refuge for hiding Mahdi Army fighters trying to elude the coalition and was believed to host Iranian agents. Sadrists ran the customs office at the airport. The deputy chief of immigration and the assistant director of air traffic control were both Sadrists. Sadrists manned the A to Z Cleaning Company, which cleaned the passenger terminals. (In a grisly act of job creation, it was later determined, fifteen employees of the company had been gunned down on the way to work at the airport so that their places could be taken by supporters from Sadr City.) More worrisome, the Mahdi Army controlled the sky marshals, who ostensibly traveled on civilian flights to protect them against terrorist attacks, and had infiltrated a British contractor, Global Risk Strategies, which was responsible for managing the checkpoint near the airport.

Their extensive network enabled the Mahdi Army to keep tabs on Sunnis who were traveling through the airport, plan kidnapping operations, smuggle money and, potentially, weapons into the country, and transport their own personnel out of the country, including those whom the Americans were trying to detain. While the United States military was conducting raids to apprehend Mahdi Army commanders in the crowded streets of Baghdad, the Sadrists were moving men, money, and matériel in and out of the country at will—all within the shadow of Casey's headquarters. Sadrist guards could monitor the comings and goings of the commandos of the Iraqi Special Operations Force, an elite brigade based on the airport grounds that had gotten on the Mahdi Army's bad side by running missions into Sadr City alongside American special operators. In several cases, Iraqi commandos would be killed as a result. The infiltration also raised the specter of sabotage. In an unpublicized incident documented by American intelligence, explosives were found on the tarmac near a Jordanian Airlines plane in March 2006. In another incident, a Global Risk employee smuggled in a small piece of C-4 and told coworkers he wanted to blow up a plane. "Jaysh al-Mahdi infiltration of key operations and security organizations at the Baghdad International Airport allows them to effectively control Baghdad's only point of entry of strategic importance," a U.S. intelligence report noted. The prime minister's office officially assumed control of the airport in October, but the report indicated the problem was deep-seated and likely to persist.

At the Health Ministry, the problems were even worse. With Sadr's backing, Hakim al-Zamili, a Mahdi Army operative, had been installed in 2005 as the deputy minister, while Hamid al-Shammari, another Mahdi Army commander, was put in charge of the ministry's Facilities Protection Service, which consisted of 150 guards and functioned as a private militia. An investigation by American officials concluded that the ministry had used ambulances and personnel to move weapons around the city and carry out killings and kidnappings. Even hospitals were used as killing grounds. So many Sunni patients and relatives were abducted and killed at Baghdad's three major hospitals—Yarmouk, Ibn al-Nafees, and Nur—that

Sunnis were afraid to use the facilities, and would often drive their sick or injured relatives all the way to Fallujah or Ramadi for treatment by fellow Sunnis. In a fall videoconference with Casey, Rumsfeld, Abizaid, and others, Chiarelli explained that more than 80 percent of the beds in the U.S. military's combat support hospitals were devoted to sick and wounded Iraqi troops and police. "We cannot take them to civilian hospitals," the corps commander said. "They'll be shot."[2]

These rampant abuses were challenged by one veteran official: Ammar al-Saffar, a deputy health minister, who had opposed Saddam during his exile in London, returned to Iraq after the invasion, and had been laboring at the ministry prior to Zamili and Shammari's arrival. Chronicling the crimes with an eye toward exposing them, Saffar was abducted from his home in November 2006, in front of his eighty-year-old mother, before he could reveal them. Saffar later appeared as a hostage in a video that purportedly had been made by Sunni Al-Qaeda but that American intelligence believed was a ruse orchestrated by Zamili in order to cover up his own role in the kidnapping. Saffar was presumed dead; his body was never found, and his case would later become a test of the United States' ability to insist on accountability in Iraq's legal system and usher in some rudimentary rule of law.

Even as the militias swamped the ministries, American commanders like Lieutenant Colonel Jim Danna were struggling to contain them on the streets in Operation Together Forward II. Danna's battalion, 2-6 Infantry, had been ordered to Baghdad in March for what was to have been a mere thirty-day deployment during Operation Scales of Justice, but he never left. By the fall, 2-6 was struggling to maintain order in the West Rashid District of the city and doing its best to work with a brigade of the Interior Ministry's National Police, a former Public Order Brigade that was manned almost entirely by poor Shiites from East Baghdad—the same recruiting pool as the Mahdi Army.

The Iraqi Army had provided only two of the six battalions of additional troops that the Americans had requested to carry out Together Forward II, which meant that the U.S. Army and the Iraqi National Police had to pick up the slack. With 15,600 American soldiers participating in the clearing operation, compared with just 9,600 Iraqis, there were more American soldiers involved in the operation than Iraqi troops. More than 30,000 National Police and regular police officers were given the critical task of securing the neighborhoods after the Americans had cleared them. But the National Police, in particular, had been infiltrated by the very Shiite militias Together Forward II was intended to curb, Badr and the Mahdi Army. "Training and leadership of National Police is inadequate," Casey had blandly briefed President Bush in an August videoconference on the new operation. That description did not begin to capture the scope of the problem with the forces under the Interior Ministry.

Over the summer, Danna observed that the Shiite-dominated National Police had their own way of operating. At first, it seemed to him that they had set up too many checkpoints, limiting the number of troops they had available for patrols. Many of the checkpoints also seemed ill positioned to interrupt the movement of weapons and militias. As the summer wore on, Danna realized that there was a sinister logic to the scheme. Baghdad residents had several pressing needs: access to markets to buy food, liquid propane and gas for cooking, and access to health clinics. The checkpoints sat astride the routes Iraqis needed to travel to procure these necessities. "It took me a while to figure it out," Danna recalled. "The forces were in place not to protect, but to facilitate attacks on the population, to intimidate and dominate the Sunni population and support the militias that were doing the dirty work."[3]

Determined to break the stranglehold, Danna ordered the National Police to take down some of the checkpoints and had his own soldiers plow them down with armored bulldozers when they did not. But even the conduct of raids on the part of the Iraqis was problematic. To mount a raid, National Police units were required to get "battle-space clearance." The targeting instructions would be issued by the Iraqi Interior Ministry, which would share the plan with American advisers there, who would relay it to J. D. Thurman's 4th Infantry Division, which would then pass it down the American chain of command until it eventually reached Danna around midnight—just hours before the assault was to take place. To many officers at Casey's command, just a few miles away but seemingly far out of touch, the approach seemed to work well—the Iraqis were taking initiative and in the lead. But Danna saw through the charade. When the Americans conducted raids they had to have a targeting package, photos of the suspects they wanted to detain, and some account of the evidence that had been arrayed against them. But when Danna received Iraqi targeting information, it was no more than a list of names—Sunni names. Never once was there a Shiite target on the list. Exercising his prerogative as the Iraqis' American partner, Danna began vetoing the operations. "The

Iraqis worked us brilliantly," Danna recalled. "They did it late in the game. About 2130 we would hear that these guys want to hit a target at 1 a.m. It would come to me and I would say: 'What target do they have? What evidence do they have?' To the defense of my chain of command if I said no it did not happen. I said no 90 percent of the time."[4]

Faced with Danna's scrutiny, the National Police played their trump card. Insisting that they had a right to conduct independent operations, the police began to go out at night to round up Sunnis without coordinating with Danna. "Together Forward" had become a curious misnomer. The Americans and Iraqis were no longer working together in Danna's areas; instead of making headway against sectarian violence, the police were abetting it. And the more the police preyed on the Sunnis, the more the Sunnis responded with bombings and ambushes. Trying to break the cycle, Danna ordered his soldiers to shadow the National Police every time they attempted to carry out a unilateral raid, figuring that the presence of the American troops would curtail the worst abuses or at least scrap the element of surprise.

Next door in the Bayaa neighborhood, Lieutenant Colonel John Norris was running into similar obstacles. Norris's battalion, 4-23 Infantry, was part of the 172nd Stryker Brigade, which had been extended and brought to Baghdad for Together Forward II. On October 1 he came upon several Sunni women in black abayas who were wailing over a body sprawled near a mosque. Distraught relatives were smearing the dead man's blood on their faces. Norris tried to wave down an Iraqi National Police truck for help, but the driver gave him a cold stare and drove on. An investigation by Norris's soldiers later determined that the victim was a Sunni officer who had been assassinated by two men armed with 9mm pistols, who had sped away, unchallenged, past a National Police checkpoint.

If that incident merely raised Norris's suspicions that the National Police were involved in sectarian killings, proof positive came shortly thereafter. Although Norris did not know it at the time, that same day twenty-two Iraqis were accosted at a Sunni-owned meatpacking plant elsewhere in Baghdad's huge southern Rashid District. According to some witnesses, the assailants wore woodland-pattern camouflage uniforms and carried Glock 9mm pistols, both of which were customarily issued to the National Police. They checked identity documents to separate the Sunnis from the Shiites. The Sunnis were blindfolded, thrown into meat trucks, and driven off.

Several days later, a unit in nearby East Rashid that had also been brought in for Together Forward II, Lieutenant Colonel Jeff Peterson's 1-14 Cavalry, found seven victims in a field it had taken to calling "Dead Man's Corner" because so many bodies had been dumped there. One was still alive; he crawled toward the American patrol, was given first aid, and excitedly told the soldiers what had happened. Peterson's troops went to the execution site and found bullet casings consistent with the Glock pistols used by the National Police. "We went to the National Police that were on duty down here at a checkpoint, secured their weapons and magazines. And sure enough, their magazines were empty by the exact same number of rounds, of casings that we found," Peterson recalled.[5]

The assault set off an uproar in the Bayaa neighborhood. The next day a group of Sunnis lobbed four mortar shells and fired machine guns at a National Police checkpoint. That was followed by an angry demonstration. Faced with a deteriorating security situation, J. D. Thurman, who as the commander of the 4th Infantry Division was the senior American commander in Baghdad, recommended that the National Police unit be withdrawn and retrained. On his second day in his new sector, Colonel Norris had the delicate task of informing the unit that it was relieved of its duties. Norris expected that the police would be replaced by an Iraqi Army unit, which he hoped would be more acceptable to the neighborhood's residents. But Iraqi soldiers were in short supply, so he was given another National Police unit. This turned out to be good news after all: the new unit the Americans would be working with was led by Colonel Ali Ibrahim Daboun, a commander from Ghazaliya well respected for his professionalism. Still, the Americans had a problem on their hands. Sunni residents had continued to shoot at the National Police, killing one of the colonel's officers and wounding several others. To encourage cooperation, Norris organized a meeting of tribal sheikhs and neighborhood leaders. He did not tell the local officials that the National Police would be there, for fear it would scare them away.[6]

At the meeting, Sunni representatives railed against the police for failing to stop Shiite militia attacks or protect residents when notices were posted on their door warning them to flee or be killed. Norris told the officials that their complaints were justified, but there was a new team in town and it wanted to make a fresh start. Seeking to win over the representatives, Ali took the floor. He declared boldly that he was not a Shiite or a Sunni but an Iraqi and would enforce the law in an evenhanded way. With so many men running around in uniforms and renegade militias running rampant, one participant asked, how could the citizens tell good policemen from those who meant them harm? Ali offered advice that said a great deal about the long road ahead: if an Iraqi policeman comes to your door, he advised, you should not open it unless he is accompanied by an American soldier.

Things became even more confounding. For instance, in Peterson's area National Police troops attacked a Sunni mosque, where insurgents may or may not have been hiding, and called on U.S. soldiers as backup. The same thing happened again the next day at another mosque. Peterson became convinced that the overwhelmingly Shiite troops were starting fights in Sunni neighborhoods and drawing his men into them to intimidate the residents. "The Sunnis lose the fight and now it appears, from the Sunni perspective, that we are aligned with a uniformed Shia militia against them," Peterson said. "They were using us to cleanse areas of Sunni presence, and we essentially have no option because we're supposed to partner with these guys." At the same time, the National Police unit seemed complicit in attacks on American troops: on several nights, some of Peterson's patrols were hit by IEDs only seconds after passing through National Police checkpoints and seeing police cars flash their blue lights—apparently a signal. In a last-ditch effort to tamp down the violence, Peterson created a "security zone" around the Sunni portion of his area, from which he banned the National Police entirely.[7]

The meatpacking plant massacre that Norris and Peterson dealt with resulted, in October, in the mass arrest of officers of the offending 8th Brigade, 2nd National Police Division. But the problem of abusive, sectarian, and often murderous Interior Ministry forces was much bigger than one brigade's leadership, subsuming much of the National Police and much of the ministry itself, even though Maliki had replaced Bayan Jabr as minister over the summer with a new official, Jawad al-Bolani. In the most brazen instance, on November 14 fifty National Police trucks pulled up to the Baghdad offices of the Higher Education Ministry. Armed men in National Police uniforms dismounted, entered the ministry, and departed after rounding up more than one hundred people, many of whom were never seen again. It was the fifth "mass kidnapping" of ten or more people since June, a report by Casey's intelligence staff noted, all five of which had been conducted by men in the uniforms and vehicles of government security forces.[8]

Just two days after the Higher Education Ministry kidnapping, Casey and Chiarelli were reporting to Abizaid and Rumsfeld by videoconference when the defense secretary asked a question about the Interior Ministry's forces. "When I think back to the brief I got on the police, I got the impression everything was okay," he said. "But now you're telling me they are not okay."

"That's because the briefing you got was about the process of training them—the mechanics—and they are going well," Casey explained. "The briefing wasn't about their performance. It didn't address loyalty issues."[9] Casey, in fact, had begun a long-term program to vet and retrain the National Police. But in late 2006, it was far from clear that it would be adequate.

By the beginning of October, two months into Together Forward II, Thurman's outlook on the difference his division was making was grim. "We drive the violence down, and then it comes right back up, because you've got to get at the real sectarian problem," he told an Army historian who visited his headquarters in Iraq. "We're in the low-grade stage of a civil war here." With no more American forces available in Iraq, Thurman had no choice but to request the deployment of three thousand more troops from the more reliable Iraqi Army to the capital.[10]

A more graphic description of the failure of the series of offensives came from Major David Hansen, a military intelligence officer who in late 2006 was working for a military task force charged with keeping track of sectarian murders. The team to which Hansen was assigned, the EJK Task Force—EJK stood for "extra-judicial killings"—would make visits to Baghdad morgues. "I remember days when we'd have up to one hundred murders a day. It was getting pretty gruesome in terms of bodies getting stacked up in morgues and not being able to burn them in a timely manner," he said. "We're talking bodies stacked six to seven feet high. I don't mean to be gross; this is just what happened. Body fluids would get six to eight inches on the floor."[11]

At his headquarters at Camp Victory, Chiarelli was distressed by the way the operation was unfolding. A core assumption behind the plan was that the Iraqi government would work as hard as the Americans to stop the violence in an evenhanded way. Instead, much of the government seemed to have taken the Shiites' side. Throughout his career, Chiarelli had maintained good relations with the media and in September he invited a group of reporters to his residence at Camp Victory. Many were flown by helicopter to the Victory Base from LZ Washington, the helipad in the Green Zone. To encourage free discussion, the session was off the record, with the understanding that the reporters would clear any quotes they wanted to use, remarks that would be ascribed to a "senior military official."

Two days later a spate of articles appeared citing concerns about the Iraqi government. Time was growing short to root out the militias receiving support from Iraqi ministries. "We are now at a time when we have a little bit of influence there. There is going to come a time when I would argue we are going to have to force this issue," the senior official said. "I can tell you in every single ministry how they are using that ministry to fill the coffers of the political parties. They are doing that because that is exactly what Saddam Hussein did."[12]

When Casey read the newspaper accounts, he was concerned. Once again, senior American officers were publicly casting aspersions on the United States' partner, albeit under the cloak of anonymity. The commander rushed out a statement asserting that Maliki was trying to do a good job in a challenging situation. "These unattributed comments do not reflect the close partnership between the government of Iraq," the statement noted, "and Multi-National Force—Iraq."[13] But the issue did not stop there. Colonel Barry Johnson, a senior public affairs officer in Baghdad, called the reporters whose bylines appeared on the articles, asking that they reveal their source. Johnson did not relish his job, but he was under orders. The journalists stayed mum, but word got back to Chiarelli's public affairs officer, who complained that Casey's command was engaging in a witch hunt. Casey never mentioned the episode to Chiarelli, but their relationship remained strained.

While the Americans struggled to keep Baghdad from imploding, Al-Qaeda in Iraq was stepping up its operations to fuel the cycle of violence. By the fall of 2006, Al-Qaeda had consolidated control of a large proportion of Iraq's Sunni insurgent groups under the Mujahideen Shura Council. Its ferocious campaign of car and truck bombings had helped ignite a civil war between Sunni and Shiite Iraqis. Yet Al-Qaeda had suffered major setbacks in Ramadi, the city it had declared its third capital after being kicked out of Fallujah and Qaim, and it had lost its leader to the formidable and growing kill-capture machine that was Stan McChrystal's JSOC task force.

Despite some internal dissension, after Abu Musab al-Zarqawi's death Al-Qaeda in Iraq named as its new leader Abu Ayyub al-Masri. An Egyptian in his late thirties, Masri had joined Islamic Jihad in 1982, been an associate of Ayman al-Zawahiri in Egypt, and traveled to Afghanistan in

1999, where he spent time at Al-Qaeda training camps and met Zarqawi, whom he then joined in Iraq ahead of the 2003 invasion. Since then, Masri had helped Zarqawi establish his terrorist group, had fought in Fallujah in 2004, and claimed to have personally executed hostages. Although the two men had collaborated in the founding of Al-Qaeda in Iraq, they shared different visions for the organization, which later became apparent when American troops captured Al-Qaeda's emir of southwestern Baghdad, who described the differences between the two men to his interrogators. According to a military translation of his interrogation, he said that "the difference between AMZ [Abu Musab al-Zarqawi] and AAM [Abu Ayyub al-Masri] is that AMZ truly believed he was fighting for the Sunnis in Iraq, while AAM believed Iraq can be used to fight Western ideology world-wide. AAM sees Iraq as only a part of a larger war. Sheik Abd al-Rahman [Zarqawi's "spiritual adviser" who was killed along with the Al-Qaeda leader] thought AAM was dangerous in the fact that peace is not part of his vision."

Masri was less charismatic than Zarqawi, but also more careful. Under new orders he issued, subordinates could be punished for falsely report-ing positive news, and those who spoke frankly were promised rewards. Although he had no real intention to reverse Zarqawi's strategy of target-ing Shiite civilians to foment reprisals and unrest, he repaired his group's ties to its Pakistan-based superiors at Al-Qaeda central, who had often clashed with Zarqawi over his strategy to foment civil war. On orders from his higher-ups, in October Masri gave the group a public-image overhaul. As he sought to put an Iraqi face on his organization, he declared that Al-Qaeda was merely part of a religious-political front called the Islamic State of Iraq, led ostensibly by a nebulous figure named Abu Omar al-Baghdadi, who the Americans were not sure even existed. Masri also requested a new religious adviser to replace Abd al-Rahman, the cleric whose car had led JSOC to Zarqawi.[14]

The group that Masri led was by now much different from the small organization he had helped Zarqawi build in 2003. Across the border in Syria, Al-Qaeda leader Abu Ghadiya oversaw a network of training camps, including those run by more secular former Baath insurgents; he also met regularly with Syrian military intelligence officials, including Asif Shawkat, the country's intelligence chief and brother-in-law to President Bashar al-Assad.

Its leaders had learned from McChrystal's campaign against them, and rarely spoke on the phone or used real names. Cells often had a sophisticated approach to electronic media, employing videographers and editors. "Most AQI cells now designate their most computer literate member as their Google Earth expert," said one American intelligence report.[15] The captured Baghdad emir also told his interrogators that when he visited Masri's mobile command post, Arab fighters were usually editing and uploading propaganda videos on computers there—that was their job until they were needed for suicide bombings.

In Iraq itself, money was flowing into the organization from its various criminal enterprises, particularly oil smuggling at the huge Bayji Oil Refinery. Though Al-Qaeda in Iraq welcomed funds from wealthy donors in the Gulf states and Saudi Arabia, by 2006 it was a self-financing organization that actually turned a large profit from its smuggling, extortion, and kidnapping activities. "External support is not critical to the operations of insurgent groups, as criminal activity can support insurgent operating expenses many times over," a DIA report assessed. "Even a limited survey of revenue streams available to the insurgency strongly suggests revenues far exceed expenses."[16]

Even captured insurgents continued to cause problems. Inside Camp Bucca, the largest American detention facility since Abu Ghraib had been closed, there was an Al-Qaeda cell that taught prisoners classes in Islamic law, operational security, and basic counterinterrogation tactics.

The group's bomb making was becoming sophisticated and large-scale, targeting bridges and other parts of the infrastructure as well as markets and civilian gatherings. What the military termed "VBIEDs"—vehicle-borne IEDS—were more than just car bombs; they were often built around dump trucks and semi-rigs and were sometimes "up-armored" with steel plates. On Masri's orders, some bomb engineers were dabbling—unsuccessfully—in chemical weapons, trying to incorporate chlorine canisters from abandoned weapons (and in one case, from the water treatment plant that supplied much of Baghdad) into car and truck bombs.

The most important change, however, was Masri's effort to dig his group's cells into physical and tribal terrain in the rural areas surrounding Baghdad, where the American troop presence was light. The capital itself, awash with Mahdi Army and government forces, was inhospitable terrain, as a report from one Al-Qaeda leader to another that was seized in December but written early in the fall explained.[17] The writer of the document prioritized enemies by level of danger. The worst, he wrote, were the National Police, followed by the Badr Corps, the "black turbans" of the Mahdi Army, and Maliki's Dawa Party. The CIA ranked fifth, warranting an instruction to "shell their location in the Green Zone," with "Mossad and the Kurds" in sixth place, and the American military in seventh. Another list suggested specific targets to be attacked, like checkpoints, telephone switchboards, bridges, Christian churches, and, intriguingly, not just police cars but ambulances and trash collectors, all seen as arms of the "Rafida" or Shiites. The report also quoted an update from Abu Nur, then the emir of Al-Qaeda in Shiite-dominated East Baghdad and later of Baghdad overall. "Work there is difficult—purely Rafida area," he wrote of the area east of the Army Canal. Sadr City, he added, "is considered the most dangerous Rafida area—it holds the army of the imposter," the Mahdi Army.

In the countryside and the small towns ringing the capital, though, there were far fewer troops, both American and Iraqi, and a largely Sunni and tribal population. That made it easier for Al-Qaeda in Iraq's cells to find shelter and rest, and to stage and build their deadly car bombs. Abu Nur noted that his bomb makers were based not in his own area, but south of the city, in Arab Jabour, a rural area along the Tigris. Casey's strategy— the consolidation of bases throughout the country, the limited number of American forces, and the focus on Bagdhad—had, in effect, given Al-Qaeda room to maneuver in the rural areas around the city, areas it referred to as Baghdad's "belts."

The evolution in Al-Qaeda's strategy was confirmed when McChrystal's commandos netted an Al-Qaeda figure named Wathiq, who was the brother-in-law of Zarqawi's late religious adviser. Wathiq told his interrogators that Al-Qaeda had divided the greater Baghdad area into sectors: a city sector, and five others surrounding the city.[18]

In December, troops from a field artillery battalion stopped a vehicle near Taji, and after one occupant ran, one was captured, and the third detonated a suicide vest, they found a hard drive and a thumb drive inside the car. Both devices were full of internal Al-Qaeda documents, including reports from the "emirs" of various sectors of the belts, further confirming the theory. In the northern belt, Al-Qaeda in Iraq had a pocket of largely unchallenged control around the town of Tarmiya, an area that had been a Sunni insurgent hotbed since Ray Odierno's troops fought there in 2003, but over which Al-Qaeda had recently wrested control from other groups. The Al-Qaeda cell there was led by an innovative commander/emir named Abu Ghazwan, a former detainee who arrived in Tarmiya in August 2006 from Diyala, bringing with him a nucleus of veteran fighters. "Some of the insurgents in Tarmiyah have started to wear clothing similar to Pakistani fighters to show support for Al Qaida," an intelligence report asserted in the fall, after Abu Ghazwan's arrival. "The clothing consists of very baggy shirts and pants." So free was Abu Ghazwan to act in Tarmiya that for his personal vehicle he "confiscated a white Nissan truck from the Tarmiyah Iraqi police" and painted over its police insignia. He also had a ferryboat at his disposal, which he had stolen from the nearby Karkh Water Treatment Plant in a raid and which he used to cross the Tigris when American troops ventured into the Tarmiya area. His fighters had a nickname for the American personnel they considered most dangerous, those who wore beards and drove SUVs (typically special operations forces and intelligence operatives): they called them "Mossad."[19]

The hard drives and thumb drives of the December Taji document trove—what U.S. military intelligence dubbed the "Taji DOCEX"—also included fall updates from Abu Ghazwan. He had six subordinate units of Al-Qaeda fighters, he said, three of them based in Tarmiya, and also two units of Jaish al-Islami fighters who had agreed to switch their banner to Al-Qaeda en masse. "The work now is three-quarters by our organization and one-quarter by other groups," he said of Al-Qaeda's expanding control. "As for the administration of the district, it is under our control as far as companies, fuel stations, and the city council," he wrote, as were the oil police. "We are running the district, the people's affairs, and the administrative services, and we have committees to run the district headed by my brother Abu Bakr." Abu Ghazwan also described in detail the American disposition in his area. "The Americans move in patrols, and there is a headquarters at Huda School in Tarmiya that we can strike any time, but because it is in a residential area we do not strike it now," he wrote, referring to the outpost in Tarmiya that would later be heavily damaged by a vehicle bomb. "They are now inside Camp Taji and never leave it," he said of the Iraqi Army. "As for the police, there is a small force that could be dismantled, as they are from the local community. Every now and then I order them to stay home."

A twenty-seven-year-old Al-Qaeda member captured in late 2006 and interrogated at Camp Cropper described the workings of a car bomb cell under Abu Ghazwan's overall command. The cell had been established only recently, by a militant named Mazin Abu Abd al-Rahman, who had been released from Camp Bucca in September. During his nearly two years in detention, Mazin had benefited from the extensive network of Al-Qaeda operatives who made use of their time in Bucca to train new recruits, taking classes inside the prison on religious law and on building bombs. "Mazin entered Camp Bucca as an ignorant donkey," the detainee from his cell explained to interrogators, but as soon as he emerged, he made contact with a senior bomb maker named Abu Nur, who helped him establish a new cell in the northern belt, which would build bombs to detonate later in the capital. It took Mazin and two other men two days to build each car bomb in the Tarmiya farmhouse they used as a workshop, the detainee explained, using stolen cars driven up from a parking lot where they were stored in Adhamiya and a combination of plastic and homemade explosives. The evening before an attack, the completed car bomb would be driven from Tarmiya back into Baghdad, where it would be stored overnight in a parking lot or garage before the bomber drove it to its final destination and blew it up.[20]

In some parts of the belts, American units sought to push back. During the fall, a new unit, the 10th Mountain Division's 2nd Brigade, commanded by Colonel Michael Kershaw, sought to reclaim ground from Al-Qaeda in the southwestern belt around Yusifiyah. A student of unconventional warfare who had led a Ranger battalion in Afghanistan and Iraq, Kershaw took advantage of the relative remoteness of his unit, while ignoring guidance from on high encouraging consolidation of outposts. Patrol bases, he reasoned, provided better control over the area and better intelligence—something he knew from studying Algeria, Vietnam, and other counterinsurgencies and from American units that had applied the approach earlier in the war, like the 3rd ACR or his predecessor in Yusifiyah, the 2nd Brigade, 101st Airborne. McChrystal's task force, which had been reinforced by a battalion from the 82nd Airborne called Task Force Falcon, spent the fall hitting one rural "no-go zone" after another, softening them up for more raids by Delta Force and British SAS commando teams. After a series of seven JSOC raids against one such place, the thermal power plant on the banks of the Euphrates that had been a hub of antiaircraft and kidnapping activity, Kershaw's troops settled in to stay in an outpost there, denying the place to Al-Qaeda in a way that no number of commando raids could have.[21]

One of the updates pulled from the captured Taji files, by the emir of Al-Qaeda in the southern belt, alluded to the success of American troops against his men and discussed the steps Al-Qaeda had taken in response. Bad operational security habits, he wrote, had "led to break-ins, bombardments, and landings against the brothers"—likely a description of the raids being conducted by American troops, with "landings" referring to helicopter raids like those of JSOC's commandos and Task Force Falcon—"leading to the killing of about 60 of the brothers and the capture of others. This was a result of not caring about security issues, and because brothers were involved in a military operation in the area that exposed them. Now the security situation is better and the number of landings has decreased. There was a vicious campaign against spies, and the mobiles were cut, which led to the decrease in landings. Now there are random landings, not directly on the brothers as it used to be."

Almost everywhere else in the belts, though, Al-Qaeda continued to gain ground. In Arab Jabour and Salman Pak, along the Tigris on Baghdad's southeastern outskirts, the American troop presence was almost nil, except for a few static road checkpoints and the occasional JSOC raid. To the west, Karma and Abu Ghraib—on the boundary between the Army in Baghdad and the Marines in Anbar—received similarly scant attention from American forces. And in the north, Abu Ghazwan's territory, an uptick in sophisticated attacks against American helicopters signaled that the Sunni insurgent group was digging in.

In a daylight mission on November 27, a team of JSOC commandos flew in MH-60 Black Hawk and MH-6 Little Bird helicopters, escorted by armed AH-6 Little Birds, to a remote "laager" site in the desert between Taji and Lake Tharthar, Objective Royal Oak. The plan was to wait there until a silver sedan carrying a senior Al-Qaeda logistician passed through, and intercept it. As the helicopters flew from one laager to another, though, one of the AH-6s, call sign Varmint 42, was hit in the tail rotor by an RPG, forcing it down. The rest of the strike force landed and the Black Hawks flew off with Varmint 42's crew. Before long, the commandos and six pilots, who were clustered around the downed Little Bird, saw trucks approaching. When the trucks opened fire with antiaircraft machine guns, Chief Warrant Officer 5 David Cooper, the pilot of the remaining AH-6, Varmint 41, took off and began shooting back, first at the trucks and then at a house from which insurgents had been lobbing mortars and RPGs at the Americans. Varmint 41's barrage of minigun and rocket fire, delivered in repeated and perilous gun runs, scared the attacking force off. Cooper would be awarded the Distinguished Service Cross for his heroics, but the mission ended tragically when an F-16 that was pursuing the retreating insurgents came in too low and crashed, killing its pilot.[22]

"Of significance to this entire operation were the sheer numbers of [insurgent] personnel and weaponry," a report by the commander of the JSOC mission noted:

They were driving around in great numbers and very motivated to try and engage our operators and aircraft. This is a signature that has not been seen in recent months, and is indicative of the lack of coalition forces presence in the area, the limited operations from our task force, and quite possibly the presence of high-level AQI figures. It is very similar to the type of enemy witnessed in the Yusifiyah area before our targeting increased significantly. Although several insurgents were killed during this action, many were able to scatter and regroup for future fights. During the time that the ground force was in contact with the enemy, we were clearly out-gunned and out-numbered. They were placing effective fire on us with heavy anti-aircraft weapons, and we were limited to small arms. The only reason they were forced to break contact was because of the actions of attack helos. After they broke from our position, FW CAS's [fixed-wing close air support's] aggressive attacks on the enemy were single-handedly responsible for ensuring that they did not regroup their forces or establish mortar firing positions within range of the ground force.

In nearby Diyala Province, a particularly strategic crossroads just north of Baghdad that included a substantial Shiite as well as Sunni population, Al-Qaeda sought to take advantage of the modest American presence, which had been halved in late 2005. The Iraqi Army's Shiite-dominated 5th Division also committed a number of abuses, which drove locals into the arms of Al-Qaeda. The insurgents fortified their bastions with huge, deep-buried bombs. "It was unbelievable, the amount of IEDs," said Lieutenant Colonel Mo Goins, whose 1-12 Cavalry arrived in Baqubah late in the fall. His battalion quickly started losing Bradleys and tanks to these enormous bombs buried under dirt or cement. In November a paratroop unit stumbled onto an Al-Qaeda enclave near the Diyala town of Turki, fortified with 23mm antiaircraft cannons.[23]

The flight of Sunnis from the sectarian violence in Baghdad sometimes fueled hostilities. As Sunni families left besieged mixed neighborhoods in the city that the militia was taking over, many of them resettled in the belts. Young male refugees with a bone to pick with Shiite militias were perfect recruits for Al-Qaeda. In the town of Saab al-Bor, just north of Baghdad, the sectarian struggle over the belts broke into the open in October. In late September, an American cavalry squadron closed its outpost in Saab al-Bor and handed over the mixed Sunni-Shiite town of more than fifty thousand to a police force of a hundred and fifty men. Over the next two weeks, residents began to flee the town and on September 29, Al-Qaeda fighters attacked it and shelled the Shiite quarter with 81mm and 120mm mortars. Over the next week, the town's population dropped to as few as ten thousand as Sunni fighters burned homes, destroyed cars and ambulances, and continued mortar and rocket attacks.

Surprised by the heightened violence, the American squadron pushed back into the town. By now, though, Maliki himself had grown concerned about happenings in Saab al-Bor. On October 11 he met with refugees from the town and told General Ali Ghaidan Majid of the Iraqi Ground Forces Command that American and Iraqi troops needed to transfer their efforts from the Together Forward offensive to operations in Saab al-Bor, Salman Pak, Khan Bani Saad, and the Mahmudiyah-Yusifiyah area—areas in the belts that were important to the Shiites. The next day Ali hosted a meeting about Saab al-Bor with J. D. Thurman and, two days after that, intelligence officers at Camp Liberty briefed John Abizaid on Shiite expansion in Baghdad and the belts. Abizaid asked what would happen if the United States let the Iraqis "fight it out," but Thurman warned him that it would result in a huge bloodletting.[24]

With Iraq engulfed by a rising sea of violence, a team of intelligence officers, led by Lieutenant Colonel Nycki Brooks, began a new assessment. A former college basketball star, Brooks had been immersed in the world of Iraq intelligence almost from the start. She had served as an aide to Barbara Fast, the two-star general who was assigned as the senior intelligence officer to Ricardo Sanchez. By August 2006, Brooks had returned for her second tour in Iraq, this time as the head of a several-hundred strong intelligence cell that served corps commander Pete Chiarelli and would stay on to serve his successor, Ray Odierno, who was also returning for his second Iraq tour. Brooks was soon joined by two intelligence planners, Lieutenant Colonel Monica Miller and Major Ketti Davison, forming an all-female brain trust that one irreverent officer dubbed "the coven."

During her first deployment in Iraq in 2004, Brooks had met with officials from SCIRI, the Hakims' political party, and the officials had brought out a map. The way to control Baghdad, they argued, was to put a stranglehold around the capital. Saddam Hussein's concept for the defense of Baghdad had involved concentric rings of Republican Guard forces outside the city. The Special Republican Guard would be inside the city and would link up with the other Republican Guard forces at the periphery. SCIRI explained that Al-Qaeda was using a similar concept. If the coalition wanted to secure Baghdad, it needed to control the "fiyahs"—Yusifiyah, Latifiyah and the like in the southwest. In the southeast, it was imperative to control Salman Pak. In the northeast, Husseiniyah was a gateway for Shiites, especially the Mahdi Army in Sadr City. In the northwest, the Taji and Tarmiya corridors were gateways for Al-Qaeda. "If you control these corridors you will control Baghdad," the SCIRI officials said. Fallujah, where the coalition had just fought a bloody battle to evict Zarqawi, did not figure in the picture.

The message had not made an impression on Brooks at the time, when she was unfamiliar with the belts concept, but now it did, in retrospect. Other American officials heard similar plans from their Iraqi counterparts, but largely discounted them as sectarian based—Shiite parties' ideas about how to attack the Sunni insurgency outside the capital, where they wanted to limit American interference.[25]

As the violence soared in 2006, Brooks met with two of the 4th Infantry Division's senior intelligence officers, Lieutenant Colonel Ivan Shidlovsky and Lieutenant Colonel Andy Gordon. With the drawdown in forces, Thurman's division had responsibility not only for Baghdad but also for much of south-central Iraq. During the session they discussed Mahmudiyah, which had been a 75 percent Sunni town and was now 80 percent Shiite, a sweeping change that had occurred in just one year. Brooks had a sense of déjà vu and dug out her notes from the November 2004 meeting with SCIRI. It seemed that the Shiites were enforcing Saddam's strategy for retaining Baghdad. The Shiites and the Sunnis were fighting over the corridors to the city.

Sunni and Shiite alike understood that to control Baghdad one had to control what Iraqis knew as the belts. "Everybody else came up with this plan except us," Brooks said. "We are trying to control Baghdad from within, and you can't do it."[26] This strategic problem was compounded by the Mahdi Army's influence within the Health, Transportation, Agriculture, and Interior ministries, which was undermining whatever success the U.S. military was having inside Baghdad. Only $2 million of the $37 million in promised reconstruction funds to Tal Afar had been provided. Of the $200 million in reconstruction funds promised for Anbar, no projects had been started.

Brooks briefed Chiarelli on her findings. To control the Iraqi capital, U.S. forces needed to do more than clear neighborhoods one by one; it needed to control the belts. Within the city, the operation Casey and Chiarelli were mounting was backfiring. The three-pronged program—forcing insurgents to flee certain areas, holding the areas down with Iraqi forces, and then channeling reconstruction funds to them—was not working, because militias had penetrated the national and regular police. The American cordons and checkpoints were limiting the Sunnis' mobility and holding them in place so the Shiite militias could go after them.

Chiarelli was taken aback by Brooks's assessment. The situation she was describing, Chiarelli said, sounded like the "perfect storm." Chiarelli pulled Brooks and Celeste Ward, his political adviser, into a meeting, took out a black marker, and began to draw on a whiteboard. What were the options? Start over? Make adjustments? Chiarelli did not have the authority to devise his own strategy—that was Casey's responsibility and, moreover, any strategy required the concurrence, or at least acquiescence, of the Iraqi government.

Chiarelli asked Brooks to write a paper on how the United States might respond if its strategy were not constrained by politics and decisions already made. Brooks elaborated on her analysis in a classified document marked "NOFORN," not to be shared with other coalition partners. The conflict in Baghdad, she wrote, "is shifting to a self-sustaining armed conflict among ethno-sectarian groups seeking to maximize self-interest. Population movements, both voluntary and coerced, are occurring to the increased violence and decreased security." A big problem, she added, was the fact that the Health and Interior ministries were "complicit in attacks on Sunnis."

In a list of recommendations, Brooks stated provocatively that the coalition needed to fundamentally change its approach. "The overall numbers of forces within Baghdad will have to be increased with the mission changed to one of Peace Enforcement Operations," she stated. The warring Sunni and Shiite factions had to be forcibly disengaged and the refugees resettled. Ultimately, the Sunnis had to be given a viable future. If not, the United States would inadvertently boost the Al-Qaeda movement in Iraq and create a base of support for it throughout the Middle East. Appropriating the phrase from Chiarelli, she titled the paper "The Perfect Storm."

Brooks did not state in her analysis how many additional troops might be needed. But her calculations suggested reinforcements of thirty thousand to forty thousand troops, though not all needed to be American.[27] Chiarelli sent a copy of Brooks's paper and troop calculations to Ray Odierno, who would soon be replacing him. Hers was a provocative recommendation, but not remotely close to what Casey would have in mind.

Out West

There was one place where the American military had begun to make some headway: Ramadi. The provincial capital of Anbar had been so far beyond the coalition's reach that it had served defiantly as Al-Qaeda's capital. By the summer of 2006, the brigade of National Guard troops that had struggled to contain the violence there was due to return home, and Colonel Sean MacFarland's 1st Brigade, 1st Armored Division was coming south from Tal Afar to take its place.

The guidance MacFarland received from George Casey was minimal: he was to "fix Ramadi without doing Fallujah."[1] It was not an enviable mission. Each American brigade that had fought in Ramadi had lost more troops than the last. MacFarland, a devout Catholic who had served on Ricardo Sanchez's staff in 2003 and had a quieter demeanor than many brigade commanders, did not want to be sucked into the same situation as his predecessors—bogged down, with few troops, little flexibility, and mounting casualties.

He also had a small window in which to change the situation. When he got the mission, it seemed likely that either Operation Together Forward or the Pentagon's regular deployment schedule would draw some of his forces away by the fall. In short, there was much to do and not much at hand with which to do it. When he arrived at the gates of the city, there were only three police stations and a hundred policemen. In northern Ramadi, Marines, soldiers, and a small group of Navy SEALs were fighting constant gun battles in their effort to secure Route Michigan, the east-west highway through the city. South of that main artery, insurgents ran the show, protecting their neighborhoods with huge IEDs buried under the dirt or pavement. The number of enemy attacks his troops had experienced in Tal Afar over the course of a week could easily happen in just one day in Ramadi. "The enemy sees Ramadi as their Super Bowl, the place they come to fight Americans, period," MacFarland noted in his diary soon after he arrived.

While the violence was spiking in Baghdad, Anbar had been slowly deteriorating for years. There were virtually no Shiites in Anbar, so sectarian killings were rarely the issue. The problem was that Al-Qaeda in Iraq had sought to turn the province into a platform for expanding its operations to the north and east. According to materials recovered by American intelligence, Abu Musab al-Zarqawi had used a forty-one-slide PowerPoint presentation at a May 4 meeting with subordinates near Lake Tharthar to outline his plan to connect Al-Qaeda's power base in Anbar to new ones the group was developing in Salahuddin and Diyala. Ramadi was to be declared the capital of the expanding Al-Qaeda "emirate."[2]

By the summer of 2006, Al-Qaeda had every reason to be confident about its hold on the province. American forces had taken back Fallujah in 2004 and established control of Qaim in the far west a year later with the help of the Desert Protectors. But since then, the mission in Anbar had been characterized as, in military parlance, "economy of force," meaning it was of secondary importance compared to Baghdad and was being executed with fewer forces than the Marine headquarters at Camp Fallujah would have liked.

Iraqis who chafed under Al-Qaeda's domination, for their part, had been too weak to put up much resistance since the destruction of the Anbar People's Committee in January. At the same time, Al-Qaeda had brought the bulk of the Anbar insurgency into its orbit under the banner of the Mujahideen Shura Council.

The dearth of reliable Iraqi allies, among the tribes or within the local government, presented the Americans with a considerable problem. For the U.S. to hand responsibility over to the Iraqis in Anbar, local government and security forces were needed to take over. But Anbar's governor, Mamun Sami Rashid al-Alwani, who hailed from the Sunni Iraqi Islamic Party, was a virtual prisoner in his compound in Ramadi, having survived more than two dozen assassination attempts. His provincial council had fled altogether. As for Iraqi security forces, there were two underwhelming Iraqi divisions in Anbar, one of them largely Shiite.

The Iraqi police in the province were virtually nonexistent. As part of their effort to build up the Iraqis' capability to ensure their own security, the American command had proclaimed 2006 to be "the year of the police." But with Al-Qaeda casting a long shadow, there were few volunteers. There were no police forces whatsoever in the Euphrates River towns of Rutbah, Anah, or Haditha, where the local police had been lined up and executed after the Marines pulled their forces from the town for the Fallujah fight in late 2004. Some policemen had been recruited in Rawa until insurgents captured a police lieutenant, beheaded him, and displayed the severed head in a fruit basket in front of a local mosque. "The MOI saw what was happening, and they basically fired all the IPs [Iraqi Policemen] for their safety," observed Joseph D'Amico, an Alaska state trooper who was overseeing the police training program for the Marine regiment in western Anbar. "They said, 'Go home, don't police anymore,' because the IPs were getting killed at a pretty alarming rate."[3]

One exception was the town of Baghdadi, near the American base at Al-Asad, where Colonel Shaban Barzan al-Ubaydi had enlisted the support of hundreds of tribesmen and appealed to the Americans for ammunition and weapons after his brother was killed by a suicide car bomb. His force operated out of a former Iraqi Air Force barracks not far from the sprawling Al-Asad Air Base, where the RCT-7 headquarters was located. Bold and outspoken, Shaban cooperated openly with the Marines and participated in joint military operations, but even he seemed to have doubts about the future. Meeting with Marine advisers, he repeatedly pressed for information on how he might emigrate to the United States.

The absence of effective Iraqi partners wore heavily on many American troops, who often found themselves with insufficient manpower to control cities and villages in the province or to liaise with a frightened population that was caught between Al-Qaeda and the occupiers and wished the American military would take its war elsewhere. "We don't even know who we can trust," said Staff Sergeant Ryan Poetsch, who was based at an outpost in Hit, a city on the Euphrates that had been one of Saddam Hussein's first stops on his flight from Baghdad.[4]

The priority to restore order in Baghdad did not help the effort to stand up Iraqi security forces in Anbar. Several U.S. Army military police units had been earmarked for Anbar duty as part of "the year of the police," but were redirected to Baghdad once Operation Together Forward got under way. With little in the way of local security, the insurgents destroyed Anbar's one remaining telephone switch facility, cutting out landlines across much of the province. (Anbar's cell phone towers had already been destroyed in

2005.) With the sectarian killings in Baghdad, Sunni refugees were flowing to Karma, providing an ideal recruiting pool for Al-Qaeda.

Of all the problem areas in Anbar, Ramadi was the worst. Encouraged by its operation to stoke sectarian passions by bombing the Askari Mosque in Samarra, Al-Qaeda followed up with a concerted push in Ramadi. The Anbari capital had proved one of the war's toughest battlefields for the 2nd Brigade, 28th Infantry Division, an assemblage of Pennsylvania, Vermont, and Utah National Guard and active-duty soldiers and Marines in the second half of its costly tour. Stretched thin and having suffered heavy casualties, the commander of the brigade, Colonel John Gronski, pulled his forces back to the edge of Ramadi, cordoned off parts of the city, and tried to keep IED attacks down on its main thoroughfare, Route Michigan.

Taking advantage of the defensive American posture, over the winter Al-Qaeda brought new waves of fighters and pushed into the urban neighborhood of Tamim and the rural, tribal areas to the north and west of the city. Groups of fighters patrolled the streets openly in the neighborhoods they controlled, and sent suspected informants and violators of their form of Islamic law to a secret prison north of the city near Lake Tharthar. The city's hospitals served as headquarters for an insurgent command structure that placed each city district under a different emir and launched frequent complex attacks on American patrols with IEDs, snipers, and squad- and platoon-sized ambushes, which were sometimes planned out on sand tables.[5]

Its cinder block buildings pockmarked with scars from bullets and shells, Ramadi had seen its population drop from 500,000 to as few as 300,000 residents as the war dragged on. Left alone in the southern half of the city, save the occasional commando raid, Al-Qaeda cells were able to emplace massive bombs in the roads, big enough to destroy Bradley fighting vehicles or even tanks. In the Malaab neighborhood of eastern Ramadi, troops from one battalion, 1-506 Infantry, uncovered frighteningly sophisticated IED workshops. "They would take an industrial saw with a carbite-tipped blade, and they would cut a piece of asphalt out of the road," explained the battalion commander, Lieutenant Colonel Ron Clark. "They would just cut the road, probably a two-by-two-foot square, put in as much ordnance as they wanted to, and then basically heat the asphalt back up and drop the piece back on top of it."[6]

At Government Center, a small, heavily fortified complex downtown, a company of Marines dodged sniper fire to protect the unpopular governor. American intelligence later determined that much of the city and provincial government—including Governor Mamun's own secretary, many members of the tiny police force, and nearly the entire highway patrol—were on Al-Qaeda's payroll. By controlling the black market, especially for oil moving through Anbar from Salahuddin's Bayji Oil Refinery, Al-Qaeda was able to make more money in Ramadi than it spent. In fact, Al-Qaeda in Iraq became so flush with cash that, according to a 2006 intelligence assessment, the organization was exporting money to its other franchises.

There were stirrings of resistance by locals who were frustrated with Al-Qaeda's brutal tactics and resented its preying on local women and cutting into the region's profitable smuggling business. Both the Albu Dhiyab and Albu Aetha tribes saw leaders kidnapped in the spring, but were too frightened to retaliate. Tribes that had previously kept their distance from Al-Qaeda, like the Albu Soda, fell in line, while other tribes split on the issue, sometimes violently. An underground resistance began to form: in Ramadi and nearby Habbaniya, a small number of policemen, insurgents, and others who had lost family to Al-Qaeda were going vigilante, kidnapping and killing Al-Qaeda members. Though the activity took place at night and often in areas where American troops rarely ventured, the CIA established contact with the "Thawar al-Anbar," or Anbar Revolutionaries, as the vigilantes called themselves.[7]

American commanders in Anbar had long identified the need for more forces. When George Casey and Pete Chiarelli flew west in May 2006 to Camp Ramadi, the dusty American base just west of the city, Gronski briefed the two generals on the situation in Iraq's most violent city, where his brigade had been fighting for nearly a year.

A native of Moosic, Pennsylvania, Gronski painted a grim picture. Just across a canal from the camp was a city partly in ruins and largely under the control of Al-Qaeda in Iraq. Ramadi had already cost Gronski nearly eighty men. Stan McChrystal's elite JSOC troops were hard at work in Ramadi too, spending their nights looking for the Al-Qaeda leaders who used the city as their base of operations, but even they were losing men there: in recent weeks, two Rangers and a Delta Force commando had been killed.

How many more troops, Casey asked Gronski, would be needed to control Ramadi? Three full brigades, Gronski said—one for the city itself, one for the rural areas around it, and one for the Habbaniya area to the east, for which he was also responsible. That was as many combat troops as had been committed to Fallujah in November 2004. "They didn't blow me off on that assessment or anything," Gronski remembered. "But I just remember General Chiarelli sincerely looking at General Casey and saying, 'There's no way we can come up with that.' "[8] As part of his strategy to hand over Iraq, Casey later that month would cut the total number of brigades in Iraq from fifteen to fourteen. And Ramadi, in the view of the two commanders, was a sideshow.

As the Pennsylvania brigade's tour came to an end in May, it had little to show for its sacrifices. To give his successor a better chance to prevail, Casey paired MacFarland's brigade with two battalions he had been holding back in Kuwait as a reserve. (A third battalion, led by Jim Danna, had gone to Baghdad after the Samarra mosque bombing.) Where Gronski had had three combat battalions, his successor would have five. It was not two extra brigades, but it was something.

With new troops arriving, Ramadi's population sensed that some sort of attack was coming. It was not clear to the Iraqis that MacFarland's brigade was replacing Gronski's, and rumors flew that the Americans were massing forces for an all-out assault along the lines of Fallujah. Al-Qaeda leaders left the city, temporarily going to ground in rural areas to the north and east like Jazira and Julayba, and in the Malaab, a major insurgent stronghold inside the city, residents prepared to evacuate. In other neighborhoods, insurgents seeded the streets with defensive IEDs. In effect, MacFarland had reaped the benefits of an unintended psychological operation: the enemy and the locals were expecting something far bigger than the Americans had in mind.

MacFarland planned to launch his offensive late in June. The colonel was drawn to the slow-and-steady tactics he had inherited from H. R. McMaster's 3rd ACR in Tal Afar, though on a much larger scale and a longer timeline, and facing much more entrenched resistance. The brigade planned to use its spare battalion, 1-37 Armor, to push into the heart of the area Al-Qaeda controlled—southern Ramadi, where the National Guard had kept no troops—to wrest control of the major facilities the enemy had used, such as the hospitals, the train station, and the soccer stadium near the Malaab, whose press box a fighter jet had blown up with a Maverick laser-guided missile during a firefight. The troops would build a web of mutually supporting outposts in the areas they seized, patrol from the outposts, and then introduce Iraqi soldiers and police as the neighborhoods around the outposts calmed. Later in the summer the brigade would repeat the plan, pushing into new areas and building more outposts before consolidating. Aware that Casey's command was making a priority effort to improve security in Baghdad, MacFarland did not think he would have enough troops to go much farther than that. In his view, he had been given enough forces "to start—not enough to finish."

Then, on June 7, word came that Stan McChrystal's JSOC task force had killed Zarqawi, and on June 10, a raid near Fallujah caught Al-Qaeda's emir of Ramadi. Marine commanders reasoned that, combined with insurgent leaders' flight from the city, it presented an opportunity to speed things up. "LTG McChrystal told me that no matter what I did, people will be unhappy," MacFarland wrote in his diary. "He advised audacity."

On June 15, three days ahead of the scheduled attack, Maliki told Casey and Zalmay Khalilzad that he had reservations about the impending assault—the timing did not seem right, and he was nervous that American forces would use tanks and air strikes. Casey tried to reassure the prime minister, explaining, according to a State Department cable, "that this operation would be larger than normal but would not entail a clearing of neighborhoods."[9]

In fact, when the push into southern Ramadi kicked off on the night of June 18 it spiraled into weeks of heavy fighting that would entail both the large-scale clearing of neighborhoods as American troops built their outposts and spread outward and the liberal use of tanks, air strikes, and other heavy ordnance. The CIA had told MacFarland that the shadowy vigilante group called the Thawar al-Anbar would welcome his troops into some areas, but for the most part the welcome was RPGs and gunfire. Tanks were not off-limits to the insurgents: when one was destroyed, its burning carcass became so hot that no one could approach it and the wheels in its tracks melted into aluminum puddles, and one replacement tank was destroyed while still on its tractor-trailer carrier.

The first night, companies of infantry, tanks, and Bradley fighting vehicles pushed into southern Ramadi, took over three sites that attached Navy SEALs had previously scouted—including the train station and the stadium—and began to build outposts there. Engineers oversaw the emplacement of concrete barricades and gravel-filled Hesco barriers, often under fire, and back at the main American base west of the city, no one was allowed into the mess hall without filling up a sandbag to help with the fortification of the outposts. A third new outpost, this one taking up a whole city block, went in on June 26, a day after insurgents stormed Ramadi's branch of the Rafidain Bank and made off with $7 million. After Iraqi and American commandos seized the general hospital on July 5, the Marines built yet another outpost adjacent to it.

Around two thousand Iraqi Army troops worked alongside 1-1 AD in Ramadi. The Iraqi brigade in the east of the city was competent and had combat experience from Qaim. Reinforcements that had arrived for the push into southern Ramadi, though, were a disappointment. "We requested an IA Brigade, were promised a Battalion, and are getting a Company . . . maybe," MacFarland wrote. When a battalion from northern Iraq finally reached Ramadi, it was at only half strength, and performed abysmally in the June 26 push. On July 3, MacFarland told his superiors at the Marine headquarters that the battalion's parent unit in the north could have them back, and that he wanted it officially recorded that the troops had displayed "cowardice in the face of the enemy." In his diary, he wrote, "I want them out of my AO before their poisonous attitudes infect the other IA units who are fighting."[10]

Al-Qaeda pushed back against the American advance immediately. Tactical leaders who had left the city ahead of the expected offensive returned, and they brought new fighters with them—in one case, two Al-Qaeda operatives who had left Lebanon because of the concurrent Israeli offensive there showed up in Ramadi. "Within 48 to 72 hours of us setting up a combat outpost, they would attack it and they would essentially impale themselves on it," MacFarland said. From rural base areas, insurgents shelled the new outposts with 120mm mortars, and others attacked American foot patrols as they pushed out from their new outposts into the neighborhoods around them. The fighting was intense, with twenty-four American troops and as many as two hundred insurgents killed in June and July. By late July, the brigade had lost five Abrams tanks and four Bradleys to IEDs; in one instance, when a tank's fuel cell was set aflame troops had to fight all day and all night while the wreck of the vehicle was recovered.

Navy SEAL snipers—who wore Army uniforms, worked alongside Army sniper teams, and were affectionately known as "Army SEALs"— gave the infantry and tank companies in these fights an edge. So did the firepower the troops were able to call in: the heavy cinder block construction of many of Ramadi's buildings necessitated the use of Abrams tank rounds, GMLRS rockets, and guided missiles and bombs launched from fighter jets and from Army and Marine attack helicopters. "I could talk to a Marine pilot," said the battalion commander in southern Ramadi, Lieutenant Colonel V. J. Tedesco, "and I could tell him, 'I want you to put a thermobaric Hellfire in the second window from the right on the third floor of Building 53 in Patrol Zone Papa 3,' and he could do it from the cockpit."[11]

The insurgent counteroffensive against the net of outposts culminated on July 24. That day, Al-Qaeda launched twenty-four large-scale attacks within the space of half an hour, all across the city. Predictably, they were beaten back with heavy losses. One soldier killed in the July 24 attacks was Captain Jason West. At Camp Ramadi, soldiers assembled solemnly to watch the ceremony in which the fallen officer's body was transported from the camp morgue to a landing pad for pickup by helicopter. "As we stood there with the others in the pitch dark waiting," a civilian interpreter with the brigade named Sterling Jensen wrote in his journal, "we heard the helos' purring and then in a distance saw them as great white sharks in the dark sea approach the pad." In his own diary, MacFarland observed, "I'm glad Jason made it to Mass on Sunday."[12]

Two weeks later, in early August, MacFarland's troops launched the second wave of their outpost-building campaign, pushing into new neighborhoods deeper in the city. 1-1 AD had moved into Ramadi to stay—at least as long as it had the troops to keep pushing.

Despite all the fighting in Ramadi, the Marine command did not see it as a game changer. In August, General Peter Pace visited Camp Fallujah. Colonel Peter Devlin, the chief of the Marines' intelligence staff, briefed the Joint Chiefs chairman on the fraught situation, a briefing he later turned into a classified paper. Without the deployment of an additional American division and the injection of billions of dollars, Devlin concluded, there was little the United States could do to stifle the insurgency in Anbar. "The social and political situation has deteriorated to a point that MNF and ISF are no longer capable of militarily defeating the insurgency," he and his deputy, Major Ben Connable, wrote.[13]

As it turned out, before MacFarland's brigade in Ramadi ran out of track, a new source of manpower appeared.

While MacFarland and three of his battalions spent the summer focused on their campaign into the city, Lieutenant Colonel Jim Lechner, his deputy commander, operated in the rural areas across the Euphrates and the Habbaniya Canal from the city's urban sprawl. Lechner, an abrasive officer who had been wounded in the battle of Mogadishu in 1993, had served as an adviser to Iraqi troops in Samarra and spent years in the secretive world of McChrystal's special operations forces.

MacFarland charged him with handling police recruitment—really, with starting police recruitment from scratch. Lechner formed a team: himself; a Marine Reservist named Major Ted Gates, who was a police officer in civilian life; Captain Travis Patriquin, who spoke Arabic and had served with special operations forces in Latin America and Afghanistan; and the interpreter Jensen, who had spent years studying Arabic in Jerusalem and Syria. The tribal sheikhs were puzzled by Jensen's refusal to sip tea or any caffeinated drinks, but were accepting once he explained that it stemmed from his Mormon faith. Some faith, even in a Christian God, was better than none.[14]

Recruiting inside urban Ramadi, where daily gunfights around the network of outposts often ended only when tanks or attack helicopters got involved and where soldiers and Marines were dying nearly every other day, was not feasible. In the rural areas outside the city, it was more realistic. In Jazira, north of the Euphrates, some tribes, like the Albu Obayd, were firmly aligned with Al-Qaeda. Others, though, like the Albu Dhiyab, had been associated with the Anbar People's Committee, and on occasion their villages had formed militias to keep Al-Qaeda, or the fighters of rival tribes associated with Al-Qaeda, away.

Gates suggested that by building a police station in the tribal areas and recruiting there, instead of in the city, Lechner could tap into their interest in self-defense. There had been inklings that the tribes might be a source of support. When Celeste Ward, Chiarelli's political adviser, visited Ramadi in January 2006, a local sheikh assured her that he could protect her by securing a road. But until Gates, there had not been a focused effort to work with them. The Jazira police station opened in the middle of July, after a successful recruiting drive at the beginning of the month had yielded ninety men—not a huge number, but much more than the ten to twenty who had been showing up to the National Guard brigade's recruiting drives.

As recruiting in the rural areas continued, some tribal leaders decided to throw their support behind the effort to retake Ramadi itself. Three tribes made this move—a dangerous one—in the early summer and cooperated wholesale with the police recruiting efforts: the Albu Risha to the west of Ramadi, and the more influential Albu Dhiyab and Albu Ali Jassim to the northwest, led by the highly respected senior Albu Ali Jassim sheikh, Khalid Araq al-Ataymi. By the brigade's count, that put six of the twenty-one

Ramadi-area tribes on their side, mostly in the country northwest of the city, compared to twelve on the side of Al-Qaeda, mostly in the east, and three on the fence.

The Albu Risha sheikh, Abd al-Sattar al-Rishawi, allowed the Americans to hold a police recruiting drive at his family's compound across the road from Camp Ramadi on July 4. At the urging of Khalid Araq, ninety men from his tribe and the Albu Dhiyab signed up, even though mortar shells were falling around the compound. Sterling Jensen spent the day striking up conversations with the recruits, many of whom he suspected had taken up arms against Americans before. "How much would it really cost for you to kill an American?" the interpreter asked several young men, alluding to the pay Al-Qaeda gave for planting IEDs or other attacks. "I hope I wouldn't do it," one of the men said. "We were fighting the Americans, but we don't want to anymore," said another. "We want to fight Al-Qaeda." Later in the month, another drive in Jazira yielded twice that. The CIA had a hand in the success, handing out cash bonuses to recruits, but more than anything else it was the newfound cooperation of a handful of tribal leaders that allowed it, especially Khalid Araq.[15]

Al-Qaeda reacted to the threat in August, shifting its focus from fighting the Americans in the city to trying to quash the tribal police recruiting in Jazira. One of the first tribes Al-Qaeda attacked, the Albu Fahad, came to the negotiating table after a brief round of kidnappings and counter-kidnappings. Then, on August 21, a truck bomb attacked the Jazira police station, detonating outside the gates and sweeping the place with flames. Eleven of the thirty officers on duty, mostly from the Albu Ali Jassim and Albu Dhiyab, died, and most of a squad of American military policemen suffered severe burns. MacFarland was out with his security detail and, seeing the mushroom cloud from the explosion, rushed to help evacuate the wounded. To the colonel's surprise, instead of fleeing their posts, the police commander and those of his men who had escaped the flames insisted on staying.

Late that night, Al-Qaeda fighters killed Khalid Araq, along with his nephew and son, and dumped the bodies in the countryside instead of returning them. Albu Ali Jassim tribesmen called up the American commander in Jazira and told him they were going after their attackers and wanted help. When the Americans were slow to commit, the tribesmen went ahead without them. "We used that as a pretense to start the revolution," a sheikh from Jazira would later say. With Khalid Araq dead, the tribes who had sent their young men into the police over the summer and quietly participated in the Thawar al-Anbar vigilante operations rallied around a new leader: Sheikh Abd al-Sattar al-Rishawi, at whose compound the first successful recruiting drive had taken place.

Abd al-Sattar was a mid-level sheikh in a mid-level tribe. With a revolver at his side and a flair for the dramatic, he had a reputation for disreputable dealings and a taste for Scotch. As a young man he had spent six months in prison for deserting from the army after the 1991 Gulf War. But he and his brother Ahmed were the only Albu Risha leaders who had not fled Anbar for good, and the Albu Risha was one of only a few tribes that had neither bowed to Al-Qaeda nor been gutted by them.

The Rishawi brothers' compound across the street from Camp Ramadi had been raided by American troops in 2003 and 2004, and Abd al-Sattar had once been detained by American commandos for suspected links to the insurgency through the family business, which consisted of smuggling cars and fuel and possibly kidnapping for profit. At least two Rishawi brothers, however, had been killed by Al-Qaeda, including one who had been a police lieutenant colonel in Ramadi, as had their father, Bezia, so their anti-Al-Qaeda credentials had been paid for in blood. In the years since the invasion, the brothers had also maintained ties with local American commanders and with intelligence officers.

As the summer continued, Jim Lechner's police recruiting team linked up with Abd al-Sattar. The sheikh took an instant liking to Travis Patriquin, Lechner's mustached, Arabic-speaking captain, and the team came to realize the role that Abd al-Sattar was playing in coordinating the Albu Dhiyab and Albu Ali Jassim police recruitment—and the role that his associates, like Hamid al-Hayis, were playing in the Thawar al-Anbar's nighttime killings of Al-Qaeda operatives.

After the assassination of Khalid Araq on August 21, events began to move more quickly, and Abd al-Sattar was at the center of them. On September 2, Tony Deane, a battalion commander in MacFarland's brigade, paid the Rishawi compound a visit, and found the sheikh gathered with a group of twenty other tribal leaders and advisers. The sheikhs were preparing to declare a "state of emergency" in Anbar Province. They wanted to declare all-out war against Al-Qaeda, replace the sitting governor with one of their own, and meet with a high-ranking American general right away. Taken aback, Deane took the news back to MacFarland.

A week later, on September 9, MacFarland himself attended a meeting at the compound. Dressed in a white keffiyah with gold trim, Abd al-Sattar introduced himself as the spokesman of a new movement including representatives from seventeen tribes, called the Anbar Emergency Council, with Hamid al-Hayis its elected head. The eleven goals that Abd al-Sattar laid out were groundbreaking: they left no doubt that this new group was firmly and publicly aligned not only against Al-Qaeda, but with the Americans.

Ten of the eleven goals were spot-on, MacFarland recalled, "and then the eleventh one was a bit negative about the governor of Al-Anbar, to the point where they kind of left open the implication that they might whack him."[16] MacFarland urged the sheikhs to drop that plank, and instead they drafted a letter to the Interior Ministry requesting Governor Mamun's replacement. From September 16 on, MacFarland's priority was backing the Anbar Emergency Council, which was soon renamed the Sahwa al-Anbar, or Anbar Awakening. On September 19 he and the CIA chief in Ramadi met with the Marine division commander Major General Richard Zilmer, and convinced him that supporting the Anbar Awakening was the thing to do. "Managed to talk the CG [commanding general] into seeing the merit of it," MacFarland wrote that night.

For the next month, Abd al-Sattar and his associates worked frantically to increase the power and profile of their group. At the same time, MacFarland scrambled to ensure that his superiors were on board with his decision to back the Anbar Awakening—hardly a sure thing, given the coup-like implications of the sheikhs' original platform and the ties to various insurgent groups that many of the leaders, including Sattar, had. On September 20 and 25 the brigade commander hosted visits to Ramadi by Casey and Chiarelli, both of whom he found supportive. "Keep Sattar alive," Casey told him.[17]

Maliki, who had a deep-seated fear of both Baathists and Al-Qaeda, was open to a modicum of cooperation with the Sunni tribes—at least in distant Anbar. Anbar Awakening representatives had met with Maliki adviser Shirwan al-Waeli and the deputy speaker of the Council of Representatives, who promised parliamentary backing for the movement. During one meeting in early October, MacFarland noted that Abd al-Sattar was taking personal phone calls from Maliki, who acquiesced to his appointment as Anbar's "counterterrorism director" and that of a retired general from the Awakening as the new provincial police chief, and, after some resistance, to the appointment of eight members of the group to the exiled provincial council. On October 17, with Zilmer mediating, Abd al-Sattar and Mamun met at Camp Fallujah and hashed out their differences—although it was clear that profound disagreements still remained. Two weeks later,

Abd al-Sattar again advocated doing away with the governor, MacFarland wrote in his journal. "Sittar said if we would let him, he would kill the Governor," the colonel wrote. "Told him that wasn't going to happen."[18]

As Abd al-Sattar's star rose, tribal police recruitment continued—four hundred recruits in October and five hundred in November. But not all of the recruits were able to meet the Interior Ministry's requirements to qualify for police training; in particular, the literacy requirement was a sticking point. Further delays came from the police training itself: recruits had to be shipped to a police academy across the border in Jordan, where they went through several weeks of training. The process was a source of great frustration to both the sheikhs and the Americans, because it meant that in the interim the police recruits' hometowns would be completely abandoned and vulnerable to Al-Qaeda. MacFarland and Abd al-Sattar would find themselves with fewer troops during a turning point in the war just because a bureaucratic process had to be satisfied.

To get around the problem, Abd al-Sattar proposed that his group build separate paramilitary units from the best of the excess recruits, a plan he persuaded Maliki to approve before the Marines even knew what was happening. By early November, when the brigade in Ramadi was ready to train the new recruits, hundreds of them were already helping the tribal police man their new stations in Jazira. Outfitted in green camouflage fatigues and organized into three battalion-sized units by tribe members with experience in Saddam's military, these new forces were called Emergency Response Units, ERUs, and by early December they numbered more than 2,200 men. Eventually, Lechner was able to negotiate an arrangement under which the new units answered to the provincial police chief, an Awakening member, and they would be paid by the Interior Ministry.

Another bureaucratic hurdle was that all of greater Ramadi was allotted only nine police stations by the Interior Ministry, and not all of those were in places where they would be useful. The workaround Lechner found for this problem was to establish new police outposts, but then call them "substations," even if the official station to which they were notionally attached was in a completely different area. New substations went up wherever the tribes provided recruits, even if the area lacked security. "They sucked down VBIED after VBIED," Tony Deane said of one new substation in his battalion's area. "These guys, they were plenty brave."[19]

Not everyone in the American military command in Anbar was on board. When the Marine Reserve colonel in charge of police training and administration found out that the brigade had been going over his head to get ERU members added to Interior Ministry payrolls in Baghdad, he told MacFarland he would not cooperate. MacFarland was incredulous. The Awakening members were bearing arms side by side with the Americans, and now bureaucracy was going to put the strategy in jeopardy.

When MacFarland's soldiers went to see the Marine colonel, he refused to let them access the safe that held the money to pay the Awakening ERU members. MacFarland promptly threatened to detain him and dispatched a military police detail to do the job, which was en route when Brigadier General Robert Neller, one of the Marine Expeditionary Force deputy commanders, called from Camp Fallujah and told MacFarland to rescind his order. "Sean, you're not going to detain this guy," Neller said, trying to calm the situation down. "He's preventing me from doing what I need to do," MacFarland insisted. The Marine was not arrested, but he made his feelings known to Neller: "MacFarland's lost his mind."[20]

So far, the Awakening and its tribal police initiatives had been a rural phenomenon, restricted to the villages north and west of Ramadi. There had been no change inside the city, where tribes were more mixed and held less sway, and the rural areas east of the city, in Sufiya and Julayba, remained Al-Qaeda strongholds. By the end of the month, American outposts and new police stations had been introduced to both areas, and two tribes that had until recently provided manpower to the insurgency, the Albu Alwan and the Albu Soda, had largely switched to the side of the Americans and the Anbar Awakening.

During the fall, four of MacFarland's combat battalions rotated home and a new battalion, 1/6 Marines, assumed responsibility for downtown Ramadi, including the embattled Government Center, in September. The battalion's commander, Lieutenant Colonel William Jurney, was close friends with Dale Alford, who had led sister battalion 3/6 Marines in Qaim a year before and embraced the Hamza Battalion and Desert Protector program there. Jurney had spent hours discussing the lessons of Qaim with Alford before deploying. But when his Marines arrived in Ramadi, their sector—the urban northwest section of the city—was a heavily contested battleground, with no sign of the Awakening or of tribal police. On the new battalion's first day on the streets, it killed twenty-four insurgents. Through September and October, American forces in urban Ramadi, joined by some effective Iraqi units like the 1st Brigade, 1st Iraqi Army Division, continued to push forward, establishing new combat outposts and pushing the pockets of security around them closer together.

In mid-October, Al-Qaeda fighters held a public parade on Seventeenth Street, which the Marines called "the Racetrack," to celebrate Abu Ayyub al-Masri's declaration of a new front for the group, the Islamic State of Iraq. At the end of the month Jurney's battalion pushed into the area and established a combined Marine outpost and Iraqi police station there, at the notorious "Firecracker" intersection. For days afterward, rocket and mortar fire rained down on the outpost and the neighborhoods around it. To reinforce its remaining urban strongholds, Al-Qaeda brought fresh fighters into the city disguised as construction workers.

The rural tribes that had joined Abd al-Sattar had no influence downtown; Ramadi's rural and urban communities were suspicious of one another, and the role of tribal leaders in day-to-day life was much greater in the countryside. To the extent that there was one dominant tribe in the Marine battalion's urban sector, it was the Albu Alwan. Many local insurgents, both those loyal to Al-Qaeda and secular fighters, were Alwani; so was Governor Mamun. In late October, around the same time that Jurney's battalion installed the Seventeeth Street outpost, infighting began between Alwani insurgents who wanted to stick with Al-Qaeda and members of the tribe, including some insurgents, who wanted to reach out to the Americans. Mamun approached Jurney with a list of 120 Alwani candidates for the police, and within twenty-four hours Jurney had established a new police station where his Marines could partner with the men, some of whom had been insurgents just weeks, if not days, before.

The faction of the Ramadi Albu Alwan that made this switch was motivated in part by suspicion of the burgeoning cooperation between rural Ramadi tribes and the Americans: fearing that rural tribal policemen would be sent into the city where they were not wanted and would be on unfamiliar ground, they decided to cooperate with the Marines and do the policing themselves.

The Albu Alwan policemen were led by Major Salaam al-Alwani, an intimidating-looking former smuggler with ties to both Abd al-Sattar and the insurgency who soon became Jurney's partner in the urban battle. "I am a man of war," Salaam said to Jim Lechner during their first meeting; "God made me that way."[21] As the Marines cleared new areas, more recruits showed up. The process, as Jurney remembered it, was this: new recruits would appear, the Marines would build a joint police station, and then the Marines and the police would stand by for the inevitable insurgent attack. The Marine battalion supplied the new policemen with blue shirts to reduce the risk of fratricide and tapped its company executive officers as police advisers; it also attached a platoon of Abrams tanks to the police to

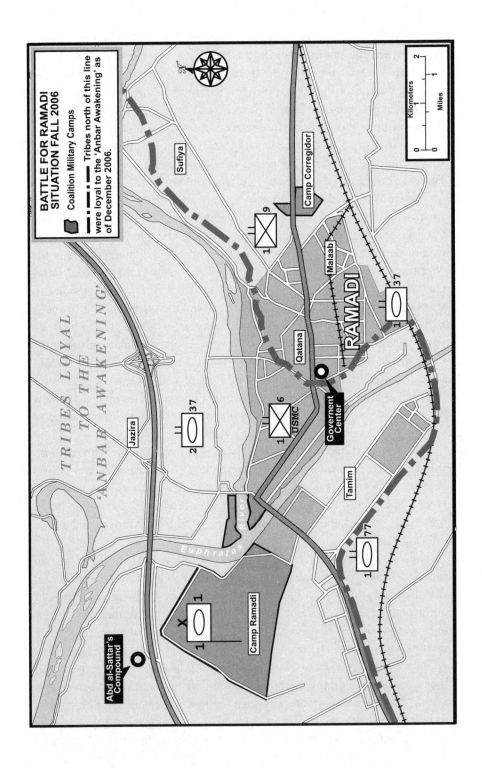

BATTLE FOR RAMADI
SITUATION FALL 2006

Coalition Military Camps

Tribes north of this line
were loyal to the 'Anbar Awakening' as
of December 2006.

Sufiya

Camp Corregidor

1 9

Malaab

RAMADI

1 37

Qatana

Jazira

2 37

1 6
USMC

Governent
Center

Tamim

1 77

TRIBES LOYAL
TO THE
'ANBAR AWAKENING'

Euphrates River

1 1

Camp Ramadi

Abd al-Sattar's
Compound

Kilometers
0 1 2

Miles
0 1

give them firepower. The Albu Alwan force considered itself separate from the tribal Awakening, and there was tension between the urban police leaders and Abd al-Sattar when the latter tried to give the former orders. But in spite of the tension, the Anbar Awakening and the police had come to urban Ramadi, changing the nature of the battle there. After the Marines cleared Qatana in December, only three urban neighborhoods remained under insurgent control.

Late in the fall, Lieutenant Colonel Chuck Ferry's battalion took over the sector that included both the urban Malaab and rural Sufiya and Julayba. A career light infantryman, Ferry had been a lieutenant in the 10th Mountain Division column that fought through Mogadishu in 1993 to rescue the JSOC strike force that included Jim Lechner and Mike Steele. Ferry's first order of business was to lead a battalion-size push into the Malaab, a new phase in the brigade's campaign to gradually build outposts in all of the neighborhoods the insurgents controlled.

On the afternoon of November 25, two days before the Malaab clearance was supposed to kick off, Ferry's interpreter got a call on his cell phone. It was Sheikh Jassim al-Suwadawi, who was under siege from as many as one hundred Al-Qaeda and Ansar al-Sunna militants in his village of Sufiya. He was begging for help. Al-Qaeda leaders had judged that the Albu Soda, small and isolated from other pro-coalition tribes, were the weakest link in the Awakening council, and had decided to destroy them to send a message to the other tribes. The day before, November 24, Al-Qaeda leaders had met with Jassim and given him an ultimatum, which he rejected. In the American headquarters, the feed from a drone showed fighters advancing through Sufiya, setting houses on fire and killing people. With MacFarland on leave for two weeks in the United States, Ferry had to make a major decision: should he push ahead with the carefully planned Malaab operation, or respond to a call for help from a sheikh he had never met?[22]

After consulting with Lechner, Ferry decided to go to Jassim's aid. It was the sort of improvisation that broke with the Army's penchant for carefully synchronized activity, but it was essential for building trust with the best ally the Americans had, the tribes. By late afternoon, an Army Shadow drone, an armed Predator drone belonging to JSOC, and two Marine F/A-18 fighters were over the battlefield. The Albu Soda and Al-Qaeda fighters were too mixed up and too close together for the jets to fire their cannons, even after Travis Patriquin, on a satellite phone with Jassim, had the friendly fighters mark their positions by waving white towels. While the jets flew low-altitude passes to scare the Al-Qaeda fighters away, the artillery at Camp Ramadi fired 155mm smoke and high-explosive shells as close as they safely could for the same purpose. As darkness fell, Jassim's fighters built a bonfire to identify their position.

Meanwhile, Ferry led a company of his infantry east from their headquarters at the edge of the city around 5:30 p.m. Abrams tanks led the way, using main gun rounds to blast obstacles out of the way—IEDs and palm trees that insurgents had cut down to block the roads. The soldiers killed a few insurgents on the battlefield, but most of the Al-Qaeda force had pulled back ahead of the American column. Four Al-Qaeda trucks were defiantly dragging the corpses of Albu Soda tribesmen down the road in Julayba when the F/A-18s destroyed three of them and the JSOC Predator destroyed the fourth with a Hellfire missile.

When Jassim's bonfire blazed onto the tanks' thermal sights hours later, Ferry and his infantrymen dismounted, scouring the area for friendly and enemy fighters with night goggles and flashlights. Once they had linked up, the soldiers distributed glowing chemical light sticks to the tribesmen to aid in identification, and a Marine small boat unit landed from the Euphrates to bring the Albu Soda food and medical supplies. Lechner and Patriquin brought in a Bradley full of captured assault rifles and ammunition. "I will not leave you," Ferry told Jassim before having him and his wounded evacuated by helicopter.[23] The next day, a company from Ferry's battalion flew into Sufiya, where it built an outpost and began to spread out through the district, patrolling alongside armed Albu Soda fighters who were not yet part of any police force.

The November 25 battle of Sufiya opened a new front for the joint force of Americans and Iraqis fighting in Ramadi: now Al-Qaeda's eastern route into Ramadi was cut off too. Through December and into January, Ferry's 1-9 Infantry would push farther east, pushing Al-Qaeda out of Julayba and enlisting the help of local men. "In a lot of these areas, I'd start with dropping bombs," Ferry said afterward. Once his battalion had shown it meant business, local tribes would join, and Al-Qaeda would disappear, falling back onto the next stronghold.

By mid-December, the situation in and around Ramadi had changed dramatically. The average daily number of insurgent attacks had fallen a small but significant amount, from eighteen and nineteen daily over the summer and early fall to fourteen and fifteen in December. Despite continuous, steady pushes by MacFarland's battalions, Al-Qaeda was still dug in deep in some areas—in the city, the Malaab, Sharika, and Iskan neighborhoods, and in the rural areas, the Albu Obayd, Albu Fahad, and Albu Bali tribal zones. The fighting against these redoubts remained fierce. On December 23, the brigade estimated that the number of insurgents it had killed in Ramadi had passed the one thousand mark.

Among those who were excited about the turnaround in Ramadi and believed that it could expand further were the Anbar representatives of the State Department and the CIA. The agency, whose shadowy hand had helped the Thawar al-Anbar with its vigilante killings and had poured money into Ramadi's tribal police, reported to Langley late in the fall that what was going on in Ramadi was significant—success could be had; support was needed—an assessment that MacFarland believed was hugely helpful. At the beginning of January, the CIA's deputy director would pay MacFarland a visit, promising agency funds to pay the police and immediately going to Baghdad to brief Lieutenant General Ray Odierno, the new Army corps commander in Iraq, on what he had seen. On the State Department side, a Foreign Service officer named Jim Soriano had arrived in Ramadi in the fall to head up the provincial reconstruction team for Anbar. The security in the area had been too dicey for the PRT to do much, in the view of military officers there, but Soriano had contributed to the fight with his reports to Washington.

On December 11, Soriano was participating in a secure videoconference with his superiors back in Washington when President Bush stopped by State for a visit. Bush asked what was going on in Anbar. "Things are starting to turn," Soriano said. Ten days later he repeated that analysis in more detail in a classified cable. Violence in Anbar remained higher than it had been just a year earlier, he acknowledged—430 attacks in December 2006 versus 230 in December 2005—but that comparison masked the surprising decrease since the summer, and the nature of the fighting. "The tribes of Ramadi would not be standing up to AQI and the city's youth would not be applying for police jobs if they doubted the CF's staying power," he wrote.[24]

One sign of both the severity of the situation and the potential for change came in early December. On December 6, an IED killed Travis Patriquin, along with another soldier and Megan McClung, the first female Marine officer to be killed in combat in Iraq. American troops had often objected to the presence of Iraqis at memorial services for fallen soldiers and Marines, but the service for the three was attended by Abd al-Sattar, Jassim al-Suwadawi, Hamid al-Hayis, and other sheikhs. A detachment of blue-shirted policemen from the force that Patriquin had helped swell by fortyfold was there, too.[25] After rendering the final honors at the service and trying to comfort a burly Marine major who had broken down in tears, MacFarland began to cry as well. "Later that night, we had the opportunity to kill some IED emplacers who we observed on our UAV" using an F/A-18 jet fighter, the colonel wrote in his diary. "Watching them die felt good."

When he launched his offensive in Ramadi in June, MacFarland had doubted that he would be able to finish it without receiving additional combat units, which had never been in the cards. Now his brigade had enough forces to do the job. No extra American battalions had come to Ramadi. The new forces were all Iraqi, and irregular ones, at that, but their ability to operate on their home turf and the intelligence they brought to the fight exceeded anything the CIA might have provided.

Abd al-Sattar and the other sheikhs had viewed the arrival of MacFarland's brigade as a sign that American combat power was being built up in the area, and as a last opportunity to forge an alliance with a force that could help them wrest back control of their towns and villages. By massing what reinforcements he had into an urban offensive, applying the lessons of the operation he had inherited from H.R. McMaster in Tal Afar, and digging in his heels with successive combat outposts, MacFarland had tapped into a "force multiplier" that was far more effective than sending an extra American battalion and far quicker than training an Iraqi Army brigade. For Casey and Chiarelli, Ramadi was now less of a worry but Baghdad was still the main effort.

Back in Baghdad, a British officer saw what Marine and Army troops were accomplishing in Anbar and tried to connect it to something bigger. In September, just as the Anbar Awakening was kicking off, Lieutenant General Graeme Lamb had arrived in Iraq as Casey's latest British deputy.

Born and raised in Scotland, Lamb was a different sort of officer from the polished aristocrats who populated much of the British Army's senior ranks. He had gained his officer's commission from Sandhurst in 1973, and, after four years in the infantry, was selected for the SAS. Lamb joined the organization at a time when the U.S. Army was establishing Delta Force in its image, and it was in those years that Lamb began his long association with JSOC. In the months after the fall of Baghdad, he commanded the British division in Basra at the same time that Petraeus, Odierno, and Dempsey were division commanders in the north.

Lamb arrived in early September, and was told by Casey that his job as the British deputy would entail dealing with the power and energy port-folio—and also "thinking about thinking about" engagement with Sunni insurgent leaders, something Marine generals had done in Anbar the previous year but which had since stalled. Casey did not actually want Lamb to go out and meet with the enemy; he just wanted to strategize about how it might be done, and how Washington, Baghdad, and the military would split the task up.

"You always end up talking," was Lamb's view. Before deploying, he'd even mulled the notion over with Petraeus when the Fort Leavenworth commander visited Britain. So Lamb began to consult with the CIA and British intelligence.

Before the end of September, Lamb made a trip to Anbar to meet with Marine commanders, MacFarland, and Abd al-Sattar (who surprised the British general by expressing interest in acquiring a British wife). That month, Lamb also flew to Balad to see McChrystal, whom he'd known since the two worked together on the Scud problem in Desert Storm. No one, he believed, knew Al-Qaeda and the Sunni insurgency at a country-wide level better than McChrystal, and engagement with the insurgents could not happen without the support of the JSOC commander and his team. McChrystal not only backed Lamb, but lent him an intelligence analyst and a Delta Force colonel to form the nucleus of a small engagement cell. JSOC had been fighting the insurgency for three years now, though, and the idea of reconciling with the enemy was hardly unanimously popular at its Balad headquarters. During a visit to the commandos' corner of the sprawling air base, though, Lamb's borrowed Delta officer helped his case hugely in a room full of senior special operators. "We can kill them all," the officer said, then paused. "It'll take us 247 years." The message sank in; JSOC would be an unlikely ally in Lamb's efforts to talk with the enemy.

Next, Lamb started talking to Maliki and to his point man, Mowaffak al-Rubaie. The latter was skeptical. "Why would you invite an alligator into your bedroom?" he asked. But Lamb could point to a precedent: the prime minister had already put his weight behind the Anbar Awakening. To gain Rubaie's trust, Lamb laid out an edict: he would do nothing the government did not approve. That might slow things down, but it made them less likely to be scuttled in the long run.

In the fall, in October or November, after laying out the ground rules with Rubaie, Lamb went back to Balad and asked JSOC which of the insurgent leaders languishing in Camp Cropper he should talk to first. "They're an interested audience, and they can't go anywhere," Lamb explained. Leaders of Al-Qaeda in Iraq were out of the question; the ones Lamb wanted were those affiliated with Al-Qaeda's cousin, Ansar al-Sunna, and with various smaller Sunni groups, all of which Al-Qaeda had spent the past year trying to devour into its own organization, with great success. The best ones to meet with, he judged, would be captured religious emirs, who had tremendous influence within their groups. They were also well educated, and perhaps more likely than others to see Al-Qaeda in Iraq's tactics as un-Islamic.

The first handful of meetings with detained Sunni militants took place not at Camp Cropper, but at Maude House, the small Green Zone palace where senior British officials like Lamb lived. An oasis where alcohol could be drunk and British English spoken, Maude House was named after another British three-star who had preceded Lamb in Baghdad: Sir Frederick Maude, the officer who oversaw the seizure of the capital from the Ottomans by British and Indian troops in 1917.

American guards brought Lamb's guests across the city goggled, manacled, and in orange jumpsuits. Once they were delivered to Maude House, Lamb had the men unlocked, then dismissed their guards, gave them a fresh set of clothes, and served them tea. Only he, his interpreter, and sometimes one other person would be in the room. The insurgent visitor, who typically was high in his organization, would see Lamb's British uniform and his three stars—he wore American rank for clarity's sake—and realize that he was dealing with one of the most senior members of the occupying army.

"How does this end?" Lamb would ask the guest after introducing himself, echoing Petraeus's famous question from 2003. He avoided specific questions that might have hinted at intelligence collection or fishing for a deal. The point was to create a relationship: Lamb brought only a few select men to Maude House, but he often brought them there over and over again across a period of months, giving them time to think the conversations over.

The next step was to meet with insurgent leaders who were still at large. This was a touchier proposition, both for the Iraqi government and for JSOC, neither of which liked the idea of holding off on killing or capturing insurgent leaders when they knew exactly where they were. In December, Lamb met with Rubaie and proposed arranging meetings with three insurgent leaders. One of the men would have had to come in for the meeting from outside the country—many top figures in the groups spent most of their time in Jordan or, especially, Syria. At that prospect Rubaie balked—and much to his surprise, Lamb backed down. "I could have wheeled the guy in and they never would have known, and it might have been quite useful," Lamb recalled. But doing so would have risked turning Rubaie against the project completely. Dropping that one meeting when Rubaie well knew he could go ahead with it alone, on the other hand, gained the national security adviser's trust.

By December Lamb had been bringing a small number of detainees to Maude House for nearly two months. One man with whom the conversations had been reasonable was an Ansar al-Sunna religious emir—a cleric who espoused the same religious teachings as Al-Qaeda, but had no direct ties to Al-Qaeda in Iraq. By virtue of the areas where its cells operated, Ansar al-Sunna was also privy to what was happening in Anbar.

The emir explained that he and his associates in Camp Cropper were no longer as sure as they had once been of how to view the foreign force occupying their country. "General, you and I have established this mutual respect, but you are a force of occupation and you are unwelcome here," Lamb recalled the man saying over tea. "The Koran makes clear that a force of occupation can be resisted for however many years it takes, because it represents a challenge to your faith and your way of life." Lamb said he understood, but there was more. "We have watched you in Anbar for three and a half years," the detainee continued. "We have concluded that you do not threaten our faith or our way of life. Al-Qaeda does." Coming from a cleric in a group that was Al-Qaeda in Iraq's Salafist fellow traveler, it was a remarkable statement.

At the time, since Casey was still out of the country and Lamb was acting commander, the British general ordered the emir released. Lamb never saw the Ansar al-Sunna detainee again. But the very fact that the strange episode had occurred was evidence that the relationship between the American military and some elements of the Sunni insurgency was taking a new and radically different turn.

PART 2

Double Down

The Surge and Its Aftermath, 2006–2008

CHAPTER 15

Some Friendly Advice

On August 31, 2006, Jim Baker and Lee Hamilton were sitting in the jump seats in the cockpit as the C-130 landed at Baghdad International Airport. For nearly six months, the two pillars of the foreign policy establishment had been leading a bipartisan review of the Bush administration's strategy and working to chart a new—and politically acceptable—path forward. The rest of the panel and a smattering of aides were scattered among the webbed seats along the side of the cargo hold with a couple of squads of infantrymen who, armed to the teeth, were returning to the fight after a brief break.

As soon as the plane landed on the baking tarmac, the team was whisked into a Rhino, an armored military bus, given a safety briefing by the embassy's security officer, and then walked to waiting Huey helicopters for the short hop to the Green Zone. George Casey's forces were only a couple of weeks into Together Forward II when the group arrived for what would be its first and only visit to Iraq. Three of the ten members skipped the trip.

The son of a Texas attorney, Baker was uniquely positioned for his task. He went to the finest schools, did a stint in the Marines, and then, following in his father's footsteps, began to practice law. A confidant of an up-and-coming politician, George H. W. Bush, he had managed several presidential campaigns, including Ronald Reagan's triumphant re-election, and gone on to serve as Reagan's treasury secretary and Bush's secretary of state before taking over as the White House chief of staff. Like Hamilton, a Democrat and former chairman of the House Foreign Affairs Committee, he was a throwback to an era when powerful and pragmatic insiders forged compromises across party lines. Baker, in fact, was so valued by the Bush family that in 2005 George W. Bush sounded him out about taking Rumsfeld's place at the Pentagon. Baker, then seventy-five, demurred.

Without Baker, the Iraq panel might not have gotten off the ground. The idea to convene a number of graybeards had started with Representative Frank Wolf, a Virginia Republican, who was worried that the Bush administration was losing credibility with the voters on the Iraq issue. The White House had been deeply skeptical at the start, and it had taken Baker's participation as cochair of the group to persuade the president and his team to cooperate, which was vital if the panel was to talk with the generals and diplomats and make its way, however briefly, to the war zone.

One of the White House's first stipulations, which Baker put on the table, was that the group not be described as another "commission"; the administration feared the word would elevate the group's status—all the more so after the 9/11 Commission became nearly iconic. "The Iraq Review Group" did not pass muster with the White House, either: that implied that the body would be passing judgment on the Bush administration's strategy. It was Steve Hadley, Bush's lawyerly national security adviser, who coined the phrase "Iraq Study Group."[1] By 2006, cooking up strategies for Iraq had practically become a cottage industry in Washington. If the Bush team did not like the group's recommendations, it could treat it as just another study.

Baker and Hamilton were less concerned with semantics than with selecting members who would confer legitimacy on the effort. For the Republicans, Baker picked Robert Gates, the former CIA director and deputy national security adviser during the George H. W. Bush administration; Rudy Giuliani, the former New York city mayor whose dwindling political fortunes had been reversed by his public response to the 9/11 terrorist attacks; Alan Simpson, the conservative former senator from Wyoming; and Sandra Day O'Connor, a former Supreme Court justice. For the Democrats, Hamilton selected William Perry, the defense secretary for President Clinton and an expert on military technology; Leon Panetta, Clinton's former chief of staff; Charles Robb, the former Virginia senator and governor; and Vernon Jordan, the attorney and Democratic Party insider. The theory was that the judgments reached by any group this broad and well connected would carry enormous weight in Washington. What nobody could know then was that two of the panelists, Gates and Panetta, would run the Pentagon and CIA, respectively, in the next Democratic administration.

The group had barely gotten under way when Giuliani, who had failed to show up for the group's first two sessions, resigned so he could focus on his presidential ambitions. Pouncing on the development, the Democratic National Committee submitted a freedom of information request seeking all records related to his participation. It was a rare instance in which partisan politics impinged on the group's activities. Edwin Meese, Reagan's attorney general and a retired colonel in the Army Reserve, took Giuliani's place.

At its first meeting in April, the group had heard from Tom Fingar, the same intelligence official who had overseen the 2004 paper that suggested Anbar was a lost cause. Now Fingar was the deputy director of national intelligence under John Negroponte, who had left Baghdad early to assume the intelligence portfolio. Not surprisingly, Fingar painted a discouraging picture. The foreign fighters, who he said were crossing the Syrian border at the rate of fifty to a few hundred a month, were exacerbating the security situation, as was Iran, which was providing lethal support to the Shiite militias. But stopping the flow of jihadists would not end the insurgency, which Fingar said was neither planned nor under a single organization's command and control. Fingar acknowledged that the American military presence served as both a target and a rallying cry for the insurgents but argued that it was critical for maintaining a modicum of order. A U.S. withdrawal would not only fail to reduce the violence, he said, but would also "redirect it against Iraq's Shiite-dominated government." As for Iraq's security forces, they did not include enough Sunnis and were often sectarian.

Iraq's politicians, he assessed, were "parochial rather than nationalist" in nature. What little civic culture had survived Saddam's regime had been overtaken by "a winner-take-all mentality that bred cronyism, corruption, and a desire to exact payback." In the current political environment, few leaders were "rising above the fray." The lagging efforts to provide services and rebuild the country had led to "anger and alienation" among the population. Oil exports were down, largely because of insurgent attacks and vandalism. While it was critical that the oil infrastructure be rebuilt, the Iraqi government lacked the capacity to do so on its own.[2]

At this point in Fingar's presentation, Gates interrupted and asked whether it was possible to internationalize the reconstruction effort, and whether the United Nations might provide cover for other countries to get involved, perhaps even the Russians and the Chinese. "We need to push beyond Iraq as simply a U.S. problem," Gates said. "Others see the dangers but are unwilling to climb on board a sinking ship." Panetta jumped on that theme. Could the United States convene a forum of other nations so they could get involved? he asked.

Fingar said nothing was happening on that front but something might be possible. Baker suggested that Muslim countries like Indonesia or Malaysia might provide some help with security, though he doubted they would serve in Anbar or had the skills to train the Iraqis.[3] Here was an idea that had caught the Pentagon's fancy in 2004 yet had failed to materialize, but the group was just getting started.

When the group met again five weeks later, the discussion focused on American troop levels and the prospects for withdrawal. James Jeffrey, who had returned to the State Department to become the secretary's special adviser on Iraq after leaving Baghdad in 2005, said the command's unpublished timeline was to stand up the Iraqi Army by the end of the year. "Should we be seeking a less visible U.S. presence?" Hamilton asked.

"That is a big debate right now," Jeffrey responded, alluding to discussions within the administration about the pitfalls of the Casey strategy. "A better Tal Afar–style approach may be compatible with our overall goals." Jeffrey and Philip Zelikow would later work on a paper on "selective counterinsurgency," which elaborated on Rice's "clear, hold, and build" testimony, and allowed for additional American forces.

David Petraeus, then a lieutenant general who had just returned from two years of training the Iraqi Army and was now running the Army's Combined Arms Center at Fort Leavenworth, spoke to the panel next. Only a three-star in rank, Petraeus was reluctant to criticize his superiors' planning and was just beginning the task of rewriting the military's counterinsurgency manual. His testimony rocked no boats: "The overall U.S. strategy is sound," said Petraeus. "The Iraqis need to control the militias and strip off the Sunni support for the insurgency. The U.S. is less of a factor."

The next day, Colin Powell, now very much a private citizen, engaged in an extended diatribe about the mistakes the Bush administration had made. There had not been enough troops from the beginning. The Bush team did not understand the demands of the occupation and had somehow assumed Iraq would just "snap together." There had been complete confusion on the American side. Jay Garner's background as a former Army air defense officer made him ill-equipped for the job of dealing with post-invasion Iraq. Jerry Bremer had made his own job a lot harder by refusing to let Zalmay Khalilzad continue as an envoy to the Iraqi politicians. The decision to disband the army was a mistake and was not properly discussed. The de-Baathification program was hijacked by Ahmed Chalabi, who used it to purge a vast number of officials. There had been "no common superior" in Baghdad, meaning that the lines of authority between Bremer and Rick Sanchez were never clear. Sectarianism was a greater threat there than the insurgency, and American forces had little capacity to stop it or control events. The goal should not be democracy, Powell argued, but reform of the Iraqi political system. "Does our government know what it is doing?" Gates asked pointedly after Powell unburdened himself. "No," Powell responded. The NSC process did not work.[4]

On the day before the group left for Baghdad they stopped by the State Department to see David Satterfield, who had replaced Jeffrey as Rice's top deputy on Iraq. Satterfield, a Foreign Service officer who had served throughout the Middle East and in the American embassy in Iraq, described Maliki as the "leader of a faction who became prime minister by coincidence" and whose closest advisers were made up of Dawa Party faithful who were still afraid of a Baathist coup. The underlying "U.S. message," Satterfield said, needs to be that Maliki "has to act now or we fail. We can help with security support, but he has to bite the bullet." Toward the end of the briefing, Satterfield and Zelikow reiterated that the U.S. needed to see progress on security, reconciliation, and governance by the end of the year.[5]

Not all the members would make the trip. Alan Simpson wanted to go, but the trip coincided with his seventy-fifth birthday. Family obligations precluded Sandra Day O'Connor from traveling. Vernon Jordan, who as early as April expressed his lack of interest in visiting Iraq, did not come either. The remainder of the study team and a nine-member support staff flew to Kuwait on a C-40 before switching to a C-130 for the final leg.

George Casey was the first official in Baghdad to see the panel and, despite early indications that Together Forward was running into problems, he perceived the glass as half full. In terms of security, Casey noted that it generally took nine to twelve years to defeat an insurgency. A premature U.S. withdrawal would be "horrific," but Casey stressed that the Iraqi Army only needed another "twelve to eighteen months" before it would be strong enough to "deal with Iraq's security issues." Asked about the Iraqis' political will, Casey replied, "So far, so good, but it's early in the process." The U.S. should be in a much better position to assess the situation in December, Casey said, and if things were showing progress by then, the Maliki government would "likely be able to expand their success" beyond the confines of Baghdad.

Khalilzad was traveling, so the group met with Dan Speckhard, the embassy's chargé d'affaires, who was even more bullish on Together Forward. The diplomat told the panel that the operation would "inspire confidence in the Maliki government," and would establish a base on which the country's politics could develop.[6]

To many of the group's members, Pete Chiarelli seemed to possess the most nuanced understanding of the political and military environment in Iraq. It was not the first time Chiarelli had played host to one of the study group principals. As a young captain in 1981, Chiarelli had served as Ed Meese's escort officer during a trip the latter made to West Point when he worked at the Reagan White House. Informed by the lessons he had learned during his first deployment in 2004, Chiarelli said that establishing a functioning infrastructure capable of providing essential services was "as important as creating a secure environment if we hope to succeed in Iraq." But he also noted a nagging concern: the "Ministries of Health, Transportation, and Agriculture were controlled by the Sadrists." On the preparedness of the U.S. military at home, Chiarelli asserted that nearly two-thirds of the Army brigade combat teams based in the U.S. were not combat ready, a fact that particularly interested former secretary of defense Bill Perry.

In contrast, Major General Joseph Peterson, who commanded the coalition's police training team, left most members of the group believing that he was in acute denial over the efficacy of his own efforts. Nearly every expert the group had spoken to up to this point had told them that the Iraqi police were largely corrupt, infiltrated by sectarian militias, and actually contributing to the security problem. These conclusions were reiterated by several Iraqi leaders with whom the ISG had spoken in Baghdad, but Peterson insisted that this was an "unfair depiction" of a police force that was "inaccurately depicted by the media." He also flatly denied that Iraq's Ministry of Interior was dysfunctional, which prompted one staffer present at the briefing to "wonder where this guy has been for the last year."[7]

Most of the Iraqis projected an air of confidence. Maliki assured the panel that Iraq was not headed toward civil war, but he was light on details as to how it might be avoided. Jalal Talabani, despite noting problems with the Iraqi police and interference from Syria and Saudi Arabia, insisted that he supported Maliki and believed that "the government would improve markedly" by the end of 2006.

Iraq's Sunni vice president, Tariq al-Hashimi, identified the country's three biggest challenges as "terrorism, militias, and the Ministry of Interior." Reflecting a common Sunni view on the latter two problems, Hashimi said that "the militias could be better managed" if coalition forces "dealt with them more aggressively."

Abd al-Aziz al-Hakim lacked a formal position in the government but remained one of the most important power brokers in the entire country as the leader of the Supreme Council for the Islamic Revolution in Iraq. The meeting with Hakim was among the last the group conducted, and by that time the members had become accustomed to hosting Iraqi leaders in their temporary quarters in Saddam's old presidential palace or visiting the Iraqis at their government offices. For the SCIRI meeting, though, the group had to travel to the private home of Adil Abd al-Mahdi, the Shiite vice president.

When they arrived at the house, they saw several unexpected faces. Every SCIRI cabinet minister was also in attendance, including the minister for national reconciliation and Minister of Finance Bayan Jabr, who had been transferred only months before from the Ministry of Interior, where he presided over the infiltration of Shiite militias.

During the meeting Baker and Hamilton urged Hakim to support the Maliki government. For his part, though, Hakim did not seem to view this as a problem, nor did he express any sense of urgency to reconcile with the Sunnis. "If Iraq already has a government of national unity, why does it need a national reconciliation program?" Hakim asked the group. It is possible that SCIRI can reconcile with "the other Shiite militias," he continued, but "we will never reconcile with the Saddamists. They were killing us for the last thirty-five years, and now we are paying them back." The United States, Hakim insisted, would have to "deal" with the Sunnis. Abd al-Mahdi was seated beside Hakim during this meeting and did not say a word the entire time.

One of the staunchest allies the United States had within the government was Barham Salih, the deputy prime minister, a Kurd. As one of the United States' most sincere interlocutors in the Iraqi government, Salih was less circumspect. Mistrust between the Sunnis and the Shiites, he acknowledged pointedly, had led to a "debilitating lack of cooperation" within the Iraqi government. Federalism might eventually work in Iraq, but there was a role for the United States in the meantime—a bigger role than many American politicians appeared to accept. The United States, Salih said, "never had enough troops in Iraq to stabilize the country, and they still don't have enough."[8]

Bill Perry had arrived in Iraq sympathetic to Salih's position, which he explored in a series of private meetings with Casey and Chiarelli. Perry had cut his teeth as an expert in military technology. Drafted into the Army as the Second World War came to a close, Perry missed the combat but served in occupied Japan. After getting a doctorate in mathematics from Penn State, he had a successful career in the defense industry and was named to run the Pentagon's research and engineering office during the Carter administration, where he played a key role in the development of the stealth bomber and other Cold War–era weaponry. After leaving the Pentagon, he was a managing director of a San Francisco–based investment firm that focused on the defense sector. Perry returned to the Pentagon as deputy defense secretary, typically a job involving the nitty-gritty of massive budgets and programs, and was elevated to secretary of defense after Les Aspin, President Clinton's first secretary of defense, was fired. His decades of experience had made him a formidable figure on defense, but while he had run the Pentagon during the Bosnia conflict he had no experience in fighting an entrenched insurgency.

Huddling with Casey, Perry pressed the commander on the troop issue. "I pushed him very hard and said, 'Look, if I were the president and came to you and said I'm going to provide you with another thirty thousand to forty thousand troops for three to six months with this expressed purpose of gaining complete control and bringing order in Baghdad, would you be positive about that directive?'" Perry recalled. "Casey was very strongly opposed to that, and as nearly as I could determine Chiarelli and Dempsey were going along with him."[9] Martin Dempsey, who oversaw the training of Iraqi troops and later emerged as Obama's pick to serve as chairman of the Joint Chiefs, was not enthusiastic about a troop surge. Chiarelli's view, as he recalled it years later, was more subtle: he was not opposed to sending more troops but did not think they would do any good unless the Maliki government was prepared to overcome its sectarian biases.[10] All in all, however, Perry had read the generals correctly. There were no demands for more troops among the brass in Baghdad.

During the blizzard of meetings, only one member of the panel ventured outside the Green Zone: Chuck Robb, the sixty-seven-year-old former governor and senator from Virginia who had met one of Lyndon Johnson's daughters when he served as an aide at the White House and later married her. A former Marine, Robb had done two tours in Vietnam, including as the commander of a rifle company. During a pre-departure briefing at the Pentagon, Gordon England, the deputy secretary of defense, had urged the group to try to go outside the international zone to get a clear view of the country. Robb planned to do just that. After a day and a half in the Green Zone, Robb used his contacts to travel to Camp Fallujah, where the Marine headquarters in Anbar was located. Robb wanted more than some military "dog and pony show," and he urged the Marines to take him to Ramadi, then the scene of some of the bitterest fighting in Iraq, only to have the embassy's security officer put a halt to the adventure. Whatever England might have advised the study group, the embassy was not about to risk the loss of a VIP.

Livid at the intervention, Robb returned to Baghdad and stormed into one of the study group's meetings "mad as a wet hen," according to Paul Hughes, a retired Army colonel, who was on the group's staff.[11] Shortly thereafter, an order came down from Casey to allow Robb to travel wherever he wanted. With time running short, the military offered him a trip to the Dora neighborhood in Baghdad, a sectarian killing ground that had just been cleared by U.S. forces, who were about to reopen its marketplace. "It looked interesting enough," Robb recalled. "So I said, 'Okay, let me go to Dora.'" A small convoy was formed to take him around the city, and, unlike his earlier trip to Fallujah, Robb was permitted to get a firsthand view of the area and talk to some of the jobless residents congregating on a street corner. A few days after returning to the States Robb read that more than thirty headless bodies had recently been found in the neighborhood.

What Robb heard and saw during his two forays outside the Green Zone disturbed him. Robb believed that the U.S. had a strong moral obligation not to leave behind an Iraqi government unequipped to establish and guarantee security and seemingly destined to fail. The U.S. military could not simply keep reshuffling troops throughout Iraq, playing a never-ending game of "whack-a-mole." Before drawing down, he reasoned, the United States needed to carry out a temporary troop surge to regain the tactical momentum. Instead of accepting the military's judgment from on high, Robb had relied more on his interactions with lower-ranking military officers, his brief foray into the field, and his own combat experience. He was genuinely surprised that the senior military leadership was not insisting on more troops.[12]

After its three days of meetings were done, the group left Baghdad on the night of September 3 in a military transport plane. Sitting in a webbed seat, Perry began drafting recommendations on a small laptop in the cargo hold. There were many points on which all the participants agreed, but a troop surge was not one of them. Perry, in fact, was coming to the view that Casey's transition plan should proceed and that the United States should insist on a clear deadline for getting the combat brigades out and handing over to the Iraqis. Aware that he held a minority position among the group,

Robb later wrote a brief memo that he asked be distributed at the panel's next meeting in Washington.

Without being overly dramatic, I believe the Battle for Baghdad is the make or break element of whatever impact we're going to have on Iraq and the entire region for at least a decade—and probably much longer. In my judgment we cannot afford to fail and we cannot maintain the status quo. The views expressed inside the Green Zone, particularly by the weak Iraqi leaders who spend most of their time there, simply don't square with facts. In spite of some notable progress, the situation is deteriorating far more rapidly than most are willing to acknowledge.

My sense is that we need, right away, a significant short-term surge in U.S. forces on the ground, augmented where possible by coalition partners, and, with very few exceptions, they will have to come from outside the current theater of operations. . . . It's time to let our military do what they're trained to do on offense—without being overly constrained by a zero casualties or collateral damage approach. . . . We can integrate Iraqis wherever they have the capability, but the clock is running on the U.S. and we need to show results very quickly. It's going to cost more in the short term, just as we'll temporarily sustain higher casualty rates on the military side, but both costs and casualties will be reduced in the long run.[13]

Once the group was back in Washington, it continued to sound out the notables. In late September, the panel heard from a number of lawmakers, including Joe Biden, the senior Democrat on the Senate Foreign Relations Committee. For years, Biden had lambasted Rumsfeld for failing to send sufficient forces to control the Iraqi capital, keep order in the country, and provide enough security for nation-building efforts. One morning in March 2006, Biden had been on a shuttle flight from New York to Washington and bumped into Les Gelb, the president of the Council on Foreign Relations, when their flight was delayed for three hours on the runway.

Gelb had begun to argue for a plan to create a decentralized federal system of Shiite, Sunni, and Kurdish regions. The plan owed a lot to the complex arrangements that had been imposed in Bosnia to stop the civil war between the Serbs, Muslims, and Croats. Gelb had outlined his thinking at a several-hour lunch with the ambassadors from Egypt, Iraq, Saudi Arabia, and Jordan, who were worried about the effect it might have on their own countries. In particular, the Saudi ambassador expressed concern that if federalism caught on in the Arab world it would give too much autonomy to their oil-rich eastern province and might even encourage the Shiite population there to try to secede. Defending his position, Gelb insisted that the political forces pulling Iraq apart could be quenched through either federalism or centralized tyranny.

Biden, who had also backed the decision to intervene in the Balkans, was an easier sell. "I'm into this, let's do it together," Biden said.[14] The plan seemingly provided something few lawmakers had: a political strategy for resolving issues in Iraq. It also gave Biden a way to ease off his earlier criticism that the United States had not sent enough troops to Iraq. Sending more force to maintain order seemed like a more appealing platform for McCain than for a Democrat contemplating a run for the presidency. Gelb later met with Biden in Washington, and they agreed to write an article together for the *New York Times,* which Gelb drafted and Biden's staff edited. Their first op-ed was published on May 1, 2006: titled "Unity Through Autonomy in Iraq," it spelled out their views on federalism.[15]

At the ISG, Biden used the opportunity to promote the Biden-Gelb plan. There were five things that could be done to promote it that were consistent with the Iraqi constitution, argued Biden, who in his enthusiasm listed six: a decentralization of power in Iraq; arrangements to ensure that Sunnis received a portion of the oil revenue; a more effective program to rebuild the nation's infrastructure; a regional nonaggression pact; international financial assistance; and a gradual redeployment of United States troops that would reduce the American military presence to twenty thousand to thirty thousand troops by the end of 2007. "Our objective in Iraq should be a loose federation within secure borders, not liberal democracy," Biden said. "It is not too late. It is in everyone's interest to stabilize Iraq, but the current course has no prospect of success."[16]

The Biden-Gelb plan was itself problematic. Many Sunnis opposed it. Hashimi told the ISG that he was afraid it would lead to the soft partition and even fragmentation of Iraq. Regardless of whatever assurances Biden might provide, he feared that the Sunnis might find themselves with only a rump state with no oil and wholly dependent on the goodwill of the Shiite government in Baghdad to get their fair share of oil proceeds. Without Sunni endorsement of the plan, the insurgency would continue. And though Biden did not emphasize the point it seemed likely that a substantial number of international forces would be needed to enforce the agreement and secure the boundaries between the different sects and ethnic groups just as they had in Bosnia and Kosovo. Baghdad and Diyala Province were just two prominent places that had mixed Sunni and Shiite populations. Biden and Gelb argued that their vision of federalism was embodied in the Iraqi constitution. But apart from the Kurds in the north, and the Iranian-backed SCIRI party, which favored the establishment of a largely autonomous Shiite sector in the south, which Tehran might dominate, the plan had few supporters in Iraq. When Congress passed a nonbinding resolution a year later endorsing the plan, the backlash in Iraq was so severe that the American embassy issued a statement all but disowning it.

As secretary of state during the George H. W. Bush administration, Baker had been skillful in dealing with the media. And the study group put aside two days to solicit their views. Some of the commentators had never been to Iraq, but they were influential voices in the debate. The journalists were divided into two panels—one conservative, the other more liberal—and were received on September 21. "How do you get more troops?" Leon Panetta asked during the session with the conservatives. "The president will not ask for more troops," George Will confidently predicted. During a session with other pundits, Tom Ricks, a *Washington Post* reporter who later left the paper to concentrate on a career as a military blogger and author, urged that a presidential apology be issued to the Iraqis and that the effort to train and advise Iraqi forces be revamped. A skeptic of the surge, he recommended that the United States cut the number of U.S. troops.[17]

Around mid-October Hamilton and Baker directed their key aides to begin writing a draft of the group's report. The vast majority of the recommendations enjoyed widespread bipartisan support and centered around three main areas: transitioning the U.S. military mission in Iraq from direct combat to training the Iraqi forces; pressing the Iraqi government to achieve key milestones of political development; and initiating diplomatic efforts to engage Iran and Syria and to pursue the Arab-Israeli peace process. The members of the group recognized the need to reach a consensus to maximize the group's influence. But resolving differences on the issue of troop withdrawals was not easy.

Casey's goal for handing over security responsibility to the Iraqis—eighteen months—was agreed to as the group's core military recommendation with little dissent. Differences began to emerge as the debate shifted to whether that timeline should be rigid or based on conditions. "The biggest issue really all along in this deal was the firm deadline," Baker said.

In Congress, a number of liberal Democrats, including John Murtha and Nancy Pelosi, advocated setting a firm date for getting out. On the other hand, several Clinton administration officials, including Sandy Berger, Richard Holbrooke, and Bill Clinton himself, voiced their opposition to a fixed timetable. After the administration promised in December 1995 that the American forces headed to Bosnia for peacekeeping duty would be out in a year, they had learned the hard way that conditions on the ground had a way of interfering with the best of intentions.

Within the group, Perry, with some support from Panetta, provided the most ardent defense of the deadline. Having accepted the gist of the Casey strategy, Perry argued that an open-ended U.S. commitment discouraged the Iraqis from standing up and taking full responsibility themselves. But Hamilton and Robb, along with the Republicans on the panel, opposed the establishing of a hard and final date.

During a divisive session at the Woodrow Wilson Center, Baker and Perry squared off over the issue. Perry initially insisted that he could not sign onto a report without a deadline, and Baker countered that if Perry felt that strongly about it, then the group would not have a consensus report. Once they recognized that neither would abandon these core principles, though, the two used the timeline they were given by Casey during their Baghdad trip as the basis for a compromise. As Baker later recalled, the final compromise essentially stated that "if we do the things we recommended," such as changing the military mission and diplomatic engagement, "then we *could*—not would or should—but we *could* meet General Casey's March [2008] deadline."[18]

Ed Meese and Perry later engaged in a similar battle of semantics over a possible surge. The initial draft report made no mention of a surge, but both Meese and Robb felt strongly that they at least had to state the possibility. Hamilton helped broker the compromise surge language, but its careful wording and placement made clear that Casey's views still carried significant weight with the group. The surge clause was not listed among the seventy-nine official recommendations, but included in the text with some key qualifications:

> Adding more American troops could conceivably worsen those aspects of the security problem that are fed by the view that the U.S. presence is intended to be a long-term "occupation." We could, however, support a short-term redeployment or surge of American combat forces to stabilize Baghdad, or to speed up the training and equipping mission, if the U.S. commander in Iraq determines that such steps would be effective.[19]

In explaining the reasoning behind the language, particularly the deference to ground commanders, Baker said, "We did that because Chuck was very strongly in favor of a surge, but the military in Baghdad had clearly indicated to us that a surge of less than 100,000" would not be enough. Perry also thought that, given the way the report was written, the implementation of a surge would be a long shot at best. "It got in there as sort of an 'on the other hand'" statement, Perry said. "It was still in my mind something not to be considered."[20]

The final report would not be released until December. The group's recommendation that the United States try to engage Iran and Syria broke with the Bush administration's foreign policy. But for all the expectation that the group would come up with an alternative strategy on military matters, it largely favored the status quo: a gradual handover to the Iraqis and an American drawdown, with the hope that a strategy that had not worked in 2005 and most of 2006 would somehow bear fruit over the next eighteen months. Casey noted as much in an account of his Iraq strategy, which he issued years after leaving. "I found the report a useful validation of what we were doing," he said of the ISG assessment.[21] It was a lowest common denominator approach that appealed to much of the Washington establishment. But the strategy the group was putting forward was not working in Iraq.

One group of experts barely consulted by the Iraq Study Group was its own military experts. To lend credibility to its effort, the group had organized a panel of senior military advisers—four generals and one admiral, including Jack Keane and Joe Ralston, the retired Air Force general and former NATO commander.

Among them, Keane's military experience was the most recent—and on Iraq, to boot. As the vice chief of staff of the Army during the lead-up to the war, Keane was familiar with the planning and had contacts at the highest levels of the administration. He had also been Rumsfeld's choice to succeed Eric Shinseki as Army chief, a post he had to turn down due to concerns about his wife's health. After Shinseki famously told the Senate Armed Services Committee that "several hundred" thousand troops would be needed to keep the peace after the regime change and was publicly dressed down by Rumsfeld and Paul Wolfowitz, the general never pressed his view internally at the Pentagon. As far as he was concerned, he had fulfilled his duty to testify honestly to Congress and had no intention of being a policy advocate.[22]

Keane had assumed a different role. He blamed the chiefs and himself for failing to anticipate the insurgency and had sought in his final months at the Pentagon to sound alarms, including to superiors who were not eager to hear his bad news. As a member of the Defense Policy Board, an advisory group to the Defense Department, he had proselytized on behalf of Derek Harvey's analysis, both within the Pentagon and to his contacts at the White House, and had stayed in touch with the situation on the ground through regular visits. By the summer of 2006, Keane was deeply worried that the strategy in Iraq had failed.

In late June, the group had convened its one and only meeting with its military advisers. The meeting was held at the Woodrow Wilson Center in Washington, but Keane and Ralston participated via conference call. Citing Harvey's analysis, Keane said there had been a "significant under-reporting of violence" and the situation was less secure than Casey's command implied. The last few years of "kill and capture" had been a mistake, Keane added, referring to Casey's strategy. "We need to protect the Iraqi people. Clear, hold, and build is good, but there are not enough forces."

Perry asked Keane about the state of the U.S. military. "How long can we sustain the force without it having an impact on our recruitment or capability?" Perry asked. Keane did not accept the argument that the Army was stretched too thin to take on the Iraq mission. "The Army can do this," Keane responded. "The key is retention of the career force, particularly good retention for those who have already served in Iraq."

Some in the group were skeptical. "Should we consider bringing back the draft?" Vernon Jordan inquired. Keane and Ralston responded negatively. In the view of most senior officials, the all-volunteer force the military had developed after Vietnam was far better than an army of conscripts.

"What about a withdrawal?" Hamilton interrupted. "What is realistic?" "We have to tell people the consequences of a precipitous withdrawal," Ralston said. "This is a long-term project, and we need at least three years."

"Should we defer to commanders on the ground regarding the question of troop levels?" Gates asked at the end of the meeting. It was an important question, given that the word coming out of Casey's headquarters was that no extra troops were needed. Keane responded that it was legitimate for the civilian leadership to play a role.[23] Even though he did not say so, Keane had lost faith in the generals in charge who believed their strategy was working, and he had already concluded that the White House and the Defense Department needed to step in and redirect the Iraq strategy. But the study group gave little weight to the panel. "It was too early on," Perry recalled. "At that time, we weren't close enough to thinking of conclusions." As all of the ISG members and staff would recall later, it was not until after their trip to Baghdad that the report really began to take shape. The study group would later list the military panel among the experts it had consulted for its final report, but the panel was not shown the group's recommendations before the report's publication. Keane, for one, was sharply critical and dismissed the report's military recommendations as irrelevant.

Before the study group headed to Iraq, Keane had pursued his own contacts. Keane told Newt Gingrich, a fellow member of the Defense Policy Board, that the U.S. Iraq strategy was faltering and shared his worries with Wolfowitz, each of whom urged him to take his views to Rumsfeld and the president. Keane started with Rumsfeld and went to see him at the Pentagon in September. Pete Pace, the chairman of the Joint Chiefs, also attended.

Urging a change of strategy, Keane advised Rumsfeld to read David Galula's famous book on counterinsurgency, even providing the chapters and page numbers that focused on urban operations. Keane said that 8 to 10 additional combat brigades—that is, between 24,000 and 50,000 troops— were needed in Iraq, stressing that this was his back-of-the-envelope calculation and that more analysis was needed to pin down the number.

As news of Keane's position spread, Chris DeMuth, the head of the American Enterprise Institute (AEI), asked him to come talk with Fred Kagan, a former professor at West Point who had shared an office at the academy with a young Army officer and fellow teacher, H.R. McMaster, and who was working on a parallel track. Kagan had also talked to the Iraq Study Group and argued that the transition strategy Casey and Rumsfeld were trumpeting was failing. He did not see a military solution for Iraq, but he believed that a strong military effort would be needed for any political strategy that had a prayer of success. With Iraq spiraling out of control, he argued, the United States was approaching its "last window of opportunity" to take on the security problems in Baghdad.

Kagan had estimated that as many as ten additional brigades might be needed, an increase of some 50,000 troops or even more. Paul Hughes, who had served in Iraq with Jay Garner before joining the think-tank world, thought the idea was completely wacky. "That was the dumbest idea I have ever heard," he observed. The Pentagon did not have lots of troops to spare, and the country would not support a massive call-up of reserves.[24]

Unperturbed, Kagan had continued to refine his plan, benefiting from some recently retired Army officers who had served with H.R. McMaster in Tal Afar. Kagan and the former officers worked the problem two ways. They tried to pin down what was needed for the greater Baghdad area and to reinforce the gains in Anbar. And they accessed the Army's Force

Generation model on the Internet to see what was available. The answer was five additional Army brigades and two additional Marine battalions. It would be a strain on the military, to be sure, but there were just enough forces to reclaim the Iraqi capital.

When Keane came by AEI to discuss Iraq, he still thought more forces than that would be needed. But after conferring with Dick Cody, the Army vice chief of staff, Keane concluded that Kagan was right about the number of available reinforcements. If there were to be a surge, Keane thought, the military would need to make the most of the situation. Both Keane and Kagan agreed that it would be a mistake to immediately send the troops into Sadr City. This would be the toughest challenge the U.S. would have to undertake in Baghdad, and they did not want to do it at the inception of the new strategy. Keane also suggested that combat outputs be established at the platoon level. What would be on the street would be small units, squads, and platoons, day and night and primarily on foot and living with the population. Kagan asked Keane to put his name on the report, but Keane demurred. He had helped considerably, but he had not written it. He did, however, share a copy with Ray Odierno, who had independently begun his own strategy review.[25]

The role of the Joint Chiefs was to train and provide forces for military contingencies. By the summer of 2006, they were worried that the operations in Iraq were badly straining the armed forces. By and large, they had brought the problem upon themselves. In January 2004, Pete Pace, then the vice chairman, had argued that it would be foolhardy to expand the size of the military. It would take two years to build a new division from scratch, Pace argued, and by that time the size of the American deployment in Iraq was slated to go down. "That number will change sooner than we could build the force, even if we wanted to build it, which I have never recommended," Pace told a seminar.[26]

At Keane's prodding, Pace had canceled a foreign trip and pulled together his own team of advisers, a smattering of smart young officers, which for reasons of Pentagon politics were drawn more or less equally from all four services and known around the Defense Department as the Council of Colonels. After convening in mid-September, the council set as its initial task to examine the global War on Terror, of which Iraq hostilities were officially a subset. The chiefs took a while to warm to the subject. On October 6, the team met with the JCS, and the chiefs were visibly uneasy with the lack of public support for an increasingly unpopular war and the modest help the military was receiving from other parts of the U.S. government. Bush's vision of a democratic Iraq seemed a bridge too far.

Buzz Moseley, the Air Force chief of staff, mused, "Some folks talk about us shoving Jeffersonian democracy down people's throats." "I have told POTUS that 'democracy' is not as effective a term as 'representative government.' We need to soften our use of 'democracy,'" Pace responded. "We need to look at things we can do better to win the war. There needs to be a recognition that the military is not going to win it alone."

"We got a complex, long war going on, but we are being perceived as cultural imperialists," said Pete Schoomaker, the Army chief of staff. "We should work to avoid the clash of civilizations. It is not inevitable," Moseley said, referencing Samuel Huntington's famous treatise positing the conflict between Eastern and Western civilizations.

Mike Mullen, the chief of naval operations and future chairman of the Joint Chiefs, was skeptical: "How do we avoid it? Iran has moved up the escalation curve." To the admiral, a clash with the Islamic Republic, which was seemingly bent on acquiring nuclear weapons, was a worry. "We have moved it up," Moseley said. "We are starting to identify Iran as an enemy." "We have handed Iraq to Iran," Schoomaker added gloomily.

When the JCS met with the Council of Colonels a week later, Pace was unhappy. There had been leaks. Mullen suggested that the review "be put into a special compartment." The first topic was instability in the Middle East. Schoomaker recommended that the chiefs read President Musharraf's new autobiography, *In the Line of Fire,* which chronicled the troubled history of India and Pakistan. Mullen recommended David Fromkin's magnum opus, *A Peace to End All Peace,* which showed how the fall of the Ottoman Empire had shaped the modern Middle East.

Then the discussion edged to Iraq. "Casey thinks the militias are a huge problem, but the Iraqi government does not want to take them down right now," Schoomaker said. "Casey does not think at this time that the militias can be dissolved."

"Let's avoid minutia and focus on the big ideas," Schoomaker continued. "One of the things we need to do is reduce dependence on oil. We are supposed to be thinking strategically, not tactically."

"Yes, oil is a major factor. We have got to reduce the American dependence on oil," Mullen said.

"We need to look at this from a long-term perspective. We need some altitude," Schoomaker said. "These are twenty-year wars, not ten-year wars. We have a short-war strategy for a long war. That is our problem."

Pace brought the bull session down to earth: "We need to spin out some ideas to Casey so he can share them with Khalilzad." Mullen argued that the United States was running short of time. "Time is a factor," Mullen said. "How long will Maliki survive? We can establish the benchmarks. But even if Maliki agrees, does the Iraqi timeline match our timeline?"

"The immediate center of gravity is the U.S. public," Pace said, echoing the thinking in Casey's first campaign plan. "We have got to promulgate new benchmarks with timelines to keep the American people engaged. Casey has a four-year timeline and we have about ninety days left with the U.S. public. SECDEF [Secretary of Defense] is pushing benchmarks, and we need to give our message in a more loud and comprehensive manner. The enemy thinks that two years is a short period of time."

"How do we prepare the American people for the long haul?" Mullen asked. Mike Hagee, the commandant of the Marine Corps, joined the discussion. "We don't. They are spectators right now. We are not asking them to change their ways or lives," he said bluntly. "The end state is when the troops come home. The long war ends when the troops come home."

"Two years from now we will have a new POTUS, and whoever that is probably will be under pressure to bring the troops home," Moseley said.[27]

On November 3, the Council of Colonels presented their assessment. The team mapped out six options. One was a massive surge of reinforcements that would involve sending all available forces and extending the deployment of the troops that were already there. This plan was known as "Go Big" and was championed virtually alone by H.R. McMaster. Another option was to reduce the American military presence, lower the U.S. casualty toll, and make the war more politically sustainable at home. It was known as "Go Long" and backed by Pete Mansoor, the Army colonel who had commanded a brigade in Iraq in 2004. The council even looked at an option to withdraw all troops, called "Go Home," which was supported initially by Tom Greenwood, a Marine colonel who had led a Marine expeditionary unit in the Triangle of Death, the Sunni provinces surrounding Baghdad, and who had returned to oversee the training effort for the Iraqi Army and police in Anbar.

The Council of Colonel's main contribution, however, was not to propose solutions, which their structure and mandate made them ill-disposed to do, but to define the problem. The group identified six major trends in

Iraq, all negative. The current strategy was not working. The Iraqi government was incapable of producing tangible results in the eyes of the Iraqi people. Much of Iraq's security force was weak, particularly the police. There was a debilitating cycle of sectarian violence, which Al-Qaeda was exploiting. Efforts to establish the rule of law had faltered, and there was little economic progress. Iraqis believed that the removal of Saddam would be followed by international assistance to revitalize the economy, but that aid had not been effective.

As for impediments, the colonels thought that the United States needed to acknowledge that it was involved in a complex insurgency as well as an escalating civil war. Properly characterizing the war was critical. The United States had to overcome its short-war mentality and develop a strategy to succeed in a protracted fight.

Greenwood put the colonels' conclusion on a PowerPoint slide. "Finally, after three years of sacrifice we think we are running out of time. . . . As the invading foreign power the burden is on us to win or at least show credible progress in Iraq. Because this is not happening at a rate that is convincing the Iraqi people, the American people, and the international community, our group of colonels thinks we are losing in Iraq today," the slide read. "We are not winning so we are losing."

Sensitive to the Bush administration's public relations requirements, Pace used that sentence at an off-the-record event, but with a not too subtle change that took the sting out and substantially altered the meaning: "We are not winning, but we're not losing."

CHAPTER 16

Back to the Drawing Board

On October 29, National Security Adviser Steve Hadley arrived in Baghdad to take his own look at the situation. Hadley had presided over dozens of White House meetings on the war and worked to keep the NSC machinery running. With a law degree from Yale, Hadley had worked for the NSC during the Nixon and Ford administrations. As counsel for the Tower Commission, which was established in the wake of the Iran-contra scandal, he had helped draft the panel's recommendation on how the NSC should operate. Hadley had held a senior Pentagon position on NATO and European security issues when Dick Cheney was defense secretary, and he had published a clarion call for building a national missile defense when George W. Bush was running for president. Nuclear matters and arms control had been his forte, not wars in the Middle East. With an indefatigable appetite for work, however, Hadley was a loyal and punctilious advocate for his client, the president. By August the president himself was interested in taking a second look at the strategy for Iraq, so Hadley was making his first trip to the Iraqi capital.

With the Baker-Hamilton study group preparing to endorse a troop drawdown, Joe Biden pressing for an ambitious version of federalism, and Jack Keane building a case for more troops, Hadley had quietly begun his own review on the president's behalf.

The NSC review had been a while in the making. In early June, Brett McGurk, an aide on the NSC who had just been assigned to Baghdad for several months, wrote a scathing ten-page trip report, which he shared with Meghan O'Sullivan and Brigadier General Kevin Bergner, who made up the Iraq team on the NSC. "Gen. Casey still has no serious plan for stabilizing the capital," McGurk wrote. He had spent nearly a year in Iraq in

2004 and now—two years later—described a "disintegration" outside the Green Zone, recommending a "radical" course correction "to match the facts as we find them, with substantial U.S. forces deployed to Baghdad."

O'Sullivan agreed that more troops were almost certainly needed—in a spring meeting with Bush she had told the president that conditions in Baghdad were "hell"—but she and Bergner explained that the president would be leading a two-day strategy review later that month at Camp David. O'Sullivan instructed McGurk to tone down his memo by starting positive and then bringing up some of the uncomfortable issues. O'Sullivan had also grown uneasy with Casey's strategy but did not think that an emotional memo from the field was the way to build the case for a new approach within the White House. In his three-page revision, McGurk reported that the situation in Baghdad had worsened and urged a long-term strategy, but left out the appeal for more forces. The Camp David review was curtailed when Bush suddenly went to Baghdad to meet Maliki.

As Bush's doubts mounted over the summer, however, Hadley told O'Sullivan in late August that the president had finally decided to mount a White House strategy review, and that she was to help lead it. Other sections of the NSC staff were drawn in as well. In early October, Hadley turned to his deputy, J. D. Crouch, and suggested that he also involve Bill Luti, a former Navy aviator who had flown in the 1991 Persian Gulf War, gone to work for the Rumsfeld team at the Pentagon after retiring from the military, and then taken a slot as the NSC staff member on defense issues. Luti, who had seen that the situation was deteriorating during a July trip to Iraq and thought a strategy review was long overdue, was to look at how a troop surge might work.[1]

One of Luti's aides in his NSC office, a military officer, used his contacts at the Pentagon to determine how many forces might be available if the president wanted to double down. Luti got the same answer that Keane had from his Defense Department contacts: if the Army pulled out all the stops, it could provide five brigades—or some twenty thousand additional combat troops. Drawing on the information, Luti submitted a confidential briefing, "Changing the Dynamics in Iraq: Surge and Fight, Create Breathing Space and Then Accelerate the Transition." As far as Luti was concerned, the White House had the essential information it needed to make a decision. Casey's strategy was failing; political support at home was evaporating; and more troops were available. There was nothing to be gained by waiting. A difficult situation would only become worse.[2] Hadley believed that the situation was more complicated. With the military stretched thin, the Joint Chiefs were not interested in sending more troops. The challenge, he thought, was not just to formulate an effective strategy but also to avoid a damaging breach with the military.

Hadley began his Baghdad stay at a breakfast meeting with Casey, Chiarelli, and other senior staff officers at Camp Victory. His next stop was the headquarters of J. D. Thurman's 4th Infantry Division, which had the frustrating mission of implementing Together Forward II. Along with his aides from the NSC—O'Sullivan, Bergner, and Peter Feaver—Hadley was ushered into a conference room full of battalion commanders and sergeants major. With the exception of Chuck Robb, nobody on the Iraq Study Group had met with any military man in Baghdad below the rank of general. But it was the battalion commanders and sergeant majors who knew better than anyone what it was like to operate on Baghdad's streets.

Lieutenant Colonel Gian Gentile, whose troops had responsibility for the Ameriya neighborhood, came right to the point. In order for the American strategy to work, the people needed to believe that the Iraqi government wanted to help them—and the Sunnis did not believe that. A local Sunni imam, Gentile related, had observed that the Iraqis required an iron fist to deal with the situation, and that fist was the Americans. "They think this is a sectarian government out to crush them."

"People don't trust the government," added Ronald Riling, the division's sergeant major, who had earned a Silver Star for rescuing a squad of Marines in Ramadi in 2004. Riling then related a story of how Iraqi women had been shot by the police for speaking with American soldiers.

Lieutenant Colonel Christopher Hall, a battalion commander with the 101st, reported that "people are petrified to leave their enclaves." Of the Iraqi forces, the army was trusted more than the police. Colonel Mike Beech, who led a brigade that operated in central Baghdad, reported that the Shiite militias had become a big part of the problem. Hadley suggested that the Shiites and the Sunnis had been relatively restrained until the February 22 bombing of the Askari Mosque in Samarra. "Maybe," Beech replied. "But I am not sure that I know who is running the government."[3]

As the discussion continued, Chiarelli and Thurman were pulled out of the meeting to take a conference call in Thurman's office. A U.S. Army interpreter, Specialist Ahmed Altaie, had made an unauthorized excursion into Baghdad to meet his Iraqi wife, and been kidnapped and hauled off to Sadr City. For a week, Chiarelli and Thurman had been mounting a desperate effort to get him back, even as they struggled to stop the Shiite militias from leaving their bastion in Sadr City to venture into the Sunni neighborhoods. To that end, the Americans had set up a series of checkpoints on the roads crossing the Army Canal separating Sadr City from the rest of Baghdad.

But Prime Minister Maliki was under pressure from the Sadrists. This junior partner in his government had complained that the checkpoints were hampering the traffic in and out of Sadr City. In a meeting with Casey, Khalilzad, and his aide, Ali Khedery, Maliki insisted that Sadr City could not be sealed off and went so far as to suggest that as an Iraqi-American, Altaie was not worth the trouble. "This guy is one of us, not one of you," Maliki said. To the befuddlement of Khedery, himself an American of Iraqi descent, the general and ambassador did not say a word. Casey later wrote that he had determined that the checkpoints were no longer of great utility in the search for Altaie before informing Chiarelli they were to be lifted.[4]

For Chiarelli, it was one of his darkest moments in Iraq. Here was proof of what battalion commanders had been saying about the Iraqi government: that it was tolerant of, if not complicit in, the violence engulfing the country. And as Chiarelli saw it, the beleaguered American forces could not do what was necessary to tamp down the violence.[5] (Chiarelli and Thurman were not the only ones taken aback by the episode. In a video-conference, Rumsfeld made clear that he was unhappy with news reports that suggested that Casey was being pushed around. "You don't work for the prime minister," the defense secretary said sternly. "You report through us—[John] Abizaid and SECDEF—then to POTUS, and we decide. He's not your political leader.")[6]

Chiarelli was surprised that Hadley seemed to be taking in the scope of the problem for the first time. The policymakers in Washington, he thought, always seemed to be six months behind the curve. At the end of his visit, Chiarelli rode to the airport with Hadley. The national security adviser made a candid acknowledgment: "I should have come here before."[7]

One week after visiting Baghdad, Hadley and his NSC team drafted a classified memo for Bush that outlined the administration's dilemma. The document was one of the most candid and significant pieces of internal documentation of the war. Maliki was not acting as the nationalist leader the White House had been waiting for when he was summoned by Khalilzad and encouraged to seek the prime minister post. He did not seem to be a Shiite Saddam, but neither did he seem to be working hard to confront the sectarianism in the Shiite ranks. The choice the Americans had to make was whether they could work with Maliki and how. As Hadley wrote in a confidential note to President Bush:

We returned from Iraq convinced we need to determine if Prime Minister Maliki is both willing and able to rise above the sectarian agendas being promoted by others. Do we and Prime Minister Maliki share the same vision for Iraq? If so, is he able to curb those who seek Shia hegemony or the reassertion of Sunni power? The answers to these questions are key in determining whether we have the right strategy in Iraq.

Maliki reiterated a vision of Shia, Sunni, and Kurdish partnership, and in my one-on-one meeting with him, he impressed me as a leader who wanted to be strong but was having difficulty figuring out how to do so. Maliki pointed to incidents, such as the use of Iraqi forces in Shia Karbala, to demonstrate his even hand. Perhaps because he is frustrated over his limited ability to command Iraqi forces against terrorists and insurgents, Maliki has been trying to show strength by standing up to the coalition. Hence the public spats with us over benchmarks and the Sadr City roadblocks.

Despite Maliki's reassuring words, repeated reports from our commanders on the ground contributed to our concerns about Maliki's government. Reports of nondelivery of services to Sunni areas, intervention by the prime minister's office to stop military action against Shia targets and to encourage them against Sunni ones, removal of Iraq's most effective commanders on a sectarian basis, and efforts to ensure Shia majorities in all ministries—when combined with the escalation of Jaish al-Mahdi's (JAM) killings—all suggest a campaign to consolidate Shia power in Baghdad.

While there does seem to be an aggressive push to consolidate Shia power and influence, it is less clear whether Maliki is a witting participant. The information he receives is undoubtedly skewed by his small circle of Dawa advisers, coloring his actions and interpretation of reality. His intentions seem good when he talks with Americans, and sensitive reporting suggests he is trying to stand up to the Shia hierarchy and force positive change. But the reality on the streets of Baghdad suggests Maliki is either ignorant of what is going on, misrepresenting his intentions, or that his capabilities are not yet sufficient to turn his good intentions into action.[8]

Hadley's memo noted that there were a number of steps Maliki could take to demonstrate his good intentions, and he ranked them by the level of difficulty. The Iraqi prime minister could insist that his ministries provide health services and open bank branches in Sunni neighborhoods to broadcast that the government would not tolerate sectarianism. Maliki could bring Mahdi Army members who engaged in ethnic cleansing to justice.

He could shake up his cabinet by appointing nonsectarian technocrats and overhaul his own staff to reflect the diversity of Iraq. Maliki, the memo went on, could demand that government workers renounce violence as a condition for keeping their posts. He could announce his support for a status of forces agreement that would enable the United States to maintain forces in Iraq after the U.N. mandate ran out. He could suspend de-Baathification measures, sanction Iraqi police units involved in sectarian operations, and announce plans to expand the more professional Iraqi Army over the next nine months. The prime minister could back an expanded American program to train Iraqi Interior Ministry units.

Were Maliki willing to take these steps, the United States could take commensurate and fitting action: it could continue to target Al-Qaeda to show the Shiites that they did not need to turn to militias to protect their families, while encouraging Khalilzad to move to the background and allow Maliki to take more credit for positive developments. The Americans could also let Maliki have more control over Iraqi forces, while prodding Saudi businessmen to stop funding insurgent groups.

Hadley's program for reducing the violence seemed reasonable, but perhaps not one that Maliki was up to. "Pushing Maliki to take these steps without augmenting his capabilities could force him to failure," Hadley's memo noted. "We must also be mindful of Maliki's personal history as a figure in the Dawa Party—an underground conspiratorial movement—during Saddam's rule. Maliki and those around him are naturally inclined to distrust new actors, and it may take strong assurances from the United States ultimately to convince him to expand his circle of advisers or take action against the interests of his own Shia coalition and for the benefit of Iraq as a whole."

To enhance Maliki's authority, the United States might use its influence to help him form a new political coalition among Shiites, Kurds, and Sunnis. Toward that end, the United States could "consider monetary support" to moderate groups to persuade them to line up behind the prime minister. As for security, the memo said that there was a "four brigade gap" in Baghdad, which might have to be filled with American troops if not enough Iraqi forces were available. The Bush administration needed to determine if the political situation there could be salvaged, and how. "We should waste no time in our efforts to determine Maliki's intentions and, if necessary, to augment his capabilities," the memo noted.

One day after the November 7 congressional elections, Rumsfeld resigned from his post as secretary of defense at Bush's request. Two days later, the

White House officially launched its Iraq review. The Bush administration had kept a stiff upper lip through the election, which many Republicans thought was a serious political miscalculation, but now that the vote was over and the Democrats had racked up some impressive gains, the reassessment of the strategy was no longer a secret.

On November 11, Hadley, Rice, and their senior aides met to debate the strategy. Rice was skeptical there was much the United States could do militarily to stop the sectarian violence beyond preventing mass killings. "I don't think we can equate force levels with security," she said, a view that her Iraq troubleshooter, David Satterfield, endorsed. Brett McGurk pushed back, as did Peter Feaver and Meghan O'Sullivan, Hadley's aides. McGurk noted that John Charles, one of the CIA's top counterinsurgency experts, had done an assessment that showed that in areas of Iraq where the United States had a substantial military presence, it was "able to help resolve local disputes before they get out of control." But McGurk added, there had never been enough forces in Baghdad.

"We would need to be confident that an increase of that kind would work," Philip Zelikow, the State Department counselor, said skeptically. "We would be betting the house on it."

"The house and the whole farm," Hadley added.

In Baghdad, Khalilzad and Casey were convinced that they still had the answer. Hadley's memo had opened the door to sending more American troops, but Khalilzad had embraced an altogether different political strategy. In a confidential November 15 memo, Khalilzad reported that Maliki's primary interests were controlling Iraq's security forces and increasing their size. The ambassador did not perceive this development as a sign of creeping authoritarianism but as an encouraging indication that the Iraqi government wanted to be self-sufficient. Under the current plan, control of Iraq's security forces was to be transferred to the government in eighteen months. Khalilzad suggested that the goal be to make it happen by the end of 2007, and to shift American forces to an "overwatch" stance on the periphery of Iraq's major cities.

In return for giving Maliki what he wanted by way of control, Khalilzad wrote, the United States would obtain leverage to press for the long-deferred political reconciliation among Sunnis, Shiites, and Kurds. Beyond that, there were other steps Washington could take to encourage Maliki and his Shiite allies to reconcile with the Sunnis. The United States, Khalilzad wrote, should assure Maliki that if the Sunnis tried to mount a coup to unseat him American forces would intervene to "protect Iraq's democratic system." It could also commit to defending Iraq against external aggression, thus easing Maliki's worries about intervention, direct or indirect, by unfriendly Sunni Arab states.

Khalilzad had a reputation for being a freewheeling ambassador, prone to seize the moment: Maliki's very position atop the Iraqi government was proof of that. But now the ambassador stressed that he would need even more autonomy and authority. "I will need to have a broad mandate, requisite authorities and resources to incentivize the Iraqis to move in the right direction," he wrote. "We need to change their calculations, using reward and punishment, so that they feel compelled to come to terms with each other."

Khalilzad recalled that he later supported the surge, but in mid-November he did not argue that an infusion of additional troops was vital. "Sending more US forces is not a long-term solution," the ambassador wrote. "Additional forces can impact the areas where they are deployed, though the violence can simply shift to another area. Iraqis securing Iraqis is the enduring solution. As we draw down, our forces should focus on specialized roles, such as striking Al Qaeda, disrupting external interference, and reinforcing and mentoring Iraqi forces."[9]

Khalilzad's military partner, George Casey, was of the same mind. Casey and the Joint Chiefs were aware that the White House was considering sending more troops and were notably unenthusiastic. In a November 22 videoconference with the chiefs, Casey argued that adding more American troops would have only a temporary and local effect. The administration, Casey argued, needed to consider whether the tactical gain was worth the risk of unhinging the progress that had been made in getting the Iraqis to assume more responsibility for security and governance. The longer the United States delayed transferring responsibility to the Iraqis, the less incentive the Iraqis would have to settle their own problems. Casey also believed that speeding up the transfer might be a lure to get the Maliki government to take some of the difficult steps the Americans were urging. Nor was it clear that Maliki, who was chafing to assert more control, would even accept the American reinforcements. "I don't think we need additional forces at this time," Casey said.

If the White House was determined to send additional troops, Casey suggested, they might be used to thicken U.S. positions along the periphery of Baghdad and not be thrust into the midst of the sectarian violence in the city. Another option would be to put the additional forces in Diyala or Anbar, along the border, or use them to guard infrastructure. One thing Casey was clearly not contemplating was a revamped counterinsurgency campaign. He advised that, if additional forces were sent, the United States should compel the Iraqi government to commit itself to expedited reconciliation as a precondition.

General Pete Schoomaker backed Casey. The Army chief of staff was less worried about Iraq than about the consequences of a surge: American inability to take on other crises if they arose. "We need to be concerned with the lack of capability to deal with anything else in the world right now," he said.

Pete Pace said that Casey had some good insights. To alter the situation in Iraq, Pace said, the surge would need to begin by the spring, but he worried that if he stressed this point too much the White House might assume that he was advocating the strategy. "I am not convinced we should do it at this time because of the back-end costs," he said.

Admiral Mike Mullen, the chief of naval operations, asked what the specific goals of the surge might be. "What is the end state we want by producing an extra five brigades?"

Vice Admiral Dave Nichols, the deputy commander of CENTCOM, chimed in in support of Casey. The big issue was reconciliation, but that was a chicken-or-egg scenario. A five-brigade surge might do more harm than good. Expanding the teams of advisers that accompanied Iraqi units might be a good idea. Nichols added that he did not think the United States would ever be able to fight the Mahdi Army. That would continue to be an Iraqi problem.

Schoomaker raised a question about the very nature of the mission in Iraq. Was it really clear that the United States and Iraq shared the same assumptions on how to proceed? "Maybe we won't agree on any objectives with the government of Iraq," Mullen added. "How can we make progress in Iraq if we can't change these assumptions?"

Casey said that perhaps the United States should develop some benchmarks for reconciliation. But the absence of progress on reconciliation, he said, would not by itself cause "strategic failure." The only way the strategy could utterly fail, Casey said, would be if the Iraqi Army collapsed after it took control.[10]

While Casey did not believe there was an immediate possibility of strategic failure, U.S. intelligence agencies were less forgiving. A classified CIA report in November interpreted the conditions in Iraq as a "civil war." The speedy withdrawal of American troops would end any hope of forming an inclusive government, let alone the democracy Bush had hoped to establish. It would also undermine the confidence of Saudi and other Arab states in Washington. Quoting a private conversation with the Saudi crown prince, the agency reported that he had observed that a quick American withdrawal would be tantamount to "following idiocy with crime."[11]

At the White House, there was a sense of urgency. President Bush wanted to announce a new phase of the Iraq strategy by January. He had arranged to meet Maliki in Amman, Jordan, on November 30 to discuss how to cope with the growing crisis. Hadley's memo had raised the question of whether Maliki was an adequate strategic partner, but Bush had made the call: The United States would give the Iraqi prime minister the benefit of the doubt. It would try to work with him and find ways to make him more effective.

Maliki had his own ideas of what he wanted from the Amman meeting. In the weeks preceding the session, he and Mowaffak al-Rubaie developed a plan to move American forces to the periphery of Baghdad; Iraqis would be chiefly responsible for battling Al-Qaeda and Sunni insurgents. Additional Iraqi forces, including Kurdish units—some of the few brigades the Iraqi government could deploy without fear of widespread desertion—would be brought to Baghdad to help Iraqi forces already there restore order. The city would be divided into seven military districts, and command and control of the Baghdad region would no longer be solely an American prerogative but would be shared. The Iraqi Army would be expanded, and the police vetted. A high-level panel would consider arrangements under which the United States would protect the democratic system internally and safeguard Iraq from external enemies. Knowing the American penchant for PowerPoint, Rubaie had the plan turned into a series of slides, which he and the prime minister intended to present. Casey had been kept informed of the Iraqi plan, and had even given the Iraqis quiet assistance from the side.[12]

The flight to Amman was filled with drama. The Sadrists had threatened to bolt from the government if Maliki met with the Americans. Following through with the meeting would rip apart Maliki's governing coalition. But American support was far more important to the prime minister at this stage than the prospect of Sadrist defection. As Maliki headed to Jordan, the Sadrists pulled their ministers from his cabinet, but kept their mid-level officials in the Health and Transportation ministries, as well as at the Baghdad Airport. The Sadrist strategy was to undermine the Maliki government but maintain their influence within the state's governing structures.

The public relations crisis shadowed the meeting between Bush and Maliki. The morning before it took place, an account of Hadley's memo, including the full text of the document, with its unvarnished portrait of the prime minister, had been published in the *New York Times*.[13] As a rule, Maliki did not care one way or another what was written about him in the Western media. He was focused first and foremost on the Iraqi and Arab press. Still, Rubaie wanted to avoid any unnecessary unpleasantness and did not translate the article for the prime minister. When Maliki arrived in Amman the Iraqis canceled the state dinner that had been planned that night, a move that led American pundits to speculate that the prime minister was expressing his unhappiness over Hadley's memo and the fact that it had been leaked. The truth, however, was different: the cancellation of the state dinner was meant as a slight to the Jordanian hosts, who Maliki felt were being presumptuous and behaving too grandly for their own good by hosting the dinner. Maliki had come to talk with Bush, not with the leader of a Sunni Arab state.[14]

The next day, Bush and Maliki met, along with their top aides. As the meeting got under way, Bush sought to defuse the controversy in the media over the disclosure of the Hadley memo. "Prime Minister, you will want to see Steve Hadley," Bush quipped. "He's the guy who wrote the memo." Maliki went up to Hadley, took his hand, and said that it had been a pleasure to meet him in Baghdad and he could come back any time. There were big issues to grapple with, and neither side was going to allow the memo to be a distraction. Once they got down to business, Maliki and Rubaie went through the plan to have Iraqi troops assume security in Baghdad. Bush turned to Casey and asked if he had been involved. "George, do you know anything about this?" the president asked. Casey acknowledged that he had had a role, but played it down.

Bush applauded Maliki's willingness to take the initiative. During a break, however, Bush asked Casey whether the Iraqis were prepared to handle Baghdad security all on their own. Casey reported that the handover to the Iraqis could be accelerated if militias were disbanded and there was progress toward political reconciliation. But Bush believed that the way the violence was raging, time was running out. Bush wanted results much faster. The president sought to prepare the ground for sending additional American troops. The United States could lend Iraq the forces until their own troops were better prepared. But neither Maliki nor Rubaie had given up on their vision. At the end of the session, Rubaie handed the Americans a copy of their plan and told them to keep it. "We trust you," he quipped. The Iraqis were also capable of joking about the Hadley memo.[15]

Even as Bush, the Joint Chiefs, and Casey were debating the way ahead, it was time for Chiarelli to hand over his responsibilities as multinational corps commander. It was a sour moment for Chiarelli. He was leaving Iraq in midstream and without accomplishing his mission; Baghdad was even worse off than when he arrived. He had been appalled by the sectarian violence, and Nycki Brooks's briefings had convinced him that there was a Shiite method to their apparent sectarian madness—a strategy at work to secure key terrain in Baghdad, the route to the Shiite power centers in Najaf and Karbala, and the roads through Diyala to Iran. Discouraged, Chiarelli thought the United States needed a plan to deal with the possibility that the Americans and the Iraqi government did not share the same goal: an inclusive, pluralistic Iraq. With Celeste Ward's help, he put together a secret briefing, "Analysis of Iraqi and Coalition End States." While the Americans favored a unified Iraq that respected the rule of law, Iraq's disputatious groups had other objectives. The Shiites, the briefing said, wanted "dominance." The Sunnis were fragmented, and the Kurds wanted autonomy. If current trends continued, the brief asserted, the Iraqi government in Baghdad would be weak and mostly in the hands of the Sadrists. The nine southern provinces would have considerable autonomy and be heavily influenced by Hakim's SCIRI. The Kurds would have a lot of leeway to run their own affairs, and the Sunnis might be "in the wilderness." If Iraq was headed toward this sort of fragmentation, would there be a soft landing or a hard landing?[16] The implication was that the United States needed to have a "Plan B" to encourage a soft landing. Chiarelli gave the briefing to Casey at his villa at Camp Victory, but the commander did not respond. Casey's silence spoke volumes: he was not persuaded that his transition plan had failed.[17]

Chiarelli's replacement was Ray Odierno, the towering, bald commander who had announced the capture of Saddam Hussein and also played bad guy to Dave Petraeus's good guy as commander of the 4th Infantry Division in northern Iraq in 2003. Since then, Odierno had had plenty of time to think and plenty to think about. His son, a captain in the 1st Cavalry Division, had been badly wounded, losing an arm to an RPG on Baghdad's infamous Route Irish in 2004. Odierno took a wholly different approach to his job as corps commander than his predecessors had. Over the years the corps command in Baghdad had often struggled to find a role for itself, overshadowed as it was by a four-star headquarters just down the street on Camp Victory. The nebulous job of an Army corps commander was to execute the "operational level of war," the doctrinal level between the strategic and the tactical, in a conflict in which strategic and tactical often overlapped. The "operational level" could be tricky to define and execute well on a conventional battlefield (the term was coined to describe the huge Eastern Front campaigns in World War II), and not everyone in the Army was convinced that the operational level even existed in a counterinsurgency. The way Odierno tied together the "kinetic" and "non-kinetic" operations of many brigades in geographically disparate areas would convince many skeptics.

To Odierno and his staff, Brooks's analysis of the belts around Baghdad made perfect sense. The belts were vital to both enemy groups, Al-Qaeda and the militia; that was why they were fighting over them. Brooks's report was also fortified by a separate analysis by Colonel Jim Hickey, whom Odierno brought with him to Iraq and put in charge of an ad hoc cell called the Counter-IED Operations Integration Center, which the general hoped would help him find the enemy's sanctuaries and decide where to attack.[18]

"If I was graded on my ability to grow ISF, I would get an A," said Jim Pasquarette, the brigade commander who was leaving the northern belt as Odierno was arriving. "If I was graded on my ability to secure my area over the course of our year, I would get an F."[19] Keeping a lid on Baghdad itself was important, but it was not sufficient; to get results in the capital different from those of the Together Forward operations, units would have to push out into the belts and kick the enemy out—not merely engage in quick forays like JSOC's, but fight for the long haul, as Mike Kershaw's brigade was doing in Yusifiyah, dug into platoon- and company-sized outposts. For this to become a reality, however, Odierno's headquarters would need many more troops.

Before leaving for Iraq, Odierno had stopped by the office of Eric Edelman, the undersecretary of defense for policy. It was an awkward period: Rumsfeld had resigned but would continue to serve as defense secretary until Robert Gates took over. Gates had been serving as the president of Texas A&M when he was picked to replace Rumsfeld, and he had insisted that he not formally take over his Pentagon duties until he had presided over the winter commencement at the university, which was scheduled for December 16. Two secretaries of defense, in effect, inhabited the same building, the departing one in his old suite on the third floor of the Pentagon, and the incoming one in a vacated Navy office a floor above. Officials ran back and forth, briefing each on the key issues. In his closed-door meeting with Edelman, Odierno indicated that he had some ideas about how to fix Baghdad, but would need more troops. Edelman indicated that he understood the need but that the current secretary of defense would not be sympathetic. As far as the Pentagon was concerned, it would be hard to have a serious discussion about sending more forces until Rumsfeld was gone.[20] Odierno was scheduled to take over the corps in Baghdad on December 12, and Gates would formally become defense secretary a week after that.

Events and intelligence in Iraq reinforced Odierno's and Hickey's intuition of what would be needed. When 1st Cavalry Division troops stopped a car in December and captured the so-called Taji DOCEX, the trove of internal Al-Qaeda reports made the importance of the belts obvious with its updates from various belt-sector commanders like Abu Ghazwan. "The most important battle, which is happening now, is the battle of the Baghdad belt," one document read, and another acknowledged that in the southern belt, where Mike Kershaw's brigade was fighting, Al-Qaeda was losing ground.[21]

A map included in the Taji trove also identified the areas within Baghdad that Al-Qaeda intended to fortify as Sunni strongholds against the Mahdi Army and Iraqi security forces, describing how the demographics of each neighborhood were changing due to war. The areas the group identified as its urban centers—Adhamiya in East Baghdad, the only remaining Sunni-majority area there, and Dora and Ameriya in West Baghdad—were all places where American troops were running into rising numbers of the deadly deep-buried bombs that were Al-Qaeda's signature weapon. Adhamiya had been left uncovered for months by the drawdown of American forces in Baghdad, and when a new battalion arrived there from Germany in the fall, 1-26 Infantry, it found itself in one of the toughest fights in the country. On December 4, a nineteen-year-old private first class in the unit, Ross McGinnis, covered a live hand grenade with his body after it was tossed into his gunner's hatch, saving the rest of the Humvee crew. Like Michael Monsoor, the SEAL in Ramadi who had jumped on a grenade nine weeks earlier, McGinnis would be awarded a posthumous Medal of Honor, the fourth of the Iraq War.[22]

Odierno wanted more forces, but other senior officers in Iraq felt that more could be accomplished in Baghdad by relocating troops there from elsewhere in the country, as during Together Forward II. On December 12, Casey summoned him and nine other general officers to brief a revised Baghdad Security Plan that would incorporate two extra American brigades. Before the meeting adjourned, according to participants, Casey took an informal poll of the ten generals in his office: should the two

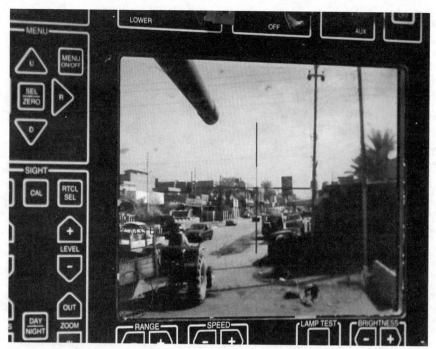

The streets of Baghdad, as seen through the targeting system of a Stryker armored vehicle during Operation Together Forward in 2006. (JIM WILSON/*New York Times*)

American soldiers stand guard as the father of Latif Abd al-Kathum Hilal al-Janabi weeps outside of a morgue in Baghdad while waiting to collect his son's body. Latif, a Sunni, was killed by assailants, and his family was afraid to go to the Shiite-controlled hospital without an American military escort. (JIM WILSON/*New York Times*)

An explosive ordance disposal robot begins a mission in Baghdad. The Academy Award–winning film *The Hurt Locker* portrayed EOD technicians as cowboys who would walk up to a bomb to disarm it wearing only a heavy suit. Far more often, they used robots to place explosive charges on a bomb and detonate it from a safe distance. (JIM WILSON/*New York Times*)

Colonel Shaban Barzan al-Ubaydi, the police chief of the Anbari town of Baghdadi, walks with his men during the summer of 2006. (JIM WILSON/*New York Times*)

General David Petraeus talks with Anbar Awakening leader Sheikh Abd al-Sattar al-Rishawi in Ramadi in February 2007. Sterling Jensen, a civilian interpreter with the 1st Brigade, 1st Armored Division is between them. (COURTESY STERLING JENSEN)

1st Cavalry Division commander Major General Joseph Fil (left) talks with Ambassador Ryan Crocker in Baghdad during the early months of the 2007 surge. (MAJOR STEPHEN LAMB/MND-B PUBLIC AFFAIRS)

Sheikh Ali Majid al-Dulaimi, a tribal leader and former insurgent, uses a U.S. Army megaphone to speak to the residents of Hawr Rajab. Sheikh Ali explained that the soldiers had come to the town center to conduct a humanitarian mission. (BEN LOWY)

1-40 Cavalry commander Lieutenant Colonel Mark Odom (left) and two Awakening leaders—Sheikh Mahir Sarhan Morab al-Muini and Sheikh Ali Majid al-Dulaimi—discuss plans for a night raid, as Captain Chad Klascius looks on. (BEN LOWY)

As a medevac helicopter lands, medics treat Specialist Jose Collazo for injuries sustained when his Husky mine-clearing vehicle was destroyed by an IED on August 4, 2007, in Hawr Rajab. Collazo was evacuated to Texas, where he recovered from his injuries. (BEN LOWY)

Sheikh Abd al-Sattar al-Rishawi (right) gestures to Mamun Sami Rashid, governor of Anbar Province, during the Anbar Forum on September 6, 2007. The two men were at the heart of Iraq's Sunni Awakening, and Abd al-Sattar would be killed seven days later. (LANCE CORPORAL JULIAN BILLMAIR/U.S. MARINE CORPS)

Admirals Mike Mullen (left) and William "Fox" Fallon held two of the most important positions in the American armed forces at a time when the military was embroiled in two land wars. Mullen was chairman of the Joint Chiefs of Staff from August 2007 until September 2011; Fallon commanded CENTCOM during 2007 and early 2008, where he clashed with Petraeus over Iraq strategy. (MASS COMMUNICATION SPECIALIST 1ST CLASS CHAD J. MCNEELEY, U.S. NAVY/DEPARTMENT OF DEFENSE)

Iraqi national security adviser Mowaffak al-Rubaie took General David Petraeus outside in the middle of a March 21, 2008, planning dinner to give him some news: Prime Minister Maliki had decided to launch Operation Charge of the Knights in Basra the next day. "You're kidding," Petraeus replied. (COURTESY LIEUTENANT GENERAL JIM DUBIK, RETIRED)

A gaggle of photographers surround Ambassador Ryan Crocker and General David Petraeus during a break in their testimony to Congress on April 7, 2008.

American Soldiers run from a building to their vehicles under the cover of a smoke grenade during the May 2008 battle for Route Gold in Sadr City. (ROBERT NICKELSBERG/*New York Times*)

extra brigades come from elsewhere in Iraq, or should they come from the United States? The assembled generals were evenly split. Five came down on side of bringing in additional troops from stateside. The other five backed the internal option.

Through an unofficial channel back to the Pentagon, Odierno learned that the most combat brigades the Army could come up with was five. That, he figured, was what he should shoot for. He had an ally in Jack Keane, who was pushing the surge in Washington. On one occasion, Keane had come by the Pentagon and insisted that he needed to talk through some issues with Odierno on a secure line. Pace was out of town, and a secretary led Keane to Pace's office. There may have been no more apt metaphor for the influence Keane had begun to exert. The retired Army general not only held more sway at the White House than Pace; on this occasion he was literally operating from the chairman's office.

There were fundamental differences between Odierno's emerging plan and that of Keane, who had sent the general a copy of Fred Kagan's report. While Odierno wanted to go after the enemy in the belts, the plan Keane had developed with Kagan focused more on Baghdad. But Keane realized that Odierno was on the scene, had valuable intelligence on the enemy in the belts, and was probably right: the surge force needed to operate in Baghdad and the belts simultaneously.[23]

December was a critical month for the administration's review of the surge. There were almost daily NSC meetings, attended by a badly divided administration. At the State Department, Condoleezza Rice and her counselor, Philip Zelikow, strongly opposed the surge. They had been advocates of "clear, hold, build" just a year earlier, but by 2006 they had concluded that the moment for the military to change the dynamic in Iraq had passed. In effect, Rice and Zelikow had lost confidence in the Iraq commanders and had been led to believe by the Pentagon that reinforcing Baghdad would take more troops than were available. As an alternative, Rice proposed a variation of the Maliki plan. American forces would go to the periphery of Baghdad and stay out of the sectarian clashes in the city. Only if the killings rose to the level of Srebenica—the massacre in which Bosnian Serbs killed more than eight thousand Bosnian Muslims—would the American military intervene.

Rice's plan became known, unflatteringly, as "Srebenica" within the administration and was vigorously opposed by Dick Cheney, among others, who had met privately with Derek Harvey and H.R. McMaster in recent months and insisted that the situation in Baghdad had to be fixed.[24] Cheney's staff had its own controversial plan. John Hannah, Cheney's top deputy on Middle East issues, argued that Khalilzad and George Casey's effort to bring the Sunnis into the political fold in Iraq had backfired and aggravated Shiite anxieties. By aggressively courting the Sunnis, the Americans were antagonizing the Shiites and, he argued, driving them toward Iran. In a classified think piece, Hannah argued that the United States should try to shore up its relations with the Shiites and the Kurds, who made up 80 to 85 percent of the Iraqi population. Hannah proposed a "concerted effort to regain Shia confidence."[25]

While the NSC process was finally coming to its conclusion behind closed doors, the Iraq Study Group came to the White House on December 6 to present their plan for a gradual handover to the Iraqis and a new effort to engage with Iran and Syria. With all ten study group members and most of the cabinet officials in attendance, there was little space in the conference room to spare. It was one of the few White House meetings Ed Meese could recall where the president's chief of staff and the chairman of the Joint Chiefs were both forced to sit with the support staff in the outer ring of chairs lining the wall rather than at the conference table itself.

Despite the close quarters, President Bush spent a lot of time speaking about the United States' goals in Iraq and alluded to his own strategy review. The vice president was not so receptive. Cheney had been present during the two previous meetings the group held with Bush and had failed to utter a word. Making light of the situation, Alan Simpson singled out Cheney by using his middle name. "Everybody ought to be willing to talk to people, and that includes you, Bruce," he said.

Chuck Robb, the main advocate of a troop reinforcement on the panel, sat to the right of Bush and at the end of the meeting, Robb advised him to "take a look at that surge concept, Mr. President." The previous month, Robb had met privately with Hadley and O'Sullivan. Afterward, O'Sullivan told Luti where Hadley stood: the national security adviser was for a surge, but only if the military could be brought along. Soon after, Hadley gave Luti's briefing to the JCS staff for their evaluation.

On December 7, the president heard from the man whose transition strategy had been echoed by much of the Iraq Study Group's report: George Casey. Seeing the handwriting on the wall, though, Casey argued for a scaled-down version of the surge at the December 7 Principals Committee meeting. Speaking by videoconference, the general insisted that only one brigade—at most two—would be needed. More than that would do nothing for the city's security. Casey's plan was to pair American battalions with Iraqi brigades in the city and deploy expanded teams of advisers and quick reaction forces (QRF) to Iraqi police stations in the city—in effect, a souped-up version of his transition plan. As for the rest of the five brigades the Pentagon had identified as potential reinforcements, Casey said, one could be kept in Kuwait as a reserve and two could be on alert in the United States or Europe to be sent if needed.[26]

This did not go far enough for the advocates of the surge, including the president. Relying too much on the Iraqi government was the flaw in Together Forward, and it could be the Achilles' heel in the new plan as well. In the NSC meeting the next day, however, Casey kept to his argument. No matter what surge option was chosen, the Iraqis needed to be in the lead by the summer of 2007. Bush asked if this would be "more of the same." It was imperative that the coalition and the Iraqis take on the Shiite militias before the summer. If the prime minister did not have the will to do that, Bush said, "Maliki may not be our guy." In the NSC meeting on December 9, the president stressed that it was important that Maliki request additional American forces soon.[27]

Keane had been invited by Hadley's office to meet with Bush along with several other military experts: Barry McCaffrey, who had led the 24th Mechanized Division in the Persian Gulf War; Wayne Downing, who had commanded JSOC; Eliot Cohen, the military historian; and Steve Biddle, an analyst at the Council on Foreign Relations. Before heading to the White House Keane consulted Newt Gingrich, who was on the Defense Policy Board. Gingrich told Keane that people who get invited to meet with the president tend to hold back and that Keane should not pull his punches.

Before the meeting Hadley asked for a commitment from the experts that they not talk to the media after the session with the president. But McCaffrey and Downing had contracts with NBC and insisted that they would have to do interviews with the network, even if they held back key details. Keane, who had a contract with ABC News, declined to talk to the media.

Cohen argued for getting rid of the generals in Iraq if they were not accomplishing the mission. Bush asked who Casey's successor should be if he were to be replaced: the consensus was Dave Petraeus. McCaffrey argued for increasing the number of Iraqi forces, but opposed sending more American troops. Downing, drawing on his background in special operations, argued for using Special Forces to train the Iraqi troops. If they replaced conventional advisers, he said, the war would be over in six months. Keane presented his plan to send five brigades of American forces to Baghdad. None of the Iraq Study Group options would work, he said. Training the Iraqis could not be the primary mission. As for Casey's strategy, its goal was not to defeat the insurgency but to hand over the fight to the Iraqis, and that strategy had failed. The new strategy had to be counterinsurgency, decentralized to the lowest level, where their mission would be to work with and protect the people. If more troops were sent they should be deployed first in mixed Sunni-Shiite neighborhoods at the platoon level. Once the people saw that the Americans were prepared to protect them they would provide information about the enemy. Operations in Sadr City could be put off for the time being. That was too challenging to make it the first order of business.[28] Even so, there would be a spike in American casualties at the start. Biddle supported Keane's basic argument, noting that American forces were limiting the scale of the violence. If the mission shifted to focus on training, violence would increase. Cheney, who had previously asked to meet with Keane afterward, listened to the arguments again but in much more detail.[29] Keane emphasized to Cheney that if the United States surged more troops without a change in strategy it would still fail.

That night, Hannah called and told Keane that he had given the White House the confidence that a surge could succeed. Cheney and Hadley called the next night. They wanted to know if Keane was willing to come out of retirement to command the new strategy in Iraq or take a post as a White House war czar, who would backstop the two wars. It was a difficult moment for Keane, who had left the Army because of his wife's illness and finally made his peace with retirement. Keane responded that such a move would be perceived as an act of desperation. Besides, he said, a stellar candidate was already available for the new Iraq mission: his former protégé Dave Petraeus.[30]

While Bush had agreed that a surge was needed—using a sports analogy, he described it as a "slow-motion lateral" to Iraqi control—the White House had yet to determine its size: should the surge consist of one brigade, two, or all five? It also wanted to line up the military's support for the plan.[31]

On December 13, Bush went to the Pentagon to meet with the Joint Chiefs. Schoomaker and the other chiefs expressed their worries that the military was stretched too thin. Rumsfeld and Gates both attended the session, but neither spoke. The chiefs outlined their reservations about the strain on the military and on Maliki's ability to produce. Bush made clear where he stood. The one thing that was worse than an overstretched military was a defeated military. The White House would push to increase ground forces, indicated Bush, who brought the military along.[32]

Getting Maliki's support was more complicated. Khalilzad had informed the White House that the Iraqi prime minister would be giving a major speech that would outline an ambitious and long-awaited program of political reform. But when Maliki spoke on December 16, his address fell well short of expectations. Maliki did not fire any Sadrist officials. Contrary to what he had told Khalilzad, he did not announce the formation of a five-party "Moderate Front," consisting of the two Kurdish parties, the Sunnis, SCIRI, and Dawa. There was no mention of an expedited constitutional review or amnesty for former Baathists—or a request for U.S. troops. Bush's team told Khalilzad that he needed to prompt Maliki to follow up with a speech on security, one that would not overlook the problem posed by the Shiite militias.[33]

Bush had hoped to announce the surge before Christmas but delayed his speech so his new defense secretary, Bob Gates, who was officially sworn in on December 18, could first make a trip to Baghdad. Two days after he officially took office, Gates arrived in Iraq along with an interagency team, which included Edelman and Hannah. John Abizaid, the CENTCOM commander, met them at the airport in Baghdad. He was not amused by the deliberations in Washington. "I guess a think tank is now designing our Iraq strategy," Abizaid said, referring to the Keane and Kagan effort at the American Enterprise Institute.[34]

Khalilzad hosted a dinner for Gates in Baghdad, and Talabani used the session to raise his concerns about the surge. If the United States needed to send additional troops to Baghdad, it would be better not to increase the overall level but to bring troops that were already in the country to the capital. Maliki was also worried about the political fallout from bringing more American troops to Iraq. Gates sought to reassure the prime minister that the United States planned only a "modest" reinforcement whose numbers would be smaller than the ones being bandied about in the media.

In Gates's consultations with American commanders, the Marines and Odierno wanted to send two battalions to Anbar to buttress the success there. But Casey was not persuaded that the troops were needed. Casey had also made clear that two brigades in reinforcements were the most that was needed in Baghdad. Martin Dempsey, now in charge of training Iraqi forces, was also not a surge proponent. "I was neither for it nor against it," he recalled. "I did advise that the more we did—the U.S. military—the less Iraq's leaders would be inclined to do."

On the flight back from Iraq Gates began to work on his formal recommendation: two brigades, perhaps with limited reinforcements for Anbar—some ten thousand troops in all—seemed like what the traffic would bear. American battalions could be paired with Iraqi brigades. Expanded training teams might be based at police stations to improve the performance of the Iraqi forces.[35] Hannah was uneasy about Gates's position; sending two brigades would be another incremental response, one that was just big enough to fail.

After he returned to Washington, Gates met privately with Bush at Camp David. The classified talking points for his meeting with the president outlined his advice:

> I believe we are at a pivot point in Iraq. . . . After extensive discussions with U.S. Commanders, there appears to be broad agreement—from John Abizaid on down—on a highly targeted, modest increase of up to two brigades in support of operations in Baghdad, contingent on commensurate political and economic increase.
>
> The idea would be to have these brigades directly support the Iraqi plan. The key elements of the plan are: Name an overall Iraqi commander for security operations in Baghdad. Assign one-half of the city to each of two Iraqi divisions. Divide the city into nine districts, with a U.S. battalion in support of each. Put an Iraqi brigade into each district. Focus on police stations in each district, with a U.S. company partnered with Iraqi Army and Police at each station. This force would function as a quick reaction force in support of and then after clearing operations. Operations would begin in ethnically-mixed neighborhoods and spread from there.
>
> The two additional U.S. brigades would enable George Casey and Lieutenant General Odierno . . . to have two brigades on each side of the Tigris in Baghdad (as opposed to the current one on each side) and give them enough combat capability to support clear and hold operations. Three U.S. brigades would continue their missions encircling Baghdad, and one would continue its mission of securing the Green Zone. (Six current would go to eight.) . . .
>
> George thinks he can get Maliki to agree to bring in one brigade by about January 15 to support Baghdad security operations. A second brigade would be brought forward to Kuwait on/about February 15 to reconstitute George's reserve. It would be available to be brought forward to accomplish the mission set out above (as needed), perhaps in mid-February. . . .
>
> Our commanders do not want more additional force than these approximately 10,000. It would be difficult to resource a more aggressive U.S. approach due to the stresses and strains on the force that you well know, and without forcing it on an Iraqi government clearly reluctant to see a large increase in the footprint of the U.S. Forces in Iraq.

Forcing it on a balky Iraqi government would undermine much of what we have accomplished over the past two years.

I believe prudence obliges us to give you some thoughts on Plan B, should the Baghdad effort fail to show much success. I have specifically asked Pete Pace to work with George Casey to develop such a plan. It might use existing forces in Iraq for different purposes. For instance, it might redirect some of Gen. McChrystal's efforts more toward targeting death squad leadership in Baghdad. The Plan B surge of internal capabilities, if it proved practical, would have a smaller U.S. footprint and could be more easily accepted by Maliki's government. It might even be incorporated into Plan A, if it was thought desirable. . . .

The process will probably unfold painfully slowly, on a typically Iraqi timeline. It will not be like D-Day. Maliki will have to announce his intentions and then demonstrate his ability to execute before I would recommend executing our reinforcement of his initial success.

I think your speech might have more weight coming after Maliki has taken some concrete actions, as opposed to announcing good intentions. We will need to condition the public and Congress to the fact that this will not unfold overnight. Ultimately, Pete Pace, John Abizaid, George Casey, and I believe we probably have enough U.S. force and Iraqi capability in place to avoid a catastrophe. The worst case is that we continue to make very little progress. If that were to be the result, then we would need to think seriously about more drastic options to prevent our long-term failure in Iraq.

The "big idea" here is the "pivot point"—a "genuine effort to transfer leadership and primary responsibility for security in Iraq to Iraqis, with the United States in a support role. As they gain confidence and show success, we can begin to stand down.[36]

Faced with a debate between proponents of sending five brigades and proponents of sticking with the current strategy, Gates had come down squarely in the middle, with the caveat that none of it might work. He had backed a modest increase of force but one that would be in the service of Casey's old strategy, one that sought to keep the Iraqis in the lead in spite of evidence that they were not up to the task. And even before the surge was launched, Gates wanted to get working on "Plan B." A December 28 National Security Council meeting had been arranged at Bush's ranch in Crawford, Texas.

Pace and the Joint Chiefs were still skittish. Throughout the war, Pace had supported the commanders in the field, Casey and Abizaid, and they were adamantly against a large surge force. As preparations for the NSC meeting were under way, Keane had a conversation with Mike Barbero, a two-star general on the Joint Staff. Pace, Barbero reported, had indicated that he supported the deployment of two additional brigades to Baghdad and two battalions to Anbar, while holding three brigades in reserve. The JCS chief was worried that the White House would conclude that this was not enough and was canvassing his staff for arguments to make his case.

Barbero was convinced that Pace's plan offered too little to make a difference, and he let Keane know what was going on. If the Bush administration ordered so limited a surge, it would only be proceeding incrementally in the fashion of Operations Scales of Justice and Together Forward I and II. Keane called John Hannah and said that when Pace showed up in Crawford he should be asked a key question: "Do you believe that such a small deployment will be decisive?"[37]

As far as Dave Petraeus was concerned, if five brigades were available he wanted all five. Most importantly, Bush—the ultimate "decider"—was persuaded that five brigades were needed. On January 4, Bush spoke to Maliki by videoconference. The prime minister would need to overcome his reservations about a major infusion of American troops. "I'll put my neck out if you put out yours," Bush told Maliki.[38] As White House officials worked on Bush's January 10 speech announcing the increase, one draft had the president saying he would send "up to five" combat brigades. Aides at the NSC took the issue directly to Bush, who made his commitment explicit. "I've committed more than twenty thousand additional troops to Iraq," Bush said in his televised address. "The vast majority of them—five brigades—will be deployed to Baghdad."[39] The president was clear: he was going all in on Iraq.

It was not just the troop numbers that were impressive. To pave the way for a new approach, Bush had shaken up his entire national security team. Rumsfeld was gone. Casey, who learned from a reporter that he would be leaving Iraq early, was shifted to the Pentagon and made the Army chief of staff. Abizaid was later offered the job John Negroponte had held—director of national intelligence—but turned it down and retired from government. Khalilzad would leave Baghdad and be made the United States ambassador to the United Nations.

The paternity of the surge would be long debated, all the more so once it became clear that it succeeded militarily. There was no question that Bush's decision to opt for a five-brigade surge had been bold. But the decision was belated. The Red Team had suggested a counterinsurgency strategy in August 2005, and by the time Bush announced the surge a multi-brigade counterinsurgency strategy had already been proposed publicly by a Washington-based think tank and developed quietly by Odierno in Baghdad. The NSC staff had lobbied hard for the change of strategy, but Keane had played an important role by giving Bush and Cheney the confidence to proceed.

Even once the decision was made, not all of its implications were understood. The White House also lacked an operational plan for how the forces were actually to be used in Iraq: that was to be decided by the new generals on the ground. The idea of using the surge force to expand the Anbar Awakening beyond Anbar had never been discussed. Nor did the White House have a sense about how long the surge would need to last or the daunting logistics of the operation. In a conversation with Keane, Hadley suggested that the White House could send five brigades, get the surge done in six months, and remove the additional troops, which would blunt opposition to the war from the Congress and much of the public. Keane disabused Hadley of that notion: it would take six months just to get all of the surge forces to Iraq; and the operation would need another twelve to eighteen months to succeed.

At the Pentagon, Barbero called CENTCOM to work out the mechanics of getting the five brigades to Iraq. The response was not what he had expected. The CENTCOM team said that they had never asked for all five brigades and were not about to figure out the timeline for getting them to Iraq. Barbero and his fellow officers on the Joint Staff should sort out the details on their own.[40]

While the Americans were calling the shots on the surge, Maliki had other matters on his mind. Saddam Hussein had been a prisoner at Camp Cropper near the Victory Base Complex for three years. The former dictator had been placed on trial in an Iraqi court, convicted, and sentenced to death. Although there was ample evidence to prove that he had killed thousands of his own people, the crime that sent Saddam to the gallows was the murder of 146 citizens in the Shiite village of Dujayl.

During his time in American custody, Saddam had entertained himself by listening to an old radio, tending a small garden, and writing poems to his first wife. While he was angry at Bush and Rumsfeld, the former Iraqi leader had spent years regaling his American jailers with jokes and dispensing advice in his gradually improving English. Some developed a genuine affection for Saddam, according to official Army oral histories. In one of his more reflective moments, Saddam insisted that he wanted to be shot like a soldier and not hanged like a criminal. At other times, he appeared to be hoping that there might somehow be a way out other than a death sentence. But neither of Saddam's wishes would be granted.

On December 26, Saddam's final appeal was denied and the order was given to execute him posthaste. The Americans did not anticipate or appreciate the timing. Khalilzad had left for a break on Christmas Eve, hoping to link up with his family. Dan Speckhard, the deputy chief of mission, was also on leave. Casey had left for a break in Arizona. Maliki, however, was determined to put the matter behind him, once and for all.

Khalilzad, who had made his way to Dubai on a swing through the Gulf, was told by Margaret Scobey, the embassy's political counselor and the senior diplomat left in Baghdad, that the Iraqis were planning to execute Saddam on December 30. It would be the first day of the Islamic holiday of Eid al-Adha, one of the holiest days for Muslims and the festival of mercy. Khalilzad was adamant: Saddam's execution had to be delayed.

A phone call between Maliki and Khalilzad was arranged. The Iraqi prime minister argued that he had to act because there was a Baathist plot to overrun the Green Zone and prevent the execution. The issue was bumped up to Rice, who also talked with the prime minister.

In Baghdad, Maliki deputized Mowaffak al-Rubaie to get the paperwork in order so the Iraqis could have the American jailers hand over their prisoner. According to Iraqi law, execution had to be approved by the Presidency Council, which was led by Jalal Talabani and included the two vice presidents, Adil Abd al-Mahdi and Tariq al-Hashimi. But Saddam had been tried by a special tribunal, which Rubaie insisted might be an exception. Talabani, who was at his home in Sulaymaniyah in Kurdistan, opposed capital punishment. Abd al-Mahdi was visiting Mecca in Saudi Arabia, and Hashimi, a Sunni, had long made it clear that he did not intend to sign Saddam's death warrant.

Not for the last time, Iraq's chief justice, Medhat al-Mahmoud, suggested a convenient workaround. Rubaie could write the legal argument that approval by the Presidency Council was not required to execute Saddam. Then, Talabani could endorse the argument on his own letterhead. The Iraqi president would not be signing off on the execution, but merely affirming the argument that his approval was not needed.

The Americans also wanted a signature from the minister of justice, who was in Paris. So Maliki appointed an acting minister, who put his name on the paperwork. The last hurdle was the easiest: the Americans wanted a doctor's signature, so Rubaie, who had worked as a neurologist during his London exile, affixed his name.

With the paperwork seemingly in hand, the Americans at Camp Cropper told Saddam that his day had come. Saddam shook the hands of guards and was taken to FOB Justice, a base in a Shiite section of Baghdad where there was a gallows. In a small concession to religious tradition, Saddam would be executed before sunrise, which Maliki's aides insisted meant that it had not happened on Eid.

No Americans were present at the hanging. Saddam was read his sentence and began shouting out slogans in favor of Palestine and the resistance, and against Iran. Some of the Shiite guards, who were from the Ministry of Justice, began chanting, "Long live Muhammad Baqir al-Sadr!" Muqtada's father-in-law had been executed by Saddam's agents; now Shiite followers of the younger Sadr were completing a bloody circle in Iraqi history. "Muqtada, Muqtada, Muqtada," they chanted excitedly.

"God curse you," Saddam replied. Then he began to pray. The executioner wanted to put a hood over Saddam's head. "I don't need that," he said.

When the trapdoor opened Saddam's neck was instantly broken. The procedure called for waiting several minutes, but Rubaie asked that the body be taken down early. He was afraid that Saddam's head might come off.

Ali Khedery was at a party with a member of the Saudi royal family when he got an early morning call from the State Department operations center: Saddam had been executed and Iraq's state television was playing the video. Someone had snuck in a cell phone and recorded the entire proceedings on its grainy camera. Khedery was dumbfounded. He had translated the call between Khalilzad and Maliki and had been sure the execution would be delayed.

In Baghdad, a Maliki aide named Bassam al-Husseini spoke to reporters. "This was an Eid gift to the Iraqi people," he said.[41]

CHAPTER 17

League of the Righteous

Late in the afternoon on January 20, 2007, five black SUVs carrying a dozen men drove up to the gate of the provincial headquarters in the Shiite city of Karbala. Wearing gray American-style digital camouflage and carrying black M4-style rifles, the men told the Iraqi guards that they were commandos from Baghdad and were waved through. Jumping out of their SUVs, the men started shooting and lobbing hand grenades, and then headed for the command center, where a small team of American military advisers was located.

By the time Apache attack helicopters and jet fighters arrived overhead, a half hour later, one soldier was dead, three were wounded, and four more had been hustled away by the attackers. As Iraqi police closed in on the kidnappers, the assailants ditched their vehicles near the town of Mahawil, along with their uniforms, boots, radios, and a foreign-made copy of an American M4 carbine.[1]

A press release issued by the American military in Baghdad that night claimed that five American soldiers were killed "while repelling the attack," but that fragmentary account was not close to the real story.

Two American soldiers who were handcuffed together were found in the backseat with execution-style bullet wounds to the head. A third American soldier lay dead on the ground. The fourth, Captain Brian Freeman, a civil affairs specialist in the Army Reserve, severely wounded but alive, was rushed to the American embassy's branch office in Hilla, only to die en route.

Within two days, American special operations forces had captured four men suspected of taking part in the deadly raid. Although Karbala was a Shiite city with a heavy Sadrist influence, the men were not members of the Mahdi Army, but of a splinter group called Asaib Ahl al-Haq, or the League of the Righteous. Founded the previous summer, Asaib Ahl al-Haq was commanded by Qais al-Khazali, a cleric who had split with Muqtada al-Sadr and received training, funding, arms, and guidance from Iran's Quds Force. Indeed, American intelligence later learned that shortly before the attack an undercover Iranian Quds Force officer was evacuated from the Iranian consulate in Karbala.

Soon after the bloody raid, Jalal Talabani visited Zalmay Khalilzad with an interesting message. The Iraqi president had just returned from a trip to Syria where he had met with Brigadier General Qasim Suleimani, the Quds Force leader. Suleimani had given Talabani a message to relay to Khalilzad. The message was vague—just a statement that America and Iran had common interests in Iraq—but the implication was that Suleimani, not other arms of the Iranian government like the Foreign Ministry, was the person in Tehran with the Iraq portfolio. As Talabani recounted it to Khalilzad, who then put the conversation in a cable, Suleimani "admitted to having hundreds of agents in Iraq at his disposal but denied ever using them against U.S. forces," saying, "I swear on the grave of Khomeini I haven't authorized a bullet against the U.S."[2] He acknowledged, though, that the Quds Force had targeted the British.

Days before, on January 11, JSOC commandos had captured five Iranians in the Kurdish city of Irbil in a nearly unprecedented raid targeted against the Quds Force. The captured men, Suleimani told Talabani, were members of Iran's Revolutionary Guard, but not, he said, of the Quds Force. Suleimani also suggested three possible channels for the United States and Iran to discuss Iraq, Khalilzad noted in his cable: "messages through Talabani, a bilateral meeting (U.S.-Iran), or an Iraq-Iran bilateral meeting with the U.S. present in an advisory capacity." It was not the only time that Suleimani would propose that the Americans accept the Quds Force's influence in Iraq and discuss some sort of accommodation.

While Bush announced the surge on January 10, the United States, in effect, was caught between two strategies: a Casey strategy that the president himself had rejected, and a surge strategy that was more of a concept than a fully developed plan and would take five months to put into place. Iran and the militias it had backed, however, had been engaging in a shadow war in Iraq for years and had no intention of waiting for Petraeus and all of his additional brigades to take the field.

Over the years, the American military's understanding of the scope of Iran's role in Iraq, both political and military, had steadily grown, as had the involvement itself. In the Iranian system, it was the Quds Force, not the Foreign Ministry or the Ministry of Intelligence and National Security, that was responsible for blending intelligence gathering, paramilitary activity, and political engagement in conflict areas like Iraq and Lebanon. The Quds Force had separate bureaus for the regions that interested Iran: the Nabi al-Akram Corps for Pakistan, the Hamza Corps for Turkey, the Ansar Corps for Afghanistan, and the largest of them, the Ramazan Corps, for Iraq.

Suleimani, the leader of the Quds Force, was familiar to every senior Iraqi politician and official, even if he was unknown to his own countrymen. During the Iran-Iraq War, Suleimani, who had been born in 1957 in rural Iran, had risen from lieutenant to general, commanding a Revolutionary Guard division during bloody battles late in the conflict. "For Qasim Suleimani, the Iran-Iraq War never really ended," American diplomat Ryan Crocker would later say. In the 1990s, Suleimani shifted into the more secretive side of Iran's security apparatus. Within the Revolutionary Guard, a small group called Birun Marzi, or "Outside the Borders," had spent the 1980s helping Lebanese Hezbollah get on its feet, and, with the end of the Iran-Iraq War it evolved into the Quds Force. By the late 1990s, when Suleimani took over the Quds Force after helping run Iranian counternarcotics operations in Afghanistan, the group's Iraq-focused headquarters, called Department 1000, or the Ramazan Corps, was actively helping the Iran-based Badr Corps fight Saddam's army in Iraq. Ironically, it was doing so out of a command post on the grounds of the pre-1979 American embassy in Tehran.[3]

By the time of the American invasion, Suleimani was already a well-known figure among the exiled Iraqi leaders, and in the years after 2003 he and his operatives were a constant presence just off the stage in Iraq politics. After the United States and its allies invaded Iraq in 2003, the Quds Force found new proxies within the Mahdi Army—accounting for the flow of EFPs that had been dogging American troops in Shiite areas since 2004—and was using old Badr hands who had stayed on in Iranian service as the nuclei of the bomb-smuggling groups. But Qasim Suleimani also maintained his higher-level connections; it helped that the same men the Quds Force had helped fight Saddam as guerrillas were now in many cases senior Iraqi politicians, whether in Baghdad or in Kurdistan.

Certainly, Suleimani's representatives were active and on the scene and operating under diplomatic cover. In April 2006, shortly before the Maliki government was seated, Tehran promoted the charge d'affaires in its Baghdad embassy, Ali Reza Hassan Kazemi-Qomi, to ambassador. Kazemi-Qomi was a veteran Quds Force officer with an impressive resume: experience in Lebanon as a Quds Force operative, former assistant to Supreme Leader Khamenei, a previous stint as a senior diplomat in Baghdad, and a tour as Iran's ambassador in Afghanistan.[5]

The behind-the-scenes maneuvering among Iraq's political parties and millions of dollars in under-the-table contributions to its politicians were just two means of exerting influence. Another was the training and equipping of Shiite militias. Hezbollah, whose fighters were native Arabic speakers and who had employed EFPs against Israeli forces in southern Lebanon, helped train the Iraqi militants at a camp near Tehran, according to reports from interrogations of some of the militants who were caught trying to sneak back into Iraq, and supplied advisers to some cells.

Hints of Iranian operations in Iraq, both by the Quds Force and by MOIS, Iran's other intelligence organization, had been showing up since the early days of the war. In 2004, an American intelligence report estimated that twenty members of the Iranian embassy's staff were Quds Force operatives. By fall of that year, it was estimated that in Basra alone the force had established ten undercover intelligence collection offices, including one in the headquarters of an Iraqi National Guard brigade. And in September, a highly classified American report indicated that an MOIS official had arranged an October meeting in Kiev with counterparts in Ukrainian intelligence to try to convince that country's secret service not to report to the Americans on Iranian activities in the portion of southern Iraq patrolled by Ukrainian troops, the border province of Wasit, just across from the Iranian city of Mehran, where several Quds Force command posts were located.

Other Quds Force operations focused not on intelligence collection but on score-settling: there were many former Baath Party officials in Iraq who had Iranian blood on their hands from the Iran-Iraq War, and if a few were killed here and there by Iranian-run agents, it was unlikely that the American military would even notice against the backdrop of insurgent, criminal, and political killings constantly taking place around the country and the capital. Much later in the war, American commandos captured a 1-gigabyte thumb drive used by Iranian operatives, and among the deleted files recovered from it was a report on Ramazan Corps activities in Iraq

between April 2004 and April 2005. Of the eighty-seven individual operations the report described, more than half targeted Baath officials from the
old regime.[6]

While most of the Quds Force operations were carried out by Iraqi allies
and proxies, the group maintained a small number of actual officers in
Iraq, some undercover with organizations like the Kosar Bureau and oth-
ers in sections at consulates and liaison offices in Najaf, Karbala, Basra,
Sulaymaniyah, and Irbil. According to a report by the National Ground
Intelligence Center, an American military intelligence agency, each of these
offices housed between ten and twenty "officers and guests," actual Quds
Force members and their Iraqi and Lebanese partners. The consulate in
Sulaymaniyah, the NGIC report said, housed a Quds Force section on its
grounds, while in Irbil Quds Force officers lived and worked in a safe house
nearby. Other officers made periodic trips to Iraq. Every forty-five days,
for example, the same NGIC report claimed, a Quds Force officer based
in the Iranian border city of Kermanshah traveled to the Diyala and Wasit
provinces to pay Iraqi operatives, which he did in Iranian rials.[7]

To American forces, EFPs were the big worry, and evidence about Iran's
role in furnishing them kept surfacing. The year 2006 had been a busy
one for the Quds Force. At the same time that the Ramazan Corps was
escalating its activities in Iraq, Department 2000 had had to deal with
the month-long summer war between Lebanese Hezbollah and Israel. A
report by the NGIC described how the Quds Force had surged personnel
from other departments to Lebanon to support Department 2000 during
the fighting, and how, after the war, the command wrote a lessons-learned
report for Hezbollah, which adopted a number of its recommendations for
organizational changes.[8]

During Israel's summer 2006 invasion of southern Lebanon, according
to a classified document prepared by the Joint Staff, Lebanese Hezbollah
fighters were using EFPs that had electronics and other components that
were identical to those recovered by the Americans in Iraq. An American
intelligence assessment in August 2006 reported that the copper discs that,
when heated, became molten armor-penetrating slugs, were being manufactured at a Revolutionary Guard facility near the southern Iranian city
of Ahvaz.

Major David Hansen, an Army intelligence officer in Baghdad who
worked first on a sectarian murders task force but later on intelligence

related to Iran, described in an interview with an Army historian the methods by which EFPs were traced back to Iran after they were captured. "When you examine the EFPs and their copper plating, the density of the copper can tell you if it's from the same copper mine or not," he said. "You can determine the chemical properties of copper to ascertain where copper may have come from." The analysis revealed that the discs were made on the same press.[9]

As the American military began to confront the Shiite militias, the EFP attacks increased. Though the EFPs represented a small portion of attacks, they accounted for a significant portion of American casualties. According to classified data gathered by the American military, EFP attacks were responsible for 18 percent of combat deaths of Americans and allied troops in Iraq in the last quarter of 2006. Adversaries had found new ways to employ the weapon: two arrays of EFPs were used in early 2007 to attack a British Air Force C-130 as it landed on an airstrip in Maysan Province, the first time the device was used to attack an aircraft. Allied forces later destroyed the aircraft with a 1,000-pound bomb to keep militants from pilfering equipment. Given the modest size of the British contribution, the episode, an American military report noted dryly, had resulted in the loss of half of the British tactical airlift in the Iraq theater.[10]

In a development that Abizaid's CENTCOM staff found troubling coming on the heels of the Lebanon war, more sophisticated weapons were beginning to trickle into Iraq, albeit in much smaller numbers than EFPs and rockets. Hezbollah had made widespread and effective use of the RPG-29, a modern Russian antiarmor rocket supplied to the group by either Syria or Iran, during the conflict, and very soon afterward, in August, the same weapon had made its debut in Iraq in the hands of Shiite militants, first in Baghdad and then in Basra. EFPs were already common in Iraq after having once been a rarity, Abizaid briefed Pace and other members of the chiefs by videoconference in early September, and now the RPG-29 had been added to the mix, penetrating the hull of a British Challenger tank in Maysan on August 22 and then hitting the turret of an American Abrams in East Baghdad on August 30. In addition, an Iranian-made Misagh-1 antiaircraft missile had been fired, unsuccessfully, at a C-130 taking off from Baghdad International Airport. In Lebanon, Hezbollah had used a variety of other sophisticated weapons against Israeli armor, almost all of it supplied by Iran or Syria, alongside EFPs, and Abizaid feared that the same could become true of Iraq—that the Quds Force could put deadlier ordnance than the EFP in the hands of the Mahdi Army and its offshoots.

Wary of prompting the Iranians to become more active, the American military had been slow to react. The same year that the United States lodged a formal diplomatic protest with Iran because of its smuggling of EFPs into Iraq, the Pentagon issued a top-secret order to learn more about how the Quds Force was operating and to gather targeting information in case the United States decided to do something about it. As secretary of defense, Rumsfeld had vastly expanded the role of the military in intelligence gathering, justifying the move on the grounds that the military needed to gather information that would help them plan operations.

With Suleimani playing a greater role in Iraq, the Pentagon issued a plan in May 2005, known only to a handful of ranking officials. CENTCOM would vet and train "non-US" personnel to gather intelligence in Iran about safe havens for militants, training areas, and transit points into Iraq, as well as funding and logistical arrangements the Iranians carried out to support insurgents in Iraq and other terrorist groups. Among other purposes, the intelligence would be used, the highly classified order stated, to "set conditions for potential future operations by US forces against terrorist groups and anti-coalition forces/insurgents in Iran." In layman's terms, the United States had authorized an operation to gather targeting data in case it decided to take the war into Iranian territory. The secret order established some important limits, stating explicitly that it did not authorize U.S. forces to enter Iran. And the personnel used were not to be directed to carry out other, more sensitive operations. Sabotage, raids, or other forms of "direct action" were not permitted. A new order would be needed for that. There were news reports—inaccurate, as it turned out—that American special operations forces had crossed into Iran to carry out attacks (or, in the parlance of the military, "advanced force operations"), which the American embassy and the Pentagon roundly denied. The actual program was subtler, more institutionalized, highly compartmentalized, and less risky, sending only foreign nationals across the border.[11]

For all of its secrecy, the operation left unclear what was to be done about the Iranian activities in Iraq or even in Iran. The United States never used the intelligence it gathered to strike training camps or EFP factories in Iran. During the first part of 2006, recalled Philip Zelikow, the Bush administration was nervous about confronting the Iranians inside Iraq and the forces they backed too aggressively, fearing that it would prompt the Quds Force to escalate its attacks. "For many months American officials were torn between a desire to do something and a wish to avoid confrontation," he recalled. "When a government is conflicted about what to do, the usual result is inaction."[12]

None of it, however, appeared to inhibit the Iranians. One military intelligence report in January 2006 described a meeting at which Quds Force Lieutenant Colonel Mahmud Farhadi and a Lebanese Hezbollah officer provided a number of EFPs to an unnamed Iraqi operative. The same month—in a development that was not linked specifically to EFPs but that fit into the same pattern—police in the southern city of Amara, near the Iranian border, captured seventy blocks of TNT and seventy-nine blocks of plastic explosive, all with markings and lot numbers showing that they were products of the Iranian Defense Industries Organization. The markings matched those of another large batch of explosives that Israeli forces had captured in 2002 aboard the *Karine A,* a ship intercepted while bringing supplies from Iran to Palestinian militant groups, the support of which was also part of the Quds Force's foreign operations portfolio.[13]

As the Bush administration pondered how hard to press the Iranians, tensions ran high along Iran's long border with Iraq. On September 7, a platoon from an 82nd Airborne squadron, 5-73 Cavalry, was patrolling the border with Iraqi troops in Diyala, looking for insurgents crossing through with EFPs and other weapons. Because the patrol was taking place at a time when the United States was pressing the U.N. Security Council to enact sanctions against Iran over its nuclear program, the platoon was told to be especially careful not to enflame Iran's "special sensitivities" and to stay a kilometer clear of the border itself. But Iranian border guards had a penchant for firing on people who wandered too close to the border—whether American or Iraqi patrols or fishermen. With Iraqi troops leading the column, an Iranian soldier approached on a motorcycle, followed by two trucks that each carried eight more soldiers. An Iranian captain engaged the Iraqi soldiers in a discussion over tea, but the American platoon leader was nervous, and when two more trucks full of Iranian troops pulled up, he ordered his men to slowly back up their Humvees.

Before the vehicles could leave, however, a group of Iranian soldiers opened fire, and the lieutenant ordered his paratroopers to shoot back. "The entire column was under fire and returned fire as they conducted U-turns to leave the area," a report on the incident noted. As one Iranian soldier raised an RPG launcher to fire, an American turret gunner killed him with his Humvee's .50-caliber machine gun. As the patrol drove away, the Iraqi soldiers who had come with them did not follow, and the Iranians continued to fire RPGs in their direction, "well inside Iraqi territory and west of the border castle," according to the report. Four Iraqi soldiers were detained by the Iranians but later released.[14]

One voice calling for more aggressive pushback against Iran in Iraq was Rumsfeld's. In a videoconference on November 3, he discussed Iran with George Casey, John Abizaid, Pete Pace, and others. All the time, Rumsfeld said, he was being told that the military had this piece of intelligence or that piece of intelligence describing the specifics of Iranian influence in Iraq—like the existence of Quds Force safehouses in various southern and Kurdish cities.

"Is the intel as precise as it seems?" Rumsfeld asked. "I would think if it was, you would be attacking."

The problem, Casey responded, was that while there was a lot of intelligence about Iranian activities, very little of it was "targetable." Abizaid chimed in that the same was true of networks supporting Al-Qaeda out of Syria, like Abu Ghadiya's—if the intelligence on Abu Ghadiya were good enough, McChrystal's JSOC would have taken him out.

"Neither Syria nor Iran are worried enough," Rumsfeld asserted. "They are getting bolder. We need to get focused intel on these guys, and we may need to shift McChrystal's guys onto Syria and Iran." The United States needed to "bloody them," he said. What, he inquired, were JSOC's targeting priorities?

JSOC remained focused purely on Al-Qaeda and its affiliates, Abizaid explained; he and Casey had discussed setting JSOC loose on Shiite death squads, but had settled on giving that job to the Special Forces group in Iraq rather than to McChrystal's task force.

What about telling JSOC to hit Quds Force sites in Iraq? Rumsfeld asked. "We're getting hurt worse by Iran in Iraq than we are by Al-Qaeda."

"We're not there yet," Casey corrected, "but I agree that their level of effort has moved beyond tactical to strategic. I will package something to show you what we can do." The United States was already pushing back against Iran outside Iraq, Abizaid added, by sending Patriot missiles to Qatar and kicking off naval and air defense exercises with allies in the Persian Gulf. And, he added, backing up Casey, "I don't think Iran is hurting us as bad as Al-Qaeda."

"I don't disagree," Rumsfeld replied. "But U.S. success in Iraq depends on the Maliki government and if Iran gets at him through Sadr and can threaten and intimidate him, that puts our success in Iraq at greater risk than from Al-Qaeda." It was time, he said, to talk to the CIA and DIA and tell them the military needed actionable intelligence on Iranian targets in Iraq. "Maybe McChrystal needs to do some actions and see if he can develop some intel that way."

Both Abizaid and Casey pushed back. "The Iranians in Iraq are acting the same way as they did in Lebanon—through surrogates, indirectly," Abizaid said. "That complicates the targeting solution." Casey added that he did "not see the Iranian hand behind Maliki as much as you imply." The Iranians, he said, wanted Maliki to succeed and the United States to fail—not for both to fail.[15]

By late fall the White House had decided that, vis-à-vis Iran, the military needed to be more assertive within the borders of Iraq. In October, Pace had ordered Abizaid to draw up plans for countering Iranian influence in both Iraq and the Persian Gulf, an initiative entitled "Contain, Protect, Deter," or CPD. "Iran actively pursues activities that counter Coalition interests in Iraq and Afghanistan through support to proxy terrorist organizations and surrogate forces to further its foreign policy goals and facilitate attacks outside of Iranian borders," the order read. The report also noted Iran's capacity to quickly escalate to higher levels of conflict by launching missiles "with very little notice" and its ability to "interdict the flow of strategic resources through the Strait of Hormuz and the pipelines through the Caspian, Caucasus, Indian, Pakistani, and Iraqi regions." Another Joint Staff document added, "Iran sees deniable terrorist operations as a low-cost way to project power while seeking to avoid escalation to major conventional warfare."[16]

CENTCOM sent its CPD plan to the Joint Staff for approval in late November. Most of the plan focused on deterring Iranian aggression outside of Iraq by bolstering military cooperation with American allies in the Persian Gulf, but the plan also allowed for what Rumsfeld had been pushing earlier in the month: the targeting of Iranian operatives and proxies in Iraq by JSOC. For the first time, elements of McChrystal's organization would focus on Iranian networks rather than Al-Qaeda—and for the first time, Iranian nationals in the Quds Force would be targeted in raids.[17]

Four nights before Christmas 2006, with the U.S. embassy in Baghdad emptying out for the holiday and most attention on Iraq focused on the surge debates, Ali Khedery was summoned into the office of Major General Dave Fastabend. The bespectacled Iraqi-American staffer had stayed in Iraq almost nonstop since his days working for Bremer at the Coalition Provisional Authority, and at the age of twenty-four was now one of the closest advisers to Khalilzad. Fastabend was the operations chief for Casey's four-star headquarters.

In his office, Fastabend was staring at a video screen and fielding calls from the Balad headquarters of JSOC. The general asked Khedery if he knew what he was seeing on the screen. Yes, Khedery said; it was footage from an overhead drone of the heavily protected headquarters compound of SCIRI, on Baghdad's Karada Peninsula, just across the Tigris from the Green Zone. Khedery understood immediately the significance of the footage. Just the previous month, SCIRI had entered a "strategic dialogue" with the United States, a large step for a political party whose much closer ties were to Iran's Quds Force, and at the beginning of December SCIRI's leader, Abd al-Aziz al-Hakim, had traveled to Washington to meet with George Bush. But, Fastabend explained to Khedery, there was more. The drone feed of the SCIRI compound represented JSOC's first chance to capture an actual Quds Force officer—and not just any Quds Force officer, but Mohsen Chizari, who as commander of the organization's Department 600, or operations staff, was the equivalent of the operations officer like Fastabend in a Western military headquarters.

What, Fastabend asked Khedery, would happen if McChrystal's commandos raided the compound to arrest Chizari? Earlier in the day, JSOC helicopters tracking Chizari's cell phone had followed two silver Mercedes to a Baghdad mosque, and then, after the cars left the mosque, landed and cornered the vehicle they thought held Chizari. Unfortunately, it was the wrong car. The men the commandos detained turned out to be members of the Iranian operative's staff and a visiting Quds Force operative from the Persian Gulf, not Chizari himself, who fled to the SCIRI compound. Ensconced in the residential block of the compound belonging to Hadi al-Amari—the Badr Organization head and a man who had logged plenty of time working with the Quds Force before the war—Chizari likely believed that he was untouchable there. But to Khedery and Fastabend, JSOC seemed like it was closer than it had ever been to dealing a serious blow to the group that had been killing Americans and Britons by proxy since 2003 and meddling in Iraqi politics with its extensive Shiite and Kurdish connections for a decade before that.

The two men walked over to Khalilzad's nearby residence, and Fastabend briefed the pajama-clad ambassador on what JSOC had in mind, expecting the plan to be overruled. To the surprise of everyone there, though, Khalilzad approved the raid, and when called to confirm the order,

Casey did the same. Fastabend called Balad and gave McChrystal's troops the go-ahead.

As Khedery returned to his office, he could hear the whir of an AC-130 gunship as it came on station overhead to support the JSOC raid. Then, as Khedery was sitting in bed, the phone rang. On the line, he could hear one of Hakim's staffers explain that their compound was being raided, and then he could hear a JSOC commando roughly ordering the staffer to hang up the phone. The raid on what JSOC had dubbed Objective Clarke IV was a success; the strike force arrested not only Chizari but also the Quds Force's Baghdad and Dubai station chiefs, both in the Iraqi capital for a meeting.

Although the surprised prisoners had destroyed some of the documents they had with them before they were captured, they had plenty more with them, illustrating both sides of their command's involvement in Iraq: specifically, its weapons smuggling to the Mahdi Army and other Shiite groups, and the economic and humanitarian aid that it provided to help build goodwill toward Iran and provide covers for its officers. On a wall in the room where they were staying, the officers had hung a large map of Baghdad depicting the demographic changes Baghdad was undergoing; except for its Farsi labels and the fact that it used different colors than the Americans typically did to represent Shiite and Sunni areas, the map would not have looked out of place in an American military briefing.[18]

The strike force "captured reams of documents, photographs, and maps that provided additional insight into IRGC-QF operations in Iraq," noted a military report on the results of the raid:

Among the 10 detainees were two Iranian IRGC-QF officials that were detained under suspicion of being involved in anti-Coalition activity and encouraging sectarian violence in Iraq. The two Iranian officials were IRGC-QF Operations Department Chief Mohsen Chizari and IRGC-QF Operations Department Official Reza Diyanati. At least one of these officials came into Iraq under the cover of a Diplomat and had a Diplomatic passport under a different name in his possession. Coalition officials believe this is a fairly common practice to ensure IRGC-QF officials have some semblance of diplomatic immunity if detained. During questioning, the detainees provided further insight into Iran's policy of providing lethal aid to these militias and corroborated much of the information Coalition officials had already obtained. They also provided additional information previously unknown about Iran's involvement in anti-Coalition activities in Iraq.

Within a week, though, the military had been pressured by the Iraqi government, and American diplomats, to free both Chizari and the other senior Iranian officers captured in the raid. In private, the raid had been a success, but in public, the military was quick to back off when the Iraqi government pressed, a situation not helped by the fact that after the raid Khalilzad had gone home for Christmas, leaving diplomat Margaret Scobey, who was not inclined to pull Iran's tail, in charge at the embassy.

Jalal Talabani quickly vouched for two of the four captured officers, saying they were in Baghdad at his invitation, and the American embassy accepted his claim, even though it turned out that he had issued the Iranians diplomatic visas only retroactively, after the raid.

In private meetings, Khalilzad took the raid as a chance to press the Shiite and Kurdish politicians who had the closest ties to the Quds Force, especially those in SCIRI and Maliki's Dawa, to trim down their relationships with Iranian intelligence operatives. While he understood that they had a long shared history in opposition to Saddam, Khalilzad told SCIRI's top leaders in early January, the paramilitary Quds Force was no longer an "appropriate interlocutor" for what should be diplomatic discussions.

The ambassador managed in one early January meeting to extract a promise from Maliki that if another party of Quds Force operatives was discovered venturing into Iraq, JSOC would not be forced to release them. (As the discussion continued, Mowaffak al-Rubaie suggested that part of the problem was that the Quds Force had no direct counterpart in Iraq with which to liaise. In response, Bayan Jabr "joked that JAM was the Quds Force counterpart," getting "a hearty laugh from the group," Khalilzad recounted in a cable.)[19]

But the December 21 SCIRI raid served as the opening chapter in a new phase of the Iraq War: a shadow conflict between the Quds Force and America's top special operations troops. It would not be long before JSOC would take another crack at disrupting Iran's malicious influence in Iraq. Under the terms of the CPD plan, Stan McChrystal's JSOC was to stand up a new task force in Iraq with the mission of "countering Iranian influence." Since the existing JSOC unit hunting Al-Qaeda in Iraq (led by Delta Force) was known as Task Force 16, the new unit, which stood up in January 2007, was dubbed Task Force 17.[20]

The next chance came on January 11, three weeks after the SCIRI compound raid and one day after Bush had singled Iran out in his surge speech. "Last time it was the big fish," recalled one embassy hand. "This time it was the whale." American intelligence was tracking the movements deep inside Iran of a senior Iranian official, who by some accounts was Brigadier General Mohammad Ali Jaafari, a senior military officer who would go on to command the entire Revolutionary Guard, and by other accounts was Mohammad Javad Jaafari, a Quds Force veteran who was Iran's deputy national security officer and often liaised with Kurdish leaders. Unaware that the Americans were monitoring him, the official and his entourage made for the Iranian border with Iraqi Kurdistan, apparently for a quiet visit there with Talabani and Massoud Barzani.

The military asked the embassy if they should act; yes, Ali Khedery advised. McChrystal's commandos were planning an ambush in a wooded, mountainous border area, and even if Talabani's PUK was sending armed men to meet the Iranians at the border, as seemed certain, it was nothing that a Delta Force team with attack aircraft in support could not handle, and the payoff would be extremely high. But the military demurred at the idea of a raid at the border, choosing instead to wait until the Iranian party reached Irbil.

Once the Iranians and their hosts had reached Irbil, JSOC made its move, flying commando teams first to Talabani's guest house and then to the Irbil airport. But the raid missed the mark—the commandos arrested five junior and mid-level Quds Force officers, but the target of the raid was nowhere to be found. Though his capture would have made a far bigger splash, the capture of the "Irbil Five" was still a warning shot across the Quds Force's bow—and, true to his word, Maliki did not press to have the men released from Camp Cropper, the high-value target jail on Victory Base Complex where Saddam Hussein had been held until his execution.[21]

In the aftermath of the capture of the Irbil Five, Iran locked down its Iraqi consulates and pulled most of its Quds Force officers out of the country. Unless it decided to send operatives back in, the task of carrying out Iran's covert activities in Iraq now fell on the Quds Force's Iraqi partners—the groups of Shiite militants both inside and outside the Mahdi Army that it trained and equipped with weapons.

The American military had only a foggy picture of who answered to whom within the Sadrist movement, but since late 2006 Iraqi officials had been calling these increasingly active and violent Mahdi Army splinter cells *al-majamee al-khaasa*, or the "Special Groups," a term the American military adopted. Some Special Groups were rogue units within the Mahdi Army that were outside of anyone's control but their own, killing Sunnis out of anger and fear or in other cases intimidating them in order to take a cut of the illicit real estate system in which the abandoned homes of Sunni families were rented for low prices to poor Shiite families brought in from elsewhere in Iraq.

Others were units in the Mahdi Army charged by their commanders with sensitive tasks, like carrying out kidnappings and executions. In the brutal environment of 2006 Baghdad, the commanders of these units could gain outsized authority and become well-known bogeymen—and they could also come into conflict with the Mahdi Army chain of command that had raised them. An example was Ismail Hafiz al-Lami, known by the alias Abu Dura, or "Father of Armor." A Sadr City native, Abu Dura had deserted from Saddam's army, but after the fall of Baghdad he joined the Mahdi Army, fighting in the 2004 battle of Najaf. By 2006 he was a Mahdi Army commander back in the capital, but he was also making a name for himself overseeing death squads that Sadr did not officially condone, and began making visits to Iran to meet with Quds Force officers independently. Known across the capital, Abu Dura became the number-one target for units in East Baghdad that operated between the militia's base in Sadr City and the Sunni districts it was attacking. But a January intelligence report described the complex dynamic between Abu Dura's Special Group and the Mahdi Army. "Multiple sources indicate that MAS does not approve of the brutal tactics used by Abu Dura; however MAS's own goals coincide with the outcome of Abu Dura's operations," the report stated, using the acronym for Sadr's name. "JAM splinter groups will continue their activity with the goal of expelling CF from Iraq. Sadr is aware of these activities, but there is no evidence he is providing guidance or support. However, it is likely other senior officials within OMS such as Abd al-Hadi al-Darraji . . . are clandestinely supporting these groups." It would later emerge that Darraji and Abu Dura were both working behind the scenes with Asaib Ahl al-Haq.[22]

More dangerous than Abu Dura's Special Group and with much higher-level connections to both Sadr and the Quds Force, Asaib Ahl al-Haq was a fledgling offshoot of the Mahdi Army. The group's founder and leader was Qais al-Khazali, a senior aide to Muqtada al-Sadr and former student of his martyred father, Muhammad Sadiq al-Sadr (and, according to General Muhammad Shawani, the chief of Iraq's CIA-backed intelligence service, the son of a prominent Baghdad madam).

Qais had split with his childhood friend Sadr in 2004 over his handling of the second Mahdi Army uprising that year, but then the two had reconciled. In June 2005, Qais was believed to be in Sadr's inner circle and a major influence on him. Then, in June 2006, the rift reemerged, and Qais formed Asaib Ahl al-Haq. The group quickly began to train in specialized military-style operations outside the capacity of the mainstream Mahdi Army, and used the resources of the Quds Force to do so. It was later discovered that the Quds Force assigned the new group an adviser from Lebanese Hezbollah, an organization whose field experience and Arabic-language skills made it more suited to providing direct advisers than the Quds Force itself. The adviser selected was Ali Musa Daqduq, the deputy commander of Hezbollah's special operations wing, Department 2800; in May 2006, shortly before the creation of Asaib Ahl al-Haq, Daqduq had traveled to Tehran and met there with the Quds Force's commander and one of his deputies, Suleimani and Abdul Reza Shahlai. Like Abu Dura's group, Asaib Ahl al-Haq occupied a complex position within the Sadrist movement, responding directly to guidance and resources from Iran but also remaining, at least for appearances' sake, affiliated with Sadr and his Mahdi Army.

Even as Suleimani distanced himself from Asaib Ahl al-Haq's January 20 Karbala raid, there was evidence that Iran was setting up a new Special Group to supplement Khazali's organization, called Kataib Hezbollah. Since being elected to the Iraqi Council of Representatives in 2005, the veteran arms smuggler and Suleimani adviser Abu Mahdi al-Muhandis had returned to Iran to join other old Badr hands like Abu Mustafa al-Sheibani in pushing EFPs and other weapons from the hands of the Quds Force to the hands of the Mahdi Army and Special Groups.

In January 2007, parliamentarian Qasim Daoud reported to American diplomats that during a recent Iran visit, he had met with Suleimani, and Suleimani had introduced him to Muhandis. (The visit alarmed Daoud, who "said he was shocked to see the influence Iran has on Iraq's political process, saying he concluded Tehran controls nearly two-thirds of the Council of Representatives seats"—although Muhandis, an Iraqi parliamentarian living in Iran and running weapons for the Quds Force, was an extreme case.[23]) In January or February, acting on Quds Force directions and with assistance from Lebanese Hezbollah advisers, Muhandis established Kataib Hezbollah, and by March this new group would be implicated in attacks on American troops.

In mid-January, though, even before the first surge forces arrived, Sadr himself left for Iran and issued guidance to his followers not to contest the coming Baghdad security crackdown. Even as the Special Groups were ramping up their attacks, Sadr was telling his mainstream militia to stay quiet. The discrepancy pointed to an unanticipated benefit of Bush's January 10 surge announcement: even ahead of the new troops' arrival, American forces in Baghdad were taking a new, more aggressive stance, and their opponents were reacting already both to the new American tactics and to the president's announcement of a strategic about-face.

On the instructions of Odierno's corps, the 1st Cavalry Division spent January launching what it called a "New Year's Offensive," pushing back into areas of Baghdad that the 4th Infantry Division had spent 2006 pulling away from and paving the way for the surge units. An important aspect of the new plan was the building of new outposts, urban bases manned in some cases only by American soldiers and in others by both Americans and Iraqis. The first two of the new outposts were established at the end of December, one in the Al-Qaeda hotbed of Dora and one on the edge of Sadr City with the reoccupation of FOB Hope, where no American troops had lived in a year. Camp Justice, where Saddam had been hanged, became home to yet another outpost in January.

Neither the promised surge of American troops nor its new commander, David Petraeus, had arrived yet, and the major counteroffensive that Odierno wanted to mount was only in the planning phase. But in Baghdad in January 2007, in the weeks before Petraeus arrived, Bush's announcement of the surge, the mounting activity of Task Force 17, and the 1st Cavalry Division's push into new outposts had already helped convince Sadr to back down, at least temporarily, leaving the dirty work to Special Groups like Asaib Ahl al-Haq and Kataib Hezbollah.

CHAPTER 18

Petraeus Takes Command

On February 5, David Petraeus and a small cluster of aides boarded a Gulfstream jet from Kansas City to London for a series of meetings with Tony Blair and British defense officials. Antiwar fever was running high in Britain, the coalition had shrunk measurably, and with the surge about to unfold it was important to keep the British on board. By February 7, the general was on his way to Kuwait, where he switched to a C-12, equipped with countermeasures to throw off antiaircraft missiles, and headed to Baghdad.

Everything in Petraeus's career seemed to point the way to his new command. Growing up in the shadow of West Point, Petraeus had entered the military academy while the Vietnam War raged and left in 1974, just after it ended, graduating near the top of his class. Fate had looked kindly on the ambitious officer, who married the daughter of a West Point superintendent. Shot in the chest during a training exercise as he stood beside Jack Keane, then the deputy commander of the 101st Airborne, Petraeus was airlifted to Vanderbilt University's hospital, where he was operated on by Bill Frist, the future Senate majority leader.

Petraeus was bright and doggedly disciplined. As a captain in the 1980s, he had passed up a prestigious slot in the Ranger Regiment in order to attend graduate school at Princeton, where he earned a Ph.D. and wrote a dissertation on the lessons of Vietnam. He was hypercompetitive in everything he did, and he became legendary for his devotion to physical fitness—two days after getting shot, Petraeus famously demanded to be released early from the Vanderbilt hospital; when the doctors objected, he did fifty push-ups on the spot to convince them. Creating a mythos of toughness was a means for the cerebral officer—and, at five foot nine, a somewhat diminutive one—to keep climbing in the sometimes anti-intellectual world of the infantry. Staff officers were expected to keep up with him on his six-mile morning runs and soldiers decades younger were challenged to push-up contests. Tapped to throw out the first pitch at the 2008 World Series in Tampa, Petraeus hauled his security detail to the Washington Nationals stadium so he could practice his throw.

When Petraeus was young, his mother had taken him on annual trips to Walden Pond in Massachusetts to read Thoreau, and he had become a voracious reader. Among his favorite books as a young man was *The Royal Road to Romance*, an adventure tale by professional globetrotter Richard Halliburton. Years later at Princeton, he liked to work in the library's Halliburton Map Room.

Later, Petraeus latched on to Jean Lartéguy's *The Centurions*, an out-of-print novel about French paratroop officers in Indochina and Algeria that was a cult classic among cerebral paratroopers and Rangers like Petraeus and Stan McChrystal. Petraeus carried a signed photograph of Marcel Bigeard, the French officer on whom the central character of *The Centurions* was based, from job to job, and over the years he lifted lessons from the novel to apply to units he commanded. Bigeard's fictional counterpart drew his regiment together in Algeria by forcing his men to wear odd-looking "lizard caps," which spurred ridicule from troops in other units. As a battalion commander, Petraeus made his men button the top button of their fatigues—he called it the "battle button"—for the same purpose.

Though Petraeus followed the textbook path to generalship, commanding in airborne and mechanized units and serving as aide to high-profile generals, his efforts to get into the 1991 Desert Storm campaign failed, and despite deployments to Haiti and Bosnia he never saw combat before he led the 101st Airborne into Iraq in 2003.

As the commander of the 101st in Mosul, he had a full division with which to occupy northern Iraq in 2003 and the first part of 2004, a troop level the United States would never again match. Operating far from Bremer's Baghdad-centric CPA, Petraeus had pushed the edge of the nation-building envelope. Instead of waiting for guidance from on high, he quickly stood up a local government and security forces, began local reconstruction projects, and sought to boost the economy in Nineveh Province by opening the border crossing with Syria. Less than six months after he left the country with the 101st, Petraeus returned to Iraq to run the training command that was building the new Iraqi Army and police, a post he held for fifteen months. By the time he left Iraq in September 2005 to run the

Army's Combined Arms Center at Fort Leavenworth, Kansas, there were mounting indications that George Casey's strategy was off track and that the Iraqi security forces were not ready to shoulder most of the burden for fighting the insurgency. In the spring of 2006, Petraeus endorsed Casey's strategy in a conference call with the Baker-Hamilton panel, but in the ensuing months he worked to lay the building blocks for a new approach—and to position himself to lead it. Along with Marine Lieutenant General Jim Mattis, he oversaw the drafting of a new counterinsurgency manual and brought an old West Point classmate, Conrad Crane, in to write it.

No sooner was Petraeus appointed than the skeptics sought to use his counterinsurgency manual against him, arguing that the 21,500 additional troops Bush administration officials said would be provided would be too few to turn the situation around. The guidelines in FM 3-24, as the Petraeus-Mattis manual was known, suggested that 20 or more soldiers would be needed for each 1,000 civilians, which meant that 150,000 troops would be needed for Baghdad alone.[1] Petraeus sought to fend off questions about this in his Senate confirmation hearing by noting that the counterinsurgency force would also include Iraqis and that even contractors could contribute by taking on guard duties, but still there was no disguising that fact that the surge—despite including every available combat brigade in the Army—would still leave the Americans shorthanded.

With feelings running high in Congress, the normally adroit Petraeus did not escape the hearing unscathed. When John McCain asked if approval of a Senate resolution assailing President Bush's new strategy could hurt the morale of American troops, the general replied, "It would not be a beneficial effect, sir." That answer sparked admonishments by critics, who insisted the purpose was to pressure Maliki to follow through on his promises. John Warner, the Virginia Republican and long-serving chairman of the Armed Services Committee who had turned against the war, cautioned General Petraeus to be sure that "this colloquy has not entrapped you into some responses that you might later regret."[2]

The same day, Joe Biden held a separate hearing to promote the Biden-Gelb plan for a soft partition of Iraq.[3] Later that month, Barack Obama introduced his own legislation. A young assistant to Lee Hamilton, Ben Rhodes, had helped draft the Iraq Study Group report in the fall. Drawing heavily on the study group assessment, he began to write Obama's Iraq War De-escalation Act as well. Obama's bill called for removing American combat brigades by the end of March 2008—the same timeline as the Baker-Hamilton report—while allowing a small force to remain for "training, counterterrorism and the protection of the American Embassy and its personnel." There was one important difference between it and the Baker-Hamilton recommendations: while the study group had stopped short of stipulating a hard and fast date for removing all American combat troops, Obama had an immutable deadline.[4]

Although there was opposition to the surge among most Democrats and even some Republicans in Congress, there was no chance that Obama's bill would be enacted. A National Intelligence Estimate issued that month asserted that a withdrawal of American troops would "almost certainly" lead to an increase in sectarian violence.[5] The political strategy on Capitol Hill was to lay responsibility for the conflict at Bush's doorstep and run against the war during the presidential campaign. Mandating troop withdrawals or cutting off funds for the war would make the lawmakers equally responsible for the outcome in Iraq.

Still, Obama was laying down his campaign position, one that was more insistent on a troop withdrawal schedule than what was suggested in *The Audacity of Hope*, Obama's political biography, which was published in the fall of 2006.[6] The Baker-Hamilton study had left no imprint on the Bush administration's strategy, but it had provided the foundation for Obama's future policy.

On his third day back in Iraq, in a ceremony presided over by outgoing CENTCOM commander John Abizaid, Petraeus relieved Casey and took charge of the war. In their final meeting, Maliki gave Casey a copy of the Iraqi constitution signed by himself and the Presidency Council, and Casey gave Maliki the Army-issue pistol he had carried every day in Iraq for thirty-two months.[7]

The surge review, and Petraeus's late appointment, had reversed the natural order of campaign planning. In theory, the commander would be in place before the operation and would develop the strategy, which would determine how many forces would be needed. In the case of the surge, everything had, perforce, been done backward. The number of forces had been decided, a very general strategy had been approved, and then the general who would run the operation had been brought in at the end.

Petraeus would need to field his new forces and flesh out his plan even as he fought the enemy. Much would need to be developed with his new civilian partner, Ryan Crocker, and it would be another six weeks before Crocker arrived in Baghdad to take over from Khalilzad. Petraeus quickly established a routine. He used his morning run with staff officers to learn what was happening without going through echelons of bureaucracy. During the morning he would read the latest operations and sensitive intelligence briefings, then preside over a carefully choreographed Battlefield Update Assessment, or BUA, at Al-Faw Palace, and spend the day visiting Iraqi officials and brigades in the field before returning to the wing of the embassy in the Green Zone where part of his headquarters worked.

Petraeus brought with him new senior staff, and kept some old hands on. He predictably tapped into the military-academic clique of West Point's social sciences department, and brought on other "soldier-scholars" with academic backgrounds like H.R. McMaster. But he also reached into Stan McChrystal's community, to bring JSOC's nighttime world at Balad closer to his own headquarters in Baghdad.

In the evening, the general would often attend the memorial ceremonies for soldiers killed around the capital. Another habit was to fly over Baghdad in one of the UH-60 Black Hawks dedicated to transporting him and his staff, checking where the lights were on and where they were not, where there was traffic, and where markets and later swimming pools were open. (As relations deteriorated with Ahmed Chalabi, whose standing with the Americans shrank rapidly as he grew overtly sectarian throughout the course of the war, Petraeus would occasionally have his helicopters hover over the Chalabi compound just to unnerve him.)[8] At night, he would read a few pages from a book before going to sleep, and then he'd do it all over again the next day; when he first arrived, he read *Grant Takes Command*, a book given to him by a historian friend before he left the United States.[9]

Every Monday, Petraeus briefed the NSC back in Washington on the week's events in Iraq via videoconference. These briefings, and more detailed letters that Petraeus sent to Gates beforehand on the same topics, showed the parts of the war not visible to reporters or the public—raids by McChrystal's JSOC commandos, for example, which Petraeus covered in detail, and meetings with senior Iraqi officials, either private or in settings like the weekly meeting of Maliki's equivalent of the NSC, the Ministerial Committee for National Security, or MCNS. These discussions could be contentious, and Petraeus was more given to losing his cool than the unflappable Crocker—though he often insisted that when he raised his voice he was merely acting a part.[10]

On the day that Petraeus officially took charge, he witnessed firsthand the sectarian tensions within the Iraqi government. As Khalilzad hosted a working dinner, Mahmoud al-Mashhadani, the Sunni speaker of parliament, railed at Abd al-Qadir al-Obeidi, the Sunni defense minister, casting him as no more than a front man for a Shiite-dominated regime who was unwilling to stop the killing of his own people. The defense minister returned the favor, chastising Mashhadani for claiming to support the coalition even as he occasionally justified the Sunni resistance. Petraeus, who knew Abd al-Qadir from his days as head of the training command, leapt to the defense minister's defense and bluntly told Mashhadani that it was vital that Sunni politicians renounce the insurgency and encourage Sunni men to join the Iraqi Army. Because the Sunnis were not joining, the strength of Iraqi divisions in Anbar, the general added, was less than 50 percent of what it should be. The evening went downhill from there as Mashhadani exploded, lambasted Abd al-Qadir as a "filthy" traitor, threatened to "smash" him in the head, and stormed out of the dinner. Khalilzad later sent a cable to the State Department, its heading summarizing the proceedings: "Mashhadani Threatens, Spews Venom and Leaves."[11]

Shiite leaders brought their own baggage as well. Despite the announcements in Washington, there were indications that Maliki and his advisers viewed the coming Baghdad offensive—called Operation Fardh al-Qanun, or Enforcing the Law—in a sharply different way than Petraeus did. On January 26, the prime minister met with Nancy Pelosi and other visiting lawmakers. He told the surprised delegation that he believed between 50,000 and 60,000 U.S. troops should be withdrawn in three to six months and that by June Iraqi troops would be in full control of Baghdad, much as he had proposed to Bush in Amman—just the opposite of the surge plan.[12]

A month later, Petraeus had an unsettling interaction with Mowaffak al-Rubaie that suggested the Iraqi national security adviser, too, was not on board with the surge. Late in February, Rubaie confronted the general with a list of demands that was completely at odds with the strategy he had come to Iraq to execute. Echoing the plan Maliki had presented to Bush in Amman, Rubaie said he wanted all American troops diverted from Baghdad to its outskirts, which would have vitiated the surge strategy. "Over the past week it has become much clearer that the issue of sovereignty animates nearly all discussions with Iraqi senior leaders," Petraeus wrote to Gates, referring to Rubaie. "The demands he provided would have constrained our mission at unacceptable levels."[13]

During his sixteen-month absence from Iraq, Petraeus had kept in constant contact with officers on the ground, but his first visits to units in Baghdad's bad neighborhoods in the second week of February, and his first evening helicopter flights over the city, shocked him. Ghazaliya and Dora, neighborhoods that he visited early on, had deteriorated drastically since he had last walked their streets in 2005. When Petraeus visited Ramadi a week later, what he saw looked like a rubbled battlefield, far worse than it had been when he was last there.[14]

Petraeus's plan was to use the first two surge brigades in Baghdad especially to protect Sunni neighborhoods—while rooting out Al-Qaeda cells from those neighborhoods—from Shiite militias and to safeguard what was left of mixed areas. The Sadr City sanctuary of the Mahdi Army and Iranian-backed Special Groups posed a problem too formidable to address as the first order of business. It would need to wait. The top priority was slowing the violence where it was worst. JSOC's British SAS squadron, Task Force Knight, would help by targeting Al-Qaeda's East and West Baghdad VBIED networks in nightly raids called Operations Fly and Spider.

Before Petraeus arrived, Major General Joe Fil's 1st Cavalry Division had begun building thirty-five new outposts, including along sectarian fault lines in Ghazaliya and Hurriya. The outposts had been blessed by Casey as a way for American troops to live and work with Iraqi security forces and, thus, hasten the eventual transition to Iraqi control. But under Petraeus's surge they became a means of better protecting the Iraqi population and conducting counterinsurgency in the capital, and the number of planned bases was doubled.[15]

To control Iraqi forces in the new offensive, the government announced the creation of a new, three-star headquarters that would oversee all Iraqi security forces in Baghdad. The Americans welcomed the announcement of this Baghdad Operations Command, but when a "crisis committee" of key officials met on January 11, the American representatives found that their own picks to lead the new headquarters had been ignored. Instead, Maliki had chosen Lieutenant General Abud Qanbar. A Shiite from the southern city of Amara, Abud had commanded a naval infantry unit in Kuwait during the 1991 Gulf War, briefly been an American prisoner, and then resumed his military career. In the fall, Maliki had appointed Abud as director of his own Office of the Commander in Chief, or OCINC, a new body which the American military feared was evolving into a shadow headquarters that could bypass the established chain of command and give orders directly to units in the field. The Americans were wary of Abud and at first resisted his selection, but as the Baghdad Operations Command stood up, they found him to be a competent partner.

The first of the five surge brigades arrived in February. The 82nd Airborne Division's 2nd Brigade had been on call as the national crisis response force, and one of its battalions had been supporting JSOC in Iraq during the summer and fall as Task Force Falcon. That battalion turned around after barely a month at home and returned to Kuwait, where it had left its gear and where the rest of the brigade soon joined it. From Kuwait, the brigade flew on to Camp Taji, north of Baghdad. The battalion that had fought with JSOC went from there to northwest Baghdad, where its companies split up to occupy various outposts in the Hurriya-Kadhimiya area that Stryker troops had been manning for them. The rest of the brigade was assigned to East Baghdad, where until now there had been just one American brigade. One new outpost was on Sadr City's southwestern edge—the American military's only foothold there in the year to come.

A week into Petraeus's tenure, American commanders began a larger effort to tie all of the disparate fights in Baghdad together and coordinate American and Iraqi operations and resources. Abud Qanbar's new Baghdad Operations Command was central to that effort. The BOC and 1st Cavalry divided Baghdad into ten administrative security districts to make sure the Iraqis and Americans were working from the same map, which had not always been the case.

The deployment in March of the second surge brigade—the 1st Infantry Division's 4th Brigade—followed the pattern of the first, setting up a string of outposts in East and West Rashid. West Rashid was a sectarian battleground where the Mahdi Army was gaining ground, while East Rashid included Dora, an emerging Al-Qaeda stronghold where troops had been encountering bigger and more sophisticated IEDs. Petraeus's headquarters in Baghdad tracked the establishment of new outposts on a map included in weekly briefings; when the second surge brigade had finished its first few days of operations, about half of the outposts planned for Baghdad were in place, thirty-two out of sixty-six.

Typically during the winter and spring of 2007, a new American unit would arrive and spend a period of days or weeks getting to know its sector and figuring out what areas were insurgent havens, sectarian fault lines, and so on. Special operations raids helped the new unit begin to attack enemy cells in their area. Then the unit began putting in outposts, often with the help of highly mobile Stryker units. Each outpost was usually manned by a company, and, in the case of a joint security station, or JSS, Iraqi police and soldiers. The availability of engineers and their cranes and bulldozers limited how quickly outposts could be built, and the availability of suitable sites limited where they could be built. The first surge brigade built COP Callahan in an abandoned shopping complex in the Shaab-Ur area; the second built COP Attack in what had once been a public rec-

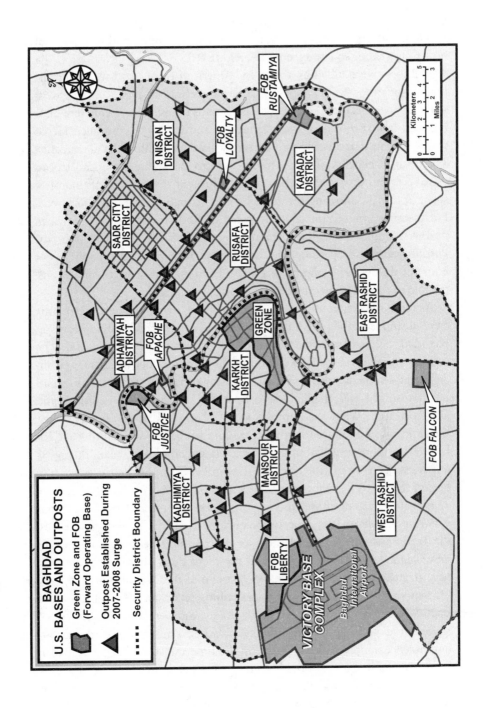

BAGHDAD
U.S. BASES AND OUTPOSTS

- Green Zone and FOB (Forward Operating Base)
- Outpost Established During 2007-2008 Surge
- Security District Boundary

9 NISAN DISTRICT

FOB LOYALTY

FOB RUSTAMIYA

KARADA DISTRICT

SADR CITY DISTRICT

RUSAFA DISTRICT

ADHAMIYAH DISTRICT

FOB APACHE

GREEN ZONE

KARKH DISTRICT

EAST RASHID DISTRICT

FOB JUSTICE

FOB FALCON

KADHIMIYA DISTRICT

MANSOUR DISTRICT

WEST RASHID DISTRICT

FOB LIBERTY

VICTORY BASE COMPLEX

Baghdad International Airport

Kilometers
0 1 2 3 4 5
Miles
0 1 2 3

reation center in the Aamel neighborhood. As troops turned abandoned buildings into barracks and command posts, they often had to figure out how to get rid of squatters, corpses, and IEDs.

Outposts were billed as a way for American troops to live among the populations they were supposed to be protecting. In practice, the extensive fortifications that the threat of car bombs necessitated—concrete blast barriers, bulletproof glass, sniper screens, and mazes of sand-filled Hesco walls—meant that an outpost was rarely very accessible to local residents. The greatest benefits of the outposts were to show that American troops were recommitting to the urban fight and to cut the amount of time they spent in transit, allowing for more time to actually patrol neighborhoods. For instance, many units that operated in Kadhimiya and Adhamiya in northern Baghdad had their headquarters at Camp Taji, outside the city. Putting platoons and companies at outposts near their patrol sectors cut hours of driving from the units' daily schedules, and made them less vulnerable to the IEDs encountered on long commutes.

As the surge began to take effect in Baghdad, overall violence across the city fell. In December, the military's estimate of monthly civilian deaths in Baghdad, derived from both American and Iraqi reports, was 3,700. The January number fell to 3,500, and the February number to 2,300. Specifically ethno-sectarian deaths followed a similar pattern, peaking in December at around 1,600, then falling to 1,500 in January, 800 in February, and 500 in March. What the numbers show clearly is that in January, when the surge was announced and when Muqtada al-Sadr decided to leave for Iran rather than publicly oppose the new Baghdad security plan, there was a modest decrease in violence, and then in February, as the surge actually began, there was a sharper one.

Especially among those who lived it, there is a heated debate over what was responsible for the drop in violence over this particular period. Did the appearance of American outposts and reinforcements in a handful of new neighborhoods, combined with President Bush's announcement of a new strategy and a new commander, convince the Mahdi Army to back off temporarily, slowing and in places halting its westward advance across Baghdad for the winter? If so, did it do so simply to wait the American surge out, expecting that it would last only a few months? Had the sectarian violence simply run its course by the time the surge began, or had it been stopped in its tracks by the surge? Measuring the success of the new strategy would be difficult, and in the first few months it would hardly be obvious whether the surge was working or not.

In the belts, Sunni insurgents responded by making a concerted effort to attack new American outposts with car and truck bombs. Inside the city, Al-Qaeda redoubled its VBIED campaign against the Shiite population, to show that the new military bases did not change the basic vulnerability of public spaces to their terror campaign. The bomb attacks came almost daily, but some days were worse than others. On February 3, five VBIEDs in Rusafa and Dora killed nearly five hundred people, one of the worst sets of attacks. A March bombing wounded one of Iraq's two deputy prime ministers, Salaam al-Zobaie. As spring began, bombs began to target not just public places but infrastructure as well: on April 12, a truck bomb shattered the Sarafiya Bridge across the Tigris, isolating the east bank Sunni neighborhood of Adhamiya from other Sunni areas on the west side of the city; the same day, a bomber in a suicide vest detonated himself in the second-floor cafeteria of the Council of Representatives building in the Green Zone. That attack killed only eight people, but two were members of parliament.[16]

The American response as the car bomb campaign continued was to add another element to the Fardh al-Qanun security plan. Troops walled off markets or whole neighborhoods with the same concrete barriers that protected their outposts, making them inaccessible to vehicles and thus safe from VBIEDs. The strategy was controversial; Iraqi media and politicians complained that the Americans were walling off violent communities and turning them into ghettos. In fact, the walled neighborhood approach helped isolate Sunni communities from the Mahdi Army and other Shiite militias as well as the Shiite-dominated security forces, just as it helped isolate Shiite neighborhoods against Sunni car bombs. Soon walls were going up all around Baghdad.

The American military was equipped with millions of dollars' worth of high-tech weapons, sensors, night-vision capabilities, and the like. But one of the most effective tools it employed during the surge was concrete. In Ghazaliya, 2-12 Cavalry had been one of the first battalions to set up a new combat outpost in January, and soon afterward it walled off a portion of the surrounding district that had seen rising sectarian murders; in a week, killings within the walled area dropped by half. In Abu Tshir, a Shiite enclave in Sunni East Rashid, 1-14 Cavalry walled off four-square-block segments into what the unit's commander, Lieutenant Colonel Jeff Peterson, an MIT graduate, optimistically labeled "gated communities."[17] Most dramatically, in April the 2nd Brigade of the 82nd Airborne began building the "Great Wall of Adhamiya," three miles of twelve-foot-tall,

seven-ton barriers that would be completed in late May (only after brigade commander Colonel B. D. Farris had been shot and wounded during a visit to the wall). Maliki himself raised objections to the Adhamiya
wall, but later backed off after Ryan Crocker publicly defended it, and the
construction of new walls around vulnerable markets and neighborhoods
continued.

Huge amounts of concrete were needed for the fortification—in West
Baghdad alone, more than 42 kilometers of barriers were installed during
the surge. The coalition's concrete plant at Camp Victory could not keep
up with the demand, so orders were pushed through to Iraqi companies
outside Baghdad. The counterinsurgency field manual that Petraeus had
supervised called for separating insurgents from the population, but in
practice, it was just as important in Baghdad to separate warring populations from each other. To make sure that the logistics commanders involved
in the "surge of concrete" knew how instrumental their role in this was,
Petraeus took to giving them unusual tokens of his appreciation: copies
of his "commander's coin" embedded within a small model of a concrete
barrier segment.

An essential element of Operation Fardh al-Qanun was the participation
of Iraqi security forces. But as American troops spread out into new areas
of Baghdad, the Iraqi units they were working with often proved deeply
troublesome in their own particular ways. At one end of the spectrum were
Kurdish units reluctant to leave the north for the violent capital; once they
were deployed, though, these units acquitted themselves well. At the other
end of the spectrum were majority-Shiite units, especially the National
Police, which sometimes continued to work hand in hand with the Mahdi
Army as they had during the Together Forward offensives.

East Rashid saw some of the worst offenses by National Police units.
Jeff Peterson's squadron in the southern part of the district had already
banned the National Police from operating in certain neighborhoods in
the fall because it was so obvious that policemen were involved in sectarian killings. In Dora, Lieutenant Colonel Steve Michael took the less drastic step of banning the National Police from patrolling without American
accompaniment, after finding that when the police were attacked—as they
were constantly, since they were a symbol of creeping Shiite influence in
a Sunni insurgent stronghold—police convoys would fire indiscriminately
into residential blocks.[18] "They would mass 40 vehicles into the neighborhood and drive down the main street firing at storefronts," wrote Captain

Jim Keirsey, an infantry company commander in Dora.[19] In some areas, insurgents targeted National Police patrols more heavily than they did Americans, seeing the latter as more of a neutral force but the police as the Shiite enemy. Lieutenant Colonel Jim Crider, a squadron commander in East Rashid, noted that sometimes IED triggermen would let American Humvees pass by unscathed, targeting National Police trucks behind them instead.[20] Lieutenant Colonel Dale Kuehl, whose 1-5 Cavalry operated in Ameriya, saw the same phenomenon. After an IED destroyed an American Humvee, a local man asked Kuehl whether there had been National Police on the patrol. When Kuehl said there had not, the man cryptically replied, "That's not supposed to happen."[21]

One of the most extraordinary American confrontations with the Iraqi security forces was largely kept under wraps. In Kadhimiya, the main Shiite enclave in West Baghdad, it seemed to Colonel J. B. Burton, commander of the 2nd Brigade, 1st Infantry Division, that the entire Iraqi security apparatus—Army, National Police, local police, government—was in the pocket of a small group of Sadrist officials, especially the prominent Araji family. To keep an eye on the Iraqis, Burton had his deputy commander, Lieutenant Colonel Steve Miska, set up a command post at Camp Justice in Kadhimiya. Burton's worst fears were confirmed when Miska reported back that the National Police brigade at Justice was running an off-the-books detention facility crammed with Sunni suspects.

Complicating the problem, the Sadrists in charge of the area were extremely well connected. A Sadrist cleric, Hazem al-Araji, controlled the Kadhimiya Shrine, which was one of the holiest sites in Shiite Islam and thus was enormously profitable as a pilgrimage site. Hazem's brother Baha al-Araji was a prominent Sadrist member of parliament whom Petraeus's staff routinely went to when they had a message for Sadr. Hazem's cousin, Lieutenant General Farouk al-Araji, was the new director of Maliki's shadow headquarters, the Office of the Commander in Chief, or OCINC.

Using this web of connections, Baha took advantage of the rush to expand the Iraqi security forces by arranging to have a Sadrist militia unit loyal to him folded into the Iraqi Army as the Kadhimiya Battalion, complete with a subunit called the Baha al-Araji Company. As Burton's brigade looked into the ties between Sadrist leaders and the security forces in their area, they realized that some of the soldiers had dual loyalties. A private in the Kadhimiya Battalion might be a mid-level leader in the local Mahdi Army unit, and a leader in the Kadhimiya Battalion might have an off-the-books position as a junior militiaman. All of them were now on the Iraqi government's payroll.

The whole thing stank to Burton, and at the end of 2006 he had pre-sented a plan to Odierno called Operation Seventh Veil, in which his own units and intelligence staff would dig into the ties among the Arajis, the Mahdi Army, and Iraqi security forces and arrest those who needed to be arrested. Odierno told him to keep digging up evidence. Then in February, Burton took Petraeus to Camp Justice, the base in Kadhimiya that was both one of the American brigade's major installations and a nexus of corrup-tion and government-militia collusion. On the hood of a Humvee, Burton briefed Petraeus on the Seventh Veil plan, and Petraeus gave it his blessing.

In April, under American pressure, the Baha al-Araji Company was dis-banded, but its members were incorporated into the 3-1-6 Iraqi Army bat-talion, and the company's militia-linked commander was put in charge of the whole battalion. It was a case of one step forward, one step back.

Matters came to a head on April 29. Captain Pat Work, an officer in Lieutenant Colonel Mike Richardson's 1-325 Airborne Infantry, got a call from an Iraqi company commander. A Mahdi Army leader was going to be tried near the Kadhimiya Shrine at a husseiniya, or Shiite mosque, for his failure to keep the surge battalion out of Hurriya. Several senior militia leaders whom the Americans had been hunting would be in attendance. Acting on the tip, Captain Doug Rogers's Delta Company rolled out of FOB Justice, drove the short distance to the husseiniya, and cordoned it off. As the paratroopers began to detain suspects, they could see others on the husseiniya grounds calling on cell phones for help. Before going into the husseiniya, the paratroopers called for support from an Iraqi company from the 3-1-6 Battalion.

The Iraqi company never came, though, and as Rogers and his com-pany waited for them, they came under fire—first an RPG launched from a pickup truck and then a rising barrage of small-arms fire. As the paratroop-ers shot back, Richardson left FOB Justice to join the fight and ordered his other companies to converge on the area around the husseiniya and the Kadhimiya Shrine. As Alpha Company arrived, its commander reported over the radio that he could see Iraqi Army officers from the 3-1-6 Battal-ion handing weapons out to Mahdi Army fighters.

After several hours, an Iraqi brigade commander arrived, told Richard-son that he was taking over, and urged the Americans to withdraw. Rich-ardson pushed back, knowing that his men were inflicting heavy losses on the militia, but he agreed to have his troops hold to their positions while the brigade commander went into the shrine to meet with Hazem al-Araji.

Soon afterward Hazem's brother Baha al-Araji, the parliamentarian, proclaimed that the one-square-kilometer zone around the Kadhimiya

Shrine would now be off-limits to American troops. The next day, Hazem used mosque loudspeakers to blare claims of victory over the American troops into the streets of Kadhimiya, and urged locals to take to the streets to demonstrate against the American presence. In the chaos, Iraqi troops, some in uniform and some out of uniform, again fired on American paratroopers, as did militiamen wearing Army uniforms they had been given; the Americans fired back. Over the course of two days, at least nine Iraqi soldiers had been killed while fighting for or assisting the militia.

The military had a name for this sort of battle: green-on-blue, after the colors of Iraqi and American units on a map. Throughout the war, there had been only a handful of incidents in which Iraqi security forces had attacked American forces—and nothing on such a large scale as this. But the incident showed how deeply the militia had infiltrated not only the National Police but some units of the Army as well, and how in some cases it went well beyond infiltration: the militia and the 3-1-6 Battalion in Kadhimiya, for instance, were barely distinguishable except for the uniforms the Americans had given them.

There had been little debate among American commanders on where to place the first two surge brigades. Petraeus, Odierno, and Fil had all been in agreement. But there were differences as to where to put the third, fourth, and fifth brigades, which were scheduled to reach Iraq at intervals of four to six weeks through the winter and spring. The decision would determine the character of the campaign.

From the perspective of Fil's 1st Cavalry Division, the answer was obvious: the capital, the center of Iraq's problems, a huge city that could easily absorb all of the surge forces and more. Extra troops would allow the division to take on a number of difficult tasks over the spring and summer: tackling the Al-Qaeda stronghold in East Rashid, and pushing into the southern portion of Sadr City. Without more troops, not everything in Baghdad could get done. Baghdad was the main Al-Qaeda target, and Shiites and Sunnis were battling over who would control the capital. Channeling forces elsewhere was simply a diversion from the main event.[22]

To the division staff, it seemed inevitable that at some point the order would come to take the gloves off in Sadr City, an area half the size of Manhattan. When special operations and Stryker raids were no longer enough, they would have to move into the slum and set up outposts there like in the rest of Baghdad. Sadr City had been the last and biggest problem on 1st Cav's previous deployment, and expecting that it would be again, the division had drawn up plans to blanket the district with nine new joint security stations. Going big in Sadr City would require the better part of one of the remaining surge brigades.

To Odierno's corps headquarters, though, there was much more to the Baghdad problem than Baghdad: there were also the belts, the rural support zones ringing the city that Nycki Brooks had identified in the fall and Jim Hickey was urging Odierno to attack with the remaining surge troops. Hickey's team, now a seventy-man element within Odierno's staff, was busy analyzing attack and casualty trends, and had concluded that of all the IEDs that were killing American troops in Iraq, the most potent were the huge, deep-buried bombs laid by Al-Qaeda. Their IEDs, Hickey concluded, were intended to restrict American movement into the areas the insurgents used to assemble, regroup, and build the car and truck bombs they drove into Baghdad markets. Before the surge, there was a tendency among military units to declare the IED-laced roads "black," or "not to be used." Hickey wanted to do the opposite. "I've never accepted the paradigm that counterinsurgency is fundamentally different from anything else," Hickey said. "The principles of war still apply. You go into the areas where the enemy really doesn't want you."

There were other indications that the enemy was prepared to defend its enclaves. The northern belt had seen a string of helicopters downed in sophisticated ambushes by trucks equipped with heavy antiaircraft machine guns. In late January and early February, a Black Hawk and an Apache were both shot down by fighters with truck-mounted heavy machine guns outside Taji. (The Apache had its cannon disabled by machine gun fire, then crashed after doing a nose-dive to fire rockets at the enemy gun trucks, killing both crewmen.) In the same three-week period, a contractor's helicopter was shot down in the southern belt and a Marine CH-46 Sea Knight transport crashed near Karma in what was eventually ruled a ground fire incident. One source working for American intelligence described a shootdown near Taji: "After the event, a witness reported viewing four white GMC trucks carrying approximately six males each moving away from the crash site," the report stated. "The men were all wearing black or dark clothing. Two of the white GMC trucks were identified as having missile launch base plates. DShK 12.7mm heavy machineguns (Dishka) were identified in the trucks. After the attack, the men driving the GMC trucks were seen changing out of their dark clothes and suiting up into Iraqi police uniforms."[23]

The sprinkling of outposts already in the belts also faced a sustained wave of attacks by huge VBIEDs, often constructed from large dump trucks and "up-armored" with steel plates. On February 19, a thousand-pound vehicle bomb exploded at the gate of a patrol base near Tarmiya in the northern belt, killing two soldiers, wounding almost the whole remainder of the platoon there, and destroying nine Humvees. On April 23, the worst of the spring's outpost attacks took place when two dump trucks rammed an outpost northeast of Baqubah, killing nine paratroopers by collapsing the main building on the base.

Odierno found Hickey's argument for attacking into the belts convincing. One day he called the colonel into a planning meeting on short notice. He asked Hickey to sketch out his thinking on a large military map. Hickey drew a circle around Baghdad. That had to be the main effort, on which the 1st Cavalry Division would concentrate. Then he divvied up the donut ringing the city that represented the belts, apportioning different sections to the Marine force in the west, the division in the north, and a new division headquarters that Odierno had requested and had been mulling different ways of using. Odierno was convinced. Although parts of Hickey's plan would be tweaked, the basic concept remained the same: 1st Cav would focus on Baghdad with half of the surge forces, and the other divisions would use the other half to push into the belts. Petraeus signed off on the plan, writing to Gates in a classified letter in early March, "We will not be able to reduce substantially the VBIEDs until we get the final brigades on the ground and can go after the bomb factories that we believe are located in the 'belts' around Baghdad."[24] By March the 3rd Infantry Division headquarters was on its way to Iraq, with its aviation brigade a few weeks behind to serve as an enabler for the five surge brigades. Quietly, the twenty thousand troops Bush had promised for the surge had grown to thirty thousand.

As the next set of forces began to arrive in the belts, the offensive in Baghdad continued, with mixed results. By late May, fifty-six out of sixty-eight planned outposts were in place. In some areas where the "safe market" and "safe neighborhood" walls were going up, sectarian violence was dropping. In Adhamiya, murders dropped by half during the spring. (To troops patrolling Adhamiya, though, it still seemed like a dismal place, with Sunni insurgents targeting them as much as ever.)

In other areas of Baghdad, the violence only worsened during the spring—in some places seemingly exacerbated by the influx of American and Iraqi troops. Starting in late March, Steve Townsend's Stryker battalions joined J. B. Burton's brigade and Iraqi troops in a month-long clearance operation in the Ghazaliya and Ameriya neighborhoods on Baghdad's western edge. Ghazaliya had been the site of some of the first outposts and neighborhood walls in Baghdad, and the Stryker operation helped cement gains there. In Ameriya, though, as soon as the Strykers left, Dale Kuehl's battalion faced a wave of violence. "I don't think as a clearing operation it did a damn thing," Kuehl recalled.[25] The same thing happened in Dora.[26]

Petraeus's first trip outside of Baghdad after taking command in February was to the Anbari city of Hit, which was still an under-resourced battleground. Soon afterward he went back to Anbar again to see Sean Mac-Farland. There had been a lot of talk about what was happening with the Anbar Awakening in Ramadi, and Petraeus wanted to see for himself. MacFarland's brigade was in the final days of its tour when Petraeus visited on February 12. Since December, the brigade had worked to consolidate the broad gains it made in the fall and spread them to new areas. Bill Jurney's 1/6 Marines in the city had cleared the hostile Qatana District and set up a new outpost there, in cooperation with Alwani policemen; that left only four pockets of the city as Al-Qaeda safe havens. Outside the city, American troops had pushed east, setting up new outposts and enlisting recruits into the police and neighborhood watch forces of new Awakening chapters. All this had come at a heavy price: the brigade had lost eighty-three soldiers, Marines, and sailors killed, about the same as the National Guard brigade in Ramadi but in a much shorter time. But MacFarland's brigade had a genuine turnaround to show for its sacrifice.

Three days before Petraeus's visit, a new Marine headquarters had taken over in Anbar, II Marine Expeditionary Force, led by Major General Walt Gaskin and a pair of one-star deputies. The new Marines anticipated that they would be fighting the entire year, given the sky-high levels of violence that still wracked most of the province. When Gaskin and his deputies had visited on their pre-deployment reconnaissance mission months earlier, a sustained gunfight had kept them from going to Ramadi's Government Center. They were not sure what to make of the Awakening movement, which the outgoing Marine headquarters had gingerly supported. Gaskin took the view that the Awakening was a group of upstarts led by a bandit, Abd al-Sattar al-Rishawi, and that working with it should take a backseat to networking with the group of more senior Anbari sheikhs who had spent most of the war in comfortable exile in Amman.

As MacFarland explained his dealings with Abd al-Sattar and the Anbar Awakening to Petraeus during their meeting, Gaskin put in his two cents. "These are little fish," he said. "We're dealing with the big fish"—

the sheikhs in Amman. Petraeus dismissed Gaskin's concerns. "*This* is counterinsurgency," he said of MacFarland's efforts. The Awakening had not been an important part of any of the surge reviews—not the one the White House conducted or even Odierno's assessment of Baghdad and the belts. Nothing like it had been featured in the counterinsurgency manual Petraeus had overseen. But it could help solve a big problem: the deficit in troops that the pundits and lawmakers had underscored. Petraeus had come to Iraq prepared to build outposts and use American troops to keep warring factions apart. But after two days in country he was prepared to alter the plan fundamentally by working with the rural tribes and former insurgents.[27]

As Petraeus expressed his enthusiasm for MacFarland's efforts, Gaskin was "squirming in his chair," recalled one of the battalion commanders who was present. As the meeting ended, MacFarland felt like a project that had always been at the edges of legitimacy, encouraged by some higher commanders but never really embraced, had received the highest possible stamp of approval. From now on the job of the Marines and the brigade in Ramadi was to spread and legitimize the Awakening. Petraeus had told them so.

When Petraeus was introduced to Abd al-Sattar, the sheikh did not immediately know who the general was. Then, remembered Sterling Jensen, the Mormon interpreter in MacFarland's brigade, Abd al-Sattar saw the rank insignia on Petraeus's cap and shirt. "I could see him count, one, two, three, four stars," Jensen recalled. ("The first thing out of Petraeus's mouth was '*ya habibi*,'" an Arabic term of affection, he added.) The meeting was not completely comforting, however. "We have two enemies," the sheikh told the general: "Al-Qaeda and the Iraqi Islamic Party," the Sunni political party. Abd al-Sattar had still not given up on his idea of getting rid of Anbar's Governor Mamun.

Though Petraeus wanted commanders outside Anbar to begin emulating MacFarland's brigade immediately, the job the unit had started in Ramadi still had to be finished. The new unit in the city was the 1st Brigade, 3rd Infantry Division, which had been to Iraq twice before and was led by Colonel John Charlton. An introverted officer who had spent 2005 in Baghdad, Charlton had also, as a battalion commander during the 2003 fall of Baghdad, been investigated and cleared for shooting a fallen enemy fighter whom he suspected of being a suicide bomber. In the terms of mechanized doctrine that both MacFarland and Charlton had grown up with, the outgoing unit had been the "breach" force, punching a hole in Al-Qaeda's formidable defenses in Anbar, both literal and conceptual. The new brigade's job was to "exploit" that breach, pushing through it and helping the changes to both stick and spread.

On February 18, the day that it assumed control in Ramadi, Charlton's brigade began a series of three large clearance operations intended to push Al-Qaeda out of its remaining strongholds inside the city. The first operation was in the Malaab, the district that Chuck Ferry's 1-9 Infantry had delayed clearing in order to go to the aid of the Albu Soda tribe in the November battle of Sufiya. Now Ferry's troops and an Iraqi battalion cleared the Malaab and set up police stations and prefabricated "COP-in-a-box" outposts there. In the first half of March, Bill Jurney's 1/6 Marines followed up with a similar operation in the neighborhood on which Al-Qaeda had fallen back after being pushed out of Qatana in December. Finally, in the second half of March, two Army battalions joined a fresh Marine surge battalion in clearing the last two pockets in the south of the city. After that, no more pockets were left—Al-Qaeda had been kicked out of its onetime capital in urban Ramadi, and the city was now saturated with police stations and American outposts.

Although levels of violence in the city had already dropped—the worst day in February saw only half as many attacks as bad days in the fall—Charlton's brigade still saw hard fighting during its three-part urban offensive. By the end of February, the battalion in southern Ramadi had lost five Abrams tanks and seven Bradleys to IEDs. (One of the tanks was lost after insurgents snuck onto the outpost where it was parked and placed bombs under it, right under the noses of American troops.) Tellingly, though, as Charlton's battalions pushed into the remaining insurgent strongholds, most of the IEDs they encountered were "surface-laid" rather than buried—Al-Qaeda no longer had the level of control that had previously allowed it to safely dig huge bombs into the roads, especially under pavement. As the last of the three operations wound down, violence inside Ramadi dropped off to almost nothing. The worst day in April saw only three insurgent attacks in the city, a level that would have been unthinkable even as MacFarland's brigade was leaving, and on several days there were no attacks at all.

The next step was to help the Anbar Awakening spread its influence—something it was doing already whether the Americans offered their assistance or not. Outside Ramadi, the west of Anbar had also calmed down as American troops and Iraqi police cleared Haditha and Hit and tribal leaders associated with the Awakening sent their men on recruiting drives. There was progress, too, in eastern Anbar. The Awakening had a foothold within the Albu Issa tribe near Fallujah already, and over the winter American troops worked to strengthen that foothold by helping Issawi leader Khamis al-Hasnawi and his armed fighters in their struggle against the Al-Qaeda-aligned factions of the tribe. In one instance American snipers helped an Albu Issa militia. In another, at the end of February, after Khamis went to American commanders and asked for assistance, his men and the police fought off an Al-Qaeda attack with the help of American counterbattery artillery fire. In Fallujah itself, the vigilantes of the Thawar al-Anbar were also working alongside the police force to push back against Al-Qaeda's efforts to infiltrate the city now that it had been pushed out of Ramadi. In early February the vigilantes posted a list in downtown Fallujah with the names of 134 Al-Qaeda operatives.

The spread of tribal resistance to Al-Qaeda into eastern Anbar was eased by the growing political legitimacy of the Awakening. A variety of the exiled Anbari sheikhs in Amman, who held greater sway in the Fallujah area than they did anywhere else, remained opposed to the upstart movement, but others were now getting on board, meeting with the group's delegations in Jordan and offering their support. In February, Ahmed Abd al-Ghafur al-Samarrai, the head of the Sunni Endowment, gathered a conference of Sunni clerics in Amman, including some disaffected religious figures from the pro-insurgent Association of Muslim Scholars, and gave the Awakening his blessing—a significant step because it conferred upon the movement a degree of clerical backing. Bolstered by this support, in early March the Awakening changed its name from the Sahwa al-Anbar to the Sahwa al-Iraq.

In keeping with Petraeus's guidance, the Marine command jettisoned its reservations about Abd al-Sattar and played its own part in helping to bring together the three groups that were jockeying for a role in the rapidly changing political landscape of Anbar: the Awakening council in Ramadi, the more senior sheikhs who remained in exile, and the provincial government, which consisted of Governor Mamun in his Marine-guarded compound in downtown Ramadi and a Baghdad-based provincial council that was too frightened to set foot in the province it was supposed to be governing. This work fell not to Gaskin but to his more capable deputy, Brigadier General John Allen, who would later become the top American commander in Afghanistan under President Obama. An Arab enthusiast who had taught Middle Eastern politics at Annapolis, Allen liked to say that he would have preferred the life of British Iraq specialist Gertrude Bell. Flying to Jordan and various Gulf states on Marine C-130s, Allen and his staff convinced more tribal leaders to return to Anbar, helping the spread of the Awakening in the Fallujah area.

More important, Allen made it his goal to coax the Anbar provincial council back from their exile in Baghdad so that they and Governor

Mamun could actually play a role in the province. Petraeus had convinced Maliki that he needed to visit Ramadi, where he had not been since taking office. The trip took place on March 13, midway through the second of John Charlton's three urban clearance operations, and was a success, boosting the standing of the Awakening and its cooperation with the government. Allen had convinced the provincial council that they needed to be present for Maliki's appearance. But on the eve of Maliki's trip, troops from the Iraqi Army's 6th Division raided the provincial council's offices in Baghdad, arresting their guards and seizing their cars and weapons. Only a late-night intervention by Petraeus and Crocker with Maliki smoothed the situation over and ensured that both the prime minister and the provincial council went to Ramadi the next day. In the weeks after that, Allen met with the council's leaders again in Qatar and got them to agree to return to Ramadi on a more permanent basis. In April the council held its first session on Anbari soil since it had fled the previous spring. Finally, Anbar's provincial government comprised more than the lone figure of Governor Mamun.

The element of the Anbar Awakening that the military least liked to advertise was its cohort of former insurgents, including insurgent leaders. Quietly, Graeme Lamb, the British deputy commander in Baghdad, had been talking with—and in some cases releasing—just such people since the late fall. Under Petraeus, Lamb was encouraged to continue his meetings and make more of them, both at Maude House in the Green Zone and in the countryside, where the British general would sometimes fly to covert meetings with just one or two guards. With Petraeus's approval, Lamb released a small number of additional high-level detainees, and McChrystal, now fully on board with the project, continued to hold his Task Force 16 commandos in check when necessary, even as they went after Al-Qaeda in Iraq harder than ever. With luck, Lamb was hoping, some of his efforts might help local insurgent groups "flip" against Al-Qaeda in the belts and elsewhere as they had been doing for months in Anbar.

The first frantic weeks of the surge had been eventful. Petraeus's surge force had secured a toehold in Baghdad. The general had reaffirmed Odierno's decision to take the surge into the belts. He had also called an important audible, throwing his full weight behind the Awakening in Ramadi; and he had given the American commanders there the leeway and authority to help it spread. The expansion of the Awakening movement had not been foreseen before the surge, but Petraeus had recognized the opportunity and was decisive enough to grasp it. But much of the strategy had yet to be defined. Even as the rest of the surge forces flowed in, Petraeus and his aides needed to develop their plan.

CHAPTER 19

The Enemy Within

On March 20, a team of British SAS commandos, backed up by a column of Challenger tanks and Warrior fighting vehicles, closed in on Objective Setanta, a hideout in Basra where they hoped to find Laith al-Khazali. A token number of American Special Forces troops accompanied the raid to take him into custody, a technicality that would allow the prisoner to be transferred to the American detention system.

Laith was one of the leaders of Asaib Ahl al-Haq, which had carried out the botched kidnapping that had killed five American soldiers in Karbala. But when the raid occurred, it netted an unexpected bonus: the British troops also captured six other individuals, including Laith's brother Qais.

In captivity, both Laith and Qais confessed to being Asaib Ahl al-Haq's leaders, to their cooperation with the Quds Force, and to associating with the planners of the raid. A twenty-two-page document found on a hard drive at the Basra raid site laid out the planning, execution, and aftermath of the Karbala attack. The contents of the wallet belonging to one of the American soldiers killed in Karbala, scanned and cataloged, was also on the hard drive.

Kept in a separate cell, Laith played a card that he hoped would lead to his release: he suggested that he knew the location where Specialist Ahmed Altaie, the 4th Infantry Division interpreter who had been kidnapped in October, was being held, and that he could facilitate the missing soldier's return. But intelligence analysts believed that some of the claims Laith made about the Iraqi-American soldier were outdated, misinformed, or deliberately false, and nothing he said proved to be a usable lead.

Nevertheless, as the interrogations continued, Qais remained cagey about his own role in any activities that had resulted in the deaths of American troops, including the January 20 Karbala raid. But he described to his captors the evolution of his relationship with his childhood friend Muqtada al-Sadr, from whom he had eventually split to create Asaib Ahl al-Haq, and the Quds Force's role in shipping EFPs to Iraq. Soon after the fall of Baghdad, he explained, he had been among the senior advisers that Sadr had brought on his first trip to Iran, where they had been hosted by the Quds Force's Qasim Suleimani and Abdul Reza Shahlai. In a subsequent trip he secured Iran's backing for his own movement. Asked on video by his interrogators about Iran's support for his group, Qais laughed and threw up his hands; Iran was integral to everything he did.[1]

Maliki had never wanted Qais to be taken into custody in the first place and had earlier insisted that he be taken off the American target list, ostensibly because of an offer by Khazali to help rein in the militias but also to win over some of the Sadrists and split the movement. It was not the first time that Maliki had made such a request. In a February meeting, the prime minister had told Petraeus that some American officers were "more Sunni than the Sunnis" and too quick to go after Shiite militias. At Maliki's request, the American military had even released two clerics, Salah al-Obaydi and Ahmed al-Sheibani, who had served as Sadrist spokesmen before being detained for their connection to the Mahdi Army. Both men returned to the Sadrist movement, taking up high-ranking positions in the political-religious hierarchy in Najaf, but neither one made any of the tangible steps toward reconciliation that the Americans had hoped for.

Having stumbled upon Qais, however, the Americans were not inclined to surrender him. Petraeus later laid out the evidence to Maliki, including a five-page statement from Qais signed with his inked fingerprint and a picture of a slain American soldier's wife and children that had turned up on the hard drive. "This week's most significant event was the capture of prominent Sadrist and leader of an Iranian-linked EFP network, Qais al-Khazali, and his brother Layth, also a ranking member of the network. We have incontrovertible evidence implicating them in the murder of five US soldiers in Karbala in January, which we shared with the Prime Minister and which he has accepted without further petition on Khazali's behalf," Petraeus wrote Gates in a classified letter on March 23. "As you know, we were targeting Layth Khazali, not Qais, as the PM had asked for a delay on operations to detain Qais due to his work to help keep the Sadr Militias under control. I explained this to the PM, but noted that it is good, for the long term, that Qais has been detained. The PM understands and was visibly disappointed to learn that the individual with whom he was dealing through an intermediary, was implicated in the Karbala operation."[2]

The very day Petraeus sent his letter, two small boats from the Royal Navy frigate HMS *Cornwall* were operating near the Shatt al-Arab waterway that separates Iran and Iraq when eight Iranian Revolutionary Guard patrol vessels descended on them. The Iranian sailors detained fifteen British sailors and marines who were on board the boats and brought them back onto Iranian soil, where they were sent all the way to Tehran. Iran claimed that the British craft had strayed from Iraqi waters, and in captivity and under duress some of the Britons wrote or signed letters admitting that they had violated Iranian territorial sovereignty. The British government denied the charges.

Taking prisoners to use as negotiating chips would not have been a new Iranian tactic; it was suspected that the botched kidnapping in Karbala allegedly masterminded by the Khazalis had been an effort to secure hostages to trade for Quds Force members who had been detained in Irbil nine days prior. Whatever the Iranian motivations might have been in seizing the British personnel, several days later Petraeus reported in his weekly letter to Gates that "Iran is asking for a trade of Qais for the 15 UK Marines."

It would take several more weeks before the Americans learned that the March 20 catch was even more valuable than they had realized. For nearly six weeks, the third detainee had refused to breathe a word, earning him the nickname "Hamid the Mute." Using a message board to communicate with his captors, he indicated that he would talk, but not before May 1. When he did, the Americans learned that his real name was Ali Musa Daqduq, and that he was a senior Lebanese Hezbollah officer assigned by the Quds Force to advise Asaib Ahl al-Haq. American intelligence had long suspected that Hezbollah kept operatives in Iraq on behalf of the Quds Force; since its men spoke Arabic and were often combat veterans, they were thus better suited for field work among Iraqi Arab militants than native Persians were. A Hezbollah operative since 1983, Daqduq had led special operations teams in Lebanon and had overseen the personal security detail of Hassan Nasrallah, Hezbollah's supreme leader. Since 2005, he had been working on and off in Iraq as the deputy commander of Department 2800, Hezbollah's external operations unit, and in the year before his capture he had visited Quds Force headquarters in Iran four times. His decision to stay silent for six weeks prevented the Americans from learning his true identity, which his Lebanese accent might have revealed. It also gave other operatives a safe interval in which to flee Iraq.[3]

The episode opened a window into Maliki's machinations, his efforts to build up his credentials with the Sadrists, and the challenges of shaping politics in Iraq. A bedrock principle of counterinsurgency was persuasion of militias to put down their arms and join the political system—essentially, diminishing the number of "irreconcilables" determined to fight to the end. But the case of Qais al-Khazali showed that, in his political struggle with Sadr, Maliki was tempted to reconcile with factions that were actively kidnapping and executing Americans.

Petraeus had a penchant for assembling his own brain trust, a conglomeration of free-thinking military officers, iconoclastic intelligence analysts, academics, and historians. When he was laboring over counterinsurgency doctrine at Fort Leavenworth Petraeus had imported some of the best and the brightest civilians to discuss and refine the manual. The stakes were much higher in Iraq. Given the antiwar politics in Congress, Petraeus figured that he had six months to start showing results. By September, he and Ryan Crocker would need to report to Congress.

H.R. McMaster, the only member of Pete Pace's Council of Colonels to press for major reinforcements, was one of the first officers to join Petraeus's team. Soon after arriving in Iraq, McMaster had escorted Jack Keane on a fact-finding trip throughout the country and it was clear to him that the very nature of the conflict had changed. The insurgency that had once preoccupied the American command had been superseded by the bloody sectarian strife he had seen in Tal Afar. Preventing a full-fledged civil war was the challenge, and Casey's plan was only making a difficult problem worse. It amounted to little more, McMaster told a colleague in a moment of frustration, than "handing the Iraqis a flaming bag of feces." Ray Odierno had a plan to take the fight to the belts, which Petraeus had embraced. What was needed, McMaster thought, was a comprehensive strategy to connect Iraqi politics and military operations. After Keane returned to the United States McMaster helped him prepare his trip report, which recommended that a group of advisers be assembled to reassess the situation and help Petraeus develop a new campaign plan. McMaster had, in effect, drafted the marching orders for his next assignment.[4]

Petraeus made McMaster the lead military member of the twenty-four-member group. Ryan Crocker, who was still in Washington awaiting Senate confirmation, picked David Pearce—an embassy political officer, Arabist, and former journalist—to serve as McMaster's civilian counterpart. The rest of the group ranged from diplomats to soldiers to academics. Robert Ford, who had become ambassador to Algeria after his two earlier years in Iraq, cut short a vacation in Libya to participate. David Kilcullen, a retired Australian officer who had served as a counter-insurgency adviser in East Timor and had gone on to work for the U.S. State Department, joined the group. So did Toby Dodge, a British historian of Iraq; Steve Biddle, a brainy military expert from the Council on Foreign Relations; a CIA official with long Iraq experience; and Andrew Rathmell of the British government's Foreign and Commonwealth Office. On the military side, McMaster was joined by Colonel Rick Waddell, a West Point graduate, Rhodes scholar, and Reservist who had worked for a South American oil company; Derek Harvey; Major Joel Rayburn, a Middle East expert who had worked for CENTCOM; and Colonel Martin Stanton, who had extensive experience in the region and had the dubious distinction of having been captured by Saddam's forces during the 1991 invasion of Kuwait. Other military and State Department personnel rounded out the nineteen-member team.

The Red Team that had advocated the "ink spot" strategy in August 2005 to Casey to no avail had largely concentrated on the military dimensions of the struggle for Iraq. The new team was tasked with looking at counterinsurgency in the broadest sense, including the vicissitudes of governance in Iraq. By March, the Joint Strategic Assessment Team was born.

Not all the members were convinced that the surge would succeed. Biddle thought the surge was a long shot and that the group should draw up a "Plan B" that could be employed if it failed. While he believed counterinsurgency was worth trying, Kilcullen recalled that he, too, "was not particularly convinced the surge was going to work" and stressed the importance of developing measures to determine if the strategy was on track. McMaster did not object to developing the metrics, but in a dramatic meeting with the JSAT team, he put his foot down on talk of "Plan B." Bush, he said, had already set the policy, and the JSAT owed it to the troops in the field to work as hard as possible to make things work at the political and strategic levels as they were trying at the tactical level. The group's mission was to concentrate on "Plan A"—making the surge work.

At the end of March the JSAT reported to Petraeus and Crocker on its initial assessment. "The team has a number of real notables," Petraeus wrote to Gates in one of his weekly notes, "and their assessment of the situation here was accurate, forthright, and a bit disheartening."[5] The JSAT's classified assessment of the American occupation of Iraq was, indeed, discouraging—and not just because of the rising violence it acknowledged.

Some of the still-classified assessment reads like a miniature version of the Pentagon Papers—a damning account of false assumptions and miscalculations as U.S. involvement in Iraq deepened. The Baker-Hamilton report, which had received enormous attention in the media and from Congress but had largely ratified the Casey strategy, was tame by comparison. The JSAT critique was intended to be a merciless chronicling of problems that needed fixing under Petraeus.

Its central point was that the war had been grievously misunderstood: the entire character of the conflict had changed, but U.S. military strategy had been unresponsive, increasingly irrelevant, and, at times, counterproductive to boot. During the first three years of the war, the JSAT noted, the Americans had concentrated on the insurgency by Sunni Arab groups, who were distressed by their diminished position in the new Iraq. As the war raged, these mainstream insurgents had made common cause with foreign jihadists determined to derail the American project by polarizing Iraqis along sectarian lines.

The American response only made things worse. Even as American forces focused first and foremost on fighting the Sunni insurgency while only occasionally confronting Sadrists and Iranian-backed militias, the Americans had assumed that their very presence in Iraq served as a recruiting tool for their foes. So their goal had been to build up the Iraqi government and transition the fight to Iraqi troops—the sooner, the better. "Pressed into what was for us an unfamiliar fight, we rediscovered and implemented counterinsurgency doctrine against the Sunni insurgent threat, and worked to build an indigenous counterinsurgency capability in the nascent Iraqi Security Forces," the report summarized.[6]

But neither the insurgency nor the militias, dangerous though they were, characterized the heart of the problem: the collapse and co-option of the Iraqi state. It was the erosion of national institutions that had pushed Iraqis to take refuge in their sectarian and ethnic identities, and to fight for control. The nation was in the middle of a "communal power struggle" among Shiite, Sunni, and Kurdish factions squabbling and killing each other—violence that had not been inevitable, but was a development the American command had misdiagnosed and inadvertently abetted. In its desire to empower the new Iraqi state and bring democracy to the country, the United States had built up the capabilities of the Shiite-dominated government and security forces and had willy-nilly taken sides in a brewing civil war. "Focused on supporting an elected government and defeating the terrorists and insurgents that initiated the cycle of violence, we began to empower one side of what was becoming a bloody communal power struggle," the JSAT assessment read. "Focused on the Sunni insurgency, we pursued a strategy of handing over responsibility for Iraq's security as quickly as possible to the Shi'a-dominated government we had helped to create. We were, however, rushing to failure."[7]

All of the problems had been aggravated by Iran's Quds Force, which the JSAT report bluntly asserted was "prosecuting a proxy war" against the United States, in which it went so far as to fund Al-Qaeda terrorists; and by Syria, which had provided insurgents with a safe haven. Their goal was to increase pressure on the United States to withdraw its troops and "to keep Iraq divided, unstable, weak, and malleable." By 2007, much of the Iraqi government was operating at cross-purposes with the United States, while acting "in concert" with Iran.

In addition to defeating the insurgents and militias as well as persuading the Iranians and the Syrians to refrain from intervening, the United States needed to find a way to influence the Maliki government, which was more an amalgamation of competing factions than a functioning administration. As closely as the United States had worked with its Iraqi counterparts, the JSAT report disclosed, it still knew little about how they operated. "The government has a formal decision-making process that works in fits and starts, but it also has informal, opaque mechanisms." Whatever actions the American-led coalition took, the government was key. A lot was riding on the surge, the JSAT noted. The American presence was the "primary counter weight to open civil war."[8]

The JSAT observed that there were a number of political or military shocks that could upend the surge strategy. The group identified nine and listed them in a concise section that bore the title "Events to Be Avoided (2007–8)." It was a collection of horrors, all of which were possible, were generally beyond the control of the American-led coalition, and would pose enormous political or military challenges for the surge:

> a. Open conflict with Iran: Iranian escalation significantly beyond their current level of covert action, sponsorship of insurgents, or intelligence and propaganda activity, which results in overt armed clashes between Coalition and Iranian forces. This includes events occurring outside Iraq (e.g., in the Arabian Gulf), and involving forces not under MNF-I control.
>
> b. Mass-casualty attack on the U.S. Embassy: including an indirect fire attack resulting in more than 20 casualties, or a Tet-offensive-like large-scale ground attack (even one that fails).

　　c. Mass kidnapping and/or murder of coalition civilian personnel—possibly coordinated to occur simultaneously across the country and focusing on PRT or political personnel.

　　d. Seizure of a district or provincial capital, a coalition FOB or another major installation—even if the captured installation cannot be held for more than a few hours/days by the enemy.

　　e. Assassination or kidnapping of a major Coalition official—e.g., an Ambassador, the CG [commanding general of] MNF-I or a visiting dignitary (e.g., a CODEL [congressional delegation] member, presidential candidate, visiting foreign leader).

　　f. Major attack that severely damages or destroys a key religious shrine (e.g., Hanafi tomb in Baghdad, pilgrimage sites in Karbala or Najaf).

　　g. Assassination of an influential, popular Iraqi political or religious figure (e.g., al-Hakim, al-Sadr, key Sunni tribal sheikh[s] in Anbar).

　　h. Mass casualty terrorist attack or coordinated attacks (measuring in hundreds of deaths) targeting civilians from one confession.

　　i. Military intervention by one of Iraq's neighbors (e.g., Turkey into Kurdistan, Saudi Arabia or Jordan into Anbar).

If any of the following events occurred prior to December 2008, the JSAT advised in an almost deadpan manner, "a contingency plan should be considered for prompt execution."[9]

After a month of deliberations, briefings to Petraeus and Crocker, and internal debate, the group developed a lengthy list of serious recommendations intended to form the core of a new campaign plan.

　　The group's real innovation had to do with political strategy, which Dodge and Ford worked hard to elaborate. The goal was to move Iraq's communities toward some sort of political accommodation and break the cycle of violence that Harvey had so often described. Toward this end, it should try to shape the evolution of the Iraqi state. The inclusive government the Bush administration had hoped for was little more than a fantasy. Sectarian Shiite political parties had extended their tentacles into the "service provision ministries," the government agencies that were in a position to deprive Sunnis—or rival Shiite factions in some cases—of daily necessities. The Interior and Health ministries were the worst, but the Transportation, Education, and Finance ministries were also complicit in this pattern of sectarian deprivation. The culprits needed to be identified and persuaded to change their behavior; if necessary, Maliki had to be pressed to remove them.[10]

Ford, after long hours of debate among the JSAT members about the feasibility of changing the Iraqi ruling elite, emerged as among the most adamant that action be taken against sectarian officials with blood on their hands. In meetings with Petraeus and Crocker, he urged a "lamp post strategy": Iraq had hanged many a terrorist and insurgent; the Iraqi government should publicly hang officials who had been behind the sectarian cleansing as well. Petraeus and Crocker, and even some of his colleagues on the JSAT, thought that Ford was just making a point for effect, but the underlying frustration with sectarian officials was real and heartfelt.[11]

The JSAT report did not go that far, but it did recommend that if the Iraqi government was not prepared to fire sectarian officials, American forces should be prepared to act unilaterally to detain them, so long as the reasons were explained thoroughly to Maliki, the Presidency Council, and Ayatollah Sistani. There was a precedent for this, which McMaster viewed as a good one: in February, American Special Forces and Iraqi commandos had entered the headquarters building of the Health Ministry, one of the ministries most deeply implicated in abuses against Sunnis, and arrested Sadrist deputy health minister Hakim al-Zamili.

To encourage the evenhanded administration of justice, the JSAT report recommended that special "Rule of Law Green Zones" be built—essentially fortified complexes where judges, their families, and investigators would be protected from threats of reprisal.[12] Curiously, the administration of justice had had unintended consequences for the Americans. Outlining the problems with the network of prisons and jails the United States used to lock up suspected terrorists and insurgents it apprehended, Major Joel Rayburn noted that the detention policy was "in crisis." Since there was not enough prison capacity, hard-core terrorists—the report estimated there were 1,350 at Camp Bucca out of a prison population of 15,000—mingled with less dangerous inmates. The prisons had become veritable recruiting centers for Al-Qaeda.[13]

Iraq's security organs were even more problematic. The CIA had, at great trouble and expense, stood up Muhammad Shawani's Iraqi National Intelligence Service. But Maliki was reluctant to trust it, not only because of its provenance but because it had a largely Sunni staff. The prime minister was bedeviled by his fear of possible conspiracies and coups and had surrounded himself with Dawa Party stalwarts who questioned whether the INIS was working for them or for the Americans. Maliki's solution was typical of many Third World leaders who do not fully trust their own government: he made sure there were six competing officials in the Iraqi intelligence community. First among equals was Shirwan al-Waeli, the minister of state for national security affairs, who had 3,500 personnel at his disposal and links to Iranian intelligence. The more Waeli's agency sidelined the INIS, the greater the prospects for "sectarian political maneuverings and infiltration from sectarian militias and foreign intelligence services, mostly Iran," the JSAT concluded. Waeli had to go.

As for Maliki's Office of the Commander in Chief, the organization was ostensibly established by Maliki as a means of coordinating national security policy. But OCINC had emerged as an extra-constitutional shadow headquarters that issued orders—often sectarian orders—directly to Iraqi units in the field. OCINC's first director, Abud Qanbar, a Maliki loyalist who had a background in naval infantry and had been trained in the Soviet Union, had been put in charge of the Baghdad Operations Command, which ran the Iraqi side of the security operation in the country's capital. The Americans had sought unsuccessfully to block his appointment by arguing that he was a mere major general and the head of the new command should be a lieutenant general—a hurdle Maliki overcame by promoting him.

Abud had turned out to be more professional than the Americans had expected, but his replacement at OCINC, Lieutenant General Farouk al-Araji, was another matter. He had retired from Saddam's military as a lieutenant colonel only to be elevated by Maliki to the rank of lieutenant general after taking over OCINC in 2006. A cousin of Sadrist leaders Baha and Hazem al-Araji, he had used his perch to bypass the Defense Ministry and politicize security. Dr. Bassima al-Jaidri was another major player. An expert in military technology partial to wearing a pink nylon hijab, Bassima was a rarity in Iraq: unmarried and determined to make her way in the largely male-dominated world of national security. She had overcome her humble beginnings as a Shiite from Sadr City by studying hard. One of her role models was an Israeli rocket expert from Haifa University, and Bassima chose a similar career path. After earning advanced degrees in missile and radar technology, she worked in the military industry during Saddam's rule. Later on, as a Sadrist member of parliament, she served with Maliki on the defense committee. When he became prime minister, Bassima was brought into his inner circle and soon became a trusted confidant.

With Maliki's assent, Bassima and other aides wanted to strengthen the role of the new prime minister and purge the security forces of commanders who were deemed to be too weak or who seemed to have divided loyalties. When OCINC was stood up on November 15 Bassima was one of its founding members. In March, she had directed the Interior Ministry to release three Mahdi Army members who had been detained in Mosul. The next month, she had intervened in Samarra, where a new National Police brigade was being formed. The brigade was to be 40 percent Sunni and 60 percent Shiite, reflecting the makeup of the population, but Bassima supplied a new list that was 87 percent Shiite. Bassima and Engineer Ahmed, the former Badr Corps member who had overseen the Jadriya Bunker and had since been transferred to OCINC, had been identified by the American intelligence community as among the "worst offenders." Petraeus intervened with Maliki to preserve the original Samarra list, but, if anything, the powers of OCINC were expanding. Since January, a subordinate civilian body under OCINC, the Counter-Terrorism Service, had assumed partial control over Iraq's ISOF commando brigade, the crack unit American Special Forces had been advising since 2004.

Even outside of OCINC, there were problems. The Americans had forged a good working relationship with certain leading Iraqis, among them Lieutenant General Babaker al-Zebari, the Kurdish head of the military joint headquarters; Abd al-Qadir al-Obeidi, a Sunni and the minister of defense; and Jawad Bolani, the Shiite minister of interior. But in addition to OCINC Maliki had other workarounds to avoid going through official channels, an arrangement the JSAT referred to as a "shadow government" and which enabled him and a small group of Dawa loyalists and political allies to bypass many government ministries. Instead of relying on Abd al-Qadir, Maliki often turned to General Mohan al-Furayji, who had been released in 2005 by the Defense Ministry, which had been unhappy with his work. Instead of relying on Babaker, Maliki turned to Abd al-Aziz al-Kubaisi, an intelligence official in his headquarters. Within the Interior Ministry, Maliki turned not to its nominal director, Bolani, but to a loyalist named Adnan al-Asadi, as when he moved to form a nine-hundred-strong "unity brigade" to protect the south. Bolani later told Petraeus the move was made without his knowledge.[14]

Maliki's connection with Major General Mahdi Sabih Hashim al-Gharawi was particularly troubling. Mahdi had been the commander of the National Police's 2nd Division, which had been accused of carrying out a wave of sectarian murders and had kept prisoners at an illegal facility known as Site 4. "Mehdi has proven valuable enough to Maliki," Crocker noted in a cable, "that he rebuffed our request that he execute an Iraqi warrant for Mehdi's arrest."[15] To block the arrest, Maliki invoked a provision of the Iraqi criminal code that allowed the prime minister to invalidate an arrest warrant if the suspect was carrying out official duties. Instead of going to jail, Mahdi was made a senior adviser in the Interior Ministry.

As for the Iraqi security forces, however, the JSAT proposed some major changes. Marty Dempsey ran the MNSTC-I headquarters, which was standing up the Iraqi military. The "T" in the command's title stood not for "training" but for "transition," and under Dempsey, it had focused on exactly that: preparing Iraqi forces for the day when they were still there and the American military was not. Iraq's security forces had a ceiling of 400,000 and had grown to 330,000 under Dempsey's tenure. But their strength on any given day was much lower because of desertion and absenteeism. "The landings at Gallipoli are right on schedule," McMaster quipped to one of Dempsey's officers during the JSAT review.[16] Dempsey's command was executing its plan well, he implied; the problem was with what came afterward, when the force turned out to be too small and riddled with sectarianism. Dempsey was open to the JSAT evaluation and ordered a new planning effort before he handed the command over to Lieutenant General Jim Dubik.

The training command did have a program in place to combat sectarian behavior in the National Police, called "re-bluing." The program sent National Police brigades, of which there were nine, to a base near Numaniyah, southeast of Baghdad, where they were retrained and certified for operations. But "retraining" was a misnomer; this was, in fact, the first real training many of the police had undergone. Re-bluing was slow, though, since it trained only one brigade at a time, and it was not always successful. The notorious Wolf Brigade—the 1st National Police Division's 2nd Brigade—was re-blued between February and April, and the training hardly rid the brigade of its sectarian virus. After re-bluing, the brigade moved into West Rashid, an area of Baghdad where sectarian violence persisted as the Mahdi Army squeezed the small remaining pockets of Sunni residents.

Not all of the group's recommendations entailed taking a tougher stance. To broaden the political base in Iraq, the report also advocated that the United States try to initiate a dialogue with the Sadrists and assure Sadr that as far as the Americans were concerned, he was not a target. To reach out to the insurgents and try to bring them into the fold, David Kilcullen proposed the establishment of a cell that would sift through intelligence data and decide which insurgent groups to approach—a bureaucratic innovation that became the Force Strategic Engagement Cell, or FSEC. There would also be steps taken to reach out to Syria and Iran, noted the report's diplomatic annex, which David Pearce drafted. If the Syrians reciprocated by staunching the flow of foreign fighters into Iraq, the American ambassador—whom the Bush administration had withdrawn over a suspected Syrian connection to the assassination of Rafiq al-Hariri, the former Lebanese prime minister—should be reinstated in Damascus. If the Iranians showed interest in cooperating, the JSAT proposed a meeting between Secretary of State Condoleezza Rice and Iran's foreign minister.

The JSAT's recommendations on foreign policy appeared out of sync with the White House's hard-line policies. A suggestion by Elliott Abrams, the senior Middle East aide on the NSC, that the United States intervene militarily to shut down the Damascus International Airport to stop the flow of foreign fighters had been shelved after John Abizaid argued against it. But the Bush team no longer seemed to have an appetite for engaging the Syrian or Iranian regimes.

Finally, the JSAT report did not take for granted that the United States should continue to back Maliki. "Consideration must be given to when and if policy should move beyond the Maliki government," it said. For instance, if the Maliki government came "under greater Iranian sway or influence" than was already the case. If diplomacy and other pressure failed to dissuade Maliki's team from moving even closer to Iran, American decision makers in Baghdad and Washington "must decide if we can still work with and support this particular [government of Iraq]."

The main purpose of the JSAT study was to provide a foundation for the drafting of the actual Joint Campaign Plan, which Petraeus and Crocker were to jointly issue. But some embassy officials, including Deputy Chief of Mission Daniel Speckhard and former ambassador to Syria Margaret Scobey, pushed back hard against the JSAT's recommendations, particularly its advocacy of the removal of senior Iraqi officials. When the campaign plan was finally published over the summer, the JSAT's language had been toned down significantly, and the section on political strategy gave priority not to efforts to clean up the ministries and security forces but to the passage of such key legislation as a provincial powers law, a provincial elections law, and a de-Baathification law—the kind of legislation that Khalilzad, the Iraq Study Group, and the U.S. Congress had tended to equate with progress.[17]

The final plan acknowledged the malign role of OCINC and other offices and tasked the American intelligence community with identifying those in government who were complicit in the violence. It proposed dealing with the culprits through disincentives and incentives, including "visas, travel, passes," and housing in the Green Zone. In an assertion that seemed at odds with the JSAT's assessment that sectarianism was deeply entrenched, the plan noted that Iraqi government "leaders can be made to see the importance of removing malign actors and will acquiesce if provided sufficient evidence that given individuals are hampering progress." If American forces ever were actually to detain senior Iraqi officials, or urge their detention by Iraqi forces, they would do so "as a last resort" and only with the authorization, not merely the knowledge, of Maliki and the Presidency Council. The possibility of American troops detaining senior Iraqi officials unilaterally and without permission was not left open. Persuasion, not coercion, was to be the means for righting Iraq's ship of state. The campaign plan had taken much of its inspiration from the team's assessment, but in the end it was JSAT Lite.

The strongest action was taken at Baghdad International Airport, which had been taken over by the Sadrists. Instead of purging Shirwan al-Waeli, the U.S. decided to work with him. Major General Mike Barbero, Petraeus's operations officer, met with Waeli, who also doubled as the acting transportation minister, and asked for his and Maliki's cooperation. The airport's chief of security and head of the sky marshals needed to be detained immediately while other marshals were polygraphed to determine the degree of their complicity. The operation, which was code-named Silver Saber, was carried out quietly to avoid alerting other personnel who needed to be detained, including those that had penetrated the British contractor that controlled the checkpoint near the airport, the settlement near the airport, the cleaning service, and other arms of the Transportation Ministry. Special Forces accompanied an elite Interior Ministry Commando unit to arrest the airport figures suspected of the worst offenses.

A fortified "Rule of Law" complex was constructed in the Rusafa district in Baghdad and provisions were made to try Zamili, the former Health Ministry deputy official, and other detained sectarian officials there. Five thousand new guards came from the Iraqi government.

Reforming OCINC proved to be the most difficult task. Petraeus informed Gates that his command was working to reduce the organization's power, if not do away with it altogether. To limit its influence, the U.S. pressed to shrink the office. The number of personnel, in fact, was reduced from sixty-four to twenty-four, but of the remaining staff twenty were Shiite and only four were Sunni.

Other efforts to limit the power of the office did not come easily. On April 24, an American diplomat visited OCINC to meet with Farouk, but when he arrived he was told that the meeting had been called off and would likely not be rescheduled. Another cable three weeks later described how both Defense Minister Abd al-Qadir and Iraq's senior uniformed officer, Kurdish lieutenant general Babaker al-Zebari, had likened Maliki's concentration of power with OCINC to the methods of Saddam Hussein.

Petraeus raised the matter directly with Maliki in early May, providing examples of how OCINC was meddling in operations or encouraging sectarian actions. Maliki insisted that was not his intention. But while there were coalition advisers to the ministries of Defense, Interior, and other agencies, Maliki never allowed the Americans to insert an adviser into the OCINC bureaucracy. In early June, Petraeus matter-of-factly summed up his frustrations in a letter to Gates.

"My J-2 met with members of the Office of the Commander in Chief (OCINC) this past week (the personal inspector general–like organization of the Prime Minister). While they promised access to all records (once the Prime Minister approved it), the meeting made it clear that they were interested neither in providing transparency of their activities nor in closer partnership with the Coalition," Petraeus wrote. "From our perspective, OCINC is a distinctly Iraqi creation that we must co-opt, as putting an end to it seems highly unlikely. We'll continue to monitor their activities and try to get a liaison officer accepted into this office, while working with the Prime Minister to use and empower his ministries for their institutionally appointed functions, rather than relying on the OCINC to work around them."[18]

The bold vision the JSAT outlined to remove sectarian commanders had indeed given way to a sense of pragmatism, if not compromise. Waeli was more powerful than ever, and Maliki had no intention of dispensing with OCINC or allowing American liaison officers into his inner sanctum. Instead of removing OCINC root and branch, Petraeus and Crocker would generally follow the campaign plan's tamer vision of incentivizing the office, pushing, prodding, and trying to work with it as best they could.

Other JSAT recommendations were carried forward. Intriguingly, the JSAT report included a section on military cyberspace operations, which was partially enacted. Electronic attacks against computer networks used by the enemy were among the most sensitive and classified military operations, in part because the United States did not want adversaries to know who had interfered with their Internet access and browsing or had blocked their sites, but also because the American government did not want to encourage other nations to engage in cyber operations. Under long-standing rules of engagement, any cyber attack required approval from the secretary of defense.

In March Petraeus asked Gates for the authority to at least use the Internet for some psychological operations, short of network attacks. Although the JSAT recommended that Petraeus be given the authority to order attacks on enemy computer networks, he did not receive it, but he did get help on the issue. On April 30, the NSC Principals Committee approved a Defense Department order that would allow a military task force, led by Lieutenant General Keith Alexander, the director of the National Security Agency, to begin cyber operations against networks used by Al-Qaeda and its allies, both in Iraq and elsewhere, after briefing Bush and, in classified sessions, the House and Senate Armed Services committees. Taking advantage of the initiative, Petraeus discussed the issue with Dick Cheney and the new commander of CENTCOM, Admiral William Fallon, in the second week of May. Days later, the first new network attack was carried out.

On May 12, Sunni insurgents snuck up on a small American position south of Baghdad, isolated it with IEDs, set Humvees on fire, and dragged three soldiers off alive. The military quickly poured a Stryker battalion and extra commandos, helicopters, drones, and cadaver dogs into the area in a vain effort to find the missing soldiers before their captors killed them. When American intelligence learned that the kidnappers had taken a video of the men, Alexander's cyber unit blocked its publication on Islamist Web sites, something for which Petraeus told Gates to pass along his thanks to Alexander.[19] This was a promising step, but in Petraeus's judgment, it was not enough. Three months after this cyber operation against Al-Qaeda in Iraq, Petraeus would brief James Clapper, the undersecretary of defense for intelligence, that "the cyber battlespace has been ceded to individuals and groups attacking U.S. forces," and that the United States remained "too risk averse" on the issue.[20]

Odierno's strategy of putting two brigades in Baghdad and then mounting a counteroffensive with the remaining three brigades in Baghdad's belts was the gist of the JSAT's security recommendations. Petraeus had already decided as much.

In May, Lieutenant General Jim Dubik, an old acquaintance of Petraeus who had held a variety of positions in Ranger and infantry units and had earned a master's degree in philosophy from Johns Hopkins, arrived at MNSTC-I to replace Marty Dempsey. Dubik wholeheartedly agreed with the JSAT recommendation to expand the Iraqi security forces, especially given average present-for-duty rates of 67 percent. His main concern was giving Odierno everything he needed to fight the insurgency.

Dubik used information from Odierno's corps, Dempsey's outgoing assessment, the Center for Army Analysis, and the Defense and Interior ministries to estimate how much Iraqi forces needed to grow. The numbers suggested to Dubik that over the next two and a half years, the total number of Iraqis in uniform needed to reach somewhere between 600,000 and 650,000, a 50 percent increase over the earlier plan.

This was an enormously ambitious project, to be sure, but the American and Iraqi commands charged with implementing it had a few advantages. The most important was money—there was already enough of it sitting around to fund the expansion without going to Washington for additional funds. Because of the extraordinarily slow way Iraqi bureaucracies spent money, MNSTC-I had between $800 and $900 million of American-supplied funds left over in various accounts. The money had to be spent by October 1, 2007, when it would cease to be available.[21] Over the summer, training centers around Iraq began churning out new units for the army, National Police, and other organs. The JSAT recommendation that the Iraqi security forces be expanded would be followed.

Some of the sectarian commanders of the National Police were purged or at least put in administrative positions where they could do less harm. In the early summer, Interior Minister Bolani and the National Police's overall commander, Lieutenant General Hussein Jassim al-Awadi, relieved both of the force's division commanders, all nine brigade commanders, and eighteen out of twenty-seven battalion commanders. Eradicating all of the sectarian elements from the National Police, however, was difficult. Lieutenant Colonel Andrew Yerkes, the leader of the eleven-man National Police Training Team, or NPTT, assigned to the 1st battalion of the 2nd National Police Brigade noted in an internal after-action report that many of the problems continued in the contested Saydiya neighborhood, even after re-bluing. The operations, he wrote, "normally had sectarian undertones and the NPTTs went on these raids to disrupt these sectarian activities." As the advisers became savvy to what their advisees were doing, though, the Iraqi officers tried to schedule raids for periods when they knew their American counterparts would be unavailable, or would use so many police in an operation that it would be impossible for the advisers to watch them all.[22]

On the morning of June 13, it appeared that the Americans had run into one of those "Events to Be Avoided" of which the JSAT had warned: the Askari Mosque in Samarra had been bombed—again. The Al-Qaeda bombing of the Shiite shrine sixteen months before, in February 2006, had collapsed the mosque's golden dome and sparked a surge in sectarian violence. This time the bombers destroyed the mosque's two 118-foot minarets, and in Baghdad the military feared that the bombing would reverse the trend of decreasing sectarian murders that had characterized the late winter and spring.

The Iraqi government ordered a curfew in the capital, effective that evening. Odierno ordered his command to keep careful track of violence against mosques, both Sunni-against-Shiite and Shiite-against-Sunni, and then he began arranging a visit to Samarra by himself and senior Iraqi leaders to show them that American and Iraqi troops had the situation in hand. Along with Maliki and the defense and interior ministers, Odierno flew from Baghdad to an American outpost in Samarra later that day, piled the delegation into Humvees, and headed to the badly damaged mosque.

Odierno feared that in the hours and days that followed the bombing, busloads of Mahdi Army fighters would head north into Sunni territory from the Shiite slums of Sadr City and Shula. He also feared that the National Police, only some of whose brigades had gone through re-bluing, would react badly by behaving aggressively in Sunni neighborhoods and sparking reprisals.[23] Neither happened. As an extra Iraqi Army brigade was deployed to Samarra to ensure calm, the war continued to take its normal, albeit deadly, course—a disaster seemed to have narrowly missed derailing the American project in Iraq. The only major negative consequence of the bombing came when Maliki fired the commander in Samarra, the long-serving and competent Major General Adnan Thabit, and replaced him with a National Police division commander known to have Sadrist connections, Major General Rashid al-Halifi. It was a fresh reminder of the virulent and seemingly intractable sectarianism of the Maliki government.

CHAPTER 20

The Former-Insurgent Counterinsurgency

With the surge brigades trickling in at a rate of one a month, Ray Odierno had decided in March to make his first major foray into the Baghdad belts: one of Steve Townsend's Stryker battalions would be pulled out of Baghdad and sent to Diyala, where it would be joined by a paratroop squadron.[1]

Located just northeast of the Iraqi capital, Diyala was a strategically vital region. The province was a haven for die-hard insurgents who wanted to mount attacks in Baghdad. It was a crossroads that led to the Kurdish lands to the north and Iran to the east. And, to the dismay of a long line of American commanders, it was a sectarian battleground. With the Mahdi Army on the prowl in Baghdad, many Sunnis had fled north, swelling the Sunni population in Diyala and fueling tensions with the Shiites, who, despite their minority status, had managed to gain control of the provincial government and police. The National Police's notoriously sectarian Wolf Brigade had been dispatched to Diyala in late 2005; its Shiite members enthusiastically joined the hunt for Sunni insurgents.

The strategy the Americans had embraced prior to the surge had succeeded primarily in pouring gasoline on the fire. Striving to put the Iraqi military in the lead, American forces had been drawn down and the 5th Iraqi Army Division had been given the main role for safeguarding the province. Soon after arriving at his Diyala post in July 2006, Brigadier General Shakir Hulail Hussein al-Kaabi drew up a list of suspects to be apprehended that included many of the Sunni notables who could be expected to play a role in shaping the province's political future. When American officers questioned why the Sunnis had been singled out, Shakir said simply that their names had come on a list from Baghdad, which was all the Shiite commander needed to know.

By the time Petraeus and Odierno returned to Iraq, the sectarian chain reaction resembled the cycle of violence in one of Derek Harvey's Power-Point briefs. Sunni insurgent attacks had sparked abuses on the part of Shiites, many committed by the Iraqi government's own forces. The cascade of violence had opened the door to Al-Qaeda in Iraq, which was under pressure in Anbar and eager to cast itself as the protector of the Sunnis in Diyala. By 2007, Al-Qaeda fighters had thoroughly penetrated Baqubah, defiantly proclaiming the city to be the new capital of their caliphate and flexing their muscles by establishing Islamic courts and decreeing an austere set of mores, which included a ban on the sale of cigarettes. A city of 300,000 just an hour's drive from Baghdad, Baqubah was divided by a river with date palm groves on each side. Despite the best efforts of the American battalion assigned to Diyala, which was led by Lieutenant Colonel Morris "Mo" Goins, much of the city was for all intents and purposes "red"—under enemy control.

South of Baqubah and east of the Diyala River, Al-Qaeda fighters were also ensconced in a sprawling palm-grove-laden sanctuary, an area so replete with arms caches, insurgent leaders, fighters, and their supporters that American soldiers took to calling it the Al-Qaeda FOB—forward operating base, in American military jargon. The supply lines between Baqubah and Al-Qaeda's rural staging area ran through Buhriz, a former Baathist community of cinder block homes and wood and mud shacks. Consolidating their hold on the town, the insurgents raised funds by kidnapping local Iraqis, secured housing by evicting some residents from their homes, and killed with abandon when anyone got in their way. A small group of bearded black-clad militants took down the Iraqi flag and raised the black banner of their self-proclaimed Islamic State of Iraq. "They used religion as a ploy to get in and exploit people's passions," said Haidar, a local resident who did a stint as an interpreter for the Americans. "They were Iraqis and other Arabs from Syria, Afghanistan, Jordan, Saudi Arabia, and Egypt. They started kicking people out of their houses and getting ransom from rich people. They would shoot people in front of their houses to scare the others."[2]

While the focus was on Baghdad, an undermanned complement of American troops was saddled with somehow holding the line in Diyala. Much of the burden fell on Goins, a seasoned soldier whose father had served in Vietnam and who had been in the 3rd Infantry Division during the initial push to Baghdad. When Goins's battalion, 1-12 Cavalry, was deployed to Diyala in late 2006, it was not expecting a no-holds-barred fight. The unit that preceded it had left much of their heavy armor on FOB Warhorse, a dusty American base just three miles north of Baqubah, and traveled around in Humvees. But security was rapidly deteriorating in Diyala. Given a vast area to cover, Goins distributed his tank and infantry companies and platoons to several key cities and towns. It did not take long for Al-Qaeda to react.

When Captain Chris Connolly moved Alpha Company to a police building in western Baqubah, he was met by a barrage of hand grenades, RPGs, and sniper fire. From that point on, the route from Warhorse to Baqubah was dense with IEDs as Al-Qaeda sought to block the Americans' access to the city. The rest of the province was just as ominous. The thick palm groves were perfect hideaways.[3]

In traffic-jammed Baghdad there was little opportunity to dig bombs into the earth: Iranian-supplied EFPs, disguised as piles of refuse along roads, were the deadliest weapons. The Sunni insurgents did not have EFPs. But Diyala's dirt roads and poorly monitored streets were especially well suited for employing an equally deadly weapon: huge buried bombs that were all but invisible to the naked eye. In the macabre race between the IED designers and the high-tech American military bureaucracy trying to defeat them, the bomb manufacturers had the upper hand.

In Diyala, the insurgents used these bombs promiscuously to ambush the Americans and turn the areas they controlled into virtual no-go zones. "Deep-buried" IEDs, as they were known by the soldiers, contained hundreds of pounds of ordnance, land mines, or homemade explosives. They were powerful enough to separate the hull of a Bradley from its turret or turn a seventy-ton Abrams tank into a "Code F" piece of equipment—a tangled piece of metal that was beyond repair. In one attack on Goins's battalion, an IED exploded under a Bradley, killing the driver. As an armored M88 towing vehicle was hauling the Bradley back to FOB Warhorse, a deep-buried IED struck it as well, blowing the M88 commander out of the hatch and setting him on fire. Soldiers rushed to put out the flames with a fire extinguisher, but three other soldiers in the M88 were killed, and the commander did not survive. The insurgents also laid deep-buried IEDs to keep the Americans away from their headquarters and bed-down areas. The U.S. military had its bases, and the insurgents had created their own sanctuaries.

Desperate to reduce the IED threat, Goins convened a meeting of all of his officers and noncommissioned officers to brainstorm about the problem. A solution offered was the Krill Device, named after the soldier who invented it. A Humvee with mannequins inside was towed with an unusually long bar, so it appeared as if the vehicle were moving on its own. Once an IED went off, the soldiers would go hunting for the triggermen, who were sometimes as far as 500 meters off the road. But with too few forces to control the increasingly hostile terrain, this was little more than a gimmick. The casualties kept mounting. In February, Goins had one of his darkest days. The commander was at a memorial service at Warhorse for one of his soldiers when he received an urgent report that Delta Company had run into a new and even more insidious type of bomb: a house that had been rigged to explode as soon as the soldiers touched a trip wire inside. The house bomb had killed three and wounded four more. Bombs were no longer only under the street. Even a house off the bomb-laden road could be a death trap.

By the time Goins's battalion was midway through its twelve-month deployment, he had lost nearly twenty soldiers, had many more wounded, and had seen eight Abrams tanks, fifteen Bradleys, and eighteen Humvees turned into useless scraps of junk. It took everything Goins could do to keep his soldiers' focus on the fight. When the surge began, however, Goins drew the line. Ordered to construct a defensive line north of Khan Bani Saad to slow the flow of insurgents toward Baghdad while also covering his previous battle space, Goins went to Colonel Dave Sutherland, the brigade commander, and told him that he simply did not have the resources to execute the mission. The battalion's strength had dwindled too much.

When Odierno arrived to check on the situation in Diyala that month, Goins briefed him that the battalion had suffered major casualties, had received little in the way of replacements, and was at 74 percent strength—just a shade above the threshold at which a unit is considered by the Army to be combat ineffective. Goins was talking with local sheikhs and trying to get them on board. But the sheikhs had reservations: on the few occasions they provided tips they expected immediate action, but the battalion had neither the control of the battle area nor the resources to regain it.

Maliki recognized the danger as well, though not his government's role in stoking the sectarian passions that fueled Al-Qaeda in Diyala. In a March 11 meeting with his cabinet, Maliki described Diyala as the "most dangerous place in Iraq." Abd al-Qadir, Maliki's minister of defense, echoed the sentiment later in the spring, saying that Baqubah was "becoming another Fallujah" and should be second only to Baghdad as a military priority. Randy Mixon, the two-star general who commanded northern

Iraq, wanted an entire brigade to do the job. Odierno saw the need for reinforcements as well. By March, however, only two of the five surge brigades had arrived in Iraq. Diyala was to get an infusion of troops, but for now only a Stryker battalion—Lieutenant Colonel Bruce Antonia's 5-20 Infantry—and a paratroop squadron would have to suffice.

The arrival of the reinforcements was not a surprise. Before Antonia's unit even got there, leaflets were distributed in Baqubah proclaiming that more American forces were headed to Diyala and that they would lay down the law. "In the brigade brief that we got several days prior to coming up we asked for the flyers not to be disseminated," recalled Captain Anthony Gore, the commander of Bravo Company. "We just did not want people to know that we were coming into their areas. They had some message that 'we own the night' or something weird on the flyer. We just thought that was not necessary. Why give your enemy a heads-up?"[4]

On March 13, Antonia's battalion drove north to FOB Warhorse, passing an ominous number of IED craters on the way. After arriving at the base, Sutherland instructed Antonia to take control of Baqubah and its suburbs while the rest of Sutherland's brigade handled the other areas in Diyala. Mixon's guidance was that the battalion should be out and on the streets of Baqubah within twenty-four hours after arriving at Warhorse. The order, recalled Major Jack Vantress, the battalion's chief operations officer, was "get out, get seen, and let them know you are here."[5]

As deadly as the region had been, the new soldiers had only a vague idea of how the enemy operated and even where they were. Since Goins's 1-12 had been so overextended, American forces did not have a detailed understanding of the city. Much of Baqubah looked quieter than it actually was only because no American troops had been there, meaning Al-Qaeda had not needed to fight and no military reporting was coming out of the area. "We pulled SIGACTS from all the databases," recalled Captain Tim Bagley, the battalion's intelligence officer. "There was nothing there to indicate that this place was all that bad. We walked into Baqubah with absolutely no idea what the true enemy picture was."[6]

After a night at Warhorse, the battalion linked up with Goins's soldiers and headed into Baqubah. Staff Sergeant Mike Marker from Bravo Company had a sense that the soldiers were headed for trouble—he could see that children near a local school had stuck their fingers in their ears. A moment later there was a huge explosion: a Stryker had hit a deep-buried

IED and, its hull breached, had flipped over on its side. In all its months in Baghdad and Mosul, the battalion had never had one of its Strykers upended. Corporal Brian Chevalier was thrown out of the driver's hatch and killed instantly. Fire seemed to be coming from all directions.

The soldiers of 1-14 Cavalry's Bronco Troop, which was attached to 5-20 Infantry, were just as surprised. "We were confident in ourselves," said Captain Ben Richards, Bronco Troop's commander. "We were the Stryker guys, the strike force. We had been doing a lot of the high-speed stuff in Baghdad. When we found out there were no EFPs in Baqubah it was like, 'Oh, we'll be pretty safe.'"[7]

Assigned to secure Buhriz, on the southeastern side of city, Richards's troops came under fire from multiple directions. Richards's tank platoon "shot black" on main gun rounds—that is, they ran out of ammunition. Air weapons teams—pairs of Apache attack helicopters armed with Hellfire missiles—pulverized buildings the insurgents were using, something Richards had never seen during his months in Baghdad, until the helicopters also ran black. There seemed to be an IED every 30 meters, often strategically placed so that when the American explosive ordnance disposal (EOD) units stopped to deploy their small counter-IED robots the robots would come under fire. Richards's soldiers had never carried grenades in Baghdad during their patrols. Now, they were heaving them in combat for the first time. "If I could take you back to that day and you could see the look on the faces of my troopers: it was a realization that we were up against something we had never come up against, and most of the guys there were on second or third tours," Richards recalled.[8]

At the end of the fight Richards's troop and other elements of the battalion stayed in Baqubah, eventually moving into an abandoned police station that had been taken over by Al-Qaeda in the fall and set aflame, leaving black, sooty streaks on the walls. The residents in Buhriz seemed as surprised at that development as the insurgents. Unlike earlier operations, the Americans had shown up in force and had not quickly withdrawn. For townspeople and even local insurgents who chafed under Al-Qaeda's dominance, it was time to push back.

During that first day, the battalion had one KIA and fourteen wounded. "They were ready for us," said Vantress. "The fact that they knew we were coming led to the fact that we got engaged decisively on both sides of the river" that bisected the town.[9] After two days of tangling with Al-Qaeda, the battalion was ordered south to clear the palm groves west of Buhriz, which Sutherland suspected were the insurgents' main sanctuary. Pushing through the weeds, the soldiers came upon bales of barbed wire and finally, after two days, a Soviet-made DShK antiaircraft gun hidden in a small farmhouse. Richards's troops and the combat engineers were ordered to secure the urban area to the east of the palm groves. The streets were so narrow that only one Stryker could go down the road at a time. As the operation got under way, an IED built into a cinder block wall exploded, disabling a Stryker the battalion's combat engineers were using, and injuring several of the soldiers.

"I never saw it. Nobody ever saw it," recalled Staff Sergeant Shawn McGuire, an engineer squad leader. A wall of enemy fire followed as Richards's soldiers and the engineers struggled to move up the street to help the stricken unit. Al-Qaeda's battlefield skills were far superior to anything McGuire had seen in Baghdad. "I have never seen, before or since, organization like that. They were organized. They were well trained. They shot. They could hit things. Instead of just poking around corners and shooting and running, they would bound and maneuver on you. It was almost like watching U.S. soldiers train."[10]

By early April, there were two wars in Buhriz—one between the Americans and the insurgents and another among the insurgents themselves, what the Americans called red-on-red. But Sutherland, who spent considerable effort trying to arrange an Anbar Awakening–style group by meeting with sheikhs, who mostly came from rural areas, was wary of any attempts to work with former insurgents. As the internecine fighting heated up, Abu Talib, a small, plump, and fiery member of the 1920 Revolution Brigades, arranged a meeting with the brigade and battalion staffs at FOB Gabe. Abu Talib wanted ammunition. The Americans were not inclined to give it to him, and the session ended with an angry exchange. Abu Talib threatened the Americans, who wondered why they should arm insurgents who had been firing on them just weeks earlier.

As the fighting escalated, Al-Qaeda was gaining the upper hand, and 1,200 residents fled Buhriz on foot. Soon after, an Iraqi who called himself Abu Ali approached Iraqi soldiers in town and arranged to meet Richards at his burned-out police station on April 7. Ali was by local standards prosperous—his family owned a store in Buhriz—had served twenty years in the Iraqi Army, and insisted that he had no association with the 1920 Brigades. Like Abu Talib, however, he was looking for ammunition. Richards was not afraid to reach out to the Iraqis, but just who he might work with was unclear. Were the Americans watching a turf fight or something more? "We were not sure what was going on," Richards recalled. "We were not sure we could trust the people not to turn on us afterward."[11]

With Al-Qaeda growing in strength, there was not much time to ponder the question. Richards suggested to Abu Ali that his men should tip off the Americans on which Iraqis belonged to Al-Qaeda and where they had buried their bombs. Initially, more than a dozen volunteers came forward. Richards dubbed them "Kit Carson Scouts." Antonia decided to use the exodus as an opportunity to clear the town of Al-Qaeda fighters. The battalion called in an airstrike on April 10 on a house which turned out to be the Al-Qaeda command center in the city, and then entered Buhriz. They were greeted not with gunfire but with groups of local men who wanted to stand up an armed neighborhood watch group. The town had flipped. "The locals had gone out and put markers on all the IEDs," recalled Command Sergeant Major Jeffrey Huggins. "We were looking down there—bag, can, rock. Got it."[12]

But Richards continued to push the envelope. Al-Qaeda had occupied the bread mills and food stores that were supposed to feed the area as a means of exerting leverage on the population, which was cut off from the supplies by IEDs and insurgents. So Richards and some Strykers drove out of their sector in search of a warehouse, losing one vehicle to an IED along the way. On another occasion, Richards drove the Kit Carson Scout leaders to meet the local police chief in the hopes of getting them hired as part of the province's security forces. In late April, Antonia called Richards in for counseling; he noted that his soldiers were questioning his aggressive outreach to the Iraqis and added that if he had a captain to spare he would replace him.

When the word got around that there was a price on his head—and that of the Kit Carson Scouts, as well—Richards figured he was making headway. On May 13, Richards was standing in the hatch of his Stryker, and headed to Warhorse for a meeting, as he approached an intersection that was a notorious sniper's alley. No sooner had he ducked into the vehicle to avoid the rounds when there was an enormous blast. A suicide car bomber had maneuvered his vehicle ten feet from the Stryker and exploded. Concussed and wobbly, Richards and his soldiers stumbled onto the street only to hear rounds pinging off the disabled Stryker: they were caught in what the military called a "complex attack." As a squad of Al-Qaeda fighters armed with RPGs moved toward the stricken vehicles, an Abrams, which was rolling down the road, dispatched the enemy with a canister round. Buhriz had once been the epicenter of the storm, but now it was an island: it was much safer in the town, but the enemy was lurking just outside. Richards would make it through the war, but because of the effects of the concussion he would eventually be medically retired from the Army.[13]

Still, the battalion had provided only half of the combat power that was needed. The western part of the city was still under Al-Qaeda control, and the battle of Baqubah was far from over. As it sought to clear the Tahrir area of the city, the battalion suffered its greatest single loss. On May 6, a Stryker from Apache Company struck a huge IED, an explosion so massive that it turned the vehicle into a twisted, unrecognizable hulk. Staff Sergeant David Plush scampered to the vehicle and peered at the wreckage. There appeared to be nobody inside. Plush yelled to see if anybody was left, and a voice answered. The driver had survived but was pinned in the flipped-over vehicle, his hand snagged in a hatch door. The soldiers needed to rescue him—and fast. Al-Qaeda fighters were all around. An enemy machine gun had opened up shortly before and nobody could pinpoint the source of the fire.

Taking off his body armor to slip underneath the vehicle, Plush and other members of the battalion furiously struggled to jack up the Stryker. Specialist Christopher Waiters, a medic, numbed the driver's fingers and grabbed a makeshift amputation kit: some gauze and a scalpel. If the driver could not be yanked free they would need to cut off his fingers to get him out. Otherwise, Al-Qaeda might move in and they would never escape. Antonia stopped the medic before he began to cut. Enemy fire or not, they needed to make one last try. With another burst of exertion, the soldiers managed to jack up the vehicle enough for the driver to yank his hand free. Six soldiers and a Russian photographer had been killed instantly in the blast and their bodies had been pulverized and thrown clear. The driver was the only survivor.

In Baghdad's western belt, around Abu Ghraib, reports were surfacing of insurgent infighting similar to that in Buhriz. In one instance, an informant reporting to Task Force Knight, JSOC's British SAS squadron, described how in Abu Ghraib, Al-Qaeda fighters were setting up checkpoints to restrict the movement of their sometime allies in the 1920 Revolution Brigades. A few weeks afterward, another SAS informant described witnessing an ambush northwest of Baghdad in which local insurgents attacked a convoy they believed was carrying Abu Ayyub al-Masri, Al-Qaeda in Iraq's overall chief. Before the 1920 Brigades fighters were able to approach, Al-Qaeda reinforcements arrived. (Masri survived.)[14]

The American commander in Abu Ghraib was Lieutenant Colonel Kurt Pinkerton, a former CENTCOM planner whose under-strength battalion,

2-5 Cavalry, had been taking heavy casualties from IEDs since deploying in the fall. In December, frustrated by mounting deaths, Pinkerton arranged to meet with the Delta Force colonel who was helping Graeme Lamb run his hush-hush insurgent outreach cell. The American colonel told Pinkerton that he had someone for him to meet, and in January, in another meeting in a room at the U.S. embassy, he introduced the battalion commander to a Jaish al-Islami commander who went by the name of Abu Azzam. The insurgent leader got right down to business, gesturing toward a box on a wall map of Abu Ghraib. "I can gain control of this area and help you," he said plainly.[15]

Pinkerton was intrigued but cautious. Abu Azzam said that he had links to the Anbar Awakening but had chosen not to cooperate with them directly; he was cagey about why and about his own past. As the winter continued, the American commander kept Abu Azzam's grand plans at arm's length, but continued to meet with him, hoping to use his connections to recruit for an unarmed or self-armed neighborhood watch group and a trash collection project. Quietly, men supplied by Abu Azzam began to provide Pinkerton's troops with intelligence tips, but the neighborhood watch idea bogged down in January. Abu Azzam's recruits wanted weapons, like the Marines were handing out to Anbar Awakening groups, but Pinkerton had no intention of arming them. On February 6, though, he accepted an invitation from Abu Azzam to meet at a remote warehouse in Abu Ghraib with a dozen leaders of the local insurgency who wanted to help.

In Abu Ghraib, there was more to the local volunteers' motivations than hatred of Al-Qaeda. Abu Ghraib's rural Sunni tribes were fighting two conflicts, and losing both of them: one, like the sheikhs of the Anbar Awakening, against encroaching and abusive Al-Qaeda cells, and the other against heavily Shiite Iraqi Army troops who were not only oppressive in their tactics, but also actively taking part in the kind of resettlement gerrymandering that was spreading Shiite influence in Baghdad and its surroundings.

By late April, Abu Azzam and his followers were itching to do something more than provide intelligence and hear promises about future police slots. "If you meet me at this location tomorrow," Abu Azzam said, pointing out a rural schoolhouse on a map, "I'll have three thousand people there." To Pinkerton's shock, the crowd of young men at the schoolhouse the next day, April 23, really did look three thousand strong. One of the first men the colonel met as he arrived at the recruiting drive was one of its organizers, a local insurgent leader who went by the name of Abu Marouf and worked for Abu Azzam. One of Pinkerton's soldiers recognized Abu Marouf's face immediately: he was number seven on the battalion's list of insurgent targets. The colonel knew that in Abu Ghraib, the Awakening had just moved from a potential phenomenon to a real one.

Three days later, on April 26, Pinkerton got a radio call saying that the same schoolhouse, where many of the mostly Sunni recruits were still assembled, was under attack by the 6th Iraqi Army Division's 3rd "Muthana" Brigade. The American colonel grabbed the dozen soldiers of his security detail and headed west toward the schoolhouse, and as their Humvees pulled up they found a scene of complete chaos bordering on a violent riot. How exactly the standoff had started was unclear, but an Iraqi Army platoon that had gone to the schoolhouse had been pinned down by a mob and a soldier had been hauled away by the crowd.

Feeling that he and his security detail were in an untenable situation and might not survive it, Pinkerton got on the radio and called in a pair of British GR4 Tornado fighters to do a low, loud pass as a show of force. The flyby allowed the Iraqi platoon to get its missing soldier back from the crowd, but to the colonel it still seemed like a dangerous situation, so he called the British jets back in to jettison bundles of the aluminum chaff that they used to jam radar. The third time the Tornados came, Pinkerton told Abu Azzam, they would come in with authority to fire their cannons.

As soon as the scene calmed down, Pinkerton got a call saying that Brigadier General Nasr al-Hiti, the Muthana Brigade commander, was headed for the Green Zone to report on the morning's events to the Defense Ministry. Not believing that Nasr would give a truthful account, Pinkerton and his security detail raced downtown as well to tell their and Abu Azzam's side of the story.

Soon Pinkerton had a motley collection of more than three thousand local men on his hands, some armed and some unarmed, some insurgents and some farmers, mostly Sunnis but some Shiites, all loosely represented by Abu Azzam. Pinkerton's hope was that as many as 1,900 of them could be hired into the police, but in the meantime they were out manning intersections and checkpoints, risking their lives and drawing interest from on high. To help protect them, Pinkerton's troops distributed infrared chemlights to some of the volunteers on duty at remote checkpoints, so that when they came under attack at night, drones and attack helicopters could see them and ground troops could find them. He also continued to work closely with both Abu Azzam and Abu Marouf, whom the American colonel trusted less but saw as a competent leader. "Abu Marouf was lean, wiry," he recalled. "When he smiles at you, it's more of a smirk. He would say, 'I want to take you to my men,' and he would take me to his house and show me his people cleaning their weapons with goat milk, saying, 'This guy will go on patrol with two bullets, he's not scared.'"

In Radwaniyah, south of Abu Ghraib, Lieutenant Colonel John Valledor began to hear the same sort of reports of insurgent infighting that had preceded the dramatic turn of events in Kurt Pinkerton's neighboring sector. For Valledor the phenomenon was happening just in time. His battalion, 2-14 Infantry, had arrived in Iraq during the summer of 2006 and had been given a large and hostile region to control—one that had cost his predecessor twenty-five killed. Instead of hunkering down, Valledor maintained a series of patrol bases in the canal-laden and largely agrarian region he was responsible for. In October, he added one more: after getting mortared from the Russian power plant that dominated the Euphrates River valley he mounted an operation to take it back. The patrol bases he established entailed some risks. To resupply them, his battalion had to drive along the roads; by the winter he had lost twenty-five armored vehicles and was enduring more than twenty attacks a day.

An even bigger worry was that for the stretch of terrain in the west of his zone that bordered Anbar, Valledor did not have enough troops to establish another patrol base: only two platoons were in the western reach of his area of operations at any one time. And it was far from quiet. For the first five months of 2007, Valledor received regular reports of mysterious firefights in the area. There were green tracers going back and forth in the distance. The Americans would find bodies in the canals. But whenever they pressed the locals for answers they came up against a wall of silence. "I kept getting reports from my company commander, 'Hey sir, there's a fight going on out here. We think it's AQ fighting with somebody else, and it ain't us. And it ain't the Marines.' So the most that we could do was kind of talk to the locals and try to get a feel. But the sensing was that the locals were afraid to talk to us because something was going on," Valledor recalled. "I didn't have the combat power to push into that area and explore further."[16]

A turning point came in late spring when Valledor got a call from one of his companies in the west. A band of heavily armed tribesmen had stopped an infantry platoon waving a white flag made from a burlap bag and said they wanted to talk. "So I drove down there and I ran into a group of what

I called insurgents. These were local Iraqi tribesmen, heavily armed, they looked like AQ, they smelled like AQ, and they talked like AQ, but they were waving a white flag. So this was kind of a strange phenomenon."[17]

Valledor's troops were not the only ones being approached. Lieutenant Colonel Mark Suich, 1-89 Cavalry's commander, a Mogadishu veteran and a wrestler who stood out for his physical fitness even in the world of light infantrymen, had begun to work with the local Ghartani tribe, allowing the tribesmen to set up neighborhood watch groups within their villages. Soon his soldiers were being approached by the mysterious insurgents in the west as well.

A meeting was arranged in an abandoned home in the Radwaniyah area so Valledor and Suich could talk face-to-face with the extremists; both sides were armed. The insurgent leader who came was Abu Marouf, the same man Pinkerton had met not long before at the schoolhouse in Abu Ghraib. Abu Marouf came to the point: he wanted to join forces with the Americans to fight Al-Qaeda. Valledor and Suich looked at each other in disbelief. Abu Marouf had connections to the 1920 Revolutionary Brigades; he had not come to the meeting with clean hands. But every time he spoke up at the session, the men he brought with him from the Zobai tribe listened, so he was clearly a person of some influence. He was also aware of the Anbar Awakening and seemed determined to carry on his version of it.

Valledor told his battalion's intelligence officer to give the Iraqis the names of the top ten Al-Qaeda figures the Americans were looking for. If Abu Marouf was serious, he would find the suspects. To facilitate the next linkup, the intelligence officer handed him a cell phone. As he left the session, Valledor had second thoughts about the encounter. Maybe the Americans should have grabbed Abu Marouf when they had had a chance.

A week later, however, Abu Marouf called to set up another meeting in Radwaniyah. Pulling out a cell phone, the Iraqi leader played a video. A group of tribesmen in a truck drove up to a house, dragged one of the Americans' top ten suspects out of the home, tied him up, threw him in the back of the truck, drove him out to a canal, and shot him. "Scratch him off your list," Abu Marouf said. This was not what Valledor had expected, but now he had one fewer name on his wanted list. Valledor reported the development to his brigade commander, Mike Kershaw.

As the meetings with Abu Marouf continued, his men helped the Americans find IEDs. The soldiers would add a Sunni to their squad—like Ben Richards, they called them Kit Carson Scouts—and go searching for weapons caches and Al-Qaeda safe houses. Soon Abu Marouf wanted to take the collaboration a step further. The Sunni tribesmen and the Americans would do a combined attack. American troops would control the roads, and the tribesmen would clear an area from Route Tampa down to the river. Valledor agreed. Since the tribesmen had no uniforms, Valledor waived off the attack helicopters: there would be no way for them to tell friend from foe. Valledor also told the commander of the largely Shiite Iraqi Army battalion he worked with to keep away: there was not much chance he would approve of Americans who fought with a Sunni militia.

Abu Marouf's fighters went in at night and killed their enemies or chased them across the river. The attack was successful. As reports about the operation trickled up the chain of command there was considerable attention, and it was not all positive. In the early days of the Awakening, the movement was a bottom-up phenomenon driven by local Iraqis and the American units they encountered in the field. It was not something the generals in Baghdad or CENTCOM had organized from on high. Like Richards in Buhriz, Valledor was making up some of the rules as he went along. But while no policy on how to use former insurgents had been set, it was not customary to use them as a maneuver unit—to form a cordon on the road and let the former insurgents do the fighting. Apache pilots from Colonel Dan Ball's aviation brigade stated that they had been flying over hostilities, reporting firefights beneath them involving Iraqis who looked like insurgents, and that Valledor had told them not to attack. The pilots were angry at not being allowed to go after the targets. Valledor had the tribesmen wear reflective school crossing belts to identify themselves.

Suich worked with the Zobai fighters in the same way. The fighters were so fierce and effective that Kershaw and his officers took to calling the tribal volunteers "shock companies." But soon the word came down from Rick Lynch's 3rd Infantry Division: if there were combined operations in the future they should involve American troops and the Iraqi Army, not a band of tribal fighters. Valledor followed his orders, but he also kept having Abu Marouf's men accompany his soldiers on patrols to point out who was friendly and who was not.

With former insurgents helping his troops fight, Kershaw recalled, "It was on like Donkey Kong."[18] The fighters marked their vehicles with orange air-identification panels to keep them from being targeted by American helicopters, but the system did not always work: from the air, trucks full of volunteers with assault rifles and RPGs looked just like trucks full of insurgents, and attack helicopter pilots did not like passing up such targets. After one disaster in which attack helicopters killed a group of friendly fighters, Kershaw's brigade learned that by relying on Kiowa pilots with whom they had a better relationship and avoiding Apaches, they could mitigate the problem.

Other villages, too, began cooperating: in the village of Sadr al-Yusufiyah, company commander Captain Palmer Phillips helped members of the Albu Issa tribe—men who had not been insurgents—set up a neighborhood watch group. It was a useful demonstration of what the tribes could accomplish—or, as Kershaw put it, somewhat irreverently, a "petting zoo," where high-level American visitors could meet the sheikhs. Valledor's battalion lost its final soldier on June 1 when Staff Sergeant Travis Atkins tackled a suicide bomber (an act for which he would posthumously earn the Distinguished Service Cross, but not the Medal of Honor for which he was nominated). By then the number of attacks had plunged. Al-Qaeda made its last gasp against the battalion on June 10, when it launched a failed attack against the "petting zoo." Two suicide car bombs crashed into Phillips's outpost in Sadr al-Yusufiyah, but failed to destroy the base.

Martin Stanton, a colonel on Petraeus's staff who been taken hostage by Saddam's forces during the run-up to the 1991 Persian Gulf War and worked tribal issues, sent Kershaw a series of emails explaining what was happening with the Anbar Awakening and encouraging him to keep on forging ahead. Working with the shock companies and other groups of fighters transformed the situation in Radwaniyah and, soon, in other parts of Kershaw's brigade area as well. Kershaw's superiors in the 3rd Infantry Division headquarters, though, were wary of the arrangement. Rick Lynch, the division commander, took the stance that American troops should not be cooperating with anyone who had American "blood on their hands"—a criterion that ruled out many of the people who were most helpful to Suich and Valledor and which was stricter than what Odierno had set. Lynch's division did establish a "reconciliation cell," but his division's relationship with Kershaw's brigade, which had embraced "reconciliation" with the insurgents when the headquarters staff was still focused on American-led combat operations, remained tense.

The episodes north and south of Baghdad appeared to fit a pattern. The presence of substantial American forces in an area that had been left largely unattended—and the fact that they were digging in for a long stay—had emboldened former Iraqi foes to reach out. As word spread through the tribal grapevine, the Iraqis had taken the initiative to establish a partnership with the Americans. But it took astute leadership on the American side to see the opportunity for what it was and make it work. For years afterward, there was a heated chicken-or-egg debate on whether the Awakening or the surge had come first. But the dispute missed the point. The Awakening in Ramadi had emerged in response to the sort of counterinsurgency tactics which had been the exception rather than the rule under Casey, but which became central tenets of strategy after Petraeus and Odierno took over. The surge served as a catalyst that encouraged the Awakening to spread to Sunni areas beyond Anbar.

In practice, it was not generals but leaders at the battalion and company level who had to make quick, hard choices about whether or not to work with insurgents on the battlefield. Not all of the lower- and mid-ranking officers were rewarded for their audacity and improvisation. Kershaw was praised by many of peers for his innovative work in the southern belts. But at the end of his tour in Iraq he received a mediocre officer evaluation report, or OER, the Army's report card, from Lynch. The two officers had clashed from the start, and Kershaw's enthusiasm for using the Awakening volunteers as shock companies and his criticism of Lynch's liberal use of airpower were high on the list of issues they did not see eye-to-eye on. An OER had four grades, and Lynch gave Kershaw a "2-Block," which all but killed his chances of being promoted to general. Even Ben Richards was counseled by his superiors after his squadron lost a Stryker while he was trying to bring food to the hungry residents in Buhriz.[19]

But Petraeus and his staff did play a role in institutionalizing the emerging alliance with the tribes. A system was set up to take and inventory biometric data from the tribal volunteers—which enabled the American military to check to see if the tribal fighters had previously been arrested. Guidance was issued that they could be paid from the commanders' emergency funds and were not to be armed by the United States. (They could, of course, buy weapons with the money they received or use weapons captured from Al-Qaeda.) As with seemingly everything the military dealt with, they were given a name and an acronym: they were the "Concerned Local Citizens," or CLCs. The name stuck until an interpreter told the Americans that in Arabic the phrase came across as "very worried Iraqis." It was eventually changed to the "Sons of Iraq."

Maliki, by and large, was content with the movement as long as it was focused, first and foremost, on fighting Al-Qaeda and was located in Sunni areas away from Baghdad. But the closer the movement came to the Iraqi capital the more uneasy the prime minister and his Shiite-dominated government grew. They did not embrace the terminology regarding the Awakening or CLCs. Simply put, the Awakening volunteers were just "armed groups" to them. Petraeus explained the situation to Gates in a letter at the beginning of June. "My sensing is that if we were to ask the Maliki government if they support Sunni tribal engagement and reconciliation they would answer yes," he wrote. "In Sunni provinces like Anbar and Salah and Din, they would likely mean yes." But the closer the Sunni groups got to Shiite population centers, the more the government would resist: "The appetite of the Shia leadership for Sunni tribal engagement lessens significantly as the issue gets closer to Shia towns and neighborhoods." The government was unsure how to respond to the appearance of Awakening volunteers in Diyala, Petraeus believed, and if the groups came to Baghdad proper, the government would likely give only lip service to support them.[20]

The first test of how the Maliki government would deal with the new Awakening groups was Abu Ghraib, where Kurt Pinkerton had 1,500 volunteers—mostly Sunnis—hoping to join the army and police. Though only a few miles separated Abu Ghraib from Anbar, where Maliki had thrown his weight behind the original Ramadi-based Awakening, from his perspective Abu Azzam's movement was a very different beast in important respects.

First and foremost, Abu Ghraib was on Baghdad's doorstep, unlike relatively remote Ramadi. And the rise of the Awakening there took place against a very different back story than in Anbar: one of sectarian strife that inherently gave the former an anti-government flavor. The tribes in Ramadi, which was not a sectarian battleground, had formed the Awakening in reaction to Al-Qaeda. In Abu Ghraib, though, Abu Azzam and his compatriots were reaching out to the American military because they faced a bigger threat: the Shiite government's troops. The 6th Iraqi Army Division's Muthana Brigade was, in effect, taking part in the sectarian struggle in Abu Ghraib on the same side as the Mahdi Army, even busing Shiite settlers into the area. That the brigade's commander was a Maliki favorite did not help matters. It was the Muthana Brigade, more so than Al-Qaeda in Iraq, that weighed on the minds of Abu Azzam's volunteers. To get back on the right side of the Americans, though, Abu Ghraib's tribal and insurgent leaders had to take on Al-Qaeda, even though some of them had worked with the group in the past.

From the American perspective, Abu Azzam and his people were taking on Al-Qaeda in a strategic district of the belts. But from where Maliki stood, the new "armed group" in Abu Ghraib looked like a case of anti-government Sunni insurgents seeking a refuge of last resort in a new alliance with the Americans. Since the Awakening group there had clashed with government forces from its very first day, when Abu Azzam's followers dragged off a Muthana Brigade soldier and Pinkerton had British jets buzz the crowd, it was predictable that the government would not embrace it.

By mid-May, the Abu Ghraib volunteers were a topic of heated discussion at the MCNS. As Petraeus relayed it to Gates, the military received reports that Maliki had ordered the closure of the Abu Ghraib unit by the Muthana Brigade, only to then reverse himself and allow Deputy Prime Minister Salaam al-Zobaie—a senior member of the tribe from which many of the Abu Ghraib volunteers came—to reach an accommodation with them. The next step was to get as many of the men as possible to join the police, as had been done wherever possible in Anbar. Here again Maliki resisted, insisting that the potential recruits travel outside their home area to pass Iraqi Army physical training tests before being considered for the police.[21]

At the end of May or beginning of June Petraeus met with senior Sunni politicians Tariq al-Hashimi, Mahmoud al-Mashhadani, and Adnan Dulaimi, all of whom expressed anger at Maliki's recent political moves, including the obstacles he was putting in the way of the Abu Ghraib volunteers.

The same week that Petraeus wrote his letter to Gates, at the end of the worst month for American casualties since 2004, the first Sunni "armed groups" arrived in Baghdad. Three of the capital's worst areas were still Al-Qaeda strongholds—the Dora, Adhamiya, and Ameriya neighborhoods. In Adhamiya, one American infantry company had taken such heavy casualties that one of its platoons staged a mental health mutiny, refusing after a visit to a combat stress center to go back out because some of the men were afraid they would take out their desire for revenge on residents. In Dora, a heavy concentration of troops was bogged down in a small amalgam of neighborhoods that increasingly resembled a mini-Ramadi or Baqubah.

In the small but nasty sector of Ameriya, Lieutenant Colonel Dale Kuehl headed a small battalion, 1-5 Cavalry. Stryker clearing operations earlier in the spring had pushed more insurgents into Ameriya, and by early May they were embracing the tactics of Anbar and Dora: huge IEDs hidden in sewers or under asphalt. On May 19, an IED in a sewer flipped over and destroyed a Bradley, killing all of its occupants just before the same company had planned an operation to install a new outpost. The same night, while the company put in its outpost and Kuehl and his sergeant major removed the remains from the destroyed Bradley's wreckage, IEDs badly damaged two Abrams tanks nearby. Not long afterward, a JSOC commando was wounded by an IED in Ameriya.

Ten days later, on the night of May 29, Kuehl was stuck in his trailer with diarrhea when a local imam called the battalion asking to talk to him. The imam told Kuehl, summoned from his trailer and still in his blue bathrobe, that the next day local fighters would be attacking Al-Qaeda in Ameriya and it would be better if American troops stayed away. Kuehl could not order his men to do that, but he did issue instructions across the battalion that his troops should exercise special restraint the next day, and should be on the lookout for armed men who looked like insurgents but were wearing white armbands.

The next afternoon, May 30, reports started coming in to Kuehl's headquarters of gunfire and speeding cars all over Ameriya, and tip lines started ringing off the hook. One Iraqi calling did so in military fashion, complete with map coordinates. This man, it turned out, went by the name Abu Abed: he had been a career soldier under Saddam, fighting the Marines in Nasiriyah in 2003 before becoming an insurgent. Now he was leading a group of fighters through Ameriya, killing and capturing Al-Qaeda suspects and burning their cars.[22]

Al-Qaeda struck back on May 31, bringing fighters into Ameriya from elsewhere in Baghdad and pinning Abu Abed and his fighters down in a mosque. Abu Abed called 1-5 Cavalry for help, and Kuehl sent two platoons; one soldier was killed in the fighting. For many soldiers it was the first time they had actually seen their enemy instead of just being stalked by invisible snipers and IED triggermen. "This is the fight we've been waiting for all year," a platoon leader told battalion staff officer Major Chip Daniels at the embattled mosque—it had taken Abu Abed and his men to spark it.[23] That night Kuehl met Abu Abed at the mosque. Also present was Abu Azzam; without the Americans' knowledge, he had been enlisted to help replicate the Abu Ghraib volunteers in Ameriya.

Starting June 1, Kuehl's troops and about forty of Abu Abed's men, who called themselves the Forsan al-Rafidayn, or "Knights of the Two Rivers," worked together routinely. No Americans armed the men or, at first, paid them; an Iraqi Army brigade commander who publicly decried the Knights covertly supplied them with ammunition at night. The Knights, usually clad in civilian clothes with black ski masks and looking just like insurgents, would climb onto the back of Bradleys, which gave them mobility and firepower. Even though corps policy said American troops could not enter mosques without high-level permission, Abu Abed set up his command post in a mosque, and that was where Kuehl and his men planned with him, on a classified map that they provided to Iraqis. On one raid, Chip Daniels, two other American soldiers, and a British SAS veteran working for an irregular warfare advisory unit accompanied Abu Abed's men as they located and burned down an Al-Qaeda media center. By the end of June the cavalry battalion and Abu Abed's Knights had locked Ameriya down; attacks had gone from a daily occurrence to a rarity, and only one more large IED attack would occur there in 2007.

At first Kuehl was nervous about what his battalion was doing. Abu Abed had obviously spent the years since 2003 fighting on the other side. One of his staff, Abu Ibrahim, had a scar on his chest that he acknowledged came from an American bullet. A *Washington Post* article quoted an intelligence officer who characterized the battalion's efforts as a "deal with the devil," prompting concern from families back home.[24] Although Kuehl had support from John Campbell, one of the two deputy commanders of the 1st Cavalry Division, he was not so sure about Joe Fil, the division commander. "I figured I was either going to jail or else we would be looking pretty good," Kuehl said.[25]

But a week into 1-5 Cavalry's cooperation with the Knights, Chip Daniels and another major in the battalion were both contacted by Petraeus's aide-de-camp, Major Everett Spain. The battalion was based on the same huge complex as Petraeus's own headquarters and residence, and the general wanted to go on morning runs with the two majors so he could hear what the battalion was doing in Ameriya. While running on June 8, Daniels nervously filled Petraeus in on his alliance with the former foe.

To Daniels's relief, Petraeus backed the program. As in Anbar and the Baghdad belts, the United States embraced and resourced Awakening groups in Baghdad as they emerged and asked for Iraqi government permission afterward, once the mix of tribal and former insurgent forces were enlisted on the American payroll. What the military had been doing before was not working; it was time to take risks and try something new. Petraeus held up two fingers to Daniels. "One, don't let our Army stop you," he said. "Two, don't let the Iraqi government stop you. Solve the problem." Daniels was relieved. He now had top cover, no matter what his division thought.[26]

CHAPTER 21

Phantom Thunder

As summer approached, Ray Odierno began to prepare for the surge's biggest offensive: Phantom Thunder, a multipronged series of operations in the Baghdad belts. For the first half of the year, the surge had been something of a misnomer. The infusion of fresh troops had been more like a steady trickle than a tidal wave. By June, however, all five combat brigades would finally be on hand, as would an aviation brigade of attack and transport helicopters and some other odds and ends that Petraeus had managed to squeeze out of Washington.

From the moment he took over as corps commander, Odierno had been interested in mounting a counteroffensive to take back Baghdad. An artilleryman by training, Odierno had been schooled in the art of synchronization, and he envisioned a multipronged effort. Even as they pressed the fight in Baghdad, the Americans would strike north and south of the capital and reclaim the belts as well.

Just what forces should be enlisted in the push, however, was a matter of heated debate among the commanders. Colonel Steve Townsend, the commander of the Stryker brigade in Baghdad, had a clear sense of where his troopers were needed: in Baqubah, where one of his battalions was already struggling to control the city. Even with the success Ben Richards had enjoyed in signing up Kit Carson Scouts in Buhriz, much of Baqubah was still in enemy hands and Diyala had been a hellacious fight.

At FOB Warhorse, the main U.S. base in Baqubah, the "Never Forget" memorial was a testament to the cost of securing Diyala. A series of sober stone slabs bore the long list of U.S. soldiers killed in action from units at that base, and it was regularly expanding. The military had a practice of naming its dining facilities and other major structures after the dead.

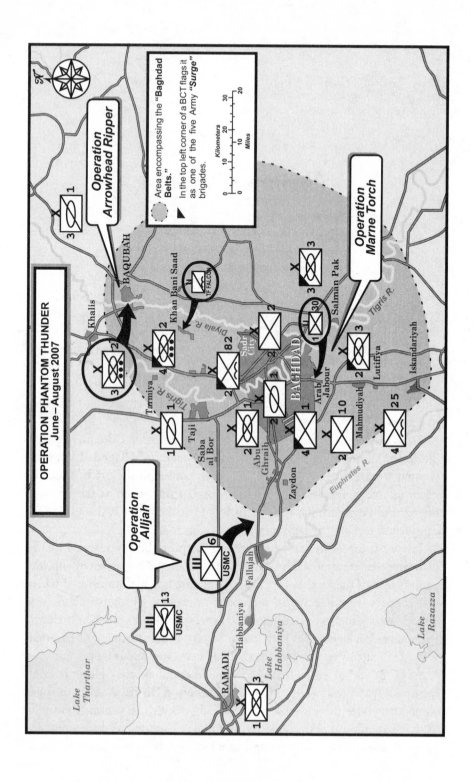

OPERATION PHANTOM THUNDER
June – August 2007

Operation Arrowhead Ripper

Operation Marne Torch

Operation Alljah

Area encompassing the "Baghdad Belts."

In the top left corner of a BCT flags it as one of the five Army "Surge" brigades.

Kilometers
0   10   20   30
0   10   20
Miles

But at Warhorse it had long ago run out of buildings. The Internet café, the gym, tactical operations centers—nearly every structure on the dusty, treeless FOB, it seemed, had been named after a soldier who had perished in the fight. Virtually every soldier appeared to have a black memorial bracelet, a band of metal the soldiers wore on the wrist that carried the name of one of their fallen friends, the day he died, and the place in Diyala where they had been blown up or shot—places that few Americans back home had even heard of. The brigade chaplain, an otherwise gregarious man whose military driver from his previous assignment at Arlington Cemetery was deployed to Iraq and killed, had seen so many gruesome scenes as he administered soldiers' last rites that even he was diagnosed with post-traumatic stress disorder. The worst experience, he confessed, was going to the combat hospital and seeing a wounded soldier lying in a bed, the sheet flat where his legs should have been.

Townsend's brigade had now been in Iraq for nearly a year and was one of the most combat-experienced units in the country, especially at the "clear" phase of operations, which it had down to a science. Still, he was appalled by the mounting losses. Every time a soldier in Bruce Antonia's 5-20 Infantry, the batallion he had sent to Baqubah, was killed Townsend made the trek to Warhorse for the memorial service. A pair of combat boots and a rifle with a Kevlar helmet pitched on top would be at the front of the podium. The chaplain would offer some somber remarks about the deceased and his sacrifice. A casket carrying the remains would be escorted to a waiting helicopter for the start of the long "hero flight" home. After the memorials, Townsend would huddle with Dave Sutherland, the commander of the lone Diyala brigade, over a few Cokes to discuss how they might put an end to the slow bleed that Diyala had become and turn the tide. The chain of command was not an issue. Townsend could work for Sutherland, or vice versa. The purpose would be to regain the momentum and reduce casualties.

The result of the discussions was a contingency plan to dispatch more of Townsend's brigade to the city. Townsend asked Antonia, whose soldiers had their hands full in the eastern half of the city, where he thought the Stryker brigade should attack first. Drawing a circle around the western half of the city, which Al-Qaeda had maintained as a haven, Antonia said, "Right here." Joe Fil, the commander of the Baghdad division and Townsend's superior, had other ideas. Fil had lost the strategy debate with Odierno over where the surge brigades should be deployed and was reconciled to the fact that at least half of the new forces arriving in Iraq would be headed to the belts and not the capital. But he was determined to hold on to those forces he already controlled, and Townsend's brigade was among them. Fil had used the Strykers in the most hostile areas of the city, like East Rashid.[1] He had lost Antonia's battalion to Diyala; the last thing he wanted was to lose more combat power.

In May, Odierno and his intelligence and operations officers swung by Townsend's headquarters to get his take on what they could do about Baqubah. Townsend was rolling through Rashid when he received an urgent message to call Fil. After heading to FOB Falcon on the southern outskirts of the city so he could call on a secure line, Townsend got an earful. Fil wanted to know why Townsend was proposing missions that would take him away from the fight in Baghdad.

"I thought I told you we weren't going to discuss that anymore," Fil barked. "I thought we agreed that was not a course of action." To the Baghdad commander, Townsend's actions bordered on insubordination. Townsend insisted that he was just obeying orders—Odierno's orders. How could the brigade's staff refuse to brief a plan if the corps commander insisted on it? Townsend asked. Fil was suspicious that Townsend had orchestrated the whole thing. Townsend denied that, but thought that going to Diyala was the right thing to do. The next day, Townsend received an order for the push to Baqubah. Townsend had estimated that it would take everything his Stryker brigade had and more to reclaim Baqubah, but as a sop to Fil he would leave a battalion behind in East Rashid, figuring he could always appeal for the unit if the city proved too much to handle. Townsend's part of the operation would be called Arrowhead Ripper. The division staff came up with the name: there had been a "Ripper" operation in Korea that Mixon's 25th Infantry Division had been involved with in 1951, and Townsend's brigade was the "Arrowhead Brigade."

For some of the units in Diyala, the reinforcements could not come soon enough. Their fight had been so tough, and the mounting toll of casualties so hard to bear, that some of the American units had resorted to calling on airpower—even in situations in which civilians were on the battlefield. Mo Goins's Delta Company, 1-12 Cavalry was engaged in an intense firefight with a group of Al-Qaeda militants in Khalis when the insurgents broke contact and ran into a house near which children were playing outside. It was a common insurgent tactic: attack the Americans and the Iraqi forces and then seek refuge near civilians. This time, however, Goins was determined not to let them get away. With his unit battered, the commander decided not to risk more casualties by mounting an infantry assault to dig them out. Apaches armed with Hellfire missiles were overhead, and Goins wanted them to strike. Taking full responsibility for the attack, Goins gave the fire support officer his initials. Asked later how he had made the decision at Warhorse, Goins said simply, "My guys." He had gone to more memorial services than he had ever wanted to. Several days later, he pulled his soldiers out to prepare for their role in Townsend's Arrowhead Ripper.[2]

From the start, Townsend was planning to do more than reoccupy Baqubah. Intelligence believed that there were three hundred to five hundred fighters in the city, mostly in the western half that Antonia's troops had not been able to clear, and the goal of Townsend's operation was to cordon off the area to catch as many of the fighters as possible. With a river to the east and a canal to the south, Baqubah offered some natural obstacles that Townsend could use to try to hem in the enemy.

To achieve an element of surprise, Lieutenant Colonel Avanulus "Van" Smiley's 1-23 Infantry would drive all night in their Strykers from Baghdad and go right into the fight instead of going first to Warhorse for final battle preparations. Other troops would be airlifted to cut off the escape routes to the south. Mixon also sent two light infantry companies to Baqubah to bolster the forces that would isolate the city, one each from Salahuddin and Kirkuk provinces. Once the western half of the city was cut off, nobody could go in or out without having to pass through the American lines. At the same time, Task Force Falcon, JSOC's conventional paratroop squadron, would helicopter into Khan Bani Saad, an insurgent-infested town to Baqubah's south.

What was known about the enemy defenses was not comforting. The main roads were laced with buried IEDs. Like the threads of a spider web, thin wires linked the IEDs to triggermen hidden in the homes and alleyways. There were so many wires that it seemed safe to assume that a single IED could have multiple triggermen. To avoid the deep-buried IEDs, the soldiers would get out of their Strykers and fight on foot, moving house to house as they pushed into the city. Only after an area had been cleared would the vehicles move forward. To help clear the IEDs the military would use a MICLIC, a cable studded with explosives that was customarily used to blast a path through minefields. Smiley also planned to have Abrams tanks fire canister rounds down the main thoroughfares in the hope that the blast would sever the trigger wires. F-16s with their satellite-guided bombs would be on station.

As Townsend's brigade neared the end of its deployment, the goal would be to secure the city and hand it off to the Iraqis within sixty to ninety days.

Even that part might be tricky. The Americans would need, in effect, to reintroduce the Iraqis to their own army. A largely Shiite force would be coming in to secure the mainly Sunni precincts in Baqubah.

Several days before the operation was to kick off, a rehearsal was held at a theater at Warhorse, which was attended by the Iraqi Army's new 5th Division commander and some of his staff. Townsend had not expected them to be there and afterward talked to Mixon about how to preserve the element of surprise. Arrowhead Ripper would start one day earlier as a purely American operation. The Americans would start the assault at night and bring their Iraqi partners into the operation the next day.

For all the secrecy, Petraeus, who was struggling to keep American public opinion and Congress on board, alluded to the operation before it kicked off. The first several months of the surge had seen an increase in violence and few of the benefits that had been promised. The planners were not surprised. It would take time to assemble all of the surge brigades and carry out the counteroffensive. But the politicians in Washington did not understand that: Harry Reid, the Senate majority leader, had pronounced the war lost in April, before all of the surge brigades had arrived. Trying to send a message that much of the work of the surge was still ahead, Petraeus hinted during a June 17 appearance on Fox News that a big operation was in the offing. "Outside of Baghdad, the Baghdad belts, as they're called, south and north of the city, are areas into which we are now going in much greater force," Petraeus said. "And then in Diyala Province, an area to which some of the Al-Qaeda fighters have moved as they have been pushed out of Anbar and out of some of the Baghdad neighborhoods, is an area that requires considerable additional attention over the coming weeks, and it will get that as well."[3] It was not easy to balance propitiating the public and maintaining operational security. This was one time that the Iraq commander had not necessarily gotten it right.

After dark on the night of June 18, Smiley's battalion drove north from Baghdad. Before light on June 19, helicopters delivered American troops to blocking positions south and west of Baqubah. While Goins's 1-12 Cavalry held down the city's east side, route clearance teams painstakingly began searching for and destroying IEDs on the main road bisecting the city. Meanwhile, Townsend's two Stryker battalions started to push into the west side. The first day showed the scope of the challenge.

Corporal Darryl Linder, a twenty-three-year-old single father who had served four years with the Marines and then enlisted in the Army, was driving a Bradley through a stretch of road in the Katun neighborhood that the Americans were convinced they had cleared and had driven through repeatedly when an IED blast flipped the vehicle and produced the only KIA of that first day. A postmortem later showed that there had been several trigger wires that led to multiple firing points. The elusive triggerman, it turned out, had been at the end of a long wire that led to the eastern part of the city, which Townsend's brigade had yet to focus on. The enemy had taken over a house on the Americans' flank, hooked up a detonating device, and used it to destroy the Bradley and kill Linder. The triggermen in Baqubah were more elusive than the Americans had suspected.

Four days later, a platoon from 1-23 Infantry's Comanche Company, inching forward in northern Baqubah, encountered an even more formidable threat. Darting across a road strewn with IED wires, the soldiers rushed into an abandoned room and took cover. A bright fireball appeared over the street and a cloud of gritty dust engulfed the house as a MICLIC blasted a path through the street. Afterward, Sergeant Philip Ness-Hunkin decided to inspect the house next door. The gate was unlocked and the front door was invitingly open. Peering through the window he saw a pressure-plate IED hidden under a piece of wood. There were IED wires from the house into the neighborhood.

"HBIED," a soldier called out, the military's acronym for a house-borne improvised explosive device—a tactic seen before in other Al-Qaeda strongholds like Fallujah, Ramadi, and the Baghdad neighborhood of Dora, where American troops were also fighting hard during Phantom Thunder. The last place the platoon wanted to be was next door to a house bomb and a series of structures that had not been cleared. If the soldiers got into a firefight and had to dart in and out of the houses along the road, they might be diving into a series of deadly booby traps.

The soldiers were instructed to move back across the road they had just crossed. Once there, the troops clambered into a two-story house. When Sergeant Gerard Mennitto got to the second floor, however, he spotted antiaircraft ammunition and a detonation cord next to two propane tanks. The platoon had escaped from one house bomb, only to find themselves in another. "Everyone get out!" he yelled.

The only safe place to go was the very house the platoon had started from in the morning. As the temperature climbed to 110 degrees, three soldiers sat down on a couch facing a large rectangular, blown-out window and looked at the street as if watching a large-screen television. "This show sucks," said one. "It's a rerun," another trooper chimed in. The insurgents, it seemed, were trying to use bombs in the road and small-arms fire to force the soldiers to take refuge in rigged houses along the route, and then blow them up. An airstrike was called in to destroy one house, and an Abrams tank destroyed more the next morning. The platoon's advance had been stymied for a day. In Arrowhead Ripper's first week, the Stryker troops found twenty-one such houses, and found twenty more over the rest of the summer.

Townsend later concluded that the company had stumbled into an entire block of HBIED houses, one of which took out a team of Iraqi troops. Townsend made an effort to clear the houses. But as a bomb disposal expert ventured into one of the houses he tripped a pressure-plate bomb, which tossed him across the room and broke his arm while collapsing the structure. At that point, Townsend recommended that the houses be destroyed with satellite-guided JDAMs.

In the intensive clearing operations that followed, the brigade, like the 3rd Infantry Division in the southern belt, brought heavy firepower to bear—forty-six JDAM bombs, fifty-seven GMLRS rockets, and four Excalibur satellite-guided artillery rounds. In addition to the forty-one house bombs it found, the brigade uncovered two hundred IEDs. After that week, Smiley's battalion settled into new outposts on the west side of Baqubah and Antonia's battalion returned to the east side. Ten days after the assault, Townsend's deputy, Lieutenant Colonel Fred Johnson, accompanied the first shipments of grain for Baqubah's hungry population from Baghdad. Nicknamed the "emir of sewage," Johnson would spend the rest of the summer presiding over Baqubah's reconstruction and making sure that insurgents did not hijack relief supplies.

American troops recorded killing about 110 insurgents during the clearing operations, and capturing another 400. None of those captured or killed were major insurgent leaders—a disappointment, given the importance the corps had attached to Baqubah as an Al-Qaeda hub, supposedly the terrorist group's new "capital" after Fallujah in 2004, Qaim in 2005, and Ramadi in 2006. Odierno estimated publicly that 80 percent of the Al-Qaeda leaders in Baqubah had escaped.[4] Despite the brigade's efforts, the house bomb threat lingered. In August, five of Smiley's troops were killed when a house bomb exploded. Soldiers had already searched the house once and had affirmed that it had been cleared.

While Townsend's Stryker brigade was battling in Baqubah, Lieutenant Colonel Kenneth Adgie was leading the other major prong of Phantom Thunder to the south. An outgoing New Jerseyan, Adgie had played football for Trenton State and joined the Army through ROTC. The battalion he led—1-30 Infantry—had an impressive lineage.

As the final battalion in the last arriving brigade, Adgie's had the last claim on resources. Upon landing in Iraq, his soldiers had been stuffed into poorly air-conditioned tents at FOB Falcon, a base on the southern outskirts of Baghdad that came under occasional mortar fire from the Mahdi Army: a mortar round in October 2006 had hit the base's ammunition stores, setting off a night-long fireworks display that miraculously produced no serious casualties.

Adgie's mission was to lead his battalion into Arab Jabour, a farming area south of Baghdad along the Tigris, and cut off the Sunni insurgent "ratline" from the region into East Rashid. The region, which drew its name from a local tribe, was a reedy, rural agricultural area laced with canals that had served as a leisure getaway for Saddam's elite. Another battalion on the other side of the Tigris would move into Salman Pak. Both areas had been hit repeatedly by Task Force Falcon ahead of the units' arrival.

There were no Iraqi Army or police units in Arab Jabour. The only American force in the area was an overextended cavalry squadron, led by Lieutenant Colonel Mark Odom, whose troops controlled Patrol Base Red, a veritable Fort Apache near a crossroads in the northern tier of Arab Jabour that had been rocked by a suicide truck bomb but was still standing. As residents fled the area, the population of thirty thousand had dwindled to about five thousand. Al-Qaeda in Iraq had become the dominant force in the area; there were no Iraqi units or even bases in Arab Jabour to use in trying to take the area back.

In early June, Adgie was told to hop on a helicopter to the Green Zone for a meeting with a few sheikhs that was organized by the Office of Regional Assessment—a thin euphemism for the CIA. As soon as the helicopter landed, he jumped into an armored Chevy Suburban, packed with muscular security guards, and raced through Baghdad to a palace along the Tigris. There, two CIA contacts, a Middle East businessman and a sheikh, greeted Adgie and used Google Earth to point out the houses of Al-Qaeda members in Arab Jabour, and promised that when his troops entered the area their "three best men" would be waiting to act as guides and informants. Adgie needed a way to find his partners in Arab Jabour, so he gave the sheikh a handful of battalion coins, which were usually handed out as mementos to the soldiers for a job well done.[5]

At 2 a.m. on June 16, 1-30 Infantry began its seventeen-mile slog to Arab Jabour. Attacking down the main route—a raised-level road cutting across numerous canals—rendered the battalion vulnerable. Since it would need to build its own forward headquarters it was lugging more than seventy truckloads of concrete T-walls and construction equipment down a narrow file that seemed tailor-made for insurgents intent on planting deep-buried IEDs: all they had to do was burrow into the side of the elevated route.

The insurgent weapon of choice was a concoction of nitric acid and fertilizer, dried and packed into a plastic five-gallon can, along with a small blasting cap, the only piece of metal in there. The bombs were all but impossible for route clearance teams to detect. Each can had the power of fifty pounds of bulk explosive, and Al-Qaeda's practice was to group several together to produce an enormous, vehicle-shattering blast. The soldiers knew the weapons as HME, or homemade explosive.

Rick Lynch's 3rd Infantry Division, which oversaw the south, was determined to fight fire with fire. Just before dawn on the 16th, Air Force B-1 bombers pounded two intersections south of Arab Jabour with satellite-guided bombs to detonate the deep-buried IEDs that American intelligence believed Al-Qaeda had taken months to plant. It was a blunderbuss solution to the IED problem, one that was intended to blunt the insurgents' main weapon. Not everybody in the division, however, was comfortable with such extensive use of firepower.

In early June, Lynch had declared open season on all boats on the Tigris in the Arab Jabour–Salman Pak area, basing his decision on intelligence that true fishermen did not use that portion of the river. By July 15, the division's attack helicopters had blown up nearly fifty boats. The brigade operating on the east bank of the Tigris nicknamed the campaign the "Boat Jihad," and in the headquarters of Kershaw's brigade to the west, soldiers wrote skits making fun of it and joked that it was why their Iraqi Army counterparts had stopped serving them fish when they visited. (The division's use of firepower escalated over time. In the fall, Odierno turned down a request from Lynch's headquarters to drop what a corps staffer remembered as "an ungodly number of bombs" on an abandoned ammunition dump south of Yusifiyah. In January, in the division's last major offensive, B-1 bombers would drop ninety-nine bombs in the area south of Arab Jabour in a single day.)

Crawling down the road as its troops scanned for IEDs and cleared houses along the way, Adgie's battalion finally arrived at a Baath Party retreat that had been used by Saddam's son Uday. The locals simply referred to the place as "the horse farm." The battalion plowed down the orchard to make room for a motor pool (vital for maintaining and fueling its vehicles) and a helicopter landing pad (critical for evacuating casualties), and installed concrete blast walls around the enclave. The base was named Patrol Base Murray. The next day all hell broke loose. The insurgents mounted nineteen attacks, using IEDs, RPGs, and small arms. On June 18 a mine-clearing vehicle called a Husky was disabled by an IED, and then as an Abrams tank went to the vehicle's aid, it ran over an even bigger bomb, which flipped the tank into a canal, killing one crewman and wounding the rest. The next day, the same thing happened—one IED disabled a Husky, and then another destroyed a Bradley as it moved to assist, killing two soldiers, including William Zapfe, a platoon sergeant and one of the most popular soldiers in the battalion.

Tanks and Bradleys were the most heavily armored vehicles in the American inventory, but on dirt roads there was no limit to the size of the bombs insurgents could plant. After the attacks, Odom told Adgie that one of the insurgents' favorite tactics was to sneak in behind the Americans and plant an IED on a stretch of cleared road. Adgie figured that the only way to keep a road clear was to form a twenty-four-hour-a-day picket: tanks and Bradleys were placed at intervals to make sure fresh IEDs were not planted surreptitiously. As the weeks went by, the stress on the soldiers increased. They had neither warm food nor real showers. Some troops were living outdoors with no air-conditioning even as the temperatures soared to 120 degrees during the day and stayed at 80 at night. There were no U.S. forces to the south, which meant that the Al-Qaeda insurgents could infiltrate north and then flee south past a protective belt of IEDs. Some of the soldiers caught Q fever, which was carried by rodents and farm animals.

The brutal heat took a devastating toll on one tank driver. The day after the Bradley was blown up, Charlie Company went to recover the vehicle. An Abrams tank that was standing guard threw some track, which required repairs in the heat of the day. Private First Class Henry Byrd III passed out from heat exhaustion and was rushed to the combat support hospital in Baghdad and then to the U.S. military hospital in Landstuhl, Germany, where he died. Byrd's core body temperature had reached 107 degrees and the doctors had been unable to cool him down.

Soon after Adgie arrived in Arab Jabour, he linked up with a relative of the sheikh the CIA had introduced him to earlier in the Green Zone: Mustafa Kamal Shabib al-Jabouri, a former brigadier general in Saddam's army who lived in Arab Jabour and worked out of an abandoned school, where he had hung a picture of Awakening leader Abd al-Sattar al-Rishawi in his office. He connected the battalion with the "three best men" the sheikh had promised. Led by a former insurgent who had recently had several relatives killed by Al-Qaeda, the three men lived in a small concrete house on Patrol Base Murray, ran a network of local informants by cell phone, and accompanied Adgie's troops on patrols. Dressed in gray American fatigues and wearing masks, the men pointed out houses where insurgents lived and picked them out at flash checkpoints—what the New Jersey–bred Adgie called "Jimmy Hoffa" checkpoints. The battalion referred to the "three best men" as their "bird dogs."

Adgie was interested in using more than a few bird dogs, however. He wanted dozens, if not hundreds, of locals to help secure the area—Iraqis who would play a role similar to that of the Kit Carson Scouts in Mike Kershaw's area to the west. Despite the promises that had been made in Baghdad, however, Mustafa was anxious about undertaking such a large scale operation. He asked for weapons, which Adgie was not allowed to provide under the guidelines supplied by his command. The former general wanted to help, but was clearly afraid of committing himself to an open war with Al-Qaeda. For weeks, Adgie made do with just a handful of bird dogs. The situation across the river in Salman Pak showed what could happen if the locals were not encouraged to help. On June 22, helicopters delivered American troops to an abandoned soda factory just outside Salman Pak, where they assisted in the installation of a new police station but did not establish their own outpost. Four days later, with the American troops gone, Al-Qaeda fighters overran the police station and destroyed it before help could arrive.

On July 6, Adgie's Bravo Company was on a dismounted night patrol when the colonel heard an enormous explosion. A pilot of an OH-58 Kiowa helicopter relayed the bad news: "We've got a squad down." Nine soldiers and a military dog had been moving through an abandoned chicken farm when the blast occurred. A quick reaction force raced to the scene. Seven of the soldiers were flat on their backs, stunned and concussed by an IED so large it left a crater bigger than a room, but two soldiers could not be found. Adgie thought immediately about the dark experience the 10th Mountain Division had had when two of its soldiers were kidnapped in May. Adgie feared that he, too, might have a kidnapping on his hands. After an exhaustive eighteen-hour search, the battalion figured out that the two soldiers had been pulverized by the blast; it was if they had simply evaporated.

Just to the west of Arab Jabour in Hawr Rajab, Lieutenant Colonel Mark Odom, commander of 1-40 Cavalry, was ahead in the Awakening game. Like his friend Kershaw, Odom was a cerebral veteran of the Ranger Regiment, which he would later command in Afghanistan. He had graduated from Middlebury College and then written his master's thesis on the Balkan conflict at King's College, London; Jean Lartéguy's *The Centurions* sat in his office at FOB Falcon alongside an inscribed copy of Zbigniew Brzezinski's *Second Chance*. His father was retired Lieutenant General William Odom, the Reagan-era NSA director and a vociferous critic of the Iraq War. The day after Bush announced the surge, the elder Odom had published a scathing op-ed: "Know When to Fold 'Em."[6]

By the time of the surge, Odom's Alaska-based squadron had already endured a hard deployment. Its memorial wall at FOB Falcon already included eight "Denali heroes." Three combat engineers had died when a massive IED destroyed a Buffalo—one of the most heavily armored vehicles in Iraq, which was used by EOD units. Two soldiers and two Iraqi interpreters perished in a furious April 12 fight at Patrol Base Dog, an outpost Odom had established on the outskirts of Adwaniyah. The insurgent attack on Patrol Base Dog had been devastating: a truck bomb had collapsed the soldiers' living quarters, burying them in rubble and prompting the survivors, many wounded, to mount a valiant defense with rifles and machine guns and to radio a "broken arrow," an urgent appeal for any available air support. Odom eventually decided that the outpost was not worth the cost and abandoned it, a rare retreat during the early months of the surge that received little attention. With the roads riddled with deep-buried IEDs, Odom and his soldiers sought to move by foot whenever possible, even if it meant a lengthy hike with heavy combat load. This was a cavalry squadron that preferred to operate dismounted.

The arrival of the surge reinforcements, including Adgie's battalion, helped Odom in one respect: it reduced the battle space he had to cover and made it possible for his squadron to move forces in and around Hawr Rajab, a town that had previously been something of a no-man's-land. But the fighting in Arab Jabour also had the effect of displacing some Al-Qaeda insurgents to the west. The Sunni residents of Hawr Rajab were soon confronted with American troops who were becoming regular visitors—and Al-Qaeda insurgents from out of town who were more ruthless than the homegrown militants.

In early July, Captain Chad Klascius, the commander of 1-40 Cavalry's Apache Troop, received a call from a local sheikh requesting a meeting. A West Point graduate, Klascius had spent several years before his Iraq duty as a member of an OPFOR unit, the opposing force in the Army's war games in Europe. The young officer had played the role of an Islamic insurgent, complete with a suicide belt. Now he was going to meet a former insurgent who wanted to make common cause with American soldiers.

Sheikh Ali Majid al-Dulaimi, by his own admission, had led somewhat of a carefree life during the Saddam years. But he wanted payback for the murder of his father by Al-Qaeda, and he wanted to restore his tribe's authority in Hawr Rajab. According to local residents, Al-Qaeda had grabbed control of one of the town's few resources: the local gas station. Fuel from the Oil Ministry was trucked to the station several times a month, though the station was rarely open and, when it was, sold gas at an inflated price. The station, the townspeople complained, was little more than a fuel distribution point for the militants and a revenue-raising operation for their cause.

Each side was apprehensive about the planned midnight meeting at Sheikh Ali's home. The Americans were worried that they might be led into an ambush and warned that any males with weapons would be shot on sight. It was agreed that the sheikh could have only unarmed bodyguards. To protect the sheikh against retaliation, the Americans concocted an elaborate ruse. A platoon of soldiers cordoned off the home as if it were a raid, pulled Ali outside, and then went into the home seemingly to conduct a search.

Once the meeting began, the sheikh acknowledged that he had been a supporter of Jaish al-Islami, the Sunni insurgent group. But that was in the past. He wanted Americans to set up a permanent base in Hawr Rajab and to drive Al-Qaeda out. He was eager to participate in the offensive, but needed several thousand dollars in financing. He wanted a local police station to be set up in town. He asked the Americans to distribute food and toys to the town's residents to encourage them to support his collaboration. And he wanted Klascius to give him a pistol to seal their new relationship.

Klascius insisted that the sheikh provide enemy names to prove that he was serious. He gave them two, members of his own tribe who lived just a few houses away. (The Americans later took them into custody.) He also gave them a seventeen-page blue spiral notebook in which he and his military adviser had recorded information about Al-Qaeda's activities in the town. With a limited number of troops, the cavalry squadron was not prepared to establish a permanent presence in the town. Nor would the sheikh receive his pistol. But the Americans promised there would be regular patrols and were able to distribute reward money for tips about the whereabouts of Al-Qaeda militants. It was clear that the sheikh's resources were limited: one of his scouts wore shoes held together by tape.[7]

Soon a fellow sheikh came forward: Mahir Sarhan Morab al-Muini, leader of another tribe in Hawr Rajab, who had been imprisoned by the Americans for two years for hiding a cache of weapons. In a region of shifting alliances, Mahir was also looking to reestablish his authority in the town. Since Klascius had only seventy-one soldiers to deal with eight thousand townspeople and several hundred insurgents, the assistance the sheikhs were offering was vital.

The first large-scale mission was set for late July. Ali and several dozen of his men would try to establish security in Hawr Rajab by going after Al-Qaeda militants. American Apache helicopters would provide air support. Ali ignored one piece of advice from the squadron's intelligence team: not to give his fighters advance word of the operation. The day before the operation was supposed to take place, Al-Qaeda made its move. Al-Qaeda had their own moles among Ali's ragtag band of fighters and mounted a preemptive strike.

When the insurgents attacked, high winds had grounded the American choppers, forcing the sheikh and his men to fight without the promised air support. It was not long before they began to pull back. One of the sheikh's aides threw his sister and her young children in a van and raced past Al-Qaeda fighters, who machine-gunned the vehicle. The woman and two of her children had their wounds treated at a checkpoint and were then driven by Iraqi soldiers to a hospital in Fallujah. The hospitals in the Iraqi capital were much closer to Hawr Rajab, but, even with the surge under way, Sunnis were still worried that the Shiite-dominated Health Ministry controlled the hospitals and were afraid of being treated there. Ali finally beat a retreat, heading south with his fighters to Yusifiyah, where he linked up with Abd al-Sattar, the Anbar Awakening leader. It was a low point for the new alliance. The American military was very powerful, but there were times, Ali thought, when it was slow to act.

The Americans' relationship with Ali was also helped by an unexpected turn of events the following week when Ali was taken into custody at a National Police checkpoint near FOB Falcon. The Shiite-dominated police force was on the verge of turning Ali over to the Mahdi Army, an all-but-certain death sentence, when he reached the Americans on his cell phone. The soldiers from Klascius's Apache Troop rushed to the scene. There was a tense standoff as the soldiers kept their weapons at the ready until the police handed the sheikh over to his American protectors. Much in Iraq was not as it seemed. The former Sunni insurgent had become the Americans' most trusted partner in Hawr Rajab, while many of the United States' supposed comrades among the Iraqi police could not be trusted.

The alliance between Ali and the Americans rebuilt, it was time to resume the battle for Hawr Rajab. On August 1, Ali led twenty-nine fighters to a checkpoint outside the town where they were fingerprinted and had their retinas scanned, the identifying information entered into an intelligence database. To identify them as "friendly," they were given traffic crossing belts by the Americans. Then Ali, Mahir, and Odom huddled inside a nearby building to discuss the tactical situation in the town.

On the morning of August 4, the Americans were to drive downtown. The day before, Klascius sketched out the plan. Two platoons, including combat engineers with heavily armored mine-detection vehicles, would clear the only road to the town. Then two more platoons would head to the town square with shipments of food and a psychological operations unit. Fliers would be distributed urging the people to take back their community from the Al-Qaeda militants by cooperating with the American-backed sheikhs.

Early in the morning the soldiers lumbered into the armored Humvees, wearing their standard kit: helmet, body armor, ballistic glasses, and Nomex gloves to protect against burns. Ali, who was wearing a tracksuit with "England" emblazoned across the front, had no protective gear as he settled into the cab of the lightly armored truck carrying the food. Several Iraqi soldiers also made the trip. It took only minutes before the operation had its first casualty. Specialist Jose Collazo was driving a Husky mine-detecting vehicle when he hit a buried bomb and was thrown fifty feet. With an open head wound, Collazo was rushed back to a sandlot to await a medevac helicopter. But soon word came that the ordnance team had cleared the route.

With wind whipping the sand, the helicopters were again grounded. After Klascius's troops reached the town center, the Humvees and the food truck formed a protective circle. The soldiers jumped down and began scanning the streets for militants. Ali got on a loudspeaker to urge the residents to come get the food. A few residents nervously approached. A soldier waved a metal detector over them to check for bombs after they entered the perimeter. But the citizens did not seem threatening, and the soldiers were preoccupied with the menace of snipers. The soldiers handed out several bags of rice, some cans of tomato paste, and powdered milk. Soon there was word: "The colonel's been hit." Odom had been on his way down to check on the food giveaway, traveling on the same road Klascius had just traversed, when he hit an IED, which flipped his Humvee. A quick reaction force raced to the scene. Corporal Jason LaFleur tied a cord to the door of Odom's Humvee so it could be yanked free by the QRF vehicle. After Odom, his interpreter, and three injured soldiers were removed and laid out on the grass, the QRF pulled to the side of the road. Suddenly there was a massive blast. The Humvee disintegrated into fragments, which rained down on the road. In addition to LaFleur, Sergeant Dustin Wakeman and Private First Class Jaron Holliday were killed instantly. The rest of the unit was trapped on a "Tier-1 IED site"—a stretch of road chockablock with buried bombs—and without air cover.

With no Apaches at the ready, the soldiers called in a show-of-force mission—an F-16 bombed an empty field. There were bodies to recover, and the grim business of collecting human remains began. Several soldiers took black bags from the Humvees and walked the fields in search of body parts. The road was a tableau of destruction: a soldier's soft cap, a can of chewing tobacco, part of a notebook, and the twisted end of a gun.

"I need another body bag," a soldier called out. A trooper asked if he had found another body. "Don't know," the first soldier replied. The three Iraqi soldiers who came with the mission—cigarettes in their mouths, cradling their weapons—pointed out some remains to the American soldiers but refrained from picking up the pieces. Ali sat in the cab of the food truck, staring straight ahead.

At FOB Falcon, the commanders imposed a procedure code-named River City—they shut down the unclassified Internet connection the soldiers used to chat with their families and to blog so that word of the casualties would not spread until next of kin were notified. That night there was another "angel flight." A formation of soldiers lined up and saluted as the caskets of the three dead soldiers were carried to the tarmac so they could be flown away. It was later determined that the militants had laid an ingenious, low-cost defensive belt of seven IEDs. That day Al-Qaeda had owned the road. It was, Klascius observed, his most violent day in Iraq, but it was just one day in a long war and not the end of the battle for the town.

On September 6, fighting broke out between local insurgents and a group of eighty volunteers, and when the cavalry troopers called in helicopters and an air strike, Ali's men scored a victory and Al-Qaeda fell back.

Soon the insurgent group had mostly disappeared from Hawr Rajab. Still, Odom was not sure that the Awakening was the answer for Iraq. Recuperating from his injuries in Alaska, Odom likened his experience with the Awakening movement to a quarterback who had heaved a long pass downfield and was waiting to see if the receiver would be there to catch it. "We have not made political progress at the national level," he said. "We have taken on a decentralized effort with the concerned citizens at the local level and somehow hope that we can tie it back into the local and national government at the end of the day."[8]

By the middle of the summer the Sunni Awakening groups were gaining traction outside of the belts and Anbar. In Baghdad, Abu Abed's Ameriya Knights had gained critical support from the Iraqi Army's 6th Division commander, Abd al-Amir Yaralla, and other groups were popping up elsewhere in the city. Just north of Ameriya, another American battalion helped form the Ghazaliya Guardians, and across the city in the Fadl neighborhood, a high-profile insurgent leader named Adil al-Mashhadani, whom the CIA had been pursuing all spring, joined forces with American paratroopers after concluding that the pressure from the Mahdi Army was too great for him to handle on his own. In late May a sheikh with ties to the Anbar Awakening announced the formation of the Salahuddin Awakening Congress, and over the summer security volunteers stepped forward, mainly focused around Tikrit, where the American brigade was handing out cash bonuses for finding IEDs. When Odierno visited the American brigade in Salahuddin at the beginning of August, its commander reported that 130 sheikhs were on board with the Awakening in the province, and half of them had already sworn allegiance to the central government.

American higher headquarters tried to regulate and standardize the bewildering array of local groups that it referred to as CLCs. In mid-June Odierno had met with the commanders responsible for training the Iraqi military and police to discuss how to manage the rise of the Sunni groups. The officer in charge of police training programs, Major General Kenneth Hunzeker, described a rough plan for 20 auxiliary "provincial support units" of 750 men each, a model apparently based on the paramilitary Emergency Response Units in Ramadi. In practice the Awakening groups in every area varied hugely in character, and attempts to regulate and manage their growth as fully as Hunzeker described were not realistic.

The more important role for senior commanders like Odierno and

Petraeus to play was to make working with local volunteer groups as easy as possible for low-level commanders—the company and battalion officers who often made first contact with insurgents willing to flip or sheikhs willing to supply neighborhood watch recruits. For one thing, that meant reassuring these young officers that they were doing the right thing and would not find themselves in hot water for cooperating with people American troops had once hunted. "I draw the line at war crimes," Odierno said, expressing a more tolerant view than Rick Lynch. "Local commanders can and will draw a more stringent line if they believe it is necessary. They understand the dynamics of their area better than I do. We reconcile at the end of any war."[9]

Another role for Odierno's corps was to make paying the Awakening or CLC groups easier. Many groups, when they appeared, did not ask for salaries at all—only "martyr pay," or compensation to their families if they were killed. That was the case in both Abu Ghraib and Taji. Eventually, most American units began to pay their Awakening groups out of the funds allocated for reconstruction and other projects, signing contracts with the groups for security akin to those they would sign with locals for cleaning or construction. Typically, volunteers made about ten dollars a day, but that could add up—Adgie's battalion alone spent a quarter-million dollars per month paying its local recruits. J. B. Burton, the brigade commander in northwest Baghdad who oversaw the battalions working with the Ameriya Knights and Ghazaliya Guardians, told Odierno in June that he needed to simplify the regulations granting company and battalion commanders the authority to pay their new allies.

To prod the Iraqi government to get behind the effort, Petraeus and Odierno visited the Presidency Council on July 10, telling President Talabani and Vice Presidents Hashimi and Abd al-Mahdi that despite the huge numbers of Sunni men signing up for Awakening groups, "national reconciliation" was lagging. Petraeus stressed that American troops were not arming any tribes (as indeed they were not, though during the early days of the Anbar Awakening, they certainly had been). Talabani stated his support for the spreading groups. Abd al-Mahdi was less sure, asking whether Petraeus believed that the groups' loyalties lay with the government. Petraeus replied that if they did not, he would not be working with them. To reassure the Iraqi officials, Petraeus and Odierno took any willing senior official on battlefield tours to places like Ameriya and Ghazaliya as soon as they seemed safe enough—a tactic he had used in Ramadi when he brought Maliki there in March. In mid-August, a soft-cap-clad Petraeus and Deputy Prime Minister Barham Salih paid a visit to Ameriya; the minister was struck by the sight of Abu Abed's Knights, who looked more like insurgents than soldiers or police.

Still, regarding the Awakening, Maliki and his close circle of Dawa Party stalwarts would serve as final arbiter. "This needs to be done," Odierno told a brigade commander, "but it can't be perfect, and we can't push the GOI so hard that they crumble." Odierno speculated about how Maliki would see the groups: "I'm Maliki, and I see the U.S. doesn't really want me as PM, it wants Allawi or Mahdi. So the U.S. is arming these groups in order to take over. I believe that the Baathists are going to come back again and they're going to be ruthless."[10]

What the Americans needed was a mechanism to legitimize the movement in the eyes of the Iraqi government, a means of transforming the "unofficial" groups into ones that the Maliki government could work with—or, at least, tolerate. With prodding from the Americans, the Maliki government set up a new organization: the Implementation and Follow-up Committee for National Reconciliation or IFCNR (pronounced "if-kinner" by the acronym-happy Americans). The committee would vet new Awakening volunteers and approve those the Iraqi authorities were prepared to work with. Led by Deputy National Security Adviser Safa al-Sheikh, the panel's nine members were largely picked from Maliki's notorious OCINC and included Bassima al-Jaidri, who had been identified in the JSAT report as one of the most sectarian officials in the government. By the summer of 2007 Petraeus had yet to meet her. A native of Sadr City, Bassima was deeply suspicious of the Americans, and believed the monumental postwar problems were a conspiracy. The United States had allowed violence to soar and the state to collapse to ensure that Iraq would be weak. How else could one explain how a superpower that put a man on the moon could take over an Arab capital and allow the situation to spiral entirely out of control?

There were plenty of American military officers who thought that Bassima and her colleagues were using their roles on the IFCNR to engineer their own conspiracy. Brigadier General David Phillips, who was in charge of efforts to train the Iraqi police, thought she should be "banned" because of the obstacles she had raised to Sunnis entering Iraq's forces. Jim Huggins, another one-star who worked for Lynch's 3rd Infantry Division, thought Bassima was a problem too.

Emma Sky, Odierno's political adviser and another strong-willed, if iconoclastic, woman who had made it in a man's world, disagreed. She thought the sectarian battles in Baghdad had brought out the worst in the Shiite leadership and that they would be capable of more statesmanlike behavior once security was under control. Bassima was close to Maliki. There was no way Sky would influence the prime minister, but perhaps she could influence the adviser who did. Sky would talk with her as an Arabist and a woman.

Petraeus was initially skeptical that the IFCNR could help, noting in one of his weekly letters to Gates that "the fact that it is led by Bassima and other sectarian OCINC personalities makes us a bit cautious as to whether it exists to rapidly assist local accommodation efforts or to protect Shia equities while dealing with these tribes and groups."[11]

A pressing issue was the more than two thousand names of Sunni volunteers from Abu Ghraib that had been submitted to the Iraqi committee. The names had been winnowed down to 1,738, but further progress was not to be had. After weeks of frustration, Petraeus headed to see Maliki for what was bound to be a difficult and even confrontational conversation.

In the meantime, Sky met with Bassima about the need to approve the list. If the former insurgents were accepted by the IFCNR, their biometric information would be known and available.

"You can control the crocodile," Sky argued. "It's a real shame we can't do this."

"What do you mean it hasn't happened?" Bassima said abruptly. "I've just processed the 1,738 names, and I don't want to talk about it anymore."

"Have you told Maliki?" Sky said.

"I'm sick of this. Everyone's talking about it, I've not told anybody. I've just done it," Bassima responded.

Sky whipped out her cell phone and rang Petraeus on his way to Maliki's palace. At least one crisis had been averted: Bassima had relented, and the Abu Ghraib names had been approved. The general was relieved. Perhaps it was possible to work with the inner Dawa Party circle after all. "Tell Bassima I will buy her dinner," Petraeus told Sky.[12]

CHAPTER 22

The USS CENTCOM

Getting Bassima al-Jaidri to cooperate with the Americans' strategy and their newfound allies in the Sunni community was just one of countless hurdles as Petraeus prosecuted the war on almost every conceivable front. His command was actively fighting against both Sunni and Shiite militants, and struggling to eliminate the pervasive sectarianism within Iraq's government and security forces—all while keeping an eye out for friendly fire emanating from Washington.

The surge had a start date, but the White House had never specified an end date, which became a matter of contention as American casualties mounted throughout the summer. Just days before the kickoff of Phantom Thunder, Nancy Pelosi had issued a letter denouncing the surge as a failure and reaffirming her intention to push for the withdrawal of nearly all combat forces.[1] With a presidential election a year and a half away, however, few in Congress wanted to be responsible if the sectarian violence increased as a result of a speedy American exit. Instead, the lawmakers' political gambit was to criticize the surge at every turn and force Republicans to cast symbolic votes supporting the unpopular president's Iraq policy, but to stop short of curtailing funding or mandating steps that would make Congress an equal partner in the endgame of the war.

CENTCOM and the Joint Chiefs of Staff were another matter. One of the major ironies of the Iraq War is that Petraeus's own superiors were skeptical of his strategy and decidedly unenthusiastic about prolonging the strain it caused on the American military. The deployment of Army brigades had already been extended to fifteen months from the usual twelve, and when brigades started to come to the end of their extended tours in the fall the surge would need to be replenished or the twenty-brigade force would slowly shrink. By July, the violence in Iraq had steadily risen, as was to be expected with the Americans seizing the offensive. Sooner or later there would need to be measurable progress that Petraeus could present not only in his upcoming September testimony to Congress but also to his own superiors.

At CENTCOM's headquarters in Tampa, Florida, Admiral William "Fox" Fallon was one of the skeptics. It was Jack Keane who had helped propel Fallon to the post. Keane had worked well with Fallon when Keane was the vice chief of staff of the Army and Fallon was serving as the vice chief of naval operations. When Pete Pace was looking for a replacement for John Abizaid, Keane had recommended Fallon, an endorsement he would later regret. George Bush had a favorable impression of Fallon as well. The president had dined with Fallon when the admiral was serving as the head of Pacific Command, on his way back from a series of Asian meetings. Pace and Rumsfeld told the White House that Fallon was a strategist who could reevaluate what the United States was doing in the region.

He was an unconventional choice in a number of respects. Traditionally, the command had been run by an Army or Marine four-star, as befitting an organization that grew out of Jimmy Carter's Rapid Deployment Joint Task Force and that was focused, first and foremost, on planning for land wars in the Middle East. CENTCOM had been the home of Army General "Storming" Norman Schwarzkopf during the 1991 Desert Storm campaign, of the Marines' Tony Zinni during the Desert Fox air strikes on Iraq, and of Tommy Franks, another Army four-star, during Bush's invasion. It had never been helmed by an admiral. If Petraeus was one of the military's youngest four-star officers, Fallon was one of the oldest. Along with Pace, he was one of the very few Vietnam veterans still in the force's senior ranks; when Petraeus was an eighteen-year-old cadet just starting at West Point, Fallon had been dodging surface-to-air missiles over Laos and North Vietnam as a navigator in an RA-5 reconnaissance jet. He was already a four-star admiral when Bush was elected in 2000.

On paper, it seemed like a match that could work. Petraeus would prosecute the surge in Iraq while Fallon would build support in the region. Fallon's previous post as the head of Pacific Command entailed considerable diplomatic involvement with nations in the region. Much the same was needed now in the Middle East. The Saudis and other authoritarian Sunni states were deeply suspicious of a Shiite-dominated and potentially democratic Iraq. Some way had to be found to stitch Iraq into the fabric of the largely Sunni Arab world, induce Arab states to post ambassadors in Baghdad, and stop the flow of jihadists and covert insurgent funding to Iraq. The admiral could play Mr. Outside while Petraeus orchestrated the war from the inside.

Fallon, however, had little interest in any of that and saw his role differently. The admiral anticipated that he would have a lead role in shaping the political and military strategy in Iraq and when necessary issue course corrections. Fallon started by putting his imprint on CENTCOM's headquarters. The J5 plans shop was moved out of the building and into a trailer to make room for an officers' mess. The tile floor was replaced with linoleum that could be buffed, as on a ship. The main stairwell in CENTCOM headquarters was briefly declared an "officers only" stairwell, something that would fly in the Navy but that smacked of snobbery to soldiers and Marines. To many of the old hands at the command, Fallon's arrival seemed informed by a sense of entitlement. Wags dubbed the headquarters "the USS CENTCOM." Fallon, for his part, chalked up the criticism to rivals and an unfriendly media who did not appreciate his need to shrink an unproductive staff that was "far too large."

Fallon did not hesitate to plunge into Iraqi politics. The Bush administration was required to submit a report to Congress in July on what, if any, headway had been made toward meeting the political benchmarks in Iraq. During a June visit, Fallon pressed Maliki to ensure the passage of a law regarding the division of oil proceeds by the following month. "You have the power," Fallon said. "Is it reasonable to expect it to be completed in July? We have to show some progress in July for the upcoming report." Maliki fended off the pressure with a disquisition on Iraq's political process as a long journey from dictatorship to democracy. "The end result will be marked in history," the prime minister said.[2] Years later, the oil law would remain unfinished business.

To put his own imprint on the military strategy, Fallon brought his protégé, Rear Admiral James "Sandy" Winnefeld, to CENTCOM. Winnefeld, who would go on to be named vice chairman of the Joint Chiefs during the Obama administration, was another naval aviator; some of the first strikes of the Afghan war had been flown off his aircraft carrier, the USS Enterprise, in 2001. A tech-savvy officer whose next post would be commander of the Sixth Fleet in the Mediterranean, Winnefeld was tasked by Fallon with putting together an alternative assessment of Iraq, one that could support a wholly different plan from the one that Petraeus and the American embassy had developed in the JSAT and Joint Campaign Plan, and one that the president had not requested.

It was an unequal competition. Petraeus had regular access to the president and did not hesitate to use it. He had done his time in Iraq, had overseen the drafting of the new counterinsurgency manual, and was working closely with Ryan Crocker and Ray Odierno, the driving force behind the campaign in the Baghdad belts. He also had a regular pipeline to Gates, which Petraeus nurtured in frequent videoconferences and through his weekly letters to the defense secretary. In a May 7 videoconference with Bush, Petraeus put the argument against curtailing the surge in terms that the Bush administration could understand: the War on Terror. Petraeus noted that he, CIA director Michael Hayden, DIA director Michael Maples, and JSOC commander Stan McChrystal were all in agreement that the global Al-Qaeda network viewed its franchise in Iraq as its "main effort," in American military terms. "Believe this is a hugely important point in any talk of a drawdown," he told the president. "It is simply shortsighted to think AQ will leave a globally connected, well-resourced position in the center of the Middle East just because we do."[3]

The access Petraeus enjoyed to the White House rankled Fallon's team. "They got to the point where they would talk about Petraeus and the hold he had over the president as though he was Rasputin," a former CENTCOM officer said. "The way they described him, it was like Petraeus had the president mesmerized. And that no one else could get between Petraeus and Bush to present a more realistic view of what was happening."[4] The mantra within Fallon's inner circle in June was that the surge strategy had run its course, and that Petraeus needed to put talk of counterinsurgency behind him and move on to a new and more realistic mission. Fallon had some natural allies, namely the Joint Chiefs, who had been uneasy about Bush's decision to opt for a five-brigade surge and who liked Petraeus's direct access to the commander in chief even less.

To get the ground truth on the war and reassert his own role and that of the Joint Chiefs, Fallon sent Winnefeld on two fact-finding trips over the summer, one in June and one in late July. The rear admiral made the rounds in London, the Gulf states, and Iraq. The Arab allies thought that if the sectarian clashes in Iraq could not be tamped down, the civil war would spin out of control. But Winnefeld took his guidance from Fallon, and it called for the development of an alternative plan.

Sketching out his scheme, Winnefeld developed a plan for a gradual step-down to a "sustainable" level of engagement, amounting to around 100,000 troops, or 10 brigades, whose chief focus would be to advise. Winnefeld's plan went into considerable technical detail: he had consulted numerous Army and Marine logisticians and training personnel. After a period, there would be further reductions. Initially, Winnefeld wanted to start troop reductions as early as August, but as he fine-tuned the plan the drawdown would instead start in November. Nothing in the plan had any connection whatsoever to the big political issues confronting Iraq: the provincial elections that were to be held in January 2009 and that had the promise, at long last, of enfranchising the Sunnis in areas outside Baghdad; the politics of legislation in the Iraqi parliament; and the like. Winnefeld's solution was to turn things over to the Iraqi government even as the JSAT held that the government itself was half the problem.

Winnefeld's visits were initially a puzzle to the officers in Baghdad. On Winnefeld's first trip, Petraeus heard that a two-star admiral was going around Iraq, and he asked to see him. "Sandy," Petraeus said. "We're just a few months into the surge."

When Winnefeld returned to Iraq in July he showed some of his findings about the war to Petraeus, who thanked him for his work and said he would look at it to see if there was anything useful. Nobody would expect, Petraeus said somewhat patronizingly, that an officer who had spent just days on the ground would have all the answers for Iraq. Petraeus and Crocker had a plan—one that the secretary of defense and the president both supported. If Fallon and his cohorts wanted to champion an alternative in Washington, Petraeus muttered to his staff in frustration, they could find themselves another Iraq commander.

As soon as Winnefeld got off his flight from Baghdad in Kuwait he got on the line with Fallon.[5] The four-star general who had overseen the counterinsurgency manual was not inclined to take strategy pointers from Navy officers who had spent virtually no time in Iraq. But by dismissing Winnefeld's briefing Petraeus was, in effect, dismissing Fallon, the Army general's nominal superior. Although Fallon could still up the ante, Petraeus had drawn a line in the sand.

Nor was Petraeus the only obstacle Winnefeld encountered. Winnefeld had met in Bahrain with Jim Mattis, the Marine commander who cowrote the counterinsurgency manual with Petraeus. Mattis had just made a trip to his old stomping grounds in Ramadi and Fallujah and been impressed with the success the Americans were having there and their thriving alliance with the Awakening. Mattis thought Winnefeld's idea about shrinking the American footprint in Anbar was crazy. The Marines and the Army had their boot on Al-Qaeda's neck, choking the life out of it. They were about to win and were practically approaching the finish line. Mattis thought

Winnefeld was utterly disconnected from the tactical realities of Iraq; Winnefeld thought Mattis was deluded.

The struggle over CENTCOM's strategy was far from over. Both sides would brief their positions to the JCS. Unless additional brigades were earmarked for deployment, the surge would slowly begin to taper off, as all the units needed to be replaced. Odierno had told Petraeus that he thought the twenty brigades initially deployed for the surge would need to be maintained in Iraq through February 2008. But as the months wore on he had become pessimistic about whether his recommendation would be carried out. In the White House, where support really counted, Bush appeared to be firmly behind the surge. But between Winnefeld's visit and the endless stream of congressional delegations passing through Baghdad only to pronounce their skepticism about the strategy back home to a war-weary public, commanders like Odierno did not have it easy. Nor were the Joint Chiefs in Petraeus's corner, notwithstanding the president's pledge to expand the Army and Marines. The chiefs, whose members now included George Casey, were not part of the chain of command, and in fact were in a weaker than usual position in the summer of 2007: in June, Gates had announced that Pete Pace would not be nominated for a second two-year term as chairman, primarily due to strong opposition in the Senate. Pace was a lame duck. The chiefs were concerned about the strain the surge was putting on the military and were getting very different signals from Fallon on what was happening in Iraq than what they were hearing from Petraeus.

At the end of June, Odierno returned to the United States for a short leave. Upon his return to Baghdad in early July, he issued instructions to his staff that made it clear that continued top-level support of the surge was not a sure thing—in fact, he thought it possible that Washington's decision to end the surge was approaching. "I see the 'writing on the wall,'" the general wrote to his aides. "Regardless of what we think of it, our country is going to change course in Iraq. A strategic decision on this may already have been made." Odierno added that he was not confident he would have the resources to sustain the surge beyond the next sixty days. "We will never know if our current strategy could have worked," he said pessimistically. Odierno said he had thought the command would have more time, but that it was now time to work on "Plan B."[6]

Just how long the surge should last would be taken up at the end of the summer. In July, Pace set the stage for a surge review, issuing a "planning order" based largely on Winnefeld's report. Fallon and Petraeus were to assess how many troops would be needed and for how long in three scenarios: if security conditions in Iraq improved sharply, if they stayed roughly the same, and if they deteriorated. In typical military fashion, the three options were presented as two extremes and a middle ground that the chiefs viewed as reasonable.

In Baghdad, the issuing of the planning order was compartmentalized so that only Petraeus and a handful of others ever saw its details. A bureaucratic master in his own right, Petraeus understood that a debate could be decided by the very way it was framed. None of the options provided by the Joint Chiefs seemed to be the proper way to frame the problem, though Petraeus had no intention of sharing this observation beforehand with anyone except the president himself. With Petraeus and Crocker scheduled to testify to Congress during the second week of September, the time to show demonstrable progress was fast approaching, but plenty had transpired in the preceding months to give even optimists like Petraeus and Odierno cause for concern.

Two weeks into Operation Phantom Thunder, Jim Hickey, who had helped to shape the belts offensive, took stock. Briefing Odierno, he showed the general a map that his staff had drawn up. Piecing together reports from combat units, Iraqi police stations, and the intelligence community— as well as documents seized from Al-Qaeda, including fifty hard drives captured in early June—Hickey's team created a "blob map," presenting the areas in which Al-Qaeda was strong as red splotches. The red blobs, Hickey showed, were shrinking and moving north, out of the belts into more remote areas like Mosul, Diyala's Hamrin Mountains, and the desert between Samarra and Lake Tharthar, where so many helicopters had been downed over the winter. Pushed out of Anbar by the Awakening and out of Diyala by Arrowhead Ripper, Al-Qaeda leaders heading for new sanctuaries farther north in June and July had to pass through towns and villages they were not familiar with, and where they stuck out and had to use cell phones that American intelligence could easily track.

There was nothing really new about such a map; in Algeria, French officers had called them "smallpox maps," and they would have looked familiar to many veterans of Vietnam as well. But they had been largely absent in Iraq, and Odierno was impressed enough that he had Hickey give the same briefing to Petraeus on the porch of his palatial residence a week later. Struck by the map, Petraeus invoked a concept from conventional war: he declared a "pursuit."[7]

To keep up the pressure, Odierno launched Operation Phantom Strike, a follow-up to Phantom Thunder that focused less on clearing new areas than it did on keeping Al-Qaeda on its heels, especially in the northern belt, where the group remained strong. As Petraeus explained in a letter to Gates, the offensive—really a series of concerted raids by commandos and conventional troops—was motivated in part by American worries that the summer's downtick in Al-Qaeda attacks might be a sign that the terrorist group was regrouping fighters, suicide bombers, and resources for a big push to coincide with Petraeus's congressional testimony.

The 13th MEU, the Marine unit that had been the last to arrive for the surge, was important to Phantom Strike, pushing into remote areas like Taji, Karma, and Lake Tharthar, transit areas that Al-Qaeda had to cross between Anbar and the north. But Stan McChrystal's special operations forces were equally important, given the offensive nature of the operation. The number of troops assigned to JSOC was small relative to the overall size of the American force in Iraq. The commandos' mission was often described as "counterterrorism"—essentially, the killing or capture of important insurgent or militia leaders and operatives—and contrasted with "counterinsurgency," protecting the population and isolating it from the enemy. In fact, the two had a synergistic relationship. When cooperation between special operations forces and conventional troops worked, as it increasingly did as the surge took hold, the two kinds of troops could complement each other and greatly increase one another's effectiveness. When JSOC's violent raids went wrong, however, it could create problems for the conventional units left to pick up the pieces the next morning. "You cannot go after AQI with just Delta and some Special Forces; that will never do it," Petraeus told a group of brigadier generals later in the surge. "There are no green doors between SF, special mission units, and conventional forces anymore."[8]

On the weekend that Phantom Thunder kicked off, JSOC's Task Force 16 had been particularly active. A strike force killed Abd al-Rahman al-Masri, an experienced foreign fighter who had fought alongside Abu Ayyub al-Masri in Afghanistan before coming to Iraq with him in 2003. A week into Phantom Thunder, on June 23, a JSOC raid in the northern city of Bayji killed Khalid and Khalil al-Turki, two foreign Al-Qaeda operatives who had entered Iraq in January to advise Masri and whose deaths, Petraeus told Gates, would send a "powerful message" to leaders of Al-Qaeda central in Pakistan.[9] And on June 29, JSOC launched Task Force Falcon into the upper reaches of the Diyala valley for Operation Quechan, the first of many "pursuit" assaults that it would launch in the valley to keep the retreating Al-Qaeda cells on the run.

Then, on July 4 in Mosul, another raid picked up Khalid Abd al-Fatah Daoud al-Mashhadani, also known as Abu Shahid. Petraeus described Abu Shahid in a classified videoconference with the NSC as Al-Qaeda in Iraq's "number two or three leader," and possibly its most senior Iraqi-born leader. In an NSC meeting on July 23, President Bush singled JSOC out for praise for its work in Iraq, and asked Petraeus to pass his thanks along to McChrystal.[10]

JSOC's various efforts against Al-Qaeda went by an array of code names—Operations Galahad and Kodiak were long-standing hunts for senior insurgent leaders like Abu Ayyub al-Masri, while Operation Mariner was the name for operations in Sulaymaniyah, where the Iranian Quds Force was believed to be assisting Al-Qaeda in a limited fashion. It was not the only instance documented in the command's classified annals in which the Shiite Iranians made common cause, albeit on a select basis, with the Sunni-led Al-Qaeda in Iraq—an application of the principle that the enemy of my enemy is my friend, at least temporarily. As the summer progressed, the pace of JSOC's nighttime raids against Al-Qaeda reached an all-time high. During one week in August, McChrystal's strike forces mounted eighty-seven missions, killing fifty-nine enemy fighters and detaining another two hundred.[11]

The American military was not the only weapon in McChrystal's arsenal. While Britain's conventional forces operated only in Basra, an eighty-strong British SAS squadron, Task Force Knight, worked under Delta Force as part of McChrystal's Task Force 16. Two of JSOC's most successful operations during the long, difficult summer of 2007 were Operations Fly and Spider, Task Force Knight's campaign against the car and truck bomb networks in Baghdad and the belts that were terrorizing Shiite markets and fueling sectarian violence. The SAS campaign averaged a raid a night, both in urban Baghdad where the bombs went off and in the rural belts where they were often assembled, and it exemplified the kind of cooperation between the most secret special operations forces and standard infantry units that Petraeus touted and that had been unthinkable a decade earlier. By summer, the car bomb cells in East Baghdad had been decimated, and the British commandos moved on to a parallel network on the west side.

In the belts, the SAS troopers would fly into a landing zone several kilometers from their target and then move in on foot, often at a run in full combat gear. It was the combination of secret SAS raids and Ken Adgie's battalion's operations that yielded the greatest dividends in Arab Jabour, according to a history of the latter unit.[12] The SAS developed a relationship with Adgie's chief bird dog and with an enlisted soldier from his head-quarters who acted as their liaison. During an intensive period of raids in August and September, the British troopers landed at Adgie's base several nights a week to pick up informants and then headed out on their raids. The cooperation culminated in a September raid in which one SAS trooper died—but so did a figure named Abu Jurra, who had led the Al-Qaeda cells in Adgie's sector of the southern belt.

Inside the city, the SAS capitalized on the difficult July clearance of East Rashid, scoring an important victory on August 7 in cooperation with the conventional units there. "On Wednesday, a combination of a conventional brigade, 4/1 ID, special operators from 22 SAS, a CIA ISR platform, and specialized intelligence unit captured three key leaders of a major VBIED cell," Petraeus wrote in his letter to Gates after the operation.[13] In another instance later in the surge, an SAS team detained an insurgent who gave up the location of an Al-Qaeda operative named Abu Yassin, whom they then captured the same night in the same West Baghdad neighborhood. Instead of taking Abu Yassin off to detention, the SAS men had him set up a meeting with a third operative, Abu Fallah. When Abu Yassin drove to the meeting site the next day, the SAS went with him, concealed in a local "Bongo" truck, and captured Abu Fallah. Later in the week, they repeated the same trick. When yet another Al-Qaeda operative tried to reach Abu Yassin on his cell phone, the British commandos again had their detainee set up a meeting, then followed him to the location of the meeting in Bongo trucks.[14]

The effect of the combined conventional-SAS operations against VBIED cells was evident later in August, during the Shiite pilgrimage commemo-rating the Seventh Imam. In years past, the Seventh Imam march, which culminated in Kadhimiya, had provided an irresistible opportunity for Al-Qaeda bombers, but in 2007 the march went off without a hitch.

Even with the surge of American troops, there were still only so many forces to go around. The success that the combined commando and con-ventional operations had against car and truck bombings in greater Bagh-dad had the effect of increasing bombings elsewhere—in northern Iraq, for example, to which Al-Qaeda was retreating and where American troops were spread as thin as they had ever been. In the case of the north's largest city, Mosul, troops were spread even thinner, and relied heavily on a JSOC force run by Rangers. One afternoon in July, for example, JSOC received a tip that an insurgent leader named Marwan was at a house in Mosul, then used a drone to follow a car for four hours as it drove away from the location. Using high-tech eavesdropping technology, an NSA team was able to listen in on one of the occupants of the car as he made a cell phone call and conclude that the voice belonged to Marwan.

The Ranger major in charge of the JSOC force in Mosul described what happened next. "I returned to my TOC, got briefed, and called the TF 16 Commander to give a final SITREP," he wrote in an e-mail report. "The vehicle stopped and the driver exited, so I gave the final order to fire a Hellfire from one of my orbiting platforms. We hit the vehicle dead-on, 2x EKIA inside. We immediately alerted the BDE TOC to get fire/rescue on scene, who were there in minutes. My element moved to the location and conducted SSE. Good news is that when my guys queried the locals on the ground, they reported that the car we hit fired on the Kiowas and the Kiowas retaliated, so there is no trace to my unit, and it is being chalked up as self-defense by the Kiowas." The Rangers saw no evidence of civilian casualties; the major added: "They checked all the ambulances and no one was present." But that night, Colonel Stephen Twitty, the brigade commander in Mosul, emailed his division headquarters that eight locals had been wounded, making the Nineveh provincial government "very upset." "Having said that," Twitty added, "I believe this was the right action to take. I will work the consequence management with the [government]."[15]

But Al-Qaeda continued to ramp up its operations in the north. On August 14, four VBIEDs attacked a pair of towns in the far west of Nineveh that were populated by Yazidis, a non-Muslim Kurdish-speaking minority. Whether the Yazidi bombings killed nearly eight hundred people, as the Iraqi Red Crescent claimed, or more than three hundred, the American military estimate, they were the deadliest of the entire war in Iraq, as Petraeus acknowledged to Gates in a letter.[16]

While Task Force 16 was pursuing Al-Qaeda, the smaller arm of McChrystal's command, Task Force 17, spent the summer pursuing Shiite targets, both Mahdi Army commanders and the leaders of the Iranian-based Special Groups. With a Shiite-dominated government in Baghdad, the task force's operations were politically sensitive, particularly if the raids were conducted in areas like Sadr City, a Shiite bastion where many militia leaders had their headquarters but whose population, if not leadership, Maliki had sought to co-opt. On June 15, for example, the Green Zone took rocket fire from East Baghdad—a common form of militia harassment of the coalition and the government in their seat of power. The next day, at a meeting with Odierno, the defense and interior ministers, and Rubaie, Prime Minister Maliki acknowledged that the rocket fire had come from

Sadr City, but proceeded to instruct Abud Qanbar, the Baghdad Operations Command chief, to avoid attacking Mahdi Army forces without government approval.[17]

One of the most politically charged operations came in late July in Husseiniya, a small town in the northeastern Baghdad belt that Shiite militants used as a support and fallback area for nearby Sadr City. After a string of EFP attacks, the artillery battalion responsible for the area cordoned off Husseiniya on July 19 and told local leaders to hand over four militia leaders. Four days later, with the cordon still in place, Odierno was approached by Tariq Abdullah, Maliki's chief of staff, who said that the prime minister did not want to hear about Husseiniya in parliament. Ahmed Chalabi was involved in negotiations over the fate of the town before the battalion and residents reached a deal on July 24. On a visit to the area a few days later, Petraeus told the artillery battalion there that the confrontation they had just been through had been one of outsized importance because of Husseiniya's significance to the militia in Sadr City and to the government.[18]

The operations were also a delicate matter for Petraeus. With no American troops except on the southern edge, the densely packed Shiite slum was effectively controlled by the militias, even its police force, and raids there could end badly. During a July 6 mission three Navy SEALs were killed in an ambush as they sought to leave Sadr City after a raid. A week later the retreat from the slum of another strike force had to be covered by an AC-130 gunship after it came under attack from local police—the raid's target, a Special Groups leader, was a policeman too. "I have asked Stan's teams going into Sadr City to look hard at their tactics," Petraeus wrote to Gates. "We're all trying to avoid a nasty ambush like the one we saw last week that cost us three SEALs."[19] As a result, raids into Sadr City had to be approved by Petraeus, who sometimes consulted with Crocker and Maliki about them as well.

Confrontations with the militia also flared up outside Baghdad, and there American forces had more leeway. In mid-June, fighting between the Mahdi Army and a paramilitary police unit in Nasiriyah led Maliki and Abd al-Mahdi to request American help; the military sent a Special Forces team, Apache attack helicopters, and an AC-130, all with Maliki's blessing, to attack any targets in Nasiriyah they deemed necessary. In Diwaniyah, the reluctance of the Polish-led multinational force to take too offensive a posture gave the Mahdi Army a free hand. On July 2, the militia fired more than seventy rockets and mortar rounds at Camp Echo, a barrage that destroyed the vehicles of the Special Forces team there and prompted a flurry of anxious phone calls from the hodgepodge of allied nations that were based there to their home capitals. A Special Forces team called in air strikes by F-16s on three buildings in the city and the Iraqi Army's 8th Division mounted an operation. Soon after, a special operations raid in the city wounded a militia leader and spurred Mahdi Army fighters to take to the streets. Again with Maliki's blessing, the small American contingent in Diwaniyah called in an AC-130.

The continued pressure from commandos and conventional forces took its toll on the Sadrists and the Special Groups. Muqtada al-Sadr had returned to Najaf from Iran in May and was trying to bring the Mahdi Army and its splinter cells back under his control. By July, however, Sadr returned to Iran, surprising the American military and embassy, and leaving Ahmed al-Sheibani in charge. With Sadr gone, the fighting between American troops and Shiite militias escalated. That month EFP attacks reached an all-time high of ninety-nine, double January's number. Because EFPs could kill whole Humvee crews and the only other similarly lethal kind of bomb, Sunni insurgents' deep-buried IED, was on the decline, these attacks accounted for an increasing proportion of overall American casualties. Two-thirds of American casualties in July were the result of attacks by Shiite groups. "I tend to agree with the assessment of Ray Odierno and see that JAM is more of a hindrance to long-term security in Iraq than is AQI," Petraeus told Gates in a classified letter at the beginning of July, after describing Mahdi Army activity in West Rashid, an area of West Baghdad where Shiite efforts to expel Sunnis from mixed neighborhoods had not yet fallen off as they had elsewhere in the city.[20]

As McChrystal's forces stepped up the pressure, Sheibani and his family followed Sadr to Iran. The increased pressure did not seem to sit well with the leadership of Lebanese Hezbollah, either, the group whose Arabic-speaking operatives often trained Special Groups on behalf of the Quds Force. "Also of regional note, we saw one intelligence report indicating that the Lebanese Hezbollah Secretary General ordered all Hezbollah out of Iraq due to the unwanted attention his organization received after the 'Hamid the Mute' exposition," Petraeus told the NSC in August, referring to Ali Musa Daqduq, the Hezbollah commander captured with the Khazalis in Basra.[21]

As the summer ended, Petraeus received an unusual message from Shirwan Waeli, the head of the parallel intelligence agency that Maliki had empowered to rival the CIA-backed INIS. Ryan Crocker had recently held a series of inconclusive and contentious meetings in Baghdad with Iranian diplomats. According to a classified cable the ambassador sent to the NSC, Crocker had even raised the issue of limited Iranian support for Al-Qaeda, something some experts had initially dismissed but of which there was growing evidence.

Despite the talks, the supply of Iranian arms to the militias had increased: on July 31, an Apache was forced to make a "hard landing" near the eastern edge of Sadr City after it was struck by an Iranian Misagh-1 missile. Bush, for one, was not impressed with the results of the sessions. "We've got nothing from U.S.-Iran talks," he complained to the NSC. "Why continue the talks?" But Condoleezza Rice pushed back, saying that it would be prudent to "keep the option for meetings open."[22]

Waeli, however, had a different message: the Americans were not dealing with the real power in Iran. In an August 12 session, Waeli told Petraeus that he had met with Iranian president Mahmoud Ahmadinejad in Tehran, and that same day met in a hotel room with Qasim Suleimani, the Quds Force commander, who wanted Waeli to relay a message. It was similar to a message received by Khalilzad in January: Suleimani—and no other Iranian official—dictated Iran's actions in Iraq.

As Petraeus reported the meeting to Gates afterward in a classified letter, Suleimani also proposed making a deal for the release of Qais al-Khazali. If Qais was released there would be a "dramatic" decrease in Quds Force activity in Iraq. "You will see results in two months," Waeli said, according to a cable Crocker sent home, classified SECRET//NODIS.[23]

"I told Waeli to relay back to Soleimani that we believe that Iran has overreached and is on the brink of attracting international isolation," Petraeus noted in his classified letter to Gates:

I pointed out that the Russians are now unwilling to provide the nuclear fuel for Iran's reactor. I noted that I am not a policy maker; however, as the commander on the ground, I am starting to think that Iran is attacking Iraqi and coalition soldiers through proxies—the JAM they have trained, funded, armed, and in some cases even directed. To provide a bit more jolt, I said that I am considering telling the President that I believe Iran is, in fact, waging war on the US in Iraq, with all of the US public and governmental responses that could come from that revelation. We'll watch for any "reflections" from this exchange. For what it's worth, I do believe that Iran has gone beyond merely striving for influence in Iraq and could be creating proxies to actively fight us, thinking that they can keep us distracted while they try to build WMD and set up JAM to act like Lebanese Hezbollah in Iraq.[24]

Even as the Sunni insurgency was being weakened, the Iranian-based militias appeared to be getting more active. By late August, violence by Sunni insurgents was on a downward slope, but violence by Shiite militias was not. Fortunately, at the end of the month, a clash in Karbala undermined Sadr's credibility and compelled him to take extreme measures to salvage what was left of his movement's unity.

The coalition presence in the cities of south-central Iraq was minimal. Instead, security was largely in the hands of Iraqi security forces: the competent 8th Iraqi Army Division, and police forces that often drew heavily on members of Badr, the armed wing of the Islamic Supreme Council of Iraq or ISCI, the newly rebranded name of SCIRI. Many police units were essentially Badr militias in government-issued uniforms. There were signs by early August that a conflict in southern Iraq between Sadrist militias and Badr loyalists in the security forces was brewing, including the assassination of two governors of southern provinces, both ISCI members: the governor of Qadisiya, the province of which Diwaniyah was the capital, on August 11 by an EFP, and the governor of Muthana on August 20.

The conflict between the Sadrists and ISCI came to a head in Karbala on August 27. Mahdi Army fighters were escorting Shiite pilgrims into the city to commemorate the birth of the Twelfth Imam when Badr-aligned security forces confronted them and tried to prevent them from carrying weapons into the shrines where the pilgrims were bound. That night Mahdi Army fighters and government forces exchanged gunfire. The next day, the situation worsened, with Mahdi militiamen firing on security forces—sometimes with RPGs—from within crowds of pilgrims. More than 50 people were killed and 280 injured. Maliki's reaction was to impose a curfew in Karbala on August 29 and travel there personally with reinforcements in a convoy of fifty-two vehicles, pistol in hand and rifle strapped to his back, and arrest or relieve various security officials in the city.

To limit the political damage, Sadr announced from his sanctuary in Iran that he was declaring a six-month cease-fire. Not all of the militia factions heeded his call, but enough did that attacks by Shiite fighters dropped.

Reflecting Sadr's incomplete—and slipping—control over the Mahdi Army and its offshoots, the cease-fire or freeze was not uniformly observed. Groups like Asaib Ahl al-Haq and Kataib Hezbollah kept fighting, as did many rogue fighters in the mainstream militia. Nonetheless, the downturn in violence in Shiite areas was real. In July 2007 nearly one hundred EFPs went off or were discovered across Iraq, but September saw just half that number.

No matter its provenance, the cease-fire compounded the effects of the spreading Sunni Awakening groups and American offensives against Al-Qaeda and the Special Groups. Sadr's cease-fire and the accompanying reduction in attacks by Shiite fighters came on the heels of a two-month-long decrease in overall attacks in Iraq. At the beginning of September, as Petraeus prepared for his return to Washington to testify before Congress, violence remained very high, but it was dropping noticeably. Attack levels were now roughly what they had been in the immediate aftermath of the first bombing of the Askari Mosque in 2006.

Two weeks before his congressional testimony, the time had finally come for Petraeus to lay out to his chain of command his thinking on when and how to wind down the surge. On August 26, Fallon and Petraeus met in Baghdad; Fallon did not know exactly what Petraeus planned to recommend, but he guessed that he would not like it. Petraeus described his recommendation in general terms to Fallon—essentially, small withdrawals of the surge forces during the fall, but protracting the rest of the withdrawals into the summer of 2008, and holding off completely on planning for further troop cuts beyond fifteen brigades.

On August 27, Petraeus presented his overall Iraq strategy by videoconference to the Joint Chiefs. To make the case for the surge, and undermine the argument for reverting to some version of the transition strategy Casey had employed, Petraeus highlighted a document his staff had dug up: Casey and Khalilzad's campaign progress review from the previous December. "Many of the risks identified within the Campaign Plan have materialized," that document's first page read. "Many of the assumptions do not hold. We are failing to achieve objectives in the Economic Development, Governance, Communicating, and Security lines of operation within the planned timeframes." Driving the point home with PowerPoint slides, Petraeus not only quoted the assessment but showed Casey's and Khalilzad's signature blocks, lifted from the December document.[25]

It was an in-your-face approach: if the JCS did not like Petraeus's plan, the leading alternative had already been pronounced a failure by its authors. Casey, participating in the videoconference from a vacation and wearing civilian clothes, was both surprised and unamused. He asked for a copy of his own document to check that he had really offered such a gloomy assessment, and would later argue that Petraeus had taken his remarks out of context. The review, Casey insisted, had not concluded that his strategy would never work but had noted that it needed more time.

As the videoconference proceeded, Petraeus thanked the chiefs for their planning order with its three options, and simultaneously dismissed it by saying that it had "informed enormously" the actual recommendation he intended to present to Bush a few days later. What, the chiefs pressed, would that recommendation be? None of the three options from the planning order, Petraeus responded. The Iraq commander would not be playing Fallon and the chiefs' game.

Three days later, in the last videoconference before his congressional testimony, Petraeus briefed Bush on the latest statistics on the drop in violence and the details of his surge drawdown plan. As a sop to critics who were clamoring for a drawdown, he recommended removing the smallest of the surge units, the 13th MEU, in September, shortly after his and Crocker's testimony, then pulling out the first full combat brigade in December and spreading out the withdrawal of the remaining four brigades over the next six months, into the summer of 2008. If anything, Bush was more cautious than Petraeus about the pace of the drawdown. The president, who understood the internal politics in the Pentagon, asked if Petraeus was suggesting the troop withdrawals in response to pressure from the Joint Chiefs and stressed that he should be careful to make sure that he remained flexible.

"Is this your recommendation?" Bush asked. "Or is it tailored to what the chiefs want? It needs to be yours." The most important thing, Bush stressed, was to succeed and to stand by the Iraqis, and if the United States needed to keep the surge forces in Iraq longer, the president was willing to do that. "If we need twenty brigades for as long as we can do it that's what we'll do," Bush added. "You better retain flexibility in your recommendation."

After a long discussion with Petraeus, the president asked Fallon, who sat in on such sessions, for his views. "Sir, I'm not sure whether this would sell on the Hill," the admiral said. That, Bush replied, was not Fallon's concern. "Let me worry about the politics of this," Bush said. Fallon then launched an odd discussion in which he sought to compare the tangled situation in Iraq to a dogfight between two fighter planes. The admiral appeared to be trying to win Bush over by alluding to the president's days as a pilot in the Texas Air National Guard. Fallon explained that when an F-16 pilot was being chased in a dogfight he had to take risks in order to shake the attacker.

"A bogey's on your tail, you try to outrun him, try to outmaneuver him, but he's still there," Fallon said, using aviator slang for an enemy aircraft. "What do you do?"

"I don't know," said Bush. "What do I do?"

"You take on some risk," the CENTCOM commander responded, "maybe slow up a bit; get that bogey in front." Moving his hands to simulate the dogfight, Fallon pushed his left hand forward: "Boom!"

Fallon was making the same argument that Casey had used, and that had failed to persuade Bush before the surge: the United States needed to draw down its forces to induce the Iraqis to step up. Years later, Fallon still held to that view. "The war was effectively over by September 2007," he insisted. "Done." With the enemy routed, Fallon argued, he was concerned about the strain on the American military, among other factors. Bush, for his part, did not buy Fallon's argument. The surge was just beginning to gain traction, and Bush was hardly persuaded that this was the time to end it.

"I'm not sure we're ready to take on more risk in Iraq," the president said. "It's still pretty early in this new plan, and I like the new plan."

Cheney was even more dismissive. "It's hard to get my head around the notion that drawing down somehow helps the Iraqis step up," the vice president said. "That's the opposite thinking behind the surge." The United States had tried that in 2006, he added, and Iraq had come "unglued."

The following weekend, on September 3, Air Force One flew into Al-Asad Air Base for a surprise visit by Bush to the province where the Awakening movement had begun. The Marine generals in charge of Anbar flew key sheikhs from across the province into Al-Asad to introduce them to the president, including both Abd al-Sattar from Ramadi and Khamis al-Issawi from Fallujah. Brigadier General John Allen, in charge of seating arrangements for Bush's session with the sheikhs and other Anbari officials, placed the sheikhs according to lineal hierarchy. Then Mamun Sami Rashid, the provincial governor whom Abd al-Sattar had on various occasions threatened to oust or kill, changed the order, putting Abd al-Sattar in the seat of honor, next to Bush. "What he has done for us, he deserves to sit here," Abd al-Sattar's sometime opponent explained to Allen.[26]

While Abd al-Sattar sat at Bush's side, across the table from the president were Iraq's most senior officials, including Maliki, Talabani, Hashimi, and Barham Salih. With a lamentable lack of foresight, Maliki, just back from eye surgery in Iran, had been placed in a Black Hawk helicopter's "hurricane seat" for the long trip from the Green Zone to Al-Asad Air Base. Getting off the helicopter at the air base, Maliki was furious, and understandably concerned about his freshly operated-upon eye. "You're insulting me on purpose," he accused. "This is meant to soften me up before I meet the president."

At times, as the Iraqis laid out their grievances against one another to Bush, the meeting became uncomfortable. When Mamun complained that Maliki's central government was not supporting Anbar, Bush quipped that when he had been governor of Texas, the federal government had not given him much in the way of support either. But when it was Abd al-Sattar's turn to talk, his message could not have been more welcome to a president who had little support at home for his decision to spend 2007 recommitting to Iraq instead of pulling out. The American troops who had died in the war—more than 3,700 of them so far—had not done so in vain, the sheikh told the president; he and the Sunni population he represented would always remember the sacrifice American families had made in sending their sons and daughters to Iraq. In a bit of hyperbole to which he was prone but which helped make him so charismatic, Abd al-Sattar even told Bush that when the war in Iraq was won, his Awakening fighters would be standing by, ready to help America defeat Al-Qaeda terrorists in Afghanistan. The president wrote that down in his notebook.[27]

Ten days later, on September 13—a year almost to the day after the announcement of the Anbar Emergency Council in Ramadi's most hellishly violent period—a bomb planted by the gate of Abd al-Sattar's compound killed him and three of his guards. Although the Marines at first suspected a rival Awakening sheikh who had publicly threatened to strangle Abd al-Sattar, Al-Qaeda claimed responsibility. Intelligence suggested that the terrorist group had had help on the inside of the compound. Fifteen hundred mourners attended the funeral, including Odierno, the defense and interior ministers, and Rubaie. In just over a year, Abd al-Sattar had gone from a mid-level sheikh viewed suspiciously for his insurgent and smuggling ties to a national martyr. In the meantime, the Sunni Awakening that he had helped spark had changed the course of the war.

General David Petraeus accompanies then-senator Barack Obama on a helicopter tour of Baghdad in July 2008. The presidential candidate took a whirlwind trip to Afghanistan and Iraq before the Democratic Convention. (STAFF SERGEANT LORIE JEWELL/MNF-I PUBLIC AFFAIRS)

Iraqi president Jalal Talabani walks with President George W. Bush on December 14, 2008. (PETTY OFFICER 1ST CLASS KRISTIN FITZSIMMONS/ U.S. NAVY)

President George W. Bush and Prime Minister Nuri al-Maliki sign the status of forces agreement between the United States and Iraq on December 14, 2008. To the left, General Ray Odierno (seated) watches. The agreement mandated that American forces leave Iraq by the end of 2011.

This card was issued to all U.S. soldiers in Iraq after the SOFA was signed. In theory, the agreement subjected American troops to Iraqi law. But American negotiators worked in a provision stipulating that American troops who were "on duty" would be immune from arrest. Whenever a soldier left the confines of a base, he would carry the card, which bore an Arabic translation on the back.

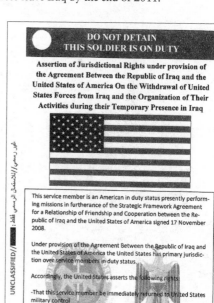

**DO NOT DETAIN
THIS SOLDIER IS ON DUTY**

Assertion of Jurisdictional Rights under provision of the Agreement Between the Republic of Iraq and the United States of America On the Withdrawal of United States Forces from Iraq and the Organization of Their Activities during their Temporary Presence in Iraq

This service member is an American in duty status presently performing missions in furtherance of the Strategic Framework Agreement for a Relationship of Friendship and Cooperation between the Republic of Iraq and the United States of America signed 17 November 2008.

Under provision of the Agreement Between the Republic of Iraq and the United States of America the United States has primary jurisdiction over service members in duty status.

Accordingly, the United States asserts the following rights:

-That this service member be immediately returned to United States military control

-This service member will provide his name and unit contact information for your report to your chain of command regarding this incident

-You may accompany this service member back to his base of operations and report this incident to his chain of command

Lloyd J. Austin III
Lieutenant General, Commanding
Multinational Corps - Iraq

The Obama-era Iraq team meets in Secretary of State Hillary Clinton's State Department office on February 19, 2010. From left: General Ray Odierno, Ambassador Christopher Hill, and Secretary Clinton. (STATE DEPARTMENT OFFICIAL PHOTO)

President Barack Obama talks on the phone with Iraqi president Jalal Talabani on November 4, 2010, from the Oval Office. He is accompanied by Vice President Joe Biden (looking out window), Tony Blinken (seated, facing camera), and Puneet Talwar. During this phone call, Obama asked Talabani to give up the presidency so that Ayad Allawi could fill the post and Iraq's government-formation process could move forward. Talabani demurred. (PETE SOUZA/OFFICIAL WHITE HOUSE PHOTO)

Undersecretary of Defense for Policy Michèle Flournoy sits next to Marine General James "Hoss" Cartwright during a December 2010 press conference. Flournoy was criticized by National Security Adviser Tom Donilon for failing to head off a letter from Admiral Mike Mullen arguing that 16,000 troops should remain in Iraq; Cartwright was embraced by the Obama administration for advocating much lower troop numbers. (CHERIE A. CULLEN/DEPARTMENT OF DEFENSE)

On October 21, 2011, President Barack Obama and his national security team informed Iraqi prime minister Nuri al-Maliki that the SOFA talks had come to an end and that the United States would complete the withdrawal of its troops from Iraq. From left, the insiders delivering the decision: Tony Blinken, Tom Donilon, Puneet Talwar, Denis McDonough, and Bill Daley. Pictured on-screen are (left to right) Prime Minister Maliki, Vice President Joe Biden, General Lloyd Austin, and Ambassador James Jeffrey. (PETE SOUZA/OFFICIAL WHITE HOUSE PHOTO)

Iraqi soldiers stand at attention in front of a poster of Prime Minister Nuri al-Maliki during a December 2006 ceremony in which Najaf Province was transferred to Iraqi control. (MATT SHERMAN)

General Lloyd Austin greets Secretary of Defense Leon Panetta (right) as Ambassador James Jeffrey looks on at the ceremony on December 15, 2011, commemorating the American troop withdrawal. (STAFF SERGEANT CALEB BARRIEAU/DEPARTMENT OF DEFENSE)

Seats were reserved for Iraqi VIPs at the ceremony. Security threats loomed over the event—each dignitary was assigned a bunker in case of rocket or mortar attack. (GREGG CARLSTROM)

President Barack Obama and Prime Minister Nuri al-Maliki shake hands during a December 12, 2011, White House visit. (LAWRENCE JACKSON/OFFICIAL WHITE HOUSE PHOTO)

U.S. and Kuwaiti soldiers close the gate at the Khabari Crossing on the Iraq-Kuwait border just after the final American convoy left Iraq on December 18, 2011. (MASTER SERGEANT MONTIGO WHITE/U.S. ARMY)

CHAPTER 23

General Petraeus Goes to Washington

Congress had set aside two days for the accounting Petraeus and Crocker were to provide on the surge. Petraeus noted in a letter to Gates that some people might have questions about "the optics" of holding an Iraq hearing on September 11, the anniversary of the Al-Qaeda attacks in New York and Washington. The critics of the surge—and they were legion—would be sure to perceive it as a clumsy effort to tie the war in Iraq to the terrorist strikes that brought down the World Trade towers and pummeled the Pentagon.[1] But the date was not up to the general: the congressional calendar was crowded, and the Baghdad team would need to appear when they were called.

Petraeus and his staff understood that he would be venturing into a political minefield. With his approval ratings in tatters, Bush was letting Petraeus walk point on the strategy, and the hearings promised to be rife with politics. As the military command prepared for the sessions, a staff member drafted a memo on "Crafting & Disseminating the Message." Petraeus's September assessment would be seen as more than a review of what had occurred on his watch. Rather, it would be treated as a verdict by the nation's foremost soldier-scholar and counterinsurgency expert on the war itself—all of which had escalated the stakes.

"P4's Honeymoon Phase is over," the memo said, P4 being military in-house shorthand for the four-star general. "The more that P4 is perceived to be partisan, the more intense the reaction. Therefore, a carefully constructed and managed message is critical to maintaining credibility." If Petraeus were to give an interview to a conservative talk show host, his staff should arrange for an interview on the liberal end of the spectrum, added the memo, which asserted that the failure to do so after the general spoke to Hugh Hewitt, an outspoken evangelical radio commentator, was a "major blunder." After offering some pointers on how Petraeus could be seen as apolitical, the memo acknowledged that the general would have an uphill battle. "Regardless of the content of his report, a majority of those in Congress may have already made up their mind." An assessment that amounted to no more than the need to "stay the course" could decisively tip the balance on Capitol Hill against the White House.[2]

For all that, late-breaking developments had bolstered Petraeus's case. Odierno's operations, Phantom Thunder and Phantom Strike, had respectively taken away many of Al-Qaeda's sanctuaries in the belts and kept the insurgents on their heels. The surge had catalyzed and expanded the Awakening movement, and Sadr's cease-fire had further reduced the number of attacks.

During the height of Phantom Thunder, enemy attacks in Iraq had reached an all-time peak of 1,600 in a single week. By August, the figure had dropped to 1,100. Nor was that the only measure of success. One of Petraeus's innovations was the decision to factor in the Iraqis' statistics on civilian casualties. Derek Harvey had established three years earlier that the SIGACTs the U.S. military gathered did not tell the entire story: there was plenty of Iraqi-on-Iraqi violence that the Americans did not observe or record. The Iraqi figures, which were drawn from the hospitals and morgues, generally ran higher than the American ones, and there were concerns that some might be the result of double counting. But it was the trend that counted, and the Iraqis' numbers were heading down too.

It was not clear how long the downturn would last or how deep it would go. But the tentative gains could be used to make the case for continuing the surge; progress was being made on the military front, but consolidating the gains would take more time. The general wondered if he should use PowerPoint slides in the hearing, and since he had good news to tell he decided to go ahead with the visual aids. "Host nation reporting" had been included in the classified databases the command used to assess the surge, and it would be included in the declassified data he planned to present to Congress as well. To buttress his claim that he would be providing independent advice, the general decided not to share his testimony in advance with the White House.

Compared to Petraeus's, Crocker's task was more complex. The Sadrists had ended their boycott of parliament in July, and limited headway had been made on Iraq's political agenda. But the Sunni political party Tawafuq had walked out of the legislature and its cabinet ministers submitted their resignations, although Maliki did not accept them. In late July, Petraeus sent Gates a letter that noted that Crocker was not going to have an easy time with Congress. "Politically, we may have lost ground this past week," Petraeus wrote to the defense secretary. "It is becoming less likely that Ryan will have much political progress to report to Congress in September."[3] Shortly after Petraeus sent that assessment to Gates, the Council of Representatives, its major work left undone, adjourned for its summer recess.

The Iraqi government's failure to match security progress on the battlefield with political progress in the Green Zone prompted Bush to wonder in an August 8 NSC meeting if the Maliki government deserved continued support. "If you dump Maliki, then ensure we get someone we can live with," he said, "definitely not Jaafari but perhaps Abd al-Mahdi." In another NSC meeting two weeks later, Bush again expressed concern when Crocker, participating by videoconference, described the Maliki government as "dysfunctional." The word, Bush said, implied that either the American mission in Iraq needed to end or the Maliki government needed to be replaced. Could the mission still succeed? Bush asked Crocker. And how, Bush continued, had Maliki responded to recent calls by Iraqi politicians for his removal? Crocker told Bush that Maliki was "no Mandela," but neither was he a new Saddam. Reassured, Bush observed stoically that for all of the frustrations, the Iraqi government was at least functioning.[4]

Even some Iraqi officials acknowledged that Crocker would have the tougher time. Mowaffak al-Rubaie told an American embassy official that Petraeus would have an easier go of it than the American ambassador. Iraq's unsteady progress toward meeting its political goals, Rubaie added, would be the American mission's Achilles' heel.[5]

On September 10, the morning Petraeus and Crocker were to appear before the House of Representatives, a full-page advertisement in the *New York Times* poured oil on the fire. Sponsored by MoveOn.org, a liberal anti-war group, it displayed a giant black-and-white photo of Petraeus, whom it dubbed "GENERAL BETRAY US," and accused him of "cooking the books for the White House." As support for its indictment, the broadside asserted that the *New York Times* had established that the Pentagon had adapted a "bizarre formula for keeping tabs on violence" that excluded car bombs.[6] It was the ad, however, that played fast and loose with the facts, as well as its sourcing. The claim that Petraeus's casualty count excluded car bombs was neither true nor an allegation that the *Times'* Baghdad bureau or Pentagon correspondents had proffered. Rather, the charge had been made by Paul Krugman, a *Times* opinion columnist, who cited as one of his main sources a mistake-laden article in the *Washington Post,* which the *Post* later corrected.[7] The *Post*'s "Fact Checker" column awarded the MoveOn.org ad "Three Pinocchios" for "specific factual errors and/or obvious contradictions," including the assertion that car bombs had been omitted from the count.[8]

More generally, the ad missed the point of the drama that was unfolding in Iraq: whether one used Iraqi or American data, the military side of the surge was clearly beginning to show results. It was Iraqi politics, as Rubaie had implied, that appeared stalemated. As a political tactic, the ad back-fired as well: much of the House hearing was consumed by a debate about the propriety of the ad rather than the war effort itself, which succeeded primarily in building sympathy for Petraeus. There were a few outbursts from demonstrators from Code Pink, an antiwar group, but otherwise the day was uneventful.

The hearings on the Senate side the next day were the main attrac-tion. Five members of the panels that were to convene the hearings—Hillary Clinton, Joe Biden, John McCain, Christopher Dodd, and Barack Obama—were running for president, and each seemed determined to take center stage.

By virtue of his seniority and his party's majority in the Senate, Biden was the chair of the Senate Foreign Relations Committee, which was host-ing Petraeus and Crocker in a morning session. A long shot as a candidate, Biden was making his second run for the presidency, his 1988 effort having been derailed by allegations that he had borrowed a stirring passage in his stump speech from Neil Kinnock, the British Labor Party leader.

Voluble, but often unfiltered and direct, Biden was part of the liberal wing of his party but had not shrunk from using military force. Like the vast majority of Democrats in Congress who remembered the political price they had paid for opposing the 1991 Persian Gulf War, Biden had voted in favor of the resolution authorizing military action, held a series of hearings on the prospective nation building problems before the invasion, and then faulted Rumsfeld for sending too few troops.

With the approach of another presidential campaign, Biden dropped his call for sending more forces, an unsustainable position for any Demo-crat running for national office, and devised the "Biden-Gelb" plan for a decentralized brand of federalism in Iraq. The plan reflected Biden's experi-ence with the Balkans and his frequent interactions with the Kurds—the group most enthusiastic about federalism—and at least meant that Biden would no longer be at odds with the Democratic base. Upon closer inspection, however, Biden's brand of federalism for Iraq was problematic. It was far from clear that it would dispense with the need for an international force: the plan that divided Bosnia into ethnic enclaves had initially been policed by 60,000 NATO troops. Nor had there been much support for the idea from Sunnis in Iraq, who did not trust the Shiite-led federal government to fairly disburse oil revenues and feared they would be left with a resource-poor rump state. Apart from Hakim's ISCI party, which had been interested in setting up a nine-province Shiite region in the oil-rich south with the encouragement of Iran, which was hoping to influence the area, there was precious little Iraqi support beyond the Kurds. By September, it was clear that the plan was going nowhere. Even Biden did not press it hard.

As the hearing came to order, Ryan Crocker led off the testimony, repeating the point he had made earlier to Bush that Iraq had no Nelson Mandela, but blaming the lack thereof on Saddam's tyranny for disposing of or dispersing all potential leadership. Deceptively soft-spoken, Crocker had a veteran diplomat's talent for making all of the points that emanated from the White House or the military without provoking much antagonism from the other side. A secure, stable, democratic Iraq, Crocker insisted, was attainable if the United States kept at it. The turning point, he said, would become apparent only in retrospect. Iraq was going through a revolution, not just regime change.

Petraeus read word for word the testimony he had given to the House the previous day, the centerpiece of which were his slides on the drop in violence. To ease the strain a bit on the military, and as a bone to the anti-surge forces that were baying for troop withdrawals, Petraeus noted that the 13th Marine Expeditionary Unit would leave Iraq in September while Dave Sutherland's brigade would depart Diyala in December without replacement. By July 2008, American forces would be down to pre-surge levels. As for further cuts, they would need to be weighed later. Projecting troops reductions down the road, Petraeus asserted, could be not only misleading but dangerous.

Biden dwelled on the lack of political progress and suggested that the decline in violence was merely a reversible blip. Crocker parried by stressing that surge forces had only reached full strength in June. The chairman had demonstrated his skepticism of the surge, and the ambassador had stuck to his stance that it was a work in progress. The exchange was a draw.[9]

The hearing under way, the junior senator from Illinois took his seat, carrying a pack of Nicorette gum. An attorney by training and temperament, Obama planned to make his opposition to the war a hallmark of his campaign and was still developing his foreign affairs platform. During the summer of 2007, Obama had read Zbigniew Brzezinski's book *Second Chance,* which critiqued the foreign policy of a succession of American presidents, and had met with Brzezinski at the Metropolitan Club. At breakfast, Obama made clear that he thought the Israeli-Palestinian issue needed to be solved sooner rather than later and indicated that he expected to be deeply involved in foreign policy should he become president; this, according to Brzezinski, would require a strong NSC. Impressed, Brzezinski told Al Hunt, a prominent Washington journalist, that Obama was his preferred candidate for president, leading to frequent communication between the former national security adviser and the aspiring politician.

Obama's own thinking on Iraq had evolved. Unlike Biden, he had little on-the-ground experience in the country: his only trip there, a January 2006 visit that occurred a month before the Samarra mosque bombing and a full year before the surge, had lasted only a day and a half and had taken him to the Green Zone, Camp Fallujah, and Kirkuk. In his best-selling book *The Audacity of Hope,* Obama had concluded that the United States should begin a phased withdrawal from Iraq but stressed that the pace of the withdrawal should be determined by the Iraqi government's ability to provide security, the degree to which the American presence motivated the insurgents, and the odds that a withdrawal would spark an all-out civil war.[10]

By January 2007, however, Obama had toughened his stance, adopting the withdrawal timeline suggested by the Iraq Study Group but dispensing with the flexibility the panel had embraced. Combat forces should leave at a rate of one to two brigades a month, and a fixed date should be set for removing all of them. Lee Hamilton, the Democrat who co-chaired the study group, was more in agreement with Obama's position in *The Audacity of Hope* than he was with the revision the senator planned to campaign on, and he advised Obama against insisting on a rigid schedule for leaving Iraq. "I've told him I do not support a deadline," Hamilton recalled. "I've made it very clear. We've had a difference at that point. I just don't think you can do it. If you set a deadline, then it drives policy. Everything then is pointed to getting out by blank date and it distorts the whole policy and it is very inflexible. You cannot react to events on the ground."[11]

But the withdrawal schedule had an obvious political advantage: it allowed Obama to outflank his main rival, Hillary Clinton, on the left. Obama had included the March 2008 deadline in the Iraq War De-escalation Act he had introduced in January and planned to stress it in a campaign speech in Iowa the next day.[12] Brzezinski would be there to introduce him.

As his turn approached to question Crocker and Petraeus, Obama was armed with a green folder, which contained a memo from Ben Rhodes, a young Hamilton protégé and one of the drafters of the Iraq Study Group report, and Denis McDonough, a trusted Obama aide with a master's degree in Latin American studies who had been working on the House Foreign Affairs Committee. Addressed to "Barack" from "Ben & Denis," the memo was titled "Iraq Speech-Differences." It was photographed by an enterprising *Washington Post* reporter who had strategically positioned himself in the balcony overlooking the lawmakers. It was not the differences with Crocker and Petraeus that Obama wanted to underscore but those with Hillary Clinton, who was to have her own opportunity to question the Baghdad team during the afternoon session of the Senate Armed Services Committee. "As you get ready for press around your speech on Iraq, we wanted to make sure you have on one piece of paper the principle [*sic*] differences between your speech on Iraq and the most comprehensive one on Iraq given by Senator Clinton," "Ben & Denis" wrote. Among the differences, they noted, "you can argue that by withdrawing 1–2 combat brigades a month you can get all those units out by the end of next year (2008)."

When it was his turn to speak, Obama reprised some of the themes of his upcoming speech. The senator started by criticizing the decision to hold the hearing on September 11, thereby reminding voters that, before the war, he had challenged the rationale for the invasion. Obama acknowledged that the surge had had some impact but insisted it was modest and unsustainable. With only seven minutes allotted to each member, Obama complained that his critique had left little time for questions.

"That's true, Senator," Biden said unsympathetically to Obama, who managed quickly to suggest a few. "At what point do we say, 'Enough?'" asked Obama. "Any set of benchmarks that have not been met?" Crocker, noting that he had already covered some of this ground before Obama arrived, quickly summarized his earlier points. Petraeus did not have a chance to respond at all.

With the presidential candidates focusing on scoring political points, it was a senator on the cusp of retirement from political life who stumped the general, at least temporarily. Was the United States safer because of its efforts in Iraq? asked John Warner, the Virginia Republican. The guidance Petraeus had internalized had been to stay away from the political debates over the War on Terror. He would be a military man carrying out his mission. "I have not sat down and sorted out in my own mind," he muttered. "What I have focused on and have been riveted on is how to accomplish the mission." Petraeus did not make many missteps, but this fumbling response was one.

Soon after the Foreign Relations Committee wound up, the Senate Armed Services Committee began its own hearing. John McCain used the hearing to broadcast his support for the surge, his past differences with Rumsfeld over troops, and his argument that it was vital to succeed in Iraq. The Arizona Republican had been criticized for a walk through a Baghdad marketplace during which he was so heavily protected by a security detail that it undermined his point that the situation was improving. McCain portrayed himself as being right from the start on the need for more troops but having a better plan than the administration's for coaxing the Iraqis to make headway politically. Crocker assured the senator that progress was still possible.

The political star that afternoon was the senator from New York, Clinton, who had secured a seat on the Armed Services Committee after entering the Senate to develop her national security credentials. Looking toward the general election, Clinton was engaging in an exercise in triangulation, intent on positioning herself between the liberal and conservative extremes. A visible opponent of the surge, Clinton had not set a firm date for withdrawing American troops; in fact, she even favored keeping a small but significant force in Iraq to train Iraqi forces, fight terrorists, and counterbalance Iran.[13]

Ignoring Petraeus's slides, Clinton stopped just short of calling the general and ambassador liars. Insisting that any fair reading of the surge was "on the downside," she lamented that Petraeus and Crocker had been pressed into service as spokesmen for a failed policy. "The reports that you provide to us really require the willing suspension of disbelief," said Clinton. The Bush administration, she added, had failed to mount a "robust" diplomatic effort to bring stability to Iraq, implying that she might be the person to do so.

The ostensible point of the hearings had been to properly assess the impact of the surge—a report card, as it were. But most members of Congress on either side of the aisle had already made up their minds and were mouthing prepared lines. Much of the time had been taken up by arguments, for and against the war, disguised as questions. Afterward, Petraeus told an associate that he was glad he had shown his slides; had he not presented his PowerPoint charts of attack and casualty data, few lawmakers might have asked about those issues.

The next day, staying true to the points emphasized in the memo from his advisers, Obama accentuated his differences with Clinton in his Iowa speech. The Bush administration's statistics on the declining violence in Iraq, the senator said, were "selective." Replacing the Maliki government with another, and presumably more inclusive, government, Obama added, would not solve the problem. The United States needed to immediately withdraw one or two combat brigades and remove all combat forces by the end of 2008. As for the tensions roiling Iraq, the deep-seated sectarian divisions should be addressed by a constitutional convention under the aegis of the United Nations. "The best way to protect our security and to pressure Iraq's leaders to resolve their civil war is to immediately begin to remove our combat troops," Obama said. "Not in six months or one year—now."[14]

On the 14th, before leaving Washington, Petraeus met with Casey. Petraeus raised the strain the war was putting on the Army, an issue on which the two disagreed. "I feel the strain should inform, not drive, our recommendations," the younger general's talking points from the meeting read. "That being said, I am keenly aware of and concerned about the strain." Focused on administrative matters, Casey was also mulling a change to the Army's dress uniform: whether to stick with the dark green "Class A" uniform that soldiers of the post-Vietnam generation had grown up with, or to switch to a new blue uniform that many soldiers complained smacked of the Air Force. "Army Class A Uniform—keep it!!" Petraeus told Casey. The advice was ignored.

Back in Baghdad, Petraeus and Crocker had a daunting mountain to climb. With their testimony, they had bought time for the surge to run until the summer of 2008. For all the rhetoric about pulling out American troops, the lawmakers in Washington were not pressing to cut off funding for the war. More than a few were planning to criticize Bush's war policy during the campaign, but they did not want Iraq to be a shared responsibility. Even the Iraqis acknowledged that there was a long way to go. Soon after getting back to Iraq, Petraeus met with Baha al-Araji, the Sadrist parliamentarian, who allowed that the testimony he and Crocker had delivered was "close to the truth."[15]

No sooner had the Americans returned than they stepped into a firestorm of their own making. On September 16, a contingent of Blackwater contractors in Mamba armored trucks opened fire on an approaching civilian vehicle in West Baghdad's Nisour Square, near the Green Zone. In about fifteen minutes of chaos that Iraqi witnesses said included aerial fire from Blackwater helicopters, some seventeen civilians were killed and another twenty wounded. Something like this was bound to happen. Since 2004, when armed contractors working for the CPA had helped defend against Mahdi Army attacks in Najaf and Kut, the military and the State Department had become deeply reliant on private gunmen from companies like Blackwater, DynCorp, EOD Technology, and ArmorGroup. The 180,000 or so private contractors in Iraq in late 2007 mostly performed a wide array of noncombat support functions, but there were an estimated 25,000 to 30,000 armed security contractors, about half of whom worked for the U.S. government.

What grated on the Iraqi government was the tendency of some of the contractors to shoot first and ask questions later. On Christmas Eve 2006, a drunk Blackwater man had fatally shot a member of Vice President Abd al-Mahdi's security detail in the Green Zone; the shooter was quickly spirited out of the country and never faced legal action. In May 2007 there had been a standoff between Blackwater and Iraqi security personnel that lasted until American troops defused it. In addition to actual killings, more or less every day Blackwater details crippled Iraqi cars that came too close to their convoys by firing bullets into their engine blocks. Though Crocker was known for reprimanding his own guards for using excessive force—and was unpopular among Blackwater personnel because of it—many other diplomats stood staunchly behind the company's gunmen no matter what they did, for the simple reason that since the beginning of the war, Blackwater had never allowed a State Department official to be killed on its watch. Adding insult to injury, a holdover decree from Paul Bremer's time in Iraq, CPA Order 17, granted foreign contractors the same immunity from Iraqi law enjoyed by American troops.

But the Nisour Square incident was the biggest contractor scandal so far. As Petraeus pointed out to Gates in a letter after the episode, personal security details from companies like Blackwater were chiefly concerned with delivering their "principals" in one piece, and so were more prone to employing excessive force. The incident also highlighted the changing face of the private security industry in Iraq, which had lowered its recruiting standards. Of the five Blackwater personnel who were eventually indicted for the Nisour Square shootings, none were special operations veterans.

While a series of Iraqi and American government probes into the shooting and the broader issues of the use and accountability of armed contractors began, there were more incidents that further angered the Iraqi government. In early October, for example, contractors from the Australian-run Unity Resources Group killed two women. "We cannot accomplish our mission in Iraq without Private Security Contractors, but we need to reduce the friction they sometimes cause before the Government of Iraq uses the sovereignty card to try to shut them down completely," Petraeus wrote to Gates after that shooting.[16] The role played by the armed contractors was underscored on October 3, when Shiite militants attacked the convoy of the Polish ambassador to Iraq in Baghdad; it was Blackwater personnel in their blue helicopters who responded and evacuated the wounded ambassador to the Green Zone.

With the contractor issue casting a pall over relations with Iraq, new issues emerged. The Iraqi prime minister had assured Bush that American forces would not have their hands tied, but as security began to improve Maliki became more difficult. Less than a week after the congressional hearings, Stan McChrystal's Task Force 17 captured Mahmud Farhadi, a Quds Force lieutenant colonel, in a raid on a hotel in Kurdistan. Although Task Force 17 had not detained a Quds Force officer since the capture of the Irbil Five nine months before, Crocker had "both privately and publicly" told Iranian ambassador Kazemi-Qomi that Quds Force members would be arrested if they were found in Iraq, Petraeus wrote to Gates. And Farhadi, one of the three regional Quds Force commanders for Iraq, was a major catch.[17]

A Kurd who had a long history of covert operations in northern Iraq against Saddam, Farhadi had close ties to Jalal Talabani, the Iraqi president. Those ties, plus Iran's threat to retaliate by closing Iran's border with Kurdistan, led Talabani, who enjoyed close relations with Tehran, to pressure Petraeus and Crocker to release Farhadi. To fend off the pressure, Major General Mike Barbero, Petraeus's operations officer, was sent to brief Talabani on the intelligence linking Farhadi to the Quds Force.

Maliki, who sought to maintain a balancing act between the United States and Iran, was not happy about the detention either. In a September 25 videoconference with Bush, Maliki complained about the raid. "If we catch them, we'll deal with them," Bush told him, referring to Quds Force officers. "This is in your interest."[18] When Maliki objected that it was the principle that mattered, since Farhadi had had a valid visa issued by the Iraqi government, Bush curtly ended the discussion. "Thank you for raising the issue," he said. (In his letter to Gates that week, Petraeus said that Maliki's raising of the issue to the presidential level was "not helpful.")[19] A month after his capture, though, Farhadi admitted his role.

A few weeks later, tensions with Maliki escalated further. Almost every night, Sadr City became a battlefield as four different forces—JSOC's Task Force 17, a covert CIA-run unit, Iraqi commandos with their American advisers, and a company of Strykers—launched politically sensitive raids into the heavily defended slum. Captain Steve Phillips, who commanded Stryker raids into Sadr City from March to July, remembered being copied on email traffic over whether specific raids would be approved or not that included Petraeus personally.

"Crossing Route Pluto was an anxious moment because the rooftop network of observers was in play and the lights would go off," Phillips remembered of the raids. "That was unnerving, to know that we have the upper hand under limited visibility conditions with thermals and night vision, but they were still willing to take that risk." Often the Strykers faced RPG fire from the first alley they passed inside the slum until they fought their way back out; when the soldiers could see families being ushered out of their houses by militiamen, they knew they were in for a fight. One night, a Stryker got a call from the next vehicle in the convoy reporting that it had a Mahdi Army fighter clambering up its ladderlike slat armor. Sergeant Greg Rayho poked his head out the Stryker's rear hatch and shot the fighter. The greatest threat was EFPs. When a new company replaced Phillips's, it welded makeshift mine plows to the front of their Strykers to push bombs out of the way.[20]

The Sadrists' anger over the raids boiled over on the night of October 20, when McChrystal's Task Force 17 drove into Sadr City looking for a ranking member of the militia led by the notorious Abu Dura. The strike force came under attack with small arms and RPGs, but the quarry was nowhere to be found. The strike force had to fight its way in and fight its way out. A Bradley vehicle was badly damaged, and the commandos had to call in help from Army attack helicopters. What was to have been a quick snatch-and-grab had turned into a melee. There would not be any mention of the violent episode in the American media, but the next day there was an uproar in the Iraqi parliament. Iraqi civilians had been killed, a Sadrist spokesman said. That day, Petraeus noted in a confidential note to Gates that the raid had caused a "significant political crisis." In particular, the general added, "Maliki was deeply affected by the very acrimonious debate that took place in the Council of Representatives today denouncing what he calls excessive Coalition Force collateral damage and lack of regard for Iraqi sovereignty."[21]

That night, Maliki convened a weekly meeting of the Ministerial Committee for National Security, a cabinet-level body, that Petraeus and Crocker also attended. Sitting at the head of the table, Maliki opened the session by decrying the Task Force 17 and Nisour Square episodes. The parliament, he said, had described the former operation as "barbarian." By Maliki's count, more than two dozen civilians had been killed. "I want a government investigation into the inhumane activities the MNF-I is conducting," Maliki said.

Crocker was diplomatic but unyielding. The ambassador sought to put the episode in context. "The Iraqis and coalition are engaged in Fardh al-Qanun to bring down the levels of violence, and we've had enormous success. We have both paid with our blood," Crocker said. "I urge the committee to consider the sacrifices that both our armies have made. We cannot blame each other. We cannot allow enemy actions through rhetoric or polemics to achieve what could not be achieved on the battlefield. We must not give back that ground."

Upset by Maliki's charge and his willingness to believe Sadrist accounts of the raid before hearing the American side of the story, Petraeus slapped the table. "We are targeting JAM Special Group criminals who kidnapped British citizens and were involved in death squad activities," Petraeus said, his voice rising. "We only used force after one of our Bradleys was disabled by RPGs. These were not innocent civilians; they were militia fighters. If there was innocent loss of life, we regret that and will pay reparations. But make no mistake: the militia extremists caused this, and you should not let opponents of the government use this to derail our success and progress. Recall what has been accomplished together. Yesterday, I was in the UAE, gaining support for this government, Mr. Prime Minister, your government." The general later told associates that he had feigned being emotional for effect, but the attendees of the meeting, including some of Petraeus's own staff, were convinced the outburst was genuine. The American side had never walked out of an MCNS meeting, and some Petraeus aides wondered if this might be a first.

Maliki backed off, but only a little. "I am very concerned, and we must find a solution. These civilian casualties decrease our chances for victory. We must decrease them. Why do coalition forces kill large numbers when we do operations with no shots fired?" he said. "Coalition forces are here by an agreement and a United Nations Security Council Resolution. The existing agreement said we would do operations with coalition support, but they do these operations with no consultations. I agree that my political opponents, other countries, and American leaders who don't want you here will use this against us. I want to calm the situation and calm the COR, and I will review the agreements with MNF-I."

Maliki's reference to "the agreements with MNF-I" raised the stakes considerably. The prime minister was hinting that the Task Force 17 episode might jeopardize his government's position on two ongoing diplomatic debates: the renewal of the U.N. Security Council resolution authorizing the American and British military presence in Iraq, and the Strategic Partnership Declaration being drafted between the United States and Iraq. "This situation is threatening the core of our political process," Maliki said.

Rubaie proposed a multipart plan to head off a confrontation. There should be a joint Iraqi and American investigation of the Sadr City episode; Petraeus should authorize the investigating group to interview the American officer who led the operation. Rubaie also insisted that the American military stay clear of Sadr City in the future. If there were any sensitive operations Petraeus's command wanted to carry out, the Iraqi government would need to approve them in advance. The Iraqis would consider renewal of the Security Council resolution. Lastly, the "victims" of the Sadr City raid should be compensated.

The Iraqis and Americans discussed who might participate in the joint investigation. The Iraqis suggested Rubaie, Interior Minister Bolani, Defense Minister Abd al-Qadir, and Shirwan al-Waeli. That Waeli might have influence over the investigation was too much for Petraeus. There was not going to be a joint investigation, and the inquiry the Americans planned would look at enemy actions as well. "We will do our own investigation," the general said. "I owe it to the commander to review this. I will examine and determine excessive use of force. But it must have been significant, to disable a Bradley. We should also discuss why the militias are able to operate openly in Sadr City. We should question this also. I take this very seriously and I ask that we not pre-judge."

A week after the meeting, Mike Barbero, the major general who served as Petraeus's chief operations officer, met with Rubaie at his Green Zone residence. The debate heated up again. The Americans had completed their investigation and concluded that most of the Iraqis who were killed were militia fighters. The Iraqis had interviewed residents in Sadr City, who they said had documented the wanton killings by the Americans. Barbero showed Rubaie the American photos and graphics of the episode and challenged the language in the Iraqi report: "This reads like it was written by JAM," Barbero said.

Eventually, they worked out an agreement. The Americans would restrict their operations in Sadr City, as the Iraqis had demanded. But a zone in which special operations could occur would be established for about a kilometer around the edge of Sadr City. That way, if Iranian-backed Special Groups leaders led raids against the Sunnis or the Americans and ducked back into their Sadr City sanctuary, McChrystal's task force could engage in hot pursuit—at least to a point. Petraeus was not unhappy about the compromise, which was implemented in January. He was not interested in risking another Mogadishu, a scenario in which American forces would be cut off within an enemy enclave and forced to fight for their lives.[22] But the understanding was a far cry from the freedom the White House had presumed the American military would have in Iraq as it carried out the surge.

Maliki's sensitivity to the Sadrists' objections was just one instance in which Shiite political movements were on his mind. Shiite Awakening groups, which at first had seemed a remote possibility, presented another problem for him. Shiite volunteers had come forward in Baghdad's West Rashid area, where the Mahdi Army had almost completely evicted Sunni residents and where Special Groups attacks continued despite the cease-fire, over the summer. Since then, the American battalion commander in the area, Lieutenant Colonel Pat Frank, a favorite of both Petraeus and Odierno, had shepherded the movement along with the help of the IFCNR, culminating in a reconciliation accord signed there in mid-October that was brokered in part by Bassima al-Jaidri and Safa al-Sheikh, IFCNR's leaders. The Shiite groups were always smaller in number than the Sunni ones and of a very different character, but the Mahdi Army cease-fire helped provide recruits and made the decision to join a volunteer group an easier one. By late October, Jeff Bannister, the brigade commander for Shiite-dominated southeastern Baghdad, had volunteer groups composed of 30 percent Sunnis and 70 percent Shiites. Other Shiite-majority groups donned the movement's ubiquitous American-supplied orange road vests in such areas of the southern belt as Mahmudiyah and Madain.

More Shiite volunteers were yielded by what the Americans referred to as the "Mid-Euphrates Awakening," a phenomenon in the fall of 2007 in which Shiite tribal leaders from southern Iraq reached out to the Sunni

Sahwa al-Iraq for help in the manner of the Anbar Awakening. Ahmed Sattar al-Rishawi, like his brother Abd al-Sattar, was interested in exporting what had worked for Anbar to other provinces, whether Sunni or Shiite. In October, a conference of seventy tribal leaders met at the Rishawi family compound in Ramadi. The gathering included sheikhs from an array of Shiite provinces: Najaf, Karbala, Babil, Qadisiya, and Muthana.

In Diwaniyah, the capital of Qadisiya, the sheikhs found an ally in Team Phoenix, an unorthodox troubleshooting team of Marines that Petraeus had first worked with in 2004 and then resurrected in 2007. The team's three members—Captains Ann Gildroy and Seth Moulton and a sniper-trained NCO, Alex Lemons, all veterans of the 2004 battle of Najaf—had come back to Iraq from civilian life at Petraeus's request. After visiting Anbar to study the lessons of the Awakening over the summer, they flew to Diwaniyah in August, shortly after the assassination of the governor there by Shiite militants.

In Diwaniyah, the team linked up with a Special Forces team and Polish troops, and also with the commander of the Iraqi Army's 8th Division, General Othman Ali Farhud, who three years earlier had written Gildroy's recommendation to Harvard Business School. A rural Qadisiya sheikh himself, Othman believed that an Awakening group could provide Diwaniyah not only with security and jobs, but also with a more secular and representative alternative to the ISCI-dominated provincial government. Gildroy agreed. "The fact that every other man will shake my hand except for the power brokers says that we are backing a very extremist regime," Gildroy said of Qadisiya's government.[23] It seemed counterintuitive to the Americans that southern Iraq's rural tribes were typically more secular than the urban populations where the Sadrist movement and religious parties like ISCI had their power base.

With Othman's help, Team Phoenix brokered an agreement with a local chief of the Jabouri tribe, which had both Sunni and Shiite branches in various parts of Iraq. At a price of $1,167 per kilometer per month, the sheikh, Taklef al-Jabouri, would provide watchmen to keep a stretch of road outside Diwaniyah clear of IEDs. Gildroy and Moulton also told Taklef they would give him information about the record of bomb explosions on the road to help his men with their new job. "Oh, I know the IED history," he said with a wink.[24] After word of the program spread, dozens of sheikhs began to approach Othman, and in mid-November the Marine team hired 268 unarmed volunteers inside Diwaniyah as well, which might just have been the beginning. From seemingly nowhere, the Shiite Awakening movement was beginning to spread.

The Mid-Euphrates Awakening did not sit well with the Maliki government. Political support for Maliki's Dawa Party was heavily contested in southern Iraq already by ISCI, the Sadrists, and smaller Shiite parties like Fadhila, and the last thing Maliki needed in the south's populous cities was even more competition. The involvement of Ahmed al-Rishawi in helping southern sheikhs was not promising: what if they sought to mount the same sort of political challenge that the upstart Sahwa al-Iraq posed to the established Iraqi Islamic Party in Anbar? Some of Maliki's rivals were concerned as well. Hamid Musa al-Khudari, the ISCI governor in Qadisiya and a strict Islamist who had spent two decades in exile in Iran, saw the movement as a challenge to his authority.

While the nascent Shiite Awakening weighed heavily on Maliki, the prime minister and his inner circle remained more wary of the much larger Sunni movement. Despite Bassima's reassurances to Emma Sky that she had submitted the 1,738 names of Abu Ghraib recruits for processing, there were still many impediments to accepting Sunni Awakening members, particularly into the police. The Maliki government had initially refused to hire any of the Abu Ghraib volunteers for police work; later, however, it offered three-month contracts to some. When Ken Adgie's 1-30 Infantry held a pair of recruiting drives in Arab Jabour in November and tried to get some recruits hired as police, the Interior Ministry foiled the plan.

During the November 11 meeting of the MCNS the Iraqis had raised the issue of insurgent infiltration of the groups and Maliki put a freeze on hiring volunteers into the security forces. "PM Maliki continues to express concern over the growth of the Concerned Local Citizen effort," Petraeus wrote to Gates. "As you would imagine, this has been a frustration for us, as we try to take advantage of what likely is a narrowing window of opportunity to reconcile with Sunni former resistance elements that now oppose AQI. The PM is, of course, naturally suspicious and inclined to believe rumors that he hears from his Shi'a advisors."[25] On November 26, Maliki raised his suspicion of terrorist infiltration of the "armed groups" with Bush personally in their videoconference.

Maliki's concern was not entirely unfounded. A squadron from the 101st Airborne that had inherited some of Mike Kershaw's thousands of volunteers detained a group of Sunni men that month who admitted to taking pay from both the American military and the insurgency—$300 per month from the Americans for deterring and uncovering insurgent activity, and $500 from the insurgents for planting the IEDs they were supposed to be stopping.[26] "Some insurgent groups could be using [the volunteer movement] as a cover to regroup, rid their areas of Al-Qaeda, and retain combat power for the future," Petraeus said of another incident in which JSOC commandos found an Awakening group with antiaircraft guns to Gates.[27]

By and large, however, the conversion the Sunni members had undergone from insurgents to the CLC movement was genuine. With the help of the Americans, the Sunnis were looking to take charge of their home turf. Switching back to the insurgency was more complicated than it seemed. The price of admission included having fingerprints and retina scans entered into an intelligence database—which meant the Americans could track down any Awakening members who fell off the wagon.

To get Maliki on board, Petraeus and Odierno took Iraqi officials with them to visit volunteer groups in the field, hoping that hearing about the effectiveness of the groups from Iraqi military and police commanders, especially Shiite ones, would sway them. In late November Odierno took Rubaie with him to Mahmudiyah, where Shiite commanders from the 5th Brigade of the 6th Division of the Iraqi Army were holding a conference that brought together Sunni and Shiite volunteers from the southern belt. The next day, Odierno brought Rubaie to Ameriya, the place where Abu Abed's Sunni insurgents had helped American troops clean Al-Qaeda out and which had marked the first appearance of security volunteers in Baghdad proper. An aide to Odierno later recalled that Rubaie seemed impressed.[28]

The suspicions, however, remained. "PM Maliki and his advisors have been very difficult partners in recent weeks, as I'm sure you sense," Petraeus wrote to Gates in late November after "a fairly tumultuous MCNS meeting during which I had to push back vigorously to PM allegations about the CLC program—spurred, we believe, by very unhelpful and often unfounded reports passed on to the PM by Mowaffak, who has very much played both sides of the issues of late (as confirmed by intel)."[29] During the November 25 MCNS meeting Rubaie suggested that Awakening groups should be banned south of Baghdad except in the area north of Hilla, a reaction to what Team Phoenix was doing around Diwaniyah; Barham Salih replied that this was a rigid and premature proscription.

The showdown over the Awakening movement was set for December 2, when the MCNS would convene again.

Petraeus, Odierno, Sky, and a variety of other officers and civilian officials would be there representing the coalition. The Iraqis included Maliki, Barham Salih, the IFCNR's Safa and Bassima, intelligence chief Shawani, Defense and Interior Ministers Abd al-Qadir and Bolani, and an array of military commanders, most opposed to the Awakening groups, including

Nasr al-Hiti, the commander of the Muthana Brigade in Abu Ghraib. The presence of Nasr was not a promising sign, but the absence of Hashimi, whose views would likely have inflamed Maliki automatically, was.

The American briefing had undergone heavy editing by Petraeus and Colonels Bill Rapp and Marty Stanton. It was a series of good-news stories that highlighted the gains the Awakening groups had made but that also acknowledged the Maliki government's apprehensions. Sky showed the briefing to Bassima, who agreed with her that a dose of what the military would likely see as negativity was needed, because, Bassima believed, the Iraqis would see it as realism. Adding negative bullets to the presentation, Bassima and Sky thought, would increase the briefing's credibility and help sell the program to the prime minister and his advisers. Violence was down, and the Americans had the Awakening members' biometric details, but some of the Awakening recruits were involved in crime and had reverted back to insurgent activity.

Odierno began the meeting with a briefing about the security situation. Maliki then turned the floor over to Abud Qanbar, in charge of the Baghdad Operations Command. Abud partly credited the Awakening groups for the drop in violence since the summer, but said that they worked better in the belts than they did in urban Baghdad. He also complained that the IFCNR was too slow in vetting the groups and recommended that the whole program be frozen at its current size until the Iraqi government, not the American military, was in control of it. Then came Ali Ghaidan Majid, who took a moderate stance. Maliki chimed in that in the future, the groups should be barred from having "political or military names"— like the Ameriya Knights or the Ghazaliya Guardians, which suggested that they had a standing independent of the Iraqi government's control.

Next Odierno presented a briefing on the Awakening movement itself. To the relief of the Americans present, Maliki seemed impressed. "We agree with General Odierno," he said. Abd al-Qadir added that he had been impressed by what he saw in Ameriya, and Bolani said that if the Iraqi government really was going to take charge of the program in the year ahead, his Interior Ministry would need the authority and money to do so.

The meeting appeared to make a breakthrough. Maliki accepted that the Awakening members could number as many as 103,000, vital for the Americans' efforts to cement the turnaround in Abu Ghraib, Yusifiyah, Diyala, and even Baghdad. The hope was that the Iraqi government would integrate at least twenty thousand—ideally thirty thousand—into the police and find ways to employ the rest. The large-scale reconciliation agenda was moving slowly in the parliament, but the Americans hoped they could achieve a more modest kind—one between grassroots Sunni movements and the Shiite-dominated central government.

But Maliki exacted a price: there would be no tribal Awakening in the Shiite south, the prime minister's power base. American officials accepted this, hoping that Iraq's security forces would be able to establish control in the south and that the Shiite tribes would find a way to pursue their political ambitions when provincial elections were held.[30]

The high-level Baghdad deliberations stayed under wraps. But in late December, Ann Gildroy received a call from Polish Major General Tadeusz Buk. Othman had called to say that Governor Khudari had ordered the Diwaniyah Awakening program shut down. "We are fighting this?" Buk asked. Gildroy said that she and Lemons would meet the next day in Othman's office to clear up the misunderstanding. After all, Khudari had earlier accepted the program. There had been many bumps in the road in Iraq, and this looked like just one more. But at the meeting it quickly became clear this was no mere bump.

As the meeting got under way, Khudari began to rail against the neighborhood-watch program, claiming it might be influenced by militias. Gildroy responded that rampant unemployment was more likely to breed mischief. To the Marines' surprise, Othman did not come to the project's defense. He had been involved in the negotiations with the sheikhs, but he appeared to have new orders from Baghdad, which he would not confide. Gildroy later talked to an American officer in Baghdad and was told that the decision had been made at senior levels of the Iraqi and American governments.

As the saga unfolded, a compromise of sorts was reached. The tribal guardians would continue to protect the roads, but the neighborhood watch would be disbanded in Diwaniyah itself. When Khudari asked for the records of the recruits in the city, Gildroy built a small fire at Camp Echo and burned them. She thought it might otherwise be used as an enemies list.[31] The Marines went from checkpoint to checkpoint, informing puzzled Iraqis that they were out of business.

CHAPTER 24

No Plan B

Even as the Americans worked to win Prime Minister Maliki's acceptance of the Awakening movement, Mike Barbero was trying hard to head off another war. A two-star Army general, Barbero had been a closet supporter of the surge during the Bush administration's deliberations and had gone on to serve as Petraeus's operations officer. He had negotiated with Mowaffak al-Rubaie over access to Sadr City and had overseen Silver Saber, the operation to reclaim Baghdad's airport.

By October he had yet another worry: Abd al-Qadir al-Obeidi, Maliki's minister of defense, wanted him to join him on a mission to Ankara to prevent Turkey's invasion of northern Iraq. "You control the air, you control the forces, you are going with me," Abd al-Qadir said. Barbero explained that before he could fly off to negotiate with a foreign government, Petraeus and Maliki would need to approve.[1] Within days, Maliki called a meeting to take up the matter.

Intrusions across Iraq's borders by its neighbors were not new. Syria had been facilitating, or at least tolerating, the flow of foreign fighters into Iraq's mayhem. Iran was providing weapons to Shiite militants and mounting artillery attacks against the Party of Free Life of Kurdistan, or PJAK, a separatist group that was struggling to mobilize the Kurds in Iran. Kurdish officials complained to the Americans about the barrages, but with the vast majority of American forces dedicated to the surge, Petraeus's command had no intention of inserting itself in that quarrel: whenever the Kurds raised the matter, Barbero reminded them that they had more leverage with their friends to the east than the Americans did. The Americans provided reports to Rubaie about the artillery attacks, but treated the matter as an Iraq-Iran issue.

But Turkey was different. The Turkish government had mounted major incursions in the late 1990s to take on the Kurdistan Workers' Party, or PKK, a separatist Kurdish group that was mounting cross-border attacks into Turkey from Iraq, and the Turkish military had never quite withdrawn from a handful of spots in Iraqi Kurdistan. Three battalions of Turkish special operations forces were based at a series of mountain outposts. Every year since 2003, the Turks had sent reinforcements during the spring thaw to the outposts. But they had refrained from carrying out a major conventional attack. Kurdish sentiment against the presence of Turkish forces was clear: when Turkey offered to send peacekeeping forces to Iraq after Saddam was overthrown, the Kurds vowed to fight them if they ventured into Iraqi territory, and Ankara's offer was withdrawn.

But a string of PKK attacks on Turkish troops in October had ratcheted tensions up to the highest level since the beginning of the American occupation of Iraq. By mid-October, Petraeus was ringing alarm bells, writing to Gates that Turkey was threatening "every kind of measure" against the PKK and that the U.S. Congress was not helping American-Turkish relations. "Additional fuel has been thrown on the fire by the Armenian genocide bill in Congress, which obviously would be exceedingly unhelpful were it to lead to the withdrawal of Turkish support and transit rights," he wrote. Massoud Barzani's Kurdish government was not in a good mood either: "I just received a letter from KRG President Barzani warning that the Kurds will fight any Turkish incursion, pulling 'their forces' from wherever they are in Iraq to do so."[2]

There was not much the United States could do to avert more fighting. The PKK was listed as a terrorist group by the State Department, and the military tended to agree with that assessment, but the surge was concentrated on securing Baghdad and the belts. There were no American troops available to chase bands of Kurdish rebels through the rugged mountains of northern Iraq. The PKK attacks were an emotional issue in Turkey, and Prime Minister Recep Tayyip Erdogan was coming under enormous pressure to do something that at least looked decisive. The prospect of the Kurds withdrawing their troops from the Iraqi Army—soldiers who were among the best trained and least sectarian in the Iraqi forces—to take on Turkey was a nightmare. The United States would be caught between a NATO ally and the nascent democracy in Iraq.

During the week that followed, Maliki convened a "crisis action team" to try to defuse the situation. For the Iraqi prime minister, the dispute was an opportunity to reinforce his primacy by consolidating control over foreign policy as well. Instead of letting Barzani discuss the matter with the Turks, Maliki would take charge. Maliki dispatched Tariq al-Hashimi, a Sunni politician who enjoyed close relations with the Turks, to Ankara to meet with Turkey's prime minister and president.

But on October 21, the PKK attacked inside Turkey again, killing twelve Turkish commandos and capturing eight, thereby further escalating the crisis. "It is appearing that the PKK is deliberately provoking the Turks to attack them," Petraeus wrote of the incident to Gates.[3] It was a ploy that had every chance of working. Four days later, Maliki decided to send another delegation, one that would include Abd al-Qadir and Barbero, to try to persuade the Turks to hold off. "We must rebuild our border security," Maliki declared. "It will be the Iraqi government, not the Kurds, that makes commitments to Turkey. Tell Turkey to give us proposals and we will work on it."[4] The Ankara meetings, however, did not go well. The Turks complained that the Kurds were doing nothing to rein in the PKK, got up, and walked out. Barbero concluded that the Turkish government and its generals never wanted a political deal. They appeared to be clearing the decks for military action.[5]

With Turkey and the Kurds nearing a precipice, Petraeus called Barzani and told him that he was coming to Irbil. The release of the eight Turkish soldiers who had been captured by the PKK, Petraeus hoped, might take the edge off the crisis, and to make sure it got done the general would deliver them himself. Petraeus and Abd al-Qadir sat at the VIP terminal in Irbil for several hours until Barzani took possession of the Turkish prisoners from the PKK and had them brought to Petraeus. The general then flew with the Turkish soldiers to the American base in Mosul, switched into helicopters, and then flew north to a Turkish military camp in the mountains of northern Iraq, where he handed over the prisoners to the lieutenant general in charge of Turkish special operations forces. The newly freed soldiers were not given the warmest of welcomes. The Turkish military, Petraeus wrote Gates, "[will] likely see the soldiers as having dishonored the Turkish Army by not fighting to the death; they were not hugged or even greeted by the Turkish 3-star on our arrival."[6]

On the same trip north, Petraeus also conducted a two-hour meeting with Barzani and his nephew, KRG Prime Minister Nechirvan Barzani, in which they promised that Kurdish security forces would take a number of new measures against the PKK, including putting up checkpoints to interdict supplies, ordering KRG hospitals to refuse to treat PKK wounded, and permitting the installation of a CIA-funded biometric security database called Pisces, which would help the Kurds identify and track down the rebel fighters. That was good as far as it went, but it seemed to be too little to head off a war. By now, Washington was heavily involved. Secretary of State Rice headed to Ankara to urge the Turks to be cautious, and soon afterward Erdogan headed to Washington for a meeting with Bush. Something more would need to be done.

The solution entailed a role reversal for Petraeus: the Americans would go from trying to ward off a Turkish attack to abetting it. The idea was to forestall a full-scale Turkish ground offensive by persuading the Turkish military that they could handle the PKK with artillery barrages and air strikes across the border with the benefit of intelligence supplied by the Americans. That put Petraeus in the awkward position of coordinating bombing attacks by a foreign power on the very country he was supposed to be securing—all for the sake of preventing a wider war, though the Kurds might not have seen it that way. In a confidential note to Gates, Petraeus wrote that it would be best if any Turkish attack did "not have MNF-I fingerprints on it as we have enough enemies on our plate right now."[7] If the United States provided the Turks with intelligence for strikes, including information gathered by Petraeus's own command, it would be best if it were conveyed by European Command, or EUCOM, and be done quietly.

The Pentagon worked out the arrangements. A command center was established in Ankara, and, just as Petraeus suggested, a military officer from EUCOM met with the Turkish General Staff to discuss sharing of ISR—intelligence, surveillance, and reconnaissance—information. The American military's rules of engagement were modified: the Kongra-Gel, the Kurdish separatists in Turkey and northern Iraq, of whom the PKK and PJAK were seen as subsets, were declared a "hostile force," meaning that the American military could play a role in providing the intelligence to help find and kill them. The intelligence itself would be gathered by Predator drones and Rivet Joint electronic surveillance aircraft, which could intercept and pinpoint the source of communications and would be based in Turkey with Kurdish-speaking linguists furnished by the Turkish government. U-2 aircraft under the authority of the EUCOM would also help pinpoint the new enemy.

An array of sensitive issues were discussed in a November 9 phone conversation following a call from Admiral Edmund Giambastiani, the vice chairman of the Joint Chiefs, to General Ergin Saygun, the Turkish deputy chief of staff. According to classified talking points for the conversation, the "ISR surge" would not be open-ended and the data would be funneled through the new command center the Americans had established, not provided directly to Turkish command centers. The Turkish attacks needed to be limited in scope and duration and should "avoid collateral damage to non-PKK targets." The Americans would not join the Turkish Air Force in carrying out the bombing raids or use JSOC in any role. In return, the Turks needed to reassure the United States that they would not initiate ground action "without prior consultation" with the Americans. The United States believed that the PKK would try to retaliate and fervently hoped that whatever force the Turks used would be proportionate.[8]

Petraeus was not pleased with the decrease in Predator support; the military had spent the year increasing its drone orbits over Iraq with Gates's help. The removal of one orbit to support the Turks coincided with JSOC's decision to shift some of its Predators to Afghanistan at the end of the year and also with the grounding of the military's fleet of P-3Cs, manned planes that provided intelligence support in Iraq but had run into technical problems. Using a valuable Predator orbit against the PKK did not seem like a good use of scarce resources; in addition, winter weather in the mountains made the drones less useful there than they could have been farther south supporting American troops.

Petraeus visited Ankara on November 20 to meet directly with General Saygun, who he told Gates was "constructive and influential," but he left unclear about the Turkish strategy. In their meetings, Petraeus wrote, the Turks did not provide a list of their targets and objectives "other than in the form of a map with expansive air clearance areas on it."[9] During the early phase of the secret collaboration, the Americans discovered that the Turkish artillery strikes often missed their targets, even with the benefit of American intelligence. "Turkey has conducted several artillery and rocket attacks on PKK groups identified by Predator, but none have been accurate enough to cause damage," Petraeus told the NSC in early December.[10]

In the middle of December, Turkish ground troops began to move to their winter quarters ahead of worsening weather, but Petraeus warned Gates that the move might be a ruse meant to lull the PKK into a state of complacency before mounting air strikes. He was right. On December 16, with only half an hour's notice given to the American command in Baghdad—significantly less than agreed upon—a dozen Turkish F-16s hit targets in the Qandil Mountains near Sulaymaniyah, and Turkish special operations troops launched targeted raids as well. In addition to the abbreviated pre-strike notice, Petraeus noted to Gates that some of the Turkish jets "flew well south of the agreed-upon box we had cleared." He added his doubts as to whether the strikes were effective: "given first-generation precision munitions, we are not sure how much damage they did to the PKK."[11]

The Turks' decision to operate beyond the parameters of their agreement with the Americans resounded at the highest levels of the White House. "They abrogated our agreement," Bush noted to the NSC the next day.[12] Adding insult to injury, there was nothing quiet about the way Turkish officials were talking about the operation. Instead of doing it discreetly, as the Americans had hoped, they were trying to maximize the political advantage by advertising how tough the Turkish military was being with the PKK.

Soon a bad situation became worse. The next day, Turkish ground troops crossed the border into Iraq pursuing a group of PKK fighters. It was the very scenario the Americans had hoped to avert: a Turkish ground offensive that the Kurds had promised to resist. That night Fuad Hussein, Barzani's chief of staff, called Barbero. If the Turkish commandos lodged in outposts in northern Iraq came off their compounds to augment the Turkish conventional forces, there would be trouble. The Peshmerga would fight them, and the much-feared Turkish-Kurdish war might be on.

Barbero rushed to contain the situation. First, he called the EUCOM officer in Ankara and told him to insist that the Turks keep their special operations forces in northern Iraq in their camps. Then he contacted Barzani, showed him a map of how shallow the Turkish conventional operation was, and urged him to not to unleash the Peshmerga. It was a night of high drama and considerable paradox: in order to head off a further escalation of hostilities, the U.S. military was providing intelligence to both sides. The Turks later complained bitterly to Petraeus that Barbero had given away their plan to the Kurds, but Barbero told him that he had had no real choice. If he had not shown the map detailing the Turkish incursion to the Kurds, the United States might have faced a major skirmish in Iraq that would have overshadowed the surge. "Roger," Petraeus said to Barbero afterward. "Don't worry about it." The Turkish conventional forces withdrew about a week later.[13]

In late December, Petraeus told Gates that he believed the Turkish military was planning another round of Qandil air strikes for the end of the month, a prospect he did not relish. The supposedly short-duration Turkish offensive was beginning to drag on. The Kurds already had a long and lengthening list of grievances with Maliki. They were unhappy over the delays in approving the oil law and in settling the boundaries of territories claimed by Arabs and Kurds, including the status of Kirkuk. More to the point, the senior Kurdish leaders, particularly Barzani, were complaining that Maliki was arrogating decisions to himself without taking other factions, especially the Kurds, into account. Instead of insulating Iraqi politics from the fight between Turkey and the Kurdish separatists, Maliki's actions only complicated the situation. The prime minister's insistence that he, not the Kurdish leadership, be the main interlocutor with the Turks had led only to a one-sided Turkish offensive.

"We do not need another Kurdish crisis to derail the politics," Petraeus wrote, referring to the possibility of Kurdish parliamentarians pulling out of the Council of Representatives in protest. "It would be most helpful if the Turks would employ some 'constructive ambiguity' and at the least remain quiet about any strikes they conduct," he continued, adding that seemed unlikely, as political concerns led Turkish officials to "shine the spotlight on their own actions, which is manifestly unhelpful to us in Iraq." As expected, the Turks did launch further strikes at the end of December. Fearful of the growing tensions between the Kurds and Maliki, Petraeus described the strikes as "generally ineffective" and said that if they continued, "we will soon be approaching the point where we will raise serious reservations about continuing to support [Turkey's] operations, given the high political cost inside Iraq."[14]

While the Americans were trying to reassure the Kurds, they received some clear signs that the political situation inside Iraq was reaching the breaking point. Barbero had gone to Irbil to meet with Barzani about Iranian influence and to encourage the Kurds to use their contacts in Tehran to tell the Quds Force to stop interfering. After a long lunch, Barzani had a message of his own. The Kurdish leadership, he said, was frustrated with Maliki and his history of broken promises—so frustrated that they were ready to withdraw from the government and try to force a parliamentary vote of no confidence against him. All they needed was the Americans' blessing and they would make their move.

During a mid-December dinner, Barzani and Barham Salih presented Petraeus with a long array of grievances about the insular Maliki inner circle. The same week Abd al-Aziz al-Hakim and Adil Abd al-Mahdi of ISCI met with Petraeus and took a similar tone. H.R. McMaster and even Jack Keane received similar hints from the Abd al-Mahdi camp. The makings of an anti-Maliki bloc were apparent. The Kurds and ISCI intended to engineer a vote of no confidence with the support of Sunnis like Hashimi and whatever other Shiites wanted to get on board. Then they could vote for Abd al-Mahdi, a longtime favorite of some White House aides like Meghan O'Sullivan. American backing, tacit or overt, would be important. The surge was at its height, and so was U.S. influence. The American military had yanked Iraq back from the brink of civil war and was committed, at least nominally, to helping Iraq's ministries become more effective and efficient. Maliki saw plots everywhere, but toward the end of 2007 he faced a real one, albeit one that sought to bring about change constitutionally and not through a coup.

For the Americans, it was a moment of truth. Maliki had been brought to the prime minister's post with the United States' quiet backing, and the process of forming his government had taken five months. Unseating him now would risk a power vacuum during the height of the surge until a successor was seated. But it might pave the way for political progress in Iraq and more consensus building. The JSAT had sought to make a change here and a switch there. This would be more radical. Change would be made at the very top, and everything else would follow from there. There were clear risks and potential gains.

On December 10, Gates reported to the NSC that in a recent meeting Talabani had described Iraq's political situation with Maliki in charge as "intolerable" and suggested that the United States take part in his removal. "What's the process?" Bush asked the NSC. "If not Maliki, who?"[15] As early as August Bush had asked the same question, and it would become a common refrain on the American side. Gates responded that it would be a mistake for the United States to get involved. The Pentagon chief and former CIA director seemed to have little confidence in the administration's ability to shape politics in Iraq. Dick Cheney disagreed, saying that the notion of unseating Maliki "merits our consideration." The vice president, and especially his aide John Hannah, had supported the earlier effort to build ties with ISCI and believed that Abd al-Mahdi, the English-speaking former vice president and former finance minister, might be more effective than Maliki.[16]

The call was the president's to make. The surge was gaining traction militarily, and Bush did not want to upset the apple cart. Beyond that, he saw his role as giving Maliki the confidence to make the tough decisions. He could only do that by letting him know that he had his back. It was decided that when Rice visited Baghdad the following week she would at once ask Talabani who he saw as the alternative to Maliki and make clear to him that the United States did not favor the notion of a successor.

The U.S. was not neutral or hanging back. The Bush administration would stick with Maliki.

In Baghdad on December 18, Rice had a busy day of meetings to tamp down the crisis. A number of high-level officials came together for a meeting with the secretary of state, including Barzani, who rarely traveled to Baghdad. Talabani told Rice that Maliki was the problem; Rice disagreed, urging him to make do with the current government. "No one supports the prime minister but the U.S.," Abd al-Mahdi added. Talabani quipped that Iran supported him too. In a one-on-one with Rice afterward, Talabani softened his position, saying that he could support Maliki but the prime minister had to change his ways—by, for instance, implementing the agreement he had made on August 26 to share top-level decision making with the Presidency Council of Talabani, Abd al-Mahdi, and Hashimi in the so-called "three-plus-one group" or "gang of four." Years later, Barzani portrayed the episode as one of the United States' biggest decisions of the war. "At the end of 2007 when a number of political leaders in Iraq wanted to replace Maliki, Secretary Rice flew from Washington to Baghdad," he recalled. "She said, 'We have no Plan B. Maliki is the prime minister and we want him to continue, and we do not want to create chaos and problems in Baghdad.'"[17]

In a meeting later in the day with Maliki, Rice reassured the prime minister that rumors that the United States was supporting his removal were not true, but added that "the government is failing, and you are failing." She said that the Presidency Council could support him, but only if he implemented the August 26 three-plus-one agreement and curbed OCINC, among other things. "Everyone is against me," Maliki told Rice, but joked, "At least I don't have to deal with Pelosi." Seemingly chastened and fearful, according to Rice's report on the meeting to the NSC the next day, the prime minister agreed to share power among the "gang of four."

In addition to Rice's mission, Bush demonstrated his support for Maliki in other ways as well. By late December, the 2008 National Defense Authorization Act, which laid out the American military's budget for the coming year, had passed both houses of Congress and been submitted for Bush's signature. Before the president signed the bill, Crocker alerted the NSC to a potential problem in it: buried within the law's more than six hundred pages was a provision designed to enable American victims of terrorist attacks to sue state sponsors of terrorism. Though the provision had been inserted with an eye toward attacks in the 1980s sponsored by Iran and Libya, Crocker noted that it "could open Iraq to claims"—Iraq had billions of dollars in assets in the United States, and American victims of terror groups linked to Saddam Hussein or Saddam's regime might conceivably sue the current Iraqi government for compensation for the crimes of the old regime.

This prospect troubled Maliki, who raised it two days after he saw Rice. In a state of agitation, he asked Bush whether Iraq should be pulling its financial assets out of the United States and urged the president to use the "line-item veto" to rid the bill of this provision. Though the American president did not actually have a line-item veto at his disposal, Bush told the prime minister, "[You] won't lose your money, we will develop a plan." A week later he promised Maliki he would veto the entire bill, and then did so. This drastic step reflected the strength of Bush's commitment to Iraq, even if it meant political costs at home. It was only the eighth bill Bush had vetoed, and congressional leaders complained that it would hold up the entire Defense Department budget, including a pay raise for American troops. Bush's gambit worked, and the president was later able to tell Maliki that Congress had amended the bill so that he, Bush, could waive the offending provision with regard to Iraq.[18]

Maliki was not out of the woods yet, though. "The unknown factor remains the behind-the-scenes scheming to replace PM Maliki, which continued in earnest over the past week," Petraeus wrote to Gates shortly before Christmas.[19] A week later, in his last letter of the year to Gates, the general added, "At this point, we don't have any additional evidence that planning for a putsch has progressed."[20] Further solidifying Maliki's position was the verdict of the Iranians. Abd al-Mahdi had taken a trip to Tehran and, according to American intelligence, received the same red light from Supreme Leader Khamenei that he had from Rice: the Iranians, too, were not in favor of "Plan B."

Still, Petraeus judged Maliki's future to be uncertain at best. With the stress of managing his job and fending off rivals, Maliki had experienced some fainting episodes. On December 27, hours after a videoconference with Bush, which focused on the defense spending bill, Maliki collapsed. A team of American doctors rushed from the combat hospital in the Green Zone to check him out, and thought he might have a heart ailment. Ali Khedery, who was working as an aide to Crocker, rang up Cheney's cardiologist, who recommended that Maliki go to George Washington University Hospital, where Cheney himself had been treated.

Maliki hated to fly and wanted to go no farther than London. To get him there, a flight on an American C-17 cargo plane was arranged, with a complete U.S. medical team on board. Within forty-eight hours, Maliki was at the Wellington Hospital for tests. In a note to Gates, Petraeus speculated that the medical problem "could give him a graceful way to bow out and obviate this plotting altogether." The prime minister could look after his health, and the Iraqis could find a more suitable leader. It could be a delicate end to a tricky situation.[21]

As soon as the plane landed in Britain, Maliki's key aides disappeared to visit their families and friends, leaving Maliki with his son Ahmed and the Americans who had come with him as he entered the hospital. Adil Mohsin, the Health Ministry inspector general whom the Americans had wanted to arrest a few months earlier for a wide variety of abuses, was on the trip as well, but spent much of his time in Britain doing what he did best—arranging questionable contracts for medical supplies.

Maliki overcame his health concern and regained his confidence. After a stent was inserted into an artery, he prepared to fly back to Baghdad the first week of January 2008. The prime minister and his team would have no more of the noisy and uncomfortable American C-17; they would fly back on an Iraqi plane. One of the anomalies of post-Saddam Iraq was that the prime minister's plane was an Airbus A300 provided as a gift by a private Iranian carrier. The aircraft bore the Iraqi flag but was operated by an Iranian flight crew, who spoke Persian and English, but not Arabic, and was outfitted with Mahan Air pillows and blankets. The prime minister used it as he wished—on a flight to London for an investment conference, the passengers watched a film adaption of *Mr. Bean,* the slapstick British comedy show—but there were definite drawbacks when it came to international travel. For three hours, Maliki and his top aides sat in the VIP terminal at Heathrow while the Iranians rushed to arrange the flight clearances. But for Maliki, it was still the better of his options: flying on the aircraft affirmed, or at least appeared to affirm, the Iraqi sovereignty that he cherished.

Less than two weeks after Petraeus's suggestion that Maliki might step down to avert being unseated, on January 10, he and Crocker dined with a prime minister the general viewed as "chastened" by his close call, and predicted that in the future he might be more cooperative as a result. "There is a chance that Maliki's newfound approach will translate into action and not dissipate as quickly as the rare snow that fell on Baghdad Friday morning," he wrote to Gates.[22]

Petraeus's assessment proved correct. The Council of Representatives had been stalled for months on several pieces of legislation that the Americans tracked as benchmarks, including the long-awaited de-Baathification reform legislation known as the "accountability and justice law," whose difficult passage Rubaie, a doctor by training, had compared in November to "a birth with forceps."[23] Part of the problem had been Maliki's own maneuverings with regard to the law, which Crocker described in an earlier cable as "manipulative, dishonest, and obstructing." But the post-potential-putsch Maliki was more cooperative, apparently mindful of advice that Bush had given him by videoconference on January 8: he needed to pass major laws in order to quiet the critics who had sought his removal. On January 12, the Council of Representatives passed the law, which Petraeus described to Gates as "the most significant Iraqi legislative accomplishment to date." When the law went to the Presidency Council, where it could conceivably have been vetoed by Tariq al-Hashimi, he agreed to let it be.[24]

The next major piece of legislation for Baghdad to deal with was the provincial powers law, which as of early February remained stalled in parliament. Walkouts by various parties had led Mahmoud al-Mashhadani, the speaker, to threaten the Council of Representatives with dissolution on February 12. The very next day, though, Petraeus was visiting a unit in West Baghdad when he received a call from Mashhadani's son saying that the parliament had just passed not only the provincial powers law but also the 2008 budget and an amnesty law.[25]

There was a hiccup with the provincial powers law two weeks later, when it went to the Presidency Council and Abd al-Mahdi vetoed it, sending it back to the Council of Representatives for revisions along with a letter to Mashhadani laying out the vice president's sixteen objections to the law as written. But in mid-March, the revised law came back to the Presidency Council for approval, and this time Abd al-Mahdi accepted it. Another major governmental hurdle had been cleared.

The provincial powers law mandated that provincial elections be held by October 1, 2008, so a provincial elections law was passed. It was Petraeus's hope that passage of the accountability and justice law and the provincial powers law would lure the Sunni Tawafuq Coalition back into the government for fear of being left out of the next set of legislation. Petraeus and Crocker also hoped that the progress on the Iraqi political front would allow the military and embassy to shift their focus to negotiating two agreements that would define the relationship between the United

States and Iraq after 2008, the status of forces agreement and the strategic framework agreement.

Still, dark clouds were gathering on another front. The Turkish strikes, which caused so much grief and aggravation for the Kurds, had continued. In one week in early February, Turkish jets struck seventy-seven targets in Iraq, and it seemed that a ground attack was looming. Fearful the situation might be spiraling out of control, Bush's NSC discussed the possibility on February 11 of attacking the PKK with American forces but decided that the cure would be worse than the disease. On February 21 or 22, about eight hundred Turkish ground troops crossed the border into Iraq for Operation Sun, which resulted in the shift of a second Predator for reconnaissance support.[26]

Bush told the NSC on February 25 that the Americans would go only so far in support of the operation.[27] If Turkish troops moved more than fifteen kilometers beyond the border, the United States would stop helping them. The cross-border force stayed short of that limit, but a Turkish Cobra attack helicopter was shot down by the PKK, demonstrating the difficulty of the operation. "My sense is it is dragging out," Petraeus told his staff a week into the fighting. "It is tough operating in three feet of snow and five thousand feet, and casualties are coming home."[28]

The next day, February 29, the Turkish ground troops pulled back to Turkey, though Turkish air and artillery strikes continued. But by the end of March, a computational error was causing Turkish artillery fire to miss its targets. The problem was first detected by the Americans, who were prepared not only to inform the Turks but to send a team of specialists from Fort Sill, Oklahoma, to help them fix it. The extent of American involvement in the Turkey-PKK fracas was never publicized. Petraeus had walked a difficult tightrope. In several conversations with Saygun, Petraeus insisted on a truth he firmly believed—a point he had constantly made about the American military effort: insofar as Turkish military operations were concerned, not air strikes, artillery, drones, and raids but politics and counterinsurgency would achieve actual results against the PKK. But it was not clear that the point registered.

While Petraeus was worried about having to support a Turkish policy that appeared to jeopardize the fragile political gains in Iraq, he was equally frustrated by Washington's refusal to let him engage Bashar al-Assad in Syria. By fall 2007, the flow of foreign fighters into northern Iraq through

Syria was shrinking as a result not of Syrian counterterrorism efforts but of problems Al-Qaeda was facing in Iraq. But there was no way to end the infiltration altogether without dealing with the insurgents' safe havens just across the border in Syria. Petraeus believed that Assad knew about the foreign fighter flow—according to American intelligence, his brother-in-law, the chief of Syrian military intelligence, was intimately involved in it—and might be more helpful, if confronted. Petraeus hoped to do this personally, along with McChrystal. As a soldier with an Iraq portfolio, Petraeus believed that he was in a position to discuss counterterrorism with the Syrians without being sidetracked by other topics of concern to Assad such as the Golan Heights or Syria's alleged involvement in the 2005 assassination of Lebanese prime minister Rafiq al-Hariri, the issue that had led the Bush administration to withdraw the American ambassador. From his earliest months in Iraq, Petraeus had had something to do, directly or indirectly, with policy toward Syria. As the commander of the 101st Airborne Division in 2003, for instance, he had opened up the border crossing between Syria and Nineveh Province for commerce.

Assad had made it clear through back channels that he was open to a meeting with Petraeus, sending messages to that effect through several Syrian ministers, including the finance minister. Petraeus reciprocated by sending intelligence about extremists in Syria to the Syrian government via the Jordanians, but he wanted to do more.

Starting in October, Petraeus raised the idea of a Syria visit in his letters to Gates and in meetings with Fox Fallon and the NSC's "war czar," Lieutenant General Doug Lute. On November 29, Petraeus mentioned the idea to Maliki. The next month, Petraeus again raised the issue, with Lieutenant General Ron Burgess, the DIA director, and yet again at the December 21 NSC meeting, to no avail.[29]

In a January letter to Gates, Petraeus wrote about Syria again. "The further we get our hands around the throats of Al-Qaeda in Iraq, the more I feel it is time for a brief visit by me and Stan McChrystal to Syria to ask for their help on stemming the flow of foreign fighters and taking on known AQ personalities who sometimes use Syrian soil," he wrote. "Because of the baggage and linkage to other Syrian demands that other American leaders might bring to Damascus, Stan and I are well-suited to engage the Syrians on the AQ threat without needing to bargain quid pro quo."[30]

Bush had given Petraeus all of the troops he had requested and had nothing but praise for the general. But he had no interest in initiating a dialogue with Assad. When Maliki, in a videoconference, asked in August if American diplomats could take part in trilateral negotiations with Syria as they had with Iran, Bush responded that the Syrians first needed to cut back on the flow of foreign suicide bombers and militants. The onus was on Assad to take the first step. When Petraeus doggedly raised the idea of a Damascus trip at the January 8 NSC session, Bush told him, "Stay patient," and changed the subject by asking whether the general was still sure he would be comfortable with fifteen brigades in Iraq when the surge forces were gone the following summer.[31]

Five days later, Petraeus and McChrystal were at an intelligence briefing in Baghdad, and Petraeus joked about the rebuff he had received in Washington from the president—prompted, he suggested, by the secretary of state. "While the briefer was saying something about Lebanon," a note taker at the briefing wrote, Petraeus "interjected an item for McChrystal, telling him that he, Petraeus, tried out the idea of the two of them going to Damascus to discuss interdicting foreign fighters on POTUS." Rice was quick to intervene, and so the idea did not get very far with Bush. "Some woman kicked him under the table," the note taker quoted Petraeus as quipping, in reference to Rice, and the answer was no.[32] As Petraeus made his pitch about Syria at the beginning of the new year, Odierno's and McChrystal's troops were pushing Al-Qaeda deeper into northern Iraq. In early December, JSOC's Task Force Falcon had flown into the lush area of Diyala where Al-Qaeda had fallen back since summer, called the "Breadbasket," killing two dozen enemy fighters, some of them in prepared, infantry-style fighting positions protected by 12.7mm and 14.5mm antiaircraft guns. The next phase of the offensive, involving conventional troops, was called Operation Phantom Phoenix, a follow-up to Phantom Thunder and Phantom Strike.

In a videoconference with the Bush on the day Phantom Phoenix was scheduled to kick off, Petraeus answered a question the president had posed to him in December: How many insurgents were American troops killing? More American troops had died in 2007 than in any other year of the war, although during the fall the toll had plunged. The numbers of insurgents killed were much higher. In total, Petraeus told Bush, American troops had killed about 7,400 enemy fighters in 2007, 50 percent more than the 5,000 estimated to have been killed in 2006. A refrain of Petraeus's was that in a counterinsurgency, a military force could not "kill its way to victory," and his command was careful not to publicly flaunt enemy body counts. But during the surge, American troops had done quite a lot of killing.

CHAPTER 25

Charge of the Knights

As March 2008 began, General Mohan Hafidh Fahad al-Furayji came to Baghdad to discuss his plan to reclaim Basra, the southern city of two million Shiites that was Iraq's economic crown jewel and had spiraled into chaos replete with militias and gangs. A close friend of Abd al-Qadir al-Obeidi, the defense minister, with whom he was imprisoned in Abu Ghraib during the Saddam years, Mohan was volatile at times, occasionally melodramatic, and not known for his sensitivity to the ethnic tensions roiling Iraq. When Bob Caslen, the two-star American general who later oversaw northern Iraq, warned about the possibility of an Arab-Kurdish confrontation, Mohan blithely noted that the Americans had had their civil war, implying that the Iraqis should be allowed to have theirs. In the spring of 2008, Mohan had no authority for the north but his responsibilities were no less significant. As head of the Basra Operations Command, he was charged with restoring some semblance of order to Iraq's second-largest city and the nearby town of Umm Qasr, the nation's only port.

The oil-rich region of southeastern Iraq had been assigned during the early years of the war to the British, who cast themselves as the masters of counterinsurgency and, touting their decades-long experience in Northern Ireland, had continued wearing soft caps whenever possible instead of helmets. But Basra was not a soft cap kind of place. Large portions of the city's security apparatus were in league with the militia. As early as December 2004, according to American intelligence, the top government security officials in Basra had struck a deal with the Mahdi Army allowing the militia freedom of movement in the city provided they attacked only British forces and not Iraqi soldiers and police.

By the beginning of 2006, after three years of British occupation, Basra was in serious trouble. On March 6, five U.S. government civilians were driving near Basra Palace when police vehicles boxed in their Audi and BMW and refused to let them leave as an angry crowd gathered, throwing rocks and firing guns. When a quick reaction force of British troops tried to reach the scene, it was halted by crowds and a police roadblock, where the police told the British they were surrounding a suspected car bomb rather than American diplomats. Finally, Triple Canopy contractors were able to ram through the surrounding police vehicles and rescue the stranded personnel under fire. One of the rescued Americans suffered a gunshot wound to the hand and four Iraqis were shot, including two policemen. The close call was never revealed publicly, consigned to the secret annals of the war.[1]

Throughout 2006 the British military hunkered down in preparation for a withdrawal. But just as with the American military in the north, hunkering down had its risks. In the spring a British Lynx helicopter was shot down over Basra, leading the British to restrict flying hours to their main city base at Basra Palace, and after a barrage of Mahdi Army rockets targeted that base during a birthday bash for the queen, British civilian staff began to pull back to an isolated base at Basra Airport west of the city.[2] Over the summer, as their civilian employees began to be killed off by Shiite militiamen, the American consulate and CIA followed suit.[3]

With the militias more active than ever, American officials were unhappy with the British military, who, confronted by political pressures at home to extract themselves from what was increasingly portrayed as George Bush's war, persisted in portraying Basra as a city in which the glass was three-quarters full. After the British, using a color-coded system, portrayed security in Basra as "green," meaning generally permissive, the Americans pointedly asked for a clarification. The British changed the assessment to "yellow," though as far as the Americans were concerned it was clearly "red."[4] In Baghdad, Pete Chiarelli sensed that the British were losing the fight. After Major General Sir Richard Shirreff, the British commander in southern Iraq, flew in to brief the corps commander, Chiarelli offered him reinforcements: an American battalion. As Shirreff later told an official British inquiry on the war, "the idea of American troops on the streets of Basra did not go down particularly well in London."[5]

Over the course of 2007, while the United States surged, Britain pulled back from Basra. On February 18, ten days after Petraeus arrived in Baghdad to change the strategy everywhere else in Iraq, Tony Blair announced plans to cut British troop numbers from seven thousand to four thousand, and in March a series of base closures in the city began, leaving only a single battle group of 550 British troops at Basra Palace and two other outposts, all planned for transfer by the end of the summer. To resource Britain's escalating campaign in Afghanistan, its attack helicopters were pulled out of Basra, and the only drone the British division at Basra Airport had access to was on loan from the American corps headquarters. After the Iraqi Army unit in Basra, the 10th Division, was deemed so ineffective and militia-influenced that it was moved to another province in 2007, the city was left in the hands of the police—almost all beholden to either the Mahdi Army or Basra's other powerful Shiite parties, ISCI and Fadhila—and a newly formed and incomplete unit, the 14th Division. Stark evidence, as if more were needed, of the degree to which the enemy had infiltrated the Basra police force came during the spring when two British soldiers were killed by a sniper in two days—a police sniper, according to a document prepared for Petraeus's meeting with the local governor.[6] "It's going round in circles," one soldier manning Basra Palace said in July. "People are getting killed for us to resupply ourselves, and if we weren't resupplying ourselves, people wouldn't be getting killed."[7]

Britain's withdrawal from its last and largest outpost in the city, Basra Palace, was scheduled for early September. In the months leading up to this closure, British intelligence and the division headquarters in Basra cooked up a secret plan, which they did not share initially either with Mohan, the senior Iraqi general in Basra, or with Graeme Lamb, the senior British general in Iraq. Ahmed al-Fartusi, a Mahdi Army commander who had trained in Lebanon and been detained by the SAS in 2005 for running an EFP smuggling cell, still resided in a British-run prison, and British division commander Major General Jonathan Shaw and the senior British Secret Intelligence Service officer in Basra began to visit him there. In central Iraq the United States was making increasingly frequent deals with Sunni insurgent leaders, and Graeme Lamb had even released a senior member of Ansar al-Sunna. The British officials in Basra who were in on the secret talks reasoned that what they were doing was little different. Step by step over the summer, the British worked out a deal whereby they and Fartusi would grant each other a series of quid pro quos, starting with the release of a small number of Fartusi's associates in return for a three-day cease-fire.

In Baghdad, Lamb was only made aware of the negotiations with Fartusi well into them, near the end of his tour as deputy commander of allied troops in Iraq, when he read about it in an intelligence report submitted to London. Lamb certainly did not object to releasing high-level detainees, but he objected strongly to just about every other aspect of what his countrymen were doing with Fartusi: negotiating without getting the Iraqi government's buy-in, doing so not from a position of strength but from one of weakness, and making specific tit-for-tat arrangements, all things that he and American commanders had consciously avoided doing when dealing with Sunni insurgents in central Iraq. He quickly informed Petraeus's headquarters, which had not known about the deal; directed the British division to put the Fartusi effort on hold until Rubaie could be brought into the process; and had Shaw come to Baghdad and brief him fully.[8]

After Lamb's departure, Shaw and British intelligence went ahead with the negotiations, now keeping Rubaie in the loop, and in July came to a final deal. The British battle group in the city continued to draw back, closing all of its bases except Basra Palace, and in return Fartusi saw to it—from his prison cell—that Mahdi Army attacks on British troops fell. In July, thirteen EFPs had exploded or been found in Basra; in August, the number was only three. In the final stage of the plan, the militia would allow Britain to leave Basra Palace without incident, and once they were gone would cease to fire rockets and mortars at the two large British bases outside the city. In return, the British would release 120 militiamen from detention, to eventually include Fartusi himself, and after they left the palace, they would keep their forces out of Basra City.

As Fartusi had promised, on September 3, 2007, the huge British convoy pulled back without incident from the palace to the airport, which would now serve as the main hub for all British operations. The arrangement had important implications for the Americans since without the use of British armored vehicles, the contingent of Iraqi commandos and American Special Forces advisers at the airport had to stop operating in Basra as well. Though it came just a week after Sadr declared his cease-fire, the British pullout from Basra Palace was an indication that the fight against the Mahdi Army and Special Groups had not been nearly as successful as efforts against Al-Qaeda in Iraq.

In late September and early October, Petraeus met with British prime minister Gordon Brown, as well as senior British defense officials. Petraeus's briefing for them noted that British troops had "been holding off on kinetic operations for a month and in response JAM has shown discipline in not targeting them," but he also came armed with an intelligence assessment by an American lieutenant colonel that raised some disturbing questions about the durability of the arrangement with the Mahdi Army. The classified assessment asserted that British forces were caught between Mohan, bluntly described as a "snake," and the Mahdi Army, starkly described as "the devil." By making a "deal with the devil" the British had merely created the veneer of stability. "Ahmed Fartusi hasn't given up anything yet that warrants wholesale buy-in," the assessment noted. It recommended that Fartusi prove his bona fides by helping the coalition capture senior militia commanders, such as Abu Mustafa al-Sheibani, the militia leader who smuggled EFPs into Iraq, or perhaps "a QF agent."[9] With British troops absent from Basra's streets, "Shi'a militias and criminal gangs continue to terrorize Basrawis through a campaign of murder, intimidation, kidnappings, rape, and torture," an American cable from Basra reported in October. "In what was once considered Iraq's open city, people are now afraid to venture out at night." A briefing prepared in late November by the corps headquarters in Baghdad judged that Basra was "reaching boiling point."[10] The British painted the opposite picture—but the American embassy branch office had an idea why, reporting that when the British left Basra Palace, almost all the informants in their "human intelligence" network were quickly rolled up by the Mahdi Army and police.[11]

Politically, the move gave the British what they needed: a milestone to justify the transition of Basra to "provincial Iraqi control," an official designation that, in theory, was settled on after careful deliberation by American and Iraqi officials and signified that the Iraqis had been given the lead role for security. Developments in Maysan, the province just north of Basra that served as a shipping route for Iran's arms to Shiite militias, illustrated some of the risks of expediting the handover. A soldier from the U.S. 82nd Airborne Division, which had troops in the south, noted somewhat irreverently that Maysan was a "PIC province" in a sense the coalition never intended: that is, under "provincial Iranian control."[12] The decision to move ahead with the transition to "provincial Iraqi control" in Basra made little sense in terms of developments on the ground, but was an integral part of Britain's strategy to gradually extricate itself from Iraq. As one aide to Petraeus put it, "Whitehall was in tactical command of the British forces in Basra."[13]

The British formally transferred Basra Province to the Iraqis on December 16. Soon afterward, they freed Fartusi. Crocker paid a visit in late January to the air base west of Basra where almost the entire British contingent was based, and he came away shaken. He was unable to enter the city and the Iraqi leaders he met with painted a picture of urban chaos, with gangs roaming freely and the Mahdi Army enforcing a strict version of Islamic law on the formerly secular city. Moreover, the air base was taking regular mortar and rocket fire, forcing British troops there to sleep in coffinlike bunkers they termed "Stonehenges." While the British were holding up their end of the summer's secret agreement, the Mahdi Army was not holding up Fartusi's. "The British had taken great care not to provoke JAM. They did such things as they stayed out of the city. They did not use attack aviation, and so on. But there were other groups not under Fartusi's control, so little by little the IDF [indirect fire] intensified," said Major Joel Rayburn, a Petraeus aide, in a classified interview with a military historian.[14]

A new British division commander, Major General Barney White-Spunner, who had experience in Bosnia and Afghanistan and had led a NATO force to disarm Albanian rebels in Macedonia in 2001, arrived in February 2008. He recognized this contradiction and lifted the ban on operations in the city. But with the British bases in the city abandoned, Whitehall set on a policy of withdrawal, and the size of the British force already significantly smaller than it had been in September, there was not much he could do.

With the British on the sidelines and Maliki increasingly distrustful of their performance, Mohan began to develop his own strategy to retake the city. The offensive he intended to command would be no small undertaking. Mohan would lead a six-month campaign, which would culminate before the provincial elections tentatively scheduled for October. It would be the first time that an Iraqi general designed, planned, and ran a major campaign. The Americans would be expected to help, but there was no question that the plan was Mohan's through and through.

Outlining his plan in Arabic and English in a series of slides on March 14 in Baghdad, Mohan explained that the current situation in Basra involved an "agreement with the Mahdi Army" but said that this was "tactical and temporary" and would soon give way to what might be the "last great urban battle in Iraq." In the first stage, lasting from March through May, the Iraqi forces near the city would be beefed up. Some would be inserted into the city and virtually an entire division would be aligned along the border with Iran to cut off the arms smuggling routes. All told, there would be twenty-one company-sized outposts and thirty-five prefabricated rooftop observation posts. In the second stage, lasting into mid-July, the prime minister would declare Basra a "weapons-free city" and security forces would run an arms buyback program. Then for another six weeks, Mohan's troops would execute the third stage, which he called "confrontation." The first two phases had their flaws, but the third was where things utterly broke down: during the offensive operations, Mohan wanted to use attack helicopters and artillery to harass and bombard cordoned-off neighborhoods like Hayyaniyah and Qibla, Basra slums where the Mahdi Army was strong.[15] When the plan was briefed to him, former prime minister Jaafari implied that it reminded him of the tactics Saddam's forces had used to suppress the Shiite rebellion in the southern cities in 1991.[16]

Petraeus was not impressed either. Mohan's inability to explain how he would use special operations forces and reconstruction money worried him. "There is a reason you were selected as a four-star general," Petraeus said pointedly to Mohan at one meeting, "and if you can't handle it, we will find somebody who can."[17] From the American perspective, Basra was one of two major military problems that would have to be dealt with in 2008—and not the most important one at that. February had seen the arrival in Baghdad of a new corps headquarters to replace Odierno's III Corps, Lieutenant General Lloyd Austin's XVIII Airborne Corps. Austin inherited a shrinking force; only two surge brigades had left Iraq so far, but a third was set to go home in March and by the middle of the summer the other two would be gone as well, bringing the total American force back down to fifteen combat brigades. That meant addressing one problem at a time. Following Petraeus's guidance, the corps's first order of business was to reinforce the 1st Armored Division's efforts in Mosul with the uninspiring name "Operation Defeat Al-Qaeda in the North." Only after that would Austin shift what mobile resources he had at his disposal, like drones and Special Forces teams partnered with Iraqi commandos, down to Basra for "Operation Look South."

Still, if the Basra campaign was to unfold, Petraeus wanted to ensure that it would be done right. Petraeus directed that a committee of Iraqis and Americans led by Jim Dubik, the three-star head of the training command, review and revise Mohan's plan. In an indication of the high political priority Maliki placed on the operation, Rubaie suggested that OCINC director Farouk al-Araji cochair the committee. But the Americans wanted to diminish, not expand, OCINC's role and Rubaie's idea was ignored. In two weeks, Petraeus said, he would visit Basra. In the meantime, Basra would be discussed at the March 16 meeting of the MCNS and the plan refined further in a series of follow-on meetings.

The MCNS meeting provided a clue about the diverging Iraqi and American military priorities. Maliki opened the session by raising his concerns about Basra and its port, Umm Qasr, where the Sadrists were reported to control the security forces and customs apparatus and thus a huge chunk of Iraq's seaborne imports. After Barham Salih chimed in that Basra needed its own Operation Fardh al-Qanun, Mohan discussed his plan, volunteering that he could speed things up. Lieutenant General Bill Rollo, Petraeus's British deputy, moved quickly to reinforce the coalition's priorities: the military campaign plan called for dealing with Mosul first, and there could not be two simultaneous "main efforts" during the spring. When Rubaie suggested that a large part of the problem in Basra was a number of organized crime families, Maliki commanded, impractically, "I order you to detain those families." As the meeting wound down, Maliki announced that he wanted to go to Basra to see the situation for himself. "The PM stated that he would go to Basrah to show the people of southern Iraq that they were part of the country and that the central government would act for their security," an American embassy cable on the meeting reported. It seemed as if the prime minister simply meant he wanted to visit the city to get a better understanding of the situation, something Petraeus intended to do in the coming weeks as well.[18]

The next Friday evening, March 21, Petraeus and other American and Iraqi military and security officials convened again to take up Mohan's revised plan. Some new units were now en route to Basra to strengthen the government's hand; an Interior Ministry commando force, the Baghdad Emergency Response Unit, had left the capital for Basra a few days earlier. The question of how to revamp Mohan's plan was on the table when Rubaie pulled Petraeus aside and said that he needed to talk to him in the courtyard. The prime minister wanted a meeting the next morning and the subject was a much-accelerated operation in Basra. "You're kidding," Petraeus replied—although American intelligence had picked up hints of Iraqi units getting orders for Basra—but Rubaie explained that he was deadly serious.[19] To the Americans, the timing was off. Not only had Petraeus determined that Mosul should be the next priority—some Iraqi forces were already headed north as part of a gradual buildup there—but the general and Ryan Crocker were due to report to Congress in April on progress made in the war, their first testimony to the lawmakers since their heated September session the previous year. A hasty and ill-defined operation did not seem the best prelude to a hearing where Petraeus hoped to point to hard-won successes.

The next morning, Saturday, March 22, Petraeus visited Maliki at his palace in the Green Zone along with Mike Barbero, Sadi Othman, and an officer from Lloyd Austin's corps headquarters. With Rubaie translating, the prime minister spent the first ten minutes of the meeting railing against the British, whom he blamed for allowing Basra to fall into the militias' hands. "I have heard from all of the religious leaders in Basra; they have been calling me," Maliki said, according to notes of an American participant. "There is a mass migration of professionals."

"My security forces are ready to go to Basra on Monday and I will also go," added Maliki, stunning the Americans. The prime minister explained that a brigade of National Police intended for Mosul would head to Basra instead, along with Iraqi special operations forces. Maliki made clear that he did not expect a large battle and would be taking a team of judges to try the miscreants he intended to have arrested. To set the conditions for the fight, Maliki said he would close the border with Iran and Kuwait, allowing only oil exports, for several days. But he wanted to know if the American-led coalition could provide air support and its own Special Forces.

Petraeus was unhappy with the change of priorities, but because Maliki was determined to go ahead, the general focused on how to make the operation work. Both sides agreed that it should be Iraqi-led, especially since American forces were already overextended. Petraeus advised Maliki to take with him the general in charge of his Counter-Terrorism Service, which oversaw the elite Iraqi special operations forces or ISOF, noting that American Special Forces were embedded with them and could call in AC-130 gunships and other forms of air support. Petraeus also advised Maliki to deploy the first helicopters the Iraqis had acquired for their air force and to consider bringing in fresh troops who had just been trained at the Besmaya training camp. "Your big challenge is going to be logistics," the American general added. "You need to take money, to buy supplies." Maliki promised Petraeus that once he got to Basra, he would do nothing rash—just use the extra forces outside the city as leverage in his dealings with tribal leaders while American assets were readied to support the next step.[20]

Maliki did not explain his thinking to the Americans, who were left to ponder why he felt the operation was so urgent. The first and simplest theory was that Maliki, spurred by reports of militia brutality in Basra, had finally become tired of the Mahdi Army and its criminal offshoots. "DIA assesses Maliki's primary motivations for conducting military operations in Basrah were to address deteriorating security and economic conditions and a desire to decrease the Sadrist threat to Basrah and the central government," a classified American intelligence report stated. "He also may have believed the timing was advantageous because of increased personal backing within the government and the recently renewed Sadrist freeze on operations."[21]

Another view was that with provincial elections in the offing, Maliki wanted to ensure that he had military control in Basra, a city in which the Dawa Party had little sway. The Maliki government, in effect, would not make the mistake the Palestinian National Authority had made when it supported the 2006 elections in Gaza only to see its rival Hamas prevail at the polls. If provincial elections were to be held in the Shiite city, they would be taking place in a setting where the prime minister's military and political influence had expanded.

A third theory that H.R. McMaster developed while interviewing Iraqi officials for a spring study on the country's governance was that Maliki was acting to head off what he thought was yet another threat to his rule. According to McMaster's analysis, in the wake of the Kurds' and ISCI's December plot to oust Maliki through a no-confidence vote, another plan for such a vote was in the works, this time by the Sadrists and two men who wished to replace the prime minister, Ahmed Chalabi and Ibrahim al-Jaafari. The idea, according to McMaster and others who believed the theory, was that at the end of its next cease-fire—renewed in February—the Mahdi Army and Sadrist Special Groups like Asaib Ahl al-Haq would barrage the Green Zone with rockets, and that barrage would be the pretext for a no-confidence vote sponsored by the Sadrists, Chalabi, and Jaafari. In late March, the theory went, Hadi al-Amari—whose Badr Organization, along with ISCI, were excluded from the alleged plot—tipped Maliki off, and he made the decision to go to Basra immediately in order to preempt the Sadrists in a stronghold where Dawa could also stand to gain popularity and power.[22]

Petraeus discounted the theory completely, believing that Maliki had merely become overconfident in the Iraqi Army and in his own leadership abilities after his foray to Karbala in August. In a videoconference with the NSC a few months earlier, Odierno and Crocker had raised the subject. "I can loan him the 'Mission Accomplished' banner," Bush joked.[23]

In any event, Maliki's decision showed that shoring up the security of the Shiite south and his political base of support were more important to him than taking on the remnants of Al-Qaeda in Nineveh Province. While the Americans were fixated on Al-Qaeda, Maliki was trying to neutralize the Shiite groups that resisted his rule. What was also abundantly clear was that Maliki intended to oversee an operation in Basra much like a larger version of what he had done in Karbala seven months before: as he saw it, he would effect a quick series of arrests that would restore security and boost his own image as a defender of law and order. Maliki, Crocker later observed, wanted to relive his "Karbala moment." He had made no provision for an extended military operation against an entrenched foe. But Basra was a far larger and more violent city than Karbala, with nowhere near the forces necessary to secure it in place.

Flying south, Prime Minister Maliki arrived at Basra Palace, the base the British had abandoned in September, on Monday, March 24. The prime minister had come south with a huge entourage of security officials, staff, and guards, along with military and police units that had been based in central Iraq. The palace grounds were quickly transformed from a deserted outpost to a cramped headquarters. Defense Minister Abd al-Qadir al-Obeidi had made the trip but Interior Minister Bolani, who feared IED-laced highways less than he did air travel, insisted on driving south in a convoy that fended off attacks along the way.

Lieutenant Colonel Mark Grdovic, the Special Forces officer who had snuck into Kurdistan before the war kicked off, accompanied Maliki to Basra. Maliki's first request to Grdovic was to have American jets fly over the city in a show of force. Grdovic arranged for two F-16s to make a pass high above the city, but it was not what the prime minister had in mind: he had wanted the jets roaring in low, and he made his disappointment clear. Maliki had such a dismal view of the British that he did not even try to coordinate with them, and sometimes kicked Grdovic's British counterpart out of the room.[24] On a skiing vacation in Switzerland at the time, Barney White-Spunner, the British division commander, was completely blindsided by Maliki's operation.

Shortly after sunrise the next morning, the fighting began as Iraqi troops pushed into the city's Tamimiya neighborhood and came under attack by Mahdi Army fighters. Dubbed Operation Sawlat al-Forsan, or "Charge of the Knights," the Basra offensive ran into trouble almost immediately. By the end of the first day, Tuesday, it was obvious that it would not be the reprise of Karbala that the prime minister was hoping for.

The first day saw heavy militia resistance not just in Mahdi Army strongholds like Hayyaniyah, but in neighborhoods across the city. The largest government force, the 14th Iraqi Army Division, was utterly unprepared for the fight. Formed only the previous fall, it had just two full brigades, with a third forming, and relied heavily on local Basrawi recruits. The division's 52nd Brigade, which had not even existed two months before, broke down as it came under militia attack. Half of its three thousand soldiers shed their uniforms and vanished into the city, and when what was left of the brigade retreated, it left behind one-third of its Humvees and other vehicles. Since the British had no advisers embedded with Iraqi units below brigade level—a result of their push to hand operations over to the Iraqis—American and British officers at the Shaibah training base west of the city first realized that something was badly wrong only when the 52nd Brigade's remnants began to stream back to the camp in disarray.

Adding to the confusion, the headquarters controlling the operation

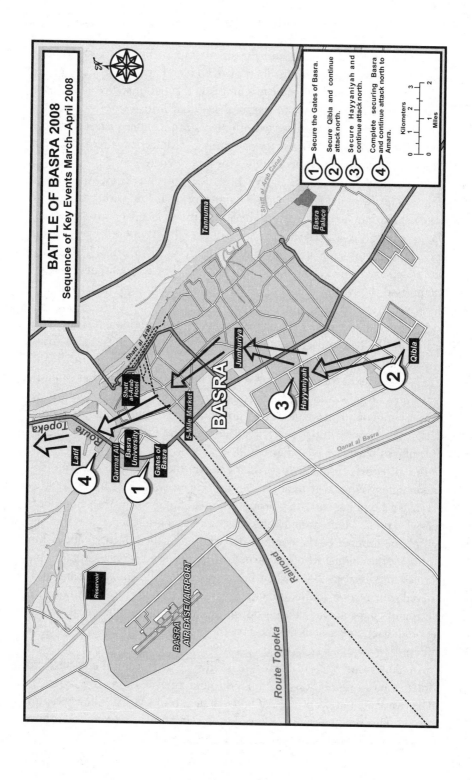

were split: General Mohan and the small staff of his Basra Operations Command were located in the Shatt al-Arab Hotel at the north end of the city, while Maliki and his ministers and generals had installed themselves in the Basra Palace grounds to the southeast that British troops had abandoned in September. On Tuesday both places came under sustained rocket and mortar barrages. "The sky was burning," Maliki later recalled in an interview. "I saw the rockets coming from everywhere."[25]

Maliki had intended to relieve both Mohan and Basra's provincial police chief, Major General Jalil Khalaf Shuwayl. But with the fighting far tougher than he had expected, he left them in place, and on the second day of the battle, March 26, announced a seventy-two-hour deadline for the Mahdi Army and other militias to put down their arms. The decree had no effect; the next day, video was released showing militiamen parading around the wreck of an Iraqi BMP armored fighting vehicle, a pair of destroyed armored cars, and a captured Humvee.

By now, the offensive had sparked more limited fighting in other southern cities like Kut and Hilla, and in a reprise of the spring Mahdi Army uprising of 2004, it had also spread to Baghdad. But to Petraeus and Crocker, it was Basra that mattered most. It seemed possible that Maliki's Basra adventure would end disastrously, and such a defeat would lead to the very no-confidence vote Maliki hoped to avoid. But Maliki dug in his heels, and Petraeus and Crocker realized they had little choice but to support him in whatever way they could.

Initial reports from the first Americans on the scene in Basra were not encouraging. When a group of Iraqi staff officers wanted Mark Grdovic to arrange a bombing run, they brought him a napkin with Arabic numbers scrawled on it, which turned out to be not a set of grid coordinates, but the cell phone number of the commander who had called in the request. Jim Coffman, the colonel who had earned a Distinguished Service Cross for his heroics in Mosul in 2004 when Petraeus headed the training command, arrived shortly after to link up with Bolani and the Interior Ministry team. He found chaos at the palace—no one seemed to be in charge. Coffman reported back to Petraeus that he gave the whole undertaking "50–50 odds at best."[26]

An American Special Forces team dispatched from the airfield to Mohan's Basra Operations Command found an even more dire situation. "The overwatch areas of the BaOC were held by JAM," a military report noted. "The perimeter was under regular gunfire. . . . Across the river, mortars were launched from boats and were spot on." And Mohan's headquarters had no plan for staying supplied with food, ammunition, or other essentials. Enlisted soldiers at Mohan's command post, the same report noted, "were told to go out into the city to forage for food and fuel without the necessary funds to purchase these critical items."[27] That did not bode well for the units actually fighting inside Basra. One police unit that had been deployed on short notice phoned its American advisers back in Karbala, over three hundred miles away, after it took casualties, hoping that they would be able to arrange a medevac since there was no functioning Iraqi support structure in Basra.

It was obvious that the Americans would need to provide some military support, and there needed to be a chain of command to coordinate the operation. First Petraeus dispatched Rear Admiral Edward Winters, a Navy SEAL who was in charge of training Iraqi commandos. After traversing Basra with a small party that had to defuse several IEDs on its own, Winters and a CIA team set up shop in the area of the palace compound that had previously housed the British diplomatic section. Next, corps commander Lloyd Austin flew to Basra on March 27 with Marcie Ries, an official from the embassy in Baghdad, and a corps tactical command post was scheduled to follow them the next day. Arriving at Basra Palace, Austin and Ries were told by Sadiq al-Rikabi, one of Maliki's most trusted advisers, that they were not needed. All he wanted was American firepower, since the small number of Iraqi UH-1 and Mi-17 helicopters flying over Basra had no attack capability. When Austin met with Maliki, the prime minister insisted that the senior British commander, Brigadier Julian Free, wait outside the room.

To provide the Iraqis greater access to air support, Austin wanted part of his corps command post, which arrived on Friday the 28th, to embed with Mohan's Basra Operations Command. At first Maliki refused, just as he was refusing to allow the British 1 Scots Guards battle group to use its armor to help out in the city. Maliki had taken ownership of the situation and did not see why American jets could not simply drop bombs on coordinates Mohan provided. Eventually, though, he agreed that Austin's deputy, Marine Major General George Flynn, could set up shop at the Basra airfield and place intelligence and fire support officers in Mohan's hotel headquarters. Flynn arrived that night, and found that coordinating air support was going to be the easy part of his job—militiamen in Basra, unlike those in Baghdad, were used to a city without drones or attack helicopters overhead. But Mohan's headquarters was a mess. "I came here to augment the Basra Operations Command," Flynn observed, "but there is no Basra Operations Command. There is only Mohan at a table with eight cell phones."[28] Simply preventing Mohan from ordering precipitous and unsupported attacks into Mahdi Army bastions like Hayyaniyah and Qibla became one of the Americans' most pressing tasks.

At the end of the first week, Iraqi troops and the assortment of Mahdi Army fighters and gangs had fought each other to a stalemate. Rocket fire continued to take a toll at Basra Palace, killing Interior Minister Bolani's chief of staff. In one bout of shelling, the militia "walked" 120mm mortar shells right into the central area of the palace, zeroing in on the old British consulate building that housed Winters, the SEAL admiral, and the CIA contingent. One shell exploded in the door of the adjacent building, killing one of Maliki's favorite bodyguards.

One of the few units in Basra to see any kind of success that week was a battalion dispatched from the Anbar-based 1st Iraqi Army Division, a battle-tested unit that, critically, brought along a large team of Marine advisers and ANGLICO fire-support specialists, led by Lieutenant Colonel Charles Western and Major Tim Bleidestel. The battalion—the lead element of a larger force from Anbar including the 1st Division headquarters and the rest of a brigade—arrived outside Basra early in the week and became engaged in tough fighting at a cloverleaf just west of the city near Basra University. Bleidestel's Marines were able to call in strikes from F/A-18 jets and Predator drones overhead, and, starting on March 28, from AC-130 gunships and British artillery.

Among the handful of other units with the capability to call in air support were Iraqi special operations troops, who, accompanied by Special Forces advisers and their link to jets, gunships, and medevac helicopters, acquitted themselves well in nighttime raids into some of Basra's most dangerous districts. A battle group equipped with Warrior armored vehicles, 1 Scots Guards, was one of the few British units allowed into combat. Although the unit was never sent into Basra on its own, constrained both by national rules of engagement and by Maliki's insistence on keeping British officers at arm's length, their Warriors provided the American and Iraqi commandos with armored support, accompanying them seventeen times on raids into tough areas like Qibla. When one special operations raid was ambushed and Mark Grdovic arranged to have the wounded Iraqi commandos helicoptered out of Basra Palace, the prime minister went so far as to insist that the casualties be flown to an American field hospital instead of the much closer British one.

Overall, though, the Iraqi forces were in over their heads. "By the third day Maliki thinks the city has been cleared three times, because every time he asks a new general, he gets these unrealistic answers, and he looks at me like I'm an idiot when I tell him the city's not secure," Grdovic recalled. When a colonel from Austin's staff, Marty Stanton, arrived at the palace a few days later, he saw hungry Iraqi soldiers fishing by tossing hand grenades into the palace's decorative lakes and the Shatt al-Arab.[29] Publicly, Petraeus and Crocker sought to put the best face on the operation. To discourage unflattering news coverage of the Iraqis' performance and disguise the extent of American assistance, Petraeus's command did not allow journalists to embed with the teams of American advisers who were assigned to the Iraqi troops in Basra, even though such arrangements were allowed in other parts of Iraq, a lapse for a headquarters that otherwise strove for transparency.

The classified assessments Petraeus and Crocker sent home were more worrisome. According to a cable from Crocker that week, Sadrist representatives were urging Talabani to support a no-confidence vote, and Jaafari and Baha al-Araji were trying to arrange an emergency session of the Council of Representatives where the vote could occur. "Frankly, if Maliki comes back having failed he will be doomed," Rubaie said in a meeting with American diplomats. "Absolutely, the knives will be out."[30] From an ISCI-KRG summit in Sulaymaniyah, Iraq's Kurdish leaders and Adil Abd al-Mahdi were "watching like vultures" to see how events in Basra would unfold, one American general recalled.[31]

"At this point, my assessment is that Prime Minister Maliki has bit off more than he can chew in Basra," Petraeus wrote to Gates at the end of the week. He continued:

> Concerned that Maliki may not have been receiving entirely frank reports from his subordinates, I gave Maliki my perspective during a conversation Ryan [Crocker] and I had with him on Saturday. I assured him we were doing everything possible to help him to refine and develop a viable plan, but that even with our support, he needs to be more modest in his objectives given the Iraqi Security Forces available and the level of their capability. Iraqi Security Forces are unlikely to be capable of securing and holding the districts they are targeting. Ryan added his view that it was time for Maliki to think hard about a political agreement to enable this to come to as good a conclusion as possible. We will continue to do our utmost to put Maliki in an advantageous position for any future negotiations.[32]

The Americans approached Barham Salih, whom Maliki had left in charge in the capital, to try to convince the prime minister to come home, but Salih declined. Six days into the fighting, American diplomats met with

Sadiq al-Rikabi in Baghdad. In an anxious state and with his English falter-ing as a result, Rikabi said that Maliki did not know what a serious situa-tion he was in. "We are working to convince him," Rikabi said, but Maliki "doesn't like bad news."[33]

The arrival of additional American personnel and resources both on the ground and in the air, however, began to turn things in Maliki's favor. Overhead, the efforts of a collection of strike fighters, Predator drones, AC-130 gunships, and surveillance and command and control aircraft pro-vided a huge morale boost to Iraqi troops, as did the arrival of Apache attack helicopters flying from Tallil Air Base; Britain's attack helicopters had long since left Basra for Afghanistan. Black Hawk and Pave Hawk helicopters helped, too, both with medevac support and by ferrying Iraqi leaders around the city—Mohan, for instance, was unwilling to fly on Iraqi UH-1 or Mi-17 helicopters or even brand-new British Merlins, but did not mind Black Hawks.

To use the airpower more effectively and buck up the Iraqis, Austin turned to the 82nd Airborne Division's 1st Brigade, which had spent most of the year providing security along Route Tampa, the military's main sup-ply route from Kuwait, and were neither organized nor trained as advisers. "We knew that the Iraqis were pretty much getting their asses handed to them, but we didn't envision at all that they would ask us to participate," one of the soldiers recalled.[34]

The brigade contributed its headquarters and a company of paratroop-ers, Delta Company, 2-504 Parachute Infantry, which reached Basra under Captain Bill Checher on March 29, just before a deal was reached to limit the fighting. It would not be a typical advisory arrangement. Each of the company's three rifle platoons would partner with an Iraqi battalion, so that they could call in air strikes, encourage the Iraqis to stand up to the militias, and, if necessary, join the fray themselves. Upon departing Tallil, they were instructed to configure their convoys and conduct themselves so they would "appear larger than you are."[35]

Rumors that the 82nd's whole 1st Brigade was heading south, not just a company, helped, too. "On March 28, JAM elements believed that up to 4,000 U.S. combat troops had reached Basrah, and that both U.S. and Brit-ish troops were involved in the attacks on them," the DIA judged.[36] The paratroopers' efforts to appear bigger than they were paid more dividends than they had anticipated.

Still, the results inside Basra remained mixed, with only fourteen of the thirty-eight Iraqi units involved paired with advisers by April 1. Strikes by Iraqi commandos and their American advisers continued to work well, and in the area around Basra University hard fighting by the battalion from Anbar and the accompanying Marines spurred locals to help drive the Mahdi Army away on the night of March 29–30, establishing a toehold in the north of the city. But other Iraqi operations did not work so well: on March 29 the militia repulsed strikes into the Tariq and Kindi neighborhoods, and the next day a two-battalion push into the Five-Mile Market area was a disappointment.

In the end, the militias, and their Iranian backers, decided that with the Americans committed and Maliki determined to succeed at whatever cost, the fighting had swung against them. On March 29, an Iraqi government delegation met with Sadr in Iran to negotiate a deal. On Maliki's behalf, Hadi al-Amari of Badr and Ali al-Adeeb of Dawa hashed out a nine-point cease-fire agreement with Sadr. Maliki would get his victory, but the Mahdi Army would not be required to hand over its heavy weapons. Sadr announced the agreement on March 30, with the terms effective that day at noon. Soon afterward Talabani also visited Iran, meeting Qasim Suleimani near the border.[37]

Flush with success, the Iraqis were determined to move on to the port of Umm Qasr. Fearing that it was a bridge too far, Petraeus urged the Iraqis not to go because they already had their hands full with Basra. Once again, Maliki ignored the Americans and the Iraqi forces raced to the port, as did Bolani, the interior minister, who brought along three hundred of his guards. Coffman went with them and reported to Petraeus that the foray to Umm Qasr had turned out all right—there had been no resistance at all, with the expected Mahdi Army units there long gone.[38]

For the British, the battle of Basra punctuated a bruising and unflattering experience in Iraq. The British military had begun the war as the reputed masters of counterinsurgency—an army that supposedly knew how to build ties with allies among the locals and that was discriminating in its use of force, that had demonstrated its skills in Northern Ireland and any number of colonial and postcolonial hotspots over the years, and that, in theory, had much to teach the bulls in the china shop, the Americans. By the end of the Basra fight that reputation was in tatters. The British had ceded control of one of Iraq's major cities and lost the trust of the Iraqi prime minister. The

British main effort at reconciliation with Fartusi had come to naught. Nor did their enemies fear them. British officers could note with some justification that they had had their hands tied by the politicians at home. Nonetheless, it was the Americans who had forged alliances with the tribes and given their battalion and company commanders the authority, autonomy, and funds to wage an effective counterinsurgency campaign on a large scale.[39]

While the battle was clearly a defeat for the Mahdi Army, it was less clear what the net value was for Iran's Iraq chief, Suleimani, who had helped instigate the fighting and then played a critical role in arranging the ceasefire with top Iraqi leaders. "The most sobering surprise of the week was probably the extent of direct Iranian involvement in Iraqi political intrigue," Petraeus wrote to Gates. "Suleimani met with Talabani (twice), VP Adel, the leaders of ISCI, Dawa, and the Sadr trend. Talabani and Adel relayed that Iran recognizes that it is not in their interest to see an unstable Iraq fail. They noted Suleimani does not trust Sadr, would like to see JAM dismantled, supports Maliki remaining in power, and supports the SFA, and would like to have secret talks with US reps!" To Crocker, Talabani's Iran trip undercut Maliki's demonstration of his authority that the prime minster had made with his bold, if rash, decision to go to Basra. "Another Iranian tactic is to invite many political leaders to Tehran for talks," he noted in a cable, listing the Iraqi politicians who had recently visited Iran or soon would: Jaafari, Chalabi, Hakim, Qasim Daoud, and Dawa's Ali al-Adeeb and Falih al-Fayadh. "The message, taken from the Syrian-Iranian playbook in Lebanon, is that Iran can solve problems and create them."[40]

Maliki's impulsive foray into Basra had been a greater gamble than he realized, and it had diverted Petraeus and Crocker from their carefully elaborated campaign plan. In an intra-Shiite war, Maliki had raised the stakes, but it was a political victory nonetheless. The military success was far from complete. But Maliki had bloodied the Mahdi Army enough that Iran stepped in to broker yet another cease-fire with Sadr.[41]

Two days after the cease-fire, on the evening of April 1, Maliki flew from Basra Palace to the airfield on an Iraqi Mi-17, and from there flew back to Baghdad on his usual Airbus jet. Cease-fire notwithstanding, the day had seen combat in Basra; several Iraqi battalions had conducted a desultory sweep in Five-Mile Market, pulling back as soon as they were attacked, while American Apaches had fired their cannon in support of special operations teams three times and a British Tornado jet dropped a thousand-pound bomb on a rocket team. Ostensibly, however, the operations targeted criminal gangs, not the Mahdi Army.

During his first week back in Baghdad, the prime minister faced a renewed push for a no-confidence vote that the Sadrists had been plotting while he was down in Basra. But he handily fended off the challenge. On April 5, most of Iraq's senior political leaders assembled at Talabani's Green Zone residence for a meeting of the Political Council on National Security, or PCNS. Maliki, Talabani, and the vice presidents and deputy prime ministers attended; so did the foreign minister and representatives from all the main blocs of the Council of Representatives. The Sadrists had been boycotting PCNS sessions, but they sent two representatives to the meeting, suggesting confidence that their opposition to Maliki would find support among those assembled.

Instead, in a landmark four-hour meeting that many of the participants described in detail to American diplomats afterward, the Maliki foes found themselves isolated. Even the representatives of other parties who had been staunchly opposed to Maliki before Basra, like Fadhila, shouted down the Sadrists, and as the meeting continued it became a referendum not on Maliki's performance but on the Sadrists and the Mahdi Army. According to one participant's account the Sadrists "were repeatedly challenged to declare whether their party intended to remain inside the Iraqi political process or not." The committee proceeded to draft a fifteen-point statement calling for militias to be disbanded across Iraq, a shot across the Mahdi Army's bow.

The unified front shown at the April 5 PCNS meeting left the Sadrists politically shaken and isolated. "That leaves the Sadrist Trend alone in the Iraqi political wilderness," an American embassy cable concluded.[42] Operation Charge of the Knights had temporarily united Iraq's bickering political leaders behind Maliki and shelved any possibility of a no-confidence vote. It was a success few American officials had expected, but one they hoped he would make the most of in the months ahead.

CHAPTER 26

March Madness

The worst of the fighting in Basra was behind him when Maliki returned to Baghdad on April 1. But the prime minister was not coming home to a peaceful capital. As in every previous Sadrist uprising, when one city in the south flared into violence, so did the other southern cities and so did Baghdad's Sadr City and Shula districts.[1]

Even before the prime minister's impulsive lunge to Basra there were mounting signs that the Maliki government was headed for conflict with the Mahdi Army and its offshoots, the very Sadrist groups it had often tried to shield from the U.S. military in the past. As the end of Sadr's six-month cease-fire neared, during the January Ashura holiday, Mowaffak al-Rubaie had a frightening run-in with the militants at a mosque in Shula. Surrounded by gunmen and hunkered down inside the mosque, Rubaie was informed that his bodyguards had been disarmed and that the tires on his vehicles had been shot out. After he made a few frantic calls for help, an envoy from the attackers entered the mosque and handed him a cell phone. On the other end was someone purporting to be Muqtada al-Sadr with an offer of safe passage. Concluding that the call was a ruse, Rubaie believed that he was being targeted by either Asaib Ahl al-Haq or Kataib Hezbollah, which were trying to take him hostage or worse.

The national security adviser prepared himself to be kidnapped or martyred until Maliki's own security detail raced to the scene along with Jawad al-Bolani, the minister of interior, and Sami al-Askari, one of the prime minister's close aides. Arriving outside the mosque, the convoy of armored SUVs found that the police were waiting blocks away. There were no Iraqi Army troops in sight, and teenagers were throwing rocks at the mosque while plainclothes militiamen walked around its perimeter. The security detail hustled Rubaie into one of the SUVs and drove him away. After-ward, an enraged Rubaie told Petraeus that he was "ready to declare war" on the Iranian-backed Special Groups.[2]

The quiet hunt for Special Groups leaders by Task Force 17 contin-ued to amass evidence of Iran's covert aid to Sadrist militants in spite of the cease-fire. Run since the fall by the storied 75th Ranger Regiment, the JSOC task force had been hampered all fall by Maliki's restrictions on Sadr City operations, but by early February its commandos were back in busi-ness. In the meantime they had continued their raids elsewhere. One strike force captured a father-and-son pair of militia operatives, one of whom had on him a flash drive that contained more than four thousand Quds Force intelligence reports from Iraq, including documents that detailed sur-veillance efforts against American bases in Baghdad and elsewhere, flight schedules in and out of Balad Air Base, and other documentation of Quds Force activities in Iraq between 2005 and late 2007.[3] It seemed that within the Mahdi Army, some factions, like those in league with Asaib Ahl al-Haq and with the Sadr City warlord Abu Dura, were getting ready for another round of fighting, whether Sadr renewed his cease-fire at the end of six months or not.

In an effort to persuade the Special Groups to toe the line after a spate of EFP attacks, Petraeus passed messages through third parties to Sadrist leaders that unless the militias were more restrained than they had been in January, American conventional troops would resume offensive opera-tions in militia areas like Shula, West Rashid, and even Sadr City. "If recent spate of attacks on CF continues, result will be M-1s rolling through Shia neighborhoods," Petraeus said, according to notes of a February 1 meet-ing.[4] The next day Petraeus advised his aides to tell the Sadrist official Salah al-Obeidi that if the Mahdi Army did not get the Special Groups in West Baghdad under control, he would "declare war" on the militia. "In the past couple of days, we have sent strong messages to our Shi'a contacts that we are about to place our full kinetic attention on the JAM/Special Group threat if it continues," the general wrote to Gates afterward.[5]

From the Iranian city of Qom, Sadr responded on February 4 by reiter-ating his August cease-fire, and later in the month by announcing via sealed letters to his subordinate clerics that when the six months of the truce had passed, he would extend it for another six months. Then in early March he puzzled the American military by announcing that he would be staying in Iran for the foreseeable future, prioritizing his religious studies over the day-to-day management of the Sadrist movement in Iraq. Baha al-Araji explained Sadr's highly ambitious course of study in a meeting with American diplomats. The thirty-four-year-old cleric would become an ayatollah in two years, Araji generously predicted, because he was studying sixteen hours a day in Qom, and his father had also completed the necessary studies in less than the usual time.[6] "At this point, the Sadr movement appears divided, uncertain, and defensive," Petraeus wrote to Gates.[7] February EFP attacks were fewer again, suggesting that Petraeus's threats worked. The pilgrimage during Arbaeen, a major Shiite holiday, was the most peaceful since 2004, and February wound up being the fifth straight month in which the number of attacks across Iraq stayed at levels last seen in the summer of 2005.

Maliki's decision to confront the Shiite militias in Basra and other southern cities and—if H.R. McMaster's theory was right—preempt their offensive against the Green Zone, however, dramatically raised the stakes for the militias. In late March, the militias abandoned whatever restraint they had mustered. Militants took to the streets in Kut and other southern cities as news of Charge of the Knights spread, though the fighting was far more limited in scope than in the 2004 southern uprising. In one clash in a south-central city, according to American intelligence, a senior Quds Force officer was wounded and had to be evacuated to Iran.

In Baghdad, the fighting started on Sunday, March 23, with sustained rocketing of the Green Zone even before Maliki had left for Basra— possibly part of a plot being executed prematurely, or possibly just because the Sadrists had gotten wind of the prime minister's intention to attack them in the south. On March 24, a U.S. infantry platoon and a team of advisers to the National Police killed or wounded seventy-five Mahdi Army fighters as they attacked Joint Security Station Obeidi, an outpost built over the winter at the edge of Sadr City. The next day, militiamen poured out of Sadr City and into the streets across East Baghdad and Shiite areas of West Baghdad like Shula and Kadhimiya. Half of the Iraqi military and police checkpoints ringing Sadr City were overrun. In Shula, 230 police deserted their posts and handed over their weapons and vehicles to the Mahdi Army, and within two days a battalion of the 4th Brigade, 1st National Police Division, had seen over 400 of its 550 members disappear. In firefights near FOB Hope—the outpost by Sadr City's eastern corner that American troops had abandoned in 2006 and then reoccupied early in the surge—militiamen fought wearing recently captured helmets and body armor. Of greater concern, American intelligence reported, some fighters were likely to be armed with American M16s confiscated from surrendering Iraqi troops.[8]

As Iraqi units folded left and right, Major General Jeffrey Hammond, whose 4th Infantry Division was now running the show in Baghdad, suggested in frustration during a briefing that perhaps the Iraqis should be permitted to fail, to teach them the hardest kind of lesson. Petraeus, also attending the meeting, was not pleased. "This is not a training exercise," he admonished the general. "This is a pivotal battle of the war. Neither we nor the Iraqis can afford to make this into a learning episode."[9]

The Mahdi Army and Special Groups had amassed an enormous supply of rockets, mortars, and IEDs in Sadr City, and were using its garbage-strewn lots and alleyways as launching pads—POO, or point-of-origin sites, in the vernacular of the American military. The vast majority of the projectiles were 107mm rockets, which could be fired from Jamila and Thawra 1, the southernmost segments of Sadr City. The daily fusillades, which some of the soldiers dubbed "March Madness," turned life in the Green Zone upside down. Virtually overnight, the international zone was transformed from a small island of stability and creature comforts in a sea of violence to a bull's-eye for militias furious at Maliki's attempt to rein in their brethren in the south. Salvos of mortars and rockets began to rain down on the barricaded seat of the Iraqi government and—thanks to the ineptitude of some rocket crews—on hapless Iraqis whose neighborhoods happened to be along the projectiles' flight path. One rocket hit Tariq al-Hashimi's office, killing two of his guards. Other salvos damaged Crocker's residence and four Blackwater helicopters. Roy Alcala, a coalition adviser to Rubaie, returned to his Green Zone trailer after working late one night only to find that it had been pulverized by a rocket.

At the time, the 4th Infantry Division, the American headquarters in Baghdad, described the enemy it was fighting in the capital in public statements as Special Groups and "rogue elements," implying that the mainstream Mahdi Army remained in compliance with the cease-fire Sadr had renewed in February. In fact, both in Basra and in the opening days of fighting in Baghdad, large swaths of the mainstream militia, including senior commanders, were fighting American troops, not just hard-liners from Asaib Ahl al-Haq and Kataib Hezbollah. "Mainstream Jaysh al-Mahdi (JAM) and its 'special groups' coordinated with one another to carry out unified attacks on U.S. forces throughout Baghdad which began on 23 March 2008," a CENTCOM report concluded. "The coordination occurred at the highest levels of JAM command," including Kazim al-Issawi, the senior Mahdi Army commander in Baghdad. But while the initial barrage was conducted with the approval of the militia's Sadr City brigade commander, it "may have occurred prematurely per plan."[10]

Maliki and his American partners were paying the price for the years he and Jaafari had put Sadr City off-limits to the United States or otherwise constrained operations there. Having asserted sovereignty and prevented the Americans from having a free hand in Sadr City, Maliki was no longer sovereign of a sprawling neighborhood that was home to more than two million of the capital's citizens. That reality appeared not to have troubled him as long as the militia attacks were mainly directed at the Americans and the Sadrists remained uneasy members of his governing coalition. But now many of the militias that had declared war on Maliki were ensconced in Sadr City within rocket range of the prime minister's government.

Caught off-guard, American units that were operating near Sadr City moved quickly to reclaim the checkpoints that had been occupied by the militias. On March 25 and March 26, a pair of American battalions, 1-2 Stryker Cavalry and 1-68 Armor, pushed into Jamila and Thawra 1 to take away the launch areas. Reinforced by five companies of Strykers and heavier tanks and Bradleys rushed from the Sunni belts, where the main activity was managing the burgeoning numbers of Awakening volunteers, the soldiers were told they might be needed in Sadr City for a few days. Establishing a toehold, they moved into abandoned homes or schools, hanging blankets over the windows to foil militia gunmen and uncovering concealed, sandbagged fighting positions as they went. Lieutenant Colonel Dan Barnett initially had to sign off on any use of 120mm main gun rounds from the Abrams tanks attached to his 1-2 Stryker Cavalry, but he quickly delegated that authority to his company commanders, and soon the rules of engagement were loosened to allow troops to shoot any spotter they thought was reporting their position on a cell phone.[11]

There were constraints on where the Americans could maneuver, as always. In deference to the Maliki government's opposition to any extensive American military engagement deep inside the slum, Quds Street, the thoroughfare where Jamila and Thawra 1 ended and the older area of Sadr City began, was chosen as the limit of advance—no American troops could venture beyond it. On the other side of the boulevard, which the Americans knew as Route Gold, militia commanders like Arkan al-Hasnawi and Abu Dura still had a sanctuary, but one at the outer limit of their rockets' range against the Green Zone. While American troops could not go north of Route Gold, nothing stopped the militias' fighters from walking south of the boundary, carrying their weapons at night, or moving unarmed during the day and accessing hidden weapons caches south of the boundary. After laying IEDs or firing off a few rounds, the fighters could melt into the urban landscape among an easily intimidated, if not sympathetic, population. Many of the local residents knew when an attack was imminent: a telltale sign was when the crowds in the street mysteriously vanished.

Sadr's August cease-fire, even imperfectly observed, had made Iraq more manageable during the fall and winter, and the explosion of fighting between the Special Groups and the Maliki government was an unwelcome development and a politically awkward one that had come virtually on the eve of Petraeus's and Crocker's return to the United States to update Congress on the war in Iraq. But it was an expression of Maliki's priorities and the Americans were determined to see him through it. Petraeus aptly summed up the situation in a classified letter to Gates: "We have shifted our stance in many areas from nation-building back to war-fighting."[12]

On March 27, Petraeus called Colonel John Hort, the commander of the 3rd Brigade, 4th Infantry Division, who was overseeing the Sadr City fight from his headquarters at Taji, to offer him the use of Shadow drones, armed Predators, and anything else he needed. Below the drones, Apache attack helicopters would hunt militia rocket teams while a CIA-managed Iraqi force did so on the ground. Above, U-2 spy planes and E-8 Joint STARS surveillance planes, which used a sophisticated radar to monitor ground movements, and a Global Hawk drone would help monitor the battle. Though ground operations were not permitted north of Route Gold, nothing prevented the Apaches and Predator drones from firing Hellfire missiles at targets north of the street, if the drones and aircraft could find them.

Despite this surge of high-technology resources, there was only so much they could do in a street fight. By the end of the first week there had been 373 attacks in Baghdad compared to 83 in the week that preceded Maliki's Basra offensive. The Stryker squadron in southern Sadr City had lost six of its armored vehicles to EFPs. Anxious to foil the IED triggermen, the Stryker unit yanked down many of the tangled webs of wires that were slung low over the streets and which mainly included the Rube Goldberg system of electrical wiring that powered much of the neighborhood, a bit of inadvertent collateral damage that plunged many of Sadr City's homes and apartments into darkness. A dead donkey, the victim of a crossfire quickly forgotten, lay for days in one of the main intersections. With the already lagging city services suspended by the gunfire, mountains of trash grew in the streets. When a market was set aflame by an errant American smoke grenade, it took forever for a lone fire truck to arrive, prompting residents to mount a desperate and fruitless effort to douse the flames. As the fighting intensified and lasted beyond the four to five days that the brigade had expected, Hort ordered the troops in his armored and mechanized units to leave their Humvees on base and go out in the tanks and Bradleys that had so far seen little use on the deployment. It was the first time the armored vehicles had been seen on a large scale in Sadr City since 2005.[13]

After his triumph in Basra, assisted though it was by the Americans, Maliki was initially adamant that the Iraqi military mount a quick and decisive operation in Baghdad as well. But Lieutenant General Abud Qanbar, a trusted Maliki aide and the head of the Baghdad Operations Command, urged the prime minister to proceed slowly and methodically.

Although many Iraqi units, notably from the National Police, had dissolved in East Baghdad, Abud's command brokered a deal with tribal leaders in the Sadr City area in which a battalion from the Iraqi Army's 42nd Brigade would be able to join the Americans in the southern sector of Sadr City, from which most of the rockets had been fired. The understanding did not go unchallenged. While Abud and Hammond gave a joint press conference at JSS Sadr City, the lone American outpost below Route Gold, Mahdi Army fighters attacked the arriving Iraqi battalion. Only reinforcement by American Strykers, tanks, and airpower, and efforts by deputy brigade commander Lieutenant Colonel Michael Pemrick and other advisers, kept the Iraqi unit fighting long enough for a second battalion to arrive to reinforce it. Gunfire echoed in the distance, and the shriek of incoming, but fortunately wayward mortar rounds caused the media to duck in the middle of the event. By the end of the day two American soldiers had been killed in Sadr City and seventeen more wounded. Despite the presence of Predators and Apaches overhead, rockets continued to arc to the Green Zone, killing another soldier there.

Virtually overnight, the violence in Sadr City had made the fight a testing ground for the Iraqi military, one that was no longer in a faraway city like Basra but in the nation's capital for all Iraqis to see. As with Basra, Maliki's solution was to mobilize a newly formed Iraqi Army division—in this case, the 11th—which meant that there were more than the usual array of problems. Since the division was just being stood up it suffered from a shortage of experienced noncommissioned officers. One of the division's battalions was assigned to the west side of Baghdad, diminishing its combat power, which was already limited when it came to bomb disposal, engineers, medical units, and logistics.

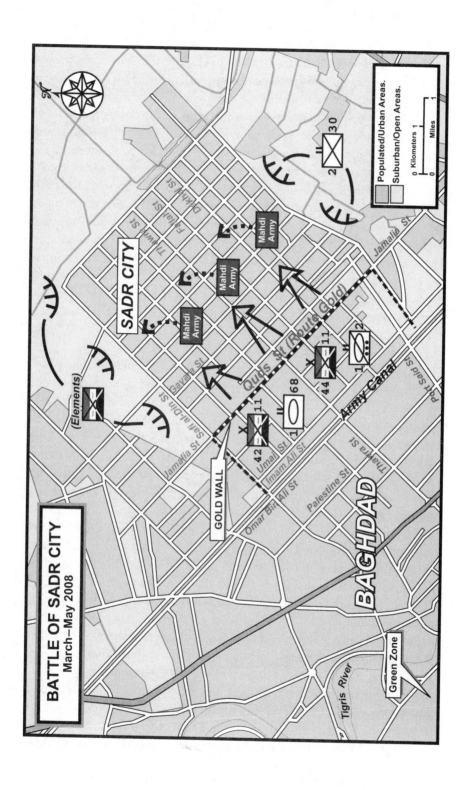

Seeking to put an Iraqi face on the operation, the Americans pushed Iraqi forces to take up positions near Route Gold. American troopers were several hundred meters to their rear, close enough to rush to their aid if necessary, but neither partnered with the Iraqi forces nor in the heart of Sadr City. Persuading the Iraqis to move to their forward positions and stand their ground was dangerous work. Major Mark Rosenberg, the thirty-two-year-old leader of an advisory team that worked with Lieutenant Colonel Yahya al-Zubaidi, a battalion commander in the 11th Division, was riding in his armored Humvee when an EFP, which was wedged into a gap between the ground and the concrete slabs the Americans used to protect their main routes, fired its projectile into the side of his vehicle. The gunner on his vehicle lost both of his legs while Rosenberg's interpreter lost one leg. Rosenberg lost a leg as well and suffered other wounds; he died soon after. In a separate EFP attack, Corporal Steven Candelo, a twenty-year-old member of the team that advised 11th Division commander Major General Mizher Shaher Latif, was also killed when Mizher ran into a complex ambush on his way to FOB Hope.

Once the Iraqis established their positions they generally stayed in place, rarely patrolled down the alleyways or side streets, and demonstrated poor fire discipline. Trying to take advantage of the Iraqi soldiers' limitations, militiamen would dart between Iraqi units, trying to provoke them to fire at one another. Some militia fighters called the Iraqi soldiers, many of whom were recruited from Sadr City, on their cell phones and warned them not to fight. Without Americans continuously stationed at the Iraqi positions, or even in some cases without direct radio communication between the Iraqi and American forces, the American role was restricted to periodic visits to instruct the Iraqis on how best to defend themselves and to exhort them to hold their ground. The Americans advised that under the rules of engagement strangers on rooftops who appeared to be reporting on Iraqi and American positions were fair game. So were the pigeon keepers if it appeared they were releasing their birds to signal the approach of an Iraqi or American unit.

Conserving ammunition and avoiding a dangerous resupply mission up a Sadr City gauntlet was a persistent problem and one that was never solved. "They would receive one or two sniper rounds and the whole platoon would open up at every window and everywhere," Colonel Richard Jung, the commander of the advisory team that worked with Mizher, told the author of a classified analysis of the battle. "You want to be on the inside of the bloom, not on the outside. The next thing you know is the IA

[Iraqi Army] commander is pulling his unit back because they are out of ammunition."[14]

The day that Major Rosenberg was killed a platoon of Stryker soldiers was holed up in an apartment building south of Route Gold with blankets shielding the windows from snipers when the electricity flared on and David Petraeus appeared on one apartment's television. Seven months after their September bout, the general and the ambassador were before Congress again to report on the surge. The thrust of Petraeus's testimony was a sober assessment of the gains since September, all the more so in light of the violence that had wracked Shiite Iraq since March 25. "The Champagne bottle has been pushed to the back of the refrigerator," the general said in response to a question by Indiana senator Evan Bayh. "And the progress, while real, is fragile and reversible."[15] No additional troop cuts would even be considered, Petraeus said, until forty-five days after the withdrawal of the final surge brigade in July brought the force down to fifteen brigades.

Although the whole episode was nowhere near as grueling as the September testimony, Petraeus and Crocker faced tough questions even from supporters like John McCain, and grim assessments from Democratic presidential candidates Clinton and Obama. "We're no longer staring into the abyss of defeat, and we can now look ahead to the prospect of success," McCain said, but asked in reference to the Iraqi 52nd Brigade's performance in Basra, "What's the lesson we're to draw from that, that 1,000 Iraqi Army and police deserted or underperformed?" Clinton, who before the testimony told ABC that "clearly the surge hasn't worked," was harsher. "It might well be irresponsible to continue the policy that has not produced the results that have been promised time and time again," she said.[16] When Obama's turn came, he promised again to set a timeline, if elected, for the withdrawal of all combat troops and to open talks with Iran.[17] When it came to Iraq, the partisan battle lines were already drawn and there was little that was happening on the ground that would change them.

In contrast, Sadr City was still fraught with problems. One of the Iraqi Army's darkest days came on April 16 when the remnants of an eighty-strong company of Iraqi soldiers loaded up their trucks with furniture and abandoned their post near Route Gold, leaving a crucial stretch of road undefended for hours. "Every house in Sadr City probably has one of their sons in the Mahdi Army," said the Iraqi company commander. "So it is hard to convince people to believe in the Iraqi Army." Captain Logan Veath, whose Stryker company from the 25th Infantry Division had been rushed to Sadr City for the battle, implored the Iraqis to return to the front. "If you turn around and go back up the street those soldiers will follow you," Veath said. "If you tuck tail and cowardly run away they will follow up that way, too. You went through a whole battle and are now removing yourself? Are any of your men dead?"

The Iraqi commander acknowledged that his unit had several wounded but none killed, but insisted his unit was short of ammunition and had no means to communicate directly with the American troops. "That is an excuse, and you know it," Veath shot back, arguing that the Iraqis could have sent a runner to the American soldiers a hundred yards to their rear to ask for him.

Dozens of excited Iraqi soldiers began to join in the discussion. As tempers flared and voices rose, First Sergeant Martin Angulo ordered the company's soldiers to form a protective circle around the captain. The Iraqi commander continued his retreat only to be detained by Iraqi generals, who were hugely embarrassed by the episode. Senior Iraqi commanders hurried to the scene and a special Iraqi reconnaissance unit was ordered to advance up the road. With the help of an American bomb-clearing unit, Stryker vehicles, and attack helicopters, the Iraqis rumbled north, preemptively spraying rounds as they went. The furious Iraqi fire on their drive toward the abandoned base endangered the American soldiers who were bringing supplies to one of their platoons, and an American officer issued a plea over the tactical radio. "They are lighting up everything," he said. "Tell them to knock it off."[18]

After the battle the American television program *60 Minutes* would credit American technology with turning the fight around.[19] But the move that did more than anything else to change the balance on the ground was the construction of an immense concrete wall across the length of Route Gold, bisecting Sadr City. It became known as the Gold Wall.

Brigadier General Will Grimsley, a deputy division commander who often visited the forces during the fight, summed it up this way: "East Berlin, West Berlin." Noting that militiamen were still sneaking EFPs and infiltrating bands of fighters south into the Thawra 1 area American and Iraqi troops were occupying, the division began the project under cover of darkness. Starting in mid-April, large cranes operated by contractors lifted twelve-foot-high, nine-ton segments of concrete T-wall into place, working from the far end and planning to link up in the middle. It did not take long before the contractors decided that undertaking a massive project under fire was not worth the risk and Army engineers had to be brought in. As the project plodded along, Hammond decreed that the construction be carried out during daylight hours as well, which led to an escalation of the fighting with the militias, who were determined that the project would not succeed.

By now, there was little attempt to put an Iraqi face on the force opposing the militias on Route Gold. In the time that it took to build the wall, the battalions fighting along Gold fired and called in an extraordinary amount of ordnance. The brigade's tanks along the route fired over eight hundred main gun rounds during the two-month battle, many at sniper positions north of the dividing line. Army commanders also called in Apache attack helicopters equipped with Hellfire missiles as well as air strikes with satellite-guided bombs, leveling buildings. For the militias' part, an Army study noted that "Route Gold was completely saturated" with EFPs. Army explosive ordnance teams regularly found ten to fifteen EFPs along each seventy-five-meter stretch of road, which they sought to clear under fire, their spotlights blazing in the night. To keep up, engineers were authorized to detonate the bombs with machine guns instead of the usual painstaking recovery.[20]

On April 25, a statement from Sadr was read at Friday prayers at mosques in Sadr City and elsewhere around the country. The statement, which took the form of eight edicts, clarified the little-obeyed March 30 cease-fire: while Sadr instructed his followers not to attack Iraqi troops or police, he urged them "to wage open war against the Americans." Three days later, under the cover of another dust storm that grounded aircraft, Mahdi Army fighters more than doubled their rocket attacks against the Green Zone and American bases and again launched coordinated attacks on Iraqi and American positions in southern Sadr City.

On April 28, attacks with a new type of rocket, called an IRAM (improvised rocket-assisted mortar), against Barnett's outpost at JSS Sadr City and another East Baghdad base wounded fifteen soldiers. The next day, Logan Veath's Stryker company was drawn into a fierce gun battle. After rescuing an injured crewmember from an Abrams that had been hit with an EFP, Veath's own Stryker was also hit by an IED and its camouflage netting and reserve fuel cans caught on fire. Under fire from militia armed with AK-47s, rocket-propelled grenades, and machine guns, Veath, with one of his sergeants, ran fifty meters to the burning vehicle and was horrified to see his gunner, Specialist Andrew Howard, burst out of the hatch on fire.

Veath threw Howard to the ground to extinguish the flames and carried him to safety, shooting back at the enemy as bullets struck the dirt near his feet. His commanders nominated him for a Silver Star but the award was downgraded to a Bronze Star with a "V" for valor under fire. The grade inflation that had seen generals given combat decorations for their presence on the battlefield during the invasion had given way to a stinginess regarding awards.

By the end of April, with construction of the wall well under way, the next question was what to do about the remaining three-quarters of Sadr City north of Route Gold. Eight senior Special Groups leaders were believed to be inside the area, and so far American air strikes had not targeted them—only suspected rocket teams. Although American and Iraqi commandos were still not allowed north of the wall, on May 1, JSOC's Task Force 17 began three days of aerial attacks targeting the leaders, killing one with a Hellfire missle. But these measures did not get at the heart of the problem, in part because, as one May JSOC assessment noted, "Lack of near real time HUMINT to confirm locations of HVIs/DHIs in Sadr City" made targeting there difficult. The bulk of Sadr City remained a safe haven for the Mahdi Army and Special Groups.

With the militias still active north of Route Gold and no resolution of the battle in sight, tensions grew among the American commanders who were prosecuting the fight. Hammond was pressing for the establishment of another outpost in a police station near Gold, called JSS Thawra II. The 1st Cavalry Division had planned all through 2007 to do this, but was never able to. Hammond had inherited their plan and meant to stick to it. A demanding general and former quarterback at the University of Mississippi who distributed division coins with the image of a football helmet, Hammond was not known for his patience. When a lieutenant colonel wrote a provocative article criticizing the generalship in the Iraq War, Hammond gathered two hundred captains at Fort Hood and insisted that the author was not competent to judge since he had never worn the shoes of a general officer. Hammond believed that by establishing the second JSS near the dividing line the Americans could force the Iraqi Army to take on more responsibility for securing Sadr City. But the site was a one-story building in an open courtyard surrounded by tall buildings on all sides, regularly attacked with mortars and vulnerable to RPGs.

Both John Hort, the brigade commander, and Barnett, the 1-2 Stryker Cavalry squadron commander, believed that the strategic utility of the new

JSS was negligible and the risk to the American soldiers who would have to establish it was too high. To Hort, the police station simply did not make sense as an outpost—it was a low-set building surrounded by high-rises, in effect making it surrounded by high ground and vulnerable to constant harassing fire, including from tall buildings in the untouchable area beyond Gold. Under pressure to man the station with Americans, Hort directed that platoons go there but be rotated every twelve hours to minimize the time they were vulnerable; still, half a dozen Iraqi soldiers were killed there.

With tensions high between the division and the brigade, Hammond flew into Combat Outpost Old MOD, to the west of the battle area, for a memorial ceremony for one of Hort's troops. Before the service began, Hammond grabbed Hort from his seat in the outpost's makeshift chapel and pulled him into a side room, where he berated the colonel for not building the wall fast enough. Hort protested that his men were doing the best they could under extremely difficult conditions—and then offered his resignation as commander. He pulled the Velcro rank patch off his uniform and tried to hand it to Hammond, but the general refused to take it. For weeks afterward, Hammond left the brigade alone.[21]

The work on the new joint security station proceeded, but at a cost. On May 1, RPG fire there wounded Sergeant John Daggett, an infantryman with one of the Stryker companies that had been pulled down from Taji. Daggett was rushed to an American military hospital in Germany. While being moved to the United States, his condition deteriorated so rapidly that the plane was forced to make an emergency landing in Nova Scotia. But it was too late to save him. Hort, who was in the area at the time Daggett was hit, quickly called in three Apaches that were circling above and had them each fire three Hellfires into the building where the fire had originated—fire had been coming from the building for some time, and Daggett's wounding was the last straw.[22]

Not only the Americans were at odds, however. The Iraqis were struggling for a way to bring the fight to a close as well. Maliki's preferred solution was a large-scale assault, à la Charge of the Knights. The Baghdad Operations Command and Hammond's division drew up a six-month plan for bringing Sadr City under control. Under this plan, troops would spend May continuing to occupy the area below Route Gold and cordoning off the rest of the slum. Then during June and July, they would push north of the wall to clear and hold a specific chunk of the rest of the city before spending another three months—through October—using two full Iraqi brigades to push slowly north from Gold through the length of Sadr City. In addition to Iraqi units, the plan called for shifting most of a Stryker brigade from the Taji area to Sadr City, where it would make its headquarters at FOB Hope and establish footholds in the district's less densely populated northern and eastern corners.[23]

Although this plan, with American assistance, was better and more carefully thought out than Mohan's six-month Basra plan, Maliki reacted with similar impatience when it was presented to him on April 28. A six-month campaign was far too long, the prime minister said; he wanted the whole operation done in two to three days. Although Baghdad Operations Command chief Abud Qanbar reacted to this by saying that he could speed the timeline up to a week or so with reinforcement, Defense Minister Abd al-Qadir al-Obeidi shot back that because of operations in Basra and Mosul no extra troops were immediately available. Rubaie urged caution; Babaker al-Zebari, the head of the Iraqi general staff, bluntly called the idea of contracting a six-month plan into three days impossible.

Maliki was not deterred. If it took six months to secure Sadr City, "the state"—meaning his government—would collapse. "Time is a sword to be used against the Iraqi government," he said. When Petraeus replied that he had to act as Iraq's prime minister, not just the Dawa Party's, Maliki melodramatically shot back that he meant what he said—the state itself, not the Dawa Party, would be in jeopardy if Sadr City were not taken quickly.[24]

Convinced that Maliki was digging his heels in and would accelerate the Sadr City operation no matter what, Babaker suggested bringing up two extra battalions from Karbala, and Petraeus suggested bringing a Kurdish brigade down from the north. Abud asked for seventy-two hours to revise his planning. When the same "crisis action cell" convened again on May 6, little progress had been made. The military realities of Sadr City and the limited availability of extra units had precluded the overly quick offensive that Maliki had been pushing.

While the Iraqis and Americans struggled to settle on a plan, the war of attrition continued. In early May, a troop of thirty Navy SEALs arrived on Route Gold. Brought in from Anbar on short notice to replicate the results their snipers had produced in Ramadi and other battles, the SEALs found themselves in the center of a 360-degree ambush on the first of their five Sadr City missions, and had to be retrieved by Strykers after running low on ammunition. After that, the Navy commandos used Bradleys and MRAPs for their insertions.

To blend in with the Army troops, the sailors wore gray Army uniforms— they had bartered unit coins in exchange for conventional Army ACUs from supply officers at Al-Asad—and cut their hair as short as possible.

Acting like a rodeo clown to distract a raging bull, the SEALs would allow themselves to be observed as they were dropped a hundred meters ahead of where the work on the Gold Wall was proceeding, drawing the militia fighters away from the construction and toward kill zones where they would find themselves confronted with Navy snipers armed with high-powered rifles. Because of Sadr City's grid layout, the SEALs positioned themselves along its perimeter and could see straight down the slum's streets and kill fighters a mile inside it. The SEAL snipers would shoot at the militiamen as they advanced as well as at the men who tried to retrieve the bodies. During one thirty-six-hour dust storm on May 11, they killed forty-six militiamen, a significant number of either the seven hundred militants that the American military would claim were killed during the month-long Sadr City battle or the Mahdi Army's own estimate of one thousand.[25] It was an example of how special operations forces and the conventional military could be devastatingly effective in battle when used together.

On May 3, intelligence pinpointed a fortified complex set of trailers well north of the wall as the headquarters of Arkan al-Hasnawi, known to JSOC as Objective Jerry, a former Mahdi Army brigade commander who had gone rogue and was implicated both in rocket fire and in a campaign to kill Awakening volunteers elsewhere in Baghdad. Unfortunately, the complex was located dangerously close to Sadr General Hospital. Austin's corps headquarters had given Hammond's 4th ID the authority to call in strikes by GMLRS long-range missiles if certain criteria were met, and in spite of the complex's touchy location, Hammond and brigade commander Hort felt that it met those criteria. Without seeking specific approval from corps, they gave the order for an artillery unit east of the city to fire between five and seven GMLRS rockets at the target, which they did, wounding but not killing Hasnawi—and, the Mahdi Army claimed, two dozen civilians. The attack came as a surprise to Lloyd Austin, the corps commander, who a senior officer reported became "animated" upon hearing of it.[26]

As with Basra a month earlier, once the militia leaders saw they were overmatched they sought a face-saving way out. At first, Maliki showed little interest in letting his adversaries live to fight another day. On April 26, Ahmed Chalabi had called Petraeus offering to negotiate on behalf of the Special Groups. "Of course we will not consider such an agreement," Petraeus wrote to Gates.[27] Three days later Maliki expressed his antipathy for Sadr to Bush by videoconference, calling him an "ugly thug." On May 3 Major General Chris Hughes, the British officer in charge of both Sunni and Shiite reconciliation projects, told Petraeus's staff, "We have seen senior Sadrists who believe they should talk to us, but express that they're forbidden to."[28]

Nonetheless, negotiation appeared to be the only way to avoid an even tougher fight against a prepared defense north of Route Gold, which the Iraqi forces would be hard-pressed to handle by themselves. An elaborate series of meetings was held to prepare for this possibility, though. As in Basra, Abud and the other Iraqi generals made it clear that they wanted American support. That meant that American military personnel would need to accompany the Iraqis north of Route Gold to call in the strikes, and to do that Hammond wanted an American platoon to go with them for protection. Masking the American presence in historic Sadr City would not be easy. And if there was major fighting, thousands of residents would need to be evacuated.

In late April, between the 28th and the 30th, a delegation including ISCI and Dawa members visited Iran to negotiate an end to the fighting but was "rebuffed" by Qasim Suleimani, Petraeus told Gates. Still, negotiations continued. According to Rubaie, Maliki authorized the talks at his suggestion; during a Sadr City planning meeting in which the unrealistic idea of evacuating the quarter-million residents of Jamila and housing them in a stadium was floated, Rubaie became frustrated and recommended negotiating. "I said, 'One man can resolve this,' " Rubaie recalled. " 'His name is Muqtada al-Sadr. Give me one week, and I'll go see him.' "[29]

On May 10, after being contacted by Iraqi officials, Sadr agreed to a temporary, four-day cease-fire in Sadr City beginning the next day to allow further negotiations. Along Route Gold, it was predictably hard to tell that anything had changed. On May 10 a helicopter flying near Sadr City was fired at by a shoulder-launched antiaircraft missile, the first launch of such a weapon during the battle, and some militia commanders said publicly that they would not stop fighting until Sadr issued a formal statement. On May 12, an Iraqi soldier along the wall—now 80 percent complete—was shot in the head with a .50-caliber sniper rifle, prompting a Hellfire strike. In 2005, the Austrian company Steyr Mannlicher, despite demarches from the United States and European nations, had sold more than 800 of its HS .50 anti-matériel rifles to Iranian security forces before the Austrian government blocked the sale of an additional 1,200 rifles. Now they or unlicensed copies were turning up in Iraq, as Iranian "lethal aid," just like EFPs and rockets.[30]

However ineffectual it was at the street level, the four-day truce allowed another Iraqi delegation headed by Dawa politician Ali al-Adeeb to travel to Iran for more formal talks with Sadr and Suleimani. The parties arrived at an understanding that averted the need for a bloody push north but allowed what was left of the militias and their leaders to fade away to Iran and fight another day.

Under the deal's terms, after the four-day truce expired, Iraqi troops—unaccompanied by Americans—would be able to move north of the Gold Wall and secure the rest of Sadr City. In return, there would be no call for the general dissolution of the Mahdi Army, contrary to aggressive statements Maliki had been making since Basra. Nor would militiamen be required to voluntarily hand over heavy weapons, although Iraqi troops would have the right to confiscate them—a subtle semantic distinction but one that diluted another demand Maliki had been making publicly. "The sixteen-point agreement incorporates the gist of an agreement that a UIA [United Iraqi Alliance] delegation had worked out with Quds Force Commander Qassim Soleimani and other Iranian officials during a May 1–3 visit to Tehran," Crocker explained in a cable.[31]

The American military had made the deal possible and the Iraqi government later portrayed the outcome as another military victory. Crocker's assessment of the agreement's long-term potential was pessimistic. Although the deal would, if executed, obviate the need for the huge clearance operation the Iraqi military was planning, its terms made a later renewal of fighting between the government and Sadrists likely, the ambassador judged. "When such violence occurs, it seems likely that the parties will again trudge to Tehran and ask Qassim Soleimani to sort out the chaos that he has been instrumental in creating and perpetuating," he cabled home.

During the first days after the formal agreement, fighting along Route Gold continued. On May 13, for instance, an Abrams dropped a building north of the wall with three main gun rounds after taking fire from it. As the planning for an Iraqi operation north of Route Gold continued, it became clear that some sort of political arrangement was afoot. Hammond and the division's intelligence officer were adamant that the Iraqis needed to maneuver around the militias' defenses north of Gold and strike the enemy in the flanks. Ignoring that advice, Abud was planning a thrust directly north, an operation that could work only if the maneuver went uncontested. By May 17, though, the fighting was tapering off, and American troops along the now completed wall were ordered to fire only in self-defense.

American troops took down slabs of the wall at six points on the night of May 19, guarding the gaps with Abrams tanks. At five o'clock the next morning, six Iraqi Army battalions—including T-72 tanks from the 9th Division, veteran troops from Anbar's 1st Division, and the 11th Division's

44th Brigade—advanced north on parallel routes into the northern part of Sadr City. Although Apaches, Predators, and Shadows circled overhead, no American advisers accompanied the columns. The tanks, Humvees, and armored vehicles flew the newly adopted national flag, on which the words "God Is Great" had been rewritten in a new font (the old font was allegedly Saddam Hussein's own handwriting) and from which the three stars that had first represented the potential union of Iraq, Egypt, and Syria and later the three tenets of the Baath Party motto had been removed. By early afternoon, the Iraqi Army columns had spread out to the Sadr and Imam Ali hospitals, former police stations, intersections, and the Sadrist political headquarters—the first sustained presence of government forces north of Quds Street since 2006. There was no resistance, but also no militia leaders to be found. Iraqi soldiers parked their vehicles on the streets and relaxed by their tanks.

A month after the Iraqis pushed north of the wall there was a sign, as Crocker had intimated, that the fight in Sadr City was not quite over. A team of civilians and soldiers from Hort's embedded provincial reconstruction team were scheduled to meet with Hassan Shama, a candidate in Sadr City's first district council election in two years. A larger meeting was scheduled to be held in the district council building's main chamber, but when the American team arrived, they went first to Hassan's office, which had not been cleared according to the military's procedures.

As the team members chatted with their Iraqi hosts, one American diplomat got up, fortuitously, to use the restroom. While he was gone a "sticky bomb" attached to the back of his chair exploded, killing diplomat Steven Farley, the deputy leader of the provincial reconstruction team, along with a contractor and two soldiers. Hort concluded that the attack was an inside job carried out by the Special Groups commander Hajji Jawad in collusion with the Sadrist former district council president, who had quit his job the week before amid threats.[32] Intelligence also linked Ali Faisal al-Lami, a protégé of Ahmed Chalabi who was working with Asaib Ahl al-Haq, to the attack. The district council reconvened two days later at 11th Division headquarters in what American officials hailed as a sign that residents were willing to stand up to the militias. Hassan Shama, who had been wounded in the blast, was elected in absentia.

In the weeks that followed, Iraqi and American leaders pondered the significance of the fighting in Baghdad, Maysan, and Basra. "Recent events may have brought on a sea change in Iraqi politics with regard to the acceptability of militias," Petraeus wrote Gates in mid-April.[33] Though many Iraqi units had performed remarkably poorly in the battles of Basra and Sadr City, they demonstrated Maliki's willingness to take on Shiite militias.

The spring fighting was a major blow to the Mahdi Army and Special Groups across Baghdad and southern Iraq. Lieutenant Colonel Joe McLamb, whose 1-502 Infantry had fought the militia in Kadhimiya and Shula that spring, explained how the fighting had helped break the Mahdi Army's hold on the Shiite population in his area. "I think it's hard sometimes for an American to understand the relationship that the Shia community and Jaish al-Mahdi had at that point," before the spring of 2008, McLamb said. "I believe that the Shia in this area, honestly, in their hearts, believe that if it were not for the protection of the Jaish al-Mahdi, they would have all been killed by the Sunnis, that they would have been driven out of their homes" in 2006 and 2007.[34] But by early 2008 the Sunni threat no longer seemed imminent, and internal conflicts among the mainstream Mahdi Army, Special Groups, and criminal elements undermined the militia's legitimacy. Then in March, government forces in Kadhimiya stood up to the militia and prevailed. A year earlier, the government security forces had been either in collusion with or less competent and more abusive than the militia; with the reverse now the case, the militia lost much of its sheen for locals.

Sadr's complex relationship with Iran also suffered as a result of the spring uprising, after which hundreds of fighters had sought refuge across the border. In early July, for example, a Mahdi Army fighter fatally shot a member of the Iranian government security forces. "Iran is cracking down" and "may deport some," according to notes taken at a July 9 briefing that covered the incident.[35]

Sadr's task in the wake of the spring battles was to decide how to continue without losing further ground in the eyes of the Iraqi populace and inviting further military defeats from an emboldened Maliki, and also without completely losing his military power. Had he chosen simply to rebuild and reorganize the Mahdi Army under cover of a cease-fire he lacked the power to fully enforce, as he had done in 2004 and 2007, he might have been defeated on the battlefield. Had he chosen to disband his militia altogether and play an exclusively political role, he would have been doing so from a position of weakness.

Instead, the cleric, still based in Qom, chose to retain a smaller cadre of militiamen. Sadr "appears to be attempting to reshape his movement to preclude its further marginalization," Petraeus wrote to Gates in mid-June. "After Friday prayers, Sadr issued a statement that future resistance to the Coalition would be carried out by a new, elite Special Group, which will be ultra-secret."[36] The more disciplined covert militia, called the Muqawi-mun, was later renamed the Promised Day Brigades. As the fighting ended, Petraeus's command had sent out orders for a new long-term effort called Operation Big Red, in which conventional forces, Task Force 17, and the CIA would work together to keep up the pressure on both the Special Groups and their Iranian friends.

Maliki himself would call Charge of the Knights, in a meeting with American diplomats three weeks after his troops crossed Route Gold, the "magic key" for dealing with the Sadrist Trend.[37] And in late June, Tala-bani described the political effects of the spring fighting in Baghdad and Sadr City to Bush in a videoconference. Before Basra, Talabani said, the only people in Baghdad who had supported the prime minister were him-self, Crocker, and Iranian ambassador Kazemi-Qomi. Now, in the wake of Basra and Sadr City, the only people who did *not* support him were the Iranian ambassador and Muqtada al-Sadr.[38]

What remained unknown was whether the Sadr City and Basra opera-tions signalled that Maliki was rising above sectarianism, or merely was determined to prevent any challenges to his rule, even from within the Shiite ranks.

CHAPTER 27

Strange Justice

There were times during Maliki's campaign in Basra and Sadr City when Petraeus wondered if the collision course the prime minister had charted with the Shiite militias might lead to such wide-scale violence that it would force the command to overhaul its campaign plan. With the end of the Sadr City fight, however, the violence in Iraq was once again sloping downward and Petraeus and Crocker shifted their focus to the Maliki government's faltering efforts to administer the country.

As the Joint Strategic Assessment Team had made clear a year earlier, the military operations against Al-Qaeda and the militias were just one element of the strategy to right Iraq and head off a bloody multisided war. There was also an unglamorous but essential dimension of the surge that was carried out behind closed doors, rarely entailed visible military operations, and that the legions of reporters, embedded or otherwise, rarely observed: the effort to purge, through pressure or arrest, militia operatives and overtly sectarian officials from the organs of government, prod the ministries to deliver services like health care, education, and electricity to Sunni and Shiite alike, nurture the anemic economy, and make good on vows to establish the rule of law.

Some semblance of an inclusive and representative government was needed to give the Iraqi public a stake in the system that was being administered from the Green Zone and to encourage the insurgents and militias to put down their arms and carry out their struggle for political power through nonviolent means. This was part and parcel of Petraeus and Crocker's campaign plan and also a political requirement in the United States. After he returned from his April appearance before Congress, Petraeus told a meeting of his commanders on April 19 that the success the military had enjoyed in driving down attacks had bought some more time from Congress for the surge, but that the lawmakers' patience was being frustrated by the cost of the war in light of the state of the American economy and by the strain on the troops. Their support for the surge was hardly open-ended. "We have gained some time on the clock," Petraeus told the group of officers, but at home there was a sense that "the Iraqis are not doing enough."[1] The Iraqi government needed to start acting like a proper government, and the Americans needed to do what they could to help.

The preceding months had demonstrated just what an uphill climb Petraeus and Crocker faced. While attention was concentrated on Odierno's Baghdad belts campaign and Phantom Thunder, Petraeus had, without any press releases or media fanfare, cleansed Baghdad International Airport of Mahdi Army operatives and set the stage for legal proceedings that would enable the Maliki government to demonstrate that it was intent on—as the very name it had given to the first surge operation suggested—enforcing the law. To insulate the legal process from outside pressure, political and worse, Petraeus's command had designed, organized, and built a judicial Green Zone—a fortified compound in the Rusafa District of Baghdad in which Iraqi judges, their families, and Iraqi investigators would live and work, safe from retaliation. The Americans had provided a fifty-five-member team of criminal investigators, Justice Department lawyers, and a paralegal staff to train the Iraqi investigators and help them run the complex. The Maliki government had agreed to take on the cost of protecting and operating the legal Green Zone to the tune of $49 million a year. It was impossible to protect all of the judicial fraternity in their individual homes and throughout their travels around the capital, so the Americans eliminated the need to commute.

The court's first defendant, a Syrian militant known by the nom de guerre Abu Qatada, had been convicted of kidnapping and murder and had been sentenced to death by a panel of judges safe from Al-Qaeda's threats of car bombs and assassinations. The next step in the project of state building was to test whether the Iraqi judicial system was capable of trying a former high-ranking official from the Maliki government who had been accused of a crime, and a Shiite, at that. This was not an abstract issue. One day before Petraeus officially took command, but with his knowledge and blessing, American and Iraqi commandos had barged into the Ministry of Health and detained two high-ranking officials: Hakim al-Zamili, a deputy health minister, and Hamid al-Shammari, the head of the fifteen-thousand-strong guard service, on charges that they were running Shiite death squads through an agency officially dedicated to the public's well-being.[2]

The perverse role played by the Health Ministry was well known to Sunnis, who avoided hospitals like the plague, fearing that if they had the misfortune to be treated at Yarmouk, Ibn al-Nafree, or Nur—the three major hospitals in Baghdad—they might be abducted and killed as would any relatives so bold as to visit them. Nor had it been a secret among American troops. In October 2006, during the waning months of Operation Together Forward, Captain Matthew Albertus, a thirty-year-old company commander in John Norris's Stryker battalion, had been approached by the distraught wife of a murder victim. Latif Abd al-Kathum Hilal al-Janabi, the owner of a cell phone shop and a member of a prominent Sunni tribe had been killed; his wife had waited at the gate of a police station, to plead for help in securing the release of her husband's body from the morgue for burial. Taking matters into his own hands, Albertus told the local police chief to get the needed documentation, drove with him to the hospital in his Stryker, and insisted that the morgue yield the body, which was placed in a simple plywood coffin and tied to the roof of the family's Chevrolet Caprice. Captain Albertus's company formed a convoy around the car and escorted it through Baghdad's streets.[3]

The hallways within the ministry were brimming with fear. During Ibrahim al-Jaafari's tenure, the Ministry of Health had been packed with his cronies from the Dawa Party; in the early years of Maliki's prime ministership, when Maliki brought the Sadrists into his governing coalition, Muqtada al-Sadr and his inner circle had selected senior ministry officials, including Zamili. The focus on hospitals was in keeping with Sadr's efforts to model his movement on Hezbollah; halls of the ministry were plastered with posters of Sadr and his father, Muhammad Sadiq al-Sadr.

Dr. Ali al-Shammari, the minister of health, who had served in Najaf as the family doctor for Sadr and his father and brother during Saddam's years in power, had been asked by the Sadrists to return from his exile in Qatar to take up the post. But the minister told Crocker that he was "sandwiched" between Dawa and Mahdi Army operatives, who seemed to have everything but improving the nation's health on their minds, and he would later write in an email to the family of a slain ministry official that he was "surrounded by killers."[4] Ali al-Shammari insisted in the email that he had wanted to fire Zamili "but criminal armed militia do not want that."

Zamili was not the only problem. A unit in Petraeus's headquarters called the Malign Actors Exploitation Cell kept track of Iraqi officials whom American Special Forces might be called upon to detain, as they had Zamili and several sky marshals. As of August 2007, the cell had "target pack-ages," which were never executed, on a variety of other Health Ministry officials, including the ministry's directors general for both East and West Baghdad, its new chief of security, and, ironically, the ministry's inspec-tor general, Dr. Adil Mohsin al-Khazali, who was also head of Maliki's Anti-Corruption Advisory Committee. "Current intel suggests vast corrup-tion, but nothing legally actionable," a report noted of Mohsin.[5] Accord-ing to American intelligence, his bodyguards brought a kidnap victim to the basement of the ministry, tortured him, and then dragged him to the city morgue where he was executed in front of the morgue staff. On one occasion Mohsin himself choked a staff member and ordered him brought to the basement torture area, declaring that he had discovered a ring of "corrupt Sunnis." To make Maliki's anti-cholera campaign and efforts to improve Baghdad security appear better than they were, Mohsin gave orders in September that the actual number of casualties reported by the hospitals in Baghdad be cut in half.

Mohsin had defrauded the Iraqi government out of millions of dollars, selling pharmaceuticals intended for the Iraqi public at a mark-up to for-eign firms and providing them to Iranian contacts at a discount. When the Commission on Public Integrity opened an investigation into some of the shenanigans at the ministry, Mohsin visited the organization and demanded that the inquiry be closed. After he was rebuffed, he sent a signal that he was not to be trifled with: two of the commission's guards service were killed. "Adel Mohsin's reputation undermines the Prime Minister's efforts to bring accountability, reconciliation, and reform to his government," read a highly classified American report, which noted that its information could only be shared orally with Maliki and Rubaie. "At best, Mohsin is an impediment to reform within the Ministry of Health. At worst, he is a criminal JAM facilitator, who has embezzled public funds and has ties to kidnappings, murders, and ethno-sectarian violence. A body of evi-dence suggests that, in either case, he is unsuited to serve as the Inspector General of the Ministry of Health or as the Head of the Prime Minister's Anti-Corruption [Advisory Committee]."[6]

A lot was rotten in the Ministry of Health. Despite sensitive information the Americans passed to Maliki about Mohsin he remained untouched and in his post. The Zamili case would be an opportunity to purge the ministry of sectarianism and show the Sunnis that Maliki was above taking sides. Michael Walther, an American Justice Department official who was advis-ing the Iraqis, said the case was more important than the Saddam Hussein trial. There was a perception among Sunnis that Iraq's legal system was an instrument for imposing the tyranny of the majority; now it seemed prepared to prosecute one of its own.

Building the case against Zamili, an Iraqi investigator gathered testimony from nine witnesses who discussed how he and Hamid al-Shammari used the ministry to organize attacks against Sunnis in hospitals with the aim of driving Sunnis out of the capital. Under Zamili and Shammari's direction, about 150 members of the agency's protection service were organized into a company that acted like a private militia. Using Health Ministry identification to move freely around Baghdad and ambulances to ferry weapons, they carried out hundreds of sectarian killings and kidnappings from 2005 to early 2007, the investigation reported.[7]

Those who were murdered included Ammar al-Saffar, a deputy Health Ministry official who told friends he had been threatened by Zamili after mounting his own investigation. A car full of masked men drove to his Baghdad home and took him away; he was never to be seen again. Ammar's son Ali, who was living in London, later approached no less a figure than Jaafari about the episode and was told Zamili was involved. Ali later received an apologetic email from Ali al-Shammari, the health minister. "I was working alone in the ministry against so many illiterate and corrupted people so I asked your father to stay with me," he wrote.[8]

To ensure the trial went ahead, Walther and Colonel Mark Martins, Petraeus's chief legal officer, arranged for some of the Iraqi witnesses to be relocated to the United States for their protection. Under Iraqi law, a government official could not be prosecuted—even for murder—unless Maliki waived immunity, a step Iraq's Interior Ministry and the prime minister had declined to take earlier in the year when the Americans wanted to prosecute Major General Mahdi al-Gharawi, the commander of the 2nd National Police Division, which had committed many sectarian abuses. With the Americans insistent that the case against Zamili and Hamid al-Shammari go forward, and Maliki increasingly at odds with Sadr, the prime minister decided to allow the case to proceed.

In the months leading up to the trial it became clear that Zamili had cards to play as well. His supporters acquired a copy of the supposedly confidential investigation report from the panel of three judges, which included the list of protected witnesses. Soon his relatives and Ahmed al-Sheibani, an aide to Sadr, began intimidating the witnesses and threatening their families. After the Americans learned through electronic eavesdropping that one of the judges was being pressured, Petraeus's command approached Medhat al-Mahmoud, Iraq's chief justice, who arranged for the judge to be replaced for "administrative reasons." But the intimidation did not stop. When the proceedings came to a head one witness said she was so afraid that she no longer had a fixed address while another recanted his testimony altogether. In early March, Zamili and Hamid al-Shammari were acquitted.[9]

Some American officials concluded that senior members of the Iraqi government, including Medhat, had acquiesced in the outcome. The American embassy took the extraordinary step of issuing a statement expressing its disappointment in the verdict, while aides to Petraeus suggested that they were looking at ways to get the charges reinstated. But the Zamili case was dead. If the performance of Iraq's government was to improve, Petraeus and Crocker would need to find another way. To develop a new strategy, Petraeus turned again to H.R. McMaster, the main architect of the JSAT. Even before the charges against Zamili and Shammari had been dropped, McMaster had launched a reassessment of Iraqi governance, along with Larry Napper, an academic from Texas A&M who had worked on assistance programs in the Balkans and former Soviet Union and had been tapped by Charlie Ries, the embassy's senior economic officer, to lead the civilian side of the effort. Together with a dozen staffers and experts, they were known as the Governance Assessment Team.

As rocket fire lit up the Green Zone, McMaster and Napper visited the main ministries and Iraq's far-flung provinces. Apart from the pernicious sectarianism, it was clear that the Iraqis were saddled with a bureaucracy hobbled by the flight of experienced professionals: this bureaucracy was reluctant to make decisions, coordinate across ministerial boundaries, or take action without awaiting instructions from the very top—a holdover from the days in which Saddam ruled Iraq with an iron fist, and from fear of the sectarian parties that had grabbed control of the levers of power in Baghdad.

One major reform the Governance Assessment Team considered was to persuade the Maliki government to issue block grants, thereby decentralizing some of its budget authority. Bayan Jabr's Finance Ministry was dribbling out its funds to the provinces, which meant that projects were moving in a halting manner and at a glacial pace. Beyond that, McMaster and Napper believed that if provincial governments were given a pool of funds to work with they would have more motivation than federal authorities and could be held accountable in local elections, all of which would help Iraq develop a more democratic and representative government.

Jabr, a Shiite official who had run the Ministry of Interior when the abuses in the Jadriya Bunker were exposed before moving to Finance, kept one eye on television reports about the latest oil prices as Napper outlined the initiative. The finance minister was singularly unenthusiastic, questioning whether all of Iraq's eighteen provinces had the capacity to spend the money efficiently, and suggested—ironically, given the many abuses the Americans had already uncovered at the country's ministries—that the type of disbursement proposed would lead to corruption. Napper responded that the U.S. embassy kept detailed reports on the Iraqi budget and spending across the country, could identify which provinces were competent, and that Jabr could reinforce those provinces and make an example. Jabr was unmoved; it became clear that he was reluctant to relinquish any of his considerable influence and authority. That was no surprise. He personally signed off on each allocation of money to the provinces. The week before Bush went to Anbar, Crocker had to demand that Jabr send money owed to the province.

After running into a brick wall with Jabr, McMaster and Napper went to see local officials in the provinces, many of whom had all but given up on getting help from Baghdad or were too beleaguered to focus on governance. In Najaf, Napper and the team met the governor at the city airport, and they were surprised at the beehive of activity around the city. The governor said he wanted people just to stay out of his business and he would see that Najaf became the center of Shiite pilgrimage, with over three million pilgrims a year, many of whom would be Iranians. He had all but given up on securing resources from the federal government. Baqubah, the capital of Diyala Province, was starved for funds, relied heavily on Baghdad's whims, and was grateful for whatever help the Americans might provide. In Mosul, where Al-Qaeda was still active and the governor's brother-in-law had recently been killed, the governor was only interested in talking about governance and budgets insofar as it would allow him to "hang on by his fingernails up there," Napper reported. In Kirkuk, the leaders were distracted by the debate over power-sharing among Kurds, Arabs, and Turkmen. In Basra, local officials appeared preoccupied with the turmoil. Even as the ministries in Baghdad protected their power and perquisites with grim determination, the officials in the provinces were so focused on mere survival that they found it hard to concentrate on the road ahead.

For their part, the Americans were also hampered by bureaucracy. Petraeus and Crocker famously got along, but the American civilians serving as mentors to the Iraqi ministries were not as effective as they could have been. Crocker had made it clear to Bush before taking up his post in Baghdad that embassy personnel would need to take risks and might suffer casualties, like the military, and the president had accepted the prospect. In practice, however, the embassy's security officials imposed such stringent requirements that civilian advisers were spending little time at the agencies they were supposed to be advising. Nor were the embassy's efforts in Baghdad connected in any way to the work being done across Iraq by the civilian-led provincial reconstruction teams.

When McMaster and Napper's Governance Assessment Team returned to Baghdad, they prepared a blunt report—typed by staff wearing body armor in a small building near the embassy, as mortars rained down on the Green Zone. A major thrust of the report was to find ways to bolster the autonomy of senior civil servants, the directors general, against first the militias in their ministries but increasingly against the prime minister.

Completed on April 24, the report noted that sectarian control of the ministries had changed little since the JSAT report a year before. "In spite of significant improvements in the security situation over the past year, key ministry buildings in Baghdad are still controlled by sectarian militia creating an environment of danger and intimidation both for Iraqi civil servants and their coalition advisors," they wrote. Zamili's acquittal and the tendency of senior officials to insist that their subordinates be immune from prosecution, the report continued, "have sent a signal that those in government are above the law." Adding to the dysfunction in Baghdad, eleven of Iraq's thirty-two ministries were led by temporary acting ministers or had no top officials at all—a sign both of Iraqi governmental inertia and, in retrospect, of the Maliki government's interest in keeping ministries leaderless in order to control them.[10]

As for the efforts by the American-led coalition, the report concluded that they were "best described as fragmented and incoherent" and not focused on the most important ministries. "A majority of advisors do not speak Arabic and can only work through interpreters, making it difficult to provide technical assistance in a system still driven largely by paper documents. Current Diplomatic Security (DS) policies and procedures, and insufficient security assets, restrict face-to-face work to only a few hours per week. The requirement to provide at least 72 hours of prior notice to arrange security, excludes advisers from key impromptu GOI [government of Iraq] meetings where many key decisions are made. Under these conditions advisors do not gain essential insight and understanding into the work of the ministries and cannot establish the presence needed to be more effective."

Attempts to persuade the tangle of government agencies, contractors, and military organizations to cooperate often ran into resistance. The problems included "contractors refusing to share information, some civilian officers' fears of a 'military takeover' of assistance programs, some military officers' resistance to assuming more of the security burden for civilian-led teams, and the persistent goal of some in the USM-I [the U.S. embassy] to achieve 'normal bilateral operations' as quickly as possible, irrespective of the goals in the Joint Campaign Plan."

Tasked with proposing a course correction, the team outlined a list of recommendations. As a general strategy, the report noted that Iraq was to hold provincial elections in 2008 and national elections a year later. That, the report observed optimistically, would provide the United States with an opportunity to encourage Iraqi politicians to support competent government, if only to improve their prospects at the polls. Toward this end, the report recommended that spending authority be devolved to the provinces, and that "ghost employees" be stripped from the ministries' rolls.

To root out abuses, the study recommended, as the JSAT had a year before, the Iraqi government should be pushed to arrest and prosecute—not merely fire or "freeze"—sectarian officials in the guard services of the Health, Transportation, Electricity, and Agriculture ministries by the beginning of July. Even sooner—by the beginning of May—it called for American forces to "take immediate steps to marginalize/remove current acting MoJ [minister of justice] and chief judge HJC" meaning Judge Medhat of the Higher Judicial Council, whom the report blamed for botching the Zamili case and demonstrating a lackluster approach to other prosecutions.

Medhat, contrary to the recommendation in the report, continued in his post and would play an important and controversial role in Maliki's efforts to consolidate his power. But Petraeus's command was able to press for some arrests. On May 22 the Americans convinced the Interior Ministry to sign off on the arrest of General Jumma Hussein Zamel, the top official in Iraq's correctional system, who, Petraeus wrote to Gates, had "been accused of abusing and torturing prisoners, extortion, providing lethal support for JAM, and extra-judicial killings." Because Jumma seemed aware of the suspicions against him and poised to flee the country, the ministry allowed its top-tier Interior Ministry commando unit that had fought in Basra, the U.S. Special Forces–advised Emergency Response Unit, to make the arrest before Jumma got away.[11]

To improve the American-led effort to advise Iraq's ministries on financial issues, the report recommended that a new czar for assistance—the coordinator for economic transition—be appointed in Washington, a step that was never taken. In a parallel move, McMaster wanted to create a powerful new cell in Baghdad that would coordinate the work that the military and civilians did on governance, corruption, and a host of other issues. But faced with bureaucratic resistance within the American government, the recommendation was toned down. Instead, the report proposed that a Public Finance Management Group be established to try to get the Iraqi ministries to spend their budgets more efficiently, a move that was implemented.

To facilitate access by American advisers to Iraqi ministries and address anxiety within the embassy about the risks of operating in the East Baghdad area where many of the ministries were based, the study recommended stripping Blackwater, Triple Canopy, and the other civilian security contractors of the job of protecting the embassy's convoys, and giving the task to the military instead, in spite of the implied drain on manpower. But this recommendation would have required a sea change in how the military and civilians operated in Baghdad, and it went nowhere.

In the years that followed the surge, the campaign would be portrayed as a lesson in how to conduct counterinsurgency. Viewed from within, the surge was a testament to the valor and dedication of the military, and to the desire of many Iraqis to put the sectarian conflict behind them. But as the governance report made clear, many of the officials who comprised the civilian arm of the surge lacked the expertise and expeditionary spirit required to turn around a war gone wrong.

By the spring of 2008, the White House and its team in Baghdad were under enormous pressure to begin winding down the surge. Indeed, the president had already begun to focus on negotiating a status of forces agreement (SOFA) that would provide a legal basis for American forces to remain in Iraq once the United Nations mandate had expired at the end of the year and a strategic framework accord to guide American-Iraqi relations in the future. As the Bush administration pondered what remained to be done in its final months in office, securing the twin agreements with the Iraqis became a higher priority than stepping up the pressure to remake the Iraqi government, politically and administratively. The delays in deciding on a surge strategy for Iraq had come at a price. In the end, the governance report was more of a guide to the many hurdles that remained than a plan for the administration's final year of dealing with Iraq.

The agreements sought by the Bush administration—the SOFA and the strategic framework agreement—were of great interest to Iran. In early June, Maliki visited Iran and met with Grand Ayatollah Ali Khamenei, Iran's supreme leader.

Despite American efforts in 2007 to blunt its sway, Iran still had considerable influence in Iraq, as it had shown during the spring Mahdi Army uprising by both supplying the militia with arms and hosting the backroom negotiations that allowed Maliki to claim victory in Basra and cross the Gold Wall uncontested in Sadr City. Operation Canines, Task Force 17's effort to track and detain Quds Force officers, had caused Iran to pull out many of its front-line operatives, and the defeat of its proxies in Sadr City had compounded the blow. But Iran was exercising an ever-increasing amount of "soft power" in Iraq. Much of Iran's investment in Iraq was sponsored by the Quds Force or its soft power arm, the Kosar Bureau—because Iraq was so dangerous, private Iranian investors had shied away from it. An American diplomatic cable claimed, citing Iranian sources and the British ambassador in Tehran, that "only former IRGC officials have the courage and the connections to operate in the insecure climate in Iraq," a reference to Iran's Islamic Revolutionary Guard Corps, the parent organization of the Quds Force.[12] In May 2007, Iranian economic interests in Iraq gained a foothold when the Iraqi government granted a license to open a Baghdad branch of Bank Sepah, a major Iranian financial concern that served not only a legitimate but an underhanded purpose, handling and facilitating Quds Force transactions. Bank Melli, a similar Iranian financial institution, received its own license to open shop in June. Both banks would eventually come under U.S. sanctions.

In March 2008, Iranian president Mahmoud Ahmadinejad, who had limited authority over Iran's dealings in Iraq compared to the supreme leader's man, Qasim Suleimani, had visited Baghdad. Afterward, Rubaie discussed the visit with American diplomats David Satterfield and Marcie Ries and NSC representative Brett McGurk. "Curiously, Rubai noted that throughout the visit, Ahmadi-Nejad never once mentioned the United States during his private meetings and indeed acted 'as if there were no foreign troops in Iraq,' " the State Department cable on these meetings recounted.

According to Rubaie, the Iranian president was devout enough that many of his Iraqi interlocutors found it unusual. "Rubai said Ahmadi-Nejad appeared to be obsessed with occultation and the 'Hidden Imam,' " or the Mahdi, the twelfth rightful descendant of the prophet whose eventual reappearance, Shiite doctrine held, would accompany that of Jesus Christ, the same State Department cable noted. For example, one of the president's last meetings before returning to Tehran took place at Abd al-Aziz al-Hakim's residence. "In a room full of 30–40 people, Ahmadi-Nejad lectured for an hour about the return of the Mahdi, claiming that the wait united both Arab and Persian Shia," the cable read, citing Rubaie. Ahmadinejad ended his lecture and departed after being passed a note by Iranian ambassador Kazemi-Qomi. Maliki, Abd al-Mahdi, and Ahmed Chalabi were all present, as was a prominent Iraqi Shiite cleric, Ayatollah Muhammad Bahr al-Ulum. "Rubai noted that some Shia had been quietly bewildered by the display and that Bahr al-Ulum had joked about Ahmadi-Nejad's religious fervor, claiming that 'he should go back to the hawza,' " or religious school, the cable noted dryly.[13]

A few weeks after Ahmadinejad's visit, Iraqi foreign minister Zebari met with Petraeus, Crocker, and McGurk and discussed what he had heard about the aftermath of the trip back in Tehran. "Zebari reported that after his March 2–3 visit to Iraq, Iranian President Ahmadinejad lobbied Supreme Leader Ayatollah Khamani for complete control of the Iraq portfolio, arguing that he had successfully guided Iran's nuclear confrontation with the United States crowned by the December 2007 NIE, which had concluded that Iran had suspended nuclear weapons work, and that he could duplicate the feat in Iraq," the cable on the meeting explained.

Apparently, Khamenei's response was negative; the Quds Force remained in charge of Iraq policy, and, according to Zebari, "Iran ha[s] settled on a policy of increased confrontation with the United States in Iraq." The foreign minister said, "Coalition kinetic activities were having a substantial effect on Iranian activities but Iran remained determined to increase its influence by getting IRGC-QF members into Iraq."[14]

After his June Iran trip, Maliki told American officials that he had raised the issue of Iran's weapon shipments to the Special Groups, providing details of what had been captured in Iraq, but that Khamenei and Suleimani denied that they had anything to do with training or arms flow. "Someone must be violating my orders," the supreme leader said when shown the evidence, according to Maliki. Suleimani took a similar line, claiming "that the training and weapons supply must have been done 'without authorization' and would be investigated."

In his postmortem with American officials, Maliki offered his own views on the relationship between the two men, supreme leader and Quds Force commander. "Commenting on the relationship between Soleimani and Khamenei, Maliki said that it was a 'mistake' to see Soleimani as an independent actor," the cable reported, and quoted the prime minister directly on the Quds Force general: "He follows Khamenei's line completely and without Khamenei he would be nothing." It was a revealing assessment. Like much of the American intelligence community, Maliki believed that Iran's support for the militias in Iraq and the operations it had encouraged there could not have been undertaken without the approval of the highest authority in Tehran.[15]

By the summer, Iraq's relationship with its neighbor to the east was increasingly being overshadowed by concerns over Iran's nuclear program, Israeli calculations, and private Bush administration discussions about how to nurture progress in Iraq while keeping the pressure on Tehran to forswear its nuclear weapons ambitions. Iran's worries about a potential Israeli strike on its nuclear facilities were palpable. In September, Israeli aircraft had attacked a nuclear facility deep in Syria in Operation Orchard, and nine months later, at the beginning of June, they conducted a long-range strike exercise in the Mediterranean that simulated the distance between Israel and the Iranian facilities at Natanz and Isfahan. In December, the United States had issued a National Intelligence Estimate stating that as of 2003 Iran's nuclear program had been suspended. Israel had disagreed, and its recent military actions had prompted the Iranian military to become increasingly paranoid about an impending strike, as evidenced by mistakes aplenty committed by jittery Iranian air defense troops.

According to highly classified American reports, in June 2007 a Revolutionary Guard air defense unit had fired a TOR-M1 antiaircraft missile at a civilian airliner that it mistook for a potential attacker. In May 2008 antiaircraft units fired on another civilian airliner, an Iranian drone, and an Iranian F-14 fighter, and in June there were two more instances against civilian aircraft. Iran was "concerned attack aircraft may attempt to mimic the flight profile of a commercial airliner," a classified Pentagon report explained. On June 15, the commander of the Iranian Air Force "ordered fighters from all units to conduct daily air-to-ground attack training (GAT) at firing ranges resembling the Israeli city of Haifa and the Israeli nuclear facility at Dimona," according to another military report. "This is the first time a specific reference to Israeli targets has been noted," added the report, which also stressed that such attacks were generally beyond the Iranians' capability.[16]

During the summer of the surge, with little fanfare, Crocker, David Pearce, and other American diplomats had conducted three formal discussions with Iraqi and Iranian representatives in Baghdad. The trilateral talks proved useful to nobody, and, Petraeus noted in a letter to Gates, appeared designed to build up the stature of the Iraqi Foreign Ministry. The discussions had been narrowly focused and entirely unproductive. Crocker had repeatedly raised the issue of Iranian support for Shiite militias and even Al-Qaeda in Iraq. Following one session, Crocker told Abd al-Mahdi that the United States did not need the Iranians to acknowledge their role in smuggling EFPs, rockets, and other weapons to Iraq; he just wanted them to stop doing it. As Crocker discussed the issue, he noted in a cable, mortar or rocket fire rattled the windows in Abd al-Mahdi's office, prompting the Iraqi official to recall a discussion he had had with Suleimani in Tehran. Abd al-Mahdi recalled that he had asked Suleimani if he was behind any rocket attacks in Iraq; the Iranian had joked that if the fire "was accurate, it was his."[17]

While the official talks floundered, a strange back channel remained open between Petraeus and Suleimani himself. At the end of March, with Maliki in Basra, Ahmed Chalabi had relayed a message from the Quds Force commander to the top American general, the second such message after the one Shirwan al-Waeli had delivered in August 2007. "Qods Force Commander Soleimani sent me a message this evening via the ubiquitous Dr. Chalabi . . . that he 'strongly opposed' shelling of the Green Zone and has spent a lot of effort in the past two days to stop the firing," Petraeus wrote to Gates. "Given Chalabi's maneuvering of late, I don't doubt he actually got such a message (my second from Soleimani, a truly evil figure, as you know)."[18] Petraeus responded to the messages through the intermediaries who brought them, but never addressed the demands Suleimani made, like the release of Qais and Laith al-Khazali. A message was conveyed back to Suleimani at one point by Hadi al-Amari with an explanation for why Petraeus, unlike all senior Iraqi officials, would not deal with Suleimani directly: the Iranian general was only a one-star, while Petraeus was a four-star. The excuse was tongue-in-cheek—the Iranian Revolutionary Guard only had two general officer ranks, one-star and two-star, and Suleimani was among the most senior security advisers to the supreme leader.[19]

A weekly briefing to Petraeus and his staff on Iraqi media and politics always included a collection of the week's editorial cartoons from Iraqi and other Middle East newspapers. One featured a cartoon that depicted Iran as a vulture dragging off a dead deer representing Iraq that a hunter symbolizing the United States had shot. "Not a bad thought, and fairly accurate, too," Petraeus quipped to his staff.[20]

For all of its concern about Iran's nuclear program and distaste for the leadership in Tehran, the Bush administration was wary about taking on a new military challenge, one that could jeopardize the headway it was finally beginning to make in Iraq. Bush had made it clear to the Pentagon during the deliberations on whether to mount the surge that he was wary of taking steps that might inadvertently lead to a wider war with Iran. While he shared Israel's worries about Tehran's nuclear ambitions, he did not want Israel to take any action that might inflame the situation in Iraq.

"I don't want Israel to bomb Iran," Bush told the NSC bluntly on June 18. In a June 20 meeting at the White House, Gates recommended that the United States ask Israel not to strike for at least a year in return for help with Israel's antimissile defense. American officials also hoped that a new program of covert action in Iran, beyond CENTCOM's highly classified third-party forays from 2005, might help the United States buy time with the Israelis. Hopefully, the new program—apparently including the Stuxnet cyberattack—would be "on autopilot on 20 January 2009," Gates told NSC members on June 26.[21]

In Baghdad, however, the possibility of American or Israeli action against Iran weighed heavily on Maliki's mind. In early July, the Iraqi prime minister went with Petraeus and Rubaie to visit JSOC headquarters in Balad. After nearly five years in Iraq, Stan McChrystal had recently given up command there to Vice Admiral Bill McRaven, a Navy SEAL. Task Force 17's raids on Shiite targets were always a sensitive political issue for Maliki, and on top of that, just a few days before, a JSOC raid had gone wrong and killed one of the prime minister's cousins. Petraeus wanted to impress the prime minister with JSOC's capabilities and explain how the task force was starting to work more with the Iraqi commando units that previously had been included only in Special Forces, not JSOC, operations. In an extraordinary display, the Delta Force, Ranger, and other JSOC troops performed a "layout" for the prime minister, showing him their gear and demonstrating their capabilities as they might to an extremely high-ranking American back at Fort Bragg.

But the Iraqi leadership had other concerns on their minds during the visit. Rubaie had read a report in *The New Yorker* that JSOC was launching missions into Iran from Iraq, and he asked the force's new commander, McRaven, whether the report was true. "Bill reassured Mowaffak and the Prime Minister that none of his forces are operating in Iran," Petraeus wrote to Gates.[22] Although Bush would authorize strikes in Syria and Pakistan using McRaven's JSOC forces in the waning weeks of his presidency, he would never do the same on Iran.

Later that day, Maliki opened a videoconference with Bush by expressing his concern over talk of strikes against Iran by either the United States or Israel. If Israel violated Iraqi airspace, he said, he would have no choice but to hold the United States responsible—he could not allow Iraq to "become a battleground." Eager to keep things on track and to work out long-term arrangements with Iraq, Bush sought to reassure the Iraqi prime minister. "Nothing is more important to me than success in Iraq," he said, according to notes of the conversation. There could be no Israeli or American flights to Iran over Iraqi territory, Maliki repeated. "I hear you loud and clear," Bush said.[23]

PART III

New Dawn

Obama, Maliki, and Beyond, 2008–2012

CHAPTER 28

Let's Make a Deal

Robert Loftis had just completed a semester of teaching at the National Defense University in Washington when he was tapped for a special mission. Loftis had spent years in the State Department's Bureau of Political-Military Affairs negotiating status of forces agreements and base access accords in Africa, East Asia, Latin America, and, most recently, Eastern Europe. But now Condoleezza Rice wanted him to take on the most important negotiation of his entire career: Iraq.

Throughout the occupation, the legal cover for the American military presence in Iraq had been provided by a United Nations Security Council resolution, but by late 2007, Iraq's leaders were eager to reassert their own sovereignty and George Bush was anxious to cement a relationship with post-occupation Iraq that would endure beyond his administration.

To secure the hard-fought security gains in Iraq and provide a new legal basis for keeping American troops there, a bilateral SOFA would be needed in 2008 to replace the increasingly untenable U.N. framework.[1] There was little room for error and Bush was determined to hand over a policy to his successor that carried forward his vision of a new Iraq.

Even for a diplomat as experienced as Loftis, Iraq would be an enormous challenge. It would be the first SOFA negotiated in a wartime environment, and his team's main negotiating partner would be a fractious Iraqi government that was involved in a seemingly unending series of internal political struggles. Further complicating the picture, the terms of the SOFA would be made public. The transparency would be a step toward the democratic Iraq the Americans insisted they wanted to see, but it was guaranteed to provide fodder for a vigorous political debate in a country with deep cultural sensitivities to foreign occupation.

In order to prepare for the challenge, Loftis and his team sequestered themselves in a poorly lit, barely ventilated conference room in the Pentagon basement. For three days they scoured existing peacetime status of forces agreements, which provided the legal underpinning for the deployment of American forces abroad. Generally speaking, there were two types of agreements: long-form SOFAs cover the full gamut of interactions between United States forces and the country in which they are stationed and can run as long as thirty pages. On the other hand, shorter SOFAs might only involve a simple exchange of diplomatic notes for a single joint military exercise.

Loftis and his team decided that the sheer number of U.S. troops in Iraq, the length of time they would be there, and the nature of their mission required the longer approach. They identified about thirty-five provisions they believed should be included in the initial draft, including legal immunity for civilian contractors, airtight legal protections for the troops, and the assurance that American forces would be able to operate in Iraq as they deemed necessary.

Ambassador Crocker and NSC staffer Brett McGurk, who had been dispatched by the White House in the fall of 2007 to close negotiations on the declaration of principles on the long-term bilateral relationship, thought that Loftis had it exactly backward. The lawyerly demands for blanket immunities and broad latitude in conducting operations, including detaining Iraqi citizens, were politically charged issues bound to be portrayed by Muqtada al-Sadr and Iran as a devious effort to extend the occupation indefinitely. The British had rammed through a military agreement in 1948 that sought to give them levers to influence Iraqi security policy even as British troops withdrew, Crocker noted, and there were bound to be plenty of suspicions in Baghdad and Tehran that the United States would try to do the same. The Crocker-led embassy had an ally in Doug Lute, who had assumed the role of Iraq czar at the White House during the surge. The sort of negotiation Loftis was planning could take a year or more, if it worked at all, he thought, and Bush no longer had that kind of time. The president wanted the agreement signed, sealed, and delivered by the end of 2008 because he was not about to leave the issue to the next president.

Iraqi politicians, for their part, had their own ideas of what they wanted out of a new agreement with the United States, and it looked nothing like any of the SOFA provisions that Loftis had in mind. During McGurk's negotiations of the declaration of principles in the fall of 2007, a close Maliki aide presented a four-point proposal that outlined what the Iraqis were hoping to get out of the SOFA talks: a commitment to defend Iraq against attack, no small matter since Iraq's army would not have the ability to defend itself against external foes for years; a promise to defend the Iraqi regime against a potential coup; an assurance that the United States would work to have Iraq's international debts from the Saddam era forgiven; and a strenuous American effort to ensure that United Nations sanctions from that period were lifted.

With sharp divisions among the Americans over how to proceed with the upcoming negotiations, a meeting of top-level officials, minus the president, was arranged in early February. The United States needed to find a basis to remain in Iraq. Loftis's opening position carried the risk of a serious backlash, argued Crocker and McGurk, who believed a security agreement needed to be part of a broader package of economic and diplomatic assistance. A security-only approach might be perceived by the Iraqis as a self-interested American gambit that ignored their sovereignty and needs. But Crocker's argument fell on deaf ears. Nearly all the Pentagon officials, including Gates, firmly backed the Loftis approach. An uneasy compromise was reached: Loftis would lead the SOFA talks and would present his negotiating position, but McGurk would head a wider set of discussions on a strategic framework agreement, or SFA, that would cover cooperation on the full range of economic, diplomatic, and security issues. Loftis was tasked with delivering the security side of the overall agreement, while McGurk concentrated on the more comprehensive effort. Both men reported to Crocker, who oversaw both efforts.[2]

Stephen Hadley rationalized the decision as a bureaucratic necessity. Just as with the surge, he argued, it was not possible to overrule the Pentagon on its own area of expertise. If Crocker and McGurk were right it was important to bring the Defense establishment around to their view.[3] It was a prescription for maintaining harmony within the ranks of the U.S. government, at least in the short run, but as with the deliberations over the new surge strategy it was an approach that would eat up valuable time.

One step that the Bush administration did not insist on was that the agreement be submitted to the Iraqi parliament for ratification. Asked by Massachusetts congressman Bill Delahunt if Bush would accept an agreement with Iraq that had not been formally endorsed by the Council of Representatives, Crocker provided a terse, but unqualified, written response, one that was vetted by the White House and other government agencies. Approval by Iraq's parliament was not a requirement, the statement implied. "We are confident Iraq will meet its domestic legal requirements for approval of the Strategic Framework and the Status of Forces Agreement," Crocker wrote. "We do not believe it appropriate for the United States to specify the procedures the government of Iraq must follow to meet the requirements of Iraqi law."[4] Even an agreement that was merely read to the Iraqi parliament but not put to a vote, some Bush administration officials indicated, would be acceptable.

In the end, Maliki decided that he would submit the agreement to the Iraqi parliament, but his reasons for doing so were primarily political. Cementing an agreement that allowed the American military to stay in Iraq after the United Nations mandate expired was replete with political risk, which the prime minister was eager to distribute as widely as possible. This procedural point was a secondary issue in 2008, but it would prove critical three years later.

Loftis's talks in Baghdad began in mid-March 2008, the same week that Mahmoud Ahmadinejad, the Iranian president, made an official visit to Iraq and Admiral Fox Fallon announced his resignation as CENTCOM commander.[5] With the Mahdi Army challenging Maliki and rockets raining down on the Green Zone, the Loftis team somewhat paradoxically found that it was actually safer to meet with the Iraqis at the Foreign Ministry building, well outside the protected enclave. Embassy security officers nonetheless required that the team keep their body armor and helmets with them at all times. After an initial failed attempt to cram the team and all of their gear into the building's elevators, the negotiators resigned themselves to lugging their gear up several flights of stairs to the ministry conference room each day.

Back in the Green Zone, their work was regularly disrupted by warning sirens that forced them to gather in the relative safety of the presidential palace's interior hallways until the all-clear signal was given. During these interruptions, Loftis and some of his staff gathered around a portable DVD player and watched the film *Team America: World Police*. The disruptions caused by incoming fire were so frequent that Loftis and his team watched the film all the way through at least twice.[6] But real dangers underlaid these work breaks. As Elissa Slotkin, an intelligence analyst who was seconded to the NSC and assigned to the Loftis team, was approaching her trailer near Saddam's former presidential palace after a long day of talks, the embassy's counter-rocket system alerted everyone to incoming fire. Slotkin ran for cover to the nearest duck-and-cover bunker. When she finally reached the concrete shell, a Jordanian translator whose friend had been killed in a similar attack only a day earlier zealously pressed her face-first against the ground. After the all-clear message came through, Slotkin thought she had escaped the attack with only a new dry cleaning expense and a mouthful of sand, but when she dressed for another round of negotiations two days later, she noticed a large piece of shrapnel lodged in the high heel of her shoe. Despite their insistence on carrying body armor into the meetings, the State Department still required proper attire to avoid offending a host country during formal negotiations. As Slotkin discovered, heels were less than ideal garb for dodging explosive projectiles, so after the near miss she switched to wearing flats.

The negotiations were slow going. Rubaie thought the initial American approach was doomed, and he derisively referred to Loftis as "the American SOFAlogist." The Iraqis had never wanted to separate the SOFA and SFA agreements in the first place and continued pressing for one overarching accord to cover the full range of the U.S.-Iraqi relationship.

But the Iraqis were not without responsibility for the ponderous pace. All of the major political parties, except the Sadrists, were included in the Iraqi negotiating team, but the group did not possess any real authority to make political decisions. Rather than crafting specific language and details directly with the Americans, the Iraqi team first had to run American proposals by Maliki's inner circle, which might then consult with other Shiite, Kurdish, and Sunni officials. The Iraqi team would be sent back to Loftis's group with specific instructions and the process would repeat itself anew.

By mid-May, the SOFA appeared to be stalled on the big issues the Iraqis wanted most and making headway only on the lower-level matters such as tariffs, entry visas, uniforms, and other technical issues. When the talks broke after the third round of three-week meetings, Iraq's negotiating team flew to South Korea and Japan to see how SOFA agreements worked there, as if the two sides had all the time in the world.

With Iraqi patience wearing thin on the unyielding American position, Maliki decided to broach the issue directly with Secretary Rice at an international conference on the Iraqi economy in Stockholm at the end of May. According to one participant, Maliki told Rice that the negotiations would have to start over from the beginning because "my government will fall if I continue to go in the direction that this is proceeding." On June 2, Bush convened an NSC meeting to reappraise the strategy and Rice laid out the problem Maliki described for her days earlier in Sweden: Sadr and Iran had been defeated on the battlefield in Sadr City and Basra, but they could be expected to rise like a phoenix by exploiting the SOFA negotiations for political gain. Just a few days earlier, about five thousand people had gathered in Sadr City to demonstrate against the SOFA, and similar demonstrations were expected to continue in the months ahead. Throughout Maliki's tenure, Bush had seen himself as a politician who had a feel for the political vicissitudes the prime minister was trying to navigate, and he now sought to impart some of this insight to the less politically attuned civil servants.[7]

"This SOFA is not like the others," Bush told his top advisers. The trick, the president stressed, was to find a way to give the Iraqis a "win" while at the same time putting in the appropriate safeguards for American troops and making the "DOD comfortable."[8] To move the SOFA talks along, the White House decided to hand the baton over to the people who knew Iraqi politics best and were skeptical of the Loftis process to begin with. McGurk and David Satterfield, Rice's senior adviser on Iraq at the State Department, would be the new leads.

The order was a tall one; indeed, there were hints that it might be impossible. During a meeting of senior officials on June 18, Hadley instructed the Director of National Intelligence to find out whether Maliki really intended to sign the strategic framework agreement and status of forces agreement because some intelligence reports suggested otherwise. When Bush led an NSC meeting later that day the principals zeroed in on the three most important things the SOFA needed to have from their perspective: support of the government of Iraq, authorities for military operations, and legal protections for U.S. troops. Despite his feel for Maliki as a politician, Bush was beginning to harbor his own doubts. "Are they trying to force us out of Iraq?" the president asked his aides.[9]

And it was not just Maliki. Once the contents of Loftis's text became widely circulated, McGurk and Crocker found no support for the agreement among the Sunnis or even the Kurds. In a meeting with Tariq al-Hashimi in late May, he informed Crocker and McGurk that the only chance for a security agreement to win political consensus was if it included a timeline for withdrawing U.S. troops. It was the first time an Iraqi leader raised the issue of a timeline in a serious way.

Soon the situation became even more fraught. JSOC had conducted a raid at a village near Karbala and an Iraqi had been shot dead. Unfortunately the commandos had hit the wrong house; it belonged to the prime minister's sister, and the man they killed was one of Maliki's cousins. The commando raid had not been coordinated with Petraeus or the embassy, in keeping with the usual practice, but the tragic mistake dramatically raised the political stakes on immunities for U.S. troops. Lethal mistakes had happened before, but the message to the Iraqi public was clear: if the prime minister's own family could not be protected from wrongful death at the hands of the Americans, then nobody was safe.

For years, President Bush had made strong public statements opposing a strict timeline for winding down the U.S. presence. It had been an article of faith that any withdrawal would need to be "conditions-based," that is, one determined by the military circumstances at the time. But the White House was also searching for a way to respond to public opinion in Iraq. Showing flexibility on a timeline might prevent the Sadrists from exploiting the lingering resentment at the occupation and, more generally, make the SOFA more acceptable in Baghdad by signaling that there would indeed be a quantifiable end to the presence of U.S. troops.

Before McGurk departed for Iraq he was asked to come to Camp David on the weekend of June 7 to discuss the dynamics in Iraq with Bush and Hadley. Now that he had been named the lead negotiator, McGurk advised the president that the United States probably had to arrive with some sort of grand gesture that would indicate a new willingness to compromise and get the negotiations back on track. Bush listened and then to McGurk's surprise suggested that there could be some give in the American position on a withdrawal schedule.

When he arrived in Baghdad a couple of days later, McGurk was authorized to make a number of concessions as a gesture of good faith, including definitively dropping immunity for private contractors, an issue that the United States had put off discussing during the previous negotiations but one where even Loftis acknowledged the United States "didn't have a lot to stand on."[10] In a meeting at the Green Bean, the coffee shop in the American embassy, McGurk alluded to the far more significant concession he was authorized to offer.

"I've got something new," McGurk told Elissa Slotkin, the NSC aide who had worked for Loftis and was lamenting how much momentum had swung against the agreement. When he explained that the negotiators had a green light to talk about timelines, she responded: "Well, that changes everything."

Bush's very public opposition to timetables required a certain amount of linguistic creativity. Crocker summed up the problem in an NSC meeting on June 30. While a firm deadline might be out of the question, the ambassador said, the Iraqi government needed some sort of "time horizon" for the presence of American forces. Just as Bush had relied on Petraeus's military recommendations, he paid heed to Crocker's advice on Iraqi politics. If Crocker believed the United States needed to make a concession, even one with caveats, the president would consider it.

As outlined by the Americans, the dates would be more of a target than a hard and fast deadline, and the initial idea was to discuss them behind closed doors with their Iraqi counterparts. This approach worked for several weeks, but a string of very public statements by Iraqi politicians began trickling out in early July that made it abundantly clear they would now be seeking a withdrawal date in the security agreement with the United States. The leaks began in the Arabic-language media, but from there they quickly spilled over to the Western press. While the American negotiators had taken the initiative by floating the idea of including timelines in the agreement, the Iraqis were framing the public rollout.

With the timeline discussion now out in the open, though, President Bush addressed the issue directly with Maliki during his regular videoconference, on July 17. "Timetables used to mean defeat," the prime minister told the president, but they were "now not so sensitive," because they could be "based on success." Bush preferred to look at the time horizons as an "aspirational goal" for transition to an Iraqi lead. "Be careful," the president advised Maliki, to "leave some flexibility based on conditions to deal with the unexpected." He should look at it not as a "set timetable, but a goal based on conditions."[11]

The following day, the White House issued a statement to show that it was serious about the change in policy and to try to regain some control of the media message. "The president and the prime minister agreed that improving conditions should allow for the agreements now under negotiation to include a general time horizon for meeting aspirational goals—such as the resumption of Iraqi security control in their cities and the further reduction of US combat forces from Iraq."[12]

But Maliki had his own talking points. In an interview with the German magazine *Der Spiegel* on July 19, only two days after his videoconference with Bush, Maliki was asked about the withdrawal schedule Obama was touting in his campaign. Maliki insisted that he was not endorsing a particular candidate, but added that Obama's sixteen-month timetable for the withdrawal of combat troops "would be the right timeframe for a withdrawal, with the possibility of slight changes."[13] Maliki's allusion to

Obama was not a coincidence. As the political campaign was heating up, Obama was scheduled to visit Baghdad two days later, his first trip to Iraq since the one-and-a-half-day visit he had made in 2006 and recounted in *The Audacity of Hope.*

The Iraqi prime minister's apparent endorsement of Obama's sixteen-month timeline for withdrawal made immediate headlines around the world and upset a number of American civilian and military officials, including Petraeus, who felt that the prime minister was playing to the galleries and overselling what his forces could do without the Americans to help them. In his weekly letter to Gates, Petraeus wrote that "although a clarification was later issued by his spokesman, the PM's statement clearly was improper and an intrusion into domestic US politics."[14]

Just before Maliki's comments in the *Der Spiegel* interview were made public he also told the British ambassador that he wanted all non-U.S. forces, including those from the United Kingdom, out of Iraq by the end of the year. The timing of Maliki's request could not have been worse: Prime Minister Gordon Brown was set to visit Iraq on July 21, and Maliki's rash announcement sparked a near panic in the U.S. and British embassies. The British were eager to leave Iraq, but on their own terms: after the losses they had suffered and the political costs the British government had paid at home, they did not want to be unceremoniously evicted. To avoid a diplomatic imbroglio, Bush called Maliki to convince the Iraqi leader to ease his opposition to British forces remaining in the country. The meeting between Brown and Maliki went ahead without incident. Crocker later reported to the NSC that Brown was grateful for the president's call because it really "changed the atmosphere" and Maliki was no longer "set on a withdrawal."[15]

Maliki's erratic behavior during this particularly eventful period in July did not go unnoticed: in just three days the prime minister had discussed the issue of timelines directly with Bush, who cautioned him to avoid speaking in absolutes on withdrawal dates; then he turned around and immediately endorsed Obama's sixteen-month timetable and told the British they had to leave. Explaining these developments to Gates on July 20, Petraeus wrote, "Frankly, the PM's position changes every time the Ambassador talks to him, and it is not clear to me at all now what form the eventual agreement will take or when it is likely that it can be concluded." Petraeus then recounted the back-and-forth over British troops and concluded, "These episodes clearly reflect the range of ever-changing assessments and emotions that PM Maliki is experiencing."[16]

At a press conference the next day, Dana Perino, the White House spokesperson, had the unenviable task of doing damage control from Maliki's *Der Spiegel* interview and sought to fend off a White House press corps that was not privy to the details of the SOFA talks but had a firm recollection of the president's sound bites on Iraq. Seeking to put the best face on the now-public discussion and to "demystify" the "time horizon," as Hadley put it in an earlier meeting, Perino insisted that the concept was possible now only "because we are succeeding in Iraq," and continued to affirm that a withdrawal would be "solely based on conditions on the ground and not an arbitrary date for withdrawal."[17]

Until this point the SOFA negotiations had largely sailed under the political radar in the United States, but the timeline controversy placed the agreement squarely at the forefront of the presidential campaign. No politician had been more adamant about the need to avoid a deadline than John McCain, who was on a path to becoming the Republican Party nominee. That had been Bush's public position as well and still was, albeit in a diluted form, in the SOFA discussions. Even Hillary Clinton had been careful not to set a date for removing American troops. In contrast, it was Obama, hardening the recommendation of the Iraq Study Group, who was the foremost critic of the Bush administration's decision to go to war and the most prominent advocate of a deadline for removing combat troops in sixteen months.

Almost every question at Perino's briefing had to do with some aspect of a timeline, which put the White House in a touchy position. Perino was hard-pressed to explain how the shift in negotiating strategy was not a move toward Obama's stance. After her opening statement, the White House press corps "just ate her alive," recalled a staff member on the NSC. Complaining about the experience afterward to her White House colleagues, Perino said, "That was the worst press conference of my professional career."[18]

On July 21, the same day that Dana Perino was being lambasted by the press over withdrawal timelines, Obama strode into a cavernous room in the Republican Palace. A massive structure backed against the Tigris River, the palace had once featured four gigantic, helmeted heads that bore the likeness of Saddam Hussein. But those adornments had been lopped off during the early days of the American occupation and the palace transformed into the home of the American embassy.

In a conspicuous bit of symbolism, Obama had begun his war zone tour in Kabul, the theater of his "war of necessity," before heading to Baghdad, the epicenter of George W. Bush's audacious effort to bring democracy to Iraq. Obama and his two senatorial traveling companions—Chuck Hagel, a centrist Republican and former Army infantryman who had voted for the 2003 invasion before joining the chorus against the war, and Jack Reed, the Democratic liberal and former paratrooper who had opposed the conflict at the outset—had been whisked by Black Hawk to the Green Zone. For all the security gains, the military was not about to subject a potential commander in chief or his Capitol Hill colleagues to "Route Irish," as the American military dubbed the airport road.

The presidential election was more than three months away, but the polls were running heavily in favor of the Illinois lawmaker. During his previous encounter with Petraeus and Crocker—the rancorous September 2007 Senate Foreign Relations Committee hearing convened to hear the American team's early reports on the surge—Obama had advertised his skepticism of the surge and, to Petraeus's frustration, had done almost all of the talking. But a lot had happened in Iraq since then and the stakes were much higher now for all concerned. Come January 20 Iraq would no longer be Bush's war. Obama looked certain to inherit the conflict, which was moving into its endgame.

Taking a seat at the center of a long wooden table, Obama positioned himself between the general and the ambassador and directly opposite the large poster board charts that Petraeus planned to use to drive home his message. Befitting their lesser political station, the other senators and the retinue of khaki-clad aides sat farther to the sides.

Petraeus, who never had a chance to respond to Obama's soliloquy when he and Crocker had testified on the surge in September 2007, was determined to get his message across this time. Violence was down. Iraq had been yanked back from the precipice, and it had all happened in the face of the blizzard of criticism that had emanated from most of Congress. The question now was how to keep the killing down and push the Iraqi politicians to take on the job of building the new Iraq. Petraeus was armed with a stack of slides that charted the decline in violent incidents—SIGACTS—the growth of the Iraqi security forces, and the expansion of the Americans' new ally: the Sons of Iraq. The Iraq commander briefed all of them.

Then Ryan Crocker gave his political assessment. As the American ambassador saw it, the surge had begun to prompt some profound political changes. The tribal Awakening was more than an Anbar phenomenon. The spectacle of the Sons of Iraq attacks on Al-Qaeda had registered on the Shiites, who had begun to conclude that the Mahdi Army might not be the guardian it pretended to be. With the rejection of Sunni and Shiite extremists the parliament had scored its February 2008 "trifecta." Lurching into action, in one day the lawmakers had adopted a budget, scheduled provincial elections, and approved an amnesty for Sunnis not accused of serious crimes.

Following Maliki's operation in Basra and the confrontation with the Shiite militias in Sadr City, Amara, and other cities, the United States finally had Iraqi soldiers and police that it could work with, Crocker continued. Certainly, there had been some fortunate breaks along the way. Iraqi forces, Crocker asserted, had been able to take the port of Umm Qasr without a fight because the Mahdi Army had rushed to the sound of the guns in Basra. Still, Maliki's willingness to take on Shiite extremists had led to a rethinking by the Sunni community. As the fanatics on both sides had been weakened and violence had declined, the United Nations and the International Red Cross had been able to establish more of a presence. Some Arab states were also more willing to engage.

For all this, Crocker acknowledged, formidable challenges remained. It would take time for Iraq to develop enough economically that ordinary Iraqis would feel invested in the emerging political order. And there was still much to do to delineate the power of Iraqi regions, which were in a tug-of-war with the centralizing tendency of the Maliki government. The Kurdish-Arab disputes over the boundaries of Kurdistan were among the unfinished business. And the Americans needed to figure out a way to cope with the mortality of some of their interlocutors: Abd al-Aziz al-Hakim had been stricken with lung cancer and Talabani was hardly the picture of health. Neither might be on the scene for that much longer. Nor had the United States and Iraq yet hammered out a SOFA.

Internationally, Iran would remain a force to be reckoned with. With the success of the surge, Crocker ventured, Tehran was reconsidering its tactics but the thrust of its strategy was unlikely to change: the "Lebanonization" of Iraq. The Mahdi Army had not been as successful in Iraq as Hezbollah had been in Lebanon at creating a state within a state, observed Crocker, who had served as head of the American embassy's political section there in the early 1980s, was the first American on the ground to confirm the massacres at the Sabra and Shatila refugee camps in 1982, and had survived the American embassy bombing. But Iran, cautioned Crocker, was not inclined to abandon the strategy yet.

Now that Petraeus and Crocker had delivered their report it was

Obama's turn. He had not yet been officially nominated, but he carried himself with the confidence of a president-elect who was surveying the burdens he was certain to inherit. He had not come to Baghdad merely to listen but to redefine the discussion.

Obama began by praising Petraeus and Crocker for the success they had had in driving down the violence in Iraq; ten months after Petraeus's report in Washington most of the Democrats were no longer insisting that the military gains on the ground were illusory. But the political debate, Obama added, did not turn just on how well things were going in Iraq but on the opportunity costs. The war had to be viewed in the context of a weakened economy at home. The collapse of the housing and financial markets had created constraints. The lawmaker's job, he lectured Petraeus and Crocker, was to assess Iraq through the lens of finite resources.

Al-Qaeda and the Mahdi Army were on the run and had been beaten up, Obama observed. Were those gains reversible? If so, when might the United States reach a tipping point? When would the Sunni insurgent groups and Sadr's militia be reduced to stray elements that the Iraqi government could handle on its own? "Right now," Obama said, "you may need conventional forces to hold, but at some point, you have to realize that you are at a sustainable equilibrium."

Petraeus understood that Obama was steering the conversation to troop cuts and sought to head off the debate. The American force, he argued, had already been reduced by more than five combat brigades. He was prepared to withdraw more forces but was worried about moving too fast. The question, he said, was how to keep the enemy from gaining as the American forces drew down. "We are not just recalcitrant," Petraeus said, "hanging on to forces and not taking risk. Some of this is a bit more rhetoric than anything else. Everybody wants to sustain progress. We can do this mission with fewer forces, but this will incur greater risk."

"The enemy can come back," Petraeus added, especially the Iran-supported militias.

"Yes, they've got a patron right there," Obama interjected, pointing to Iran on the map.

Even with their support of the Special Groups, Petraeus thought there would be a limit to Iran's intervention inside Iraq. "Iran does not want to lose the Iraqi people," he said, adding that the Iranians wanted to maintain access for Iranian pilgrims in Najaf.

Petraeus returned to his theme that he was drawing down troops as fast as possible. "We are already thinned out in the south," he said. "We have gone from fourteen to six [Marine infantry battalions] in Anbar and have maintained the security level there, though AQI is trying to come back in Fallujah, which creates worry among our military commanders. This is more near term. AQI could come back to a degree because of the Bayji Oil Refinery. However, we will keep thinning out as the Iraqi surge continues. The situation can be reversed. We want to get our forces home. Nobody is more keenly aware of sacrifices than we are."

Obama reiterated his point that the commanders and the legislators were looking at the situation through different lenses. "I have no problem with you guys," Obama responded. "I'd advocate the same if I was in your shoes." Then the senator asked if the commanders were not making the best the enemy of the good. "With respect to the Iraqi security forces, which still require our support: are you sure you are not building something that the Iraqis can't sustain?"

Petraeus, who had run the training mission himself in 2004–2005, had endorsed Jim Dubik's plan to expand the Iraqi forces. There had been an Iraqi surge as well as an American one. If the Americans were gradually to reduce their combat forces the Iraqis would need the assets to fill the gap. "Well, the oil money should enable them to do it," Petraeus said.

Obama asked if Petraeus knew how fast he could grow the Iraqi forces. "We can chart it out," Petraeus replied. "Of course we don't control Iran and Syria. The foreign fighter pipeline has diminished but we need to take down Abu Ghadiya as well. We also need a way to keep Iran from dialing the violence up, and for the Iraqis to continue to generate forces, army and police." Petraeus was trying to make the point that stabilizing Iraq was more complicated than simply handing over to the Iraqis or training an abstract number of indigenous security forces. "You can't transition them to a problem they can't handle," he explained.

"Right," Obama said. "One other group gets a vote, that is Prime Minister Maliki. I assure you I didn't plan the *Der Spiegel* article. Some of it is his playing to his politics, meaning his base. Some of it is his overconfidence. But how we structure a SOFA or strategic framework agreement—"

"Got to have that," Petraeus interrupted.

"No debate about that in DC," Obama said. "But we've got to send it through Congress. You have to show a few of your cards."

"Well, the core of the agreement is going to be authorities and protections for our forces," Crocker said, shifting the focus of the discussion. "Some of it is CPA 17, which will go away and need something replacing it," he said in reference to Bremer's initial order that had established blanket immunity for coalition troops and security contractors. "We discussed with the Iraqis a broad framework agreement, which will track closely with the Baker-Hamilton report. We will talk about economic, trade, cultural exchange like Fulbrights, etc. We realize that we can't commit funds. We'll assure the Iraqis, but we will stay well away from a commitment."

"And explain to them why," Obama stressed.

The senator was making the argument that the SOFA needed to be reviewed by the Senate, an argument that reflected the Democrats' fear that it might contain some hidden commitments to defend or keep bases in Iraq. Crocker was politely deflecting the demand by trying to reassure Obama that there were no hidden commitments and by referring to the Iraq Study Group, the bible for many of the war's critics.

"We went away from security commitments in the early '60s," Crocker said. "There are two ways it can go: either a short protocol as a bridge to a final SOFA or we continue to work on SOFA-like issues, which Maliki said just today he wants. We are aware that timing is an issue for both the U.S. and Iraq, that's why we talk about time horizons."

"I sense that Iraqi politicians need a date to sell the agreement," Reed said, making the case once again for a concrete date certain to pull combat forces out of Iraq. Petraeus pushed back on that; the commander needed some flexibility and thought the Iraqis would ultimately accept that as well.

Obama once again joined the debate. "The risk is that this takes so long to do that we lose it elsewhere," Obama said. He was making the argument that taking time to solidify the situation in Iraq would deprive Afghanistan of the extra forces needed to take on a resurgent Taliban.

Petraeus rejected that argument as well. "We should not assume that this mission would take so long," he said. "We've reduced five BCTs [brigade combat teams] in just over eight months." The general believed he had done more to reduce forces than he had been given credit for.

Obama made a case for his plan. "A sixteen-month timeline is not unrealistic," he said. "We need to start planning now for things we will have to do elsewhere."

Senator Hagel leapt to Obama's defense. "A six-brigade drawdown is not something new. Every commander in Afghanistan says 'we are going to require two, three brigades.' The president says we will put more forces in Afghanistan and have forces here for the foreseeable future," he said. "Maliki emphasized that he has to go to parliament with the agreement. That means there has to be a date. What Barack is saying is, 'Where do we go from here?' You, General Petraeus, are a big part of that, but there is a larger picture here, the economy for example."

Hagel's suggestion that Petraeus take the American economy and domestic policy considerations into account in deciding on a drawdown schedule in Iraq crossed one of Petraeus's red lines. If the new political leadership in Washington wanted to change the mission, that was its right, but the general did not want to put himself in a position of trying to carry out the strategy with less than what was required.

"Those are policymakers' questions," Petraeus said. "I will do what you want me to do. But I am going to give my best military advice. You seem to want me to tailor my advice to a policy." The retort surprised a staffer who had come with the congressional delegation and she uttered a gasp.

Shifting to the subject of the Sons of Iraq, Hagel asked if they would turn back to Al-Qaeda if the Iraqi government stopped paying them. Petraeus insisted that some were being trained to take civilian jobs and that the Iraqi government was contributing $270 million toward this end. "The SOIs are worth enough to us to keep paying them," Petraeus said. "Government capacity building is the key issue. Our units are reorganizing themselves at the district and provincial level to help. "

As the session wound down, Obama returned to his main theme: the need to expedite the withdrawal from Iraq to free up more forces for Afghanistan. "The timetable is needed because of the assessment of risk," Obama said. "Afghanistan is the central front in the war on terror."

Petraeus challenged the argument. "Actually, Senator, Iraq is what Al-Qaeda says is the central front." Al-Qaeda may not have been in Iraq when the war started, but Petraeus had long argued in his letters to Gates that now that the fight was on, Al-Qaeda's leadership viewed Iraq as a prize and was determined to rout the Americans and expand its influence in Mesopotamia.

Obama thought the general was missing the point. "The Al-Qaeda leadership is not here in Iraq. They are there," he said, pointing on a map to Pakistan.

For Petraeus, the argument was a statement of the obvious and somewhat academic. Assuming that Al-Qaeda's top leadership was hiding in Pakistan, pulling forces out of Iraq would not help. The United States was not going to invade Pakistan. "Right, but how do you get in the FATA?" Petraeus argued, using the acronym for the Federally Administered Tribal Areas, the ungoverned space in Pakistan where many of the Al-Qaeda leaders were believed to be lurking.

Obama questioned whether Al-Qaeda in Iraq presented a threat to the United States. They might be profiting from kidnapping and a menace for the Iraqis but they were not threatening the American homeland. "If AQI has morphed into a kind of mafia then they are not going to be blowing up buildings," Obama said.

Petraeus challenged that argument. A terrorist attack in Scotland had been linked to Iraqi terrorists, and there was the potential for similar attacks if Al-Qaeda in Iraq was not pursued. "Well, think about the Glasgow airport," said Petraeus, who also noted the potential of AQI to expand its influence to Syria and Lebanon.

Wrapping up, Obama said the Iraqis had to pull more of their weight. There were problems to take care of in the United States and as commander in chief there would only be so much energy and so many resources he would want to channel in Iraq. "We can't pay $4.50 a gallon to Iraq because they are incompetent to spend it," Obama said. "At some point, you have to ask, 'Do you just say this is good enough?' You are so invested. You are reaching for excellence, not just adequacy."

"No, we are minimalists here," Petraeus said. "We are very happy with adequate."[19]

On the political side, Bush was determined to first wrap up the strategic framework agreement, which covered economic, diplomatic, and other nonsecurity cooperation, and then work through the thorny issues that continued to impede progress on the SOFA. Still viewing any dates as "aspirational" goals, the White House initially wanted 2015 as its ultimate date to withdraw all American troops, but that did not gain any traction with the Iraqis. For his part, Maliki was pushing for the Americans to be out of Iraq's towns and cities in early 2009 and completely out of the country by the end of 2010—a small step back from the sixteen-month Obama timeline he had previously advocated to *Der Spiegel*. As an American counter, Bush told Crocker on July 29 that he could only accept the end of 2011—the date Petraeus's campaign plan projected Iraq would be capable of taking care of its internal security—and preferred only a vague reference to transitioning American forces out of "populated areas as soon as possible."

In his videoconference with Maliki the following day, though, Bush took a more flexible position and suggested a key compromise on the dates to his Iraqi counterpart: Bush would accept a mid-2009 date to get out of

Iraqi cities if Maliki would accept the end of 2011 as the ultimate goal for removing all American troops. Because the agreement is "important for both of us, I can live with these dates," Bush said. The prime minister was ambivalent. "Yes, we have a deal," Maliki said, but he cautioned that the rest of his government could still reject the 2011 date after he proposed it.[20] The split-the-difference compromise on leaving Iraq's towns and cities would be set for the end of June 2009, but at this point the United States still insisted on including two key caveats on both dates, which essentially reserved their right to review conditions on the ground and stay longer should it prove to be necessary.

There was a secondary, but important, question about Maliki's insistence that American troops be pulled out of Iraqi cities by mid-2009. The idea of restricting American forces to the periphery of Baghdad had been pressed by Maliki when he met with Bush in Amman in 2006. Bush had ignored the demand then, but the Iraqi prime minister was insistent on it now. Not only would it allow him to demonstrate that he had restored sovereignty over Iraqi cities, but it would give him a freer hand dealing with his enemies, both real and perceived.

The agreement on the notional dates at the highest level was an important step forward, but nearly a month later, the negotiations remained stalled on immunities and other nagging issues. Secretary Rice, feeling the immense pressure to get an agreement, decided to throw her own weight behind the effort during her last trip to Iraq as secretary of state on August 21. When Rice attempted to bridge the final gaps herself in a one-on-one meeting with Maliki, she believed she had nailed down a final agreement, which included a residual force of some forty thousand U.S. soldiers to assist Iraqis with training and logistics beyond 2011.

Rice thought Maliki had promised to send those provisions on to the parliament and she was prepared to walk Bush through the details during his next videoconference with Maliki, but she later wrote in her book *No Higher Honor* that "when I got back to Washington, he reneged."[21] Maliki later apologized for the misunderstanding and promised to provide specific details on what he would need in the agreement, but when Mowaffak al-Rubaie discussed the new demands with McGurk and Satterfield during a four-and-a-half-hour meeting on August 24, they included major revisions to all the substantive issues, including military operations, detentions, immunities, and the timelines. The Americans had thought the agreement was nearly completed by this point, so when the Iraqi negotiators sought to revise nearly every important component of the deal, Washington had had enough of Iraq's gamesmanship.

In a phone conversation with Rice, Hadley expressed concern that the negotiating team members had been worn down by the endless talks and were losing their perspective. "Condi, have you looked at the latest version of the SOFA?" Hadley asked, according to an NSC aide. "I'm a little concerned that our guys in the field are tired. I feel like maybe they need to come back and reset." On August 26, Hadley told the NSC team that Secretary Rice would send a "tough message" to Maliki in two days, and then recommend a "cooling period." In the meantime, the president still wanted the NSC to find ways to "help the prime minister with his politics."

On August 28, Petraeus, McGurk, and Satterfield met with Maliki to follow up the tough message Rice had delivered over the phone. They were able to clarify that jurisdiction over U.S. troops remained the "lynchpin" of the agreement, but the rules for detaining Iraqis was also a concern. Maliki did not give any ground on the issue of jurisdictions, but Petraeus told Gates in his weekly letter that "the PM has confirmed" that the stipulation to have combat forces out of major towns and cities by mid-2009 "will not include transition teams, advisors, provincial reconstruction teams, and their security elements."[22] This had been an important concern of the Pentagon, and it ensured that McGurk and Satterfield would not return for "consultations" in Washington completely empty-handed.

Still, with just over four months left in his term, Bush was becoming frustrated with Maliki's inability to get behind the SOFA and concerned about the steps he was taking to consolidate his power at home. "A year ago we complained Maliki was too weak," Bush observed in a September 8 NSC meeting, but "now he's too strong."

When Bush met in the Oval Office with Iraq's Kurdish president, Jalal Talabani, two days later, he stated in no uncertain terms that if the two sides could not come to an agreement, then the United States "must leave." Bush asked Talabani, "Will the prime minister lead on the SOFA?"[23] Talabani said he would, but the Americans were not so sure.

CHAPTER 29

The Home Stretch

With the fate of the status of forces agreement still up in the air, the American military got a glimpse of what might unfold if it was not around to monitor the darker expressions of the sectarian impulses in Iraq. Ray Odierno's Baghdad belts campaign had succeeded in reclaiming Baqubah and much of Diyala Province from Al-Qaeda in Iraq. But that had set the stage for the political battle over who would control the strategically vital region, which was populated by Sunnis, Shiites, Turkmen, and Kurds.

On August 18, the American Special Forces who advised a detachment of the elite Iraqi special operations forces, or ISOF, in Diyala were told that the Iraqi commandos had been instructed to detain one of the leading Sunni members of the provincial government, Dr. Hussein al-Zubaidi. The Americans told the Iraqis they had no intelligence to suggest that the official should be detained and refused to support the operation. But the growing ISOF contingent in Iraq was far less dependent on its American partners than it had been just a year earlier, and it had grown accustomed to receiving orders directly from an offshoot of Maliki's Office of the Commander in Chief.

The next day the Iraqi commandos headed off on their own. What happened after that was a tragic comedy of errors. The Iraqi soldiers barged into the Diyala Government Center, grabbed Zubaidi, killed the governor's personal secretary, confiscated the guards' weapons, and then drove away in SUVs that belonged to the provincial council. No sooner did the Iraqi commandos begin to leave than they found themselves in a firefight with local police.

Setting up a checkpoint, the police held their ground as the Iraqi commandos fired back, wounding four policemen and a female civilian. From

FOB Speicher, the American base near Tikrit, a pair of Apache helicopters scrambled to check out the fighting only to find themselves under heavy machine gun fire, which followed them as they maneuvered. An American intelligence officer, reviewing the helicopter's video recording of the episode, assessed that the fire had come from Iraqi forces.

It had been an extraordinary melee. Iraqi forces had been fighting among themselves and some had even taken shots at American Apaches. Iraqi police who were doing their duty had ended up in the hospital along with a civilian, and the supposedly elite commandos had managed to get themselves trapped. The only force that was not involved was the Al-Qaeda enemy. The Iraqi commandos were stuck until their superiors called Lieutenant General Ali Ghaidan Majid, the head of the Iraqi Ground Forces Command, who was overseeing a summer offensive in Diyala, and persuaded him to pull back the police units.[1]

In Baghdad, Petraeus was irate. The ISOF, a force trained and advised by America's own elite to be the best in Iraq, had gone after a Sunni political opponent of the Maliki government. Instead of defending the Iraqi state it had been used for political repression. "Okay, CJSOTF is going to have to have a heart-to-heart with ISOF," he said, referring to the American Special Forces group that advised the Iraqi commandos. "There cannot be the kind of operations that ISOF has been doing for the last 48 hours." The Iraqi operation, Petraeus continued, had showed utter "disregard for any kind of respect for the Iraqi population." Later on that day, Petraeus talked to the American colonel who was in command of the American Special Forces group. "I will not hesitate to yank all support for the ISOF Brigade if they don't knock it off," he said. "They've done well since Karbala last year, but they've got to clean up their behavior."

"We can handle the tactical guys," the colonel replied, "but it is brigade and above that originates the problems."[2] Most ISOF troops were competent professionals, and their longtime commander, Kurdish brigadier general Fadhil Barwari, was a trusted American ally. But Maliki's Counter-Terrorism Service, led by a former Baathist general named Dhai Kanani, was increasingly calling the shots and using the ISOF as the prime minister's political targeting force. Maliki insisted after the raid that he had not authorized the operation and ordered an investigation, but according to a Petraeus aide, Kanani gave the orders.

As the complaints from Sunni politicians in Diyala drifted to American ears, it became clear that the raid—officially part of an Iraqi military offensive dubbed Operation Glad Tidings of Benevolence—was part of a bigger problem. Maliki and his inner circle had learned in the Basra, Sadr City, and Amara operations in the spring that they could use their best units, even Sunni-dominated ones like the 1st Iraqi Army Division, not merely to fight militias and insurgents but to influence important regions for the political battles to come. "This operation certainly had heavy overtones of sectarian targeting," recalled Major General Mark Hertling, the American division commander in the north.[3] The dean of the university in Diyala was arrested and his computer confiscated and some of Diyala's Awakening members felt threatened.

A few days after the ISOF raid, Saif Abd al-Rahman, an American of Iraqi descent who served as an adviser to Tariq al-Hashimi, the Sunni vice president, dismissed Maliki's call for an investigation into the episode as a "protocol response." The real purpose, he argued, was to sideline potential political opponents before the provincial elections. Some six hundred Iraqis had been detained during two weeks of raids, seventy-six of whom, Abd al-Rahman reported, were members of Hashimi's Iraqi Islamic Party. The Sunni party, he complained bitterly, had backed Maliki during his fight against the militias in Basra and Sadr City only to become the target of a new, and apparently political, phase of Maliki's operations. "If the government thinks we, the IIP, are terrorists, they should say so openly and we will prepare an appropriate political response."

In a cable to Washington, Crocker wrote that Abd al-Rahman's comments "track closely with those expressed recently by Kurdish members of Maliki's parliamentary alliance. Such sentiments indicated that while PM Maliki is acting in an increasingly self-confident and assertive manner, his actions produce significant backlash among his political partners, both Kurds and Sunni Arabs."[4]

As Iraqi troops pushed into Diyala for Operation Glad Tidings of Benevolence, they reached the eastern town of Khanaqin, a small, mostly Kurdish town near the Iranian border. The Kurds considered Khanaqin part of historic Kurdistan even though it was outside the borders of the Kurdish autonomous region. In the town, only Kurdish flags, not Iraqi ones, lined the streets. With the blessing of the Americans and the acquiescence of the Iraqi government, the Kurds had kept the 34th Peshmerga Brigade there for several years, a move that allowed Iraq's 5th Division to focus more on Baqubah and other Diyala hotspots. But with Diyala more secure thanks to Odierno's Baghdad belts campaign and Maliki feeling his oats thanks to Basra and Sadr City, the Iraqi government was now inclined to see the Peshmerga as a symbol of Kurdish encroachment.

The looming standoff over Khanaqin occurred against a background of tension between the Kurds and the Maliki government. The Iraqi government believed that the Kurds were too independent; the Kurds thought Maliki indifferent to their agenda. The two sides had a long litany of disagreements: settling the boundaries of Kurdistan, determining the status of Kirkuk, defining the revenue-sharing arrangement and oil production rights in the unfinished oil law, integrating some of the Peshmerga into the Iraqi Army, and, ultimately, coming to terms on the degree of autonomy the Kurds could exercise.

With the Americans consumed with tamping down the sectarian infighting in Baghdad and heading off a full-scale Sunni-Shiite civil war, the Bush administration had little energy left to tackle the Kurdish agenda. The surge was first and foremost about stabilizing Baghdad. Now Maliki's desire to assert control and the Kurds' lingering resentments were pushing their issues to the fore. "Tensions this week were also running high over the 34th Peshmerga Brigade in northern Diyala that had ignored orders from Baghdad and was refusing to withdraw," Petraeus reported to Gates in mid-August.[5]

On August 15, a Kurdish delegation came to Baghdad to meet with Maliki. After the session, Major General Mike Barbero and Ryan Crocker went to Barham Salih's Green Zone residence for an update. Salih had some good news. Jalal Talabani had pushed the Kurds to compromise, and the two sides had reached an agreement. The 34th Peshmerga Brigade would be formally incorporated into the Iraqi Army with much fanfare. That would address Maliki's concerns about sovereignty and would also relieve the Kurds of the expense of supporting the unit. After that ceremony, the two sides would discuss moving the unit north. Soon after the agreement was reached, it began to fall apart, with each side accusing the other of reneging. "On Sunday, however, the Kurdish side changed its position, committing only to withdraw the 34th to the north of its position and not to become part of the IA," Petraeus reported. "We'll see what the ultimate resolution is."

The resolution did not look good. Toward the end of August, an Iraqi Army unit was turned away at a Peshmerga checkpoint outside Khanaqin, and reported back to Ali Ghaidan that the Kurdish troops were digging in and concealing artillery and rocket launchers. Ghaidan gave the Kurds in the town an ultimatum to withdraw, but orders came back from Massoud

Barzani that they should stand their ground. To make matters more complicated, American Special Forces troops were embedded as advisers with the 34th Brigade and other Kurdish troops.

Just back at his Tikrit headquarters from his most recent round of shuttle diplomacy in Kurdistan, 1st Armored Division commander Mark Hertling received a call from Fuad Hussein, Barzani's chief of staff. Hussein was livid. "We know what they are doing: another Anfal," he shouted, referring to Saddam Hussein's brutal 1986–1989 campaign against the Kurds that killed tens of thousands. "You have got to call Maliki and stop this. We will tell every Kurd to leave their unit and come back to Kurdistan," Hussein threatened, alluding to the thousands of Kurds who served in the regular Iraqi Army around the country. "There will be thunder and lightning along the Green Line."[6] Hertling immediately called his boss, Lloyd Austin, to alert him to the crisis.

Equipped with tube and rocket artillery and highly disciplined, the Peshmerga troops on one side of the Khanaqin standoff seemed almost certain to come off better if it came to an actual fight. "The Peshmerga forces would have kicked the IA [Iraqi Army] forces' ass, and I wouldn't have known what to do with our forces that would have been caught in the middle of them," Hertling later told a military historian.[7] Initially, the Americans hoped this imbalance might deter Iraqi commanders from doing anything rash. But now an alarming series of communication intercepts suggested that Ali Ghaidan and Defense Minister Abd al-Qadir al-Obeidi were planning to bring up as many as three companies of T-72 tanks and were already deploying the first of them.

Satellite and Predator photos were one of the most useful dispute resolution tools that Hertling had at his disposal—overhead imagery could prove to Iraqi and Kurdish officials alike that the United States knew what was going on despite their denials. Hertling took a photo to Ali Ghaidan showing that four T-72s had already arrived at a base in eastern Diyala, and was able to trim the planned deployment to just four more tanks, all of which would remain parked in their motor pools for the duration of the crisis. Marine advisers assigned to the Iraqi 1st Division troops on the ground outside Khanaqin also drew the unusual mission of touring their Iraqi partners' lines and photographing the positions of military vehicles around the town. Hertling threatened both sides that he would withdraw American forces, including Iraqi Army advisers, to their bases.

In Baghdad, Mike Barbero got a call from Hertling telling him that Iraqi tanks were in the picture, and he phoned Mowaffak al-Rubaie. "Are you trying to start an armed confrontation with the Kurds?" Barbero asked Rubaie. "Because if you are, we are not going to participate. We are dead against this. This is not a fight to pick at this time. Why are you doing this?"[8]

Rubaie put the blame squarely on the Kurds. They had refused to withdraw their brigade in Khanaqin and, in fact, were reinforcing it. Iraqi government forces, the national security adviser insisted, should have the right to go deeper into Diyala at any time. The Peshmerga were a tool of Kurdish political interests and were outside the boundaries the Maliki government was prepared to accept for Kurdistan, and thus they had to go.

Having read Rubaie the riot act, Barbero did the same with the other side, taking his concerns to the leading Kurds in the government: Barham Salih, the deputy prime minister; Hoshyar Zebari, the foreign minister; and Babaker al-Zebari, the head of the Iraqi military joint headquarters. The Kurds insisted that they were not the ones who were escalating the tensions, but Barbero was armed with Predator photos of the Kurdish rocket launchers and a map of Peshmerga positions, which he passed around.

Over the ensuing days, the Peshmerga pulled back their rocket launchers and the Maliki government agreed not to send its forces into the town. Barbero later met with Barzani and thanked him for not escalating the crisis—although the situation in Khanaqin remained tense. "It's not an issue worth destroying everything that we've gained together," he told the Kurdish leader. But Barzani's monumental frustrations with Maliki had reached the breaking point. In a September 16 meeting with Crocker, Barzani made clear that he viewed Khanaqin as a personal betrayal. The Kurds had sheltered Maliki in the early 1980s during his exile from Saddam's Iraq. Now he was showing dictatorial tendencies, Barzani complained.

The Baqubah ISOF raid and the near confrontation between the Peshmerga and the Iraqi Army in Khanaqin pointed to an important but often overlooked role for American forces in Iraq. By threatening to withhold support from the ISOF, the American command could deter Maliki and his inner circle from going too far in their political targeting. By sharing reconnaissance photos they could let Iraq's politicians know where their own forces were being maneuvered on the battlefield and deescalate a spiraling confrontation.

The episodes also marked a new phase in Iraq's evolution. Thanks to the surge and Awakening, the fledgling Iraqi state had overcome the Sunni insurgency and avoided an all-out civil war. But Maliki was steadily accumulating power and strengthening his authority. For years, Iraqi prime

ministers had been too weak. Did Maliki's attempts to crack the whip
mean that he was, at long last, taking responsibility for Iraq, as Washington fervently hoped? Had his Basra adventure demonstrated that he was
able to rise above sectarianism, as Bush hoped? Or was Maliki determined
to stifle any and all rivals regardless of whether they emerged from the Shiite, Sunni, or Kurdish ranks, as political opponents were warning?

Crocker knew better than most that Maliki's newfound assertiveness had
already extended beyond his relations with Iraq's other political factions
and directly impacted his interactions with the United States. Maliki's
erratic and hard-line approach to the SOFA had been a major reason Washington called McGurk and Satterfield back at the end of August, but Hadley's decision to have them reset and recharge in Washington also afforded
the Bush administration a new opportunity to address the bureaucratic
infighting that had plagued the negotiations from the beginning.

After months of refusing to budge, the Pentagon was beginning to
grudgingly come around to the view that some flexibility in their negotiating position might be needed to secure an agreement.

The Defense Department's newfound realization had far less to do with
the arguments they had heard from the embassy in Baghdad than it did
with an international crisis that erupted over nine hundred miles away.
The Russian invasion of Georgia in August led to a rapid deterioration in
already strained relations with Moscow. The United States had branded
Russia the aggressor and was flying the Georgian brigade home from Iraq
so they could defend their own country. Any extension of the U.N. mandate authorizing the troop presence in Iraq would depend critically on
Russia, which held a veto in the Security Council, and under the current
circumstances any Russian cooperation there was beginning to look like
a pipe dream. According to one of the American negotiators, the military
had always approached the negotiations with the "schizophrenic view"
that the United States had to go through the motions of negotiating an
agreement, but expected all along that it would ultimately fail and Iraq
would have no choice but to reauthorize the U.N. mandate. When that
option was removed by the Georgia crisis, the clock was already ticking
down on securing an agreement that would make or break the U.S. troop
presence in Iraq.[9]

With the pressure mounting, President Bush began to actively press both
the Iraqis and his own military leaders. On the same day he asked President

Jalal Talabani if Maliki would lead on the SOFA, September 10, Bush also explained the urgency to Ray Odierno. On Jack Keane's recommendation, Bush had decided to promote Petraeus to take Fallon's place at CENTCOM and to elevate Odierno to serve as the overall Iraq commander so that the Iraq A-team would remain in charge when the next president took over. Odierno was set to take command in Baghdad in less than a week, but during an earlier meeting with McGurk he had expressed some reservations about the SOFA language, especially on immunities and the requirement to vacate Iraq's cities by June 30, 2009. Meeting in Hadley's office, Bush emphasized to his new general that finalizing a SOFA was critical to his overall strategy of locking in the gains of the surge. It would provide the foundation for American troops to stay in Iraq until 2011 and possibly beyond.

Fortunately, McGurk had already devised a creative way to bridge the gap between the Pentagon's insistence on absolute immunity and the Iraqis' preoccupation with exercising at least token sovereignty. A lawyer who had clerked at the Supreme Court, McGurk was trained to find his way through legal thickets with elaborate finesse.

The solution was outlined in a terse document McGurk drew up that became known as the "Concentric Circles Paper" and was marked "Small Group Eyes Only," a reference to Hadley, Lute, and key aides at the NSC. The Pentagon had dug in its heels on the notion of immunities for soldiers, but McGurk suggested there was a way for the Bush administration to have its cake and eat it, too.

"Can we offer the Iraqis **in principle** what they say they need to pass the SOFA while retaining **in practice** essential protections for all US military personnel in Iraq?" the paper asked before answering the question in the affirmative. The Iraqis, the paper explained, were insisting that immunity be waived for crimes like rape and murder that were committed off-base and while the soldiers were off-duty. By retaining the right to define when troops were considered to be off-duty and inserting other safeguards, the SOFA could be drafted in such a way that the chance of American military personnel falling under Iraqi law would be negligible.

To illustrate the point, the paper used a series of overlapping circles to depict legal jurisdictions over U.S. troops in various countries. The drawing showed that American troops would be much less likely to be subject to Iraqi laws than American troops in countries like South Korea and Japan, where U.S. soldiers were already subject to local jurisdiction over a wider range of crimes than the Iraqis sought to secure in the draft agreement. Besides pointing out the narrower scope of jurisdiction, McGurk's paper also asserted that the United States could build in several loopholes to further strengthen troop protections: in the small number of instances in which the Iraqis might claim jurisdiction, no trial could take place unless it was clear that the Iraqis would meet the American standards of due process, a provision suggested by Hadley that the Pentagon could always cite to refuse to turn over a soldier accused of an offense. More importantly, any soldier who was accused of a crime would be held under American custody pending any legal procedure. "The US always retains physical custody of the accused at all times and can—as a last resort—remove personnel from Iraq," the paper read.[10] One NSC aide described the paper as "the most Frankenstein-like thing you have ever seen." But it reflected the realization that the SOFA was at its core a political, as well as a legal, document.

McGurk, Hadley, and the NSC team arranged to personally brief Mullen and Gates on September 11 and walk them step-by-step through the new immunity provisions described in the paper. If the effort failed, Bush was ready to intervene personally with the Pentagon, but in a high-pressure meeting the arguments McGurk laid out were persuasive enough. Both Gates and Mullen began the meeting opposed to the changes, but after asking Petraeus if he could live with the new language, and hearing his affirmative answer, Gates switched his position. Mullen then reluctantly followed suit and the Pentagon's long-held opposition to changes in the immunity provision officially softened.[11]

After Odierno took command from Petraeus in a September 16 ceremony at Al-Faw Palace, he upped the pressure on Iraq's prime minister through his own channels.

In his first meeting with Maliki as the new four-star commander, Odierno denied rumors that the United States would remain in Iraq without a status of forces agreement. Maliki mentioned that he had already been told by Gates in a videoconference that there was no "Plan B," but to underscore what was at stake, Odierno interjected that there was one: "full withdrawal."[12] To give the Iraqis a sense of what that would mean, Odierno had his staff draw up a list of all the many ways in which the United States supported Iraqi troops, everything from guarding Iraq's airspace to providing intelligence, logistical support, and medevacs to units in the field. All of it would come to an abrupt end if an agreement was not reached and Maliki was on his own.

McGurk and Satterfield were set to resume negotiations in Baghdad near the end of the month, and on September 22, Hadley and top administration officials were briefed on the strategy the negotiators would pursue when they arrived. Heeding the advice given to them by the president, they planned to start with principles first and make the government of Iraq take "ownership." Then, once the text was closed on a particular issue, it would stay closed. This process would take longer than simply handing over the latest version and trying to leverage it through the process without further changes, but they judged it would be more likely to succeed in the end. There was still plenty to be worried about on the Iraqi political scene, but Crocker noted that the provincial elections in January made the path forward "hard, but viable."[13]

Another important step to facilitate an agreement was quietly taken by the Obama team. Throughout the campaign, Obama and his aides had publicly insisted that the SOFA needed to be subjected to Congressional review. But that raised the possibility that the Iraqis might make politically painful concessions only to see the Americans balk. Colin Kahl, a political science professor who had been advising the Obama campaign, had been invited by Odierno to Baghdad to participate in a strategy review in October. And he soon concluded that it was in the campaign's interest to support the negotiating efforts in Baghdad. The SOFA the Bush administration was working on was consistent with Obama's approach and if it failed now the new president would need to spend the first few months of his administration trying to resurrect the agreement—or dealing with the chaos in Iraq that might result from a hasty American pullout. Kahl sent the Obama campaign an email urging that it avoid criticism of the agreement. "If we win the election we don't want to have our Iraq policy consumed by renegotiating the agreement in the early portion of 2009," he wrote.[14] The Bush plan for handing off the war was now merging with Obama's expectation to assume the responsibility.

In late October, Barzani paid a visit to Washington. Bush hosted the Kurdish leader in the Oval Office, praised his support for the status of forces agreement, and hailed his leadership in building a free Iraq. Barzani publicly endorsed the SOFA after a meeting with Rice, making the Kurds the only Iraqi faction vocally supporting the accord. But in the closed-door session he had a private message as well, the same one he had delivered a year earlier. Maliki was too autocratic and unwilling to acknowledge the Kurds' concerns. "If we cannot reach agreement then I don't think the prime minister will remain the prime minister," Barzani bluntly told Rice, according to a Kurdish official.[15]

Rice's message was also consistent. The American ambassador had encouraged Maliki to seek the prime ministership in 2006. Bush had stood behind him then and in December 2007 on the premise that the Iraqi leader would make the difficult decisions if he knew he had the support of the United States. The White House had had its doubts about Maliki along the way, but it was not about to countenance any changes now. As she had a year earlier, the secretary of state made clear that the Bush administration was not interested in changing horses in midstream. When it came to Iraq's leadership the Americans had no Plan B. "We've had this conversation before because he was not strong enough," Rice said to the Kurdish leader. "Now, he's trying to act as the prime minister. I don't think Iraq has the time for a leadership struggle. You have to come together."

In the final months of Bush's term in office, the Americans sought to take care of some unfinished business. Al-Qaeda was still entrenched in parts of northern Iraq, and the terrorist logistical leader Abu Ghadiya continued to funnel foreign fighters, including suicide bombers, in from Syria. Taking care of Abu Ghadiya was not a simple proposition, though, since he spent almost all of his time on the Syrian side of the border.

An American initiative to have Abu Ghadiya designated a terrorist by the U.N. Security Council was blocked by Libya, a country that was happy to see its own radical Islamist fighters travel to Iraq rather than stay at home. A JSOC strike at a place near Sinjar called Objective Massey a year earlier had found that a disproportionate number of at least one large batch of foreign fighters had come from Libya, many of them from the town of Misurata, which would later become a center of resistance to the Qaddafi regime.

Petraeus's idea of visiting Syria to confront Assad with the evidence of Abu Ghadiya's role and pressure him into cracking down was still a non-starter with the Bush administration. "I have offered to go to Damascus, but the last time I said that, I was told to go sit under a tree until the thought passed," Petraeus told his staff on July 13.[16]

That left the administration with the decision of whether to draw on JSOC and the CIA and pursue a military option. As early as mid-March, Petraeus had recommended to the NSC that they consider launching a cross-border strike against Abu Ghadiya inside Syria. At the end of May, intercepted communications suggested that the terrorist logistician would soon move into Iraq, but if he did so, he avoided detection and made it back to Syria by mid-June. On May 30, the NSC discussed with Stan McChrystal the possibility of using a JSOC strike force under CIA authority to launch a raid seven kilometers into Syrian territory, but the raid was deferred.

Over the summer, the subject of what to do about Abu Ghadiya continued to come up at the NSC. That month, a group of NSC officials mulled an offer by Israel's covert forces to kill him inside Syria; the United States declined the offer. A month later, in mid-August, a Predator strike on the Syrian side of the border was planned, but after two days there was still no fix on the terrorist leader's position and the strike did not occur—although around the same time, at the end of the summer, JSOC did capture two of Abu Ghadiya's close associates, one in Baghdad and one in Qaim.

Then in the fall, Bush authorized two rare joint JSOC-CIA cross-border ground raids six weeks apart. Because the targets were in countries where U.S. combat operations could not be acknowledged, in both cases the JSOC strike forces were placed under the temporary authority of the CIA, as would be the case with Operation Neptune Spear three years later, the bin Laden raid. In the first, in early September, a strike force marched into Pakistan and got into a significant fight, killing as many as thirty enemy fighters, taking one American casualty, and calling in attack helicopters for support. The press attention caused by that raid deterred the NSC from allowing further Pakistan ground raids, but in a bold daylight mission on October 26 that bystanders caught snippets of on video, MH-60 Black Hawk helicopters flew a JSOC team across the border into Syria near Qaim to attack a compound where Abu Ghadiya was believed to be hiding. The commandos killed him and took his body back in the helicopters. Because the operation had been run under CIA rather than military authority, the Bush administration's response to the raid was sharply different from the fanfare that surrounded JSOC's capture of Saddam Hussein and the killing of Abu Musab al-Zarqawi—deafening silence.

The northern city of Mosul remained a battleground.[17] American troops there faced IEDs, gunfights, car bombs, and occasionally attackers among their Iraqi allies. On November 12, two platoons from the 3rd Armored Cavalry Regiment converged at an Iraqi outpost on the traffic circle in the Zanjili neighborhood of Mosul, the site of the battle four years earlier in which Jim Coffman had earned the Distinguished Service Cross as the lone American adviser with an ambushed convoy of Special Police Commandos. As the platoons' lieutenants went inside the outpost to meet with their Iraqi counterparts, the enlisted soldiers lounged in the outpost's courtyard. Without apparent provocation, an Iraqi soldier turned his assault rifle, equipped with a drum magazine, on them. One soldier, nineteen-year-old

Specialist Corey Shea, died on the spot, and seven more were wounded. The soldiers' onetime ally, the shooter, died in a hail of bullets that tore through his American-supplied body armor. A few hours later another of the wounded soldiers, Sergeant Jose Regalado, died in the same combat support hospital that Jim Coffman had snuck out of. It was one of three "green-on-blue" incidents, or shootings of American troops by the Iraqi troops with whom they were partnered, in little over a year in Nineveh. The Americans were never sure if they had been attacked by Al-Qaeda infiltrators or by Iraqi soldiers who simply snapped.[18]

With the November election fast approaching, the White House soon found itself wrestling again with the issue of a withdrawal timeline. Bush and Maliki had agreed on the mid-2009 and 2011 dates at the end of July, but Iraq's negotiators were now insisting that the words "withdrawal" and "temporary presence" be included in the official title. This drove the political advisers and communications staff in the White House into a frenzy. Some felt it would influence the election in Obama's favor. The negotiators could not understand their thinking; with the economy tanking, the outcome of the election would hardly depend on a small word in an international agreement. But at the White House, some political operatives felt the Republican cause was being undermined. When Ed Gillespie, the counselor to the president, noticed at an NSC meeting that the reference to "withdrawal" was highlighted front and center on the SOFA's first page, he interjected that "this is a surrender document!"[19]

Dismissing the outburst from his political adviser, the president nonchalantly responded, "Thank you very much, Ed," and then moved on as if nothing had happened. While she was not part of that NSC meeting, Dana Perino later wondered how she was supposed to publicly defend a title that had "withdrawal" in it. Bush was more worried about cementing the final agreements with Iraq than he was about the politics at home, though, and he soon agreed to an even more significant concession on the timeline.

Throughout the tortured negotiating process, Bush had steadfastly maintained a measure of ambiguity as to when American forces would leave Iraq. There had been discussion of goals and notional dates and time horizons, but not a hard-and-fast date for leaving the country altogether. The dates in the draft agreements had consistently included caveats that would allow the United States to review conditions on the ground, but now Maliki insisted that he needed dates. "If I take this to the parliament," Maliki said to a member of the negotiating team, "they will say, 'You really don't have firm dates. The U.S. will demand and you will have to accept a longer period.' "

Recognizing that the two sides were close to finalizing the language during the early hours of the morning in Baghdad, and that a date was needed to push the agreement over the finish line, Crocker called Lieutenant General Doug Lute at the White House and told him they needed the president's approval to include a firm deadline in the text—December 31, 2011—for withdrawing all American forces from Iraq. Bush had relied heavily on Crocker's advice, just as he had with Petraeus. Now Crocker was putting his years of experience and reputation on the line and advising the president to give in to the Iraqis on this final point.

Lute informed Hadley, who said, "Well, let's go find the president." The pair soon located the commander in chief in his White House gym, a veranda-like room overlooking the pool outside the chief of staff's office, where he was simultaneously listening to country music, sweating profusely on the exercise bike, and reading a book resting on a small stand for hands-free reading. The president turned down the music with the remote. "What do you two want?" he asked.

"Well, Doug has an issue for you," Hadley said. Lute explained that Crocker had just told him they were close to reaching an agreement on the timeline and they needed his final approval to lock in the language.

After a short discussion in which they reviewed the details of the proposed language, the president asked them, "Well, what does this mean?"

"It means it's not going to look conditions-based," Lute responded. "There is going to be a date and we've said all along that we are not going to put the commanders on a timeline."

"Okay, I agree with it," the president said. "If Ryan needs it, that's what we're doing. If this is what we need to get an agreement, this is what we'll do."

After the president gave them the green light, Lute quickly reconnected on the secure two-way link with Ambassador Crocker. "We got it," Lute said with a grin.

"You got it?" Crocker responded, somewhat surprised. "Isn't he taking it to the Principals [Committee]?"

"No," Lute said, a bit incredulous himself. "The president just decided."

Crocker wasn't the only member of the negotiating team surprised by the ease with which the final language gained the president's approval. Eager to report the breakthrough to the other members of the negotiating team, Lute told an aide that Bush had gone along with Crocker's advice.

"He agreed to it," Lute reiterated.

"Holy shit!" the aide exclaimed.

In addition to the request for firm withdrawal timelines, the Iraqis sent a list of 110 total amendments to the SOFA to the American embassy on October 30. About sixty-five of these were small technical corrections, another twenty-five the U.S. accepted with slight changes, and the rest were thrown out or renegotiated. Processing these additional requests took a few days, but on November 3, the day before the election, Bush gathered his NSC to go over the final SOFA draft. Although many were present, Bush was primarily interested in hearing from his new ground commander, Odierno.

Bush's driving philosophy throughout the entire process was to focus on the big picture and let the operators work out the details. He had told his advisers back in July that he did not want to negotiate the agreement directly with Maliki because "you don't put your friends in an uncomfortable position." Now that the two sides had finally come up with the agreement, he wanted to know if the man in charge of executing it approved.

Odierno had been deeply involved in the negotiating process since he arrived in September and had put a lot of thought into what it would mean for the long-term relationship. "I think I can live with the jurisdiction," he told the president. "I think we'll be able to conduct security operations. I'm a little nervous about the June 2009 date, but I think by recognizing their sovereignty in the end it will be better off for all of us." Petraeus, now the CENTCOM commander, concurred with Odierno's endorsement and that was good enough for the president.

The day after Obama's victory on November 4, Bush signed a letter to Maliki with the final SOFA attached. Crocker delivered this letter at noon on November 7, with the expectation that the agreement would eventually go to the Iraqi parliament for a straight up-or-down vote, but Iraqi politics tended to march to the beat of its own drum. The process was now almost completely out of America's hands.

Maliki proposed an additional change on November 10 that really hammered this point home: on the provision barring the use of Iraqi territory for hostile acts, Maliki wanted to replace the more nebulous term "harm" with "attacks" against neighboring states, a measure that seemed intended to assuage Iranian concerns. Crocker referred the requested change on "attacks" to the White House, which agreed. At the same time, Crocker advised the NSC that "with the Prime Minister's leadership, the SOFA will pass," but "without it, no."

For days, the Americans wondered if the process was finally at an end.

Two days later on November 12, Odierno was somewhat reassured when Maliki told him, "It will be signed, it is a must." The following day, Maliki followed up with a letter to Bush seeking another small change to a single paragraph, which in Crocker's estimation was actually "not bad." Crocker told the NSC that it would give Maliki "the closing issue," and that the more important aspect of the letter was that it was the first time he had written anything pertaining to the topic. Maliki was a "conspiracy theorist," so the very fact that he was willing to put something on paper should be seen as a positive sign that he intended to follow through on the agreement.

On November 16, all but one of Iraq's cabinet-level officials voted to endorse the final draft status of forces agreement and send it to the parliament for ratification, where further complications soon emerged. During the second public reading of the agreement in the parliament on Wednesday, November 19, the proceedings erupted into a shouting match.

The following day the Americans, to their surprise, received a list of grievances from Salih al-Mutlaq and Mahmoud al-Mashhadani, two Sunni politicians. Throughout the surge, the American military had in effect protected Sunni communities in Baghdad and other mixed sectarian areas from the Shiite militias. It had organized and paid the largely Sunni Sons of Iraq. But the Sunnis understood that the Americans and even Maliki at this point wanted the accord and were using the process to press their long-standing legislative demands. Even the Kurds jumped in line to use the agreement to extract concessions from Maliki; his opponents finally had some leverage over the increasingly powerful prime minister, and they were determined to use it.

One of the more significant provisions came from Tariq al-Hashimi, the Sunni vice president. Hashimi's proposal, which noted Sunni demands for the enforcement of an amnesty law for thousands of detainees in Iraqi custody and for a greater sectarian balance in the security forces, stated that a referendum on the SOFA would be held in six months, which meant July 2009, and if it failed, then U.S. forces would have to completely withdraw within a year.[20] Logically, the measure made little sense. It was the American forces that had sought to stop the Shiite security forces from harassing the Sunnis and had worked with the largely Sunni Awakening. Pulling American troops out early would merely give Maliki's forces free rein. The referendum on the SOFA never materialized. An NSC official compared the measure to a "sense of the Congress" resolution, which was difficult to enforce unless Maliki chose to implement it.

Addressing these ancillary demands on the referendum and similar requests from most of Iraq's other political parties took nearly a week, and the last-minute power plays delayed the final vote in the parliament to Thursday, November 27, Thanksgiving Day in the United States. In the end, the final deal brokering Sunni support came less than an hour before the parliament was set to go out of session for the year. The lopsided final vote in the parliament masked the enormous difficulty it had taken to arrive at that point; after nine months of tough negotiations with the Americans and among themselves, the Iraqi parliament approved the SOFA and SFA with 149 votes in favor, only 35 opposed, 14 abstentions, and 77 not present.[21] The Sadrist bloc, which had consistently opposed any agreement that would permit U.S. troops to stay in the country, accounted for all but five of the votes against the pact.

After the vote, Maliki addressed the nation: "This is the day of our sovereignty. Together we will go forward toward a free, prosperous and glorious Iraq, where Iraqis can live with pride and dignity and can be proud that they are sons of this beloved country." Grateful to his own staff for seeing the process through, President Bush called each member of his team individually to say congratulations and to extend his personal gratitude.

The agreements cleared the final hurdle when they were signed by Iraq's Presidency Council of Jalal Talabani, Adil Abd al-Mahdi, and Tariq al-Hashimi on December 3, but Maliki was feeling confident even before that. On December 1, the embassy notified the NSC that the prime minister would invite Bush to Baghdad to sign the agreements personally. Unlike the president's previous visits, though, this would be a formal ceremony with "full honors."[22]

A picture of the American president standing side by side with the Iraqi prime minister to sign an accord of tremendous import to the future relationship of both countries would create an iconic image, but the actual ceremony yielded one that neither side had anticipated.

On December 14, Bush made his final trip to Baghdad, the last foreign visit of his presidency. A velvet-covered table had been placed in front of a backdrop of alternating U.S and Iraqi flags. Two leather-bound copies of the agreements—one in Arabic, one in English—were ready for the signing, which would occur before assembled dignitaries from both countries and the television cameras.

Lute, the White House czar for Iraq policy, was sitting with Brett

McGurk among the American delegation as the media was brought in for the carefully staged and choreographed event. Exhausted by the long flight to Baghdad, Lute's mind started to drift as the proceedings began, so he was a bit startled when McGurk exclaimed: "Hey, that guy just threw a shoe at the president." A man had stood up and hurled a shoe that had missed Bush and struck the wall behind the flags. Then the protester took his other shoe off and hurled it as well. Almost defiantly, Bush sought to catch it. In the Arab world, waving a shoe was one of the gravest insults, but the president appeared to laugh it off.

Maliki's security detail was not so forgiving. They grabbed the shoe-thrower and immediately began to pummel him. The American Secret Service intervened and a senior agent moved to thrust himself between the now-expended threat and the president, striking the interpreter's boom microphone, which then swung around and struck Dana Perino in the face, giving her a shiner. Maliki was mortified. It was not only Bush who was being insulted. Maliki was being humiliated on his own turf. The prime minister shouted some orders, and Iraqi security guards hauled the dissenter into an adjoining room, where his muffled yells could still be heard as the two sides struggled to get the ceremony back on track and sign the key documents that would solidify America's "enduring relationship" with Iraq.

Maliki had arranged a banquet for both delegations after the signing. The prime minister was still flustered, struggling to compose himself and unable to take charge of what was to have been a more lighthearted event. Crocker pulled Maliki aside and spoke with him for several minutes in Arabic to calm him until he was ready to join the ceremony. To some members of the American delegation, the event seemed an apt metaphor for the entire American experience in Iraq. The event had been organized with the loftiest of intentions, had dissolved into chaos with an element of violence, and the senior American spokesperson had literally gotten a black eye before the situation was righted by a patient American diplomat.

CHAPTER 30

Change at the Top

On the day after his inauguration President Obama went to the White House Situation Room to convene a meeting of his national security team. The first order of business was clear. During the campaign, Obama had promised to summon the Joint Chiefs of Staff to the White House on his first day in office and direct them to bring the Iraq War to a "responsible close."

The Situation Room was equipped with a network of plasma screens, which, like the maestro of a small orchestra, the president could activate or mute to bring more participants into the discussion or ensure that his more candid comments never left the White House. But Obama did not want to be distracted by the hardware and he left those technical details to an aide. Ray Odierno and Ryan Crocker would be beamed into the meeting from Baghdad. Petraeus, now ensconced at CENTCOM, had been traveling abroad and had flown all night to be there in person.

The problem was staring everybody in the face. On the presidential campaign stump, Obama had vowed that he would remove a combat brigade or two a month and ensure that all combat brigades were out of Iraq within sixteen months. Obama's aides argued that the military had determined that the move was feasible, citing testimony Peter Pace had given to Congress in 2007. But Pace had been talking about what was doable logistically in terms of the port capacity in Kuwait and the like, not about what was feasible with respect to the military's mission to maintain security in Iraq and prevent the country from backsliding into civil war. Now that Obama had been elected, the White House was confronted with the task of reconciling Obama's campaign oratory with the realities on the ground in Iraq. The president recognized the challenge: he opened the session by stressing that his "only objective" was to "get this right."[1]

As the discussion got under way, Crocker noted that there had been "slow, uneven progress," which was "fragile and reversible," but it had the "potential for transforming the region." Crocker added that the political blocs in Iraq were "fragmenting" and that power sharing among Maliki and his rivals was an issue, as were the tensions between the Arabs and Kurds in disputed areas. Continued "engagement" with Iraqi leaders was "key."

Odierno stressed that Iran, using its hard and soft power, remained a long-term threat to Iraq. There were more immediate worries as well—the general asserted that 2009 would be a "pivotal year." In every provincial election in January, the incumbents had lost, and in many instances nationalist, not religious, parties had fared well. There had been 70 to 80 percent turnover in the provincial councils. The census, which was bound to be a contentious matter, if it ever happened, was scheduled for that year. And in June, American troops needed to withdraw from Iraq's cities, under the terms of the SOFA that had been signed by Bush and Maliki. Odierno noted that there was "significant risk" in drawing down troops in 2009, and the way in which the United States did so would "set the conditions" for more significant reductions in 2010. Odierno stressed that he was already recommending a drawdown of 12,000 troops in addition to the 5,000 British soldiers who were leaving in May.

Obama made clear that he wanted the Iraqis to do more on the political front, asserting that Iraq's leaders appeared to be in a "comfort zone." Vice President Joe Biden continued the theme. What leverage, he mused, did the United States have over Maliki?

Focusing on the troops issue, Obama said that there were in effect two plans on the table: the one he had inherited and his sixteen-month plan. Obama wanted an assessment of the different timelines and risks, and he wondered if the new administration might find a "sweet spot."

George Bush had talked weekly to Petraeus and Crocker in Monday morning teleconferences and had even gone on a spirited mountain bike ride with Petraeus in the Virginia countryside. But Obama was more cerebral and distant in his dealings with top commanders. An attorney at heart, Obama did not want to be swamped with briefing charts or one-upped on the strategy. Obama and his tight circle of aides would be judge and jury and Odierno and Crocker would be submitting the equivalent of a legal brief to the commander in chief for his consideration.

It was the administration's mid-level staffers who came up with an artful formula to narrow the chasm between the president's campaign promises and the sober assessments of the commanders and ambassador, a gap that had been evident during Obama's Baghdad meetings with Petraeus and Crocker. By coincidence, Elissa Slotkin had been close friends with Colin Kahl, an assistant professor at Georgetown University who headed the Obama campaign's Iraq policy group. Kahl had never been invited to brief the candidate on Iraq, but he had tracked all of the ins and outs of the Bush SOFA negotiations and funneled emails, memos, and papers to Denis McDonough and Mark Lippert, who were in the new president's inner circle. Kahl had also worked closely with Michèle Flournoy, a former Defense Department official who was slated for big things at Obama's Pentagon.

Odierno, who like Petraeus made an effort to keep influential Iraq specialists in the loop, had invited Kahl and Flournoy to participate in a Baghdad-based review of his Iraq strategy and privately provided his feedback on a paper about Iraq that they wrote. As expected, Flournoy had been tapped after the election to serve as undersecretary of defense for policy, the third-ranking civilian position in the Pentagon, and Kahl was picked to serve as her senior deputy for the Middle East. As he waited to take up his Pentagon duties, Kahl went over to Slotkin's NSC office to brainstorm about how to thread the needle on troop withdrawals.

While the candidate had billboarded the sixteen-month deadline, Kahl was familiar with the fine print. There was wiggle room to be had and in a confidential memo to the new White House team Kahl pointed it out. In accordance with sound bites from the campaign, the White House Web site noted Obama's timeline, but notably did not set a start date. Aligning the start of any withdrawal with the day the president announced his Iraq plan—not inauguration day—would add a month or so. What is more, Obama had never committed himself to the pullout of all American troops from Iraq. The candidate had discussed retaining some kind of residual force in Iraq to protect American diplomatic personnel and to target terrorists. An internal analysis that the campaign's Iraq working group had prepared and circulated to senior advisers in September 2008 suggested that a residual force of 75,000 might be required by mid-2010. Ben Rhodes, the chief communications aide on the NSC, had worked for the Iraq Study Group, whose report was the basis for Obama's Iraq policy. The group had envisioned a residual force of twenty thousand to sixty thousand troops.[2]

Slotkin took her and Kahl's solution to the withdrawal date dilemma—the notion of a residual force—to Doug Lute, the three-star Army general who had been brought to the White House by Bush to advise on the Iraq and Afghan wars and had been kept on by the Obama team. Lute saw the ingenuity of the approach and bounced it off the president's small circle of aides as well as Odierno himself.

The solution was not to move the goalposts but, in effect, to change the playing field. The security agreement Bush had signed with Maliki had two firm deadlines: June 2009 for withdrawing American troops from Iraq's cities, and the end of 2011 for withdrawing all American forces from Iraq. Instead of mechanically taking out a brigade or two a month, and ignoring the best advice from the generals, the White House would create yet another milestone—one that the United States would be sure to meet and that the president could tout as the symbolic end of the war. Obama would specify a date for ending the American "combat mission" in Iraq. Not all of the brigades would be out by then, but those that remained would be renamed "advise-and-assist" units. Odierno would retain a substantial number of troops whose stated mission would be to mentor Iraqi forces until the end of 2011 as stipulated by Bush's status of forces agreement. Domestic politics and security imperatives would thereby be balanced. The details to be settled by the Obama review, however, were vitally important: how many troops would Odierno retain in his residual force and how many months would go by before the president could trumpet the end of the American "combat mission" in Iraq?[3]

In late January, Odierno and Crocker sat at opposite ends of a long wooden table at the Republican Palace in Baghdad to pore over their recommendation to the White House. Odierno's team had initially generated Power-Point slides galore, a military propensity that drove the diplomats batty. The general's aides soon learned that this White House would countenance no such thing. "The universe has been restored to equilibrium," Crocker quipped approvingly. Now Odierno and Crocker had come together to discuss their joint paper. "Welcome to the first combined MNF-I/Embassy editorial board," exclaimed Colonel Mike Meese, the head of the Social Sciences Department at West Point, who had worked for Petraeus during the surge and been summoned back to Iraq by Odierno to work on the review.[4]

Before Obama's inauguration, in mid-January Joe Biden had made his final trip to Iraq as a senator and let Odierno know that there would not be a lot of patience for extended troop deployments. "Unemployment is going to hit 10 percent," Biden explained, according to a participant in the meeting. "The economy is really bad. We've got to wind this down."

Then borrowing a tie from Ali Khedery, who was serving as an aide to Ryan Crocker, Biden went off to see Maliki. It was another indication, if Odierno and Crocker needed one, that it might not be easy for them to make their case.[5]

There was no doubt as to Odierno's position. With vivid memories of the terrible violence that had engulfed Iraq before and during the surge, Odierno was wary about rushing the removal of combat troops. The American government had a poor track record of prognosticating events in Iraq. More importantly, the Iraqi and American political calendars were fundamentally out of sync. While Obama was taking office after a hard-fought American campaign, a political free-for-all was getting under way in Iraq. Iraq's national elections were expected to be held in late 2009 or January 2010, a vote that would seat a new parliament and, quite possibly, a new prime minister. If ever the diminished ranks of Al-Qaeda terrorists, Sunni insurgents, and Iranian-backed Special Groups—which had managed to hang on despite the surge—wanted to stage a comeback it would be then. The worst-case scenario was a series of spectacular bombings to frustrate the elections or stymie the formation of a cross-sectarian government. There was also no telling what might happen after a new parliament was picked: there had already been a few elections in Iraq, and after each parliamentary reshuffling, things had rarely fallen quickly into place.

By the evening of January 29 Odierno and Crocker's review was done and ready to be transmitted to the White House. From his CENTCOM headquarters, Petraeus proposed about a dozen changes. In keeping with the themes of the new administration, the report was entitled "Options for a Responsible Drawdown in Iraq." It began by underscoring the significance of the American project in Iraq, assuming a stance that was by no means popular among the new occupants of the White House. "Iraq is of great strategic importance to U.S. interests," it asserted. "After nearly six years of conflict, the U.S. stands on the brink of a new strategic partnership with Iraq that could significantly alter the diplomatic calculus in the Middle East." Having confirmed the stakes, the paper made the case for limiting the exodus of American forces until after Iraq's parliamentary elections took place and a new government was formed. Iraq's success in holding fair elections, the paper argued, would strengthen the "fragile state" against foreign foes and enemies within. Each Iraqi election set the stage for the next, and successful parliamentary elections would provide a strong foundation for representative government. A disputed election would beget still more problems in the future. The "window of highest risk" would be in the months before the parliamentary election and in the sixty-day period that followed.

In addition to the elections, there were many other reasons to be cautious. Tensions between Arabs and Kurds had supplanted the Sunni-Shiite divide as the main challenge facing the country. Peshmerga and Iraqi Army forces had nearly come to blows in September 2008 at Khanaqin and without an effective American role could wind up on a collision course again. Iraqi security forces had a long way to go. The Iraqi military had made numerous gains, as was demonstrated during Maliki's 2008 Basra operation. But that assault, Odierno and Crocker noted, had also exposed the Iraqis' logistical shortfalls—difficulties in coordinating artillery fire and orchestrating medical evacuation—so much so that the intervention of American forces had been necessary.

"Violence remains low due to the coalition's ability to sustain constant pressure on extremist networks," including Iranian-backed groups, the report noted, stressing the American role. Concerning Iraqi politics, there were plenty of ways the fuse might yet be lit. There was not yet a common Iraqi "national vision." Iraqis, the assessment noted, "struggle with disputed internal boundaries, the degree of federalism or centralization of government, communal rivalries between Sunni and Shia, Arab and Kurd and amongst Sunni and Shia factions." In short, there was still a need for American troops and much political spadework to do. "Consolidating the gains made in the security and governance areas in 2009 by withdrawing in a measured fashion would significantly increase the likelihood of our strategic success in Iraq," the paper said.

Having laid the groundwork for its central argument, the assessment outlined the case for bringing the combat mission to a close at the end of 2010, that is, within twenty-three months. This would provide Odierno with eleven or twelve combat brigades through the Iraqi elections. Presenting every justification the Iraq team could muster, the paper listed ten advantages to the approach:

a. Maintains the greater security presence through the window of greatest risk.

b. Provides the most opportunity to develop both security and civil capacity, hence smoothing the transition to residual force missions and tasks.

c. Preserves the feasibility to accelerate the drawdown if conditions warrant.

d. Allows the most deliberate transition of responsibility for security operations from Coalition Forces to Iraqi Security Forces, thereby keeping security incidents at the lowest possible level of incidence.

e. Provides an unambiguous message of U.S. resolve and commitment to Iraq and the region.

f. Best adheres to the underlying tenets to the Security Agreement including the deliberate transfer of bases to the GOI.

g. Most effective pressure vs AQI and balances Iranian influence in Iraq, to best deny extremist organizations the ability to regenerate organizational capacities.

h. Best prepares for the transition to the residual force mission sets by maximizing security gains to increase space for advisory and training functions to develop.

i. Ensures sufficient enablers and ground forces to safeguard Iraq's external borders, air space, waterways, and key infrastructure assets, such as the Persian Gulf oil terminals.

j. Eases the logistical burden and permits good stewardship by providing time to clean, package, load and transport supplies and equipment out of theater.[6]

As Petraeus had noted in his Baghdad meeting with Obama, troop reductions had been carried out since Bush's surge. In fact, the paper argued, there had already been a significant American drawdown. The number of American combat brigades, which had climbed to twenty during the surge, was already down to fourteen. Of the fourteen brigades that remained, two would be leaving over the next several months, as would an F-16 squadron and 4,500 British troops.

Despite these arguments, Robert Gates was pressing for a more politic middle course. Obama had asked Gates to stay on as defense secretary to provide continuity at the Pentagon and protect the new administration's right flank. When the Bush administration had decided on the surge in 2006 Gates had demonstrated his instinct for compromise by recommending that the reinforcement be limited to two combat brigades, less than half of the forces Bush ultimately decided to send. Now Gates was proposing a nineteen-month drawdown schedule. There was no particular rationale behind the number, except that it was closer to Obama's sixteen-month schedule and would enable the White House—two months before the November midterm congressional elections—to say that the combat mission in Iraq had come to a close.

Odierno and Crocker were duty-bound to consider Gates's compromise in their report and assessed that it posed "significant to high risk" because compliance with the schedule meant that some troops would have to leave before Iraqis went to the polls. Specifically, they noted, it would provide a "less than optimal operational capability," some nine or ten combat brigades, during the period when possible dangers would be greatest: "This adds a level of complexity during the window of highest risk, which is beyond that of the 23-month option." Gates's option, they argued, would also provide fewer opportunities for American forces to partner with their Iraqi security counterparts after the election and limit the support the American military could provide for the civilian effort.

As for the sixteen-month option, which in form if not in substance resembled the timeline Obama had promoted during the presidential campaign, Odierno and Crocker's assessment was unforgiving. "The overall risk is extremely high," it noted. "This option demands that U.S. forces place primary focus on withdrawal operations to include equipment withdrawal and base closure within the window of highest risk, thereby undermining the oversight necessary to ensure successful execution of key events such as national elections. Furthermore, U.S. forces will largely be unable to fulfill their role as 'honest brokers' in the resolution of contentious issues." The general and ambassador had not pulled their punches: opting for a sixteen-month timeline would be the height of irresponsibility.

At the end of the paper, Odierno and Crocker explicitly and strongly advocated their position: "We recommend that the twenty-three-month option be adopted because it best mitigates risk during the uncertain and critical period in 2009." A further advantage of the twenty-three-month option to the White House, they noted, would be that it did not preclude the president's slamming the troop withdrawal program into fast-forward should the situation in Iraq uncharacteristically turn out to be easier to manage than expected. "If conditions warrant, the president can decide to accelerate the drawdown timeline to either the 19-month or 16-month option, up until 1 August 2009. By that time, we should have a better sense of political progress in Iraq and better assess the drivers of instability." According to Odierno and Crocker, there was no urgent military reason whatsoever to rule on a withdrawal timetable in early 2009: the White House could start the ball rolling and make a decision on the pace of withdrawal once the situation was clearer.

The nature and size of the residual force that would be deployed in Iraq after the combat mission officially came to a close—whether after twenty-three, nineteen, or sixteen months—was another matter to be determined. Odierno wanted to retain a force of 50,000 to 55,000 troops, which would include six "advise-and-assist brigades," to be located at key points throughout the country. The advise-and-assist brigades would be identical in structure and weaponry to combat brigades, equipped with armored vehicles, artillery, and attack helicopters, and ready to fight if necessary, but each would have an extra complement of fifty advisers. A small number of commandos from JSOC, the Special Forces, and the Navy SEALs would also remain, mainly to accompany elite Iraqi troops on raids: the end of the combat phase would not mean the end of special operations raids against insurgents and militias, at least not until all American troops left at the end of 2011.

When Colonel Meese, the Odierno aide, initially drafted the paper on the residual force and shared it with the White House, the recommendation did not provide for any options other than the general's 50,000- to 55,000-troop configuration. Doug Ollivant, an Army lieutenant colonel who had helped plan the 1st Cavalry Division's surge operations and now worked on the NSC for Lute, saw immediately that the recommendation would not fly with the new team without some elaboration. Odierno and his aides would need to justify the residual force as well.[7]

Making his best case for the force, Odierno argued that it was needed to maintain a presence throughout the country, the better to support the training and equipping of Iraq's security forces, a mission that had been endorsed by the Iraq Study Group—the Holy Grail for Democrats. With a smaller force of 35,000, the United States could cover the Tigris valley, the stretch of central Iraq from Baghdad to Mosul, where Al-Qaeda in Iraq remained dug in and had recently killed an American cavalry battalion commander. At this troop level, however, the United States would be leaving other parts of the country unattended and would not be able to complete the training of some of Iraq's military before the departure of American forces.

The option to retain an even smaller force—some lawmakers had advocated diminishing the American presence in Iraq to as few as 10,000 to 15,000 troops—would severely hamper the American military's ability to defend itself and protect the American civilian officials it was supporting throughout Iraq. Odierno was flatly against this option. If the residual force was to be smaller than 35,000, Odierno preferred that it be withdrawn altogether: "Commander of MNF-I considers this a 'red line' and if we reach this threshold would recommend redeploying the force and transitioning the mission to a smaller security cooperation office in Baghdad."[8] As with the withdrawal timeline, Odierno stressed that there was no immediate need to determine the number of residual forces. Even according to the shortest timeline under consideration, it would take the United States well over a year to get to the point where it would have to field a residual force. It was another matter that could be settled as 2009 wore on.

One of the most important sections in Odierno and Crocker's classified submission was a brief analysis of the Americans' political leverage in Iraq. Contrary to those who argued that there was little the United States could do to shape the unfolding events there, they said, the United States still had significant, but not unlimited, influence. Many of the politicians and factions in Iraq had their own reasons for dealing with Washington. Maliki saw the American military presence as a bulwark against a Baathist-led military coup. The Sunnis saw it as a means to moderate the behavior of the Shiite-dominated government and the security forces it controlled. With no close friends in the region, the Kurds wanted to "lock in" a long-term relationship with the United States.

American participation in the Iraqi political scene would have to be subtler than ever before. Gone were the days when American diplomats would shuttle proposals back and forth among feuding Iraqi politicians. American officials might dispense general advice to Iraqi officials, but the latter were now responsible for hammering out the details. "This means that we can and often do set agendas, but we cannot compel particular outcomes or concessions that Iraqi leaders perceive as disadvantageous to their own political gain."

As for how to navigate the future, Crocker and Odierno cautioned that threatening to remove forces or cancel aid programs unless the Iraqis made political progress would simply backfire.

"Our negotiation with Iraqis in 2007 over 'benchmark legislation,' and in 2008 over the SoFA showed that how we apply our influence is hugely important," the analysis noted, adding:

> Threatening to withdraw American forces and programs from Iraq when Iraqis reject our requests appears to them to be an emotional American reaction and draws an Iraqi emotional reaction in return or, in the case of the Kurds and Sunni Arabs, a return to the bunker mentality (the Prime Minister is especially prone to this as well) in which they refuse to reach out to other Iraqis because of fear that the Americans won't be available to help. The U.S. military presence itself has significant importance but does not automatically lead to leverage on all issues. While our military presence is key for the large issue of guaranteeing an environment for progress in the political process, it does not predetermine the outcome of

that process. It is also an important factor in dissuading Kurds and Arabs from escalating to serious armed conflict.

Instead, recent experiences show that detailing realities about U.S. domestic support for the war effort, about which Iraqis usually know little, and how that support depends on progress inside Iraq, generates more positive responses. Iraqi officials realize that the war in Iraq has generated American domestic skepticism and opposition. They are nervous about the new administration's commitment. They have thus followed carefully signals from the new Administration—especially cautionary comments by the Vice President—regarding the realities of the American political and economic scene. We have underscored the changed context for U.S. decision-making, emphasizing both the need for Iraqi action in key security, political, and economic areas, and the critical requirement to avoid destabilizing actions and confrontation that will make continued U.S. engagement and support difficult. It is clear that all of Iraq's political elites wish to cultivate favor with the new Administration, or at a minimum avoid negative reaction, and we have used these levers to press, inter alia, the importance of avoiding Arab-Kurdish confrontation, a major political crisis over the Maliki government and importance of all parties working to ensure credible elections.

The message to the White House was clear: it could still shape events in Iraq, and there was a lot more to consider than how fast American troops could leave.

As the parameters of its Iraq strategy were being decided, the Obama administration still faced an important choice: who should succeed Crocker as ambassador to Iraq. It was not just another ambassadorial appointment. With the drawdown of the American military in Iraq, the diplomats would be taking on additional responsibilities and eventually take the lead. The State Department had pondered a raft of potential candidates, including Mark Parris and Marc Grossman, two former ambassadors to Turkey, who were not interested. Tony Zinni was not a former diplomat, but he had considerable experience on Iraq. The former CENTCOM commander had commissioned the Desert Crossing exercise that pointed to the many vicissitudes of a postwar Iraq. Zinni had opposed the war but had supported the surge as a way to stabilize Iraq before the Americans began to reduce their forces. He also had a good understanding of Odierno's thinking: he had participated in the strategy review the commander had convened in October.

For all that, Zinni had not given any thought to an ambassadorial post until James Jones, Obama's first national security adviser and a fellow retired Marine four-star general, called shortly before the inauguration. The administration was going to appoint several special envoys to the Middle East and other trouble spots and was also looking for ambassadors to Iraq and Afghanistan. Zinni indicated that he was interested, and Jones followed up with another call in which he offered him Baghdad. Zinni was then invited to Foggy Bottom to meet with the new secretary of state, Hillary Clinton, and her top deputies, Jim Steinberg, the deputy secretary of state, and Bill Burns, the undersecretary for political affairs and the highest-ranking career Foreign Service officer in the department. Zinni talked about the work that had been done by Paul Brinkley, who led a Defense Department task force that sought to restart Iraq's former state-owned industries to generate jobs and, the Americans hoped, give Iraqis a reason not to join the insurgency. Clinton had not heard of Brinkley and asked why the State Department, which was supposed to be taking the lead in Iraq, did not have that sort of capability.

Looking beyond the withdrawal of American troops, Zinni said it was already clear that the Iraqis would continue to need some help after American forces withdrew, especially in the realm of intelligence. Clinton and Steinberg were uneasy about maintaining any sort of military presence after 2011 that was not formally attached to the embassy's office of security cooperation, part of whose portfolio was to sell American arms and provide a modicum of security assistance. Steinberg asked whether the intelligence function might be camouflaged as part of the United States military assistance program. Zinni said that something like that might be possible and also argued that there needed to be an operations cell in that headquarters in case American forces had to be rushed back to Iraq in a crisis. An American quick reaction force might be kept in Kuwait just in case.

At the end of the session, Clinton turned to Steinberg and Burns and said that she wanted to get the paperwork moving and get an early hearing set up. Zinni, Clinton said, needed to start thinking about the deputies he would want to take with him to Baghdad. Burns would call Zinni with the details on where things stood with the nomination process. The next day Biden called Zinni to thank him for taking the job. The United States, the vice president said, was moving into a new phase in which the diplomatic and economic portfolios would be far more important than military operations.

As Zinni was being wooed by the Obama team, he received a call from the White House, which had a request. Zinni had been a vocal advocate of "smart power"—the proposition that diplomacy and development assistance were as important as military power. Obama aides thought Zinni should write an op-ed praising smart power and the new president's interest in it. If Zinni did not want to take the trouble to draft the op-ed, the Obama team would draft it for him. Zinni, in effect, would get another opportunity to proselytize on behalf of the smart power strategy and the new administration would secure a plug as it was rolling out its foreign policy. Zinni took the White House team up on its suggestion and, after concluding that the op-ed piece they had written was innocuous, submitted it to the *Washington Post*.[9]

Zinni was on the verge of canceling speaking engagements, suspending his participation on corporate boards, and generally clearing the deck for his ambassadorial appointment. But after days went by without further word from Burns, Zinni left a message for Jones saying that he needed an explanation. Jones got back to him that night: Christopher Hill, not Zinni, had been picked as ambassador to Iraq.

The next day the media was all over the story. Zinni was angry that he had been so publicly rejected for a position he had not sought—and all without the decency of a phone call. When an editor from the *Post* called to suggest some changes to Zinni's smart power op-ed he pulled the piece. As a sop, Jones told Zinni he could be ambassador to Saudi Arabia, a throwaway remark that said something about the level of attention the new administration had paid to its ties with Riyadh. Zinni told Jones to shove it. In the span of a few days, Zinni had gone from being a coveted recruit for the new administration to being a pariah who was off the team.[10]

Hill, who had ascended to the post of assistant secretary of state for East Asian and Pacific affairs after a frustrating stint as the Bush administration's negotiator with Pyongyang, was just as surprised. As the point man for talks with the North Koreans, who had defied the West by marching ahead with their nuclear weapons and missile programs, Hill had become a lightning rod for conservatives, including some hard-liners in the Bush administration itself. The negotiations, Hill observed years later, had been the right thing to do but for the wrong administration. Summoned to Clinton's seventh-floor office, Hill had assumed that he would be asked about the way ahead with North Korea.

As soon as Hill entered Clinton's State Department suite, he could see that this was not going to be a brainstorming session. Steinberg, Burns, and Cheryl Mills, Clinton's chief of staff, were also there. Clinton came right to the point: would Hill be willing to succeed Crocker as the American ambassador in Baghdad? Hill was taken aback. Of all the places he had served, the Middle East was not one of them. Hill spoke Polish, Serbo-Croatian, and Albanian, but not Arabic. He was operating on the assumption that he would need to vacate his assistant secretary post with the arrival of a new administration and had lined up a teaching fellowship at Yale. Compounding the unlikeliness of his selection, the North Koreans had maintained a clandestine uranium enrichment program even as they engaged the United States in negotiations, and the conservatives in Congress would be baying for Hill's scalp. Clinton was not worried. "We will protect you on this," she said.[11]

Hill went home to think over the offer and fielded a call from his mentor Richard Holbrooke, the veteran diplomat and Democratic Party favorite, who asked if he was going to take the job. Huddling with the staff of the Asian bureau the next morning, he decided to take the post. Hill would be America's man in Baghdad just as Iraq was moving into a critical phase. He told Clinton he would stay a year.

Odierno's argument to defer the hard calls on the withdrawal schedule and the residual force until later in the year was rejected. The president had promised to chart a new course and wanted to demonstrate as much to his base. As for the timeline, the Gates compromise option had prevailed: Odierno would have nineteen months to formally end the combat mission. Odierno was given the flexibility to manage the pace of the drawdown over those nineteen months, which the general felt was enough to make the plan work. Obama's promise to withdraw one or two brigades a month was quietly discarded.

Jockeying over the size of the residual force, however, continued until the last minute. In the interagency meetings working on the Iraq review Admiral Mike Mullen, the chairman of the Joint Chiefs, had sought to avoid a legalistic debate about counting every last soldier, including those packing up and heading south to Kuwait, as the August 2010 deadline approached. He was adamant American troops at the end of August 2010 be accounted for as "about fifty thousand." The figure was agreed upon at a top-level meeting and a memo codifying the position was sent to the president.

On February 25, the night before the president was to brief his decision to congressional leaders, Obama's small circle of aides reworked the
numbers. Overnight, the figure was changed to a range with a hard upper
limit: 35,000 to 50,000. The president was still trying to strike a balance
between satisfying his commanders and placating the antiwar wing of his
party. The next day Obama hosted the congressional leaders in the Roosevelt Room, an ornate conference room in the West Wing. Obama outlined the plan before handing the presentation off to Gates. But Mullen,
who had not been alerted to the overnight change, stuck with "about fifty
thousand." The discrepancy did not escape the attention of Carl Levin, the
Michigan Democrat and former prosecutor who headed the Senate Armed
Services Committee. Levin put the perplexed JCS chairman on the spot
until Obama intervened to clarify the matter: fifty thousand was a firm
limit and there would not be a soldier more.[12]

Nancy Pelosi, the House Speaker, was still unhappy. The experts she
had consulted, she explained, did not believe that more than fifteen thousand troops were needed. Pelosi did not name her experts, and the figure was well below the minimum troop number that Odierno said would
be required after August 2010, but the episode was an indication of the
pressure the president was under from the left wing of his party. Obama
responded by explaining that August 2010 would still signify an important
change of mission. The "end of combat" milestone that Kahl and Slotkin
had devised had served its purpose.

The review established a pattern in the White House's decisions about
Iraq and Afghanistan. From Odierno in Iraq to McChrystal and Petraeus
in Afghanistan, Obama accepted the main tenets of the generals' strategy.
The candidate who had remonstrated against the surge endorsed, however
reluctantly, the main assumptions behind the counterinsurgency program.
Jack Keane's recommendation that Bush elevate Petraeus to CENTCOM
and send Odierno to Baghdad had had its intended effect: it had locked in
the military strategy, all the more so as it had been endorsed by Crocker.
But counterinsurgency by its very nature was a troop-intensive and lengthy
approach and political pressures would lead the White House to limit the
resources and time that the commanders could have to carry it out. Military commanders would not have as much time or as many troops as they
wanted to prosecute their strategy. The Obama administration would not
wage wars; it would manage them.

The same day that Obama met with the congressional leaders, Odierno
went to brief Maliki about the plan. The general ran through its gist: all

combat operations would cease by the end of August 2010 with the important exception of special operations missions to be conducted in coordination with Iraqi troops. As for the American military's footprint, the fourteen American combat brigades would be reduced to six advise-and-assist brigades. The 350 American bases would dwindle to 30, spread throughout Iraq but outside of cities in conformity with the security agreement. Maliki was pleased about the latter stipulation.

"This is good," the Iraqi prime minister said. The presence of American forces in Iraq's cities had become a political issue, especially among the Sadrists. But Maliki also had some apprehensions about the plan. The prime minister asked when the accelerated troop drawdown would begin and was told that Obama would announce that the first step would be the withdrawal of fifteen thousand troops from Iraq over the next six months, including two Marine battalions from Anbar and an Army brigade from Diwaniyah.

"A principle must be established," Maliki said. When it came to pulling out of Iraq, American forces should leave troubled Sunni areas last. The Iraqi prime minister was particularly concerned about the withdrawal from Anbar, which had served as a sanctuary for the insurgents before the Awakening. Seeking to reassure Maliki, Odierno said that he retained the flexibility to shift some remaining Army forces to Anbar or other challenging areas if insurgents tried to make a comeback.

Turning to some of the problems Iraq had to contend with, Odierno informed Maliki that American warplanes had tracked and shot down an Iranian drone the previous day that had been flying for three hours over Iraqi territory. Maliki asked if it had entered intentionally. Odierno said that the drone appeared to be conducting reconnaissance of Camp Ashraf, the Mujahideen-e-Kalk compound, but that an Iranian helicopter that had also strayed into Iraqi territory that day was probably just lost.

As for problems of the Iraqis' own making, Odierno reported that Iraqi forces near Kirkuk were flying an old Iraqi flag that bore the slogan "Long Live Saddam." The Iraqi unit was near an area that was contested between Arabs and Kurds and the Americans were worried that the gesture would intensify the already inflamed tensions. Maliki, who had heard nothing about the episode, was upset and indicated he would remedy the situation. As a former member of the Dawa underground Maliki continued to regard Baathists as the greatest threat.[13] It was another example of how the American military provided the Iraqi leadership with information on some of the touchiest issues and worked behind the scenes to defuse ethnic and sectarian tensions.

The next day Obama took a leaf out of George Bush's playbook and, using a military base as a patriotic backdrop, traveled to Camp Lejeune, the Marine base in North Carolina, to unveil his plan on "responsibly ending the war" and announce his withdrawal timeline. Ben Rhodes, the precocious staffer who had helped write the Iraq Study Group report drafted the address. The Bush administration had asserted that the emergence of democracy in Iraq would be a catalyst of political reform throughout the Middle East. The Obama administration had a different approach. It was loath to commit itself to spread "democracy" and embraced a lesser, but still formidable, goal of fostering an Iraq that was stable, self-reliant, and had a representative government that was accountable to its citizens and a just legal system. The difference did not go unnoticed by Iraqi politicians in Baghdad, who asked American diplomats if the new administration was still committed to a democratic Iraq.

To bring stability to Iraq, the Obama administration would be pursuing "principled and sustained engagement" across the region, including with two of Iraq's most autocratic neighbors, Iran and Syria, a theme carried over from the Iraq Study Group. Bush's intention to use Iraq as a lever to fulfill his broader "freedom agenda" for the Middle East had been more of a vision than a master plan; he did not consistently apply his doctrine in Egypt or the Gulf states whose leaders had long worked closely with Washington. Still, Obama was turning the doctrine on its head. Instead of seeking to change the autocracies in Syria and Iran he hoped to strengthen ties with them and seek their tolerance of the nascent democracy in their midst. Stability in Iraq would not be achieved by using developments there to change the region but by reassuring its neighbors that the United States did not represent a threat to the old order.

Obama acknowledged the success Odierno and Petraeus had had in reducing sectarian violence and delivering a body blow against Al-Qaeda. As a month had passed since the Gates compromise option had been devised, Obama announced his plan was to remove combat brigades over eighteen months. "As a candidate for President, I made clear my support for a timeline of 16 months to carry out this drawdown, while pledging to consult closely with our military commanders upon taking office to ensure that we preserve the gains we've made and protect our troops. Those consultations are now complete, and I have chosen a timeline that will remove our combat brigades over the next 18 months," Obama said, sliding over the difference between sixteen and eighteen and the fact that the structure of the remaining brigades would be largely the same as it had always been. "Let me say this as plainly as I can," he said. "By August 31, 2010, our combat mission will end." Then the United States would initially have a "transitional" force of 35,000 to 50,000. Nobody had wanted the force to be considered "residual" and the term had been jettisoned. It was finally time to usher in an era of normalized relations with Baghdad. Chris Hill, a pragmatic and skilled diplomat who had served from Korea to Kosovo, Obama said, would be the man to do so.

The same week that Obama announced his Iraq plan, his administration moved to carry out its regional strategy. John Kerry, who chaired the Senate Foreign Relations Committee, had introduced Obama to the nation at the 2004 Democratic convention and endorsed him in the early stage of the campaign. Kerry had lost out to Clinton for the post of secretary of state, but he was close to the administration and ran interference for the White House on sensitive diplomatic undertakings.

Syria promised to be among the trickiest of Kerry's assignments. Syria had provided refuge to senior Baathists from Saddam's regime and allowed a steady trickle of foreign fighters to make their way to Iraq. American relations with Syria had taken a turn for the worse when the Bush administration concluded four years earlier that Assad's regime had been implicated in the assassination of Rafiq al-Hariri, the former Lebanese prime minister, and withdrew its ambassador. During the waning months of his term in office Bush authorized the October 26, 2008, raid by JSOC and the CIA in Syria that killed Abu Ghadiya, the militant leader who had been funneling terrorists into Iraq.[14]

Several weeks after that raid, David Miliband, the British foreign secretary, sought to pave the way for improved relations with the West by urging Assad in a November 18 meeting to take positive steps on Lebanon, the Palestinian-Israeli peace talks, and Iraq. Why, Miliband asked Assad, did the Syrian government still refer to Sunni terrorists as the "resistance" and the American effort as an "occupation" when it was trying to achieve a modicum of cooperation with Baghdad? Miliband did not receive an answer. Assad complained about the October JSOC-CIA raid in Syria that killed Abu Ghadiya. Miliband asked why Syria had not taken care of Abu Ghadiya, especially since the United States had provided the government with much information on his presence in Syria. Again, Miliband received little by way of a reply. The Syrian leader did not even acknowledge that Abu Ghadiya had been in Syria. "Even if Abu Ghadiya was there," Assad said, the U.S. strike was not the way to deal with the issue. Reporting on the visit, the American chargé d'affaires in Damascus concluded in a cable that Miliband's trip had provided the Syrian government with a modest propaganda boost for little in exchange.[15]

Kerry began a February 21 visit to Damascus by seeking to reassure Assad and his deputies that the arrival of the Obama administration signaled a fresh approach to diplomacy. The United States, Kerry insisted, was willing to take steps to demilitarize its foreign policy, including cutting its own nuclear arms. Kerry said that he had recommended that the United States shrink the nuclear arsenal to one thousand weapons. As for Iraq, Kerry said that the Obama administration wanted to withdraw troops as soon as possible. Assad was not reassured. The question, he lectured Kerry, was not when to leave Iraq but how. Before American combat brigades left, the Iraqis needed to make political progress. If reconciliation failed and the Iraqis opted for federalism, sectarian divisions would harden. The Sunni sector would be governed by Al-Qaeda, Assad asserted, and the Shiite sector by Iran. And the autonomous Kurdish enclave would become a problem for the entire Middle East, argued Assad, who appeared to be concerned that an independent Kurdistan might encourage separatist tendencies among Syria's Kurdish population.

"Maliki doesn't like us," Assad said. "He is stubborn but good, a legitimate leader." The Iraqi prime minister would move forward with greater confidence if the United States gave the Iraqis "more space." Both Maliki and Zebari, the foreign minister, had confided to the Syrians that the United States needed to understand that it could not continue to pressure the Iraqi government.[16]

In March 2009, a delegation of State Department and NSC officials traveled to Damascus for the first discussion to ease antipathy between the two countries. In the next several months, each side made some modest gestures of conciliation. The United States provided information "regarding a potential threat to a Syrian official" through Syria's Washington ambassador, Imad Mustapha, and allowed a senior aide to George Mitchell, the American Middle East envoy, to attend a holiday event at the Syrian embassy, a cable reported. Syria, for its part, allowed the Americans to reopen an English-language school and hosted a team of American military officials to discuss how better to regulate the Syria-Iraq border.

Each side, however, wanted the other to make the first major initiative. Syria kept pressing for the lifting of economic sanctions, which had crippled its aviation industry, and the Americans urged Syria to curtail its support for Hezbollah and Hamas. "The U.S. had publicly recognized its mistakes, e.g. use of torture methods, and would continue to take steps," Daniel Shapiro, a senior official on the NSC, told the Syrians in the meeting, according to a May 2009 cable. "But others needed to reciprocate to ensure that the opportunity did not pass."[17]

When Odierno and Maliki met again in March the Iraqi prime minister repeated his concerns about the pace of the American withdrawal. Some 12,500 American troops were to leave by July, and Maliki worried that Al-Qaeda was waiting for the drawdown to reconstitute and attempt a comeback. The Americans, he argued, needed to be careful about withdrawing from Anbar, Nineveh, Salahuddin, and Diyala, all provinces with substantial Sunni populations. Maliki wanted to meet with Odierno and plan the drawdown in greater detail together.

Maliki surprised Odierno with one question. The Iraqi leader had been warned that foreign fighters were training in Russia and was concerned that the militants and a new generation of weapons would infiltrate Iraq. With little in the way of foreign intelligence, Maliki was looking to his American partner for assurance. Odierno said he would look into it but suggested that if indeed fighters were training in remote parts of Russia their destination was more likely Afghanistan than Iraq.[18]

Odierno was out of the country two weeks later when it was time to confer again on March 19, so corps commander Lloyd Austin joined Patricia Butenis, the chargé d'affaires, for the session. Once again, Maliki fretted about the drawdown. The once formidable insurgency had devolved into gangs, but was still a danger. The Iraqis and Americans needed to adjust and exploit whatever intelligence they had. "Maintaining victory is much more important than achieving victory," Maliki added. The Iraqi prime minister was signaling to the Americans that he did not consider the job done.

Austin suggested that the Iraqi police might play a greater role in the security of Baghdad. As the Americans saw it, the ultimate goal was to have "police primacy" in the cities and redirect the Iraqi Army to external defense. The idea was rebuffed by Maliki. The Iraqi prime minister did not have confidence in the police and had seeded the army with loyalists. He told Austin that he did not want to risk withdrawing the Iraqi Army from Iraq's cities, particularly as the American forces drew down.

Maliki asked Butenis when Chris Hill would arrive in Baghdad. The United States had not had an ambassador in Iraq since Crocker left on February 13. Maliki wanted to know if Hill would run into any snags during his Senate confirmation hearing. Butenis noted that Hill did not have any Middle East experience, but stressed that he was a respected diplomat and would not have any problems getting confirmed. Maliki responded that he had spoken about Hill with Obama and that the president had assured him that Hill had his complete confidence and was the right man for the job.

"We welcome him to Iraq," Maliki added.[19]

CHAPTER 31

The Odd Couple

Chris Hill made it to Baghdad on the evening of April 24, 2009. As the ambassador feared, his nomination had been criticized by a pack of Senate conservatives who saw him as an avatar of the Bush administration's frustrated diplomacy with North Korea. But as Hillary Clinton had promised, the Obama administration eventually pushed his nomination through.

Two months after he was chosen for the job, his ambassadorship began with a mad dash. After presenting his credentials at the Foreign Ministry, Hill had a midnight dinner with Jalal Talabani, the Iraqi president. Hours later he was having breakfast with Leon Panetta, the CIA director, before rushing to Baghdad International Airport to greet Clinton, who was making her first visit to Iraq as secretary of state with Jim Steinberg, her top deputy, in tow. For good measure, Mike Mullen, the chairman of the Joint Chiefs, was passing through Iraq, too.

The high-level visits were intended to demonstrate that the Obama administration had not forgotten about Iraq, a message that seemed directed not only at the Iraqis but at foreign policy experts at home who had been distressed that the ambassadorial post in Baghdad had been allowed to remain vacant for almost two months. For all that, Clinton's one-day excursion to Baghdad would be the last time the Iraqis would see the secretary of state in the capital before the American troops pulled out. Biden would make regular visits, but Hill would be the point man now.

The son of a diplomat, Hill was capping off a long and varied career. After graduating from Bowdoin, Hill had done a stint in the Peace Corps, where he served in Cameroon, a West African nation that had taught him a cautionary lesson about the limits of nation-building. After discovering that the workers at a plantation were having their funds stolen by the corrupt administrators of a local credit union, Hill gave a fiery speech exposing the malfeasance only to see the villagers reelect the very officials he had condemned. The credit union officials, it turned out, reflected a careful balancing of tribal interests. From this episode Hill took that there were limits to how much the United States could do to shape a developing society. As Hill told an interviewer years later, "When something's happened, it's happened for a reason." It is important to understand the reason, Hill added, "but don't necessarily think you can change it."[1]

Hill's adventures with the Peace Corps prompted him to sign up with the Foreign Service, in which he held several important posts in the Balkans and emerged as a protégé of Richard Holbrooke. By the time Obama came to office, he had risen to the rank of career minister, the second-highest rung in the diplomatic corps. After ambassadorships in three countries, quality time wrestling with the demons in the Balkans, experience working with American generals in Seoul, and a stint negotiating with the inscrutable North Koreans, he felt up to the challenge despite his lack of Middle East experience.

As Hill saw it, the American role in Iraq had changed over the years, and with it the nature of the diplomatic assignment. A senior Iraqi official who dealt with all of Hill's predecessors characterized them this way: Jerry Bremer had been a viceroy who presided over the occupation; John Negroponte had been a skilled caretaker of the transition process; Zalmay Khalilzad had been the ultimate insider who labored hard to draw the Sunnis into the new government by drafting a permanent constitution, which was passed in a referendum; quiet and seemingly unflappable, Crocker had been the quintessential troubleshooting diplomat. He had worked hand in glove with the military, gone jogging with Petraeus, testified side by side with the Iraq commander when he came under fire in the Senate Foreign Relations Committee, been in frequent videoconferences with the president, and been deeply engaged in the political engineering in Iraq.

Hill intended to preside over a major course correction. He would move to normalize the relationship with Baghdad and wrest away from the military the lead role in Iraq for those missions the United States did retain. The lessons of political engineering that he had taken away from his Peace Corps assignment once again appeared to be apt. The word back at Foggy Bottom was that Hill was determined to be the "un-Crocker." Or as Hill himself put it sarcastically and somewhat indelicately to his staff after arriving in Baghdad, it was time to "break some crockery."[2]

To mark a fresh start in Baghdad, Hill would be working with a new team—some who had worked with him before and had records of accomplishment but little or no time on the ground in Iraq. The head of the political-military bureau whom Hill recruited was Cameron Munter, who had been called in to run the provincial reconstruction team in Mosul for six months in 2006, but whose principal expertise and diplomatic assignments had been in Europe and who, in fact, had been shifted from his ambassadorship in Serbia. Patricia Haslach, who had served in the Asia bureau and as ambassador to Laos, was made the senior coordinator for the U.S. assistance fund. Yuri Kim, who had worked for Hill in the Asia bureau, switched her assignment from the provincial reconstruction team she had volunteered to work for in Anbar to come to Baghdad and work in the political section. Gary Grappo was the senior political officer and was not recruited by Hill. A graduate of the Air Force Academy, Grappo had served as the American ambassador in Oman and been posted in Saudi Arabia and Jordan, but he had never worked in Baghdad.

There was a holdover of long standing in the embassy with considerable knowledge of Iraq. Robert Ford, who was fluent in Arabic, had begun his service in Najaf during Bremer's tenure at the CPA and returned as the political counselor under Negroponte and later Crocker, then been selected to serve as the deputy chief of mission. But Ford, who was largely marginalized and even chided by Hill when he met with his many Iraqi contacts, left the embassy later in 2009 and reemerged as the United States ambassador in Damascus. Ford thought that Adil Abd al-Mahdi, the Shiite senior politician with ISCI, would make the strongest prime minister for Iraq given his experience as finance minister and his diverse connections among the Iraqis. Maliki might have been the right leader for his time and had led the operation to restore order in Basra, but with the challenges Iraq faced in developing its economy he seemed to be a man of the past, Ford figured. But with Ford's elevation into management and eventual departure there was nobody in the embassy actively to press that case.

Hill's crockery-breaking portended strains with the military and his opposite number: Ray Odierno. By all accounts, Hill and Odierno made an unlikely pair. After the long stretch without an ambassador, Odierno had welcomed Hill's arrival. But the general and the ambassador had different visions of the American role in Iraq and disparate resources to bring to bear on its problems.

Odierno had been an activist. He had presided over the surge and was a fervent troubleshooter. Odierno had spent more than three years in Iraq by the time Hill arrived and much of his team was on its second and third deployment. Odierno's headquarters not only had a sizable staff of majors and colonels that dwarfed the embassy team but it was better connected with Iraqi politicians and had more experience than Hill's inner circle of Asian and European hands. The military's civil affairs shop was almost a mini–State Department all its own and worked on everything from oil policy to agriculture. The military's dominance in terms of resources was driven home to Hill in an early briefing he and Odierno conducted for a group of visiting American dignitaries. The American briefing team was heavily military, and the visitors had been given coffee mugs with the emblem of Odierno's headquarters. Hill was concerned, he later recalled, that the embassy he was inheriting "was not acting like an embassy but as kind of an adjunct to the military." The diplomats, he told his staff, needed to show they were really in charge.

The asymmetry led to some tension. To the enormous frustration of Hill, Odierno had his own foreign policy adviser: a petite British civilian who had become something of a modern-day Gertrude Bell. The product of Oxford's Somerville College, the alma mater of Margaret Thatcher and Indira Gandhi, Emma Sky was awarded a degree in Oriental studies and set out to work for peace between the Israelis and Palestinians and change the world. After working for the British Council in the West Bank, Gaza, and Israel for nearly a decade, Sky boasted about her opposition to the Iraq War. But after the invasion began, she went to northern Iraq for a British relief organization and later worked in Kirkuk for Bremer's CPA, living in the divided city until a mortar shell struck her local residence and forced her to the nearby base of the Army's 173rd Airborne Brigade. During the surge, she had emerged as a trusted adviser to Odierno on Iraq's tangled and internecine politics and even helped negotiate a cease-fire with Sadrists in West Rashid who had been shelling Camp Victory. As an Arabic speaker, Sky could run circles around many of the diplomats in the embassy, sometimes literally since she more freely accessed the "Red Zone" outside the embassy compound.

Hill felt strongly that it was wrong for the United States to depend so much on a foreign national, notwithstanding that Britain had been the most valued member of the American-led coalition. More than once Hill's staff meetings at the embassy were peppered with digs at Odierno's adviser—he once referred to her as a "goddamn fucking British spy." Eventually, a modus vivendi was reached. It was agreed that if Sky interacted with Iraqi officials she would brief Kim, Hill's deputy political officer, who would return the favor by keeping Sky in the loop on what was happening at the embassy. Some veteran embassy hands were convinced that neither side fully kept to the bargain.[3]

The main tension between Hill and Odierno was driven by their clashing interpretations of Iraq. Maliki had been an ally of sorts to the American military, but the command had also found itself having to deal with the consequences of his decisions, whether trying to discourage arbitrary arrests in Diyala, rushing to avert Arab-Kurdish tensions along the ill-defined periphery of Kurdistan, or hastening to support Maliki in Basra when he took the plunge only to discover that he was in over his head. Whether it had to do with Al-Qaeda, Iran, Maliki's rivals, or actions taken by the prime minister himself, Odierno was worried that hard-won gains would be reversed and Tehran's influence expanded if the United States did not stay actively involved in shaping Iraqi affairs. Odierno was always talking about the need to neutralize, or at least attenuate, the "drivers of instability," those factors that had the potential to unhinge Iraq.

Hill and some of his embassy colleagues thought such concerns said less about the political equation in Baghdad than about the military's difficulty in letting go of its lead role in Iraq and its desire to claim a victory. Hill was skeptical of the military's presumed challenges; he recoiled even at Odierno's argot. "We hate the term 'drivers of instability' and won't use it," he fumed at one embassy session. Not since the days of Jerry Bremer and Rick Sanchez had the civil-military relationship in Baghdad been fraught with so much tension.

Two weeks after arriving in Baghdad, Hill had his first meeting with Maliki. Crocker's diagnosis of the political challenges in Iraq was evident from the title of one of his last cables from Iraq: "PM Maliki: Strengthened Center or Emerging Strongman?" The prime minister, Crocker cautioned, had worked hard to build up his authority to manage what was in many ways a dysfunctional state, which was to the good. But there were clear risks as well. Maliki relied on an insular circle of conspiratorial-minded Dawa Party operatives. Building up the power of his OCINC, Maliki had gone outside the formal chain of command by assuming control of the regional operations commands, the Iraqi Army's 56th "Baghdad" Brigade and the ISOF commando brigades through the Counter-Terrorism Service. They were tools for repression and intimidation that Maliki had used in the 2008 operations in Baqubah and Khanaqin until the United States pushed back.

"Maliki has shown that he is either unwilling or unable to take the lead in the give-and-take needed to build broad consensus for the Government's policies among competing power blocs. Furthermore, the Prime Minister has appeared willing to confront his adversaries with force, as illustrated by the near-confrontation between the Iraqi Army and Peshmerga in northern Diyala province last September," Crocker wrote in his confidential cable.

"A key question posed by Maliki's evolving hold on levers of political and security power is whether the PM is becoming a non-democratic dictator bent on subordinating all authority to his hand or whether Maliki is attempting to rebalance political and security authority back to the center after five-plus years of intended and unintended dispersal to (and in some cases seizure by) actors and power structures outside Baghdad," Crocker concluded. "We believe the answer lies closer to the latter than the former."

It was a hopeful analysis but not an outcome Crocker took for granted. As he indicated in his contribution to the Obama review and at the conclusion of his cable, the United States would need to use its economic, political, and military influence to keep Iraq on course and bind it to Washington. "Faced with this situation, we should continue to emphasize our support for institutions rather than individuals, and for processes rather than personalities, even as we are mindful that Iraqi politics will remain personalized and divided for the foreseeable future," Crocker wrote. "We should press the PM on institution and political consensus building as key to sustaining and advancing our relationship and support."[4]

The question was whether the same aims could be effectively pursued by his "un-Crocker" successor. In his first meeting with Hill, Maliki cautioned that he would likely hear much criticism of the prime minister from self-interested rivals more committed to their own ambitions than to working together. The prime minister appealed for "understanding" and insisted that anti-Maliki criticism was "having a negative effect on Iraq's interests." On foreign policy, the prime minister noted that he wanted better relations with Kuwait, but was unhappy with Saudi Arabia, which he said still had the misconception that the Iraqi government was sectarian, and Turkey, which to his frustration had recently hosted Muqtada al-Sadr. To deal with the threats it still faced, Iraq would need American-supplied intelligence as well as equipment.

Of greater immediacy, Hill noted that a rocket had been fired at the American embassy compound and that the United States could tell from the weapon's fragments that it had been supplied by Iran. Maliki, seeming to relive his glory days in Basra and during the Sadr City fight, quipped that Hill was lucky that it had been only one rocket. During the 2008 clash with the Sadrists, he claimed, 730 shells and rockets had been lobbed at the Green Zone in one month. The rockets, Maliki added, were "gifts from our friends to the east and west," taking a less pointed stance on Iran and underscoring the need for the United States and Iraq to remain partners. Hill raised a problem with the student exchange program the United States had promised. Washington wanted to move ahead, but Iraq's Ministry of Education, which was in the clutches of Dawa Party appointees, wanted to prohibit female high school students from traveling to the United States. The discrimination against the female students, Hill stressed, was a non-starter for the American side. Maliki acknowledged the problem, but was noncommittal.

The big news of the session was Maliki's interest in visiting Washington soon and meeting with Obama to discuss Iraq's strategic relationship with Washington and also set the stage for an investment conference in Baghdad or Washington. Hill said that he would be returning to Washington soon and would personally pass on the message. The cable reporting Hill's first encounter with Maliki was headlined "PM Tells Ambassador That Iraq Wants Strong Relationship with Obama Administration." As best Hill could tell, he was off to a strong start.[5]

Maliki was right that his rivals saw things differently. When Bill Burns visited Baghdad several days later and met with prominent Sunnis, they rehashed their worries that the Americans might be short of breath. Unlike the United States, the Iranians appeared to be in the game for the long haul, noted Saif Abd al-Rahman, an aide to Hashimi, and Hashimi himself. The Iraqi government, Abd al-Rahman continued, was less a coherent entity than a "collection of competing interests in a state-like environment," one with a prime minister who appeared more intent on building up his power than on compromising. That same day, when Burns met with Abd al-Mahdi, the State Department official sought to assure the Iraqi vice president that the Obama team would honor the existing commitments to Iraq. Even if the security in Iraq deteriorated? Abd al-Mahdi asked. He wondered how much an American president who had pledged to pull out of Iraq would do if violence began to grow again.[6]

The major test for Odierno was the SOFA requirement that American troops be withdrawn from Iraq's urban areas by June 30. American intelligence indicated that Al-Qaeda wanted to take advantage of the transition. In March, according to intelligence reports, Al-Qaeda leadership had reorganized its remaining cells around Baghdad and issued orders to launch a campaign of coordinated high-profile VBIED attacks to make it look as if they had driven the United States out of the cities. In April, the plan, called Harvest of Prosperity, was executed, with a dozen car bombs going off around the capital at nearly the same time, but the attacks were poorly coordinated and did not cause as big a splash as planned.[7]

Odierno also had his eyes on the Shiite Special Groups. As the deadline for vacating the cities approached, two of the Shiite groups' main bases of support in the capital region, Sadr City and Husseiniya, became more violent. A June State Department cable noted that although there was still more nighttime civilian activity and liberal dress in Sadr City than there had been in years, IED attacks were rising, and there were signs of heightened activity by both Asaib Ahl al-Haq—which was ostensibly observing a cease-fire—and Sadr's own Promised Day Brigades in the area of the slum north of the Gold Wall.[8]

There were ways to hedge against the threat. The agreement's Article 24 mandated that American troops withdraw from Iraq's "cities, villages, and localities." But what exactly was a city, village, and locality was open to some interpretation—for example, the huge Victory Base Complex near the airport, where Odierno had his headquarters, and FOB Falcon were defined, by mutual consent, as being outside a city. The Iraqis' confidence in their military capabilities was growing, but they still felt more comfortable with the Americans close at hand. American forces that were pulled to the periphery of the capital could also conduct joint operations with Iraqi troops in the Baghdad belts, though on a much smaller scale than during the surge. Inside Baghdad itself there could be a small number of outposts kept open, jointly staffed by Iraqi and American troops. For their part, the Iraqi Army and National Police would need access to attack helicopters, medevac, intelligence, and other kinds of support that American adviser teams could provide, and for greater security the adviser teams would need platoons and companies of infantry nearby in case of emergency. These arrangements were consistent with the SOFA but were still touchy for the government. In a meeting at his headquarters, Odierno summed up the dilemma: it would be politically difficult for the prime minister if some American troops stayed in the cities, but perhaps even more so if it became clear that Iraqi forces were not up to the task, requiring that he ask the U.S. military to return.

As the weeks passed, Maliki showed himself to be more prepared to assume military risks than political ones. During an early May visit to Washington, Odierno told Pentagon reporters that he expected about one-fifth of the American troops still in Baghdad and Mosul to remain behind as support forces after June 30, and said that he could foresee circumstances in which the pullout might be delayed if violence worsened.[9] Maliki was not pleased with the general's remarks and raised them with a visiting Nancy Pelosi and at the May 10 meeting of the Iraqi NSC. The general's statements, Maliki insisted, were "dangerous."[10]

The commander charged with overseeing the realignment of American forces in the Iraqi capital was Major General Dan Bolger, a veteran of the effort to train and advise Iraqi forces, whose 1st Cavalry Division was back in Iraq for the third time. He had taken charge of the division headquarters for Baghdad in February. By the time Bolger arrived, the number of joint American and Iraqi outposts had already been winnowed down to about forty. COP Callahan in Adhamiya, one of the first outposts established during the surge, had been handed over to the Trade Ministry in January, and Camp Rustamiya, a larger base in East Baghdad that had served as a headquarters for American battalions and brigades since 2003, was handed over to Iraqi troops in March. At other bases, the American presence merely shrank over the winter rather than disappearing altogether, as at Camp Loyalty in Rusafa and Camp Justice in Kadhimiya, the site of Saddam's execution.

During March and April, Bolger went to work on the reorganization of American forces. Since the beginning of the surge, some American brigades had focused on the urban districts of Baghdad proper, while others operated in the rural belts. In preparation for the June 30 deadline, Bolger redrew the boundaries among his units so that each brigade owned a slice of land that included both urban and rural terrain. This reshuffling would ease the urban pullout, as thousands of troops moved from the remaining outposts inside the city to large bases on the outskirts. In West Baghdad, 7,000 of Bolger's troops left urban bases during the spring for Victory Base Complex and Camp Falcon; in East Baghdad, 5,500 troops left the city for Camp Taji to the north and Camp Hammer in the desert to the east.

How many of the residual urban outposts would remain, though, and which ones, were matters of contention between Bolger's headquarters and the Iraqi government. An April plan written by Bolger's officers called for seventeen joint American-Iraqi outposts in the city past June 30, but Abud Qanbar's Baghdad Operations Command raised objections to several of the sites the American plan specified, mainly those in close proximity to Shiite areas where Sadrist sympathies were strong and the continued presence of American troops would be politically sensitive. In dispute were a set of outposts on the periphery of Sadr City, another in Hurriya, and Old

MOD, the outpost where Jeffrey Hammond and John Hort had clashed during the battle of Sadr City a year earlier. The Iraqis got their way on some of the sites, including those around Sadr City, but not on others, including Old MOD. The number of outposts that would remain open past June 30 fell to thirteen; they would be manned by 1,000 American troops and 1,700 Iraqis.

Driven by political considerations, Maliki was loath to explain publicly that there would still be a minimal American presence in Baghdad, albeit one to support Iraqi forces. To avoid the perception that American troops were flouting an understanding that had never been properly described to the Iraqi public, Bolger decreed that all routine convoys needed to keep the outposts running, like resupply patrols, would switch to a "reverse cycle" nighttime operating schedule.[11]

On June 18, the American battalion tasked with patroling the area south of the Gold Wall, 2-5 Cavalry, formally handed authority for security in the slum to the 11th Iraqi Army Division, but the American unit continued to patrol regularly there. On June 28, the battalion commander, Lieutenant Colonel Timothy Karcher (a veteran of the 2004 battles of Najaf and Fallujah), was driving through Sadr City when his MRAP was hit by an array of several EFPs. The copper slugs penetrated the MRAP's armor and tore both of Karcher's legs off. The attack, American intelligence learned, had been conducted by a cell of the Promised Day Brigades based nearby in Shaab. Even though the Americans were leaving under the terms of the SOFA, the Iranian-backed group was determined to foster the narrative that the occupiers were being driven out.

The situation was more troubling in Mosul, which remained a violent city despite the presence of more than twenty Iraqi Army and National Police battalions. On February 20, for example, a VBIED had rammed an American MRAP in the western part of the city, killing the commander of the American cavalry battalion there, Lieutenant Colonel Gary Derby, along with three of his soldiers and his interpreter. Because of the poor security in the city, American troops handed over or closed only four of their ten outposts ahead of the June 30 deadline.

Under Iraqi pressure, however, Odierno agreed to close the remaining six. Demonstrating that the United States was prepared to follow the letter of the status of forces agreement, he concluded, was the top priority. Major General Bob Caslen, the American commander for northern Iraq, and other senior officers continued to meet with Iraqi officials in the city, but dispensed with MRAPs when they did and traveled in Iraqi Army

Humvees: lowering the American profile in the city was more important, Caslen figured, than having maximum protection.[12]

Security in Iraq was as dependent on the disposition of the country's 100,000 Awakening volunteers as it was on the American presence. The largely Sunni Sons of Iraq had the potential to fill in the gaps but could yet turn against the government if abandoned. By Odierno's arrival in the fall of 2008, Maliki had, after much persuasion, agreed that the government would take on and continue to pay 60,000 of Iraq's 100,000 Awakening volunteers, and hire half of the remaining 40,000 as security forces. In the long term, the plan called for the hiring of many other volunteers as nonsecurity personnel in government ministries. In October, the first large group of volunteers had transitioned to the Iraqi government payroll without incident. Indeed, that same month, when a dispute over the budget between the Council of Representatives and the executive branch disrupted the payment of Awakening volunteers, Maliki's solution to the problem—taking money from the Interior Ministry budget to pay the watch groups—drew praise from Odierno.

Even so, Maliki's campaign against enemies real and imagined had led him to pursue some of the very Awakening leaders the Americans had so assiduously cultivated. Lieutenant Colonel Raad Ali, whose group in Ghazaliya had been among the first to stand up inside Baghdad during the summer of the surge, was briefly detained in the spring. More arrests followed. On May 12, the 22nd Iraqi Army Brigade arrested Mutlab Ali Abbas al-Massari, who had worked closely with American forces in Ghazaliya since 2007. "They will arrest all of us, one by one," another Ghazaliya Awakening leader "predicted darkly" to American diplomats afterward.[13]

When Massari was arrested, he was taken to a detention site at Camp Justice, where the unit that apprehended him, the 22nd Brigade, was based. Although military advisers described the Camp Justice site as being akin to a "slave ship" because of its cramped and inhumane conditions, Massari had not been abused when American diplomats checked in on him there two days after his arrest. When diplomats next visited him, though, they did so at the site in the Green Zone where both OCINC and the Iraqi Army's 56th "Baghdad" Brigade, which OCINC controlled as a kind of praetorian guard for sensitive missions, were headquartered and where Massari looked much the worse for wear. The Americans were told that it would be up to OCINC director Farouk al-Araji whether Massari would ever get to meet with his lawyer. It was another example of how the prime minister's office used the extra-constitutional command structure it had established to go after its enemies.

In Diyala, American troops on the ground reported that the Maliki government's political housecleaning was making a bad situation worse. Late in the summer of 2009, the 2nd Infantry Division's 3rd Stryker Brigade—the unit that had cleared Baqubah during the surge—returned to Diyala. By the end of the year, the brigade's intelligence section had had several months to observe the disproportionate targeting of Diyala's Sunnis—including Sunnis associated with the Awakening—by the province's Shiite-dominated security forces. A secret December 2009 report by the brigade noted that the standing Sunni majority in the Diyala provincial council—twenty out of thirty seats—was potentially under threat because of these arrests; two Sunni council members had recently been detained "on questionable warrants" by the Diyala police, and there were outstanding warrants for seven more. The Sunni governor of Diyala, who later fled Iraq in 2012 after being threatened by aides working for Maliki, told State Department officials that the judges and police officials in Diyala, appointed by Baghdad, had been instructed to release Shiite prisoners and keep Sunnis under detention regardless of the evidence against them.

Aggravating the situation was the tendency of the government to defer payment it had promised to Awakening volunteers. After forty-five to fifty days without pay, the brigade's analysis observed, Awakening members would threaten to stop working or return to the insurgency; at sixty days they might abandon their checkpoints; and after a hundred or more days "it is assessed with high confidence that SoI [Sons of Iraq] would resort to limited violent action in the form of organized crime out of necessity to generate income," such as robbery or extortion at checkpoints.[14]

Reports by a mixed civilian-military unit called Human Terrain Analysis Team—Baghdad in early 2010 emphasized the same problem in the capital and the belts. "The single biggest issue we SOI leaders are worried about is the arrest warrants, against which we have little protection," Sheikh Ayad al-Jabouri told the team in December 2009, the same month as the Stryker brigade's report in Diyala. "The Americans used to protect us but now we have no one. How are we supposed to protect our areas when we and our sons are in jail? All it takes is two individuals to go to the court and accuse someone and you can get arrested. Sometimes people will blackmail you for $10,000 to $20,000 using this law."[15]

The government's process for hiring Awakening members as nonsecurity personnel as it had promised was badly dysfunctional, another report from the Baghdad human terrain analysis team explained not long afterward, in early 2010. On August 2, 2009, the government had "transitioned" the first batch of 3,331 Awakening volunteers from its Awakening payrolls to a pre-hiring limbo, nominally a step forward; by the beginning of 2010, the number of transitioned volunteers was approaching 29,000. In West Baghdad's Mansour District, for instance, the last Awakening checkpoint was handed over to the government's security forces on December 13, 2009. Upon being transitioned, Awakening volunteers were assigned to a ministry—but they still had to go to that ministry and apply for one of a limited number of available but mostly menial jobs like janitor or tea-server. Expressing a common sentiment, one man from Nasr wa Salaam said, "I would rather work in a ministry than stand outside with four bullets in my magazine." But many suspected their employment would last only a few months when the government would become an even more intractable obstacle in the already difficult hiring process. When the IFCNR that Bassima al-Jaidri served on in 2007 distributed business cards with a hotline number that "transitioning" volunteers could call, the number turned out to be dead.[16]

To be sure, there were instances when Awakening volunteers went bad. Abu Abed, the founder of the Ameriya Knights, would eventually flee Iraq after it came to light from a source in his own ranks that he was hiding the bodies of his enemies under his driveway. And there was the troublesome case of Adil al-Mashhadani, an Awakening leader in East Baghdad's Fadl neighborhood, whom Maliki insisted remained a threat. Over the summer of 2007, Mashhadani had turned on Al-Qaeda in Fadl and his fighters had allied themselves with a battalion of the 82nd Airborne.

Despite his usefulness to the Americans, however, the paratroop squadron dealing with him by 2009 found him to be volatile, erratic, and inclined to criminal activity. A June 2008 review by American military lawyers had found that the government had enough "valid evidence" to support an arrest warrant. His insurgent past also warranted continued concerns. One American intelligence report stated that Mashhadani's group was responsible for executing the crew of a downed Blackwater helicopter on January 23, 2007. As the surge took hold in Baghdad, a secret unit of Iraqi and American commandos run by the CIA, called the STU, had targeted Mashhadani and his group in a series of raids whose code names played off Mashhadani's name.[17] One of the STU raids, dubbed Barriga Mash, had ended tragically on May 11, 2007. A team of Iraqi and American commandos from the unit was going after a figure named Hajji Salih, "reported as the deputy to insurgent leader Adel al-Mashadani," when it got into a firefight, wounding four of the Iraqi commandos and killing one American—Major Doug Zembiec, on loan to the CIA from the Marine Corps. As a rifle company commander during Operation Vigilant Resolve three years earlier, the Marine officer had earned a Silver Star and two Purple Hearts along with the moniker "the Lion of Fallujah." The raid took place just months before Mashhadani's group switched sides.[18]

When Maliki began pressing Odierno for Mashhadani to be arrested and his men confronted and disarmed in early 2009, Odierno agreed to have American commandos and air support involved in the operation. He reasoned that, rather than risk a tough firefight between Maliki's troops and Mashhadani's group—possibly sparking violence from other Awakening groups—it would be better for American troops to help the Iraqis detain the rogue Awakening leader quietly.[19] The general was building up goodwill with the prime minister, which he might need in the months ahead.

Another drama that played out in Iraq in 2009 had to do with the fate of Asaib Ahl al-Haq, the Sadrist splinter group responsible for some of the most high-profile Shiite militant attacks of the war, and its leaders, Qais and Laith al-Khazali, who had been in American custody since the SAS detained them in Basra two years before. When Odierno took command in Baghdad in the fall of 2008, he viewed Asaib Ahl al-Haq as the most dangerous Shiite group on the block, more so than the Iranian-controlled Kataib Hezbollah and more so than Sadr's Promised Day Brigades. Unlike those groups, Asaib Ahl al-Haq had been involved since the spring uprising in political machinations with Ahmed Chalabi and Ibrahim al-Jaafari. "I believe AAH is more dangerous than KH, because we don't know where they are, and their threat is more insidious," Odierno told his staff on October 1, 2008, two weeks after taking command. "We need to expose them."[20]

Odierno's counterparts in the Iraqi government, though, had no desire to expose Asaib Ahl al-Haq. Instead, they negotiated a cease-fire later in October with the group's Iran-based leader, al-Khazali associate and former Mahdi Army commander Akram al-Kabi. Sadr had created the Promised Day Brigades in part to try to retain the best fighters in the Mahdi Army and draw back others who were working for Asaib Ahl al-Haq and Kataib Hezbollah, but Maliki believed that those same fighters, uncertain of their future, could be lured away from militia groups and their leaders into the political process. This effort included a plan drawn up by Safa al-Sheikh, Maliki's deputy national security adviser. In November, Safa gave the American military a list of names of militia members to consider releasing from detention, but the effort was complicated by the fact that of 256 names on the list, only 75 were actually in American custody.[21] When Maliki visited Iran in the first week of January 2009, he met with Akram al-Kabi there, according to the notes of a high-ranking American official, and the cease-fire with Asaib Ahl al-Haq was renewed.

Once the cease-fire was struck, the U.S. embassy and military put their weight behind further negotiations with Asaib Ahl al-Haq. Over the winter of 2008–2009, the United States took the step of designating Kataib Hezbollah as a foreign terrorist organization, making it subject to various sanctions and restrictions. In order to facilitate the talks being led by Safa al-Sheikh, the State Department recommended that the same not be done with Asaib Ahl al-Haq—the group that Odierno had stated the previous fall was more dangerous than Kataib Hezbollah.

Some people observing the negotiations, though, a State Department cable reported in March 2009, viewed the Asaib Ahl al-Haq talks less as real political reconciliation than an effort to arrange a simple prisoner swap: Asaib Ahl al-Haq wanted its leaders, Qais and Laith al-Khazali, released from American custody, while the government wanted Asaib Ahl al-Haq to release the five British contractors it had kidnapped in Baghdad in May 2007, and to turn over the bodies of any of the five who had been killed. Iraqi government representatives were allowed into Camp Cropper, where Qais was being detained, to meet with him. The Force Strategic Engagement Cell was involved in the negotiations as well, and some skeptics in the military headquarters felt that it had gone too far—that by now the British-led FSEC was little more than a tool used by the British government to seek a swap for its five missing men.

The view that the talks with Asaib Ahl al-Haq were less about genuine reconciliation than about a prisoner swap seemed to be borne out. At the beginning of June 2009, just ahead of the pullout from the cities, the American military handed Laith al-Khazali over to the Iraqi government for release. After being freed by the Iraqis in the Green Zone on June 6, Laith disappeared into Sadr City and then into Iran. Two weeks later, fulfilling their part of the bargain, Asaib Ahl al-Haq handed over to the Iraqi government the corpses of two of the five kidnapped Britons, and the Iraqis in turn returned them to the British government.

In an arrangement made before his release, Laith stayed in touch by cell phone with American representatives, including from inside Iran, helping the negotiations move along toward the release of his brother by setting up meetings with third parties where he would keep the United States updated on the status of Asaib Ahl al-Haq and its cease-fire. The militant group's decision to negotiate for Laith and Qais's release did not make it any friends in the Sadrist Trend; in October, armed clashes were reported in Sadr City between Asaib Ahl al-Haq and fighters loyal to Sadr's Promised Day Brigades.

In December 2009, the negotiations with Asaib Ahl al-Haq culminated with the group's release of the surviving hostage (and the handover of one remaining body) and the Iraqi government's release of Qais al-Khazali. Qais returned to Iran to join his brother and the rest of Asaib Ahl al-Haq's leadership. Shortly afterward, in January 2010, some suspicions of the Asaib Ahl al-Haq negotiations' critics were confirmed when at least a faction of the group called off its cease-fire, apparently having no more use for it with its leaders free. On January 23, the group took a new hostage, an Iraqi-American Defense Department contractor who would be released two months later, ostensibly in return for the release of four more Asaib Ahl al-Haq members from Iraqi government custody. Nonetheless, the release of the Khazalis demonstrated that the environment for Asaib Ahl al-Haq in Iraq had changed, and before long Abu Dura, the notorious Mahdi Army commander tied to the Khazalis, returned from Iran, too.

Two and a half years of captivity had only heightened Qais al-Khazali's prominence among Sadrists, and early in 2010 he and Sadr reportedly met in Qom, where Sadr offered to allow Asaib Ahl al-Haq's leaders and followers to reintegrate back into the Sadrist Trend. Qais declined—after more than five years, he was finally splitting from Sadr completely, ready to be an Iraqi political figure in his own right when the time came.

With American troops out of Iraqi cities, Maliki was ready to make his first visit to Washington since July 2006. Hill had high hopes for the trip. Crocker had wondered whether Maliki was a tyrant in the making or a misunderstood prime minister struggling to govern an unruly country. While Crocker was inclined toward the view that the glass was half-full, he had documented the many reasons for concern. Hill had a far more sympathetic view of the Iraqi prime minister and a much darker view of his rivals, which he conveyed in a cable in anticipation of Maliki's White

House meeting. Maliki, Hill reported, was a compromise candidate who had grown in the job. Constrained by a system of checks and balances, Maliki had sought to compensate by using his constitutional authority as commander in chief. The prime minister aspired to build a broad-based and cross-sectarian alliance and was intent on developing the nation's economy. The problem was that ambitious rivals, Sunnis and Kurds, who sought to persuade Americans that Maliki was dangerous, would not get with the program. "The Sunni and Kurdish 'Green Zone' set, for their part, are trapped in an 'anyone but Maliki' mindset—and may be forcing the Shia back together, since nobody but Maliki appears to have the strength or determination to break away," Hill wrote. There was more that Maliki could do to fight the perception that the arrests he had ordered were sectarian, but the prime minister insisted he was detaining more Shiite suspects than Sunni ones. Maliki was a complicated figure and "by no means the Saddam-in-the-making those rivals suggest." There were times when he even seemed to be above politics. "While he clearly wants to stay in office, he has begun in recent weeks to discuss (perhaps only half in jest) retiring to his farm south of Baghdad and growing watermelons. Maliki tells us he does not want to use the U.S. visit to bolster his political credentials in Iraq, and instead hopes to bolster enduring long-term ties between the United States and Iraq that will outlast successive Iraqi and U.S. administrations."

If there was a theme to Maliki's visit, the prime minister had told Hill, it was "launching the Strategic Framework Agreement." To the Iraqis this included securing help in organizing a conference to get companies to invest in Iraq. As for deliverables, Hill thought that the Washington meeting might facilitate a resolution of the long-standing differences between Iraq and Kuwait, which dated back to Saddam's days. The emir of Kuwait would soon be meeting with Obama as well. Maliki, Hill advised, "should be encouraged to 'help us help him' on Kuwait." Finally, as a gesture of appreciation for the sacrifice of American lives in Iraq, Maliki would be laying a wreath at Arlington Cemetery. "The Arlington visit is locked," Hill wrote.[22]

The prime minister's visit, however, did not follow Hill's script. In spite of America's military, political, and economic investment in Iraq, Maliki surprised Obama by raising the Iranian threat. Maliki first had a breakfast meeting with Biden and then an Oval Office session with the president himself. In his meeting with the vice president Maliki had played the Iran card: if the United States could not persuade the Sunni Arab countries to stop rallying the Sunnis, the Iranians would have an excuse to intervene in Iraqi politics. Later, Maliki surprised the White House and Hill even more by complaining about FSEC, the Force Strategic Engagement Cell Petraeus had established to reach out to insurgents. It had been leaked that representatives of FSEC had attended a meeting in Turkey with exiled Baathists. The meeting had fueled Maliki's preternatural fear of Baathist conspiracies. Neither Obama nor his aides knew anything about the episode and were unhappy they had not been prepared for Maliki's complaint.

While these exchanges introduced a sour note in what was supposed to have been an upbeat visit, they essentially dramatized a clash of cultures. In the United States, the president was briefed to a T and meetings between heads of state were carefully scripted and prepared. That was not the case in Iraqi culture. Agendas were not necessarily fixed in advance and talking points were not subjected to interagency scrutiny—a holdover from Saddam's reign when everything the tyrant thought was secret and everything he was told was shielded. Insofar as Maliki was concerned, he would talk about what he deemed important and the FSEC issue was on his mind.

After leaving the White House, the American and Iraqi delegations climbed into their limousines for the ride to Arlington Cemetery. Hill was livid. Yelling into his cell phone, he barked that Maliki had waited months to come to the White House and then wasted time on an FSEC engagement nobody at the top levels of the American government even knew about. The American ambassador was so angry he was indifferent to the fact that an Iraqi embassy official was riding in the car with him and listening to his every word.

Later, at his suite in the Willard Hotel, Maliki also fumed. It seemed to him that the White House and Hill had known about the Turkish meeting but played it down. The Americans did not appear to appreciate the sheer danger of their approach to try to win over insurgents. It was unclear to some Iraqi officials clustered in Maliki's hotel suite whether the prime minister was being sincere or trying to impress them with his determination to stand up to the United States, but his position was unmistakable: if the Americans did not respect his concerns they could get the hell out of Iraq.[23]

CHAPTER 32

Trouble Up North

In Nineveh Province, two hundred miles away from the Green Zone politics, Atheel al-Nujaifi had his own agenda. The theory on the American side was that the January 2009 provincial elections would enfranchise the locals, advance democracy, and help stabilize the country by bringing the Sunni Arab political class—whose 2005 election boycott had delivered Nineveh to a pro-Kurdish coalition—back into the political life of Iraq. Sunni Arabs would have a stake in representative government in the regions that concerned them most and a way to settle differences with the ballot box instead of violence.

In Nineveh, however, things were rarely that straightforward. Nujaifi, who hailed from an old and prominent family with considerable holdings throughout the province, was the leader of the Hadba Gathering coalition. Nujaifi had been a pillar of the Baathist business establishment under Saddam, but unlike others of his class, he had established ties to the Americans after the fall of the regime. His partner in Hadba was Sheikh Abdullah al-Yawar, a Sunni tribal leader from western Nineveh who had cooperated with the United States from 2003. Indeed, the sheikh's cousin Ghazi al-Yawar had been the first president of the new Iraq. For all that, Hadba had campaigned on an Arab nationalist and anti-Kurdish platform, and that portended problems, particularly after Nujaifi was elected governor.

On April 5, the day after Lieutenant General Charles Jacoby took over from Lloyd Austin as corps commander, he was briefed on a classified "tabletop exercise" that the corps had just run. Along with colonels from Bob Caslen's division and the Special Forces, Jacoby was told his planning officers had explored how to head off an Arab-Kurdish clash in northern Iraq like the one that had nearly broken out at Khanaqin. In addition to

Hadba's program there were a number of other combustible factors that added to the already considerable risks. There were no American advisers among the Peshmerga forces in the areas the Arabs and Kurds disputed, so the United States lacked knowledge of their plans, and there was a large concentration of Iraqi security forces in Nineveh, including police who were not up to professional standards. If it looked like the Arabs and Kurds were headed for trouble there would be a need for "dynamic KLEs"—key leadership engagements—with both sides' leaders. Otherwise, there was a risk that the situation could spin out of control, detracting from the fight against Al-Qaeda.[1]

Just a few weeks later, it looked like the exercise had become a real-life drama. Anxious to assert his prerogatives as governor and show that the writ of his administration extended throughout the province, Nujaifi made plans to give a speech at a sports festival at Bashiqa, a largely Yazidi town that was in a disputed area claimed by both Arabs and Kurds. Taking advantage of the imposing cliffs in the area, Iraqis would be participating in a hang gliding tournament. Two days after the governor announced his plans, a liaison officer from the Kurdistan Regional Government told Brigadier General Robert Brown, the deputy American division commander for northern Iraq, that the Kurds did not appreciate Nujaifi's parading of his authority. Though Bashiqa was several miles to the east of Mosul, Nineveh's provincial capital, the Kurds considered the town to be part of historic Kurdistan and a Nujaifi visit could lead to "a potential incident." Nujaifi's own considerable landholdings were just south of Bashiqa, near the confluence of the Great Zaab and Tigris rivers; to get to his own family property, Nujaifi had to traverse Peshmerga-controlled territory.

Eager to avert a confrontation, Alexander Laskaris, the head of the State Department's provincial reconstruction team in Mosul, called the governor and warned him against making the trip. Laskaris, who would later be appointed as the head of the first American consulate in Irbil, was a rare diplomat who had knocked around Third World trouble spots, immersed himself in the language, and was enthusiastic about navigating through the disorder and danger that was northern Iraq. The United States, Laskaris explained to Nujaifi, supported the governor's right to travel within his own province, but events were moving too fast for the United States to pull everyone together and facilitate the visit. "Don't go," Laskaris said. "It's dangerous." Nujaifi, however, would not back down. "I'm going," he said. "It's my province."

Laskaris's next call was to Colonel Gary Volesky, whose 3rd Brigade, 1st

Cavalry Division, was the main American unit in Nineveh. Volesky, who had battled the Mahdi Army in 2004 as a battalion commander in Sadr City, helicoptered directly to the checkpoints to try to calm things down. Officially, the Peshmerga fighters and Iraqi troops shared the common goal of thwarting Al-Qaeda attacks, but now they had squared off like two opposing armies. The Peshmerga troops, armed with machine guns at the first checkpoint on the road to Bashiqa, confirmed that they had "shoot to kill" orders if the governor tried to pass. Iraqi soldiers, who had their own checkpoint nearby, reported that they had been ordered to fire on the Peshmerga if they shot at the governor. Having avoided a long-dreaded confrontation at Khanaqin, the Peshmerga and the Iraqi Army seemed to be headed toward a new one now.

If ever there was a time for dynamic KLEs, this was it. Laskaris got Khasro Goran, the leader of the Kurdistan Democratic Party's branch in eastern Nineveh, which included Mosul, on the phone and insisted that Nujaifi be able to travel through the Peshmerga checkpoints without any problem. It was an act of insanity, Laskaris said, for a Peshmerga checkpoint on the outskirts of a major Arab city to threaten to kill a democratically elected governor. Goran agreed that it was a crazy order, but said the Americans needed to press the point in Irbil. Goran was a Swedish citizen, trained in Arabic at the University of Mosul, and a widely reviled figure among Mosul's Sunni Arabs. Until Nujaifi's inauguration, Goran had served as vice governor of Nineveh but American military and diplomatic officials had always viewed him as levelheaded and reasonable.

As the issue was kicked up the chain of command, Brown called Masrour Barzani, the head of intelligence in Kurdistan and the son of Massoud Barzani, the Kurdistan Regional Government's president, and delivered a demarche that had been prepared by the American embassy in Baghdad. An hour later, Masrour called back and said that he was passing on a message from his father. Barzani was not happy. "We are very sorry that you have to be in the middle of all this," Barzani replied. "Atheel Nujaifi was not elected by people in the disputed areas and they are not ready to be ruled by him. The KRG is not ready to accept someone stepping on the backs of the Kurds."

As the clock ticked down on the visit, the Iraqi military pulled its support for Nujaifi's convoy, calculating that this would compel the hotheaded governor to reconsider his trip. The Iraqi general in Mosul was a Maliki appointee and he had no sympathy for Nujaifi. But the governor was prepared to take his personal bodyguards if need be.

With few cards left to play, the American troops that Volesky had moved near the checkpoints got in their MRAPs and drove away. Laskaris called Nujaifi to be crystal clear: if a confrontation erupted American forces would not be there to bail him out. United States troops were prepared to take the fight to Al-Qaeda or Iranian-backed militias, but they were not about to interpose themselves between the Peshmerga and the Iraqi government forces.

Finally, a way out was found that saved face all around: the Ministry of Youth and Sports in Baghdad canceled the festival. There was no event to attend, and therefore no reason for Nujaifi to travel to Bashiqa. Volesky later told Laskaris that if Nujaifi insisted on heading down the road American soldiers would have made a final effort to warn him and, if need be, block the road. The move, no doubt, would have stirred up a storm of protest, but at least the governor would be alive. Summarizing the nerve-wracking episode, the embassy sent a cable home with the comment "one conflict averted, others surely waiting." Nujaifi had a political interest in exacerbating tensions, while the beleaguered Kurds appeared determined to stand their ground, however counterproductive.

"Barzani's shoot to kill order was outrageous, as even Kurdish leaders in Ninewa acknowledge, but (to quote Talleyrand) it was 'worse than a crime, it was a blunder,' as preventing Alnujaifi's trip will have been a pyrrhic Kurdish victory if it provokes a consolidated Arab political or GOI military response," the embassy's chargé d'affaires Patricia Butenis wrote. "We managed to avoid a firefight May 8, due in large part to some excellent cooperation between our civilian and Coalition colleagues, but the Arab-Kurd issues that make such incidents likely in the future remain unsolved. We will soon recommend additional follow-on action."[2]

The Bashiqa event, in fact, was not the end of the problems. Soon after, Maliki ordered Iraqi troops to take control of Mosul Dam, which had been guarded by Peshmerga troops since the early months of the war, with American acquiescence.

Like so many Maliki orders, the directive had bypassed the usual chain of command and had been transmitted from OCINC directly to the Nineveh Operations Command. A compromise was worked out. The Peshmerga troops stayed. So did Iraqi troops deployed nearby, and a small contingent of Americans. The Green Line between Kurdistan and Arab Iraq was fast becoming a tense frontier.

When it came time for Brown to say his farewell as he wound up his tour in the fall, he had lunch at Massoud Barzani's complex outside Irbil.

Citing the arrangement near Mosul Dam, the Kurdish president observed that he would not deal with the Arab and Kurdish differences over the disputed areas without the presence of American troops.

Even as the Americans were trying to manage the contention between Arabs and Kurds in northern Iraq, Al-Qaeda was trying to take advantage of the new security situation in Baghdad. The first advise-and-assist brigade—a standard combat brigade with a complement of forty-eight extra majors and colonels to serve as advisers to Iraqi troops—had been deployed to southern Iraq. Meantime, the number of forces had begun to decline: the late summer had seen the first major reduction in combat forces since the Obama review.

By September, the number of brigades fell to eleven from fourteen as three brigades left Iraq—one from the south, one from Baghdad, and one from Anbar, which marked the end of the deployment of Marine regiments to western Iraq that had begun in early 2004. The Marines were replaced by a single brigade, the 1st Brigade, 82nd Airborne Division. It was more of an advise-and-assist brigade in name than in fact since it had only sixteen additional advisers. All told, it was the lowest overall level of American forces since the American invasion in 2003. American troop levels would remain at eleven brigades through the end of 2009, with the next large set of cuts scheduled for summer 2010, ahead of the official end of the American combat mission, after which the only brigades remaining would be advise-and-assist units.

According to American intelligence, Al-Qaeda leaders decided to mass their remaining resources in the capital for a few dramatic operations, a new phase the group dubbed Prisoner's Conquest.[3] On August 19, near-simultaneous car and truck bomb attacks targeted the Foreign Ministry, the Finance Ministry, and the Al-Rashid Hotel.

The Foreign Ministry, Iraq's official face to the world, was particularly hard hit. Dozens of vehicles on the street outside the structure were charred. One side of the ministry was sheared off in places. Some floors appeared as if they might collapse altogether. The crater created by the blast was eight feet deep and thirty feet across, according to an estimate by an American combat engineer, and it filled up with water from damaged pipes. As for casualties, in the ministry alone there had been forty-two fatalities and more than sixty injured. According to foreign minister Hoshyar Zebari, the security forces within the compound—largely Peshmerga forces—had

acquitted themselves well, but he was convinced that the Maliki government had erred by taking down many of the concrete barriers and removing checkpoints, steps the prime minister had decreed to convey an air of
normalcy. What is more, the Iraqi Army and police had displayed incom-
petence. The videotape from the ministry's security cameras showed a
four-ton truck, full of red plastic water containers, maneuvering unchallenged through Baghdad traffic until it exploded in a massive fireball.

General Muhammad al-Shawani, the head of the CIA-supported Iraqi
National Intelligence Service, was in his office when the blasts rocked the
capital. When nobody called to check on his welfare or that of his team,
Shawani decamped from Iraq, never to return. With rival intelligence arms
loyal to Shiite parties on the rise, like Shirwan al-Waeli's Iranian-supported
Ministry of State for National Security Affairs, Shawani had seen the INIS
sidelined and many of his officers fired and replaced by Dawa loyalists.
With the influence of his American friends waning and a hunt for scape-
goats for the August bombing likely, Shawani decided that he had had
enough.

As far as Ray Odierno was concerned, the spectacular nature of the
attacks, the coordination, and the suicidal tactics were hallmarks of
Al-Qaeda in Iraq. Maliki, however, was inclined to see a different enemy:
the same Iraqi Baathists who had suppressed Dawa when he was a member
of the underground movement, the prime minister insisted, were behind
this attack as well, operating away from their sanctuaries in Syria. Maliki
claimed that the explosion at the Al-Rashid had, in fact, been intended for
him since he had planned to attend a conference there, and that a third car
bomb had been found before it exploded, which "looked foreign." That
Al-Qaeda in Iraq included many former Baathists complicated the issue,
but it was a Baath resurgence, not an Al-Qaeda one, that Maliki was fixated on.

In contrast to the Bush team, the Obama administration had begun to
engage Syria. Petraeus's brainstorm about going to Damascus to confront
Assad about the foreign fighter problem had been dusted off and somewhat toned down. The Americans were hoping to initiate three-way talks
with the Syrians and Iraqis about controlling the border and also to persuade Assad to moderate his behavior and join in the Middle East peace
process, if it ever got off the ground again. Now Maliki indicated that he
was uncomfortable with the Americans' engagement with the Syrians.

As Maliki's suspicions grew, he recalled the Iraqi ambassador from
Damascus, insisted that the Syrians hand over two suspects he believed were
linked to the attacks, and appealed to the United Nations secretary-general

to mount an investigation into Syria's interference. The Presidency Council chided Maliki for his insistence on an international inquiry. Their criticism, Zebari told Gary Grappo, partly reflected the fact that Maliki often bypassed the body on important issues but might also have to do with pressure from Iran. Qasim Suleimani, Zebari indicated, might have talked with Talabani and pressured him to ease off on the criticism of Syria, Grappo reported in a classified cable. The Iranians had many ways to try to influence the Iraqi government and Talabani, the Americans were convinced, was one of them.

On September 10, Chris Hill went to Capitol Hill, his first appearance before Congress since being confirmed as ambassador. Hill was the sole witness, and unlike the contentious Petraeus and Crocker hearings, which had been carried out in the spotlight, his sessions with the lawmakers were brief and almost perfunctory. After six years of war, Iraq was finally entering the "endgame," John Kerry, the chairman of the Senate Foreign Relations Committee, observed as the panel got under way. "The task ahead as we draw down our forces is to provide a nudge here and there to ensure that Iraq doesn't crash when the wheels do come off," he added, alluding to the training wheels American troops were ostensibly supplying.

Hill painted a generally reassuring picture, one that suggested that little more than regular nudging was necessary. Iraqi forces had responded well to the recent attacks, he insisted. Preparations were under way for national elections in January, which would advance the Obama administration's goal of a representative and inclusive Iraq. The United States needed to caution the Sunni Arab states, as well as the Iranians, against trying to interfere politically. "I do believe that some Sunni countries believe that somehow it was an aberration that there's a Shia-led government there, and that somehow, in January, it'll flip back, and they just need to be a little patient or show a little more effort to try to get the Sunni parties to be better funded, and somehow they could emerge victorious with a split Shia community," he said. Hill believed that if the United States used its influence to contain what he later described as "The Great Game in Mesopotamia"—the competition for influence among the Saudis, Turkey, and Iran—Iraq's political evolution would stay the course. "For the first time in decades," Hill told Kerry's committee, "Iraq has a chance to become an engine for regional stability and regional economic growth rather than a source of regional tension and dispute."[4]

After returning to Baghdad, Hill told his staff that his testimony had gone well. The Congress was supportive of the embassy and the military and comfortable enough with Iraq's trajectory. Obama had campaigned against Bush's war in Iraq, contrasting Afghanistan as a war of necessity. But with growing anxiety over the course of the Afghan war the tables appeared to have been turned. "Now Iraq is the 'good war,' " Hill quipped.

Prisoner's Conquest and the fallout from it in Baghdad, however, were not over. In a September 22 meeting with Hill, Maliki insisted that Iraqi intelligence had uncovered a fresh plot to set off four more car bombs, a plot financed by Iraqi Baathists in Syria. The Obama administration's attempts to reach out to Syria, Maliki said, would fail because Syria was coordinating its policy with Iran. Syria, Maliki declared, is "behaving like a teenager, not an adult."[5]

On October 25, two huge vehicle bombs, one a minivan and one a bus, killed more than 150 people in attacks on the Justice Ministry and the Baghdad provincial council. Petraeus was visiting Iraq that day in his capacity as CENTCOM commander, and he and Maliki discussed the state of Al-Qaeda in Iraq after the bombings. Although there were now as few as ten foreign fighters entering Iraq per month, Al-Qaeda was regaining strength in Fallujah and in the northern Baghdad belt, Petraeus said, and the group obviously maintained the capacity for large and deadly attacks every few weeks. Like Odierno, Petraeus saw a threat somewhat different from the Baathist one Maliki discerned lurking outside the Green Zone.

As the Americans struggled to keep Iraq on course, the United States embassy fielded an unsettling allegation. Maliki's son was accused of pursuing a woman who had rejected his attentions only to be abused by his guards. The woman reported that she had been raped and had taken her complaint to the embassy. To Hill, the charge came at the worst possible moment. "We need to stay the fuck away from the story," Hill told his staff at an October meeting. "There is no win for the U.S. here. There is a story. We have heard it, and it's a law enforcement issue. Our line is: law enforcement." The matter was reported to Washington, but the days when the United States would respond to every single crisis in Iraq were over. Furthermore, Iraq was supposed to be under the rule of law; the Iraqis could deal with this themselves.

In November, the Americans were caught by surprise when the plans for the January election were cast into doubt. Tariq al-Hashimi, the intemperate Sunni vice president, voted against the election law on the grounds that it would undercount Sunni Iraqis who lived abroad. The development was of deep concern to the Obama administration, which was eager to have the elections take place on time to make headway toward the August 2010 "end of combat" milestone and further troop cuts. After intense pressure from the Americans, including a blitz of calls by Biden, the election law was finally passed on December 6. The elections were back on track, though not in time for the January 31 date set by the constitution.

The next big attack came two days later when four car bombs exploded at the Finance, Justice, and Foreign ministries, killing more than 120 people. Dan Bolger's 1st Cavalry Division, which since the pullout from the cities had focused on going after insurgent cells in the belts, believed that Al-Qaeda was having a limited resurgence. By the end of the year, Bolger's staff assessed that "restrictions placed on U.S. Special Operations Forces and the drawdown of conventional forces had allowed AQI to re-group and establish new operations in and around Baghdad."[6] While Al-Qaeda was linked to the large-scale attacks, other Sunni insurgent groups were also active. This point was driven home when the Americans officially designated the Jaish Rijal al-Tariq al-Naqshabandi as a terrorist organization. The Sunni group had Baathist ties and had been causing trouble in the north since at least 2008.

Four days after the December 8 attack—the third major eruption of bombings since the June 30 American pullout from Baghdad—Maliki faced six hours of pointed questioning from the parliament. The representatives complained that there was not a clear strategy to combat terrorism and that the coordination among the Ministry of Defense, Ministry of Interior, and Baghdad Operations Command was poor. With parliamentary elections set for the following year, the prime minister was not about to relax the restrictions on Americans operating in the cities and searched instead for a scapegoat: General Abud Qanbar was removed from his post as head of the Baghdad Operations Command and kicked upstairs to a job at the Defense Ministry. The deputy interior minister, Adnan al-Asadi, told Robert Ford that Abud had been removed to placate the critics and that it would lead to little change in Baghdad security operations. "Maliki has staked his reputation on security gains achieved in Iraq, and is likely cognizant of the impact such security breaches could have on his State of Law Coalition in the upcoming national election. Recent attacks have targeted Iraqi government facilities as opposed to civilian targets such as markets and schools, which seems intended to undermine the public's confidence in the GOI's authority and ISF [Iraqi security forces] capabilities," Ford cabled home. "We will continue to urge Iraqi leaders in the government and the COR [Council of Representatives] alike to redouble their calls for national unity and resist the finger pointing which could foster public cynicism in the short term and damage to ISF credibility in public eyes if it continues."[7]

In mid-December, the embassy had an important visitor: Jeffrey Feltman, the assistant secretary of state for the Middle East. Hill had mused about Feltman, telling his embassy aides that he was surprised that the State Department official had not visited Baghdad more often. When Hill was the assistant secretary for East Asia and the Pacific, he boasted, he had traveled to China and Japan all the time. Still, Feltman was a bureaucratic ally and was visiting at a critical juncture. Iraq looked a bit shaky but, Feltman ventured, was the only success story the White House had going in the Middle East. Afghanistan and Pakistan were dicey. The Arab-Israeli peace process was stymied. As ironic as it seemed, Iraq was the only good news coming out of the region. But the embassy needed to share more with Feltman's office; there was no such thing as too much information. The NSC was a mess; it was trying to be an operational arm of the government.

The big worry in Washington, Feltman added, was that security in Iraq would deteriorate as the Iraqis struggled to form a new government after the parliamentary election. Hill wanted to know who was concerned, and Feltman said Tom Donilon, Rahm Emanuel, and the president himself. Robert Ford wanted to know if the White House was worried that it would be impossible to withdraw troops while the United States served as caretaker of a newly formed Iraqi government. According to Hill, Odierno did not foresee keeping large numbers of troops longer than planned.

In a whirlwind series of meetings, Feltman sounded out the Iraqi leadership about the way ahead. Abd al-Mahdi optimistically thought that the formation of the government would take less time than in 2005 and 2006. The new coalitions would be stronger. Once a prime minister was chosen "the rest would be easy." There was already strong support for retaining Talabani as president. Maliki portrayed himself in his December 14 meeting with Feltman as a man above sectarian strife, as he had in his first meeting with Hill. Iraq had made enormous progress, he said, and his State of Law Coalition hoped to campaign on nationalist themes. Noting that there were challenges ahead, Maliki deplored that others were more preoccupied with divisive issues and that many of Iraq's Sunni neighbors were halfhearted about supporting the Shiite-led government.

Ayad Allawi argued that the time needed to form a government could be reduced if the senior leaders—whom he defined as Barzani, Talabani, Hakim, and Hashimi—began discussing the crucial power-sharing issues in advance. Allawi touted the need for a government of unity that would include all major groups. In contrast to Maliki, who looked askance at the Saudis, Allawi said they were helpful in countering Iranian influence.

Rafi al-Issawi, a Sunni doctor who had worked in the Fallujah hospital during the Marine offensives before he entered politics, was pessimistic about prospects for the formation of the new government; he thought it would be long and drawn out. Issawi was skeptical of Maliki's nationalist and post-sectarian pretensions. The prime minister, Issawi said, had been on both sides of the de-Baathification issue in recent months. The process of reconciliation was "not fixed enough."

It did not, in fact, take long for the de-Baathification issue to emerge with full force. By the start of 2010, the parliamentary elections that had been expected in January had been postponed to early March. Worse, the Accountability and Justice Commission, the heir to the old de-Baathification Commission that had been set up by Bremer's CPA but caused much difficulty for the Americans, had taken the extraordinary step of barring more than five hundred candidates because of their ostensible Baathist ties, including Salih al-Mutlaq, one of the most prominent and outspoken Sunni politicians and a member of Allawi's Iraqiya alliance.

The commission was led by Ahmed Chalabi and his protégé Ali Faisal al-Lami. In August 2008 American commandos had detained Lami on suspicion of having helped Asaib Ahl al-Haq with a June bomb attack that killed four Americans in Sadr City, but after holding him for a year the military released him. Lami returned to his duties on the panel as if he had merely been on an extended vacation, taking time out to pen an essay alleging abuse in detention that ran on the Huffington Post. Odierno saw the Iranian hand behind the disqualifications. If hundreds of Sunnis were barred from competing, the election would seem systematically unfair to the Sunnis, who might conclude that they had been disenfranchised. All the painful efforts to get the Sunnis and Shiites to accommodate each other— "reconcile" would be too strong a term—would come to naught.

Hill was instructed to raise the matter with Maliki in what quickly became a tense January 12 meeting. Reprising the American position, Hill insisted that there were no grounds for disqualifying Mutlaq. The Iraqi voters should decide whom they wanted in the parliament. Mutlaq, in fact, had already served as a parliamentarian for several years. The disqualification was presented as an administrative matter, but the process seemed tainted and it would produce a political crisis.

Maliki gave no ground. There was no hint of post-sectarianism in his arguments now. The prime minister accused Mutlaq of conspiring with Iraqi Baathists like Izzat Ibrahim al-Duri and Mohammad Yunis al-Ahmed operating from Syria. "You need to have lived in Iraq and be intimately familiar with its history to understand the political conspiracies these people are willing to engage in, and the problems they can cause," said Maliki, who compared the Baathists to the Nazi Party of Hitler's Germany. The Americans, Maliki continued, were casting doubt on the entire Iraqi political process for the sake of a Baathist sympathizer. The Iraqi public would understand the de-Baathification rulings, by which Maliki seemed to have in mind the Shiite public. If Mutlaq did not like the ruling he could appeal to the Court of Cassation, which would take up the matter within twenty-four hours. "There is no way out of this except through the normal legal process. No one can intervene, not me, not the President or anybody else," Maliki insisted. In support of the prime minister, Sadiq al-Rikabi claimed other members of the Iraqiya coalition would hardly object. Allawi, the leader of Iraqiya, "would be one of the happiest people in Iraq" to see one of his rivals dispatched.

So that the voting could proceed, Hill suggested that ballots be printed with Mutlaq and others provisionally certified to run. They could be vetted for Baathist ties after the election but before they were seated. It was a solution that had been endorsed by Washington. Cloaking himself in the Iraqi constitution, Maliki rebuffed the suggestion, saying it would not be legal. In the new Iraq, the law seemed to be just another tool in the political fray. Hill cabled an account of the meeting to Washington with the wry comment "the 2010 Parliamentary campaign has begun."[8]

The Obama administration still had a card to play. Obama had turned over the lead for Iraq to Biden. It was part of a broader White House restructuring of Iraq responsibilities that had seen Lute and his team squeezed out. In the Obama NSC there would no longer be a senior director for Iraq; rather, it would be subsumed in the staff's broader portfolio for the Middle East. The president's most trusted political partners would run Iraq policy now, not holdovers from the previous administration, notwithstanding their role in fashioning the upcoming "end of combat" milestone that had allowed the new president to square his campaign rhetoric with the realities in Iraq. Still, Biden was determined to keep the elections, which were the best hope for a stable Iraq and a peaceful American troop withdrawal, on track. Publicly, Biden insisted that he had not come to Iraq to discuss de-Baathfication, but he pressed the case in a private one-on-one meeting with Maliki.

With the March voting just weeks away, Odierno did what he could to keep violence to a minimum. The U.S. military had been transferring three hundred prisoners per month to the Iraqi judicial system, which was free to try or release them, depending on judicial and political winds. As a precaution, Odierno would hand over only "green," or low-threat, prisoners prior to the voting. If they ended up on the streets instead of in an Iraqi courtroom they would pose little risk to the elections. More important, Odierno crafted an elaborate plan to prevent another Arab-Kurd stand-off like Khanaqin and Bashiqa. The Americans had brokered a series of meetings between officials—from Maliki's defense minister and his Ministry of Interior, and Barzani's interior minister and Ministry of Peshmerga Affairs. The result, the "Combined Security Mechanism," was a security system akin to a U.N. peacekeeping operation. The goal was to prevent an accidental conflict along a line running from Sinjar on the Syrian border to Khanaqin on the Iranian border. The arrangement, according to a classified American cable, was temporary and would last through the "volatile period of elections and government formation." Under the system, a number of disputed areas would be designated as special security zones, where no single force could operate independently. If the Peshmerga troops wanted to maneuver, they would need to secure permission from the Americans and Iraqis. To further enhance security, there would be a series of checkpoints, each of which would be jointly manned seven days a week by thirty-three American, Iraqi, and Peshmerga troops. The security zones and checkpoints were set up in three regions: Nineveh, Diyala, and Kirkuk. At the latter, a multiethnic city, there would be unique arrangements: no Iraqi or Peshmerga soldiers would be deployed. Rather, the checkpoints would be manned by local police and American troops.

Importantly, the arrangements in each of the areas would be overseen by a joint command center, which would intervene to adjudicate any disputes. If the issue needed higher-level attention, it would be bumped upstairs to a Senior Working Group at the Iraqi Ground Forces Command Headquarters at Camp Victory, which would be manned by American, Kurdish, and Arab officers and, ultimately, if need be, a ministerial committee of top officials from all groups. But if the system worked, it would not come to that. Odierno recognized that the system was just a short-term palliative that might be in effect for four to six months. So the long-term plan called for select Peshmerga and Kurdish intelligence units south of the disputed Green Line that marked the border of Kurdistan to be integrated into the

Iraqi military. Other Kurdish forces would not be absorbed into the Iraqi military but would withdraw north of the Green Line.

It looked good on paper, and the arrangements had been approved by Maliki and Barzani themselves. For the Obama administration, which had pledged to end the American combat mission, the checkpoints specified by the plan were something of a stretch, but if the "repositioning" of American troops—as it was called in the American press guidance—worked the United States would be heading off trouble before it even began. With little political headway on Arab-Kurdish issues, Odierno had been forced to do something to keep the lid on while the diplomats and Iraqis tackled the core issues.

The arrangements worked well but started off inauspiciously. Atheel Nujaifi wanted to visit two towns, Tal Kayf and Qosh, which were in areas disputed by the Arabs and Kurds. A problem cropped up almost immediately: while Tal Kayf was within one of the new security zones, Qosh was just outside it. The issue was sent to the Senior Working Group command center to be sorted out. But Barzani was traveling out of the country and no Kurdish officials were willing to authorize Nujaifi's trip without Barzani's explicit permission. Having spent months working out the system, Odierno felt obliged to support Nujaifi now that he had agreed to play within the newly established rules. Nujaifi dropped Qosh from his itinerary. He now planned to visit, in addition to Tal Kayf, the nearby town of Wana, which was also within the security zone. The Kurds continued to take the stance that they could not authorize Nujaifi's visit without word from Barzani, but the arrangement was formally in effect and the Americans provided a small military escort so the trip could go ahead. This was particularly objectionable to the Kurds, since the Christian mayor of Tal Kayf, Bassim Bello of the Assyrian Democratic Movement, was openly critical of the Kurds.

On February 1, the group headed off and quickly ran into trouble. As the convoy approached Wana, several hundred Kurds, brandishing sticks and an enormous Kurdish flag, began to pelt the Iraqi and American vehicles with rocks and tomatoes. Shots were fired at the convoy, and the mayor from Qosh, who had traveled to Wana to meet with Nujaifi, was harassed by the Assayesh, the Kurdish intelligence service. As the crowd became even more unruly, U.S. commanders feared that some of the American soldiers might be roughed up or have their weapons taken. They ordered an F-16 to buzz the crowd and Abrams tanks rumbled to the scene.

Before the episode was over, Nujaifi was claiming that he had been the target of an assassination attempt and his security detail had detained eight attackers who were said to have been firing at the convoy, bringing them back to Mosul for prosecution. The Assayesh responded by going into an Arab town and taking hostages, including local policemen. What was supposed to have been a demonstration of three-way cooperation had turned into a three-way fracas. The episode, which received scant attention in the Western media, was one of the worst moments in American-Kurdish relations. Odierno and Barzani refused to talk to each other for several days.

With the Kurds and Arabs at loggerheads, Odierno dispatched Emma Sky to Irbil. Sky had lived in northern Iraq and knew all the players. Odierno wanted a pragmatic solution, and as Sky saw it, that meant a hostage swap. To facilitate the trade, Sky flew to Kurdistan on Odierno's plane, which, navigating through thick fog, managed to land on its second attempt. Meeting with the Assayesh, Sky determined that the Arab hostages were alive and well. She phoned Rafi al-Issawi, the Sunni deputy prime minister, and reported that she had "proof of life." The first step toward solving the impasse had been taken.[9]

The next move was to arrange the release of the Kurdish detainees. Flying back to Baghdad, Sky picked up Issawi and his adviser Jaber al-Jaberi and headed to Mosul, where the Kurdish prisoners were brought to the airport so they could be flown to Kurdistan. Everything looked set for the hostage trade until an Iraqi judge decided that the Kurdish prisoners needed to appear before his court to be formally released. To reassure the Kurds that the Arabs were not reneging on the deal, Jaberi stayed at the airport with a team of Kurdish negotiators while they waited anxiously for the detainees to get back from the judge. Meanwhile, two American military helicopters flew to Kurdistan to pick up the kidnapped Arabs. After several nervous hours aggravated by poor mobile telephone reception, the swap was consummated.

As the real law in northern Iraq and the father of the new security system, Odierno was able to work things out with Barzani through Sky. After the episode died down, the Combined Security Mechanism would prove more effective. Civil-military relations on the U.S. team in the Green Zone, however, would be tested further.

CHAPTER 33

Crises of Confidence

As the March 7 parliamentary election approached, the United States had entered the period of maximum vulnerability that Ray Odierno had identified during Obama's Iraq review. The general had contended with all manner of threats—Al-Qaeda in Iraq, the Naqshabandis, and the array of Iranian-backed groups—and he had come up with a system to keep Kurdish-Arab tensions at bay.

Under American pressure, the de-Baathification campaign had been defused. The Sunnis had decided not to boycott the election. Many of the candidates who had been barred from running had been reinstated. The United States worked hard to ensure Salih al-Mutlaq would not be arrested on trumped-up charges of being a Baathist agent, and was hoping he would again be accepted into the political fold.

Still, Odierno was worried. After the March 4 Battlefield Update Assessment, Odierno huddled with Chris Hill and a small cluster of aides and vented his concerns. The opinion polls the Americans had quietly commissioned showed that Maliki's Dawa-based State of Law Coalition was hardly a sure bet to prevail at the polls, as the prime minister seemed to think. The Iraqi prime minister had operated for decades in a world of conspiracies, real and imagined. If he did not win by the rules, Odierno wondered, would Maliki try to change the very nature of the game?

The preparations for a potential power grab seemed to be staring the Americans in the face. Odierno reported that he had told the Pentagon that Maliki was cramming the senior and middle ranks of Iraq's intelligence services and army with Dawa Party operatives. Using the expanded powers of his office Maliki might declare a state of emergency, decline to relinquish power, and crack down on his opponents. An upsurge in violence during the election period, actual or provoked, would give him an excuse to act. Iraq's election law gave the winner thirty days to form a new government, and Odierno worried that this would be the time when the prime minister might make his move. The refusal of an incumbent leader to hand over power peacefully to a democratically elected successor would be an enormous setback to the American project in Iraq and a crisis for the Iraqis themselves. It was worst-case thinking, to be sure, but Odierno wanted a plan just in case.

"If he doesn't get elected," Odierno said, "he could refuse to leave." Odierno had asked Michèle Flournoy, the undersecretary of defense for policy, how he should respond if Maliki mounted a creeping coup. As the commander saw it, the United States needed a several-phase plan, one that provided for diplomatic pressure on Maliki and his inner circle to accept the election procedures, a public information campaign to encourage compliance, and, as a last resort, American military intervention to enforce the rule of law. The United States could not sit idly by while Maliki and his Dawa Party cronies stole the election, and Odierno wanted to know what the rules of engagement were in case Maliki lost, declared a state of emergency, and clung to power.

"I don't put it past Maliki at all," added Odierno, noting that Maliki was securing the loyalty of key operational commanders by promoting them to three stars. Even if Maliki did not mount a coup, other Shiite leaders might declare the election a fraud if Allawi managed to get the most votes. The government formation period, Odierno warned, could be very contentious and drawn out.

"We need a Maliki strategy," Hill chimed in. "He is the only one with the tools to screw up democracy." The ambassador was inclined to see Maliki as a necessary evil. To Hill, all of the alternatives looked less palatable. Hill believed that Allawi was too clever by half. Though led by a secular Shiite, most of Allawi's Iraqiya coalition was Sunni. To Hill, it was like arranging for the Afrikaner party to make a comeback in South Africa with a black front man. Instead of trying to figure out what to do if Maliki refused to leave, Hill was more interested in outlining a political strategy that accepted the fact that the prime minister was likely to prevail and that sought to tame his authoritarian impulses and broaden his coalition.[1]

The issue of how to respond to a Maliki crackdown was batted around inconclusively in Washington, but Odierno never heard back. The White House seemed less alarmed about the prospects for a creeping coup than its commander in the field, was decidedly unenthusiastic about intervening to set things right if it did happen, and was hoping for the best.

By Iraqi standards, the election turned out to be a model of decorum. On the day of the vote, the loudspeakers in the mosques in Fallujah urged residents in the Sunni city to go to the polls. Despite the furious controversy over Ali Faisal al-Lami and Ahmed Chalabi's efforts at de-Baathification, Sunnis did not boycott the vote as they had in January 2005. They would not make that mistake again. If anything, the de-Baathification program might have increased the Sunni turnout. In Baghdad and the south, the Sadrists mobilized their supporters as well.

The turnout was respectable: 62 percent of the electorate voted. The ballots had been gathered and deposited in clear plastic tubs. Neither the international election observers nor the Iraqi election commission reported any instances of rampant cheating. Two apartment buildings in the Ur neighborhood of northeast Baghdad were collapsed by mysterious explosions, but even in post-surge Iraq that did not exceed the expectations for insurgent-instigated mayhem. The machinery of democracy had chugged along more or less smoothly without massive demonstrations, ugly finger-pointing, or bloody car bomb attacks. After six years of occupation, the Iraqis had become proficient in organizing elections and imposing enough security precautions to keep the insurgents at bay, at least for a day. It was translating the votes into an effective government that was the problem.

To the consternation of the Hill team, Odierno had been interviewed in the days after the vote by Wolf Blitzer and Jim Lehrer. The general had spent more than four years in Iraq and commanded one unit or another during virtually every phase of the conflict. But at the embassy, Odierno's TV appearances were seen as indicative of the general's and his team's hovering over Iraq like overprotective parents reluctant to relax their grip on policy. As Hill saw it, his own tenure was supposed to usher in the new normal: the initiation of a relationship between two sovereign states, and it was the diplomats at the embassy, not the generals at Camp Victory, who ought to have the lead.

During an embassy huddle, Thomas Dougherty, the chief embassy public affairs official, suggested that McDonough's Deputies Committee in Washington issue instructions that Hill should be the one to talk about anything in Iraq that did not involve security. That way Hill would not need to assert himself every time media requests came in and say "me, me." Another senior staff member noted that, with prodding from the embassy, the NSC staff would move to block Odierno from appearing solo on the Sunday television talk shows.

When he had the bully pulpit, Hill planned to use an entirely different vernacular than the military. Petraeus had a penchant for referring to the Iranian government, which had ruthlessly put down its own pro-democracy protesters, as a "thugocracy," Hill observed. The CENTCOM commander, Hill griped, seemed to be obsessed with "-ocracies." Hill had an even dimmer view of the media. The press, he sniffed at one March meeting, had been "predicting ten of the last two crises." The media was always looking for the dark cloud and not the silver lining and seemed to believe that violence sells. Still, the media and the community of experts in Washington who influenced the press could not be overlooked and the embassy did not intend to ignore them.

To get its message across, the embassy arranged periodic background briefings for the Western media. As the wrangling over the election continued, one reporter asked how the United States might respond if Maliki staged a coup and refused to honor the balloting. Unbeknownst to the journalist, it was the very issue that Odierno had fretted about. Grappo dismissed the reporter's query as a stupid question. After the press was gone, Cameron Munter praised Grappo's handling of the question.

At Maliki's ornate palace in the Green Zone, a picture was beginning to emerge from the election returns and it was not one that the prime minister liked. Maliki had believed he was all but assured of victory. He had seen the nation through the surge and led the charge to Basra, formed "support councils" to reach out to tribal leaders throughout the south, and rebranded his political coalition as a nationalist organization committed to restoring and preserving the peace: State of Law. In fact, Maliki was so confident that his popularity and the dramatically improved security situation would seal his reelection that he had split away from his rivals in the other major Shiite bloc, the Iraqi National Accord, after they announced they would not support Maliki for another term as prime minister. Maliki's aides had assured him that State of Law would win as many as 120 seats and would be able to easily form a government without the INA and Iraqiya. That Allawi and his largely Sunni coalition could dislodge the incumbent prime minister seemed unthinkable to Maliki.

But the contest between Iraqiya and State of Law was astonishingly close and as the results trickled in to Iraq's Independent High Election Commission it appeared that Allawi's bloc might win more parliamentary seats, which could give it the right to make the first attempt to assemble a governing coalition under the Iraqi constitution. On March 17, Iraqiya held a slim nine-thousand-vote lead over Maliki's State of Law with more than 95 percent of the votes counted. The party had even done well in areas of the Shiite south, where they tallied more than 200,000 votes and elected more than ten Shiite members of parliament. The trend held up when the final results were announced nine days later. Allawi's Iraqiya had secured ninety-one seats over Maliki's State of Law, which had been awarded eighty-nine seats. The INA, the competing Shiite alliance, won seventy seats and the Kurdistan Alliance fifty-seven seats. To govern Iraq, a bloc needed to line up enough allies to control 163 seats in the 325-seat parliament.

Maliki, as Steve Hadley's impolitic 2006 memo to Bush had noted, had come of age in a world full of conspiracies. As the tallies rolled in, Maliki was convinced that he faced one more. It was unfathomable to the prime minister that a coalition that included former Baathists would fare so well. The fact that the United Nations representative in Iraq assessed the vote as fair simply indicated that the U.N. was in on the fix. The prime minister sent a confidential letter to the Americans claiming that he had been cheated. Maliki wanted a recount in Baghdad, but there were indications that he might add Mosul and Kirkuk as well.

A recount was just one way Maliki could shape the outcome. Another way was to reinvigorate the de-Baathification campaign and disqualify enough of the winning Iraqiya candidates so that State of Law came out on top. A third way was to challenge the constitutional principle that the party that won the most seats would have the right to the first crack at forming the government. In the weeks after the election, Maliki and other Shiite politicians pursued all three tracks, mounting a three-pronged assault on Iraqiya.

Chalabi and Lami's commission insisted that Iraq's courts disqualify eight of the winning candidates because of their ostensible Baathist ties. Maliki's office sent a letter to Iraq's highest court on March 21, asking for an interpretation of the "largest bloc" language in Article 76 of the constitution. Four days later, the judiciary issued its opinion: "largest bloc" could mean either the bloc that won the most seats in the election or a bloc assembled in the parliament after the vote. The ruling appeared to be a blatant reinterpretation of the framers' intent. Sheikh Humam Hammoudi, one of the drafters of the constitution, had stated in a 2004 interview that the article was meant to refer specifically to electoral blocs. The Governance Assessment Team report that was prepared for Petraeus in 2008 had noted that Judge Medhat al-Mahmoud, the head of Iraq's highest legal body, was vulnerable to political pressure. The clarification appeared to confirm as much. Faced with a decision on how to respond, the Obama administration decided to let the process unfold by itself. Maliki could have his recount and the Americans would not venture an opinion on Judge Medhat's ruling. But it would seek to limit the scope of de-Baathification.

At Camp Victory, Odierno was concerned that his apprehensions about Maliki were beginning to come true. Recounting the votes would be opening Pandora's box. Neither the United Nations nor Odierno saw any justification for it. This was the time to stand firm, Odierno argued, and nip the possibility of election skulduggery in the bud. Already there were rumors that the prime minister or a member of his inner circle had sent a text to the Iraqi electoral commission threatening to surround it with armored vehicles, rumors taken seriously enough to have been briefed at Odierno's BUA.[2] But as Odierno analyzed the situation he became convinced that Maliki honestly thought he had won and was confusing the popular vote in which State of Law had a small edge over Iraqiya with contests for seats in the parliament. "He's focused on the popular vote," Odierno told his subordinates. "That's what's making him act so wacky."

On March 25, Hill and Odierno met again to assess the situation. The Iraqi election commission was doing a hand recount of the Karkh warehouse district. The voters in this area were mainly Sunni, which was why Maliki's office wanted a recount there. Hill had a typically dyspeptic observation: "What a stinking country this is." Six of those disqualified had won seats and two were from Iraqiya, including Ibrahim al-Mutlaq, the brother of Salih al-Mutlaq. It was not clear whether the parties would be allowed to name replacements.

Odierno argued that the United States needed to get involved: "I think it should also meet our objectives." A government assembled by Qasim Suleimani would not get the support of Iraq's Sunnis, and that meant that 2011 could be very violent. Odierno was worried about the lack of Sunni buy-in. Odierno did not agree with standing back and allowing events to unfold. There needed to be an interagency decision about whether the

United States should help shape the outcome, if only to prevent the Sunnis from slipping back into the insurgency and prompting more violence.

Hill was more skeptical about the Sunnis and Iraqiya. There was no Sunni party that was not bought and paid for by the Saudis, he said, but he shared some of Odierno's concerns. The ambassador suggested that Ad Melkert, the representative of the United Nations secretary-general, should talk with Ayatollah Sistani and get him to say that this was a free and fair election. Grappo, meanwhile, asked the CIA for a psychological profile of Maliki.

On April 26, a special judicial panel upheld a decision by the Accountability and Justice Commission to disqualify fifty-two candidates because of their alleged Baathist ties. At the BUA that day, Odierno's frustrations bubbled over. The United States, he barked, needed to call Judge Medhat and "ask if he is going to do this forever." Later, Biden called Maliki to raise American concerns about undue influence on the judiciary.

The Americans, however, were not the only ones trying to shape the process. As the election results came in and confirmed the Shiites' worst fears, Iran saw a new opportunity to reconstitute the United Iraqi Alliance—the mega-Shiite bloc that had dominated Iraqi politics years earlier.[3] In March, Iraq's Shiite politicians had been invited to the Nowruz festivities in Tehran to celebrate the Persian New Year, where Iranian leaders pressed them to reunite. Though nothing was finalized on this front, on March 22 it was agreed that Talabani, who was also in attendance, ought to remain president. After more Iranian lobbying, by early May, Maliki's State of Law and his Shiite rivals in the INA had merged to create a new coalition: the National Alliance. With 159 seats in the parliament, the Shiites could now claim to have the largest bloc in the 325-seat legislature and, with Medhat's earlier opinion, the right to try to form the new government.

At the White House, Obama administration officials were not perturbed. They argued that Allawi's Iraqiya would have been unlikely to attract enough allies to form a new government and that it was a political fact of life that the prime minister of Iraq would come from the ranks of the Shiite political parties. But Sunnis saw it as a violation of the very spirit of the vote. "I mean, if the winning bloc is not the one which will form the government, why are there blocs competing for the election?" said Rafi al-Issawi, a leading Iraqiya member.

By early 2010, the bulk of Bill McRaven's JSOC strike forces had shifted from Iraq to Afghanistan, a pivot that mirrored the focus of the American military overall. A smaller JSOC task force of Ranger and Delta Force troops continued their shadow war in Iraq, though, working alongside Fadhil Barwari's ISOF commandos and the American Special Forces who advised them. Much of their time was spent chasing Al-Qaeda, which by early 2010 was no longer a broad insurgent network but rather an underground terrorist group with most of its cells based in Mosul or elsewhere in the north. The task force's first big hit of 2010 came at the beginning of January when commandos killed the Al-Qaeda chief of operations for northern Iraq. A week after that, on January 12, the Americans used electronic intercepts to mount a series of raids in Baghdad while several car bombs were en route to their targets at the Defense, Health, and Trade ministries. Later in the month, information gathered in those raids led to the killing in Mosul of an even more senior figure, Abu Khalaf, who had succeeded Abu Ghadiya at the helm of Al-Qaeda's support network in Syria after that leader's death in the October 2008 CIA-JSOC cross-border raid. Step by step, American and Iraqi special operations troops were continuing the methodical campaign to take down Al-Qaeda's leadership.

While the American commandos had a free hand in raiding Al-Qaeda targets, attacks against Shiite militias were more politically sensitive, even when they involved Iraqi forces. On the night of February 11, an Iraqi special operations team with American Special Forces advisers launched a heliborne raid on a group of Kataib Hezbollah militants near the Iranian border in Maysan, a group that was believed to be involved in smuggling weapons from Iran, including IRAMs, rocket-boosted mortars, that had been used with devastating effect against some American bases—no small concern, since the State Department–led provincial reconstruction team was located on a base in the province.

According to a classified American account of the mission, dubbed Steel Curtain, eight Iraqis were killed, including an armed woman linked to the Kataib Hezbollah militants; she was pronounced dead on arrival at a local hospital. Twenty-two were arrested.[4] No sooner did the raid occur than it provoked a furor. The Iraqi media described the mission as a unilateral American operation that had killed ten innocent civilians. Iraqi politicians demanded an investigation, though with varying degrees of fervor. After Adil Abd al-Mahdi, whose ISCI party was competing for votes in the south with the Sadrists, publicly demanded an investigation, one of his aides told an American embassy official that the declaration was "just politics," and that if he had had serious objections he would have contacted Odierno and Hill directly.[5]

The day after the Maysan raid, Farouk al-Araji, the head of Maliki's

OCINC, announced that from now on all commando operations would have to be authorized by the prime minister. The edict was so sweeping that it prompted the Basra Operations Command to suspend all operations with American commandos. Joint American and Iraqi operations were suspended even in Anbar Province, and in some parts of northern Iraq the Americans stopped collaborating with the Iraqi police altogether.

Slowly, Maliki relaxed his obstinacy. On February 15, he declared that American-Iraqi raids against Sunni targets would not require his approval, and the next day said the same thing about Shiite targets, although this retraction of the February 12 order also directed special operations forces to avoid using helicopters in their raids when possible. As a condition for the resumption of raids, the American military handed over all of the militants it had captured during the Maysan raid, whom Iraqi officials promptly released. A secret cable from Hill bluntly summed up the episode. The release of the prisoners "must be balanced with the need to maintain pressure on AQI and Shi'a extremists—especially to deny them the initiative in counter-election operations," Hill wrote. "Once the PM demanded the transfer of the detainees in accordance with the Security Agreement and threatened to cancel all high value SOF cooperation activities, USF-I [United States Forces—Iraq] weighed the loss of the detainees versus the loss of SOF cooperation and handed over the KH prisoners. This is disappointing, and it appears that more dialogue will be required."[6]

Despite Odierno's and Maliki's efforts to patch up their differences, friction lingered. In March, Iraqi troops captured Al-Qaeda's emir of Baghdad, Manaf Abd al-Rahim al-Rawi, the figure who had orchestrated the large-scale August and October 2009 bombings in Baghdad. Rawi was handed over to the Office of Special Investigations, one of the many Iraqi intelligence agencies Maliki had created in order to sideline the CIA-backed INIS and allow his inner circle to have a more complete intelligence picture than any of the agencies themselves. The system served Maliki's purposes, but it also created confusion and was especially counterproductive when the Americans were cut out of the picture. The office never bothered to report the catch to the American military.

Within a week of that capture, American commandos apprehended Rawi's twin brother and handed him over to the Interior Ministry. When Odierno learned through his sources that Maliki's investigations office had been hiding the other twin, he went to Maliki and insisted that he grant access to the detained terrorist leader. Accompanying Odierno to a meeting of his various intelligence officials, Maliki insisted and demanded that from now on they had to share information not only with each other but with the American military as well. The intelligence gap between the Americans and the Iraqis had been closed, at least insofar as Al-Qaeda targets were concerned.

At first Rawi had been uncommunicative, but when American interrogators took his twin brother to visit him, the Baghdad emir started talking, spilling details about Al-Qaeda's covert network. Raids began targeting Al-Qaeda couriers whom Rawi had given up. Following the trail of two such couriers led American intelligence to a safe house north of Samarra in mid-April. Iraqi intelligence officers wanted to attack the house at that point with a joint JSOC-Iraqi strike force that was standing by, but JSOC commanders demurred, preferring to continue tracking the two couriers. Fourteen hours later, one of the couriers, still under American surveillance, stopped at another safe house, this one in the remote Tharthar area near Salahuddin's border with Anbar.

This time, the strike force moved in and snatched the courier. Although the house appeared to be empty except for one woman and some children, the courier told his captors that it was occupied by Al-Qaeda in Iraq's top leader, Abu Ayyub al-Masri, who was holed up in a hidden basement, whose secret entrance was underneath a sink. Barging into the building, the commandos ushered the woman and children outside and began methodically to clear the structure. Sensing they were cornered, the Al-Qaeda operatives began to fire from their underground lair and the commandos responded by tossing down a few grenades.

In the basement the strike force found computers, documents, and bodies—those of Abu Ayyub al-Masri, his assistant, and another Al-Qaeda leader, Abu Omar al-Baghdadi, and his son. American and Iraqi intelligence had long debated whether Baghdadi was a real terrorist leader or merely a fictional character employed by the group to lend an Iraqi face to its senior leadership, but the April 18 raid confirmed his existence. That night, JSOC and Iraqi commandos hit eight more targets; on one of the raids, a Black Hawk helicopter crashed, killing an Army Ranger.

For all their successes, Maliki and Odierno refused to let their guard down against Al-Qaeda. As the Arbaeen pilgrimage in Karbala approached in the spring, the general took his abiding concerns about the terrorist group to Maliki. Reluctant to embrace the Awakening volunteers—the number of Sons of Iraq in the area had shrunk from more than 30,000 to a mere 8,500—the prime minister was relying heavily on the Iraqi Army to secure the southern Baghdad belts, which had gaping holes. Meeting with Maliki, the general persuaded the prime minister to quietly rehire some of the Awakening volunteers.

In April, Maliki became obsessed with the notion that Al-Qaeda was planning to mount a 9/11-style attack on the Iraqi capital. Iraqi sources, Maliki confided to Odierno, had learned that Al-Qaeda intended to hijack a civilian jet in the Middle East and crash it into the Baghdad Airport or perhaps the shrine in Najaf. With no explanation, Maliki ordered that the Baghdad and Najaf airports be closed and all civilian flights canceled. Wary of the intelligence but eager to show that he was taking the prime minister's worries seriously, Odierno rushed an air defense unit equipped with Stinger antiaircraft missiles to Baghdad and made sure that American warplanes were in the air, ready to pounce on any suspicious plane. The deployment of the air defense unit was an ironic role reversal. With no enemy air threat in Iraq, the Americans for years had used many of their air defense troops as provisional infantry and guards for military bases—so much so that they had to bring the Stingers in from Kuwait. Of the many threats Iraq had endured, this was one that never materialized. The Iraqi public was kept in the dark, the episode chronicled only in the classified records of the war.

A scandal that could not be kept under wraps, however, was prisoner abuse at some of Maliki's detention facilities, especially a secret prison the prime minister's security forces had maintained at Muthana Air Base in Baghdad. The Iraqi prisoners had been detained in Nineveh and transferred from jails there so that provincial authorities could not order their release. Not only had the prisoners been denied fair judicial review but they had been beaten, sodomized, and subjected to extortion. Huge bribes had been demanded from prisoners who wanted to call their families. The abuses had been uncovered by Wijdan Salim, the head of Iraq's Human Rights Ministry. What made the accusations all the more damning was that Salim was not a foe of Maliki but had run for parliament on the State of Law ticket. The charges were recounted in a secret embassy cable that found its way into the *Los Angeles Times*. Maliki was upset about the disclosure, the result, as he saw it, of a conspiracy to diminish his chances of becoming prime minister while boosting Allawi's prospects. To show his displeasure, he refused all meetings with Hill, the last person who would have leaked the document.

The day after the *Los Angeles Times* article, Hill convened his team for their customary huddle. He was furious that the highly classified cable had been leaked. Only half a dozen people at the embassy would have seen it. Upset about the disclosure, some members of Hill's team initially trained their suspicions on Odierno's staff.

Two days later, the subject came up at Hill's meeting with Odierno.

Grappo accentuated the positive. In the wake of the scandalous revelations, Maliki had allowed Human Rights Watch to conduct interviews with the prisoners, which he insisted was unprecedented in the Middle East. Munter agreed: the international media had gone overboard in its unflattering portrayal of Maliki.

To Odierno, however, the true story was worse than it seemed. The prime minister's office, specifically OCINC, was trying to pin the blame on the Defense Ministry. But the Ministry of Defense was only in charge of the guards on the outside of the facility. OCINC was in charge of the prison itself. Nor did Odierno believe Maliki's claim that the only reason he had recently traveled to Iran was because his opponent, Allawi, had visited Arab states. This was a bit of revisionism. If the United States did not privately remonstrate with Maliki, it would look as if the Americans were blithely consenting to his involvement with Iran.

As the summer approached, Odierno was worried that Maliki was playing for time. If the electoral process followed its course there was a good chance Maliki would not continue as prime minister. But if for whatever reason the election results were not officially certified that would be fine with Maliki. He would hang on as the interim prime minister and the extension of his term would be a fait accompli. In a meeting with American officials, Odierno noted that Sheikh Abdullah al-Yawar, a Sunni moderate, warned that in the eyes of the Sunni community, Allawi had won and the election was now being stolen from him. For Odierno, ameliorating the concerns of Iraq's Sunni population was a major concern. After all, it was Sunni discontent that had fueled the insurgency in the opening years of the war. Whoever became prime minister, Iraqiya and Allawi needed to be a conspicuous part of the process. It was important for the integrity of the election process and stability in Iraq. Certainly nobody, the general insisted, could accuse him of being biased toward the Sunnis. "I am not a Sunni lover," he said in one meeting. "I killed and arrested more Sunnis than anyone in this room."[7] Brigadier General Joe Anderson, Odierno's chief of staff, a former brigade commander in Mosul who oversaw the attack that killed Saddam's sons, Uday and Qusay, quipped that he had actually killed more Sunnis. The black humor prompted laughter and temporarily broke the tension between the civilians and military leaders at the table.

Still, the embassy saw things differently. As one observer recalled, "General Odierno believed that we should put our arms around Iraqiya and help them reach a compromise with the others, whereas the embassy put their arms around Maliki and tried to get everyone else to reach a settlement with him."[8] The debate cut to the core of American policy in Iraq, and the two sides were at loggerheads.

As concern grew that the Iraqi electoral process would drag on and the formation of a new government was not in the very near future, the Obama administration—with some prodding behind the scenes from Odierno—began to step up its involvement in Iraq.

As early as November 2009, soon after Vice President Tariq al-Hashimi had vetoed Iraq's election law, Odierno had lifted the veil on his relations with the American embassy in a videoconference with the Pentagon. The ambassador was expending so much energy monitoring which Iraqis the American military was meeting with, he said, that he did not have time to meet with the Iraqis himself. "The American ambassador keeps closer track of what I'm doing than he does of what Maliki's doing," he said, according to a participant.

When Odierno visited Washington in February he had elaborated on his frustrations in a closed-door meeting with Defense Secretary Bob Gates. Odierno had constantly pushed to get Hill to meet with Iraqi officials. The ambassador had gotten better at it but was still a far cry from Ryan Crocker. Hill was an experienced diplomat but he was not trying to build long-term relationships in a country that was all about building those kinds of ties. Gates had arranged for the general to speak with Hillary Clinton, and Odierno again laid out his worries.

In May, Gates reached out to Crocker, who was serving as a dean at the Bush School of Government and Public Service at Texas A&M, and had him flown to Washington in a government plane for a series of unpublicized meetings. Crocker was inclined to take the Iraqi developments in stride, but he had a much more activist vision of the American role than Hill. It was true, Crocker believed, that the Iraqis needed to stand on their own, but it was also the case that the United States was hardwired, as he put it, into the Iraqi system, especially during such thorny political crises as the election. There was no need to overreact, but the United States had to stay engaged and all of its best experts needed to be involved. It was an extraordinary turnaround. Hill had gone to Baghdad to "break some crockery." Now Crocker was quietly being summoned to Washington for consultations on how to improve the diplomats' performance in Iraq. Crocker met with Flournoy and then with Gates. Crocker told Gates that, in accordance with the Iraqi way of doing things, the formation of a new government was unlikely before Ramadan, which was months away.

Crocker and Gates then went to the White House for a meeting that included Biden, National Security Adviser Jim Jones, Petraeus, and Clinton. The worry was expressed that the United States might be facing 2006 all over again—a year marked by a similar delay in fielding a new government, giving the insurgency space and time to grow. Crocker again advised that there was no need to panic, but that the United States needed to act more as a catalyst of developments in Iraq, and for that it had to send its very best people to Baghdad.

The White House would buttress the embassy with an all-star team. Petraeus compiled a list of potential advisers, which included Ali Khedery, a current Petraeus aide and former aide to Crocker; Sadi Othman, a longtime adviser to Petraeus who had first worked with the general in Mosul and had once been a member of the Jordanian Olympic basketball team; and Molly Phee from the NSC staff. The State Department took some umbrage that a general was developing a list of civilians to send to Iraq, so its Near Eastern Affairs bureau began putting its own list together. One name that was common to both was Brett McGurk, who had worked on the status of forces agreement for the Bush administration and written an op-ed article criticizing the Obama administration for establishing the August 2010 deadline to get down to fifty thousand troops. McGurk would make it to Iraq after Clinton intervened to overcome Biden's reluctance to send a former Bush NSC aide to help Team Obama find its way. But Hill had no use for Khedery, who was whisked to Baghdad in a plane dispatched by Odierno only to be sent packing the day he arrived.

Crocker's White House meeting was among the most secret of his long diplomatic career. When Biden and Clinton discussed it with Hill they insisted that the topic of discussion had chiefly been Afghanistan. When Hill emailed Crocker to ask him about the session the retired ambassador was more candid, if diplomatic. Crocker responded that Iraq had come up and that he had suggested that it was important for Foreign Service officers to do more than one tour at hardship posts, a polite way of noting that Hill's team included precious few seasoned diplomats knowledgeable about Iraq. Still, the writing was on the wall. After letting Hill try things his way, the White House was going to be more involved.[9]

CHAPTER 34

Team of Rivals

As Barack Obama's point person on Iraq, Joe Biden had quickly emerged as the troubleshooter in chief. The Biden-Gelb plan for a decentralized federal government had been shelved. Biden's role was to ride herd on the Iraqi politicians, give the process a push whenever necessary, and ensure that the administration's policy stayed on track. As in the Bush administration, the Office of Vice President, and its retinue of aides, would be a major player on Iraq, its influence easily eclipsing that of the State Department.

The problem the White House faced was a vexing one. If there was no Iraqi government in place, or even steady progress toward deciding who would serve as prime minister and determining who would lead the ministries, how could the administration confidently proclaim an end to the combat mission in August and proceed with the new phase of troop withdrawals? While the White House wanted to make good on Obama's campaign promise to get the combat troops out, it did not want to be accused of allowing Iraq to slide once more into civil war.

Biden was making a trip to Iraq on July 4 to visit the troops and fully intended to take the opportunity to huddle with politicians in Baghdad and Kurdistan and move the electoral process along. Under the SOFA Bush had concluded with Maliki, American troops did not need to be out of Iraq until the end of 2011, and even then there seemed to be a strong possibility that some sort of follow-on agreement allowing some troops to remain might be agreed upon. But the White House's determination to announce a turning point at the end of August meant that Obama team was quickly running out of time. The tyranny of the deadline could be unforgiving, even if it was self-imposed.

For Chris Hill, Biden's trip was an opportunity get top-level endorsement for his plan to build a new government around Maliki. The situation, as Hill saw it, was clear. No party had won a commanding victory. Both Maliki and Allawi considered themselves the rightful prime minister. Neither was prepared to give way to the other, but one was already in the prime minister's chair. In short, there were not enough places at the top of Iraq's governing structure to accommodate the politicians who believed they were destined to lead the country and no small amount of concern about the power accumulated by the politician who did.

Brainstorming with Gary Grappo, Hill had developed what he thought was an ingenious answer. If Allawi's Iraqiya was unable to beat Maliki's State of Law—and it was Hill's verdict that despite the impressive list of seats Iraqiya won it could not and, indeed, should not prevail because of its considerable Sunni support—perhaps there could be an arrangement whereby Iraqiya would join its adversaries. If there were not enough places at the table for Maliki, Allawi, and the other factions, he reasoned, the United States could push the Iraqis to add some more chairs.

Ben Metz, the embassy's legal attaché, was tasked with addressing the fine points of the plan. The United States, Hill told Metz, had overhauled its national security structure in 1947. The National Security Act had spawned the National Security Council, the Defense Department, and the CIA, and none of that required amending the United States Constitution. Why couldn't something similar be done in Iraq? The last thing the Obama administration would want was for the seating of a new government to be delayed by months of wrangling over constitutional issues.

The embassy's proposal was outlined in a "non-paper," a confidential document that the diplomats could disown if it ever leaked. A top-level body would be established—"The Coordinating Council on National Strategic Policy"—to guide foreign policy and economic decisions, including issues involving the oil sector. To ensure that the body would be more than a debating society and deal with the apprehensions about Maliki's expanding powers, the council would have some concrete responsibilities. It would review the budget for Iraq's security forces, oversee weapons purchases, confer before major military operations, as Maliki had pointedly refrained from doing before mounting his Charge of the Knights operation in Basra, and oversee the policy on detainees, no small concern given the allegations that Maliki had had potential foes locked away in secret prisons.

Significantly, the council would have the authority to nominate military officers above the rank of brigadier general. Maliki had been seeding the ranks of the military and intelligence service with Dawa Party loyalists.

As the American military drew down, having the council handle military appointments would go a long way toward ensuring that Iraq's military was a national institution and not a private army for the prime minister.

As for who would oversee the council, it would be led by a secretary-general for national security affairs, who would be nominated by Iraq's president and approved by a majority vote of Iraq's parliament. Significantly, the president and the prime minister would be mere cochairs. Other council members would include the speaker of the parliament, the chief of the Higher Judicial Council, the president of Kurdistan, and the heads of the ministries of Defense, Foreign Affairs, Interior, Finance, and Oil. If the discussion called for it, the heads of Iraq's various intelligence services and of the armed forces could attend, and other officials might be invited. The body would be required to meet at least once a month and could be convened more often by the secretary-general, president, or prime minister.

To make the plan more palatable to Maliki, Hill instructed Metz to avoid using terms like the "transfer" of power, which for the prime minister would be like waving a red flag in front of a bull. "Nothing in this concept should be construed as curtailing or altering the constitutional authority of the Prime Minister, President or the Council of Ministers, and Council of Representatives by the Iraqi Constitution," the paper noted. That was true in a literal sense. But much of the point of the exercise was to curb Maliki's extra-constitutional powers by reaffirming limits that the prime minister had overstepped.[1]

There were drawbacks to the plan, to be sure. All of the rivalries within the Iraqi political system would be imported into the new governing structure. It would be like having an American administration in which Obama presided over a cabinet with the likes of John McCain, Ralph Nader, and Newt Gingrich. But the alternative to the "partnership government," as the idea came to be known, would be to have a parliamentary majority do political battle against a loyal opposition. In a country that had only recently emerged from years of brutal sectarian fighting, Hill figured that inefficiency was preferable to leaving major factions outside the tent.

In the spring, Hill test-marketed the idea of a Maliki-Allawi government with Kenneth Pollack, the Brookings Institution scholar and former NSC hand during the Clinton administration, without providing much by way of details. Pollack thought the approach was spot-on and took it upon himself to argue the case to Dennis Ross, a senior NSC hand on the Middle East for Obama, and Jeffrey Feltman, the assistant secretary of state for Near Eastern affairs, neither of whom was thought to be a staunch supporter of Maliki. If Maliki's role was circumscribed, Allawi was given substantial responsibilities, and the administration was to act swiftly to cement the arrangements in place, Pollack thought the plan for the new council could work.[2]

After his many years in government, Hill was not about to send his plan for interagency review, where it would be analyzed, debated, modified, and picked apart. He waited to outline the plan directly to Biden, who was anxious to have a roadmap for the way ahead. Biden embraced the plan and later described it in general terms. Unlike the neoconservatives, Biden did not believe that a democratic Iraq would have a catalytic effect, spreading representative government throughout the Middle East. But he thought that it was important for all of Iraq's major parties and sectarian groupings to be under one tent. "It is important that it become a democracy because that is the only vehicle by which you can hold together such a diverse population that has such a history and inclination to actually be at each other's throats," Biden observed.

In developing the plan, Hill had not been so bold as to spell out which political figures would occupy the top posts of the new government. The administration's formal position was that it was not picking Iraq's leaders. But during his July 4 visit Biden was quick to fill in the blanks. The prime minister's post would be filled by the man who was already in the chair—Maliki—while Allawi would get the consolation prize: head of the new council.

Among other Baghdad hands there was a range of views. Robert Ford, an Arabist and the most experienced diplomat at the embassy when Hill first arrived in Baghdad, had thought that Adil Abd al-Mahdi was the best choice to lead Iraq. Abd al-Mahdi had run the Finance Ministry, which seemed more relevant to the challenges Iraq faced in building its economy than the strongman role Maliki appeared to relish. Emma Sky, Odierno's political adviser, shared her boss's worries about Maliki's incipient authoritarianism. Allawi had his flaws, but Sky thought Iraqiya offered a promising cross-sectarian and secular vision for the new Iraq. Because Odierno did not have the policy lead in Iraq, Hill and his team had little patience for Sky, whom he routinely assailed in embassy staff meetings as a British interloper with a soft spot for former exiles who had lived in London. Ali Khedery, who had served as Crocker's aide and had worked for every senior American civilian in Iraq from Jerry Bremer on, was also wary of Maliki and thought he was too susceptible to Iranian influence, but Khedery had been sent packing by Hill.

Hill, for his part, thought Biden had it exactly right. Allawi, Hill thought, had little chance of running Iraq as the head of a coalition with so many Sunni members, and Hill once dismissed him as "the smartest and laziest man in Iraq." Abd al-Mahdi was an attractive politician, but one, Hill thought, with not nearly enough support to make it to the top. The ambassador was not looking for a sea change in Iraqi politics, but a course correction that accepted what Hill deemed to be the political reality that Maliki would stay in place but would make his role less of a bitter pill for his rivals to swallow. For all of his flaws, Maliki, Hill thought, was somebody with whom the United States could work.

If carried out right, the establishment of a new bureaucratic decision-making structure could serve another, and increasingly important, purpose. Odierno had done his best to sensitize the Pentagon to Maliki's authoritarian tendencies, and two Pentagon officials—Colin Kahl and his aide Sam Parker—had drafted a paper during a visit to Camp Victory proposing that the United States look for opportunities to roll back Maliki's extra-constitutional power over the military and intelligence agencies and preserve some semblance of a system of checks and balances by, for example, ensuring that Iraq's president retain his veto authority. The paper was sent to Denis McDonough's Deputies Committee and had been approved as the basis for going forward.[3] That guidance, too, could be included in the plan.

Establishing an Iraqi team of rivals promised to be tricky. The Americans were not merely trying to assemble a cast that had spent years trying to outmaneuver each other; they were also trying to redefine the powers of Iraq's leader and create posts that had not existed. It was clear that advocacy of the plan in Baghdad was not going to be easy, as Hill learned when he tried out the idea on a few prominent Iraqis, including Ali al-Dabbagh, the government spokesman and a close Maliki aide. There was nobody like Dabbagh in the American political system. Dabbagh was the public face of the government, a consummate political operative, successful businessman, and diplomatic envoy, all rolled up into one. Born in Karbala, Dabbagh had obtained a doctorate in business administration from a British university and spent much of his time in exile during the Saddam years running a successful trading business in Dubai. Fluent in English and impeccably tailored, he also spoke French, Farsi, as well as some Urdu; had connections in Turkey, Syria, and the Arab world; and appeared to be among the most Westernized members of Maliki's inner circle.

Meeting in the living room of Dabbagh's Green Zone home with Grappo and Metz in tow, Hill explained the plan, which had some obvious advantages for Maliki, the most important being that it appeared to presume that Maliki would remain as prime minister. But Dabbagh was wary: the plan diminished Maliki's powers as commander in chief and would never be accepted in its present form by the prime minister or his State of Law Coalition, he cautioned.[4]

Although Dabbagh was skeptical that Maliki would go along with the council proposal, he made an effort to facilitate it. Playing shuttle diplomacy between Maliki and Allawi, Dabbagh succeeded in bringing the two archrivals together for a Tuesday night dinner on July 20 in Maliki's office, along with Allawi's cousin Mohammed Allawi. At one point, Allawi told Maliki in front of the other guests that he would support him if the prime minister adhered to a genuine power-sharing agreement with Iraqiya. After a forty-minute one-on-one meeting, however, Maliki and Allawi walked out without enthusiasm. "No use," Dabbagh expressed in frustration.

Hill's meeting with Allawi promised to be trickier still. Hill's attitude toward Allawi was no secret, and he did not want the Iraqiya leader to think that the American ambassador had decided on his own that Allawi would not be prime minister. After getting his talking points from the NSC reaffirmed by Tony Blinken, Biden's top aide on national security issues, Hill met with Allawi and made clear that he was reading his instructions from Washington. "Have you talked to the neighbors?" Allawi asked. Allawi had invested heavily in building support for himself in Turkey and in Arab states and was calculating that they could influence the situation in Iraq. Hill responded that the Obama administration planned to do so.

Contemplating Hill's idea, Allawi wondered whether the Obama administration wanted him to serve as secretary-general of the council or just as a representative of Iraqiya. "We're talking about you as the leader," Hill replied. Allawi said he would consult his allies in Iraqiya and get back to the Americans, but it was clear that he did not like the arrangement. He was still holding out for the prime ministership.

Even as he weighed the Obama administration's proposal, Allawi was quietly meeting with the regional powers to line up support for a government in which he would be assured of an important position. A day before he met with Maliki, the Iraqiya leader traveled to Damascus to meet with Bashar al-Assad, where Allawi suggested he might support Adil Abd al-Mahdi if he was given the presidency.

Assad promised to relay the message to Iran, but mentioned that the Iranians had a "red line" against Allawi. "Are you going to negotiate with Tehran, or are you going to listen to what they have to tell you?" Allawi asked. Assad said that he would negotiate, but the next day one of his deputies called Allawi from Tehran and said that the Iranians were adamant: the only prime minister they could accept was Maliki.

By coincidence, Muqtada al-Sadr was also visiting Damascus at the same time as Allawi, and the two men met face-to-face for the first time. As interim prime minister, Allawi had wanted to arrest Sadr for the Mahdi Army's antics in Najaf. But facing a common enemy years later, they attempted to reconcile. "You know, I know most of your family, including your father and your uncle," Allawi said to Sadr. "They never believed in sectarianism."

"Yes," Sadr replied. "I don't believe in this." The unlikely pair discussed generally how to reconcile and form a government.

Russia was another stop. In talks with Vladimir Putin, after arriving in Moscow on August 21, Allawi sounded out the Russian prime minister. Putin reiterated the Iranian objections and also related that Hillary Clinton had told him that Allawi would never become prime minister. Allawi's gambit to reach out to Iran through its allies had come up short.

Even in Washington there were also some well-placed skeptics. On the NSC, Dennis Ross, who served as senior aide for the Middle East, had serious reservations. He had not been persuaded when Pollack broached a version of the plan, nor was he convinced now. Instead of finalizing an arrangement that would keep Maliki in power, Ross thought it was wiser to let the electoral process play itself out and see if a compromise candidate emerged.

But the most determined challenge to Hill came from James Steinberg, the deputy secretary of state, who represented his agency in Deputies Committee meetings. Steinberg was not convinced that Maliki was the best the United States could do and also had qualms about the strategy itself. Much of the administration seemed preoccupied with a demonstrably inclusive Iraqi government without pondering its consequences: intense mutual antagonism at its core and unending gridlock. The more traditional approach—a majority government and a loyal opposition—would have a better chance of promoting efficient governance. Instead of trying to make the best of a bad situation, Steinberg thought the Obama administration might be better off encouraging alternatives. What looked like the course of least resistance might actually create serious problems down the road. "I think that some of the people, including Chris, felt that [Maliki] was likely to be the best choice to us. And I was less persuaded," Steinberg recalled. "I wasn't against him, but I was less persuaded that he was somebody who was so obviously preferable from our point of view that we should be part of trying to encourage that outcome."[5]

As was to be expected, there had been substantial pushback from Maliki's camp, which did not take kindly to circumscribing the prime minister's powers, and which was deeply suspicious of the role Allawi would play. The NSC's lead staffer on the Middle East and the second-ranking State Department official were dubious. Obama's decision to give Biden the lead for Iraq, however, was critical. The biggest worry for a White House that was trying to put the Iraq conflict in the rearview mirror was that the political drift in Iraq would leave the country rudderless and raise pointed questions about the feasibility of the American troop withdrawal schedule. As the summer dragged on it was not yet clear if the Iraqis were on board but the White House was committed to the strategy. It would stick with the devil it knew, Maliki, and try to soothe hurt feelings all over Baghdad, hoping to tamp down the risk of sectarian violence by ensuring that Allawi and other rival figures were in decisive roles. "You wouldn't believe the problems I had with the State Department, including Steinberg," Biden told Hill.[6]

The Americans were not the only foreign power that was trying to influence events in Iraq. The Turks were deeply suspicious of Maliki, whom they saw as too susceptible to Iranian influence. Maliki's efforts to concentrate power and the 2010 de-Baathification push added to their concerns, all the more so since American forces were set to draw down and possibly withdraw altogether by the end of 2011. At the center of Turkey's policy in Iraq was its highly charismatic and skillful ambassador Murat Ozcelik, whose name in Turkish meant "genuine steel." Before becoming ambassador in 2009, Ozcelik had served as special envoy to Iraq, leading Turkey's rapprochement with the Kurds. His essential argument was that instead of focusing on the narrow objective of militarily defeating the separatist PKK, it would be more effective if Ankara mended its relations with Irbil and invested heavily in the Kurdish economy.

The gradual turnaround in Turkey's foreign policy had expanded Ankara's influence in Iraq. Consulates had opened in Irbil, Mosul, and Basra. As a further counterweight to the Iranians, Ozcelik had played a role in securing Sunni support for the SOFA agreement the Bush administration negotiated. While Maliki had his supporters in the Obama administration and there was reason to think the Iranians would endorse him for another term, his inner circle wanted to get the Turks on board.

In May, Iraqi government spokesman Ali al-Dabbagh had traveled to Istanbul but made no headway in a private meeting with Turkish prime minister Recep Tayyip Erdogan. When Dabbagh insisted that the Turks could not cherry-pick the Iraqi leadership, Erdogan pointed the finger at Tehran, reminding the Iraqi what had happened in the spring when Iran summoned Iraqi Shiite leaders to a meeting during the Nowruz holiday. "Iran nominated Talabani to remain as president," Erdogan alleged. Dabbagh agreed: "I know, that wasn't right."

Dabbagh's next trip to Turkey was more successful. On July 31, Dabbagh traveled to the resort city of Bodrum in Turkey to meet with Ahmet Davutoglu, the Turkish foreign minister. The engagement resulted in what was dubbed "The Bodrum Paper," which stipulated that Maliki would remain as prime minister for a second term, while the Kurds would retain the presidency. To satisfy Iraqiya, the bloc would be given the speakership of the parliament while Allawi would head the yet-to-be-established council, later renamed the National Council for Higher Policies.

A week after the Bodrum Paper, Maliki took the process a step further by working out a secret understanding with Barzani on how the new government should be configured. A secret document the two leaders signed reaffirmed the essence of the Bodrum deal. "In line with the national interest and for the purpose of expediting the government formation," the handwritten document read, each side committed to retaining Maliki as prime minister and Talabani as president while Allawi would oversee the council on higher policies. The Interior Ministry, Defense Ministry, and intelligence agencies would be run by "independent individuals" who would be approved by Maliki and the Kurds. The Iraqi government would commit itself to solving the Kurds' outstanding issues, and a "supreme committee" headed by Maliki and Barzani would be formed to forge a consensus on strategic issues.

Sensing that Washington and Tehran could each accept Maliki, and with no Shiite alternative in sight, Barzani calculated that by throwing his support to Maliki he could extract concessions from him. The Americans knew nothing about the deal and would only hear about it months later.

Hill's sixteen-month tenure in Iraq ended on a sour note in mid-August. The man Obama had entrusted to bring the Iraq project to a dignified close—who had negotiated with Slobodan Milosevic and contended with North Korea, the protégé of Richard Holbrooke—had broken his ax on

Iraqi politics. Hill had delayed his retirement from the Foreign Service to try to conclude a deal that would be the capstone of a long career. But instead, he would be leaving in his wake strained relations with the military, the media, and the Iraqis themselves.

American officials in Baghdad had heard him apply a slew of unflattering sobriquets to the Iraqi officials who frustrated him so, most of which he would later deny ever saying. Memorable Hill-isms were well known. "I won't have a long Christmas card list for anyone here," he exclaimed during one huddle with Odierno and his aides. "I am so sick of this violence," Hill said another time. "I just want to shoot these people."[7] As he prepared to depart, some Iraqis returned the favor. Mowaffak al-Rubaie publicly complained that the Obama administration had sent a diplomat with no Middle East background to a sensitive post. "The most merciful comment I can make is that Chris Hill's legacy in his time here was uneventful, from the American government's side, while Iraq was full of events," Rubaie said.

Najmaldin Karim, the governor of Kirkuk, made a similar comment to a senior American military officer: "General, we like Chris Hill, but why is it he doesn't want to be here in Iraq?"

Hill chafed under the criticism. The diplomat provocateur who had been so free with invective was especially bitter about an unflattering profile by Anthony Shadid, the late *New York Times* reporter. "So, if you ever hear my name again, please try to forget u ever knew me. I'll do the same for u," Hill emailed Shadid in a fit of pique after the article came out.[8]

On September 1, the United States conducted its formal ceremony to mark the end of its "combat mission." In the months leading up to the event, Odierno had been adamant in his message to Washington: the Obama administration should stop claiming that the date would mark the withdrawal of combat troops, fearing that the loose talk would simply embolden the insurgents and militias that remained in Iraq to go after the remaining force.

Held in the marble rotunda of Al-Faw Palace at Camp Victory, the September 1 ceremony was a made-for-television event. Odierno would hand over command to Lloyd Austin, who would preside over Operation New Dawn, as the post-combat mission would be named. "We stood together in difficult times, we fought together, we laughed together and sometimes cried together," said Odierno, who insisted that the milestone "in no way signals the end of our commitment to the people of Iraq." He ended his remarks with his military sign-off: "Lion 6—Out."[9] Bob Gates took a markedly anti-triumphalist tone. American troops, he said, "have accomplished something really quite extraordinary here. How it all weighs in the balance over time I think remains to be seen."

The military had arranged for an NBC news crew to ride out with the final "combat brigade," and the network had issued a breathless report that the war was over. The show said little about the fraught situation that remained, about either the continued Iranian-backed attacks on American troops or the six advise-and-assist brigades that would carry on in Iraq.

One week after the declaration of the end of combat, the Americans found themselves back in the fray. Several hundred Iraqi soldiers and police were involved in a five-day exercise in Diyala when the Iraqi forces came under attack from insurgents near Al-Hadid. Late on September 11, the Iraqis asked for American help, and the Americans responded. All told, forty-nine American soldiers were on the ground in support, including two Stryker platoons and a ten-person Special Forces detachment. Apache helicopters attacked with 30mm cannon fire and Kiowa helicopters fired their machine guns. F-16s dropped bombs. Iraqi helicopters and armored personnel carriers were also involved in the operation. "This operation demonstrates the importance and dangers of the mission in Iraq during Operation New Dawn," observed Colonel Malcolm Frost, the commander of the 2nd Advise and Assist Brigade, 25th Infantry Division. "This was a grinding, slow, close combat fight."[10]

The political debate stymied, the military situation unsettled, Biden used his official visit to Iraq to conduct another round of consultations with the Iraqis, but the American goal to forge a partnership government seemed as elusive as ever. In his public pronouncements, Biden sought to downplay the continued stalemate. Even as the wrangling continued, he insisted, Iraq had a functioning government. But if Iraqi politicians failed to cobble together a government over the next several months, the Iraqi military might take matters into its own hands. "My worry will be that generals in the military will start saying: 'Wait a minute, which way is this going to go? Which way is this going to go?' I worry then that it goes from right now everybody saying, 'Salute Iraq' to 'Whoa, let's figure this out,' " Biden said. "That's when I would begin to worry because then everybody might start to say: 'What's my calculus here? It looks like they are not going to pull this together.' "[11]

With the Iraq debate as polarized as ever, James Jeffrey had taken over as ambassador. Jeffrey had served as Negroponte's top deputy in Baghdad in 2003 and 2004 and held a number of Iraq-related posts in Washington. A former Army officer with a thick Boston accent, Jeffrey brought Iraq experience to the post and was not entirely enamored of the Maliki-led partnership government the Americans were trying to broker.

During his first week in Baghdad, Jeffrey hosted a dinner for Biden, which he used to tee up the debate so the vice president could hear all sides. Biden's top national security hand, Tony Blinken, was there, as was Jim Mattis, the new CENTCOM commander. Ali Khedery had returned as an aide to Jeffrey, and he used the occasion to present the case against Maliki. A majority of the Iraqi public, Khedery insisted, had voted for nonsectarian parties like Iraqiya and State of Law. But Maliki, Khedery argued, was an autocrat in the making and too sympathetic to Iran. The United States should stand by its secular allies in Iraq who supported democracy. Brett McGurk argued the opposite: Allawi was just not viable. Jeffrey's position was that Iraqiya's support was largely Sunni, and Khedery was mistaken. Biden seemed to agree: he still thought the idea of forming a partnership government around Maliki as prime minister was valid.

One Iraqi politician who had a different idea of how to proceed was ISCI's Abd al-Mahdi. With Allawi unable to muster enough support to challenge the prime minister, Abd al-Mahdi thought he spied an opening. Ammar al-Hakim, the leader of ISCI, had sent his brother Mohsen to meet with Muqtada al-Sadr in the Iranian city of Qom and try to cut a deal. With the support of the Sadrists, Abd al-Mahdi would have at least a third of the Shiite coalition—even more if Abd al-Mahdi could lock down the support of the Badr Organization. That, ISCI figured, would meet Barzani's requirement that he would not back any alternative to Maliki who did not have sufficient Shiite support. But Abd al-Mahdi did not know about the secret understanding between Maliki and Barzani.

Iran was hardly enthusiastic about Abd al-Mahdi's plan. The Iranian strategy had been to unite the Shiite bloc behind Maliki and squeeze out Iraqiya and secular parties. During a trip to Tehran, Ammar al-Hakim had had a difficult meeting with Iran's supreme leader, Khamenei. The meeting, American officials were later told, had not gone well and had deteriorated to the point that Qasim Suleimani reprimanded Hakim afterward for standing up to Khamenei.

The United States and Iran, it seemed, were both prepared to back Maliki but in different political configurations. For Washington, Maliki would be the head of a cross-sectarian government, balanced by Allawi as head of the new Council on Strategic Policies. For Tehran, he would be the head of a Shiite-dominated regime in which secular politicians friendly to the United States would be marginalized. Ammar al-Hakim summed up the situation with a quip to Tony Blinken: the Axis of Evil and the Great Satan appeared to be backing the same candidate.

During a late meeting convened in Baghdad on October 1, Maliki was selected over Adil Abd al-Mahdi to represent the National Alliance as the candidate for prime minister. This ended weeks of discussion about the mechanisms for deciding between Abd al-Mahdi and Maliki. A press conference was held afterward, where Falah al-Fayyad announced the formation of a negotiating delegation to lobby the other political blocs to support Maliki's candidacy. Two minority Shiite parties, ISCI and Fadhila, challenged the manner in which Maliki was selected, which was basically by acclamation after the Sadrists switched their support from Abd al-Mahdi to Maliki. The voting procedure was not mutually agreed upon within the National Alliance. Despite the protests, the fight was effectively over: Maliki would be the candidate. A senior Kurdish lawmaker, Mahmoud Othman, told the *New York Times* at that time, "Now, he has a great possibility to become prime minister again."[14]

Sadr released a statement to his followers beforehand, explaining his decision to support Maliki, which essentially argued that politics comes down to "give and take."[15] Nobody knew exactly what concessions Maliki gave to Sadr. But aides close to Maliki confirm that concessions were indeed part of the deal.[16] Iran played a crucial role in getting the Sadrists and Bashar al-Assad on board, allegedly arranging meetings in Iraq, Iran, Syria, and even at U.N. headquarters in New York.[17]

With the majority of the Iranian-brokered National Alliance's 159 seats now in his camp, Maliki needed only a handful more to secure the prime ministership. The Kurdistan Alliance, which held 57 seats in parliament, sensed the importance of the moment. That night, Kurdish officials signaled that they would support either Iraqiya or the National Alliance's candidate for prime minister. A delegation led by Rowsch Shaways headed to Baghdad to negotiate with both blocs. The determining factor would be which side was prepared to accede to more of the Kurds' demands, which were outlined in a nineteen-point list of demands dubbed the "Kurdish paper."[18]

On October 6, Biden chaired a videoconference to discuss how the administration should proceed. Allawi had concluded that Maliki was not serious about sharing power and negotiations between the two leaders were in trouble. The partnership government was proving elusive, and the question arose whether Abd al-Mahdi might be a plausible alternative. Hill and his team had argued that there was little support for Abd al-Mahdi and thus no sense in backing him. But Khedery had argued that Iraqi politics was like a train. If it started to leave the station and pick up steam the disparate Shiite factions would jump on board. They would not want to be left behind.

Biden kicked off the session. The Kurds, he argued, were the kingmakers and Barzani was insisting that everybody participate in the government—Iraqiya, the Sadrists, all the main factions. The government could not stand as a simple majority with the rest of the Iraqi political class in opposition. Barzani had his grievances with Washington, but the Obama team had taken a number of steps to secure Barzani's support. In addition to the checkpoints Odierno had established the Americans had secretly stationed about twenty-four M1 tanks and Bradleys at a Special Forces training base near the Irbil airport. The deployment of the equipment—without troops—was heavily classified, but it was symbolic; it sent a message that there was American military capability at hand if things went bad.

In Baghdad, Jeffrey outlined the situation as he saw it. There were four possible outcomes. The first was a governing coalition that included Maliki's State of Law Coalition, Allawi's Iraqiya, and the Kurds—essentially the solution that Hill and Biden had been promoting. The problem was that Allawi was not willing to go along with the plan without real concessions on power-sharing. Would Iraqiya and the Sunnis accept Maliki? And who would be president in the new configuration?

A second scenario had Abd al-Mahdi as prime minister. Burns interjected that Allawi had told him that this option would provide too small a base of support for the new government, an indication that Allawi was still reluctant to step aside for Abd al-Mahdi. "We're trying to keep Adil's prospects alive, urging Barzani not to decide yet," Jeffrey responded. "I've talked to him many times, seen him, and talked over the phone," Jeffrey said, referring to Barzani. "He won't endorse Adil Abd al-Mahdi as PM yet because he needs full Shi'a buy-in." Abd al-Mahdi would talk with the Kurds and the Americans might use the presidency as a lure to get support for the plan.

The third imagined outcome was an Iraqi government comprising Maliki's coalition, the Sadrists, and the Kurds. The Americans did not like this since it would leave the Sunnis out of the equation and would give the Sadrists too much influence. The fourth option was a continuation of the drift, with Maliki as head of a caretaker government.

Officially, the Obama administration took the position that the formation of a new Iraqi government was entirely up to the Iraqis themselves. Behind closed doors, it was deeply involved in trying to engineer a solution. Biden was still committed to making a partnership plan that kept Maliki as prime minister work. The vice president argued this might involve moving Jalal Talabani out of the presidency and giving that job to Allawi. With Maliki as prime minister and Allawi as the president, two strong-willed men who disliked each other would be at the top of the pyramid, but Biden preferred to double down on the plan he had endorsed in July than to try to maneuver Abd al-Mahdi into the prime minister post.

That entailed helping Talabani save face by finding him another position. Going back to Kurdistan was not an option for Talabani, Biden continued, since it would inflame his rivalry with Barzani. "Massoud Barzani told me, 'I don't want him to be back in Kurdistan,' " Biden said. Biden had a suggestion for what to do with Talabani: "Let's make him foreign minister."

"Thanks a lot, Joe," quipped Hillary Clinton, observing that Biden had, in effect, cast the Foreign Ministry slot as a consolation prize for someone who could not be president.

Jeffrey said that Talabani was aware that the presidency was in play.

At that point, Lloyd Austin joined the discussion. After noting that the level of violence was down, Austin gave his views on Iraqi politics from a security perspective. The partnership government the Obama team was pursuing was Austin's favorite approach. There would only be a few changes among the leadership of the Iraqi security forces with whom the Americans were working. But the Shiite Islamists and Sunni Arab neighbors would not be happy. Building a government around Abd al-Mahdi, Austin cautioned, could be problematic. If ISCI, Iraqiya, and the Kurds formed the core of the government, Maliki and the Sadrists would object and that would create nothing but trouble. Maliki would not surrender power easily. Austin made clear that he was more comfortable with the status quo.

Jim Mattis, the CENTCOM commander, was not. The Egyptians, the Saudis, the Jordanians, and the Qataris had all told him that they did not want Maliki to stay on. If Maliki triumphed, it would send shock waves across the region, and any extension of Iranian influence on his government would work against the United States in the long term. He was reminding the group that government formation in Iraq would affect relations across the Middle East. Austin said he, for one, viewed the Sadrists as the actual kingmakers. James Clapper, the director of national intelligence, agreed with Mattis that the regional impact would be significant.

Biden claimed that the Iranians had spent $100 million backing candidates and did not want to lose that investment. He said that after his various visits to Iraq he had concluded that the Iranians wanted Maliki because they wanted a stake in the inevitable. "In my opinion, that's the best option," Biden added.

Biden asked Austin if he thought Maliki was beholden to Iran. Austin recalled that Maliki had struck at the Iranian-supported groups in Basra and predicted that he would resist Iranian control. Others were not so sure. During the discussion Clinton noted that Steinberg was also worried about Iran's influence on Maliki. "I haven't seen what Maliki's commitments to Iran are," observed Leon Panetta, the CIA director.

Jeffrey noted that the perpetuation of Maliki's rule would create a "real regional problem." But Jeffrey was a pragmatist and was prepared to work with what he had. The United States needed a renewed SOFA that would allow it to keep some limited forces in Iraq for training. It needed international oil companies to come in and increase Iraq's revenues, and it needed to preserve the democratic system. Iran could not block Maliki from implementing these policies, "but he's under significant pressure from Iran," Jeffrey said.

Along these lines, Jeffrey Feltman, the senior State Department official for the Middle East, observed that Maliki was a stubborn thinker and that Sunni Arab states thought he was under Iranian influence. "We will have regional problems if he returns, and there's a perception problem—that Iran has won, in that case," Feltman said. "We'll have to guard against that perception."

"Will full-blown Sunni participation ameliorate that?" Biden asked.

Clinton jumped in: "Our strategy has yet to bear fruit." If Maliki and the Sadrists did not offer true power-sharing, it would push the Sunnis toward taking up arms over time—a bad outcome for Iraq and the United States. "We need to go forward on getting Maliki to be more flexible, and Allawi into the government," Clinton said. That meant "moving Talabani aside and urging the Kurds to be more flexible."

As the discussion continued, Steinberg, who was participating by phone, repeated some of his earlier concerns about a partnership government. Pursuing partnership at all costs could exact a price. "Even if we broker a deal that's inclusive of all sides, will a Maliki-Allawi government hold over the long term?" Steinberg said. "Will it actually function, or will it just continue to build tensions in the government? Will Maliki continue to build bad structures in the government? We need to build sustainable structures of governance." Steering the prime minister post to Abd al-Mahdi, Steinberg thought, made more sense. "The Adil track creates more chance of real partnership. We need the Shi'a, but we also need a government, a type of government that we can live with. Deeply divided government concerns me, even if Maliki fulfills his commitments."

Countering Steinberg, Biden restated his case for building an inclusive government around Maliki. The United States would not accept a coalition that included just the Shiites and Kurds. "I have told this to Maliki. We'll just leave Iraq if he does that," Biden said. "Barzani has given me his word: he will not join a government unless it's inclusive." The vice president was not minimizing the challenges—"Maliki hates the goddamn Sunnis," he said—but he still thought the United States could get Maliki to share control and get Allawi to sign on. "I was blunt with Maliki: without devolution of powers to the Kurds and Iraqiya the U.S. will not sign on. The Kurds will not accept extrajudicial PM powers."

In a bold prediction, Biden confidently forecast that a Maliki government would conclude a new status of forces agreement that would allow a continued presence of a small number of American troops. "Maliki wants us to stick around because he does not see a future in Iraq otherwise," Biden said. "I'll bet you my vice presidency Maliki will extend the SOFA."

As the meeting drew to a close, Biden threw out a series of questions. "What are the next steps?" he asked. "Is Iraqiya splintering? If Allawi goes with Adil, what will happen? Will Allawi go with Adil or Maliki?"

"None of these guys are models of solidarity, but Iraqiya is holding," Jeffrey said. If the deal making with Maliki did not bear fruit, the ambassador cautioned, Iraqiya might splinter.

"I agree with the ambassador," Austin said. "Allawi and Adil might not work out well either as prime minister." Austin was reinforcing the point that he was more comfortable with Maliki.

"We need an action plan to stay on course," Biden said. "We need to be prepared in the next few days. Who gets what jobs?"

"Maliki has shown his capacity to be independent in the past, but Iran is clearly intervening with the Sadrists," said Steinberg, again injecting a skeptical note. "There's a new dynamic that we should be careful about. We need to be very careful about the Sadrists and we need commitments from Maliki that he will contain them."

"Our goal hasn't been an efficient government, it's been an inclusive government," Jeffrey said to Steinberg. "We need carrots and sticks to deal with all of them. Allawi has committed to continue talking to all sides. We have time to work through this, as long as the security situation permits. And I'll work on the Talabani issue."[19]

While the Obama administration appeared to be tilting strongly toward Maliki as a logical choice for prime minister, it was clear that at least some members of the administration had concerns. In Baghdad, Jeffrey decided to make one last try to see if Adil Abd al-Mahdi might yet emerge as an alternative.

Ammar al-Hakim, who had taken over as the leader of the ISCI political faction after the death of his father, had sent his brother to Iran to meet with Muqtada al-Sadr, and had, Hakim claimed, secured his support for Abd al-Mahdi. The Kurds had made it clear that they would not back a substitute for Maliki unless he had substantial Shiite support, but now Hakim was trying to accomplish this. Jeffrey sent a highly classified memo to Washington that made the case for Abd al-Mahdi. The memo, which was shared with Obama and Biden, argued that Abd al-Mahdi might be a candidate around whom secular forces could rally. Maliki, on the other hand, had undertaken a number of authoritarian steps, which were worrisome. Allawi, however, would not shelve his ambitions to be prime minister and ISCI and the Kurds were not prepared to try to appease Allawi by offering him the presidency.[20]

As the maneuvers played out, Obama chaired an NSC meeting to decide the next steps. Gates argued that enough time had elapsed and that the United States needed to make a decision. Obama made the call: Washington should accept the inevitability of Maliki as prime minister, try to secure the presidency for Allawi, and placate the Kurds by arranging for them to have the speakership of the parliament. It was a variation of the strategy Biden had hatched with Hill earlier in the year. A major obstacle, however, stood in the way: Jalal Talabani.

Born in 1933, Talabani had been a fixture in Iraqi politics for more than half a century. Known as "Mam Jalal"—Kurdish for "Uncle Jalal," a term of affection and a recognition of his status as a political godfather—Talabani was a complex figure. He had successfully navigated the dizzyingly complex series of alliances, betrayals, and machinations that constituted Kurdish politics—as a Maoist, he had made deals with Saddam only to emerge as a prominent member of the Kurdish opposition, where he clashed with

Massoud Barzani. After the invasion, Talabani had served on the Governing Council and emerged as Iraq's president in 2005, a position which made him the highest-ranking Kurd in the Iraqi government. Talabani was thus ingratiated with the Americans—his son Qubad ran the Washington office of the Kurdistan Regional Government, and his Western predilections for fine food and Churchill cigars meant he often had to travel to the Mayo Clinic for medical treatment—but he also had a long history of interactions with Iranian leaders who had backed him against Saddam. Mowaffak al-Rubaie once described him as "the ultimate pragmatist."[21]

Among Jeffrey's aides, there were divisions over the wisdom of the strategy to replace Talabani. Ali Khedery argued that the idea was foolhardy and even naive: after clawing his way to power there was no way that Talabani would vacate the office, Khedery argued. Brett McGurk was also skeptical, but noted that Talabani had worked with the Americans on the SOFA and was committed to giving it a try. There was no real debate to be had, however, since the matter had already been decided at the White House.

After a lunch at the residence of Kosrat Rasful, the vice president for the Kurdish region, Tony Blinken, Jeffrey, and Austin went to see Talabani privately. They appealed for Talabani to give up the presidency, and he declined. Hoping the Americans would not escalate the issue, Qubad Talabani advised the White House not to pursue the demand. But the Obama administration had no other plan.

On November 4, the White House arranged for a call to Talabani from Barack Obama himself. Obama had met Talabani during his visits to Iraq and had called him before. But more than a year later, the relationship between the American and Iraqi presidents was not as close as during the Bush years. Even after 2008, when Talabani went to the Mayo Clinic, he customarily called his old friend George W. Bush.

Obama was seated at his desk in the Oval Office when he asked the president of Iraq if he would step down for the sake of the White House's Iraq strategy. Biden, Blinken, and Puneet Talwar, the NSC specialist for Iraq, were on hand. An official White House photographer, documenting a potentially important occasion, captured the event for posterity. But Talabani turned down the American president. "They were afraid what would happen if the different groups of Iraq would not reach an agreement," Talabani later said. "The Kurdish leadership decided that it would be kind of humiliating, so they refused categorically."

The president was not prepared to take no for an answer. If Talabani would not yield, the Americans would go over his head. For assistance, the administration enlisted some of the sharpest critics of its Iraq policy: Lindsey Graham, John McCain, and Joe Lieberman, who were going to Iraq as a visiting congressional delegation. The lawmakers had traveled together so often and were so like-minded on the importance of Iraq that they were known as "the Three Amigos." The three were barely on the ground when Jeffrey and Austin approached them and said that intelligence confirmed that Talabani was too close to the Iranians. The United States had electronically intercepted discussions between Talabani and Iranian officials, the lawmakers were told, all of which meant that Talabani needed to be eased out of his job.

Jeffrey had encouraged Obama to make the fateful call to Talabani and was not ready to give up. He saw his job as helping to form an Iraqi government, and if Abd al-Mahdi was not a possibility, he would make a full court press for a Maliki-Allawi partnership. In an October meeting with Barzani, Jeffrey had argued that polling data collected by the State Department had indicated that Iraqiya had substantial public support, including in the Shiite south. Barzani had not been won over then, but Jeffrey would make another try.

Five days after Obama's call to the sitting president of Iraq, Jeffrey joined the lawmakers when they flew north to meet Barzani at his mountaintop home outside Irbil. Barzani received the senators, Jeffrey, and Alex Laskaris, the former provincial reconstruction team leader in Mosul who had since been appointed to stand up the new American consulate in Irbil, over a long lunch as they discussed the political conundrum in Baghdad.

Lieberman praised Barzani's leadership and stressed that he shared the same goal as the Kurdish leader: an inclusive government. Based on what the senators had been told by Jeffrey, Iraqiya needed the presidency, which meant that Barzani had to do something difficult with his old rival Talabani. "We know how hard it is," Lieberman said. "We won't forget it. We will do all we can to support you, Kurdistan, and Iraq." The broader the Iraqi government, the easier it would be for the senators to convince their colleagues at home to provide economic and security support to Kurdistan.

There was a long pause as Barzani digested the senators' analysis of Iraqi politics, which the Kurdish leader said was not correct. The Kurds, Barzani asserted, had supported Allawi, but the Obama administration had backed Maliki as prime minister. The issue was not Talabani. It was not about him. The speaker of the Council of Representatives, Iraq's parliament, had more power than the president. The problem was that the Shiites had strengthened their position. Was Barzani supposed to solve a problem between the Shiites and Sunnis at the expense of the Kurdish people? If the problem was really about Talabani, the Kurds could nominate another Kurd for the presidency. If the Sunnis had come to the Kurds privately and offered the Council of Representatives speakership in return, it might also be different. But the Sunnis had gone about their business in an unwise way, Barzani added, alluding to Tariq al-Hashimi's public proposal that a Sunni be given the presidency. "We will not make this concession because it will be considered an insult to us," Barzani said. "The problem is between the Sunnis and the Shia."

Lieberman thanked Barzani for his honesty. "But if you can find another way to make Iraqiya feel as though it's sharing power," the senator said, "then God bless you."

McCain then asked Barzani: "What is your solution?"

"Allawi is a close friend," Barzani said. "I would have wished to see him as prime minister or president. He did not get the opportunity to form the government. He deserved it," Barzani added, referring to the legal opinion that had allowed Maliki to assemble the "largest bloc" even though he won fewer seats, an opinion the American embassy had not challenged. "Until this moment, Allawi had not told me that he wants to be president. Allawi is a Shia and I think the Sunnis will not accept him as president." Barzani was making an obvious point. Allawi's Iraqiya coalition included many Sunnis, yet, as the American partnership government had it, the top officials of the proposed government would be Shiite.

Barzani suggested that there could be a power-sharing arrangement that involved the new council the Americans wanted to create.

"Will Maliki accept this?" Lieberman asked.

"Well, if he doesn't we won't form a government with him," Barzani responded.

Jeffrey finally intervened to put forth the position of the White House. For President Obama, this was not a Shiite problem or a Sunni problem. It was an Iraq problem. "He is offering one solution, which you have told me is very hard. If there is another solution you need to make it work."

"If there is a government without Kurdish representation, if you sit out that's also not going to be acceptable," Lieberman said. "I've spent my whole life fighting for this cause," Barzani replied. "Since I was sixteen years old I've fought for my people. It's very difficult for me to accept this. People will say, 'The Shia got what they wanted, the Sunnis got what they wanted, and you betrayed us.' Allawi, Maliki, they are all Arabs. We are Kurds. The main question is whether we are part of the future of this country."

Graham was getting frustrated. "I am not going to ask my country to spend another dime on a country that can't come together. If it is truly better for the Kurdish people to have the speakership, don't let someone else's mistake deny them that," he said.

McCain chimed in: "I've studied Kurdish history. You've been murdered, massacred. I fully understand your concerns about the future. We just ask you to do what is best in these meetings."

Lunch with Barzani had solved nothing. When it was almost over, Jeffrey showed Graham a letter from Obama addressed to the Kurdish leader. Graham glanced at the missive. It was a list of ways in which the United States might help the Kurds—aid programs and the like—stating that the Obama administration favored a new nominee for the presidency and requesting Barzani's backing. Jeffrey had just received the letter from Washington, and he wanted the senators to hand it to the Kurdish leader as a demonstration of bipartisan support for the American position. Both the Democratic president who had pledged to get American troops out of Iraq and the Republican lawmakers who wholeheartedly supported the war would back the request.

Graham, who had made numerous trips to Iraq and had even done Reserve duty there during his breaks from the Senate as an Air Force lawyer, was dubious. "You know what he is going to say, don't you?" Graham told Jeffrey. "You don't give a politician a letter from the president of the United States making a request in writing unless you know what he is going to say," Graham added. "You don't ask Barzani to do something that he can't deliver." Jeffrey indicated that for all his stated objections Barzani's final response could not be assumed. The Obama administration wanted to ratchet up the pressure. "This is what we want to do," he said.

Graham handed Barzani the letter after lunch. The Kurdish leader glanced at it and put it in his pocket.[22] He seemed to have been anticipating such a gambit and made clear that it overstepped a line. The Kurds had been taking their complaints to Washington for years. They had bemoaned Maliki's abuses to Condoleezza Rice during the Bush years and had been told repeatedly that there was no Plan B. The Kurds had never stood up to the Americans before or flatly rejected an American demand. Whether the issue was the election law or the constitutional debate, they had tended to go along with the American position. But now the Kurdish leaders felt taken for granted. They would just say no.

Now that Obama's initiative on Talabani had run its course another way would need to be found to stand up a new government. Time was running out. There was a constitutional requirement for forming a new government and the Iraqis were at the limit. Barzani said he would meet with Iraqi leaders in Baghdad and try to broker a deal. The Kurdish leader hitched a ride with Jeffrey on a State Department aircraft along with forty Peshmerga fighters. Jeffrey, a former Army officer who served in Vietnam, supervised the removal of the ammunition magazines from the Peshmerga's Kalashnikovs as they climbed into the airplane.

After arriving in Baghdad on November 10, Barzani hosted a meeting of political leaders in his Green Zone offices for a final push to form the government.

The contours of a deal soon emerged: Maliki would be prime minister. Talabani would remain president. Allawi would head the new National Council for Higher Policies—the "extra chair" that Hill had proposed. Salih al-Mutlaq and two others would be taken off the de-Baathification list. It was still necessary to find an acceptable Iraqiya candidate to serve as speaker of the Council of Representatives. Fuad Hussein, the well-connected chief of staff to the Kurdish president, had heard from "reliable sources" that Osama al-Nujaifi was hoping he would get the speakership. After learning this, Hussein approached his boss and the two decided it would be a good idea to support Nujaifi as a "goodwill gesture," in hopes that it would improve relations between them and the powerful Sunni leader. Hussein cornered Nujaifi outside of an Iraqiya meeting later that night.

"I would like to tell you that we, the Kurds, will support you for speaker of parliament," Hussein said. The emerging Sunni leader from Mosul was surprised that Barzani would back him, given the animosity between the Kurds and his family. Just a year before, his brother Atheel al-Nujaifi, the governor of Nineveh, had almost come to armed confrontations with Kurdish Peshmerga troops on several occasions. Now, to expedite the formation of a Maliki government, the Kurds were trusting him with one of the most powerful positions in Baghdad. "When I finish the meeting, I will come personally to thank President Barzani," Nujaifi said to Hussein.

The next day, Allawi was worried that the power-sharing arrangement would not stick. In his first phone call to Allawi, Obama tried to move the process along. Allawi wanted further assurances and suggested that Jeffrey join a meeting with him, Maliki, and Barzani later that day. As the leaders were trying to finalize the arrangement an argument erupted. Allawi got up to walk out. Barzani, who had been a wrestler in his youth and enjoyed hikes in the mountains, jumped up and held Allawi in place. "Maliki wanted to leave; he was not happy," Barzani recalled, laughing. "I did not allow him to stand up. The argument became hotter, and Allawi stood up. He wanted to leave, and I told him 'No, sit down.' The important thing was that I did not allow him to leave the room." After the agreement was struck, the three leaders clasped hands.

Even that did not put an end to the dispute. Later that day when parliament convened the dispute started up again. Allawi was seated next to Maliki to show unity when he learned that Talabani's reappointment to the presidency would be announced before he got his end of the deal. Convinced that he had been double-crossed, he staged an Iraqiya walkout. The Americans argued that Allawi had mistaken a rule of procedure for a betrayal. The Turks got into the act as well. After the walkout, Dabbagh walked outside the parliament building and called his friend Davutoglu, the Turkish foreign minister, who called the new speaker, Osama al-Nujaifi, and urged him to go back to parliament and carry out his duties so the government could formally be sworn in, and Nujaifi returned to parliament. The session commenced without most of Iraqiya, but the issue of top-level appointments was finally settled.

The White House later stressed that when the final deal was cut the American ambassador was in the room. But Obama had been rebuffed in his effort to install Allawi as the Iraqi president and critical decisions to unite the Shiite bloc in support of Maliki had been taken in Tehran. More importantly, little of the agreement stuck. Rafi al-Issawi and Salih al-Mutlaq were given high-ranking posts and Nujaifi did become speaker of the parliament. But the National Council for Higher Policies was never formed. Allawi never joined the government. Nearly all the promises Maliki made to the Kurds were never fulfilled.

The partnership government the White House had lobbied for existed only on paper. Maliki had kept his prime minister post by playing for time. He continued to exercise his prerogatives as prime minister as if the election had never occurred.

CHAPTER 35

The Numbers Game

In early January 2011, Denis McDonough sat down with Tom Donilon to discuss the way ahead in Iraq. A lawyer by training, Donilon had been at the intersection of politics and policy for much of his career, with a heavy emphasis on the former. Donilon had parlayed a White House internship into a post with the Carter administration, where he worked for Hamilton Jordan, Carter's chief of staff, and was said to have drafted an important memorandum on the cabinet's failure to get behind the president's reelection. After getting his law degree, Donilon had worked on the Walter Mondale presidential campaign and then the abortive Biden run for president, during which he helped Biden with "debate prep," the laborious task of anticipating and preparing responses on key issues—or at least the ones that the media and opponents might raise. The collapse of the Biden campaign redirected but did not derail Donilon's ambitions. During the Carter administration, Donilon had come to know Warren Christopher, the deputy secretary of state, who recruited him to work at his well-heeled law firm, O'Melveny & Myers.

When Christopher became secretary of state under Bill Clinton, Donilon followed his mentor to Foggy Bottom. As Christopher's chief of staff and media adviser, Donilon was a behind-the-scenes operative who was attuned to the Congress and politics at home. As the Balkan fires raged, Christopher's State Department was among the most cautious about using military force to quell the fighting in Bosnia.

In the years after the Clinton administration, Donilon had gone on to work as an executive vice president and lobbyist for Fannie Mae, the federally chartered mortgage company whose bankruptcy had thrust it into the media glare. Donilon's had been a lucrative and unexpectedly controversial tenure, which the Republicans in Congress were certain to exploit should Donilon be nominated for a senior post—the talk was that he was to follow Christopher's path and be appointed deputy secretary of state, which required Senate confirmation.[1] The Obama team was determined to have Donilon on board and appointed him deputy national security adviser, a post that did not require the Senate's approval.

Donilon had endured a rocky relationship with Jim Jones, Obama's first national security adviser, who chastised him for his lack of on-the-ground experience in the world's crisis zones. But he was organized, worked endless hours, and was wired within the Democratic Party establishment: his brother worked as a counselor to Biden while his wife served as the chief of staff for Jill Biden.

Most importantly, he shared the president's vision and the imperative to shape policy with an eye to domestic priorities and political campaigns. Nobody worked harder to gain the president's confidence. After Donilon was named to replace Jones, he pressed the NSC staff to pore through the highly classified President's Daily Briefings and email him relevant background material so that the national security adviser could shine if the president had any questions at his morning brief. As Donilon moved up, McDonough, the former congressional staffer who had focused on "strategic communications" for the NSC, filled Donilon's old spot as deputy national security adviser.

Obama, Biden, and Clinton were all former senators who had wrestled with policy in the Congress and were attuned to the public mood. Their aides, by and large, were former congressional staffers or politicos. The team's sensitivity to the public mood was arguably an asset in building support for a foreign policy doctrine. But it also raised the question of whether politics played too large a role in formulating policy—whether the tail was wagging the dog. With the centralization of national security policy in the White House, it was sometimes said that the Obama NSC had the most powerful staff since Henry Kissinger, but was missing its Kissinger.

By 2011, the White House was practiced in reviewing military strategy in Iraq and Afghanistan. But the question of what troops to keep in Iraq after 2011 was one of the most highly charged yet. With a reelection campaign virtually around the corner, the White House did not need reminding that Obama had campaigned on Iraq being the wrong war and Afghanistan being a war of necessity. Up to this point in his presidency, Obama had essentially implemented the Bush status of forces agreement, which called for removing American troops by the end of December 2011. Some

Bush administration officials had held out hope that some sort of extension would be worked out to permit American troops to keep training
Iraqi troops and to help them carry out commando raids against the remnants of Al-Qaeda after that day, among other missions. Even during the
heat of his 2008 campaign, Obama had left the door open for a residual
troop presence for training and counterterrorism missions as well, as Colin
Kahl had repeatedly reminded the campaign staff. Still, keeping troops in
Iraq beyond 2011 would require a proactive approach with the Iraqis and
might be perceived by the Democratic base at home as a departure from
Obama's campaign promises.

A formal meeting of the Deputies Committee, which McDonough
chaired, would be held on January 26, 2011. There would be more deputies sessions to frame the issue, principals meetings led by Donilon, and
smaller offline sessions to weigh the pros and cons of a continued troop
presence in Iraq, and, finally, a meeting of the National Security Council
chaired by Obama himself.

The starting point was clear. As early as February 2009, Bob Gates had
signaled that the Obama administration might be willing to keep a modest
force in Iraq after the SOFA Bush negotiated ran out at the end of 2011.
But the details were all-important. How many American forces would the
administration actually be willing to leave in Iraq? What would be their
missions? And what conditions would the Iraqis need to meet? The issue
was too hot to handle, even internally, during the last half of 2010 when
the Democrats were headed into the midterm elections. But with less than a
year to go the questions had to be faced. The Iraqis were masters of resolving disputes at the eleventh hour. Indeed, there were times when the Iraqis
made decisions a minute after midnight and then sought to back them in.
But the formidable logistics of moving troops and equipment out of Iraq
militated against that sort of last-minute dickering now. Factoring in the
time needed to move personnel and equipment, the administration had
perhaps half a year to settle the issue, nine months at most.

In Baghdad, Lloyd Austin was tasked with providing the military's input.
A giant of a man, Austin had graduated from West Point and been commissioned as an infantry officer. He had served as the deputy commander
for maneuver when the 3rd Infantry Division marched to Baghdad in
2003 and, in keeping with the more liberal standards that governed the
awards for commanders during the opening wave of the Iraq invasion,

was awarded the Silver Star for commanding from the front. Austin had gone on to lead the 10th Mountain Division in Afghanistan only to return to Baghdad to command Multi-National Corps—Iraq, where he played an important role under Petraeus's direction in helping Maliki secure his victory in Basra.

Cautious and methodical—during his days as corps commander he was known to arrive at meetings with fellow three-stars with talking points prepared by his staff—Austin and his aides had pondered what sort of American force would be needed to keep Iraq stable and headed in the right direction after the Bush-era security agreement expired. Even with the gains on security, there was a lot to do. The United States would need to train and assist the ISOF, Iraq's special operations forces, so they could continue to go after Al-Qaeda and other militant groups. No president wanted to allow Al-Qaeda and the like to operate from Iraq's ungoverned spaces and there was no higher priority than that. The ISOF were rated as the Iraqis' best troops but remained critically dependent on the Americans for intelligence and even to get around the country. There were few Iraqi helicopters and Iraqi pilots to operate them, especially at night.[2]

As for Iraq's conventional forces, its army had grown to more than a dozen divisions and the United States needed to train enough of them to provide for the nation's external defense, which was the right of every sovereign country and all the more important if the Iraqis were to eventually stand up to Iranian pressure. The Iraqis would be fielding new M1 tanks, as well as American artillery and vehicles and probably F-16s. But it was not just a matter of helping the Iraqis learn how to operate and logistically support the weapons; they needed to be able to use them in combined operations on the battlefield. The Americans could help by training Iraqi forces at ranges at Besmaya and Taji and also by sending teams to partner with them in the field where the mentor could see how the mentee performed in actual operations.

Yet another mission stemmed from the Kurdish-Arab issues that had been deferred by the Iraqis and American diplomats so long that Odierno had been forced to come up with a stopgap: twenty-two jointly manned Arab, Kurdish, and American checkpoints to dissuade the Iraqi military and the Kurdish Peshmerga from coming to blows. Kirkuk, a city riven with ethnic tensions, was ringed by six of the checkpoints. Inside the ring of checkpoints, the city itself had a special status as a "combined security area." Outside the checkpoints, responsibility for the rest of the province was split between the Iraqi Army's 12th Division, which operated in the

Arab-heavy south and west, and a Peshmerga brigade, which operated in largely Kurdish areas. Disputes over the arrangement were to be brought to a working group comprising Lieutenant General Frank Helmick, the deputy commander for operations of the American force in Iraq; Major General David Perkins, the division commander in charge of American troops in the north; General Ali Ghaidan Majid of the Iraqi Ground Forces Command; the commander of the Federal Police; and the Kurdish general who served as chief of staff of the Peshmerga forces. The presence of an American brigade headquarters in Kirkuk ensured that there was always a senior American commander with a large staff and infantry troops at his disposal ready to respond to any crisis.

On February 25, such a crisis had emerged when protests related to the Arab Spring in the nearby town of Hawija had led to fears in Kirkuk that an Arab mob, backed by the Iraqi Army, was moving on the city to incite ethnic violence. In response the Kurds had moved their Peshmerga brigade out of its usual positions outside the city and brought in a second brigade from Irbil, violating the agreed-upon divvying up of responsibility for the province. Only when Perkins and the rest of the working group intervened was the crisis defused. The new agreement relied on an American Stryker battalion to protect the areas the Kurds had occupied. It was only a matter of time until another such crisis emerged, whether in Kirkuk or Mosul or elsewhere along the line of checkpoints separating the Kurdish Peshmerg from the Iraqi Army.

Finally, to protect Iraqi airspace until they acquired their own air force, F-16s would have to be based in the country. Some civilians urged the military to look at the option of protecting Iraqi skies from neighboring countries, but in the end that option was fraught with difficulties. It took time to scramble the jets from adjacent countries, which would not provide a sufficiently rapid response in the event the United States needed to intercept a fast-moving jet or provide support to its own troops in the country. A more feasible option was to keep an F-16 squadron at Al-Asad, including the usual complement of support troops, headquarters personnel, and quick reaction units in case Americans were at risk.

Force protection also weighed on Austin's mind. The year had begun unnervingly with a January IRAM attack at FOB Kalsu, a major coalition base south of Baghdad. The improvised rocket-assisted mortar was essentially a flying IED. A bomb was strapped to a 107mm rocket, and an array of the projectiles packed into a small truck, which was positioned close to a base. Even by the standards of Iraq, it was a nasty weapon, one that had the potential to cause scores of casualties. What also made American officials take notice was that the IRAM was of Iranian provenance and was used exclusively by Shiite Special Groups, especially Kataib Hezbollah. If ever there was a sign that Iran's Quds Force planned to keep up the pressure on the Americans this appeared to be it. Whatever missions the troops were assigned they needed to have enough forces to protect their bases and maintain quick reaction teams to protect their personnel.

When the numbers were crunched, the force Austin envisaged topped out at 20,000 to 24,000 troops, which he still believed entailed moderate risk. In addition to the military challenges, Lieutenant General Mike Barbero, Petraeus's former operations officer who had been sent back to Iraq to head the Iraqi troop training effort, had done an assessment that identified gaps in counterterrorism, air defense, intelligence fusion, and the ability to use combined arms.

The Iraqi military knew it had deficiencies, too. During a 2008 trip to the United States, Abd al-Qadir al-Obeidi, Iraq's defense minister, had ventured that his country's military would need American help in protecting its borders until at least 2018. If the decision on American troops had been left up to the American and Iraqi militaries, some sort of continued United States military presence would have been agreed upon without much controversy or fanfare. But the decision was one the politicians in each country had to take on.

The civilians at the Pentagon, who had the job of selling the plan to the White House, made it clear that Austin was thinking too big, and he and the Joint Staff at the Pentagon began to develop a range of options. As the deliberations proceeded, Austin came back with 19,000 as a favored option and two different 16,000-troop options. One of them would start at 16,000 troops and then possibly taper to 157, the size of a small office of security cooperation that would handle the sale of American military equipment to the Iraqis—depending on conditions. The other option would start at 16,000 and taper to 157 come what may over a three-year period. The intent was to show the Iraqis, as well as the White House, that even if Austin got his troops, they would not be there forever. The trajectory would be right politically if not militarily. Three years was picked because Jeffrey had advised it would make the agreement more negotiable with the Iraqis. The lowest figure in Austin's range of options was 10,000, and he did not think that option wise.[3]

Before leaving Iraq and handing over his command to Austin, Odierno had recommended a similar-sized force, telling Biden and Gates that a force of 10,000 to 15,000 would be needed. As Odierno envisioned it, an American brigade would be deployed in Kirkuk, long the epicenter of

Arab-Kurdish tension. The Americans would slowly turn over the administration of the checkpoints to the Iraqis, but would have enough troops to continue to monitor the Arab-Kurdish fault line from afar. Another brigade would be allocated to the protection of the embassy and the associated consulates while the force would be rounded out with aviation and support troops. Odierno had already demonstrated during the Bush SOFA negotiations that he was not one to insist that the Americans take on all of the military missions in Iraq and was prepared to take risks. Among the commanders with time on the ground in Iraq, there was general agreement about the minimum force that was needed.

At the White House, there was sticker shock at the numbers the military was suggesting. A Principals meeting was arranged for April 29 and the options that were on the table for discussion were 8,000, 10,000, and 16,000 troops.[4] At the meeting, Donilon put the question to Gates: could he accept a force of up to, but not more than, 10,000 troops? The defense secretary had recommended a two-brigade surge during the Bush years and had come up with the compromise nineteenth-month timeline to reduce forces to 50,000 during the Obama review. Put on the spot, Gates once again opted for the compromise solution, one that he hoped would bridge the gap between the White House and the military. He said he could accept the figure.

At the Pentagon, Mike Mullen was troubled by the turn of events. Pentagon officials had gotten an earful from Saudi Arabia and other Arab states, which were worried that the United States was pulling back from the region. The admiral did not think the Principals meeting had seriously examined the military requirements. He was in his fourth year as chairman and a veteran of any number of reviews. Mullen saw his role as conveying the advice of the American commanders in the United States' twin conflicts to the White House civilians far from the battlefield. The president and his team had already demonstrated that they were prepared to overrule the military on Iraq and Afghanistan. From Mullen's perspective, the only thing that was worse than having no troops in Iraq was having too few, and Austin's recommendation of 16,000 troops seemed to be eminently sensible.

As chairman of the JCS, Mullen had written only a handful of letters to the White House laying out his concerns. Now he prepared a confidential memo to Donilon outlining his position and that of the collective military leadership. The 1986 Goldwater-Nichols reforms had sought to get beyond the interservice rivalry and lowest-common-denominator thinking that had hobbled the military by, among other things, making the chairman of the JCS the senior military adviser to the president. Mullen would exercise his prerogative.

The memo, which was also copied to Gates, recommended keeping 16,000 troops in Iraq. The United States, Mullen argued, would continue to have five missions: supporting the counterterrorism effort to fight Al-Qaeda and other terrorist groups; protecting Iraq's airspace; defusing the tensions between Arabs and Kurds, who had nearly come to blows at Khanaqin; training the Iraqi military; and maintaining the United States influence in the region while countering Iran's malign activities. Having sufficient forces so that the Americans could protect themselves was also a major concern of Mullen. And he believed that it would be good to give the American SOFA negotiators some leeway in case the Iraqis tried to bargain them down. Mullen advised that the smaller option the White House was considering—a force of 8,000 to 10,000—would constitute high risk.

Mullen ended his note by stressing that Austin and Mattis, the CENTCOM commander, concurred with his assessment. In terms of the risks in Iraq and the opportunities to maintain influence there and shape the new Iraqi state, Mullen added he had presented "my best military advice to the president." Austin and Mattis were even of the view that if the force was too small, it would be better to have no troops at all.[5]

Mullen's letter arrived with a thud at the White House. The military's flash of independence had been exercised in classified channels and behind closed doors, but that was too much for Donilon. By presenting a unified view from the JCS chairman, the Iraq commander, and the CENTCOM commander, and putting it on paper, Donilon argued, the military was boxing in the White House and creating a potential political liability. Imagine if it leaked! The White House was still smarting from its experience in the 2009 Afghanistan review, when General Stanley McChrystal's assessment of what was needed to turn the tide became public during its deliberations. The White House did not like it when the military delivered PowerPoint briefs with "high risk" stamped in red on the low troop options, and Donilon liked Mullen's letter even less.

Furious, Donilon called Michèle Flournoy, the undersecretary of defense for policy and the third-ranking civilian at the Pentagon. Gates was a Republican holdover. Flournoy was a Democrat and a political appointee. As the Defense Department's senior policy official, Flournoy was one of the most respected defense experts in the building—so much so that there had been occasional speculation that she might one day be nominated as the first female secretary of defense. But Donilon did not like the Mullen letter and was of the opinion that Flournoy should have maintained a firmer grip on the debate within the Pentagon and even done something to stop it.

Flournoy explained that the JCS chairman had a legal responsibility—a Title 10 responsibility, as she put it, referring to the Goldwater-Nichols legislation—to provide his independent military advice to the president, one that the secretary of defense and his aides were not allowed to interfere with. After taking some soundings with the president's inner circle, Flournoy later concluded that the Obama team did not want to shut down the channel for independent advice and that the objection to Mullen's note originated with Donilon.[6]

Although Mullen's 16,000-troop recommendation was not what the national security adviser wanted, the admiral's letter never leaked. Its very existence remained a closely guarded secret within the Obama administration.

Flournoy, for her part, left the Pentagon in early 2012. She remained fiercely loyal to President Obama and his agenda. During the president's second term, her name would appear on the short list of contenders to succeed Leon Panetta as Secretary of Defense, though she eventually lost out to Chuck Hagel, the former Republican senator who had accompanied Obama to Baghdad in 2008. Still, Donilon's tirade was a low point in her distinguished public service career.

There was one outlier in the military family, a politically astute one: James "Hoss" Cartwright, vice chairman of the Joint Chiefs. A Marine aviator, Cartwright had no time on the ground in Iraq and relatively little combat experience. But Cartwright was accustomed to doing things his own way and his career had blossomed. During the Bush administration, Cartwright had been the J-8, the officer who headed the directorate for force structure, resources, and assessment, which ran the war games on Pentagon strategy and programs.

Rumsfeld had been enamored with his work. Cartwright had used his directorate to do a study that validated the basic principle of Rumsfeld's doctrine to transform the military—specifically, that fast-paced military operations and the accuracy of high-technology weapons reduced the need for large numbers of troops. Speed and accuracy, his study on the "operational availability" of forces concluded, could substitute for mass. The study, however, did not look at postwar troop requirements, the phase of the operation in which the number of forces was far more relevant than technology or the pace of their armor formations. That fatal flaw of Rumsfeld's approach to strategy had been exposed in Iraq and Afghanistan. After two years in that job, Cartwright was promoted to four stars and became the first Marine to head the United States Strategic Command, whose purview included nuclear deterrence, missile defense, information operations, and cyber warfare. When Pete Pace was forced out as chairman and his vice chairman left with him, Cartwright assumed the number-two slot on the Joint Chiefs.

After Obama took office, Cartwright offered a contrarian view on Afghanistan, one that challenged Stan McChrystal, Dave Petraeus, and the counterinsurgency proponents. Instead of carrying out an Afghan surge, Cartwright argued for more emphasis on commando raids against militant leaders. While Cartwright saw himself as an officer bold enough to challenge military orthodoxies, his critics—and he had plenty of them—muttered that he was trying to position himself as Mullen's successor by once again telling the civilians what they wanted to hear, namely that military operations could be fought with a minimum number of troops and at acceptable political costs. Certainly, there was no love lost between Cartwright and Petraeus, who had also developed a reputation for innovation. When the White House was casting about for a successor to Mullen, Cartwright was dismissive of Petraeus's prospects. "It's time for Dave to write his book," he told Jack Keane.

On Iraq, Cartwright was also contrarian. His assessment had less to do with the internal dynamics in Iraq than with his thinking on the region. During a trip to the Middle East in 2010, he had talked with Benjamin Netanyahu, the Israeli prime minister, and other leaders in the area. As the United States drew down, Cartwright argued, the region needed to be assured that American influence was not shrinking. Instead of carrying out a scaled-down version of the mission with a slimmed-down version of the force, Cartwright argued, the United States needed to define a new mission, something that would provide assurance for Israel that Iraq would never become an eastern front in a struggle with Iran.

During a stop in Iraq, Cartwright bounced his ideas off Austin and Jeffrey and ventured that he did not see much tolerance in Washington or Baghdad for more than 5,000 to 10,000 troops. Austin was not persuaded. Nobody had relieved him of his broader responsibilities, he argued, to maintain stability in Iraq and head off confrontations between the Arabs and Kurds in Kirkuk and along the Green Line. Nor was Mattis, a fellow Marine who had fought in Iraq during the invasion and later in Anbar, and who led the command that oversaw the region, persuaded. None of this deterred Cartwright.

When he saw Mullen's letter, Cartwright dissented. Mullen, he felt, was merely rubber-stamping the view from the field. Cartwright thought he could do better by expanding the options for the White House, especially those to field fewer troops. Though Mullen and his field commanders were all on the same sheet of music, the Marine general would march to the beat of his own drum.

So Cartwright took the extraordinary step of writing a dissent. It was the first time in memory that the vice chairman had sent correspondence objecting to a recommendation by the chairman and even making the case for far fewer troops. "In executing missions of advising, training, assisting the ISF," Cartwright's letter noted, "troop levels of 8,000–10,000 offer the best balance between mission execution and stewardship of taxpayer dollars." Cartwright's memo was attached to Mullen's letter and was submitted to the White House.

While Cartwright's relations with Mullen were strained, he had a warm reception at the White House. As he developed his thinking further, Cartwright argued that the United States could keep some 3,000 troops in Iraq, including special operations forces. A thousand troops could be based in the north and another 1,000 in the south to train Iraqi troops and signal to the Iranians that any intervention in Iraq would mean a confrontation with the United States. An F-16 squadron would be based at Al-Asad and the United States would store equipment in Iraq and Kuwait that could be used for exercises like the large Bright Star maneuvers in Egypt or in case the United States needed to rush forces to Iraq during a crisis. If 3,000 was more than the traffic would bear, a more modest option was to keep a mere 1,000 troops in Iraq.[7]

Cartwright discussed his ideas with Donilon and Blinken and met repeatedly with Biden. The vice president was taken by the idea of a smaller deployment than what Mullen was proposing. The Marine walked Biden through the logic of the high and the low options. The vice president was uninterested in hearing about the high, but he did want to hear about the low. The details of Cartwright's recommendations were not adopted, but his intervention was important. It was difficult for the president to overrule all of his commanders. Now a four-star general, albeit one with no Iraq experience, had lent legitimacy to the politically appealing troops levels the White House had in mind.

As the White House was pondering its options, Lindsey Graham received a call from Hillary Clinton. Graham was not surprised by the call. The Republican senator from South Carolina was a conservative Republican and a surge supporter, but he was prepared to reach across the aisle to get things done. Graham had been a severe critic of the Bush administration's authorization of "enhanced interrogation techniques" and had been willing to discuss a compromise that would have shuttered the terrorist detention facility at Guantánamo Bay. Clinton was a pragmatist, too. During the Bush administration, Clinton had remonstrated against the surge, famously telling Petraeus at a congressional hearing that his statistics on the improving security situation required a "willing suspension of disbelief." But she had kept her ties open to Jack Keane and during her campaign asked if he would serve as one of her military advisers. (He demurred.)

As a member of the Appropriations Committee, Graham had complained about the State Department's plans to keep 17,000 civilians—mostly contractors—in Iraq, as what he dismissively dubbed a "mini-State Department army." As supportive as Graham had been on Iraq, he did not favor dispatching thousands of contractors to Iraq equipped with MRAPs and helicopters to take up the mission of protecting diplomats because American forces had been withdrawn. The State Department had never undertaken a mission like that before, contractors had a checkered record in Iraq and lacked the discipline of American forces, and at more than $5 billion a year it did not appear to Graham that it would be money well spent.

Graham sensed that Clinton was not eager to see all of the troops go either and to have the entire burden for security shifted to the State Department. Indeed, the secretary of state wanted Graham to prod the Iraqis to make a decision on troops. He had close ties with Iraqi officials and Clinton was hoping he could use them. Graham called John McCain and Joe Lieberman, his close political allies on Iraq, to line up a trip to Baghdad. The lawmakers had traveled to Iraq together many times before, and Graham wanted to get the "Amigos" back together. Lieberman had a schedule conflict, but McCain was on board. The CODEL—congressional delegation—would leave in early May.

Before leaving for Iraq, Graham went to the White House to talk to Biden and Tony Blinken, his senior adviser on national security. The vice president made it clear that he believed that Maliki was somebody the United States could do business with, but he saw Allawi as more a problem than a solution. Allawi, Biden complained, had submitted a candidate for the defense minister post only to change his mind and had been traveling to Arab capitals and Iran to drum up support for his candidacy against Maliki. He was jeopardizing the power-sharing deal by making impossible demands. It was not an assessment that all Iraq specialists shared, including some in the Obama administration—but Biden had the lead for Iraq policy.

Arriving in Iraq, the senators were told by Austin that he was developing plans for a force of some 20,000 troops. Just manning the joint Kurdish-Arab checkpoints and maintaining peace in the disputed Kurdish and Arab areas could take 5,000 troops, Graham was told by one officer during a visit to one of the checkpoints. Determining the number of troops that were needed, however, was just part of the puzzle. The senators still needed to line up the Iraqis.

At a dinner with Massoud Barzani in Kurdistan, the Kurdish leader told the lawmakers that it was vital that American troops remain in Iraq but that there was no way Maliki was going to go out on a limb by asking for troops and exposing himself to his many political opponents. It was agreed that Barzani would convene the leaders of the main political factions to take up the troop issue. That would provide Maliki with the political cover he needed to ask for support from American forces.

With Jeffrey and Austin in tow, the senators next had a meeting with Maliki. The prime minister began the session by launching into a bitter attack on his rival. Allawi, Maliki complained, had been going around the region trying to undercut Maliki and was making fiery speeches against the government. "He's out to destroy me. I have got the video," Maliki exclaimed, referring to a recording of one of the speeches in question.

Graham concurred that Allawi had been counterproductive and began to make his case for the need to agree to an American military presence when the prime minister asked a surprising question.

"How many troops are you willing to leave here?" Maliki asked.

"You don't know?" Graham shot back.

"No. Nobody has ever talked to me about that," Maliki replied.[8]

In front of the prime minister, Graham turned to Jeffrey and Austin. The lawmakers had come to Iraq to push the Iraqis to agree on a troop presence only to learn that the Obama administration had not put a plan, much less a proposal, on the table. Jeffrey and Austin sheepishly explained that the White House was still in the midst of its review and had yet to settle on a number. The senators were flummoxed. While waiting for the Iraqis to say that they wanted forces, the White House had not specified to the Iraqis how many troops the Americans were prepared to provide nor what exactly they would do.

Leaving the Green Zone, the Americans went to huddle with Allawi at his Baghdad compound. As the leader of Iraqiya and a former prime minister, Allawi had been a close ally of the Americans. His coalition had won more seats than the others in the March 2010 parliamentary elections, and more than a year later he had not reconciled himself to the fact that it was Maliki who clung to the prime minister post.

Allawi wanted American forces in Iraq, but believed the Obama administration was going about it all wrong. The Americans needed to present a case for what forces needed to remain, for how long, and under what rules of engagement. The Iraqi military needed to give its assessment of such a plan. Allawi's pragmatic approach also masked a cautious political strategy. For all of Iraqiya's close ties with the United States, the troop issue was a touchy matter for them as well. Though Sunnis had been protected by American forces during the surge, they had formed the backbone of the insurgency and some still resented the American presence. Moreover, Allawi was still hoping to trade his support for a prolonged American presence for American support for the power-sharing arrangement with Maliki that had yet to be consummated. Like Maliki, Allawi did not want to be perceived as being too out front in pushing for American troops.

At Allawi's Baghdad compound, Graham lectured him on how he needed to do more to support the formation of the government. Allawi, Graham insisted, was not going to be prime minister and it was wrong for him to fly to foreign capitals to seek support for his candidacy, but he could play a role as the head of the proposed National Council for Higher Policies. Allawi suggested that the shrewdest way to build support for an American troop presence in 2012 was to have the request come from the Iraqi Army. "I'm a politician," Allawi said. "I'm not going to be able to respond to an American offer, but if my generals describe to me gaps in my defenses and they recommend to me a continuing alliance, that will sell."

On May 11, Maliki suggested that he would support an American military presence if he could garner enough support. "Realistically, there is no 100 percent consensus on such an issue," Maliki told a news conference. "We will hear the voice of the citizen and the politician and civil society," he said. "After that I will meet with the heads of blocs and officials in the state, maybe the governors of the provinces."[9] The Americans, he said, "need time to prepare and get ready for the withdrawal, so they want my decision before August," he said. The other political leaders, he added, preferred "that I shouldn't carry the responsibility alone."

Almost half of 2011 was already gone. Bush's SOFA negotiations had taken almost nine months and gone down to the wire. The Obama administration would have even less time, since it had to be prepared to start removing American forces if the talks did not pan out. And yet the White House had yet to settle on a firm set of troop numbers or outline a plan to the Iraqis. Barzani, Allawi, and even Maliki suggested privately that they understood American troops could help build Iraq's forces but neither wanted to be in the vanguard publicly on the issue.

Soon after the senators returned to the United States, Donilon called Graham and told him that their trip had been productive. Graham and McCain met at Biden's house to discuss the effort. "We said, 'Joe, you know they seem to be warming up to this, they seem to be all realizing they have got to have some American troop presence. Their general staff is going to recommend it,' " Graham recalled. "We've got to give them some options here."

" 'We're on it, we're on it, we're on it,' was Biden's response," Graham recalled. Biden said that he was going to meet with Obama in a few days and that the final troop package would soon be settled, after which he would give Graham a call, but the call never came.[10]

The president made his decision at an NSC meeting on May 19 that he used to try to redefine the terms of the debate within his administration. Obama wanted a plan that would signify that the war was in the past and that the United States and Iraq were embarking on a new relationship, one in which Iraq was not perceived as dependent on the United States. It was the vision Obama had touted during the campaign, outlined in his speech at Camp Lejeune, and would voice in his upcoming bid for reelection. Affirming the stance that Donilon had already sketched out, Obama made clear that he was prepared to keep up to 10,000 troops in Iraq. This was the floor for Mullen and the generals in the field, who were worried about the challenges of operating in Iraq, but the ceiling for the White House.

On June 2, Obama conducted a secure videoconference with Maliki, his first such discussion with the Iraqi prime minister that year. Obama did not tell Maliki how many forces the Americans were prepared to keep in Iraq in 2012. That was still a card that the Americans were keeping close to their chest. But he made a conditional offer to work closely with the Iraqis: "As long as you and your coalition partners are devoted to building a peaceful and prosperous Iraq, the U.S. will remain your partner." The president had another requirement: if there was to be a new SOFA that would enable the United States to keep troops in Iraq after 2011, the Iraqi parliament would need to approve the agreement.

On June 10, Donilon issued formal negotiating guidance to Jeffrey and Austin. They were to start with a discussion of missions and requirements and end up at how many forces might be needed. No more than 10,000 troops would be available for the mission, but the ambassador and the general were not authorized to convey that number to Maliki. The White House wanted to avoid the impression that it was anxious to keep troops in Iraq and believed that the Iraqis would want fewer American troops, if they wanted any at all.

The notion that the Iraqis would object to significant troop numbers was more widely held in Washington than by American officials in Baghdad. In June, according to an American official, Maliki had met with senior Iraqi officials and Hussein al-Shahristani and had talked about a possible American force of some 20,000 troops. The numbers game was a Washington fixation. During its Iraq and Afghanistan reviews, the White House had focused like a laser on the question of how many troops would be deployed, calculating that the figure would make headlines at home. But for the Iraqis, the question was less about the number of troops, which after all would be tasked with training the Iraqis and helping the ISOF and other Iraqi security forces fight Al-Qaeda, than it was about the burning issues of sovereignty, immunities, and compliance with Iraq's laws. If it had been up to the generals on each side, the issue of a post-2011 American troop presence in Iraq would never have been controversial. The deficiencies of the Iraqi security forces were well known. But in both Washington and Baghdad, the decisions were being made by civilians who were also influenced by political calculations and public opinion.

To buttress the negotiating team, Brett McGurk, who had left the government to write a book about his experiences in Iraq, was asked to return to Baghdad as an adviser.

In the discussions Jeffrey and McGurk had with Maliki, the Iraqi prime minister repeatedly suggested that an executive agreement—perhaps a memorandum of understanding between the Pentagon and the Iraqi Ministry of Defense—be drafted that would permit the continued presence of American troops but would dispense with the need to take the accord to the parliament, which the prime minister argued portended nothing but trouble. McGurk, who would later be nominated by the White House to succeed Jeffrey as ambassador to Iraq, agreed and quietly recommended that the White House drop the parliamentary requirement. There were benefits in keeping American forces in Iraq, he believed, and the United States had to balance the strategic risk it would assume by not having any forces in Iraq against the minimal legal risk that a circumstance might arise in which one of its troops faced Iraqi prosecution. An understanding on troops might be drafted under the terms of the strategic framework agreement, which covered broader economic, diplomatic, and security relations. As a SOFA negotiator for Bush, McGurk had seen how the parliamentary debate and the need for consensus could politicize the issue. But McGurk was a minority of one among the Americans.

In Washington, the government lawyers argued that parliamentary approval was a precedent that had been set and even Medhat al-Mahmoud, Iraq's chief justice, told American officials privately that parliamentary approval was a constitutional requirement. The demand raised the political stakes for the Iraqis. The Sadrists were in the parliament now and a major issue for the other parties was whether they could line up the support to back a position the Sadrists, among others, were sure to oppose. Allawi, in principle, supported a continued American military presence, but in a July 3 meeting he was not ready to talk about the level of American troops until the power-sharing issues were settled. The Iraqiya leader was trying to leverage American interest in a SOFA to advance his position in the wrangle over who would run Iraq.

Obama had set an August 1 deadline for the Iraqis to ask for American troops. The White House was eager to avoid the impression that it was demanding a new SOFA. The Pentagon and State Department believed it was in the United States' interest to maintain some sort of residual military presence to shore up the shaky institutions Iraq had established at such great cost and contest Iranian influence. For Obama and his loyal cluster of aides, the attitude was that the Maliki government would not be doing the president any favors by allowing American troops to stay. Obama had posed the essential question to Petraeus in his July 2008 visit to Iraq: what was good enough? Obama was willing to help to a point if the Iraqis requested it, but for the president the situation in Iraq was fast approaching "good enough."

In mid-July, Denis McDonough and Tony Blinken met with Maliki to explain that time was running out and that his government needed to meet four conditions by August. There would need to be an official request for

American troops from the Iraqi government. The Maliki government would need to seek parliamentary approval of a SOFA with the same immunities for American troops as had been negotiated in 2008. The vacuum at Iraq's Defense Ministry and other security ministries needed to be filled as progress was made on forming a new government. And Maliki needed to commit himself to pursuing the Iranian-backed Special Groups, which had been increasingly active and had been attacking American forces with EFPs and IRAMs, the deadly rocket-propelled mortars.[11]

During the spring and early summer, violence by all three major Shiite militant groups—the Khazalis' Asaib Ahl al-Haq, Kataib Hezbollah, and Sadr's Promised Day Brigades—had spiked. The American military accused Asaib Ahl al-Haq of being behind a string of assassinations of government officials during the spring, and one instance of insurgent activity by the Promised Day Brigades was highlighted in a court case in Hilla. After the 3rd Armored Cavalry Regiment captured three members of the group planting an IED and a court then acquitted them, the regiment's commander, Colonel Reginald Allen, issued an unusual press release decrying the acquittal. But the most dangerous attacks by Shiite militants were a series of strikes against American bases by Kataib Hezbollah. On June 6, an IRAM shot half a dozen rockets onto Camp Loyalty, one of the few joint American-Iraqi outposts still open inside the city. Six 1st Infantry Division soldiers died in the attack (and American commanders were frustrated when senior Iraqi officials, including Maliki, failed to attend a memorial ceremony for the six, leaving their seats empty). Another IRAM attack against a base in southern Iraq on June 15 failed to inflict any casualties, but a third, on June 29, killed three troopers from the 3rd ACR at an outpost near the Iranian border and wounded a dozen more. Two weeks after that, on July 10, a barrage of rockets hit Camp Garry Owen, the main American base in Maysan, and killed a soldier. Also in July, three Triple Canopy security contractors working for the State Department were killed in a rocket barrage.

The attacks brought the number of American combat deaths in Iraq in June to fourteen—a small figure, but the largest monthly toll since 2008—and provoked military responses from both the Iraqis and the Americans. The Iraqi response was lackluster: what the Iraqis planned as a division-level operation in Maysan in July to ferret out caches of EFPs and rockets ended up involving only a brigade. For their part, American commandos launched raids against militants involved in the attacks, sometimes unilateral strikes in which they did not bring along Iraqi troops. The battalion based at Camp Garry Owen, 3-8 Cavalry, had already been using Abrams tanks in its operations to demonstrate that it was serious about security—something most units in Iraq no longer did—and in July, it added "show of force" missions by AH-64 Apache attack helicopters and AC-130 Spectre gunships.

The day after Obama's August 1 deadline, with considerable prodding by Jeffrey and McGurk, the leaders of the Iraqi blocs convened, worked until 1 a.m., and then issued a statement. Maliki was authorized to negotiate a "memorandum of understanding" that would provide for "trainers." Maliki appointed an acting minister of defense, Sadoun al-Dulaimi, a Sunni whom Allawi had previously rejected because he did not deem him sufficiently loyal. Meanwhile, the Iraqi military had begun to mount operations in Maysan Province against Iranian-backed groups. An outstanding issue was securing approval of the agreement by the parliament.

Even so, Jeffrey and McGurk believed that the Iraqis had done enough formally to launch the negotiations. The administration had a clear "ask" from the Iraqis and an official one at that. McGurk thought he had pulled off a diplomatic coup. They had gotten all of the Iraqis into a room, persuaded them to crack down in Maysan against the Special Groups, and prodded Maliki to name an acting minister of defense and indicated that they might take the issue to the parliament. The embassy thought it was going to get the green light from the White House to begin talks. "The leaders agreed to authorize the Iraqi government to start the talks with the United States that are limited to training issues," a statement was quoted by Al-Jazeera as saying.[12]

Instead of rejoicing in the formal steps the Iraqis had taken or a call from Obama to Maliki and other leaders asking them to go the extra mile, there was an awkward silence. The American team in Baghdad was perplexed. For weeks there had not been much movement in Baghdad. But now that the Iraqis were beginning to shift their position, it was the White House that seemed to be having trouble taking yes for an answer and appeared to be reconsidering the deal.

On August 4, McDonough led a Deputies Committee meeting where it was determined that the Maliki government had not committed itself to taking the issue to the parliament and granting immunities. The White House had become exceedingly risk-averse on the immunity issue after a CIA contractor had been detained in Pakistan and put on trial in March for shooting two Pakistanis who had accosted him, notwithstanding the American insistence that he enjoyed diplomatic immunity. The contractor had been released, but it was a reminder of the sort of problems that might arise in Iraq. The odds of such a thing happening there were small, but it was a risk that the Obama administration did not want to take. Jay Carney, the White House spokesman, summed up the administration position. The United States, he said, had been waiting for a response from the Iraqis. "But that has not been forthcoming, and we are on track to withdraw by the end of the year," he said.[13]

As the wrangling within the government continued, the White House was already beginning to rethink its earlier decision to keep up to 10,000 troops in Iraq. The politics of the deficit had been heating up throughout the summer. The White House began to ready a deficit reduction plan that claimed more than $1 trillion in savings over ten years, including from winding down the wars in Iraq and Afghanistan. The calculations, in effect, projected a near-constant level of troop deployments and spending and then claimed the savings that would accrue from taking all the troops out. That keeping sizable numbers of troops in Iraq and Afghanistan for years had never been intended was conveniently overlooked by the number crunchers, who were generating largely hypothetical savings for an increasingly polarized and partisan budget debate. But the point was, the lower the number, the greater the claimed savings. At the Pentagon, there was a growing sense that the politics of the deficit was beginning to shape the Iraq debate.

But other political realities informed the White House's frustrations with the Iraqis as well. Donilon and the NSC staff argued that Obama could not be perceived as chasing an agreement he might not get. If an accord proved elusive, the United States would be rushing to get its troops out of Iraq. Instead of forging a new relationship with the Iraqis, the media would cast the president as presiding over a retreat.

The NSC staff was beginning to advocate for lower numbers as well. During their July trip to Iraq, McDonough and Blinken had met with Major General Dave Perkins, the commander in northern Iraq. In a bid to keep the peace between the Kurds and Arabs, in 2009 Odierno had established almost two dozen joint checkpoints, manned by American, Kurdish, and Iraqi troops, as well as three command centers to oversee them. Perkins figured that the United States was not going to keep many troops in Iraq and since that was the case it made sense to staff the command centers and perhaps keep a battalion in the north to visit the checkpoints should problems arise. The White House aides took those findings back to Washington and used them to argue that the military footprint could be diminished further. As more ammunition to shrink the number of the residual force, they cited a CIA report concluding that relations between Barzani and Maliki were more important to stabilizing the north than the presence of American troops.[14] That was true to a point, military officials argued, but there was always the potential for an escalating series of miscalculations as at Khanaqin. But the search was on for ever-lower numbers more consonant with Cartwright's recommendation than with Mullen, Austin, and Mattis's. By late July, Biden had led a Principals Committee meeting where the Pentagon was instructed to look at a new set of options.

At the White House's insistence, several new options were drawn up, including one that would have left half a squadron of F-16s in Iraq and 3,500 to 4,000 troops. To get the numbers down further, one option would have used American aircraft in neighboring countries to protect Iraqi skies and would have kept 2,000 troops or fewer in Iraq. In total, there were five options, ranging from 10,000 to 1,600 troops.

On August 10, another Principals meeting was held at which Leon Panetta, who had taken over from Gates at the Pentagon, urged that the negotiations continue on a troop presence of up to 10,000 and that the actual level be decided by the American and Iraqi negotiators. The military was anxious about the low numbers the White House was considering and did not see the merit in preemptively settling on a low level. Clinton supported Panetta's position. The State Department was planning to field a small contractor army to protect its diplomats and enable the civilians to continue training Iraqi police. It did not, as one official put, want to be left alone "holding the baby."

The president settled matters. On August 13, Obama convened a conference call with Panetta, Mullen, and Clinton and gave his decision. The president ruled out the 10,000-troop option and a small 7,000-troop option that would have trained Iraqi troops at three hubs. Reflecting the findings of McDonough and Blinken's trip, Obama was skeptical of the need for keeping troops in the north to discourage fighting between the Arabs and Kurds. But he thought it would be good to have special operations forces in Iraq to work with Iraqi commandos and carry out missions against Al-Qaeda and other terrorist groups. Obama was also open to keeping a small number of American aircraft inside Iraq, which the military advised was the only feasible option for protecting Iraqi airspace, provided the Iraqis asked for it.

Obama's plan called for the continuous presence of 3,500 troops and a force of up to 1,500 more that would regularly rotate through the country. The smaller force would limit its training operations to a small number of bases. The troops would not man the checkpoints to keep Arab and Kurdish forces from challenging each other, but it would include a small cell to oversee them at the command center in Kirkuk. That, plus the training element that would be located at the base near Kirkuk, it was hoped, would enable the Americans to keep an eye on the system of checkpoints Odierno had established in the north, which would now be manned exclusively by Arabs and Kurds. It would be a minimal force that would train the Iraqi military, support counterterrorism operations, and control Iraq's airspace with half a dozen F-16s stationed at Al-Asad.

If the White House was right, the small force would make the deployment more acceptable to the Iraqis, provide some counterterrorism capability, and enable the administration to say that it had ended the war. For critics of the plan, the administration was asking Maliki to take a political risk at home by trying to push the agreement through parliament for minimal gain. Washington was asking a lot and offering only a little.

There were Pentagon officers who worried that deploying such a modest force entailed unnecessary risk—to the mission and to the troops who had to carry it out. When the plan was being hashed out, one member of the Panetta's staff cautioned Blinken that shrinking the force entailed trade-offs in effectiveness and force protection. "Look, it's not a perfect world," Blinken replied.

In September, Bill Burns went to Baghdad and drove home the message that the accord required parliamentary approval, insisting that Maliki had the political leverage to get it. "Then you don't understand my country," Maliki replied. Then, in early October, Iraqi leaders assembled under President Talabani to make a final decision on a troop presence. The gathering approved U.S. military trainers but ruled out immunities. Only the Kurds supported the U.S. immunities requirement.[15]

On October 21, Obama held his second and final videoconference of the year with the Iraqi prime minister. The SOFA negotiation was over, and all American troops would be coming home. The inability of the two sides to negotiate a new SOFA was not a setback, the president's advisers concluded, because the White House never considered it a requirement. The important issue was to forge a new relationship with a sovereign Iraq. The United States had been willing to keep a modest force in Iraq if the Iraqis had been willing to accept the United States' legal demands, but maintaining a presence was not an end in itself. In short, it was a step that the United States was prepared to take to help the Iraqis but not one the White House thought was essential for stability in Iraq or the region.

"Given that the Iraqis had not come close to meeting our conditions, it was clear that keeping 10,000 troops in Iraq was going to be enormously difficult for the Iraqis and would require a significant effort on our part to jam it through when we, in fact, were not eager to have 10,000 troops in Iraq," a senior Obama administration official asserted. "As we reviewed the 10,000 option, we came to the conclusion that achieving the goal of a security partnership with Iraq was not dependent on the size of our footprint in country, and that stability in Iraq did not depend on the presence of U.S. forces."

Ryan Crocker, who had led the successful 2008 SOFA talks, later offered a different perspective. If the Obama administration had really wanted the accord, it should have begun the negotiations much earlier, he felt. And the Iraqis erred by allowing the United States to stipulate that approval by the Iraqi parliament was a requirement—a demand the Bush administration had never imposed. "I don't think either government handled it as well as it could have been handled," he said. "The U.S. side came to it late. You have got to leave a lot of latitude for difficulties, foreseen and unforeseen. On the Iraqi side, they should have said, 'If you want this, don't try to determine our own procedures.'"

The 45,000 American troops still in Iraq had already begun their final withdrawal. As more bases closed and brigades left, what was left of the American force collapsed on itself, with the last troops to go providing security for the convoys that left before them. Specialist David Hickman, a paratrooper with the 82nd Airborne's 2nd Brigade who had been in ninth grade when the United States invaded Iraq, was the last soldier to die, killed by an IED in Baghdad on November 14.

A ceremony at Al-Faw Palace on December 1, which Biden, Maliki, and Talabani attended, marked the formal closure of Camp Victory. A small corner of the airport complex remained open, now run by State Department contractors. There, on December 15, the American command in Iraq formally cased its colors in a ceremony that Maliki and Talabani did not attend. In his speech at the event, Lloyd Austin recalled the 3rd Infantry Division's battle to seize the airport eight years and eight months before. The final five thousand troops left Tallil Air Base over the next three days. The last American aircraft, a C-17 carrying two Air Force generals who had first flown over Iraq in Desert Storm, flew out of Tallil on the night of December 17. At 2:30 the next morning, the last ground convoy left the base—five hundred soldiers from the 3rd Brigade, 1st Cavalry Division, a unit that had spent four years fighting in Iraq. With a Predator drone watching from above, the convoy's 125 armored vehicles crossed the border into Kuwait four and a half hours later.

CHAPTER 36

Mission Accomplished

At his October 21 videoconference with Maliki, President Obama invited the Iraqi prime minister to visit Washington, a meeting that was intended to underscore the United States' insistence that it was not only pulling American forces out of Iraq, but had succeeded in leaving behind a stable and democratic country in its wake.

In the weeks preceding his Washington visit, the Iraqi prime minister had lost none of his anxiety about threats to his power, real and imagined. Nearly a thousand Iraqis had been detained as suspected Baathists, ostensibly because of intelligence seized by the new rebel government in Libya. American diplomats concluded that there was, in fact, no Libyan treasure trove listing diehard Saddamists. Faced with fears of a plot, Maliki's inner circle appeared to have done little more than round up their suspected enemies, many of them Shiites.[1]

Even some of Iraq's most senior generals had felt the sting. Lieutenant General Nasier al-Abadi, the vice chief of Iraq's joint command and an Air Force officer, received a letter declaring that his position had been abolished. Stripped of his bodyguards and perquisites, Abadi left for Amman. American officials later concluded that he had been cashiered because of his independent streak and close ties with the American military.

As Maliki's December visit approached, Dave Petraeus thought it would be a good opportunity to get together with Maliki. Now ensconced at the CIA, Petraeus figured that he, his wife, Sadi Othman, a trusted adviser and interpreter, and Maliki might go out to dinner. It would be both a way to indulge in nostalgia about the turnaround months of the surge and a way to discuss the thorny way ahead. By the time Maliki's visit came around, the Petraeus invitation for a quiet soiree had morphed into a lavish dinner at Blair House, which included Hillary Clinton, Biden's staff, and Maliki's traveling party.

The prime minister's entourage included Maliki loyalists and a Shiite Islamist who had been brought into Maliki's governing coalition, Badr's Hadi al-Amari, the minister of transportation and one of the intermediaries Qasim Suleimani had used with the Americans. But no prominent members of Allawi's Iraqiya were part of the delegation, which was living proof that the partnership government the Americans had labored so hard to assemble existed in name more than in fact.

After some niceties—the Americans ribbed Hadi al-Amari that in a departure from Iranian etiquette he was wearing a tie—the dinner conversation turned to issues of the moment, mainly Syria, which was in the throes of a revolution that Bashar al-Assad was doing his best to ruthlessly suppress. Of the Americans present, Petraeus pressed the issue hardest. Too much blood was flowing in Syria and Assad's loss of power, he insisted, was inevitable. Should not Maliki be joining in the international efforts to encourage a Syria without Assad? Maliki gave no ground. If Assad fell and Syria was convulsed by civil war, Maliki argued, the chaos there would spill over to Iraq, somewhat ironically making the same sort of argument that many Arab leaders made against the United States' 2003 invasion of Iraq.[2]

The next day Maliki went to the White House for a conversation with Obama about the future of the U.S.-Iraq partnership. As Iraqi and American aides scribbled notes, the president made clear that he had Iraq's neighbors on his mind, particularly the one to Iraq's east, which stood to gain from the security vacuum that might be created after the Americans pulled out, and which had supported militia attacks in Iraq against Americans. "Some people will think that our withdrawal will bring more influence by Iran. I am confident in your independent leadership and we accept that Iraq needs a normal relationship with Iran. But as partners we must say our main problem with Iran is their nuclear ambition," Obama said. "We said we would not use Iraq as a platform to attack Iran, but in Iraq there are groups supported by Iran who target our people. This is a major concern. Iran has not responded to our approaches. We would prefer to resolve the issue of the militias by diplomatic means."

Maliki insisted he was not susceptible to Iranian influence. "We have friendships with everyone, but there is no hegemony in that. Iran for example is not happy that we are buying fighter airplanes from you," he said. "Frankly, an attack on an American security or business establishment would be tantamount to an attack on Iraqi interests."

As for Iraq's neighbors to the south, Obama sought to reassure Maliki that the United States was concerned about Shiite protesters in Bahrain and to use that as an enticement to get the Iraqi leader to take a tougher stance on Syria "We must take what we say about Bahrain and we must then apply it to Syria," the president said. "We don't think al-Assad can survive. We must be against any repression. I want to hear your views. We are working with the Arab League for a peaceful transfer of power."

Maliki noted that the Shiite-led government in Iraq had been in touch with the Bahraini opposition but blamed the Saudis, who he implied wanted to keep Bahrain as part of their sphere of influence. "As for Syria, any sectarian conflict in Syria will transfer itself to Iraq. We have not interfered on the side of the regime or the opposition."

"We have no intention to intervene militarily," Obama said reassuringly. "We can look into your suggestions. We do not believe Assad can reform. The train has left the station."

In the one-on-one meeting that followed, the American president urged the Iraqi leader to honor his commitments on government formation, made clear that the United States did not want Iraq forcibly to repatriate the MEK, the Iranian opposition members who took refuge in Iraq during Saddam's rule, and expressed American concerns about Ali Musa Daqduq, the Lebanese Hezbollah leader who had been captured by the SAS along with the Khazalis in March 2007 in Basra. The Americans had handed him over to the Iraqis under the terms of the SOFA but did not want to see him released.[3]

Obama painted a glowing portrait of Iraq's achievements and prospects in the press conference afterward. Maliki was the leader of a "sovereign, self-reliant and democratic Iraq," the president said, a nation that could serve as a beacon for the region. "For the first time in two decades, Iraq is scheduled to host the next Arab League summit, and what a powerful message that will send throughout the Arab world. People throughout the region will see a new Iraq that's determining its own destiny—a country in which people from different religious sects and ethnicities can resolve their differences peacefully through the democratic process," the president added. "A war is ending. A new day is upon us."[4]

As the prime minister toured Washington one Sunni leader in Baghdad delivered a riposte. Salih al-Mutlaq, the outspoken deputy prime minister who had been targeted by Ahmed Chalabi and others during the 2010 de-Baathification fiasco, had landed a televised interview on CNN. Mutlaq, who held the services portfolio, had often complained that Maliki had him in a powerless position with no capacity to make decisions and that his job was to drink tea and smoke cigarettes all day. Mutlaq told the interviewer that he was "really shocked" to hear Obama referring to Maliki as a democratic leader. "It's either because they don't know anything in Iraq" or because "they don't want to admit the reality in Iraq, the failure in Iraq." As for Maliki, Mutlaq said with a good measure of hyperbole that he was the most dictatorial leader "we have ever seen in our history." Playing clips of the interview on his CNN show, Wolf Blitzer was astonished to hear Iraq's deputy prime minister denouncing the prime minister as a dictator, even as Maliki was in Washington meeting with the president. The remarks were part of politics as usual in Iraq, but to newcomers it appeared the United States was leaving behind a dysfunctional political system.

As he flew back to Baghdad, Maliki was angry. The prime minister was sensitive to accusations of authoritarianism. On February 25, 2011, during the Arab Spring, Basra, Kirkuk, and Mosul had erupted in the "Day of Rage" protests. Thousands of Iraqis had rallied in the streets, and Maliki and his security staff feared that Baghdad might soon be the next victim of the populist rage sweeping the Middle East. They spent the entire day in an operations center nervously tracking the developments.[5] Indeed, Maliki had been so concerned about the protests that he attempted to preempt them by announcing that he would cut his salary by half and not seek a third term.

Moreover, Mutlaq's comments implied that Maliki, the proud leader who had ridden with his security forces to Basra for Operation Charge of the Knights, was not the master of his own house. This was not the only problem Maliki faced. On December 12, the same day as his meeting with Obama, the provincial council in Diyala had decided to follow the lead of neighboring Salahuddin Province and demand more autonomy from the central government. Under the Iraqi constitution, provincial councils were allowed to request a referendum for citizens to vote on whether to become a federal region under the constitution. The Sunnis had been opposed to the Biden-Gelb plan for a decentralized federalism, but, recoiling against Maliki's efforts to centralize authority, some were now pushing back.

With tensions running high, Shiite residents of Diyala, some of whom were armed, reacted to the decision by storming the provincial council building in Baqubah. The governor and other local politicians fled to the northern city of Khanaqin, within the Kurdish protective sphere. Stunned,

Maliki activated the Iraqi security forces and placed the province under de facto martial law. Shiite militias reportedly operated checkpoints on Diyala's roads, and an arrest warrant was issued for Diyala's deputy governor. Soon, Nineveh and Anbar provinces were threatening to declare autonomy as well.[6]

In Baghdad, the prime minister had ways to show who was in charge as well. Stung by the criticism of the Iraqiya leaders, Maliki ordered tanks to take up positions near the residences of Mutlaq, Rafi al-Issawi, and Tariq al-Hashimi, the Sunni vice president. The Iraqiya leaders huddled in Hashimi's residence on December 16 and decided to boycott the parliament and the Council of Ministers. The Maliki government followed with the announcement that a bodyguard of Hashimi had been linked to an earlier bombing near the parliament. Just days after Obama had feted Maliki as an avatar of a proud and democratic Iraq there was a spiraling crisis that threatened to dwarf the detentions that Maliki had justified on the ostensible Libyan evidence. There was shock and consternation at the White House. Jeffrey did some quick checking and concluded that the prime minister had not plotted his demonstration of force before his White House visit. But that was cold comfort. The United States was still faced with a political clash that might spin out of control.

In Baghdad, Jim Jeffrey mounted a full court press to contain the crisis. Iraqiya ignored the ambassador's plea to suspend its angry denunciations of the Maliki government while the Americans urged cooler heads to prevail. Jeffrey went on a long-scheduled leave with his family to Salzburg, Austria, but after a day flew back to Baghdad. There were calls from Biden and a visit by Petraeus. With rumors that he might be arrested, Hashimi headed for Baghdad International Airport on December 18. Talabani had conveniently announced the convening of his Presidency Council in Sulaymaniyah, Kurdistan—a body that included Hashimi and Shiite vice president Khudair al-Kuzai. There were numerous delays departing. Security personnel were everywhere and even Hashimi's bodyguards were being asked to show their identification.

As the plane waited on the tarmac, Mowaffak al-Rubaie, who by happenstance was on the same flight, received a text message from Maliki insisting that the aircraft not leave.[7] After another delay, the passengers were abruptly escorted off the plane. Hashimi was eventually allowed to reboard, but his bodyguards were left off the flight and some were later arrested. One of Hashimi's bodyguards later died in custody under mysterious circumstances. Hashimi believed he was tortured in an attempt to extract a confession. After Hashimi secured refuge in Kurdistan a warrant was issued for his arrest. American officials later said that there was evidence that some of Hashimi's guards might have been tied to a car bombing but no conclusive information that Hashimi himself was aware of such a plot.

In the months after his flight to Kurdistan, Hashimi reported, he never heard from an American official.[8] Hashimi was later told that Maliki had suggested to Talabani that he find a graceful way out by leaving the country. The Americans had used their influence to contain the crisis but the fissures within the Iraqi government seemed deeper than ever.

With the approach of the Arab League summit in March, American diplomats found themselves struggling with a new set of challenges. The departure of American forces had a number of unintended consequences. Without the American military presence, no military power controlled Iraqi skies. That meant that Israel had a direct air corridor to strike nuclear sites in Iran if the Israelis decided force was needed. The operation would not require the Israeli state to take the politically difficult step of flying through American-controlled airspace, and would not run the risk of prompting Iranian retaliation against American troops on the ground in Iraq.

The security vacuum in the air opened up a new opportunity for Iran as well. Seeking to prop up the Assad regime in Syria, Iran had been flying arms on commercial flights through Turkey until the Turks began demanding that the aircraft land for inspection. With no Americans left safeguarding Iraq's skies, the Iranians had an inviting alternative route, one that they eagerly exploited. According to American intelligence, the Iranians flew about two hundred tons of arms—rockets, ammunition, mortar rounds, heavy machine guns, and assault rifles—through Iraqi airspace to Damascus. The flights did not escape the notice of the Americans, especially since the Iranians were using wide-body aircraft operated by Yas Air, an Iranian civilian carrier that was soon placed under U.S. Treasury Department sanction.

Jeffrey met with Maliki to protest the flights. "Our relationship isn't about hotels and tomatoes," the characteristically blunt ambassador started, referring to the investment projects many countries sponsored in Iraq. "This is about our military cooperation; this is about you showing the rest of the world that you are not with the Iranian camp."[9] To prod the Iraqis to take action, American diplomats provided specific information about Iranian flights believed to be carrying arms and urged the Iraqis to force them to land, a step the Iraqis were entitled to take since the Iranian aircraft were subject to United Nations sanctions. But then the Iranians started arranging for Il-76s, operated by a Syrian carrier, to ferry the arms, a shift of tactics that the Americans suspected might have been encouraged by Hadi al-Amari himself.

When the Iraqis insisted they did not have clear intelligence on what was on the aircraft, the American embassy arranged for Petraeus to call Maliki from Langley. Eventually, the Americans were able to persuade the Iraqis to clamp down, warning them that if the flights became public, it would torpedo the Iraqis' opportunity to host the Arab League summit. In an April 3, 2012, call after the summit, Obama sought to reinforce Maliki's decision to discourage the Iranian flights. But after the Assad regime was rocked by a bombing that killed several of its highest officials—including Asif Shawkat, the military intelligence chief who had long acted as Syria's liaison to the Quds Force as well as working with Al-Qaeda in Syria—Iran doubled down in supporting the Syrian regime, and the flights started up again. Another round of American pressure prompted the Iraqis to request that two of the Iranian flights land in Baghdad for inspection. No military cargo was found on those planes, but they represented only a fraction of the continued flights.

The episode illustrated a downside of the failure to secure a new SOFA. The Obama administration had been adamant that it would not countenance an agreement that did not provide ironclad immunity from prosecution for American troops. Avoiding even the slightest hint of legal risk, however, meant taking strategic risk with regard to Iran's and Israel's calculations in the region. Iraqi skies were ungoverned territory that friend or foe could use as they saw fit.

The absence of an American stay-behind force also tied in with the Syrian war in another way. By the fall of 2012, Sunni militant groups linked to Al-Qaeda in Iraq were recruiting fighters in some of their old stomping grounds, like rural Diyala, to send into the fight in Syria against the Allawite regime that had once granted Al-Qaeda fighters safe passage in the other direction. In Anbar, tribal fighters associated with the Awakening went west into Syria, too, according to Hamid al-Hayis, one of the Awakening's founders. With the JSOC task force at Balad gone, the American military and intelligence community no longer had their most sophisticated tool for monitoring or countering Al-Qaeda in Iraq's activities as they seemingly began to gain back old ground and even expand into Syria.

As the civilian mission in Iraq ran into obstacles in 2012, it shrank far beyond what had originally been planned. By the time the troops left, the State Department had not received military equipment it had asked the Pentagon for, like two-dozen Black Hawk helicopters, and it had already canceled earlier plans to establish "embassy branch offices" in Mosul and Baqubah. Although a consulate was established in Kirkuk, the consul-general charged with running it eventually began commuting to the ethni-cally divided flashpoint from Irbil. The embassy's once ambitious police training program also shrank considerably. The original American plan had envisioned 350 police trainers, but by September 2012 the program consisted of twenty-one advisers in Baghdad and fourteen in Irbil. Some of the advisers had been targeted in IED attacks, and the Iraqis complained that much of the program had been devised without adequate consultation with the Interior Ministry about what kind of training the police could really use. Adnan al-Asadi of the ministry called the whole program except a portion run by the FBI "useless," and in Basra, the Iraqis made clear that they had no interest in being trained by Americans at all.

By spring, the Iraqi political crisis had flared up with gusto. Maliki quietly sought to expand control over Iraq's electoral machinery. The Iraqi politi-cal system contained a number of independent bodies, such as the Central Bank and the Independent High Electoral Commission, the organization that oversaw voting procedures. It was no secret that Maliki was suspicious of IHEC, believing that it had somehow colluded with the U.N. to manipu-late the March 2010 electoral results against him.

In January 2011, Maliki had received another favorable ruling from Iraq's nominally independent judiciary. Thanks to the ruling, the IHEC was removed from parliament's oversight and put under the supervi-sion of the cabinet, which Maliki headed. The shake-up brought another round of suspicion from various Iraqi parties that the prime minister was steadily moving to consolidate power. Marginalizing his current rivals was not enough. Now it seemed he was trying to undermine the governmental checks on his office.

Then on April 12, 2012, Faraj al-Haydari, the IHEC chief, and a fellow commissioner found themselves sitting in a jail cell: a charge of corruption had been leveled by one of Maliki's political allies. Unable to make bail before the close of business, both men were taken into custody, a deci-sion made by the judge overseeing the case. Because it was a Thursday, the IHEC officials would have to wait until the next business day, Sunday. While in jail, the IHEC chief received a telephone call from someone he did not expect. It was the prime minister. Haydari had already suspected that Maliki had allowed the arrest to take place. The prime minister insisted that he did not know anything about the situation and would use his influence with Iraq's chief justice to get the charges dropped. "I tried to help you and I will speak with Medhat Mahmoud," Haydari recalled Maliki saying to him, referring to Iraq's top judge. To Haydari, the entire episode had been a shot across his bow, a warning of what might be in store for the commission if it stepped out of line.[10]

For the Americans, a new challenge emerged when Barzani decided that he had had enough of Maliki. In late October 2011, Barzani had flown to Tehran and told Supreme Leader Khamenei that he could no longer work with the Iraqi prime minister and that an alternative was needed. Maliki had broken too many promises to the Kurds and was beginning to amass too much power for himself. Maliki got word of the maneuver from Sheikh Abd al-Halim al-Zuhairi, a senior Dawa Party cleric who served as Maliki's interlocutor with Qasim Suleimani, and Rubaie was sent to see Barzani and try to smooth things over.

But the relationship between Barzani and Maliki soon soured to the point where it was beyond repair. In November, the Kurdish leadership signed an exploration deal with the American oil company ExxonMobil. Under the terms of the deal, Exxon would be allowed to drill for oil in six fields, and would split the revenues from any oil that was produced with the Kurdistan Regional Government. Although Maliki had not objected when informed on two occasions of the Kurds' intent to ink the contract, when they finally did so he became incensed. The deal completely bypassed the Oil Ministry in Baghdad, which—though it had dragged its feet when it came to developing the Kurdish region's natural resources—still claimed the legal authority to sign all oil contracts in Iraq. Making matters worse, it soon emerged that two of the oilfields the Kurdish government had granted Exxon permission to drill in were located entirely outside the accepted boundaries of Kurdistan, in the so-called "disputed areas" near the cities of Kirkuk and Mosul that were under de facto Kurdish control. A third field straddled the border between Dohuk Province, which was formally a part of the KRG, and Nineveh Province, which was not.[11] The Kurds had signed off on a deal that granted them sole access to oil revenues from contested territory, without checking with Baghdad first. It was a warning: if Baghdad would not acquiesce to Kurdish demands, Barzani and the Kurdish leadership were prepared to go it alone.

Having taken his case against Maliki to Iran, Barzani approached the White House soon after the last American troops departed. In an April meeting, Barzani outlined his concerns to Obama and Biden. The Kurdish leader told the Americans that he had decided Maliki was not good for Iraq and had to go. Barzani was prepared to convene a meeting of senior Iraqi leaders to secure a vote of no confidence in the prime minister. If all else failed, he would organize a referendum and the Kurdish public would vote on whether to declare independence or remain part of a Maliki-dominated Iraq.

Before his delegation left, Barzani presented the White House with a confidential paper that called into question the American talk of building a long-term strategic relationship with Maliki's government. The F-16 fighter jets that the United States was so eager to sell the Iraqi government so that the country would have air sovereignty could just as easily be used to intimidate the Kurds. With fears growing in the north over Maliki's consolidation of power Barzani proposed that Kurdistan and Washington intensify their cooperation on energy, intelligence-sharing, and security. Fuad Hussein, who as Barzani's chief of staff attended the meetings at the White House, said that the Americans listened politely but made no such commitments. "They want to keep everything quiet," he recalled, noting that the upcoming U.S. elections seemed to overshadow the conversation. "Iraq could come back into the campaign, and that's not good for the administration."[12]

To reassure the Kurds, Biden promised to escalate the American program of diplomatic visits. But the offer did not mollify Barzani, who was determined to press ahead with his two-pronged campaign to unseat Maliki and develop Kurdistan's natural resources. Barzani soon began to sound the alarm about Maliki publicly. "The F-16s must not reach the hand of this man," he told a gathering of reporters in the Kurdish capital of Irbil. "We must either prevent him from having these weapons, or if he has them, he should be in a new position."[13]

By June, the relationship between Barzani and Maliki had turned overtly hostile. Maliki's opponents were gathering in Irbil, trying to assemble enough votes to unseat the prime minister, who had managed to alienate many of the major political players in Iraq. A big question was whether the Sadrists, Kurds, ISCI, and Iraqiya would be able to maintain a unified front against him to hold a vote of no confidence. In June, Maliki himself sent a letter to the White House that attacked the ExxonMobil contracts and alleged that Atheel al-Nujaifi, the brother of the Sunni speaker of parliament, was involved in dubious transactions linked to the deal. An American official interpreted the move as a way to pressure the speaker to hold back from supporting a no-confidence vote.[14] Despite a visit to Irbil by Sadr and considerable speculation that Maliki's days might be numbered, the effort to orchestrate a no-confidence vote failed. Qasim Suleimani registered his disapproval of the scheme in an unpublicized letter to Talabani. Even without Suleimani's intervention, it was clear that Maliki's opponents were having difficulty finding enough common ground to pick an alternative to the prime minister.

The Kurds, for their part, were looking for guarantors of stability other than the United States government. Genel Energy, a Turkish company, announced plans to build a pipeline that could carry 420,000 barrels per day from the disputed territories to Dohuk, where it could be pumped on to Turkey.[15] Discussing the pipeline deal in a cable back to the United States, Jim Jeffrey warned that if construction began, it would be a casus belli for Maliki to go to war with the Kurds.[16] In September 2012, the dispute over the oil issue eased somewhat when Baghdad and Irbil, with much prompting by visiting American officials, worked out an agreement. The accord allowed the Kurds to export oil at a rate of 140,000 barrels a day—and 200,000 barrels a day in 2013—through the pipeline from Kirkuk to Ceyhan, Turkey. Under the arrangements, the Iraqi government agreed to compensate the Kurds for their costs of production and resume supplying them with 17 percent of Iraq's refined oil products. But underlying tensions over oil remained.

There were other friction points, too, particularly a tense July standoff near the Syrian border between Iraqi Army and Peshmerga forces that recalled the confrontations in 2008 over Khanaqin and 2012 over Kirkuk. The episode was spurred by Maliki's worries that the Kurds were using a pontoon bridge to ferry supplies to rebel Kurds in Syria. As at Khanaqin and Kirkuk, the Americans played a behind-the-scenes role in defusing the standoff.

In May, more unsettling news came out regarding Ali Musa Daqduq, the Lebanese Hezbollah operative believed to be linked to the 2007 Karbala attack. After Daqduq was transferred to the Iraqis under the terms of the SOFA Bush signed, an Iraqi appeals court announced that there was insufficient evidence to keep him incarcerated.[17]

Sami al-Askari, one of Maliki's advisers, had tipped off Doug Silliman, the political counselor at the U.S. embassy, to the impending release before it actually happened but sought to assure him that Daqduq would not immediately go free. Instead, Askari said he would stay in Iraqi custody for a period of not more than two months, ostensibly so that the government could verify that there were no grounds for charging him in any other incidents. Assuming that nothing was uncovered, Daqduq would quietly be put under house arrest in the Green Zone for an unspecified period of time, during which he would be granted very limited contact with outsiders. Askari had spoken with the leaders of Hezbollah, who had assured him that they would not advertise or ostentatiously celebrate his release.

Citing a 1934 extradition treaty negotiated by Franklin Delano Roosevelt's administration and the Iraqi monarchy, the Obama administration formally requested on June 1 that Iraq extradite Daqduq for trial in the United States. Under the terms of the treaty, a detainee who was arrested in Iraq pending extradition to the United States could be held for up to three months in Iraqi prison while the extradition request was being considered.[18]

Still, the Americans were not hopeful. An internal American assessment concluded that there was "no serious possibility" that Daqduq would be convicted or extradited to the United States. Rather, the Maliki government appeared to be planning to keep him in detention long enough to partially assuage the Americans, but not so long that it would be unacceptable to Iran and Hezbollah.

As the 2012 American election approached, Maliki's aides fleshed out the sort of compromise they had in mind. In an attempt to mollify the Obama administration, they proposed that Iraq would hold onto Daqduq until the election was over, a suggestion that the administration rejected as insufficient—they did not want the Hezbollah commander released at all. But two days after Obama's reelection, a senior Maliki aide told Tony Blinken in a phone call that Iraq no longer had grounds to hold Daqduq. Biden called Maliki the next week to make a last minute appeal that Daqduq not be set free. But on November 15, the Iraqis released Daqduq, who immediately left for Lebanon.

Looking back on the more than eight-year-long war, Iraq's politicians delivered their verdict. Talabani, who had defied the Obama administration to hang on to the presidency, was optimistic. "I think Iraq has a unique democracy," he said. "From the extreme left to the extreme right, there is a newspaper. Everybody is free to say what they want. So I think that we have a kind of democracy and that makes trouble for us from our brothers in Arab countries who are not in favor of democracies in their country."[19]

Allawi disagreed. "First of all, let me tell you: I don't believe that we have democracy," he said. "What lies in the heart of democracy is the respect of the elections, is the rule of law. It's the institutions that protect democracy. And we don't have this. We have a very naked kind of exploitation, intimidation, arrests. We don't have power-sharing at all. So the Americans would be leaving frankly a severely injured country. Severely injured."[20]

Adil Abd al-Mahdi, who had come close several times to being prime minister, was more optimistic. "Without democracy Iraq cannot be governed," said Abd al-Mahdi. "Even if we have a change here, people will not go backward and say we need a despotic regime or a tyrannical regime. They will ask for more democracy. They will ask for more freedom. They will ask for more constitutional acts. They will not ask to oppose the constitution. But even if they do, they will ratify another one. So I think we are on the right track. The Americans are sometimes rushing things, but they are burning what they are cooking. Because Iraq is a complicated society you need to give time so solutions will be clearer and clearer."[21]

Barham Salih, the urbane Kurd who had been in the upper rungs of the Iraqi government for years, was more skeptical. "There is mounting concern that Maliki has become too centralizing, too authoritarian," he said. "Iraqi history is unmistakable: centralizing rule in Baghdad invariably leads to dictatorship and instability. Authoritarian rule will deepen mistrust among Iraq's communities. Maliki is no Saddam, but we may be witnessing a repeat of General Kasim's tumultuous reign in 1958. The unity and stability of today's Iraq can only be kept by an inclusive government, by a leadership that can build bridges. The present government in Baghdad has proven polarizing and has deepened the sectarian and ethnic divide in the country. Yes, in the context of transitions of the Middle East, Iraq is possibly doing better than Libya and Syria, but I must admit I cannot be terribly optimistic about the future Iraq today, and that is because of a profound failure of its leadership. It failed to seize the moment, it failed to utilize unprecedented international support and abundant resources to help the country come together. Iraq could be an amazing success with good leadership."[22]

———

In his years in power, Maliki had proved to be a determined survivor—so much so that his ability to consolidate control had become a worry that eclipsed concerns over Al-Qaeda in Iraq and sectarian infighting. Jim Jeffrey had lived through most of the new Iraq's short history. As he wound up his last tour in Baghdad in June 2012, Jeffrey believed that Iraq was still a qualified success, but a somewhat precarious one.

Jeffrey had conceived of a Plan B, but it was not one that he was eager to implement. If Maliki continued on an authoritarian path, the United States could slowly start to withdraw support from the prime minister and give more backing to the Kurds, while pressing Baghdad to move to a more energetic version of federalism. But the veteran ambassador hoped that it would not come to that. To head off that danger, Jeffrey cautioned Maliki that he needed to take his critics' demands seriously and try to meet them halfway. The threat of a no-confidence vote was not to be discounted.

But Jeffrey had a message for Washington, too, which he noted in a classified cable soon before leaving his post and retiring from the Foreign Service. The very Iraqi leader the president had touted at the White House as a model for the region had "dictatorial" tendencies. The American government needed to work actively to contain them.[23]

Epilogue

During his push toward Baghdad in 2003, Major General David Petraeus posed the essential question about the Iraq War: "Tell me, how does this end?" The nearly nine years of war may be best understood as a struggle to come up with the answer.

The Bush administration's initial endgame was that the invasion would culminate in a speedy handoff to the Iraqis. "The concept was that we would defeat the army, but the institutions would hold, everything from ministries to police forces," Condoleezza Rice recalled. "You would be able to bring new leadership but that we were going to keep the body in place." That strategy said more about the Bush team's hostility to nation building than it did about the project to fill the vacuum left by Saddam Hussein's departure. And it left unspoken how the United States would ensure that the Iraq that arose from the ruins of Saddam's state would remain on the road to democracy.

After discovering that there were, in fact, no durable institutions to take over the new Iraq, the United States' dream of a turnkey operation vanished and the Bush administration embarked on a long effort to build a new Iraqi state from the ground up. In the early years, the expectation was that the machinery of democracy—a series of elections and referendums—would inexorably lead to a representative government. It was a misconception that failed to take into account the vagaries of the election procedure, the possibility of a Sunni boycott, and the tenuous nature of the security the Americans had established. A history of this period reads like a litany of chances missed and opportunities lost.

Again, a major deficiency was the ending the Americans had in mind. Faced with the daunting prospect of fighting an entrenched insurgency, the

United States' initial strategy was one of transition. The goal was not so much to defeat the enemy as it was to whittle it down to a sufficiently manageable size for the newly minted Iraq military and its nascent ministries to take over. In Washington, President Bush talked about victory, but the goal was the more modest one of shifting the fight to the Iraqi security forces that the United States had first abolished and then struggled to stand up.

There were indications within General George Casey's own command that the strategy would be inadequate to the task. In 2005, a Red Team that was commissioned to take a fresh look at the strategy made the point that if the well-trained and -equipped American military was finding it hard to fend off the insurgents, a less capable Iraqi force would discover it was utterly overmatched. The report recommended a counterinsurgency strategy to clear and hold areas, protect the population, and isolate insurgents. But despite the mounting signs of sectarian conflict, including civil strife and the systematic infiltration of the state's armed forces and ministries by militias, nothing was done. It was not until Iraq approached the precipice of an all-out civil war that the White House was prepared to undertake a major course correction.

By 2006, what had begun as a war of choice had become a war of necessity. A 1,200-year-old Arab capital was being savaged and demographically reshaped as surely as any city in the Balkans of the 1990s. New graveyards for the victims of this Iraqi-on-Iraqi war, like the Adhamiya Martyrs Cemetery in a Sunni neighborhood in the shadow of Sadr City, were filling up. By stepping back, even in the name of the sovereignty of Iraq's new government, the United States had ceded the initiative to its opponents, including Al-Qaeda, local Sunni insurgents, and the Quds Force and its Iraqi partners.

Approaching a crossroads, Bush decided to dispatch five additional combat brigades, a bold but belated move. Having opened Pandora's box, the Americans had an obligation to tamp down the violence before heading to the exit. The United States owed it to try the surge not only for the people it had sought to liberate, though, but also for the soldiers and Marines who had been fighting in Iraq for nearly four years when Petraeus took command. As bad as an overextended military was, a defeated military would have been worse. Leaving Iraq prematurely and allowing its militias and insurgents to slug it out would have haunted America's ground forces for many years to come and been a devastating setback for American policy in the region.

As a military event, the surge succeeded beyond any reasonable expectation in tamping down sectarian violence, breaking the back of Al-Qaeda in Iraq, and then, in the unexpected final chapter brought on by Maliki's Charge of the Knights, damaging and sidelining the Mahdi Army. The new strategy also served as a catalyst for the Sunni Awakening, which would make its way from Anbar to the Baghdad belts and then the capital itself. As American brigades pushed into the belts and also confronted the long-ignored Mahdi Army, violence in Iraq began to fall. As Petraeus and Crocker prepared to make their case to Bush and Congress, though, they continued to face second-guessing and attempts to narrow their options and change their strategy, not just from skeptical lawmakers but also from CENTCOM and the Joint Chiefs. But the surge's gains endured. Though Al-Qaeda in Iraq would remain the most active of Al-Qaeda's Middle East franchises to the end of America's involvement in the country, the group was dealt a crushing body blow in 2007, transforming it from a terrorist group embedded within a broad-based, terrain-controlling local insurgency to merely a terrorist group. It is a mark of how little military politics were changed by Iraq that the two most senior officers during the Obama years—General Martin Dempsey and Admiral James "Sandy" Winnefeld, the chairman and vice-chairman of the Joint Chiefs—were either agnostic about the surge when it was first proposed or actively opposed it, and that some of the war's best tactical commanders, like Colonel Mike Kershaw, never rose higher in the ranks.

The chicken-and-egg "debate" over whether the Awakening or the surge came first and which was more important in diminishing violence in Iraq misses a basic point: the Anbar Awakening came before the surge was even conceived and was barely considered in the surge debates, but it was not until American troops had recommitted themselves during the surge to areas where their presence had been sparse that the more broadly defined Awakening groups, including insurgents who "flipped," began to appear outside the borders of Sunni Anbar and have a strategic effect on the war in Baghdad and the belts. The Anbar Awakening itself took off in 2006 after Colonel Sean MacFarland's troops, in an exception to the drawdown strategy, pushed into enemy-held areas to stay, proving themselves worthy allies in the Anbari tribes' fight against Al-Qaeda. The relationship between American operations and presence and the appearance of Awakening groups elsewhere during the surge was similar: by coming in fighting and looking like they meant to stay, American troops gave Iraqi civilians—and many former insurgents—a partner they could trust. In Anbar the enemy was Al-Qaeda. In some sectarian hotspots like Abu Ghraib, though, Awakening groups sought American help not only in fighting Sunni extremists but in protecting against government forces that were feeding the cycle of violence. By lobbying the Iraqi government to accept Awakening members and to put them on its payroll, and by entering their biometric details in an intelligence database, Petraeus's and Odierno's commands institutionalized appreciation of the Awakening.

The second aim of the surge, the one that remained unfulfilled to the end according to the military's own report card, was to push Iraq's factionalized government, in which ministries themselves were battlegrounds of the civil war, to reform. In the United States at the time, "political progress" in Iraq was often measured by the rubric of how many contentious laws were passed. In reality America's efforts to reform Iraq's government and governance went much deeper than the "benchmark" laws—and the problems went much deeper, too. The solution involved prodding and purging the sectarian-minded officials who had infiltrated and in many cases taken over Iraq's ministries, particularly those involved in delivering social services or providing security, and purging those who resisted reform.

The increased security brought on by the surge and the Iraqi-driven battlefield events that took place alongside it was a necessary precondition for Iraq to move forward politically, but as H.R. McMaster's Governance Assessment Team found, it was not a sufficient one. By the team's standards, political progress was fitful and often incomplete. If the United States had switched its strategy earlier, a longer surge might have been matched by greater progress in politics and governance. And if the Bush administration had not been so narrowly focused on signing a status of forces agreement during its last year in office, it could have devoted greater attention to the deep fissures in Iraqi politics, perhaps even finding an alternative to Maliki—as many of his peers attempted to convince the administration to do in December 2007—and possibly averting Iraq's post-surge tilt toward authoritarianism.

Arriving in the White House in January 2009, the new administration of Barack Obama inherited from Bush a military situation that was vastly improved, but a political environment that was still riven by divisions and which was also developing a new and menacing facet in Maliki's tendency toward authoritarianism. The incoming administration is to be commended for one of its first actions with regard to Iraq: backtracking on its unrealistic campaign promise to remove combat forces within sixteen months. The new president heard Odierno and Crocker out on troop levels and withdrawal schedules and met them more than halfway. The administration had a fresh chance, though, to reengage with Iraq's leaders and shape its politics, a chance that came just as Iraq emerged from provincial elections in which many sectarian troublemakers had been thrown out and many more secular and nationalist candidates swept in. Obama did not act decisively on that chance, choosing instead to take a more hands-off approach on Iraq by focusing on winding down American involvement rather than energetically trying to shape the situation he had inherited.

This decision was characteristic of those Obama made on Iraq: he saw America's involvement there not as an opportunity, or even as containing opportunities, but rather as a leftover minefield, a path out of which had to be charted as quickly as possible. In seeking to find such a path and "normalize" diplomatic relations with a country in which the United States was still fighting a war, the Obama team created, by appointing Chris Hill, an unfortunate counterpoint to the model civilian-military relationship that Petraeus and Crocker had established: a toxic and dysfunctional pairing that went beyond personal differences between Hill and Odierno to deeper ones in interpretation of Iraq's politics and visions of its future.

Compared to Bush's weekly videoconferences with Maliki, Obama's direct role with Iraq's leaders was minimal, a fact made especially stark during the 2010 government formation process when Obama called Talabani, a man he barely knew, with the extraordinary request that he step down from the presidency, an appeal that was turned down. In fact, as the episode shows, Obama, like Bush, was trying behind the scenes to engineer an inclusive Iraqi government and the effort largely failed.

That the Obama administration brought the war in Iraq to an end is true, but only because of terms already negotiated by his predecessor. Obama was in office when the last American combat unit left Iraq before the end of December 2011 in accordance with the status of forces agreement Bush and Maliki signed in 2008.

Given the vicissitudes of Iraqi politics, the negotiation of a new SOFA that would have allowed a continuing if minimal American troop presence might have proven impossible under the best of circumstances. But the American effort was hindered both by the administration's ignorance of the lessons learned during the 2008 negotiations—for example, that negotiating an agreement would be a long process best begun early, and that direct and frequent engagement by the president himself was essential— and by its own ambivalence toward prolonging a military mission that Obama had very publicly pledged to end during the campaign.

The small American military presence that likely would have resulted from a new status of forces agreement may seem a pittance compared to the hundreds of thousands of troops that rotated through Iraq over the years. But this small force's absence has not been without strategic consequences. The United States leaves Iraq with no air defense capability, not even the limited capability Saddam's air force had in 1991. Without the presence of American F-16s, the skies over Iraq are an unguarded air corridor—open, at least initially, to Iran's arms shipments to the Assad regime in Syria. It has also lowered the political threshold for the Israeli strike against Iran that both Bush and Obama have expended considerable energy struggling to deter.

A less-appreciated but no less important consequence of the U.S. military's departure is that there are simply no Americans left to do the laborious tasks of tracking violent incidents and reporting on the situation in the country. The State Department's diplomats are largely confined to a handful of protected compounds; it is enormously expensive to hire the private security contractors required for frequent visits to the "red zone," and stationing personnel all around the country is difficult when there are no bases where State can piggyback off military-provided security. Even the CIA is cutting back on its officers in Baghdad. In an article in *Foreign Affairs,* Vice President Joseph Biden's national security adviser Tony Blinken asserted that Iraq was "less violent, more democratic, and more prosperous than at any time in recent history." But the claim rested on a comparison of attacks being reported today and those reported during the height of the surge in 2007–2008. A separate analysis by Michael Knights, which was briefed to several intelligence agencies, concluded that Iraqi-on-Iraqi violence had gone up 18 percent in the wake of the U.S. withdrawal. The truth may be more unsettling: the United States government has diminished awareness of events in one of the most strategically vital countries in the Middle East.

The Iraq that the United States has left behind is no longer embroiled in sectarian strife, although sectarian tensions and potential flashpoints remain. The greater threat to the country's American-initiated experiment in democracy is the authoritarianism evident in Maliki, the leader the United States and Iran have both found agreeable enough to support. When the Obama administration acquiesced in the questionable judicial opinion that prevented Ayad Allawi's bloc, after it won the most seats in 2010, from the first attempt at forming a new government, it undermined the prospects, however slim, for a compromise that might have led to a genuinely inclusive and cross-sectarian government. By the time the American military left, Iraq had still not passed a major milestone in the life of any successful new democracy: the peaceful handover of power to an opposition party. The consequences of this decision are troubling, to say the least. As Vice President Biden himself said of Iraq in a 2010 interview, "It is important that it become a democracy, because that is the only vehicle by which you can hold together such a diverse population that has such a history and inclination to actually be at each other's throats. Otherwise, what you do is, you end up having something in the form of an authoritarian government that just builds hostility, and eventually it will explode."[1]

Acknowledgments

This book would not have been possible without the help of hundreds of individuals. We are deeply indebted to everyone who added their piece to the story, many of whom by virtue of their position cannot be mentioned. But many are deserving of special recognition.

We wanted to capture the perspective of Iraqi leaders to the greatest extent possible, so that they could be active participants in the narrative. Senior Iraqi politicians helpfully made themselves available for interviews, and many spoke frankly about the decisions they still face. These included Prime Minister Nuri al-Maliki, President Jalal Talabani, the president of the Kurdish Regional Government Massoud Barzani, Deputy Prime Minister Salih al-Mutlaq, Deputy Prime Minister Rowsch Shaways, Vice President Tariq al-Hashimi, Iraqiya leader Ayad Allawi, ISCI leaders Adil Abd al-Mahdi and Ammar al-Hakim, Finance Minister Rafi al-Issawi, Foreign Minister Hoshyar Zebari, and Ahmed Chalabi. In Washington, Qubad Talabani, the envoy for the Kurdish Regional Government, and Samir Sumaidaie, Iraq's former ambassador, were very helpful.

The military story would not have been complete without the perspectives of higher headquarters and the field. Generals David Petraeus, Ray Odierno, George Casey, and Peter Chiarelli were generous with their time, as were many other generals and lower-ranking officers. Their participation allowed us to explain the war not only as it was experienced by troops on the ground. Special thanks also go to the commanders who allowed us to embed with their units, including Lieutenant Colonel Dan Barnett in Sadr City; Colonel Steve Townsend in Baqubah; Lieutenant Colonels John Norris, Jeff Peterson, and Joe McLamb in West Baghdad; Colonel

Stephen Twitty and Lieutenant Colonel Keith Barclay in Mosul; Lieutenant Colonel Owen Lovejoy in Haditha; Lieutenant Colonel Tom Graves in Hit; Lieutenant Colonel Mark Odom in Hawr Rajab; Lieutenant Colonel Ken Adgie in Arab Jabour; and Captain Ben Richards in Buhriz, among many others.

The American embassy in Baghdad was helpful. We were aided by the senior diplomats who served in Iraq, including CPA chief L. Paul "Jerry" Bremer III and Ambassadors John Negroponte, Zalmay Khalilzad, Ryan Crocker, Christopher Hill, and James Jeffrey. Each of these diplomats granted interviews to explain their crucial roles in shaping the successive Iraqi governments. A bevy of embassy deputies and aides also spoke with us to share their experiences in Iraq.

In Washington, officials at the Pentagon, State Department, and White House contributed to our knowledge, as did key lawmakers. Matt Sherman's assistance was much appreciated.

The *New York Times* Baghdad Bureau was extremely helpful, including bureau chiefs Tim Arango, Alissa Rubin, Steven Lee Mye, and John Burns. Rich Oppel and Marc Santora provided important inputs, as did Omar al-Jawoshy, one of the bureau's able Iraqi reporters and translators.

In the course of covering the war, we were privileged to work with a number of exceptional photographers. Many of them generously offered to share their photographs for this book. João Silva's contributions were especially valuable—a veteran war photographer, he shot more front-page-quality frames during his time in Iraq than most photographers capture in a lifetime. Other photographers to whom we are indebted are Ben Lowy, Jim Wilson, Robert Nickelsberg, Gregg Carlstrom, and Eros Hoagland.

Important institutional support was provided by the Institute for the Study of War, the Woodrow Wilson Center for International Scholars, and the United States Institute of Peace. A number of Iraq experts were generous with their expertise, especially Ramzy Mardini, whose understanding of Iraqi politics is unmatched. Lieutenant Colonel Joel Rayburn, Emma Sky, and Marisa Cochrane Sullivan were also extremely helpful.

Our dedicated research assistants, Steve Stoddard and Nick Hubbard, helped see the project through by digging through archives and unclassified documents, reviewing hundreds of hours of taped interviews, and editing chapter drafts. Stoddard worked in the United States Senate during the surge, and his careful research contributed greatly to the chapters on the Iraq Study Group, the 2008 status of forces agreement, and other political developments surrounding the war. Hubbard provided insightful feedback and input that helped enormously with the actual writing of the book, especially the sections on Iraq during the Obama years. We were also aided by a number of researchers, including Matthew Sinkez, Zachary Gorman, Anthony Bell, Will Bardenwerper, Josh Linden, Alexandra Shaheen, and Kate Eyerman. Joy Glasser provided valuable support.

We would also like to thank Dr. Lorry Fenner and David Palkki of the Conflict Records Research Center, who facilitated our access to English translations of Saddam Hussein's government documents that United States forces seized from various locations during the invasion. Thanks also to the Center for Army Lessons Learned at Fort Leavenworth for providing oral histories, the U.S. Army Center of Military History for letting us access archival material, and the U.S. Marine Corps Historical Center. Alexander Cochran and Major Kelly Peyton Howard, General Casey's historical advisers, were helpful guides.

Our agent, Andrew Wylie, helped shepherd the book through the publishing world. At the Knopf Doubleday Publishing Group, our patient and persistent editor, Erroll McDonald, offered thoughtful feedback on how to better present a sprawling, complex tale. Lieutenant Colonel (Retired) R. L. "Bill" Cody, our cartographer, meticulously produced all of the maps for the book from scratch. Thanks also to the entire Pantheon production team, including managing editor Altie Karper, copyeditors Fred Chase and Amy Stackhouse, text designer Kristen Bearse, production manager Lisa Montebello, jacket designer Peter Mendelsund, and editorial assistant Caroline Bleeke.

Thanks also go to our wives, Cheryl and Peggy, and our children for enduring a marathon that at times seemed as long as the war itself.

Notes

CHAPTER 1 *Desert Crossing*

1. Interviews with White House and Iraqi officials.
2. White House transcript, "Remarks by President Obama and Prime Minister al-Maliki of Iraq in a Joint Press Conference," 12 December 2011.
3. Telephone conversation between President Bush and President Ozal of Turkey, Bush Library Archives, 20 April 1991, Richard Haass Working File, 22.
4. William J. Clinton, "Statement on Signing the Iraq Liberation Act of 1998," 31 October 1998.
5. After 2003, the Iraq Survey Group, a CIA-supported task force, was asked to provide an accounting of Saddam Hussein's weapons of mass destruction programs. It was led by Charles A. Duelfer, a former senior United Nations weapons inspector. Duelfer said in an interview that Iraq's chemical, biological, and nuclear weapons programs were defunct by the time of the December 1998 raid that was ordered by President Clinton.

   "After the war the Iraq Survey Group concluded that by the time of the Desert Fox raid, Baghdad had eliminated its nuclear, chemical and biological weapons programs. Ballistic missile programs were continuing up to the very limit permitted by UN resolutions—and once inspectors left, they exceeded the UN limits," Duelfer said. "So, by December 1998, Iraq had finally revealed (after years of deception) the extent of its past WMD programs. But with such a track record of lying, and the continuing obstruction of inspection activities, the inspectors had no reason to give Saddam the benefit of the doubt. The inspectors could not verify fully the Iraqi claims."
6. Interview, Laurence Pope.
7. "Desert Crossing Seminar, After Action Report, June 28–30, 1999." A declassified version of the still-secret report was obtained by the authors through the Freedom of Information Act.
8. Interview, Martin Indyk.
9. "Iraq: Goals, Objectives, and Strategy," document shared with the authors.
10. Interview, Brent Scowcroft.
11. Interview, Stephen J. Hadley.
12. Interview, General (Retired) Anthony Zinni.

13. Interview, Zalmay Khalilzad.
14. Interviews, former senior officials.
15. Interview, Zalmay Khalilzad.
16. Hadley reports that he cannot remember making such a call, but Armitage recalls it.
17. Account provided by a military official familiar with notes of Frank's discussion.
18. "Text of President Bush's 2003 State of the Union Address," *Washington Post*, 28 January 2003.
19. James Dobbins et al., *America's Role in Nation-Building: From Germany to Iraq* (Santa Monica: RAND Corporation, 2003), pp. 167–221. The report resoundingly endorsed the "outside-in" approach in its conclusion even as it outlined a number of the problems Bremer would eventually confront: "Democratic nation-building is possible given a sufficient input of resources and a long-term commitment. However, these inputs could be very high. . . . Overly short departure deadlines are incompatible with the requirements of nation-building. The United States will only succeed in Iraq if it is willing to spend time establishing robust institutions and does not tie its departure to artificial deadlines. In this regard, setting dates for early national elections can be counterproductive. . . . Political, ethnic, and sectarian fragmentation and lack of support from neighboring states are important hindrances. Germany and Japan had homogenous societies, while Bosnia's and Kosovo's neighbors either supported transition or were powerless to disrupt the process actively. Iraq combines the worst of both cases. . . . There is no reason why Iraq cannot be democratized and establish democratic institutions and a pluralist polity. There are, however, a number of reasons why democratization will not be rapid or smooth in Iraq. The lack of a democratic experience and a tradition of authoritarian politics are complemented by the absence of agreement on power-sharing among the country's main ethnic, sectarian, and tribal groups. The hollowing out of the Iraqi middle class and a young population with little experience of the outside world do not provide a conducive environment for democratization. Existing power elites and the 'shadow state' will resist transfer of power from their hands and may retain the economic and physical authority to undermine attempts to bring in new elites and power centers." Interestingly, the report estimated that if the international community maintained the same ratio of troops to civilian population in Iraq that it did in Kosovo, 526,000 foreign troops would be required through 2005; similarly, "Bosnian levels" implied a force of 145,000 staying through 2008.
20. Interview with L. Paul "Jerry" Bremer III; Michael R. Gordon and General Bernard E. Trainor, *COBRA II: The Inside Story of the Invasion and Occupation of Iraq* (New York: Pantheon, 2006), pp. 545–50.
21. Interview, senior administration official.
22. CPA planning document provided to the authors.
23. L. Paul Bremer III, "Facts for Feith," *National Review Online*, 19 March 2008.
24. Michael R. Gordon, "Fateful Choice on Iraqi Army Bypassed Debate," *New York Times*, 17 March 2008.
25. Transcript of Jeremy Greenstock, oral evidence submitted in private to the Iraq Inquiry and later declassified, p. 46, 26 May 2010.
26. Interview, former CPA official.
27. Interview, Massoud Barzani.

28. Interview, former CPA official.
29. Transcript of Jeremy Greenstock, oral evidence submitted to the Iraq Inquiry, p. 63, 15 December 2009.
30. "Security," CPA/CJTF-7 campaign plan for Operation Iraqi Freedom, July 2003, PowerPoint presentation obtained by the authors, declassified 16 October 2009. The plan identified twenty-seven different security requirements for Iraq after February 2004, the vast majority of which were to be transferred to the Iraqis by then.
31. Military historian interview, Lieutenant Colonel Bjarne "Mike" Iverson.

CHAPTER 2 *Politics of the Gun*

1. Military historian interview, Lieutenant Colonel Bjarne "Mike" Iverson.
2. Interview, intelligence official.
3. Brian Knowlton, "Top U.S. General in Iraq Sees 'Classical Guerilla-Type' War," *New York Times,* 16 July 2003.
4. Secretary of Defense Donald Rumsfeld, Department of Defense official transcript of 18 June 2003 press conference.
5. Robert Earle, *Nights in the Pink Motel: An American Strategist's Pursuit of Peace in Iraq* (Annapolis: Naval Institute Press, 2008), p. 34.
6. Combined Joint Task Force 7 Assessments and Initiative Group—Red Cell, "Sunni Arab Resistance: 'Politics of the Gun,'" February 2004, report obtained by the authors.
7. Shortly after the First Gulf War ended, the Iraqi Intelligence Service was directed to seek out and make contact with organizations that might be suitable proxies to carry out assignments abroad. Correspondence from the Fedayeen Saddam dated March 1993 listed a number of terrorist organizations with whom they were in contact.

   The nationalities of more than one hundred foreign fighters who trained with the Fedayeen Saddam during the First Gulf War included: Palestinian, Syrian, Lebanese, Sudanese, Jordanian, Tunisian, Moroccan, Eritrean, and Egyptian. English translations of captured Iraqi government archives, reviewed by authors at the National Defense University's Conflict Records Research Center, Washington, D.C.
8. Interviews, senior military officials.
9. In a 1992 meeting, Saddam told his advisers: "We need to make people feel that they are our people and therefore these people will fulfill their duties without receiving any instructions from us. . . . You do not know Bedouins the way I know them; he will never surrender his weapon. I am familiar with them, their history. . . . Write it down . . . tell them to use the tribes." English translation of an audiotaped conversation between Saddam and his Revolutionary Command Council in February 1992; reviewed by the authors at the National Defense University's Conflict Records Research Center, Washington, D.C.
10. Interview, U.S. government official.
11. Interview, military official.
12. Notes of a meeting participant.
13. Interview, Lieutenant Colonel (Retired) Mark Grdovic. In the spring of 2002, the CIA and small numbers of soldiers from the 10th Special Forces Group formed joint "pilot teams" to advise Kurdish fighters in northern Iraq ahead of the insertion of many more Special Forces after the war began. A Special

Forces detachment, ODA 076, was split into two pilot teams of six soldiers and several CIA men each, and snuck in from Turkey in October 2002. One pilot team went to Irbil to work with the Kurdistan Democratic Party (KDP), while the other went to Sulaymaniyah to work with the Patriotic Union of Kurdistan (PUK). At the end of the year, three men from the latter team became the first U.S. soldiers to see combat in the war when, while touring the PUK's front lines, they came under mortar fire from Ansar al-Islam militants and directed Kurdish artillery fire to silence it, an action for which they received Bronze Stars.

Three weeks before the March 2003 invasion, the next wave of CIA–Special Forces pilot teams entered the country through a ruse. When an American delegation led by Zalmay Khalilzad and Lieutenant General Colby Broadwater drove into Iraq from Turkey for talks with the Kurdish leaders, six more pilot teams accompanied them, billing themselves at the border as the security detail for the delegation, but then stayed behind. Five of the six teams were able to get in before the Turkish border guards caught on. Soon afterward, those thirty-seven soldiers were joined by four more: the commanders and operations officers of two Special Forces battalions, including Grdovic. The teams paid local construction workers to complete three partially built airstrips that dated to the 1980s, so that when the invasion began, the rest of the two battalions would be able to fly in and land on MC-130 transports.

In one incident in mid-March, another group of Special Forces soldiers wound up in the thick of things. Three weapons sergeants were touring the PUK's front lines near Halabja when mortar shells began falling. The soldiers quickly took over a PUK mortar position and began returning fire, silencing the Ansar al-Islam mortar team. "We knew we had kind of broken the rules, but we were pretty proud of ourselves for doing it," Grdovic recalled of the incident, which he learned about when his three sergeants reported back to his command post about it.

14. L. Paul Bremer III, "Iraq's Path to Sovereignty," 8 September 2003.
15. Account provided to the authors by a meeting participant.
16. James Dobbins et. al., *Occupying Iraq: A History of the Coalition Provisional Authority* (Santa Monica: RAND Corporation, 2009), p. 10.
17. Interview, L. Paul Bremer III.
18. Interview, L. Paul Bremer III.
19. Account provided to the authors by a meeting participant.
20. Interview, former NSC official.
21. Interview, former administration official.
22. Personal correspondence of L. Paul Bremer III, reviewed by the authors.
23. Internal military report, reviewed by the authors.
24. Combined Joint Task Force 7, "Operation Lyon (BIAP Counter MANPADS) Brief to Deputy Secretary of Defense" (SECRET), 1 February 2004.
25. Notes of a meeting participant.
26. Duong Van Mai Elliott, *RAND in Southeast Asia: A History of the Vietnam War Era* (Santa Monica: RAND Corporation, 2010), p. 74.
27. Dobbins et al., *Occupying Iraq*, pp. 273–74.
28. Interview, former CPA official.
29. Account provided by L. Paul Bremer III.
30. Joint Staff Intelligence Directorate (J2), "Sunni Outreach to the Governing Council and Coalition Provisional Authority" (SECRET), 3 October 2003.

31. Account provided by U.S. officials.
32. Even under the oppressive authoritarian rule of the Baath Party, the power of Iraq's tribes could never be fully neutralized. The regime devoted immense amounts of energy to manipulate and control them. A memo from the General Security Directorate circa 1991–1992 indicates that Saddam's regime sought to "give the Clans a limited and changing role but not at the expense of government or party organization." Some of the key tactics the Baathist regime used to achieve this were to selectively reward tribes with gifts, such as land or fishing rights; to introduce elements of competition between tribes; influence the leadership structures within tribes; and to serve as the final arbiter for inter-tribal disputes. By selectively pitting certain tribes against others, Saddam was able to quickly rebalance his alliances if any particular tribe became powerful enough to threaten the regime's overall control.

Captured audio conversations between Saddam and his inner circle also reveal that the 1991 uprising appeared to be a turning point in how Saddam interacted with the tribes. The uprising caught the regime completely by surprise, which prompted Saddam to say "regarding the tribes, we are facing a new reality." While George H. W. Bush's lofty rhetoric during the First Gulf War may have helped spark the uprising, the war itself gave the regime some advantages in suppressing it; communications throughout the country were completely disrupted by the destruction, which left the uprising fragmented and uncoordinated. One of the key lessons Saddam learned from the experience was that tribal elements could be used as an effective supplemental security force to control the population, particularly in rural areas that had a minimal presence of the more formal state security forces.

After the First Gulf War, Saddam's regime elevated the importance of engaging tribes that live near borders with other countries. It also took more concrete steps toward integrating tribal elements into the state security apparatus. This planning is readily apparent during the lead-up to the U.S. invasion in 2003, and there are multiple accounts of how tribal elements were expected to participate in defending the Iraq homeland from an American invasion. English translations of captured Iraqi government archives, reviewed by the authors at the National Defense University's Conflict Records Research Center, Washington, D.C.
33. Army historian interview, Colonel Derek Harvey.
34. United States Special Operations Command History and Research Office, *USSOCOM History 1987–2007* (Tampa: 2007), 119–21; Lieutenant Colonel (Retired) Steve Russell, *We Got Him! A Memoir of the Hunt and Capture of Saddam Hussein* (Marietta, GA: Deeds Publishing, 2011).
35. Susan Sachs, "The Capture of Hussein: Ex-Dictator Hussein Caught in Makeshift Hideout, Bush Says 'Dark Era' for Iraqis Is Over," *New York Times*, 15 December 2003.
36. Edward Wong, "The Capture of Hussein: The Resistance—At Least 17 Die in Attack on Police Station West of Baghdad," *New York Times*, 15 December 2003.

CHAPTER 3 *"Sovereignty with Limits"*

1. Interview, Haydar al-Khoei.
2. Interview, U.N. official.

3. James Dobbins et al., *Occupying Iraq: A History of the Coalition Provisional Authority* (Santa Monica: RAND Corporation, 2009), p. 287.

4. Dobbins et al., *Occupying Iraq*, p. 270.

5. Interview, U.N. official.

6. Interview, Larry Diamond; Larry Diamond, *Squandered Victory: The American Occupation and the Bungled Effort to Bring Democracy to Iraq* (New York: Times Books, 2005), pp. 53–66.

7. Notes of a meeting participant.

8. George W. Bush, "2004 State of the Union Address," 20 January 2004.

9. Notes of a meeting participant.

10. Scott Shane and Charlie Savage, "Bin Laden Raid Revives Debate on Value of Torture," *New York Times*, 3 May 2011.

11. Notes of a meeting participant.

12. Combined Joint Task Force 7, "Operation Stuart Brief to Deputy Secretary of Defense" (SECRET), 1 February 2004.

13. Wolfowitz was briefed in detail on the plans for Operation Stuart during his February 2004 visit to Baghdad (Combined Joint Task Force 7, "Operation Stuart Brief to Deputy Secretary of Defense" [SECRET], 1 February 2004), and then later in the month on the specific authorities for the raid by the Joint Staff (Joint Staff J3, "Deputy Secretary of Defense Decision Brief: Operation STUART" [SECRET], 20 February 2004). A 14 February email from CENTCOM's Major General John Sattler to Joint Staff operations officer Lieutenant General Norton Schwartz ("Authority to Execute Operation Stuart; Arrest/Capture of Sadr" [SECRET], 14 February 2004), delved into the same issues, and also noted that Special Forces troops from the Iraq-based Joint Special Operations Task Force—Arabian Peninsula had been busy preparing. "The house indicated in the OPLAN is the one they (JSOTF-AP) have cased and rehearsed before," Sattler wrote, " . . . it belongs to one of Sadr's Lts, and is one they were rehearsed and prepared to take down last Dec."

14. Notes of a meeting participant.

15. Interview, John Negroponte.

16. Interview, John Negroponte.

CHAPTER 4 *Vigilant Resolve*

1. Memo from Brigadier General John Kelly to 1st Marine Division staff.

2. Michael R. Gordon and General Bernard E. Trainor, *COBRA II: The Inside Story of the Invasion and Occupation of Iraq* (New York: Pantheon, 2006), p. 527.

3. Gordon and Trainor, *COBRA II*, p. 527.

4. Bing West, *No True Glory: A Frontline Account of the Battle for Fallujah* (New York: Random House, 2005).

5. Lieutenant Colonel (Retired) Kenneth Estes, *U.S. Marine Corps Operations in Iraq, 2003–2006* (Quantico, VA: History Division, U.S. Marine Corps, 2009).

6. "Sheikh Ali Hatim al-Razzaq Ali al-Sulayman al-Assafi, Heir Apparent to the Paramount Sheikh of the Dulaimi Tribal Confederation and Head of the National Salvation Front Political Party," in *Al-Anbar Awakening*, eds. Colonel Gary W. Montgomery and Chief Warrant Officer 4 Timothy S. McWilliams,

vol. 2, *Iraqi Perspectives* (Quantico, VA: Marine Corps University Press, 2009), p. 108.

7. Quoted in Estes, *U.S. Marine Corps Operations in Iraq.*
8. Interviews, former Bush administration officials.
9. Quoted in *Al-Anbar Awakening*, eds. Chief Warrant Officer 4 Timothy McWilliams and Lieutenant Colonel Kurtis Wheeler, vol. 1, *American Perspectives* (Quantico, VA: Marine Corps University Press, 2009), p. 57.
10. Notes of a participant, obtained by the authors.
11. Kennedy and Royer quoted in Gregg Zoroya, "Fight for Ramadi Exacts Heavy Toll on Marines," *USA Today*, 12 July 2004.
12. Mattis quoted in *Al-Anbar Awakening*, eds. Chief Warrant Officer 4 Timothy McWilliams and Lieutenant Colonel Kurtis Wheeler, vol. 1, *American Perspectives* (Quantico, VA: Marine Corps University Press, 2009), p. 27.
13. Michael Moss, "Bloodied Marines Sound Off About Want of Armor and Men," *New York Times*, 25 April 2005.
14. Marine Corps Intelligence Activity, "Study of the Insurgency in Anbar Province, Iraq" (SECRET), 13 June 2007.
15. Michael M. Phillips, "In Combat, Marine Put Theory to Test, Comrades Believe," *Wall Street Journal*, 25 May 2004.
16. Interview, former CPA official.
17. Interview, General Peter Chiarelli.
18. Combat Studies Institute interview with Colonel Robert Abrams.
19. Interview, General Peter Chiarelli.
20. On November 29, two SUVs carrying Spanish intelligence officers were trailed by militants in a white sedan and then ambushed in Latifiyah. By the time the bloody episode was over, seven of the eight Spanish passengers had been shot and killed while the lone survivor had frantically sought to wave down passing cars for help to no avail, only to be saved from an angry mob, and a potential kidnapping, by local Iraqi police. According to an American intelligence report, a heavily armed military convoy had passed through the area without problems just minutes before. The assailants appeared to have made a calculated decision to pick on the most vulnerable and least aggressive members of the coalition.
21. Interview, Ronald Neumann.
22. Interview, former CPA official.
23. Interview, former CPA official.
24. Interview, U.S. official.
25. Marine Corps Intelligence Activity, "Study of the Insurgency in Anbar Province, Iraq" (SECRET), 13 June 2007.
26. Interview, Ronald Neumann.
27. Notes of a meeting participant.

CHAPTER 5 *A Lost Cause?*

1. Notes provided to the authors by a meeting participant.
2. Notes provided to the authors by a meeting participant.
3. Notes provided to the authors by a meeting participant.
4. George W. Bush, "5-Step Plan for Democracy in Iraq" (speech, Army War College, 24 May 2004).

5. Interviews, U.N. and CPA officials.
6. Interview, Ayad Allawi. SCIRI politician Adil Abd al-Mahdi was a fellow student at Baghdad College and, like Allawi, a vigorous water polo player. Kanan Makiya, the human rights activist who would later document Saddam's abuses in his celebrated book *Republic of Fear*, also attended as did Nizar Hamdoon, who served as Saddam's ambassador to the United Nations.
7. Interview, Ahmed Chalabi. Many of Chalabi's interactions with the U.S. government prior to the war are well known, but an April 2001 estimate from the Iraqi Intelligence Service reveals that the United States sought to expand its relations with Iraqi exile groups beyond Chalabi and the Iraqi National Congress nearly two years prior to the invasion. In part, this decision came about after Secretary of State Colin Powell discovered during a tour of the region that Chalabi "is not respected by the big countries of the region, [e]specially Turkey, Iran and Washington Arab allies who clarifies [sic] that they are not going to cooperate with the recent National Congress Command." Another reason the report cites for the desire to deepen Washington's ties to alternative exile groups was that the CIA and other elements of the bureaucracy felt that the INC had misused American money throughout the 1990s because despite millions of dollars in aid authorized by the Iraq Liberation Act, the INC's physical presence and influence in Iraq remained minimal. English translation of a captured Iraqi government document, reviewed by the authors at the National Defense University's Conflict Records Research Center, Washington, D.C.
8. Interview, Ayad Allawi.
9. Interview, Ayad Allawi.
10. Interview, Ayad Allawi.
11. Interview, former U.N. and CPA officials.
12. Interview, former CPA official.
13. Interview, Larry Diamond; Larry Diamond, *Squandered Victory: The American Occupation and the Bungled Effort to Bring Democracy to Iraq* (New York: Times Books, 2005).
14. Letter from Thomas Fingar, INR, to Secretary of State Colin Powell, forwarded to Cheney, Rumsfeld, Card, and Tenet, "Iraq, Falluja, and the Arab Sunni Heartland—A Lost Cause?" (SECRET//NOFORN), 7 April 2004.
15. Interviews, L. Paul Bremer III and former administration officials.
16. Interview, Hoshyar Zebari.
17. Interviews, former CPA officials.
18. Interview, Barham Salih.
19. Interview, John Negroponte.
20. Interview, Ron Neumann.
21. Interview, Ron Neumann.
22. Interviews, former CPA officials.
23. Embassy Baghdad cable classified by James Jeffrey, "Iraqi Government Signals Tougher Sentences for Criminals and Terrorists" (CONFIDENTIAL), 2 July 2004.

CHAPTER 6 *Our Man in Baghdad*

1. Interview, former aide to General George Casey, Jr.
2. Gregg Jaffe and David Cloud, *The Fourth Star: Four Generals and the Epic*

Struggle for the Future of the United States Army (New York: Random House, 2009).

3. Interviews, Paul Wolfowitz and General (Retired) Jack Keane.
4. Interview, U.S. Army official.
5. Interview, General George Casey, Jr.
6. Michael R. Gordon and General Bernard E. Trainor, *COBRA II: The Inside Story of the Invasion and Occupation of Iraq* (New York: Pantheon, 2006).
7. Notes of General George Casey, Jr.
8. It was for this reason that some commanders in Iraq, such as Colonel H.R. McMaster, banned PowerPoint from their commands entirely. (During a later tour in Afghanistan, McMaster told a *New York Times* reporter that the endless presentations were dangerous "because they can create the illusion of understanding and the illusion of control." McMaster emphasized that war was often much more complex than it appeared on slides: "Some problems in the world are not bullet-izable.") Elisabeth Bumiller, "Enemy Lurks in Briefings on Afghanistan," *New York Times*, 26 April 2010.
9. Interview, aide to General George Casey, Jr.
10. Rod Nordland, "Iraq's Repairman," *Newsweek*, 4 July 2004.
11. Notes of General George Casey.
12. Translated from Arabic, Abu Flus roughly means "Father of Money."
13. Email from General George Casey to General John Abizaid, copying General Richard Myers, Lieutenant General John Craddock, and Gary Helmick, "Update" (SECRET), 4 July 2004.
14. Notes of a meeting participant.
15. Interview, Robert Earle.
16. Interview, Robert Earle.
17. Red Cell report, obtained by the authors.
18. General George W. Casey, Jr., and Zalmay Khalilzad, *MNF-I/Embassy Joint Mission Statement*, 16 August 2004, declassified and obtained by the authors.
19. Interview, military official.
20. *Multi-National Force—Iraq, Campaign Plan: Operation Iraqi Freedom (Partnership: From Occupation to Constitutional Elections)*, 5 August 2004, declassified 29 September 2009, declassified and classified versions obtained by the authors.
21. Memo obtained by the authors.
22. Interview, former CPA official.
23. Embassy Baghdad cable classified by Robert Ford, "Security in Sadr City and Baghdad: Progress is Slow" (SECRET), 20 August 2004.
24. Interview, U.N. official.
25. The Hakim family had led the Dawa Party for decades before founding SCIRI. A 1995 Iraqi military intelligence assessment noted that Muhammad Mahdi al-Hakim was among the six original cofounders of Dawa in 1957, and that he fled to Iran in 1969 and was later executed; his brother Muhammad Baqir al-Hakim was also active in Dawa until he split with the group in 1982. Muhammad Baqir al-Hakim cofounded SCIRI early that year with Ayatollah Mahmoud Hashemi Shahroudi, an Iraqi-Iranian cleric who would later serve for a decade as Iran's chief justice.

Many of SCIRI's original founders were drawn from Dawa's ranks. The differences between Dawa and SCIRI revolved around their loyalty to the Iranian regime. SCIRI sought to mobilize all Islamic forces into a unified political and military direction that would execute the Islamic Revolution in Iraq, but SCIRI members also expressed complete "faith and belief in the Islamic Republic [Iran]." They considered the Khomeini regime the focal point of the international Islamic Revolution, and agreed to "the defense of its doctrines to confront the dominant international forces." This avowed loyalty to Iran and its supremacy over the Islamic Revolution did not sit well with some Iraqi Dawa Party members (including the eventual prime minister Nuri al-Maliki), who preferred to relocate to Syria or other nearby states rather than stay under the thumb of Khomeini. For this reason and because of its seniority within the Iraqi opposition, the Dawa Party tended to have greater influence and a more organized presence in the neighboring Arab countries than did SCIRI.

Differing views on Iran did not prevent Dawa and SCIRI from working together to undermine Saddam Hussein's regime, though. Abd al-Aziz al-Hakim was personally involved in creating a committee with Syrian and Iranian intelligence officials that would help smuggle Dawa Party members through Nineveh Province into training camps in Syria. English translations of captured Iraqi government archives, reviewed by authors at the National Defense University's Conflict Records Research Center, Washington, D.C.

26. Classified report on interrogation of Qais al-Khazali, March 2007, reviewed by the authors.

27. First Lieutenant Ann Gildroy, a Georgetown graduate who had tried her hand at investment banking before joining the Marines, was an aviation maintenance officer, but she had volunteered to deploy as an adviser to Iraqi troops, a job that few others wanted. The Marines in Najaf, she found, had little time or resources to spare for her Iraqi troops. From the outskirts of the city, she sent a borderline-insubordinate email to every MNSTC-I address she could think of, including Petraeus, a general she had never met, but who she knew was supposed to be in charge of training and equipping Iraqi troops. The message contained a plea for equipment and photos of wounded Iraqi soldiers with no first-aid gear and spartan facilities covered with feces because they had no latrines. Soon afterward, Petraeus came to visit. The MEU commander instructed Gildroy to remove the most damning material from her briefing to the general, but she briefed her original version anyway. Petraeus sat and listened, and then thanked her for her candor and instructed her to keep him apprised of everything she needed. Gear for her troops began to arrive, and every time she needed more, she stuffed a list into a cheap backpack and sent it to Petraeus via someone traveling to Baghdad, since there was no reliable secure email system.

28. Account provided by former NSC official.

29. Account provided by former NSC official.

30. Interview, Mowaffak al-Rubaie.

31. Intelligence report reviewed by the authors.

32. One old colleague from his Badr intelligence days with whom Abu Mahdi al-Muhandis remained close was Hadi al-Amari, who was now the head of the rebranded Badr Organization, a major Shiite political party in the new Iraq.

33. Interview, U.S. government official.

34. Interview, Ayad Allawi.

35. Interview, U.S. official.

36. Studying the battle in retrospect, American military officers found that the reporting provided by the *New York Times*'s Dexter Filkins and other Western

reporters who were embedded with the Mahdi Army in Najaf provided a better record of the militia's fortunes during the battle than many official intelligence reports. Perhaps for this reason, the Mahdi Army never again allowed reporters the kind of battlefield access it granted during the Najaf battle.

CHAPTER 7 *New Dawn*

1. Letter obtained by the authors.
2. Although Rumsfeld may have said there were 240 SEALs serving as bodyguards for Iraqi politicians, in reality the number was closer to 200.
3. Interview, Ayad Allawi.
4. Notes of a meeting participant.
5. Notes of a meeting participant.
6. Notes of a meeting participant.
7. Document reviewed by the authors.
8. Bing West, *No True Glory: A Frontline Account of the Battle for Fallujah* (New York: Random House, 2005).
9. Marine Corps Intelligence Activity, "Study of the Insurgency in Anbar Province, Iraq" (SECRET), 13 June 2007.
10. Interview, General (Retired) Stanley McChrystal.
11. Multi-National Force—Iraq C2, "CG Assessment" (SECRET), September 2004, a monthly compilation for General George Casey of reports from his staff sections.
12. Marine Corps Intelligence Activity, "Study of the Insurgency in Anbar Province, Iraq" (SECRET), 13 June 2007.
13. General (Retired) George Casey, "Operation Iraqi Freedom, July 2004–February 2007: Strategic Reflections," draft publication by National Defense University dated 3 February 2012.
14. This account of the battle draws heavily on four accounts for its details: Chief Warrant Officer 4 Timothy McWilliams and Master Gunnery Sergeant Robert Yarnell, *U.S. Marines in Battle: Al-Fallujah, 24 March 2004–30 January 2005* (Marine Corps University Press, review copy); Marine Corps Intelligence Activity, "Study of the Insurgency in Anbar Province, Iraq" (SECRET), 13 June 2007; Lieutenant Colonel (Retired) Kenneth Estes, *U.S. Marine Corps Operations in Iraq, 2003–2006* (Quantico, VA: History Division, U.S. Marine Corps, 2009); and Kendall Gott, ed., *Eyewitness to War: The U.S. Army in Operation AL-FAJR: An Oral History,* 2 vols. (Fort Leavenworth: Combat Studies Institute Press).
15. Captain Neil Prakash, quoted in *Eyewitness to War,* vol. II.
16. "Telling the Fallujah Story to the World," I MEF and MNC-I Effects Exploitation Team, 20 November 2004.
17. Most casualty and damage numbers are from Estes, *U.S. Marine Corps Operations in Iraq.*
18. Quoted in McWilliams and Yarnell, *U.S. Marines in Battle.*
19. Classified MNF-I year-end assessment. According to the report, MNF-I units killed a total of 8,400 insurgents in 2004 and detained 23,000 (not counting those released within a day). In April, 1,270 insurgents were killed; in August, 1,600; and in the second battle of Fallujah alone, 2,175.
20. Katherine Zoepf, "Why So Few Medals of Honor?," *New York Times Magazine,* 27 May 2010.

21. Quoted in Estes, *U.S. Marine Corps Operations in Iraq*.
22. Jason Whitely, *Father of Money: Buying Peace in Baghdad* (Dulles: Potomac Books, 2011).
23. Interview, Lieutenant Colonel Ed McKee.
24. Interview, Colonel Jim Coffman.

CHAPTER 8   *The Long Telegram*

1. Interview, embassy official.
2. Interview, senior U.S. official.
3. Interview, William Taylor.
4. Embassy Baghdad cable classified by Ambassador John Negroponte, "A Plan for Dealing with the Next Government of Iraq," 2 December 2004, declassified 24 September 2009.
5. Interview, John Negroponte.
6. Interview, General (Retired) Jack Keane.
7. Interviews, U.S. officials.
8. Interviews, former officials.
9. Central Intelligence Agency, "Near Term Regional Implications of Successful Iraqi Elections" (TOP SECRET), 29 October 2004.
10. Notes of a meeting participant.
11. Reservations about how successful the Iraq mission was came from other quarters besides Negroponte and the intelligence community, too. In mid-December, Newt Gingrich had sent a rambling letter to Casey, Wolfowitz, and the chairman and vice chairman of the Joint Chiefs, Dick Myers and Peter Pace, entitled "Iraq 2005: Initial Assessment and Action Plan." "We're going to need a bigger and better boat," the letter began, a quotation paraphrased from the movie *Jaws*. "We have already killed many more people than were supposed to be in the insurgency," Gingrich pointed out. "Our enemies in Iraq are more complicated, more sophisticated and better resourced then we would have expected."
12. Notes of a meeting participant.
13. Notes of a meeting participant.
14. Multi-National Force—Iraq, "MNF-I CONPLAN: Transition to Security Self-Reliance and Coalition Transformation" (SECRET), 29 April 2005.
15. Combat Studies Institute interview, Lieutenant General John Vines, July 2008.
16. Email from General George Casey to Ron Neumann, copying John Negroponte, 3 March 2005.
17. Notes of a meeting participant.
18. Embassy Baghdad cable classified by Robert Ford, "Interior Minister Worries About Future of Interior Ministry as Shia Islamists Hover" (CONFIDENTIAL), 5 April 2005.
19. Muhammad Baqir al-Hakim assumed command of the Badr Corps only two months prior to the end of the Iran-Iraq War, after Iran somewhat disingenuously transferred control to SCIRI in order to assert its "non-interference in the internal affairs of Iraq." Iran had initially formed the Badr Corps in 1985 to coordinate the training and militia operations of the main Shiite factions, which at the time included the Islamic Labor Organization, Dawa, and the Hakim-influenced Hezbollah. After Iran transferred formal control, the Supreme Council continued to build the capacity of the Badr Corps and was

aided substantially by the influx of former prisoners that Iraq repatriated or deported to Iran at the end of the war. The Iraqi report estimated that as many as two-thirds of the Badr Corps consisted of "fugitive soldiers and renegade prisoners," who were supported by Iran's Revolutionary Guard Corps and were "well trained on weapons." Despite the formal cessation of hostilities between the two nation-states, SCIRI and Badr remained active in subversive operations (both direct and indirect) across Iraq's southern and northern borders. In the north, SCIRI would frequently collaborate with Kurdish groups with whom they had made extensive contacts while fighting Saddam during the Iran-Iraq War. English translations of captured Iraqi government archives, reviewed by authors at the National Defense University's Conflict Records Research Center, Washington, D.C.

CHAPTER 9 *Papa Jaafari*

1. In 1995, Iraq's General Military Intelligence Directorate produced an extensive study of the Dawa Party. According to an English-language translation of the document, the roots of the Dawa Party can be traced back to a variety of domestic and foreign influences operating in Iraq in the late 1950s. Shiite seminaries in Najaf played an influential role early on by publishing a magazine called *al-dawa*, or "lights," which they did to raise money and increase their political power. The Dawa Party emerged out of that association in 1957. In response to the July 14, 1958 coup that overthrew the British-backed Hashemite monarchy in Iraq, Britain encouraged the Dawa Party to mimic the Muslim Brotherhood in order to bring "divisiveness between the Iraqi people and to incite wrong religious practices and ceremonies." Iran provided material and other support to Dawa from the first day it was established in order to create a fifth column in the Arab world. The study further concluded that Dawa benefited early on from the leader of the 1958 coup, Abd al-Karim Kasim, who initially fostered close relations between the Communist and Dawa parties, which raised the profile and popularity of the latter.

   The report also identified several key developments in the evolution of the Dawa Party. After Saddam executed Grand Ayatollah Muhammad Baqir al-Sadr in April 1980, the remaining Dawa leadership fled to Iran, where the party increasingly came to be dominated by Persian leaders. It quickly became an effective proxy for Iran after the Iran-Iraq War, which erupted in September. of that year. With Iran's assistance, Dawa established training camps in Iran, Syria, and Lebanon, and frequently infiltrated across the border in order to conduct what Iraqi intelligence reports described as "sabotage operations."
2. Interview, Phebe Marr.
3. Embassy Baghdad cable classified by Robert Ford, "Garden Chats with Papa Ja'fari and Crew" (SECRET), 11 July 2005.
4. Interview, U.S. official.
5. Interview, U.S. military official.
6. Combat Studies Institute interview with Lieutenant Colonel Robert Kerecz, May 2008.
7. Combat Studies Institute interview with Brigadier General Edward Cardon, March 2008.
8. Combat Studies Institute interview with Colonel Jim Blackburn, April 2008.

9. Embassy Baghdad cable classified by Robert Ford, "Islamic Human Rights Organization Alleges Iraqi Forces Detainee Abuse in Ninewa" (CONFIDENTIAL), 16 June 2005.

10. Embassy Baghdad cable classified by Robert Ford, "Sectarian Violence Hampers Sunni Participation in Political Process" (CONFIDENTIAL), 30 August 2005.

11. One unit that spent 2005 in Iraq, the 29th Brigade Combat Team of the Hawaii National Guard, had problems from the start—with its leaders. The brigade came to Iraq with three infantry battalions, and by the time it left, the commanders of two had been relieved—this in an Army that was notoriously gun-shy about firing commanders in combat zones. One commander, whose battalion was based at Camp Anaconda near Balad, attacked one of his staff officers in an argument over an order just a month after arriving in Iraq, choking the man and throwing a chair. The other commander, an eccentric Vietnam veteran who had also fought in Rhodesia on behalf of South Africa, was fired more than halfway through the tour after allegedly creating a "cult of personality" in his unit in southern Baghdad, which his superiors suspected led indirectly to abuse of detainees by his soldiers.

   Another effect of the Army's reliance on the National Guard in Iraq in 2005 was felt back home. When Hurricane Katrina hit the Gulf Coast in August 2005, three of the states in its path—Louisiana, Mississippi, and Georgia—had their main Guard formations in Iraq, complicating relief efforts and necessitating the deployment of active-duty troops and Guard formations from as far away as the Pacific Northwest.

12. Interview, Lieutenant Colonel Kevin Farrell. The most common types of EFPs were 77mm, 114mm, and 135mm across, but there were rarer bombs of larger caliber, like 152mm, as well. "All EFPs are an overmatch for the majority of U.S. vehicles," a later military assessment noted grimly; except for Abrams tanks and Bradley Fighting Vehicles, everything else in the American inventory, including up-armored Humvees and Strykers, could be destroyed by even the smaller bombs.

13. Central Intelligence Agency, "Iraq: Proliferation of Explosively Formed Projectiles to Shia Insurgents" (TOP SECRET), 24 May 2006.

14. Combined Joint Task Force Troy, "EFP Attack & Casualty Trends, 12 Feb 05–05 Jan 07," January 2007.

15. Combat Studies Institute interview with Lieutenant General William Webster, April 2008.

16. Michael Gordon, "Deadliest Bomb in Iraq Is Made by Iran, U.S. Says," *New York Times*, 10 February 2007. UK Defence Intelligence Staff, "Iranian Munitions Supply Into MND(SE) in Iraq" (UK SECRET, AUS/CAN/UK/US EYES ONLY), 19 October 2006.

17. National Ground Intelligence Center, "The Islamic Revolutionary Guard Corps in Iraq" (SECRET), 20 December 2006.

18. Military Intelligence Directorate, Israeli Defense Forces, "Hizballah—Employment of a New Type of Plate Charge (EFP)," 2002.

19. Harmony Document ISGQ—2005—00037289, quoted in Joseph Felter and Brian Fishman, "Iranian Strategy in Iraq: Politics and 'Other Means,'" Combating Terrorism Center, October 2008.

20. Central Intelligence Agency, "Iraq: Proliferation of Explosively Formed Projectiles to Shia Insurgents" (TOP SECRET), 24 May 2006. Shahlai's role

is also detailed in later reports: National Ground Intelligence Center, "EFP Smuggling Routes in Maysaan Province" (SECRET), 4 September 2007, and National Ground Intelligence Center, "Key Smuggling Routes in Wasit Province" (SECRET), 7 September 2007.

21. In the Sadrist-dominated town of Amara, British troops were allowed to patrol only in Warrior Fighting Vehicles because the bombs were so dangerous, and shortly before the Jamiat Police Station episode, Special Air Service commandos had arrested the man British intelligence believed to be behind the recent EFP deaths of the three soldiers—a Mahdi Army commander named Ahmed al-Fartusi, who would have another, larger role to play before Britain's time in Basra was over.

22. Interview, Ron Neumann.

23. "Message from the United States to the Government of Iran," 19 July 2005.

24. Embassy Baghdad cable classified by David Litt, "Navigating the Rift Between the U.S. and Iran—Rubaie on the UIA's Balancing Act" (SECRET), 19 July 2005.

25. Embassy Baghdad cable classified by David Satterfield, "Building a House on Shifting Sands: Iran's Influence in Iraq's Center-South" (SECRET), 20 July 2005.

26. An American intelligence report on a January 2005 meeting between Iranian Supreme Leader Khamenei and Ali Reza Hassan Kazemi-Qomi, the Quds Force officer who served as the Iranian chargé d'affaires in Baghdad, provided some idea. Kazemi-Qomi had three major tasks in Iraq, Khamenei told him. One was to establish a network of Shiite clerics friendly to Iran's own clerics back in Qom, the holy city that the Iranian regime hoped to make eventually eclipse Najaf as the center of Shiite Islam. The second was to peddle Iranian influence in reconstruction efforts, especially in southern Iraq, a task to be accomplished largely through companies and charitable organizations that were fronts for the Iranian government (especially as violence increased, private Iranian investors were not nearly as interested in working in Iraq as the Iranian government was). The lucrative travel business that helped hundreds of thousands of Iranian pilgrims travel to Shiite holy sites in Iraq like the shrines in Najaf, Karbala, and Kadhimiya was among the easiest venues for Quds Force involvement; the force's "soft power" arm, the Kosar Bureau, provided funding and made use of the largest pilgrim-handling travel business in Karbala, for instance, Shamsah Travel and Tourism. The third task was to keep the American military in Iraq under pressure and off balance. U.S. Army Counterintelligence Center, "Iranian Ambassador's Tasks" (SECRET).

27. Embassy Baghdad cable classified by David Litt, "Navigating the Rift Between the U.S. and Iran—Rubaie on the UIA's Balancing Act" (SECRET), 19 July 2005.

28. Years later, in 2008, American diplomats would gain insight into one of the tactics that Iranian intelligence officers used to work in Iraq early in the war during a conversation with Dr. Farshid Towfighi, an Iranian Red Crescent (IRC) official who had fled the country after being blacklisted by the Iranian regime. Towfighi claimed that the MOIS and Quds Force had routinely used Iranian Red Crescent credentials as covers for their operatives in Iraq.

"Prior to the Iraq war, a Mr. Bothani—an MOIS representative stationed in the IRC—requested that Dr. Towfighi sign the professional certificate for two or three Qods Force officers, thus providing the necessary paperwork to travel to Iraq under IRC cover," a State Department cable on the meeting with

Towfighi explained. "With the war underway, Dr. Towfighi says the number of Qods officers seeking IRC cover increased and was between ten and 30."

In September 2003, Towfighi traveled to Iraq along with a "Mr. Shootstarizadeh," a Red Crescent employee connected with the Quds Force and SCIRI, the cable continued: "In accompanying Mr. Shoostarizadeh around Iraq, Dr. Towfighi met many purported members of the IRC working in Iraq. Dr. Towfighi knew none of the purported IRC members, and concluded that they were not legitimate IRC relief workers and alleged that someone else must have been signing their professional certificates. During his subsequent investigation by the MOIS—after attending the exchange in the U.S.—Dr. Towfighi recalled being told that IRC identification cards had become more important after US forces had detained Iranian officers carrying IRGC identification cards" in Baghdad and Irbil. During another trip to Iraq, in March 2004 after Al-Qaeda bombings in Karbala killed and wounded a number of Iranian pilgrims, Towfighi "again met purported IRC officers that he assumed were Quds Force officers; at the time these officers were helping with the relief effort. While in Karbala, Dr. Towfighi met with the IRGC commander in Karbala, who chastised Dr. Towfighi for not bringing a refrigerated transport vehicle to return victims' remains to Iran. The commander then immediately authorized the purchase of such a vehicle at the cost of $40,000, surprising Dr. Towfighi that such money was readily available."

CHAPTER 10   *The Red Team*

1. Interview, Zalmay Khalilzad. When Dick Cheney was defense secretary and George H. W. Bush was president, Khalilzad found a place on the Pentagon staff where he prepared an early draft of the Defense Planning Guidance, a classified paper that was intended to guide decisions on weapons purchases and military planning. Khalilzad's paper argued that the goal of American policy should be to maintain military primacy and made the provocative case that the United States should be prepared to use force preemptively to stop nuclear proliferation.

   There were howls of outrage when the draft leaked—news reports wrongly attributed its provenance to Khalilzad's immediate boss, Paul Wolfowitz—and the White House was quick to disown it. By the time George W. Bush took office, however, the once controversial themes about preemption and coalitions of the willing were at the core of the administration's national security policy.

2. U.S. Senate Foreign Relations Committee, "Nomination of Zalmay Khalilzad to be Ambassador to Iraq," hearing chaired by Senator Richard Lugar.

3. "Securing Strategic Success," MNF-I brief obtained by the authors.

4. MNF-I Red Cell, "Red Team Report: An Integrated Counterinsurgency Strategy for Iraq" (SECRET), 31 August 2005.

5. Account provided to the authors.

6. Interview, Colonel Bruce Reider.

7. Note of 26 September, obtained by the authors.

8. By now Casey's command subscribed to the same view as Stan McChrystal's JSOC, that Zarqawi's followers, not former Baathists, were the most dangerous element of the Sunni insurgency. Though Zarqawi's Al-Qaeda in Iraq was made up largely of Iraqis, volunteers from other Arab countries played two key

roles in the group: as leaders and as suicide bombers. In a common military analogy, if car and truck bombs were Al-Qaeda's cruise missiles, its strategic weapons aimed at widening the scope of the sectarian war, then foreign bombers were the missiles' guidance packages. And those suicide bombers were entering the country from Syria. "Damascus is main entry point," a report by Casey's intelligence staff on foreign fighters noted. The majority of the men simply flew commercially from their home countries to Damascus International Airport. From there, it was the job of an underground logistical network led by a Mosul-born Al-Qaeda leader named Abu Ghadiya, or Badran Turki al-Mazidih, to help the volunteers reach and cross the Iraqi border.

9. Combat Studies Institute interview with Lieutenant General John Vines. Iraqi officials in the Defense and Interior ministries also saw the problem in a different way, advocating frequently during the spring and summer of 2005 that fresh troops be sent not to the borders but to the rural areas just outside the capital, around towns like Yusifiyah, Taji, Abu Ghraib, and Arab Jabour. Saddam had controlled Baghdad by controlling these areas, they insisted, and the Sunni insurgency was doing the same. The argument was that while the foreign suicide bombers who drove the car bombs were coming from Syria, the car bombs themselves were being assembled just beyond the Baghdad city limits. Later in the war, the United States military would come to know these areas as the "Baghdad belts" and place great emphasis on them, but in 2005 Casey's command simply did not see the problem that way. The problem was the Syrian border.

Within Vines's headquarters, some planners had also been arguing that the corps campaign plan should emphasize Iraq's Shiite majority, with its huge militias and influential political parties, over the Sunni side on which Casey was focused. Finally, the corps's operations officer pulled aside one of the main proponents of this plan, Lieutenant Colonel David Oclander. "Look," the one-star general told Oclander, "if you don't stop pitching that the Shia population is the center of gravity, the only thing you're going to be planning is how to move rubber dogshit out of the Baghdad airport."

10. Interview, Colonel H.R. McMaster.

11. Interview, Colonel H.R. McMaster. The city hospital was in a Sunni area where Shiites were afraid to venture, and the Sunni areas of town were the only ones with a functioning water supply. The tiny border towns to the west like Rabiya and Biaj, had no local security forces. The Iraqi Army's 3rd Division headquarters, northeast of Afar, was besieged, its ranks depleted due to enemy intimidation. The Shammar tribe, which had deep roots in cross-border smuggling, was in large part on the insurgent payroll, and Sunni insurgent leaders were frequently sighted in the area on their way to and from Syria.

12. Interview, Colonel H.R. McMaster.

13. Interview, Colonel H.R. McMaster.

14. Embassy Baghdad cable classified by David Satterfield, "Tal Afar Wrap-Up: Short-Term Success but Momentum Must Be Maintained" (CONFIDENTIAL), 2 October 2005.

15. Interview, Najem al-Jabouri. Some residents of Tal Afar grew apprehensive as the end of 3rd ACR's deployment neared over the winter. Shiite and Sunni sheikhs together wrote a letter addressed to President Bush asking that 3rd ACR not be allowed to leave Tal Afar. Najem al-Jabouri, the mayor, said the

same in a letter of his own, also addressed to Bush and widely publicized. "In this critical state we are shocked to learn the 3rd Armored Cavalry Regiment will leave after all these great accomplishments," Najem wrote. "Mr. President, we are asking for your compassion, to delay the re-deployment of this brave unit until our city is completely healed." Casey responded to Najem with a letter of his own. "General Casey responded by letter and said, 'The 3rd ACR soldiers have families waiting for them, but I promise you, I will bring you the finest unit in the United States Army,'" Najem recalled.

16. Quoted in *Al-Anbar Awakening*, eds. Chief Warrant Officer 4 Timothy McWilliams and Lieutenant Colonel Kurtis Wheeler, vol. 1, *American Perspectives,* (Quantico, VA: Marine Corps University Press, 2009).

17. From the get-go, the CPA had ignored and minimized the importance of tribes in Iraq, choosing to deal instead with such institutions of modern government as the military was able to help stand up, like city councils and police forces. Marine battalions in Anbar followed the CPA's lead. In Anbar, tribes played an outsized role, even in the province's cities, and with the rise of the insurgency, Anbar's city councils and police forces had either disappeared or been co-opted by Al-Qaeda almost as soon as they appeared.

   ODA 555 in Hit, a town halfway between Haditha and Ramadi, rejected this approach, cutting the infiltrated police force out of its dealings and forging ties with the local Albu Nimr tribe.

   But when ODA 555 left in the fall of 2004, a new Special Forces group headquarters chose to pull out of Anbar to focus on central Iraq. The company of Albu Nimr fighters was folded into the thoroughly infiltrated local Iraqi Civil Defense Corps battalion, where it fell apart, and the main Albu Nimr sheikh, who had led the tribe's dealings with the Special Forces, was killed by Marines. The Hit experiment in tribal outreach withered, and Al-Qaeda quickly became the dominant force in western Anbar. In early 2005 a new Marine command arrived and launched a short-term offensive in the west, but by spring, Al-Qaeda's control in the region was almost complete. In Haditha, insurgents had killed the police chief and dispersed much of the police force. In Hit, Al-Qaeda ran much of the city and had established a shadow legal system of courts, judges, and executioners. And in April Zarqawi declared Qaim, on the Syrian border, the new capital of his organization's embryonic emirate; although he himself did not set up a permanent headquarters there, his fighters created courts, took control of mosques, hung green-and-black flags from government buildings, and punished men who failed to grow beards with public whippings.

   Also during 2004, men from the Albu Mahal tribe had fought the Marines in Qaim as part of a local insurgent group called the Hamza Battalion. By the time of the November Fallujah offensive, with foreign fighters passing through and the Marines focused eastward, the Albu Mahals had begun to chafe against the Al-Qaeda presence, in part because the group's strict interpretation of Islam did not mesh with the lucrative smuggling business that had made the tribe's sheikhs wealthy. So the Albu Mahals repurposed the Hamza Battalion to keep foreign fighters out of their communities. In Ramadi and Fallujah in eastern Anbar, the fracturing of the insurgency in the wake of Fallujah and the run-up to the January elections had worked in Al-Qaeda's favor, drawing mid- and low-level Anbari insurgents away from groups that wanted to negotiate with the government and toward the side that wanted to keep fighting. In the west, where the split occurred against a backdrop of tribal discontent with the foreign Al-Qaeda presence, the opposite happened.

By spring, the Hamza Battalion in the Qaim area had grown. Under the leadership of an Albu Mahal sheikh named Sabah al-Sattam Effan Fahran al-Shurji al-Aziz, who had fought against the Marines in Fallujah and who was the brother-in-law of Anbar's new governor, the group expanded to include members of other tribes like the Albu Nimr, other insurgent groups like local cells of the 1920 Revolution Brigades, and veterans of local police forces and former Iraqi National Guard units. In the Qaim area, the Hamza Battalion was quietly but actively fighting Al-Qaeda while the Albu Nimr were doing the same in Hit; even in Ramadi, where Al-Qaeda's grip on the local insurgency was growing, there was some skirmishing.

Against this background of opening tribal conflict against Al-Qaeda, but largely ignorant of it, the American military reentered the western Euphrates in May 2005 with what would become an escalating series of offensives. Since the end of major operations in Fallujah in December 2004, Stan McChrystal's JSOC commandos—a separate group from the Special Forces—had had their hands full chasing insurgent leaders as they relocated from Fallujah to Ramadi, the rural areas south and west of Baghdad, and Mosul. The JSOC task force at Balad Air Base had begun to evolve from an organization focused on individual insurgent leaders to one that targeted insurgent networks more broadly, a machine that launched constant raids to gather more intelligence rather than gathering intelligence to launch occasional raids against major targets.

18. Special operations forces in Iraq operated under a complicated chain of command. Army Special Forces teams like ODA 555, and most Navy SEAL teams, were overseen from Balad by Combined Joint Special Operations Task Force—Arabian Peninsula (CJSOTF-AP). The Army's 5th and 10th Special Forces Groups took turns running this task force twice a year. These troops were under the "tactical control" of the three-star corps headquarters in Baghdad.

McChrystal's troops operated more independently and in greater secrecy. The JSOC troops went by an ever-changing series of numbered code-names, from Task Force 626 in 2004 and Task Force 145 in 2005 to Task Force 77, Task Force 5-15, and Task Force 88 in 2006. The general's own headquarters, which eventually settled on the name Task Force 714, was based at a base at Balad but oversaw secret operations throughout the Middle East and Afghanistan.

Also at Balad was the smaller task force that focused on Al-Qaeda in Iraq. It was led, in turns, by the commander and deputy commander of Delta Force. This task force reported to McChrystal and was used in close coordination with Casey's headquarters, pursuing Zarqawi's network with other task forces in various parts of Iraq. For the WERV campaign, a Delta squadron was moved from its usual area in Baghdad, where it worked alongside a squadron of the British SAS called Task Force Black and later Task Force Knight. In the north, a JSOC task force built around an Army Ranger battalion ran JSOC's campaign in Mosul.

The Rangers in Mosul rolled up to their targets in Strykers or flew in on helicopters, almost always at night. "I knew Mosul through the green lens of night vision," one Ranger officer recalled. On June 14, 2005, as Delta Force was surging in the WERV, the Ranger task force risked a daylight mission for the chance to capture a Zarqawi deputy they believed to be the third-ranking member of Al-Qaeda in Iraq. By a lucky chance, the Rangers captured an even more important terrorist leader, Abu Talha, Al-Qaeda's "emir of the north" and JSOC's number-two target in Iraq. The intelligence the Rangers gathered at the raid site allowed JSOC to launch thirteen more raids around Mosul in the next eight hours.

After a May visit to Iraq, Lieutenant General Jerry Boykin, the controversial former commander of Delta Force, reported glowingly to Donald Rumsfeld on JSOC's growing intelligence-collection capacity, singling out its interrogators, use of clandestine sources, and cooperation with the CIA, which lent the command some of its Predator drones. By now McChrystal's task force was focused almost purely on Zarqawi's Al-Qaeda in Iraq, whom it had nearly caught between Fallujah and Ramadi in February. Only an attached squadron of the British SAS remained focused on "former regime elements." (Rumsfeld passed Boykin's report to Dick Myers, the chairman of the Joint Chiefs, suggesting that he forward it to Bush. "He likes texture," the secretary observed.)

19. Interview, JSOC officer.
20. Central Intelligence Agency, "Iraq: Cash Seizures Provide Window into Insurgent Finances" (SECRET), 18 August 2006.
21. As Delta Force and the Rangers pressed their campaign of night raids, the other shadow struggle in the area, between Al-Qaeda and the fighters of local tribes, escalated. In May, Al-Qaeda had killed the Albu Mahal police chief for Qaim, leading the Mahals to expand their attacks on Al-Qaeda. In response, insurgents then kidnapped and later executed the governor of Anbar, a relative of the Mahals, but in June the Hamza Battalion took control of several smaller towns around Qaim. By early August, though, Al-Qaeda had counterattacked, nearly defeated the Mahal rebellion, and taken control of Qaim and the smaller towns around it.
22. In Hit, though, another Special Forces team, some of whose members were back in the same area from the previous year, was breathing life into a second round of Albu Nimr recruitment. With the blessing of the Defense Ministry and American headquarters, the Albu Nimrs promised the Special Forces and the Army National Guard field artillery unit that patrolled the area 200 recruits for a second Desert Protector unit.

    Unlike in Qaim, though, the Hit Desert Protector initiative did not receive the support it needed from above. Conventional units were passing through Hit after spending just weeks there, not enough time to become invested in the area. And on the day when the two hundred Desert Protector recruits were scheduled to be flown out for training, Marine aviation failed to show up. Belatedly, the troops in Hit were told that it was their maintenance stand-down day. The number of recruits fell from two hundred to thirty, and the program did not recover.
23. Quoted in *Al-Anbar Awakening*, eds. Chief Warrant Officer 4 Timothy McWilliams and Lieutenant Colonel Kurtis Wheeler, vol. 1: *Iraqi Perspectives,* (Quantico, VA: Marine Corps University Press, 2009).
24. Marine Corps Intelligence Activity, "Study of the Insurgency in Anbar Province, Iraq" (SECRET), 13 June 2007.
25. Quoted in *Al-Anbar Awakening,* eds. McWilliams and Wheeler, vol. 1, *American Perspectives*.
26. Interview, Philip Zelikow.

27. Interviews, U.S. officials.
28. Interview, former military official.

CHAPTER 11   *The Year of Living Dangerously*

1. Major General Peter Chiarelli and Major Patrick Michaelis, "Winning the Peace: The Requirement for Full-Spectrum Operations," *Military Review,* July–August 2005.

2. Major General Peter Chiarelli and Major Patrick Michaelis, "Winning the Peace: The Requirement for Full-Spectrum Operations," *Military Review,* July–August 2005.

3. Interview, General Peter Chiarelli.

4. Memo from chairman of the Joint Chiefs to Combatant Commands, "SECDEF Approval for CDRUSSTRATCOM to Conduct Computer Network Operational Preparation of the Environment (CNA-OPE) and Computer Network Attack (CNA) Operations to Counter Adversary Use of the Internet (CAUI) (TOP SECRET), 18 May 2007. The document describes the 2005–2006 operations as background.

5. Embassy Baghdad cable classified by Zalmay Khalilzad, "MCNS Meets to Discuss Security in Baghdad, Tal Afar, Sectarian Strife" (CONFIDENTIAL), 27 September 2005.

6. Letter from General George Casey, Jr., to Bayan Jabr, October 2005. The letter was accompanied by nine enclosures, each detailing instances of recent abuse or suspicious activity by Interior Ministry forces. In part, it read: "Multi-National Force has had numerous reports of infiltration of the Ministry of Interior by Badr members, who actively participate in policing functions and in the offices of the Special Police Commandos in Baghdad. Efforts to have the Public Order Brigades and Iraqi Army arrest these illegal militia members have been thwarted by the disappearance of those militia members once they are detained."

7. PBS *Frontline* interview with Brigadier General Karl Horst, 9 February 2007. Horst immediately contacted Jabr and asked him to check the ministry's records for evidence that the missing boy was in the Jadriya Bunker. No, Jabr said, the boy was not there. Horst told Jabr that he was going to the bunker to check for himself, and Jabr did not get in his way, but said that unless they were given advance notice the bunker's guards would not let American troops inside. When Horst demanded entry to a large room with double doors the Iraqi officer refused, saying that it was locked and the guard with the keys was on his day off. When Horst finally prevailed and got the door unlocked, there were not forty-three prisoners inside but twelve, who were blindfolded. Although nearly all of them were Sunni, the missing boy was not among them. Horst called Jabr, who promised he would come see what had been uncovered at the facility; Jabr never showed, instead sending Hussein Ali Kamal. The Americans loaded the prisoners up and sent them all to Abu Ghraib.

8. Embassy Baghdad cable classified by David Litt, "Bunker Investigation Falters, Nationwide Inspections Gather Steam" (SECRET), 15 December 2005.

9. Embassy Baghdad cable classified by Zalmay Khalilzad, "Shia Politico: Ja'afari has to go" (CONFIDENTIAL), 2 January 2006.

10. Embassy Baghdad cable classified by David Satterfield, "Zebari: Shia Far From Decision on PM Candidate, New Government Formation Also Distant" (CONFIDENTIAL), 8 January 2006.

11. Embassy Baghdad cable classified by Zalmay Khalilzad, "Shia PM Contenders: No Perfect Candidate" (SECRET), 10 February 2006.

12. O'Sullivan was pushing Abd al-Mahdi as the next prime minister. Khalilzad was skeptical of him on the grounds of SCIRI's closeness to Iran, a doubt encouraged by Ali Khedery, who had stayed on from the CPA. In one episode early in the war, he had realized that contrary to the view O'Sullivan held, SCIRI was a far greater friend to Iran than to the United States. Khedery was chatting with SCIRI leader Abd al-Aziz al-Hakim's personal driver when the driver asked him, "What do you think is the greatest country in the world?" The United States, Khedery replied; in the United States, Arab immigrants like his parents could arrive and thrive based on hard work, with few obstacles placed in their way. What, Khedery asked the driver, did he think? "Iran," the driver said simply.

13. During the lead-up to the December elections, the coalition force in Iraq had swelled, though not as much as it had a year earlier for the January elections. For most of 2005 the American force amounted to seventeen combat brigades plus Marine expeditionary units that came and left on shorter tours. During the fall, roughly an additional brigade was deployed from the 82nd Airborne Division: two paratroop battalions went to northern Iraq (one to Tal Afar and one to Badush Prison near Mosul), and a third went to Anbar to work with JSOC.

14. Combat Studies Institute interview with Colonel Steven Salazar, January 2008.

15. Multi-National Corps—Iraq slide deck on decision to off-ramp replacement for 278th Armored Cavalry Regiment, reviewed by the authors.

16. Combat Studies Institute interview with Colonel John Tully, February 2008.

17. Marine Corps Intelligence Activity, "Study of the Insurgency in Anbar Province, Iraq" (SECRET), 13 June 2007.

18. General George W. Casey, Jr., "Strategic Directive—Golden Mosque Bombing," 24 February 2006, obtained by the authors.

19. Interview, Lieutenant Colonel Gian Gentile.

20. Embassy Baghdad cable classified by Robert Ford, "Reports of Attacks Driving Families Out of Baghdad Communities" (CONFIDENTIAL), 6 March 2006.

21. Interview, Lieutenant Colonel James Danna.

22. Interviews, Western officials.

23. Interview, Phebe Marr.

24. Interviews, Western and Iraqi officials.

25. Interviews, Nuri al-Maliki, former Western officials.

26. General George W. Casey, Jr., and Zalmay Khalilzad, "Joint Campaign Plan: Transition to Iraqi Self-Reliance," 28 April 2006, campaign plan obtained by the authors.

27. Interview, former military official.

28. Major General Eldon Bargewell, Haditha Article 15-6 investigation (declassified), 15 June 2006.

29. Combat Studies Institute interview with Colonel Michael Steele, March 2008.

30. Steele was an iconoclastic character who had fought in the 1993 "Black Hawk Down" battle in Mogadishu as a Ranger company commander in the JSOC task force. Many officers who had served in the Balkans during the 1990s pointed to the experience as useful in preparing them for Iraq; Steele believed that the Balkans had warped the Army and diverted it from the job of fighting

wars. "The guy who is going to win on the far end is the one who gets violent the fastest," he told his troops in a speech before deploying.

In early 2006, Steele and the other brigade commanders in northern Iraq, including H.R. McMaster, gathered at a base near Tikrit to discuss what was working and what was not in their various sectors. McMaster, whose 3rd ACR was approaching the end of its tour in Tal Afar, gave a presentation about the importance of understanding the politics and history of any given area of Iraq. "Thank you for the history lesson, H.R.," Steele said sarcastically when McMaster was finished. When Steele gave his own brief, the deputy division commander in the north, Brigadier General Rickey Rife, noted that he had not mentioned reconstruction in Samarra, for which a $30-million-dollar fund had been set aside. Steele responded that he saw no reason to throw good money at a city full of people supporting the insurgency. "I am not going to spend a dime," he told an incredulous Rife.

Steele constantly reminded his troops of the importance of killing more enemy fighters, which raised worries among some of his officers that eventually civilians were going to wind up dead. "Colonel Steele sometimes told his officers, 'We will never cross the line, but we might get chalk all over our feet,'" reported a *New Yorker* article on his brigade (Rafi Khatchadourian, "The Kill Company," *The New Yorker*, 6 July 2009). After an airstrike that killed both insurgents and a pregnant woman, the article added, "Chiarelli's staff insisted that Steele's soldiers find and compensate the woman's family; Steele's brigade staff refused, and epithets were exchanged."

31. Embassy Baghdad cable classified by Zalmay Khalilzad, "Severe Abuse at Ministry of Interior Site 4 Detention Facility" (CONFIDENTIAL), 10 June 2006.

CHAPTER 12   *Together Forward*

1. Yochi Dreazen, "A Class of Generals," *Wall Street Journal,* 25 July 2009.
2. Combat Studies Institute interview with General George Casey, 25 January 2009.
3. Interview, Lieutenant Colonel Gian Gentile.
4. Multi-National Corps—Iraq intelligence report obtained by the authors.
5. Multi-National Corps—Iraq intelligence report obtained by the authors.
6. Multi-National Division—Baghdad unclassified monthly historical report, July 2006.
7. Interview, General Peter Chiarelli.
8. Interview, former military official.
9. General (Retired) George Casey, "Operation Iraqi Freedom, July 2004– February 2007: Strategic Reflections," draft dated 3 February 2012.
10. "Notes from SecDef SVTC, 060831," 31 August 2006.

CHAPTER 13   *The Perfect Storm*

1. Classified American intelligence assessments dating back to early 2006 reveal the extent of Sadrist control over BIAP, as Baghdad International Airport was known, but do not reveal actions to halt it until much later. An April report by the Air Force Office of Special Investigations ("AFOSI Defense Threat Assessment: Baghdad International Airport, Iraq" [SECRET] 28 April 2006),

which also touched on Russian monitoring of American communications in Iraq, reported that Global Risk Strategies had been penetrated and the Mahdi Army was smuggling explosives through the airport. A July report by Casey's intelligence staff (MNF-I Combined Intelligence Operations Center, "Daily Intelligence Summary" [SECRET] 3 July 2006) described the monitoring of coalition operations by Sadrist airport personnel. A November report by the corps intelligence staff ("Sadrist Control of BIAP" [SECRET] 27 November 2006) described the March 2006 explosives incident and the infiltration of Global Risk Strategies and the sky marshals.

More reports piled up over the winter of 2006, recording new offenses that included the killing of A to Z Cleaning Company employees, the murder of Iraqi commandos after they were followed from the airport, and the Iraqi Airlines director-general's "Jan 2007 trip where he flew Ministry of State for National Security Affairs Director (and acting MOT Director) Wa'ili to Iran. Wa'ili met with MOIS and was instructed on OPSEC procedures to counter SIGINT." A file on Major Ayyub Jaffar al-Zaydawi, the director of sky marshals and later overall director of airport security, said that he met in January with Waili to discuss "the assassination of Iraqi intelligence officers in BIAP due to their opposition to Jaysh al-Mahdi and their association with the Americans," and also "targeted Iraqi special forces for kidnapping in retaliation of raids conducted throughout Baghdad. Baghdad International Airport security personnel and Iraqi sky marshals are trying to identify members of the Iraqi special forces (ISOF), commanded by Brigadier General Fadil [al-Barwari], so they can be kidnapped." One witness explained to investigators that Zaydawi had in 2006 commanded a Mahdi Army unit in Baladiyat, near Sadr City.

A later report, from March 2007, listed a litany of recent offenses: "JAM infiltration within the commercial side of the airport is pervasive. In January 2007 the Office of the Martyr Sadr (OMS) issued orders for JAM to take control of the Iraqi sky marshals. JAM has since taken steps such as removing and displacing people to facilitate the formal employment of more JAM members. JAM members can be found among sky marshals, security personnel, contractors, and within Airport Village (APV). In addition to employment, JAM has worked to obtain housing for its members by displacing Sunnis and non-JAM Shia from APV. Intelligence reports indicate:

- "In early February 2007, Hassayn Naim Fayay (LNU)—the Director of the Sky Marshal's Office, a JAM death squad leader, and a high-ranking JAM commander—conducted assassinations for his personal gain and for JAM.
- "In early February 2007, JAM sky marshals used their positions to board international flights to escape Coalition and Iraqi Security Forces.
- "In early February 2007, BIAP security personnel and Iraqi sky marshals targeted U.S. forward operating bases and planted improvised explosive devices.
- "In early February 2007, BIAP security personnel and Iraqi sky marshals targeted Iraqi Special Forces for kidnapping in retaliation for raids conducted throughout Baghdad. [. . .]
- "In mid-October 2006, approximately ninety (90) percent of the A to Z cleaning company were JAM members.

- "In early January 2007, JAM members shot approximately 15 A to Z employees traveling by bus on their way to work at BIAP using PKC light machine guns. One survivor of the attack claimed on local news that JAM was behind the killings. No A to Z employees from Sadr City were on the bus at the time of the ambush."

2. "Notes from SecDef SVTC, 061116," 16 November 2006.
3. Interview, Colonel James Danna.
4. Interview, Colonel James Danna.
5. Interview, Colonel Jeff Peterson.
6. Michael R. Gordon, "On Baghdad Streets, a Police Partnership Falters," *New York Times,* 21 October 2006.
7. Interview, Colonel Jeff Peterson.
8. MNF-I Combined Intelligence Operations Center, "Kidnapping Trends in Iraq" (SECRET), 26 December 2006.
9. "Notes from SecDef SVTC, 061116," 16 November 2006.
10. Interview, Major General J. D. Thurman, 35th Military History Detachment, 6 October 2006.
11. Combat Studies Institute Interview, Major David Hansen, September 2010.
12. Richard A. Oppel Jr., "Military Officials Add to U.S. Criticism of Iraq Government," *New York Times,* 28 September 2006.
13. Doug Smith and Peter Spiegel, "Top U.S. Commander Defends Iraq's Premier," *Los Angeles Times,* 30 September 2006.
14. Classified report on the interrogation of a senior Al-Qaeda detainee in Iraq.
15. Marine Corps Intelligence Activity, "Study of the Insurgency in Anbar Province, Iraq" (SECRET), 13 June 2007.
16. DIA, "The State of Insurgent Finances—A Strategic Reassessment" (SECRET), 26 March 2006.
17. Recovered north of Baghdad on 19 December 2006 by troops from 1-82 Field Artillery, the "Taji DOCEX" proved to be a treasure trove. One document was a thirty-three-page report from one senior Al-Qaeda in Iraq leader to another, "Khalil." Some portions of that document were extended quotations from reports submitted by regional emirs or commanders, complete with parenthetical notes by the more senior author of the main letter. Some euphemisms were used: "Rafida," a pejorative term, refers to Shiites throughout the text. Some Al-Qaeda figures' names end with either "al-Muhajir" or "al-Ansari"; the former refers to a foreign fighter from outside Iraq, while the latter refers to a local Iraqi fighter. "Karkh" and "Rusafa" refer not to the districts of those names, but to West Baghdad and East Baghdad generally. Other documents in the Taji trove included a three-page memo listing accomplished missions and the logistical tasks of an Al-Qaeda commander, such as putting in a nomination for a colleague for an emirship and "organizing the mail"; a manual for how to behave if captured; and shorter reports to "Khalil," the recipient of the main report.
18. Marine Corps Intelligence Activity, "Study of the Insurgency in Anbar Province, Iraq" (SECRET), 13 June 2007.
19. Tactical HUMINT Team 335, "Planned Activities by Tawhid wa'al Jihad in Tarmiyah, Iraq" (SECRET), 27 October 2006.
20. "Logistics of an Al Qa'ida in Iraq VBIED Cell Led by Mazin Abu 'Abd-al-Rahman in Baghdad and Tarmiyah" (SECRET), 25 May 2007.

21. Interview, Lieutenant Colonel Michael Kershaw.
22. "OBJ Royal Oak: Executive Summary" (SECRET), 27 November 2006.
23. The squadron, 5-73 Cavalry, was commanded by the Grecophile Lieutenant Colonel Drew Poppas. After the November fight in Turki, the squadron planned to return in greater force. By late December Poppas had developed a plan for his troops to parachute into Turki to take the enemy by surprise, which would have been a first since the 173rd Airborne Brigade's drop into Kurdistan during the invasion, but that plan was vetoed. "Do not bring up vertical envelopment again or you'll be stuffed in a canteen cover," Poppas recalled being told by a superior after he continued to argue for a parachute drop.

   On January 4, 2007, Poppas's squadron and an Iraqi contingent flew into Turki by helicopter while tanks and Bradleys from Mo Goins's battalion approached on the ground. In two weeks of fighting, the paratroop squadron and the extra companies attached to it cleared trench after trench and killed attacking fighters with Abrams main gun rounds as heavy rain kept Apaches and Predators grounded. In the final assault, a pair of B-1 bombers dropped three dozen two-thousand-pound bombs on the concrete bunkers the Al-Qaeda fighters had fallen back on. In buried shipping containers, the American troops found 1,000 RPG rounds, 1,100 Katyusha rockets, nearly a million rounds of 23mm antiaircraft ammunition, and, most surprisingly, 170 American-made TOW 2 antitank missiles, complete with a receipt showing they had originally been sold to the Kuwaiti Army. 5-73 Cavalry would eventually be awarded the Presidential Unit Citation for its dogged fighting, an honor rarely given to units since Fallujah in 2004.
24. Notes of meeting participant, Multi-National Division—Baghdad briefing to General John Abizaid, 14 October 2006. Division and corps staff officers briefed Abizaid about the Mahdi Army and its advances throughout Baghdad and the belts, describing it as a "Shia expansion plan." Abizaid was told that attacks against civilians had gone up since his last visit, that the Ministry of Health had been implicated in the killing of Sunnis, that the Ministry of Finance would not open banks in Sunni areas, that the Ministry of Interior needed to be cleared of corruption and that Sunni officers were being purged from key military units.

   Abizaid asked if the briefers were sure that the Mahdi Army was trying to take and control Sunni territory and was told they were. "Why don't we let them fight it out?" the commander mused. "It's a COA," he added, using the military acronym for a course of action. Told by Thurman that this would result in a huge bloodletting, Abizaid said that sectarianism must be controlled. A big problem is that some Iraqi ministers had more faith in the Mahdi Army than in the Iraqi security forces. "This is a highly nuanced problem that we can work our way out of," Abizaid concluded. "We must find a solution."
25. Interviews, U.S. officials.
26. Interview, U.S. official.
27. MNC-I "The Perfect Storm" (SECRET), 22 October 2006.

CHAPTER 14 *Out West*

1. Combat Studies Institute interview with Colonel Sean MacFarland.
2. Marine Corps Intelligence Activity, "Study of the Insurgency in Anbar Province, Iraq" (SECRET), 13 June 2007.

3. Michael R. Gordon, "Wary Iraqis Are Recruited as Policemen," *New York Times,* 24 July 2006.

4. Michael R. Gordon, "Endurance Meets Doubt in Anbar Province," *New York Times,* 3 September 2006.

5. Marine Corps Intelligence Activity, "Study of the Insurgency in Anbar Province, Iraq" (SECRET), 13 June 2007.

6. Interview, Lieutenant Colonel Ron Clark.

7. Marine Corps Intelligence Activity, "Study of the Insurgency in Anbar Province, Iraq" (SECRET), 13 June 2007.

8. Interview with an Army historian.

9. Embassy Baghdad cable classified by Zalmay Khalilzad, "PM Discusses Baghdad Security Plan, Site 4, Basrah, Zarqawi Remains" (SECRET), 19 June 2006.

10. Journal of Colonel Sean MacFarland, reviewed by the authors.

11. Interview, Lieutenant Colonel V. J. Tedesco. "Ended up using a laser-guided Maverick missile from an F-18 against what was once an all-male dormitory that we refer to as the 'Gay Palace,' " MacFarland wrote in his diary of one fight, on June 29. Journal of Major General Sean MacFarland, reviewed by the authors.

12. Diaries of Sterling Jensen and Major General Sean MacFarland.

13. I Marine Expeditionary Force G-2, "State of the Insurgency in al-Anbar" (SECRET), 17 August 2006.

14. Interview, Sterling Jensen.

15. Interview, Sterling Jensen.

16. Combat Studies Institute interview with Colonel Sean MacFarland.

17. Journal of Colonel Sean MacFarland, reviewed by the authors.

18. Journal of Colonel Sean MacFarland, reviewed by the authors.

19. Interview, Colonel Anthony Deane.

20. Interview, Major General Sean MacFarland.

21. Interview, Sterling Jensen.

22. The battle of Sufiya is best reconstructed in William Doyle, *A Soldier's Dream: Captain Travis Patriquin and the Awakening of Iraq* (New York, NY: NAL, 2011). Our account also draws on interviews with participants like Chuck Ferry and Sterling Jensen and on the account provided by Jassim al-Suwadawi in *Al-Anbar Awakening,* eds. Colonel Gary Montgomery and Chief Warrant Officer 4 Timothy McWilliams, vol. 2: *Iraqi Perspectives* (Quantico, VA: Marine Corps University Press, 2009).

23. Interview, Colonel Chuck Ferry.

24. Embassy Baghdad cable classified by Jim Soriano, "The Security Situation in Anbar: A Year-End Review" (SECRET) 21 December 2006.

25. William Doyle, *A Soldier's Dream: Captain Travis Patriquin and the Awakening of Iraq* (New York: NAL, 2011), pp. 256–59.

CHAPTER 15 *Some Friendly Advice*

1. Interviews, Iraq Study Group and United States Institute of Peace officials.

2. Notes of a participant.

3. Notes of a participant.

4. Notes of a participant.

5. Notes of a participant.

6. Notes of a participant.

7. Notes of a participant.
8. Notes of a participant.
9. Interview, Bill Perry.
10. Interview, General Peter Chiarelli.
11. Interview, Colonel (Retired) Paul Hughes.
12. Interview, Charles Robb.
13. Memo written by Charles Robb.
14. Interview, Les Gelb.
15. Joseph R. Biden, Jr., and Leslie H. Gelb, "Unity Through Autonomy in Iraq," *New York Times,* 1 May 2006.
16. Notes of a participant.
17. Notes of a participant.
18. Interviews, Iraq Study Group officials. The exact language in the final report reads "By the first quarter of 2008, subject to unexpected developments in the security situation on the ground, all combat brigades not necessary for force protection could be out of Iraq." James A. Baker III and Lee H. Hamilton, "Iraq Study Group Report," published by United States Institute of Peace, pp. 7 and 49.
19. Iraq Study Group report, p. 50.
20. Interviews, Iraq Study Group officials.
21. General (Retired) George Casey, "Operation Iraqi Freedom, July 2004–February 2007: Strategic Reflections," draft dated 3 February 2012.
22. Interview, military official.
23. Notes of a participant, obtained by the authors.
24. Interview, Colonel (Retired) Paul Hughes.
25. Interview, General Jack Keane.
26. "A Conversation with Peter Pace," Council on Foreign Relations, 17 February 2004, discussion moderated by Michael R. Gordon, full transcript.
27. Notes of a participant.

CHAPTER 16 *Back to the Drawing Board*

1. Luti thought a strategy review was long overdue. During a July visit to Baghdad he had met with Bill Caldwell, the major general who served as Casey's top spokesman. "It's changed, hasn't it?" Luti asked. "Yes, it's changed and it's difficult to get their attention," Caldwell had responded. Luti was not sure if Caldwell was referring to Casey, the White House, or both.
2. Interview, senior officials.
3. Notes of the meeting, reviewed by the authors.
4. Interviews, military officers and diplomatic personnel.
5. Interview, General Peter Chiarelli.
6. "Notes from SECDEF SVTC, 061101," 1 November 2006. Only a random selection of the checkpoints on the Army canal, Casey explained to Rumsfeld, had been intended to be manned by Americans at any given time, but after Altaie's disappearance troops had surged onto all of them, only for Maliki to request that they be removed. Casey recalled "explaining the risks" of this to the prime minister: that he would be perceived as "assisting death squads" and "favoring the Shia over the Sunnis." "He understood the risks but asked us to suspend, so we did," Casey said.

The press, Rumsfeld told Casey, was "making it seem Maliki told you. That's the reaction in the U.S. Why are we here if we cannot do what we need, or won't be permitted to do what we need? That's what the reaction here suggests."

"The way I look at it," Casey replied, "he is the prime minister. I give him military advice. If it's not right, we won't do it. But if it's right, then we go ahead and do it."

"I don't see it that way," Rumsfeld shot back. "You don't work for the prime minister. You report through us—Abizaid and SECDEF—then to POTUS, and we decide. He's not your political leader."

"He's not my boss but my partner," Casey protested. "I will never do anything I feel will disadvantage our soldiers."

"What if he tells you to do something you don't think is in accordance with instructions?" Rumsfeld pressed. "You should tell him you have freedom to do different things to make him do different things."

"I inform him of military risks in Baghdad." Casey responded. "I didn't think I jeopardized the mission."

7. Interviews, military officer.
8. Stephen J. Hadley, 8 November 2006 memo, obtained by the authors.
9. Embassy Baghdad cable classified by Zalmay Khalilzad, "Ambassador Khalilzad's Proposed Strategy for Iraq: Sustainable Approach" (SECRET//NODIS), 15 November 2006.
10. Notes of a participant.
11. Central Intelligence Agency, "A Comparison of Strategic Approaches for Iraq" (TOP SECRET), 10 November 2006.
12. Interviews, NSC and Iraqi officials.
13. Michael R. Gordon, "Bush Adviser's Memo Cites Doubts About Iraqi Leader," *New York Times,* 29 November 2006.
14. Interview, State Department official.
15. Interviews, NSC, State Department, and Iraqi officials.
16. Multi-National Corps—Iraq, "Analysis of Iraqi and Coalition End States," declassified 26 July 2010.
17. Multi-National Corps—Iraq, "Analysis of Iraqi and Coalition End States," declassified 26 July 2010.
18. Interview, Colonel Jim Hickey.
19. Combat Studies Institute interview, Colonel Jim Pasquarette, January 2008.
20. Interview, Pentagon official.
21. Interview, U.S. official.
22. U.S. Army, "Medal of Honor—PFC Ross A. McGinnis," official citation.
23. Interview, General (Retired) Jack Keane.
24. OSD-Policy, "National Security Council Meeting: Ongoing Iraq Review" (SECRET), 8 December, 2006.
25. John Hannah, "Establishing a Political Basis for U.S. Success in Iraq" (SECRET), undated "think pieces."
26. OSD, "Iraq Policy—The New Phase—A Proposal: 'Accelerate the Transition, Refocus the Partnership, and Stabilize the Region' " (SECRET), 6 December 2006.
27. General (Retired) George Casey, "Operation Iraqi Freedom, July 2004–February 2007: Strategic Reflections," draft dated 3 February 2012.

28. As Casey, Chiarelli, and the 1st Cavalry Division debated how they would use two extra brigades, a leading option was a large offensive into Sadr City, where American troops ventured only rarely and usually on night raids. In a December 18 meeting on the New Year's offensive that the division was planning, deputy division commander John Campbell gave a sobering view of the likely success of Together Forward–style operations by American and Iraqi forces in Sadr City, according to the notes of a participant. "If you ask the ISF if they will fight in Sadr City, they will not fight," he said plainly. "Really?" Casey questioned. If the United States really wanted to clear and control all of Baghdad, including Sadr City, as many as eight extra American brigades might be required, division planner Lieutenant Colonel Doug Ollivant suggested. "That's the Stalingrad model," Casey observed.

29. Interview, Jack Keane.

30. Interview, Jack Keane.

31. While Bush concentrated on winning over the Joint Chiefs, Casey took his own soundings in Baghdad. On December 12, ten general officers from Casey's staff and subordinate commands gathered to brief him and Chiarelli on a revised Baghdad Security Plan that would incorporate two new American brigades. Before the meeting adjourned, according to participants, Casey took an informal poll of the ten generals in his office: Should the extra two brigades be repositioned from elsewhere in Iraq, or should they be new forces, brought in from the United States? Five of the generals came down on the side of bringing in additional units from stateside. The others backed the internal option.

32. Notes of a meeting participant.

33. National Security Council, "Memorandum for the Record: NSC Meeting on Iraq" (SECRET), 15 December 2006.

34. Interview, trip participant.

35. Robert Gates memo to George Bush (and others), "Trip to Iraq, December 19–22, 2006" (SECRET), 22 December 2006.

36. "SecDef Talking Points for Meeting with POTUS" (SECRET), 22 December 2006.

37. Interview, Jack Keane.

38. Account of a meeting participant.

39. Alfonso Serrano, "Full Transcript of Bush's Iraq Speech," CBS News, 19 June 2009.

40. Interview, senior military officer.

41. Interview, U.S. official; also see Michael A. Newton and Michael P. Scharf, *Enemy of the State: The Trial and Execution of Saddam Hussein* (New York: St. Martin's Press, 2008) pp. 184–206.

CHAPTER 17 *League of the Righteous*

1. "The insurgents used SUVs with fake CREW antennas, apparent ACUs, US type weapons, and some spoken English to appear like a US Contractor or Security team," a classified 1st Cavalry Division account of the Karbala attack noted. "The team entered the compound and HQ building without being engaged, and attacked US forces with rifle fire and grenades. While defending the command post, one US soldier was KIA and three others WIA by a hand

grenade thrown into the main CP office. Soldiers in the PJCC reported that the IPs fled to adjacent buildings and did not defend the compound . . . In addition to the assault team, the insurgent team appeared to include a support force and indirect fire support, all integrated and well rehearsed. The precision of the attack indicates inside knowledge of the office and security layout of the compound. This and police behavior during the attack supports possible IP complicity. The coordination and complexity of the operation exceeds that seen in JAM or Sunni militia operations against US forces, indicating possible support from outside government forces, such as Al Qods." Multi-National Division—Baghdad. "MND-B OPSUM of 21 Jan 07 Attack of PJCC in Karbala."

2. Embassy Baghdad cable classified by Zalmay Khalilzad, "Talabani Gives Readout of Syria Visit, Passes Message from Suleimani" (SECRET), 22 January 2007.

3. National Ground Intelligence Center, "The Islamic Revolutionary Guard Corps in Iraq" (SECRET), 20 December 2006.

4. Zalmay Khalilzad, U.S. embassy Baghdad diplomatic cable, obtained by the authors.

5. National Ground Intelligence Center, "The Islamic Revolutionary Guard Corps in Iraq" (SECRET), 20 December 2006.

6. Defense Intelligence Digest, "2004 IRGC-QF Document Reveals Operations Data" (TOP SECRET), 4 June 2008.

7. National Ground Intelligence Center, intelligence report reviewed by the authors.

8. NGIC report cited in Combined Joint Special Operations Task Force—Arabian Peninsula, "Iraq Internal Forces/Factors" (SECRET), 7 January 2007.

9. Combat Studies Institute interview with Major David Hansen, September 2010.

10. "Iraq: Targeting of Fixed Wing Aircraft" (SECRET), 16 February 2007.

11. Interviews, senior U.S. officials.

12. Michael R. Gordon and Scott Shane, "Behind U.S. Pressure on Iran, Long-Held Worry Over a Deadly Device in Iraq," *New York Times*, 27 March 2007.

13. "Iranian Destabilization Activities in Iraq" (SECRET), 19 January 2007.

14. Initial incident report, Task Force 5-73 Cavalry, 7 September 2006.

15. "Notes from SecDef SVTC, 061103" (SECRET), 3 November 2006.

16. "CJCS Contain, Protect, Deter Planord" (SECRET), 1 October 2006.

17. JSOC dubbed the new missions in its portfolio "Countering Iranian Influence," or CII, and "Countering Militia Influence," or CMI. The Special Forces group that was also based at Balad, Combined Joint Special Operation Task Force—Arabian Peninsula, would continue to pursue the same kind of missions, helping JSOC get on its feet in the new territory of Shiite militants and Iranian operatives.

18. Joint Staff J2, "Iranian Destabilization Activities in Iraq" (SECRET), 19 January 2007.

19. Embassy Baghdad cable classified by Zalmay Khalilzad, "January 7 MCNS: Iranian Diplomats, BSP, and PIC Among Topics Discussed" (SECRET), 8 January 2007.

20. The acronym-laden order for JSOC to create Task Force 17 read, in part: "To ensure effective, long term execution in Countering Iranian Influence (CII) in

accordance with the MNF-I CII Strategic Directive and FRAGO, OCF-I will establish a CII task force, with all portions of Find, Fix, Finish, Exploit, and Analyze (F3EA) organic to it. The development of the task force will be conducted in two phases: Interim Operational Capability (IOC) will be in place NLT 15 Jan 07 and Full Operational Capability (FOC) will be in place NLT 15 Feb 07. A cooperative C2 relationship between TF 88 and CJSOTF will enable the necessary expertise and resources to be applied. Endstate is a TF 88 CII Task Force, mirror-like in appearance to the Defeat AQI Task Force 16, but clearly separated from the AQI mission set, capable of conducting sustained operations in support of CII."

Initially, JSOC would lean heavily on the Special Forces group already in Iraq for Task Force 17's troops and missions. Over the course of the year, though, the Ranger Regiment and non-JSOC SEAL teams took over the job.

21. Multi-National Force—Iraq, "Detained Iranian Intel Officers" (SECRET), January 2007.
22. "Rogue Elements of JAM" (SECRET), 19 January 2007.
23. Embassy Baghdad cable classified by Margaret Scobey, "COR Member Qasem Daoud Discusses Tehran, POTUS Speech" (SECRET), 17 January 2007.

CHAPTER 18 PETRAEUS TAKES COMMAND

1. Although the new counterinsurgency manual did establish this guideline, it was not absolute. The relevant section of FM 3-24 reads, in full: "No force level guarantees victory for either side. During previous conflicts, planners assumed that combatants required a 10 or 15 to 1 advantage over insurgents to win. However, no predetermined, fixed ratio of friendly troops to enemy combatants ensures success in COIN. The conditions of the operational environment and the approaches insurgents use vary too widely. A better force requirement gauge is troop density, the ratio of security forces (including the host nation's military and police forces as well as foreign counterinsurgents) to inhabitants. Most density recommendations fall within a range of 20 to 25 counterinsurgents for every 1000 residents in an AO. Twenty counterinsurgents per 1000 residents is often considered the minimum troop density required for effective COIN operations; however as with any fixed ratio, such calculations remain very dependent on the situation." *Counterinsurgency Field Manual*, U.S. Army Field Manual No. 3-24, Marine Corps Warfighting Publication No. 3-33.5 (Chicago: University of Chicago Press, 2007), paragraphs 1–67.
2. U.S. Senate Armed Services Committee, "Nomination of Army Lieutenant General David Petraeus to Be General and Commander of the Multi-National Forces–Iraq," 23 January 2007, A.M. hearing chaired by Senator Carl Levin, committee chairman.
3. U.S. Senate Committee on Foreign Relations, "Alternative Plans Continued—Federalism, Side with the Majority, Strategic Redeployment, or Negotiate?," 23 January 2007, A.M. hearing chaired by Senator Joseph R. Biden Jr., committee chairman.
4. Senator Barack Obama, "S. 433—Iraq War De-escalation Act of 2007," 110th Congress, 1st session, 30 January 2007, p. 7.

5. The NIE concluded that "Coalition capabilities, including force levels, resources, and operations, remain an essential stabilizing element in Iraq. If Coalition forces were withdrawn rapidly during the term of this Estimate, we judge that this almost certainly would lead to a significant increase in the scale and scope of sectarian conflict in Iraq, intensify Sunni resistance to the Iraqi Government, and have adverse consequences for national reconciliation. If such a rapid withdrawal were to take place, we judge that the ISF would be unlikely to survive as a non-sectarian national institution; neighboring countries—invited by Iraqi factions or unilaterally—might intervene openly in the conflict; massive civilian casualties and forced population displacement would be probable; AQI would attempt to use parts of the country—particularly al-Anbar province—to plan increased attacks in and outside of Iraq; and spiraling violence and political disarray in Iraq, along with Kurdish moves to control Kirkuk and strengthen autonomy, could prompt Turkey to launch a military incursion." National intelligence estimate ("a withdrawal of American troops would 'almost certainly' lead to sectarian violence"), Office of the Director of National Intelligence, "Prospects for Iraq's Stability: A Challenging Road Ahead," National Intelligence Estimate, 30 January 2007, p. 7.

6. Even as he called for withdrawal publicly, Obama hinted at the consequences of a precipitous withdrawal in *The Audacity of Hope*. Recounting his interactions with a group of Baghdad reporters, he wrote, "I asked them if they thought a U.S. troop withdrawal might ease tensions, expecting them to answer in the affirmative. Instead, they shook their heads. 'My best guess is the country would collapse into civil war within weeks,' one of the reporters told me. 'One hundred, maybe two hundred thousand dead. We're the only thing holding this place together.' " Later on his day-and-a-half-long trip, Obama spoke with a Marine major, who told Mark Lippert that the best strategy would be to withdraw troops from the country, even though he could see the situation improving slowly. In the section of the book where he outlined his Iraq policy, Obama ultimately did not commit to any timeline for withdrawal; instead, he simply wrote, "I believe . . . our strategic goals at this point should be well defined: achieving some semblance of stability in Iraq, ensuring that those in power in Iraq are not hostile to the United States, and preventing Iraq from becoming a base for terrorist activity. In pursuit of these goals, I believe it is in the interest of both Americans and Iraqis to begin a phased withdrawal of U.S. troops by the end of 2006, although how quickly a complete withdrawal can be accomplished is a matter of imperfect judgment, based on a series of best guesses—about the ability of the Iraqi government to deliver even basic security and services to its people, the degree to which our presence drives the insurgency, and the odds that in the absence of U.S. troops Iraq would descend into all-out civil war. When battle-hardened Marine officers suggest that we pull out and skeptical foreign correspondents suggest that we stay, there are no easy answers to be had." Barack Obama, *The Audacity of Hope* (New York: Random House, 2006), pp. 352–59.

7. General (Retired) George Casey, "Operation Iraqi Freedom, July 2004–February 2007: Strategic Reflections," draft dated 3 February 2012.

8. Interview, senior military official.

9. Bruce Catton, *Grant Takes Command* (New York: Little, Brown and Company, 1994).

10. Interview, senior military official.

11. U.S. embassy Baghdad cable, classified by Zalmay Khalilzad, "Iraqi Parliament Speaker Mashdani's Meltdown" (SECRET), 13 February 2007.

12. Notes of meeting participant.

13. Weekly report from General David Petraeus to Secretary of Defense Robert Gates (SECRET), week of 24 February–2 March 2007.

14. Interview, senior military official.

15. To keep the warring sides apart and roll back the militia advance as much as possible ahead of the arrival of surge forces, 1st Cavalry relied heavily on Colonel Steve Townsend's 3rd Stryker Brigade, 2nd Infantry Division, which roamed the capital clearing neighborhoods and helping to establish outposts. In some cases, though, the Stryker operations were little different from the summer and fall's Together Forward missions. When a Stryker battalion dislodged Sunni insurgents from Haifa Street just outside the Green Zone in late January, few Iraqi troops were available for the "hold" phase. As a result, the Mahdi Army moved in, with reports quickly appearing of militia snipers taking up positions on the street's high-rises to intimidate Sunni residents. Haifa Street served as a sobering lesson to Fil's division.

   Efforts to get more Iraqi troops to the capital had been problematic, too. The first battalion of a wave of Iraqi Army reinforcements ordered in by the Defense Ministry arrived in early January. But a brigade commander in the largely Kurdish 2nd Division resisted and then delayed orders to move his troops from the northern city of Sulaymaniyah, and the commander of another Kurdish brigade, in the 4th Division, selected to move from Irbil to Baghdad, told his superiors in early January that he could not make the move in less than six months. A Shiite-majority brigade was ordered to Baghdad from Anbar, and although it went, its commander expressed concern over whether his soldiers would have to fight Shiite militias to which they were sympathetic. Department of the Army, "Morning Brief: Operation Iraqi Freedom/Operation Enduring Freedom/Operation Noble Eagle" (SECRET), 13 January 2007.

16. Alissa Rubin, "9 Die as Assassins' Blasts Wound Sunni Deputy Prime Minister," *New York Times,* 24 March 2007; Alissa Rubin, "8 Iraqis Killed in Bomb Attack at Legislature," *New York Times,* 13 April 2007.

17. Interview, Colonel Jeff Peterson.

18. Interview, Colonel Jeff Peterson; interview, Lieutenant Colonel Steve Michael.

19. Captain Jim Keirsey "Reflections of a Counterinsurgency Company Commander," *ARMY Magazine,* July 2008.

20. Interview, Colonel Jim Crider.

21. Interview, Lieutenant Colonel Dale Kuehl.

22. Interviews, U.S. military officers.

23. Department of the Army, "Morning Brief: Operation Iraqi Freedom/Operation Enduring Freedom/Operation Noble Eagle" (SECRET), 7 February 2007; CJSOTF-AP, "Insurgents in GMC Trucks with Missile Launch Base Plates Changed into Police Uniforms After Helicopter Is Shot Down" (SECRET), 7 February 2007.

24. Weekly report from General David Petraeus to Secretary of Defense Robert Gates (SECRET), week of 3–9 March.

25. Interview, Lieutenant Colonel Dale Kuehl.

26. During one raid in March, Steve Michael's troops and their National Police partners found a cache that contained two rifles with high-end scopes, a

German-made G3, and an American-made M16, hard evidence of the sniper threat that Michael's soldiers often encountered.

Much more lethal were Dora's deep-buried bombs. By mid-April, half of all the underbelly IEDs going off in Baghdad were going off in Dora. Similarly, in parts of East Baghdad where the Mahdi Army was being challenged by new forces, violence was on the rise as militia cells used EFPs to defend their territory and restrict American movement. Dora and Ameriyah had both been bad neighborhoods when the surge began, but by the end of May, they were much worse. American officers could protest that increased violence in some areas was to be expected as insurgents were challenged there and pushed out of other neighborhoods—an oft-repeated refrain of counterinsurgents is that "things will get worse before they better." In Dora, Ameriyah, and other neighborhoods that Sunni insurgents were choosing to defend heavily, things did not look like they were on their way to getting better in the late spring of 2007.

27. Interviews, U.S. military officers.

CHAPTER 19 *The Enemy Within*

1. Interrogation report of Qais al-Khazali (SECRET), 23 March 2007.
2. Weekly report from General David Petraeus to Defense Secretary Robert Gates (SECRET), week of 17–23 March 2007.
3. Weekly report from General David Petraeus to Defense Secretary Robert Gates, week of 24–30 March 2007.
4. Interview, military official.
5. Weekly report from General David Petraeus to Defense Secretary Robert Gates (SECRET), week of 24–30 March 2007.
6. Joint Strategic Assessment Team, "Draft Joint Campaign Plan and Final Report of the Joint Strategic Assessment Team" (SECRET), 20 April 2007.
7. MNF-I Joint Strategic Assessment Team final report.
8. MNF-I Joint Strategic Assessment Team final report.
9. MNF-I Joint Strategic Assessment Team final report.
10. MNF-I Joint Strategic Assessment Team final report.
11. Interview, State Department official.
12. MNF-I Joint Strategic Assessment Team final report.
13. The problem at Camp Bucca was so severe that a field artillery battalion from one of the surge brigades was diverted to the prison to bulk up the guard force.
14. Interview, military official; Embassy Baghdad cable classified by Ryan Crocker, "Maliki Reshapes the National Security System" (SECRET), 15 May 2007.
15. Embassy Baghdad cable classified by Ryan Crocker, "Maliki Reshapes the National Security System" (SECRET), 15 May 2007.
16. Interview, U.S. military officer.
17. MNF-I and U.S. Embassy Baghdad, "Joint Campaign Plan: "Operation Iraqi Freedom (SECRET), 26 July 2007.
18. Letter from General David Petraeus to Secretary of Defense Robert Gates, obtained by the authors. Weekly report from General David Petraeus to Defense Secretary Robert Gates (SECRET), week of 10–16 June 2007.
19. Weekly report from General David Petraeus to Defense Secretary Robert Gates (SECRET), week of 13–19 May 2007.

20. Commander's Initiatives Group, "Talking Points for Mr. Clapper, Deputy Secretary of Defense (Intelligence)," 14 August 2007.
21. Interview, Lieutenant General (Retired) James Dubik.
22. Lieutenant Colonel Andrew Yerkes, "Team #6121 After Action Report," December 2007.
23. Interview, military official.

CHAPTER 20 *The Former-Insurgent Counterinsurgency*

1. 5-20 Infantry was the third battalion Odierno's headquarters moved into the belts over the winter. In January, a paratroop battalion had been pulled from the Iskandariya area to Karma, between Baghdad and Fallujah. Then, at the same time as 5-20's move, the paratroop squadron that had fought in the battle of Turki and gotten into the tiff with Iranian border guards relocated to the lush valley area just north of Baqubah to complement the Stryker troops' offensive.
2. Interview, Haidar (real name redacted).
3. Interviews, U.S. soldiers.
4. Interview, Captain Anthony Gore.
5. Interview, Major Jack Vantress.
6. Interview, Captain Tim Bagley.
7. Interview, Captain Ben Richards.
8. Interview, Captain Ben Richards.
9. Interview, Major Jack Vantress.
10. Interview, Staff Sergeant Shawn McGuire.
11. Interview, Captain Ben Richards.
12. Interview, Command Sergeant Major Jeffrey Huggins.
13. Interview, Captain Ben Richards.
14. A separate DIA cable placed responsibility for the attack with a former Al-Qaeda fighter, Abu Qutayba, who had left the group in 2006, and a group of his relatives, and said the ambushers were in fact able to approach and identify Masri's corpse, which "was dressed in black Afghan-style shirt and pants and was wearing a black scarf around his head," along with eyeglasses and "a very light beard." But before they could recover the body, Al-Qaeda reinforcements arrived and took it back toward Tarmiya, the Al-Qaeda stronghold in the northern belt. Masri, it turned out, was not dead. But the reported incident hinted that in the strategically significant western belt, between Anbar and Baghdad, the same Sunni opposition to Al-Qaeda that had motivated the Anbar Awakening was simmering.
15. Interview, Colonel Kurt Pinkerton.
16. Interview, Colonel John Valledor.
17. Interview, Colonel John Valledor.
18. Interview, Colonel Michael Kershaw.
19. What low- and mid-level leaders such as Valledor, Suich, Pinkerton, and Ben Richards were now doing by working with Sunni insurgents had a strikingly close parallel in the real war in Algeria on which Jean Lartéguy's *The Centurions,* an American military cult classic, was based, a conflict that sometimes seemed spookily similar to Iraq. Exactly half a century earlier, in 1957, French ethnologist Jean Servier and a thirty-year-old commando officer, Cap-

tain Pierre Hentic, had overseen the creation of Algerian irregular units called *harkis*, often drawing on "flipped" members of the Algerian FLN insurgency. "After noting instances where villagers in the Orléansville area had killed F.L.N. scouts with hatchets," explains Alistair Horne's classic tome on Algeria, *A Savage War of Peace,* "Servier—despite considerable official opposition— had gained permission initially to create 'light companies' from some thousand men, the able-bodied and trustworthy defectors from the F.L.N." The *harki* units had spread much as Sunni Awakening groups were now spreading, and would eventually number sixty thousand men. "That mere captains, like Hentic, should come to acquire quite vast powers, both in military and civil operations, had—by May 1958—become in itself a commonplace and significant feature," Horne wrote. The same was true of 2007 Iraq.

20. Weekly report General David Petraeus to Secretary of Defense Robert Gates (SECRET), 27 May–2 June 2007.

21. Daily Intelligence Summary Multi-National Corps—Iraq (SECRET), 27 April 2007. "There is a pattern forming between the Abu Ghraib ERU and the Muthanna Brigade," it noted.

22. Interview, Colonel Dale Kuehl.

23. Interview, Lieutenant Colonel Chip Daniels.

24. Joshua Partlow, "For U.S. Unit in Baghdad, an Alliance of Last Resort," *Washington Post,* 9 June 2007.

25. Interview, Colonel Dale Kuehl.

CHAPTER 21 *Phantom Thunder*

1. The worst area in Baghdad, Petraeus told the NSC several times in his weekly videoconferences, was East Rashid, especially the Al-Qaeda redoubt of Dora. In late May, Steve Townsend's Stryker brigade spent four days fighting in three adjacent neighborhoods in Dora where Al-Qaeda was putting up the most resistance, Muhallas 822, 824, and 826. The first day ended with two Strykers burning to the ground—one hit by an IED and one by a Molotov cocktail that ignited a flammable countersniper screen. Before moving on to Baqubah, Townsend told Odierno that he thought Dora was now close to a tipping point. It was not. On June 20, after the Strykers had moved on, five soldiers from the battalion that stayed in Dora, Steve Michael's 2-12 Infantry, died in a complex ambush in Muhalla 826 in which insurgents used RKG-3s, a type of parachuting antiarmor grenade that had rarely been seen in Baghdad before. "I thought the work of the Strykers at best disrupted activity, but didn't change anything," said Michael.

Starting July 1, the Stryker battalions that had stayed behind in Baghdad when Townsend went to Baqubah returned to Dora's three problem muhallas. This time the brigade that "owned" southern Baghdad ran the operation, not the Stryker brigade, and the plan was for the extra clearance forces to stay in Dora for thirty days this time, not three. For the month of July and into August, five American battalions were concentrated in East Rashid (more than in Baqubah), three of them in the one-square-mile area represented by Muhallas 822, 824, and 826. As the battalions cleared the muhallas, this time they installed concrete barriers like those that had helped cut down violence elsewhere in Baghdad. They also went house to house collecting "biometric data"—photographs, fingerprints, and retinal scans—from every young man in every home.

The units in Dora faced some of the toughest conditions in Iraq, akin to Baqubah. After losing so many Strykers in the first few days in Dora in June, the commander of the battalion in Muhalla 822, Lieutenant Colonel Ricardo Love, ordered his troops to work dismounted, leaving their vehicles at the edge of the muhalla. As in Baqubah, there were HBIEDs, or house bombs, as well; Love's battalion, 1-38 Infantry, used 105mm tank-style guns mounted on some of their Strykers to destroy them.

A small number of effective snipers posed a nerve-racking threat. "They would aim right for your ear-hole," Love recalled. On the first day of the July operation, one of Love's soldiers was shot and killed by a sniper, and then an hour later a shot penetrated the helmet of another soldier but ricocheted around inside and left him with only a concussion. 2-12 Infantry, which spent July focused on Muhalla 826, lost two soldiers to snipers, in addition to a third soldier whose frontal lobe was grazed by a bullet, a fourth who walked away with a concussion when the back of his helmet stopped a bullet, and a fifth who survived a shot through his skull and brain because the bullet was armor-piercing and left only a small hole. When 2-12 Infantry soldiers finally killed the sniper who had been tormenting them, he turned out to be an Egyptian Al-Qaeda fighter, but when 1-38 Infantry killed theirs, he was a local man who appeared to be mildly mentally disabled.

2. Interview, Lieutenant Colonel Morris Goins.
3. "General David Petraeus," Fox News Sunday Transcript, 17 June 2007.
4. See Colonel Fred Johnson, "Arrowhead Ripper: Adaptive Leadership in Full Spectrum Operations," U.S. Army War College Personal Experience Monograph. For Odierno's estimate that 80 percent of insurgent leaders escaped, see Department of Defense, "DoD Special Briefing with Lt. Gen. Odierno," 22 June 2007. Odierno said, "Frankly, I think they knew an operation was coming in Baqubah. They watched the news. They understood we had a surge. . . . I don't think they were tipped off by Iraqi security forces. I think they were tipped off by us talking about the surge, us discussing the fact that we have a problem in Diyala province."
5. This account of 1-30 Infantry's operations in Arab Jabour is based on the author's firsthand observations, interviews with Lieutenant Colonel Adgie and other participants, the battalion's Presidential Unit Citation narrative, and a paper by the unit, "You Can't Clap with One Hand. . . . Arab Jabour: A Case Study of Counterinsurgency During OIF V," 2007. See also Michael R. Gordon, "The Former Insurgent Counterinsurgency," *New York Times Magazine,* 2 September 2007.
6. William E. Odom, "Know When to Fold 'Em," New York *Daily News,* 11 January 2007.
7. Interview, Captain Chad Klascius.
8. Interview, Lieutenant Colonel Mark Odom.
9. Interview with Lieutenant General Ray Odierno, quoted in Gordon, "The Former-Insurgent Counterinsurgency."
10. Notes of a meeting participant.
11. Weekly report from General David Petraeus to Defense Secretary Robert Gates (SECRET), week of 24–30 June 2007.
12. Interview, Emma Sky.

CHAPTER 22 *The USS* CENTCOM

1. Nancy Pelosi and Harry Reid, "Call on the President to Listen to the Will of the American People on Iraq," Speaker of the House Press Release, 13 June 2007.
2. Meeting attended by the authors.
3. Briefing by General David Petraeus, "MNF Iraq Update: POTUS SVTC" (SECRET), 7 May 2007.
4. Interview, former CENTCOM officer.
5. Interview, American military official.
6. Email from Lieutenant General Ray Odierno to MNC-I Chief of Staff, C3, C4, and C5, "Let's Steal the March on Washington" (SECRET), July 2007.
7. Interview, Colonel Jim Hickey.
8. Notes from video presentation by General David Petraeus to a military staff college in the United States, 18 July 2008.
9. Weekly report from General David Petraeus to Defense Secretary Robert Gates (SECRET), week of 24–30 June 2007.
10. Notes of 16 July and 23 July 2007 NSC videoconferences.
11. An outline of JSOC's activities during the surge can be pieced together from the periodic "Defeat Extremists" videoconferences MNF-I hosted. The slide decks for these briefings, classified SECRET, included regular updates from both Task Force 16 and Task Force 17, as well as the Special Forces group answering to Odierno's corps, listing ongoing operations, names of targets, and numbers of raids, detainees, and insurgents killed. A regularly updated headquarters document aimed at putting all the raids being conducted by various units in Baghdad into one database, the "Nightly FAIO Consolidated Roll-Up," describes every special operations mission conducted in Baghdad in slightly more detail. Sections give the basic details of raids conducted by conventional troops in the capital, by the Special Forces group and its Iraqi commando partners, by JSOC (referred to as OCF-I, or "Other Coalition Forces—Iraq"), and by a CIA-led unit whose missions were often into Sadr City.
12. Task Force 1-30 Infantry, "You Can't Clap with One Hand . . . . Arab Jabour: A Case Study of Counterinsurgency During OIF V," 2007.
13. Weekly report from General David Petraeus to Defense Secretary Robert Gates (SECRET), week of 5–11 August 2007.
14. Task Force 714, "OBJ Colenso, OBJ Flanders 4" (SECRET), 20 August 2008.
15. Email traffic between commanding officer of JSOC's Task Force Mosul and the division staff of 25th Infantry Division (SECRET), 7-8 July 2007.
16. Weekly report from General David Petraeus to Defense Secretary Robert Gates (SECRET), week of 12–18 August 2007.
17. Notes of a meeting participant.
18. Wesley Morgan, notes of visit with General David Petraeus to 2-12 Field Artillery, August 2007.
19. Weekly report from General David Petraeus to Defense Secretary Robert Gates (SECRET), week of 8–14 July 2007.
20. Weekly report from General David Petraeus to Defense Secretary Robert Gates (SECRET), week of 24–30 June 2007.
21. Briefing by General David Petraeus, "MNF Iraq Update: NSC SVTC" (SECRET), 1 August 2007.
22. Notes of a meeting participant.

23. Because of this cable's NODIS classification, it was not released in the Wikileaks trove. Embassy Baghdad cable classified by Ryan Crocker, "Iraqi Minister Relays Offer from IRGC Quds Force Commander" (SECRET//NODIS), 14 August 2007. Full cable:

"1. SUMMARY: On August 12, following his return from a trip with Prime Minister Maliki to Iran, Iraqi Minister of State for National Security Affairs (MSNSA) Shirwan al-Waili delivered a message to MNF-I Commanding General Petraeus from Iranian Brigadier General Qasem Solemani, the commander of the Quds Force of the Islamic Revolutionary Guards Corps (IRGC). Al-Waili stated that Solemani had asked him to relay the message that Iranian activity in Iraq would decrease dramatically if detained Jaish al-Mahdi (JAM) Special Groups leader Qais Khazali were released. General Petraeus responded that Iran needed to immediately cease its actions, which were tantamount to a war by proxy against Iraq and the U.S., that if it did not it would face serious consequences, and that it made no sense to release Khazali since he was a key figure who could strengthen JAM's actions against the GOI and the Coalition. END SUMMARY.

"2. MSNSA al-Waili met with MNF-I Commanding General Petraeus August 12 to deliver a message he had received from Iranian Quds Force Commander Solemani on August 10 while al-Waili was visiting Iran as part of Prime Minister Maliki's delegation. Pol-Mil Counselor and MNF-I BG Bergner were also present at the meeting. Al-Waili explained that he met Solemani in his hotel in Tehran after earlier meetings with Iranian President Ahmadinejad and National Security Council Secretary Larijani. Al-Waili claimed that these earlier meetings made it clear to him that neither Ahmadinejad nor Larijani were in control of Iranian activities in Iraq. According to al-Waili, Solemani presented himself as having sole authority over Iranian actions in Iraq.

"3. Al-Waili said the first part of the conversation with Solemani concerned whether the U.S. would attack Iran. Al-Waili said he then discussed Iranian involvement in Iraq. Solemani, he said, asked him to convey an oral message to General Petraeus. The message was that Iran would decrease activity in Iraq dramatically if the Coalition would release Jaish al-Mahdi (JAM) Special Groups leader Qais Khazali, an Iraqi in Coalition custody as a security internee. Al-Waili added that Solemani pledged 'you will see results in two months.'

"4. General Petraeus told al-Waili that Iranian actions and their provision of explosively-formed penetrators (EFPs), 240 mm rockets, and other weapons to their client militias in Iraq were very dangerous. He rejected the idea of releasing Khazali, stating that it defied logic to release someone who would unite and strengthen JAM. General Petraeus urged al-Waili to tell Solemani that Iran needed to stop its actions immediately or face the prospect of isolation or worse. He characterized Iranian actions as tantamount to a declaration of war on Iraq and the U.S. Iran needed to stop funding, equipping, and training Iraqi militants, actions which were of increasing concern in Baghdad and other Coalition capitals, and were not even in the long-term interest of Iran itself, he concluded.

"5. Al-Waili took notes and said that he had told Solemani that Iran, Iraq, and the entire region would be the losers if Iran continued its destructive actions. Al-Waili related that Solemani claimed to be disturbed that JAM was engaged in destructive activities. Furthermore, Solemani said that the ongoing trilateral U.S.-Iraq-Iran talks would not make any difference because he alone decides what the Iranian government does in Iraq.

"6. Al-Waili related his opinion that Solemani believes that his control over Iranian activities in Iraq makes him a major political deal-maker. He noted that this was his first meeting with Iranians in which they admitted to involvement in Iraq. Throughout the discussion with General Petraeus, al-Waili emphasized that he was not a messenger for Iran but rather an Iraqi patriot. General Petraeus affirmed that, as such, he would be credible when delivering our response to Solemani."

24. Weekly report from General David Petraeus to Defense Secretary Robert Gates (SECRET), week of 5–11 August 2007.
25. Multi-National Force—Iraq and U.S. Embassy Baghdad, "Campaign Progress Review, June 2006–December 2006" (SECRET), December 2006.
26. Interview, Major General John Allen.
27. Interview, senior military official.

CHAPTER 23 *General Petraeus Goes to Washington*

1. Weekly report from General David Petraeus to Defense Secretary Robert Gates (SECRET), week of 1–7 July 2007. "There is some question as to the optics of testifying on Iraq on 9–11 (whether that would be seized upon as overly politicized), but we may have no choice given the restrictive Congressional schedule," Petraeus wrote. "We'll await further guidance."
2. Multi-National Force—Iraq, "Crafting and Disseminating the Message," document prepared for General David Petraeus's congressional testimony.
3. Weekly report from General David Petraeus to Defense Secretary Robert Gates (SECRET), week of 22–28 July 2007.
4. Notes of a participant.
5. Embassy Baghdad cable classified by Patricia Butenis, "Charge's July 29 Meeting with NSA Rubaie" (SECRET), 30 July 2007.
6. "General Betray Us," MoveOn.org. MoveOn.org moved to disaffiliate itself from the ad after its publication. MoveOn removed the ad and all references to it from its website in 2010, after President Obama nominated Petraeus to replace General Stanley McChrystal in Afghanistan.
7. Karen DeYoung, "Experts Doubt Drop in Violence in Iraq," *Washington Post,* 6 September 2007.
8. "Fact Checker: General Betray Us?" *Washington Post,* 20 September 2007.
9. United States Senate, Committee on Foreign Relations, Iraq: The Crocker-Petraeus Report, Hearing 110–490, 11 September 2007, 110th Congress, 1st Session (Washington, D.C.: GPO, 2007).
10. Barack Obama, *The Audacity of Hope* (New York: Random House, 2006), pp. 352–59.
11. Interview, Lee Hamilton.
12. United States Senate. Iraq War De-Escalation Act of 2007, 110th Congress, 1st Session, S. 433 (Washington: GPO), 2007.
13. Michael R. Gordon and Patrick Healy, "Clinton Sees Some Troops Staying in Iraq If She Is Elected," *New York Times,* 14 March 2007.
14. Jeff Zeleny, "Obama's Iraq Speech," *New York Times,* 12 September 2007.
15. Embassy Baghdad cable classified by Ryan Crocker, "CG Meeting with Sadrist Council of Representatives Member" (SECRET), 29 September 2007.

16. Weekly report from General David Petraeus to Defense Secretary Robert Gates (SECRET), week of 7–13 October 2007.
17. Weekly report from General David Petraeus to Defense Secretary Robert Gates (SECRET), week of 16–22 September 2007.
18. Notes of a participant.
19. Weekly report from General David Petraeus to Defense Secretary Robert Gates (SECRET), week of 23–29 September 2007.
20. Among the soldiers on Phillips's Sadr City raids was Sergeant Robert Bales, the Stryker team leader who would go on, after fighting in Dora later in the summer and then another Iraq tour, to be charged with killing sixteen civilians in Afghanistan five years later.
21. Weekly report from General David Petraeus to Defense Secretary Robert Gates (SECRET), week of 14–20 October 2007.
22. Weekly report from General David Petraeus to Defense Secretary Robert Gates (SECRET), week of 21–27 January 2008.
23. Interview, Captain Ann Gildroy.
24. Michael R. Gordon, "The Last Battle: The Fight Among Iraq's Shiites," *New York Times Magazine,* 3 August 2008.
25. Weekly report from General David Petraeus to Defense Secretary Robert Gates (SECRET), week of 11–17 November 2007.
26. Dale Andrade, *Surging South of Baghdad: The 3rd Infantry Division and Task Force Marne in Iraq, 2007–2008* (Washington, D.C.: U.S. Army Center of Military History, 2010).
27. Weekly report from General David Petraeus to Defense Secretary Robert Gates (SECRET), week of 11–17 November 2007.
28. Interview, aide to General Raymond Odierno.
29. Weekly report from General David Petraeus to Defense Secretary Robert Gates (SECRET), week of 18–25 November 2007.
30. In the December 2 MCNS meeting, Maliki blessed the program to hire Awakening members. The meeting was a milestone, but it did not mean that he and the IFCNR were done throwing roadblocks into the CLC program's way.

    In late January 2008, IFCNR sent the Americans a list of two thousand names from Sadr City whom it had approved for hiring into the police under the auspices of the Awakening hiring program. Of course, the two thousand recruits had nothing to do with the Awakening; the government was trying to fill with more Shiites the police spaces (actually, ninety-day pre-recruitment test contracts) the Americans had intended for the Sunni volunteers. In effect, IFCNR was adopting the American system and using it to subvert itself. Shirwan al-Waeli, the head of Maliki's shadow intelligence agency the MSNSA, and the person who had passed Petraeus the August message from Suleimani, had created the list and given it to the Interior Ministry to implement, a ministry official told American advisers; another source said Bassima was behind the move.

    Brigadier General Dave Phillips scrambled to figure out where the two thousand names had come from, and on February 6 consulted with Major General Ayden Khalid Qadir, the deputy interior minister for police affairs. The list of Sadr City names, Ayden explained to him, had come from IFCNR—from Bassima herself, he said—and even he had not known about it. Instead of Sunni Awakening volunteers from Abu Ghraib being hired to police Abu Ghraib, the result OCINC and IFCNR was pushing would have had Shiite men from Sadr City policing distant Anbar.

At Petraeus's direction, Phillips visited Qadir again at his house in the Green Zone for dinner. "Are you going to hire the Abna al-Iraq?" Phillips asked, using the Arabic term for the volunteers that the Americans had recently adopted as "Sons of Iraq." Ayden said no—the ministry would not hire the men. But, he said, it would meet the Americans halfway, hiring them on a ninety-day trial basis as contractors. Phillips and his boss, Dubik, were not pleased with this solution, but Petraeus saw that it was a better deal than would be forthcoming from OCINC or IFCNR, and put his support behind it. Though IFCNR would again scrutinize and delay the recruit lists at the end of the ninety days, it bought time.

31. Interview, Captain Ann Gildroy.

CHAPTER 24 *No Plan B*

1. Interview, Lieutenant General Michael Barbero.
2. Weekly report from General David Petraeus to Defense Secretary Robert Gates (SECRET), week of 18–25 November 2007.
3. Weekly report from General David Petraeus to Defense Secretary Robert Gates (SECRET), week of 14–20 October 2007.
4. Notes of a meeting participant.
5. Interview, U.S. military official.
6. Weekly report from General David Petraeus to Defense Secretary Robert Gates (SECRET), week of 28 October3 November 3 2007.
7. Weekly report from General David Petraeus to Defense Secretary Robert Gates (SECRET), week of 21–27 October 2007.
8. Joint Chiefs of Staff slide deck, "VCJCS-VCHOD Saygun Phone Call" (SECRET), 9 November 2007.
9. Weekly report from General David Petraeus to Defense Secretary Robert Gates (SECRET), week of 18–25 November 2007.
10. Briefing by General David Petraeus, "MNF Iraq Update: NSC SVTC" (SECRET), 3 December 2007.
11. Weekly report from General David Petraeus to Defense Secretary Robert Gates (SECRET), week of 10–16 December 2007.
12. Notes of a meeting participant.
13. Interview, U.S. military official.
14. Weekly report from General David Petraeus to Defense Secretary Robert Gates (SECRET), week of 17–23 December 2007.
15. Notes of a meeting participant.
16. Notes of a meeting participant.
17. Interview, Massoud Barzani.
18. Notes of a meeting participant.
19. Weekly report from General David Petraeus to Defense Secretary Robert Gates (SECRET), week of 17–23 December 2007.
20. Weekly report from General David Petraeus to Defense Secretary Robert Gates (SECRET), week of 24–30 December 2007.
21. Weekly report from General David Petraeus to Defense Secretary Robert Gates (SECRET), week of 24–30 December 2007.

22. Weekly report from General David Petraeus to Defense Secretary Robert Gates (SECRET), week of 7–13 January 2008.
23. Embassy Baghdad cable classified by Ryan Crocker, "MCNS November 25, 2007 Addresses SPD, CLCs, AQI, Returnees, Foreign Fighters, MOI FMS Funding Delays" (SECRET), 28 November 2007.
24. Weekly report from General David Petraeus to Defense Secretary Robert Gates (SECRET), week of 7–13 January 2008.
25. Interview, military official.
26. Notes of a meeting participant.
27. Notes of a meeting participant.
28. Notes of a meeting participant.
29. Notes of a meeting participant.
30. Weekly report from General David Petraeus to Defense Secretary Robert Gates (SECRET), week of 31 December–6 January 2007.
31. Notes of meeting participant.
32. Notes of meeting participant.

CHAPTER 25 *Charge of the Knights*

1. Multi-National Division—South-East initial incident report, 6 March 2006. The State Department's close call came at a time of rising tensions between the British troops in Basra and the province's government, and especially police.

   On September 19, 2005, two undercover SAS commandos had been tailing a police captain they suspected of involvement with the Mahdi Army when they were confronted by police patrolmen. After a shootout that left one policeman dead and another wounded, the two SAS soldiers (neither of whom spoke Arabic, according to the British investigation into the incident) commandeered a car and fled the scene, only to be arrested when they reached a police checkpoint. When a negotiating team of six British soldiers went to the police compound to which the men were taken, they were not allowed to leave, prompting British troops to throw a cordon of Warrior armored vehicles around the station. That cordon was withdrawn in the afternoon after one of the Warriors was set on fire with gasoline bombs, injuring its crew and other soldiers.

   A classified report the British defense attaché in Baghdad later shared with the American embassy described what happened next. With the British division commander out of the country, figuring out how to resolve the crisis fell to Brigadier John Lorimer, who tried to negotiate the eight soldiers' release with Basra's governor and police chief. In the evening, after an intervention in Baghdad by British ambassador William Patey, Interior Minister Bayan Jabr ordered the soldiers freed, but the order was not executed. Half an hour later, Lorimer and the governor reached an agreement that at 10 p.m., British troops would approach the compound and the eight prisoners would be handed over. In the meantime, however, the British learned through high-tech eavesdropping that the two SAS soldiers had been moved from the compound; the governor claimed that the police had been "overwhelmed" by Mahdi Army members, which seemed unlikely.

   As agreed, at 10 p.m. the British force approached the compound, but, finding that their Warriors would not fit through the gate, they knocked the whole wall down, extracted the six soldiers there, and confirmed that the two SAS soldiers were gone. Luckily, British surveillance assets had tracked the movement of the two original prisoners, and an hour later an SAS raid in Hayyaniyah, a Mahdi Army stronghold analogous to Sadr City, recovered them. Throughout the episode, the British military in Basra had acted as though it were not part of a larger force, leaving the American command in Baghdad playing catch-up, and the next day, Casey dressed down his British deputy, Lieutenant General Robin Brims, for the breakdown in the chain of command. The day's events caused the provincial government to cut off contact with the British mission, a boycott that it would periodically lift and reinstate.

2. Regional Embassy Office Basra cable classified by Kenneth Gross, "British Helo Crash in Basra" (CONFIDENTIAL), 8 May 2006.

3. Regional Embassy Office Basra cable classified by Mark Marrano, "Deteriorating Security Impacting REO Basrah" (CONFIDENTIAL), 21 July 2006.

4. Interview, U.S. diplomat.

5. Testimony to the Iraq Inquiry by Lieutenant General Sir Richard Shirreff, 11 January 2010. Without receiving major reinforcements, the British division in Basra mounted one last large offensive in late 2006, mirroring the Together Forward offensives in Baghdad, called Operation Sinbad. Under pressure from Chiarelli, on Christmas Day British troops raided the Jamiat police station where they had had the ugly confrontation a year before. More than one hundred off-the-books detainees were found there—many likely held on behalf of the Mahdi Army or criminal gangs rather than for police purposes—many of them showing signs of abuse. Yet the areas British troops cleared in Operation Sinbad were quickly handed back over to the police.

6. Document prepared for General David Petraeus, "Talking Points for Mr. Muhammad al Wahili, Basra Governor," 9 April 2007.

7. Stephen Farrell, "British Pullback in Iraq Presages Hurdles for U.S.," *New York Times*, 29 July 2007.

8. Interview, British military officer.

9. Documents prepared for General David Petraeus, "Talking Points for London Visit," 12 September 2007, and "Talking Points for Meeting with PM Brown," 18 September 2007.

10. Multi-National Corps—Iraq, "IO Support to Basra PIC: Mission Analysis" (SECRET), 30 November 2007.

11. Interview, U.S. official.

12. Interview, officer with 1st Brigade Combat Team, 82nd Airborne Division.

13. Interview, U.S. military officer.

14. U.S. Army historian interview with Major Joel Rayburn (SECRET), 7 April 2008.

15. Briefing by General Mohan Hafidh Fahad al-Furayji, "Security Strategy for Basra," 14 March 2008.

16. Interview, Iraqi official.

17. Interview, Colonel Jim Coffman.

18. Notes of a meeting participant, 16 March 2008 MCNS meeting; Embassy Baghdad cable classified by Ryan Crocker, "MCNS March 16 Discusses Basrah Security, Taji Maintenance Facility, Demining Ref: Baghdad" (SECRET), 23 March 2008.

19. Interviews, Mowaffak al-Rubaie and U.S. officials.

20. Notes of a meeting participant.

21. Defense Intelligence Agency, "Shedding Light on Operation Charge of the Knights in Basra" (SECRET), 18 April 2008.
22. Interview, Brigadier General H.R. McMaster.
23. Notes of a meeting participant. Crocker also discounted the McMaster theory, but a comment Maliki made to the ambassador in the weeks before Basra indicated that his mentality was as much one of conspiracy as of overconfidence—not surprising, given the December effort by most of his political peers to unseat him. The prime minister told the ambassador that he was developing sympathy for General Abd al-Karim Kasim, who had overthrown the Iraqi monarchy in 1958 and then faced a variety of internal revolts before himself being ousted and executed by the Baath Party in 1963.
24. Interview, Lieutenant Colonel (Retired) Mark Grdovic.
25. Interview, Nuri al-Maliki.
26. Interviews, Lieutenant Colonel (Retired) Mark Grdovic and Colonel (Retired) Jim Coffman.
27. "GoI, ISF, and CF Partnering Success in Basrah, Iraq, March–April 2008" (SECRET), April 2008.
28. Interview, U.S. military officer.
29. Interview, Colonel Martin Stanton.
30. Notes of a meeting participant.
31. Interview, U.S. military officer.
32. Weekly report from General David Petraeus to Defense Secretary Robert Gates (SECRET), week of 24–30 March 2008.
33. Embassy Baghdad cable classified by Marcie Ries, "PM's Advisors Discuss Basrah Exit Strategy" (SECRET), 1 April 2008.
34. Interview, officer with 1st Brigade Combat Team, 82nd Airborne Division.
35. Lieutenant Colonel Fred Drummond and Major Jim Schreiner, " 'Appearing Larger Than We Are': The Story of the 1st Special Troops Battalion, 1st BCT, 82nd Airborne Div," 2008.
36. Defense Intelligence Agency, "Shedding Light on Operation Charge of the Knights in Basra" (SECRET), 18 April 2008.
37. As Maliki prepared to leave Basra on March 31, Petraeus received a personal message from Qasim Suleimani, who had helped broker the cease-fire, relayed by Ahmed Chalabi. The message to Petraeus was one of several pieces of evidence that Iran, having established other militant proxies like Asaib Ahl al-Haq and Kataib Hezbollah that it could rely on more than it could the ungainly Mahdi Army, wanted to control Sadr. On the same day that Petraeus met with Chalabi, Talabani and Abd al-Mahdi went to Iran to meet with Suleimani. One message "Hajji Qasim" gave them, according to Abd al-Mahdi, was that he wanted Maliki to pull out of Basra, the goal being partially accomplished by the cease-fire. The other was that Iran was tired of Sadr and the Mahdi Army. In a dinner with Petraeus and Ryan Crocker and then a meeting with Brett McGurk and Marcie Ries, Abd al-Mahdi relayed this message, along with his own assessment that it was impossible to predict the direction the Sadrist Trend would take now; it bounced like an American football, not a soccer ball, he said.

   All this was not to say that the Iraqi leaders who met regularly with Suleimani trusted him or lacked nationalism or anti-Iranian sentiment, however. The next week, KRG prime minister Nechirvan Barzani—one of the December plotters against Maliki—reported to Marcie and Charlie Ries that he and his uncle Massoud Barzani had recently declined an invitation from Suleimani to visit him in the same secure location in Iran where he had met with Talabani and Abd al-Mahdi on March 31. "Nechirvan quoted an adage of his uncle's," the Rieses' cable on the conversation reported: "Turkey will offer you either honey or poison and tell you which is which, but Iran is more dangerous—they offer you poisoned honey."

38. Interview, Colonel Jim Coffman.

39. Maliki also took a page out of the Awakening movement's book in Basra, or tried to, by reaching out to tribal leaders from the rural areas around the city, who felt disenfranchised by the ISCI- and Fadhila-dominated Basra government and threatened by the Mahdi Army. Across the Shatt al-Arab from the city in the less built-up Tannuma district, the mixed Shiite-Sunni Bani Tamim tribe had resisted the Mahdi Army during the first days of fighting. Seeking to capitalize on this, Maliki met with sheikhs from the Bani Tamim and other tribes, including his own Bani Malik tribe, and promised to help them stand up tribal Awakening battalions; in a move meant to undercut the Fadhila governor and ISCI-dominated provincial council, he also named sixteen cooperative sheikhs to a new "tribal committee" with authority to coordinate with him and his deputies in the standing up of an imagined force of ten thousand to twenty-five thousand tribal security volunteers. By early April, the sheikhs were claiming to have assembled five tribal battalions of five hundred men each in the areas outside the city.

At the very end of March, Petraeus dispatched a group of American officers to investigate and support the Basra tribal Awakening that Maliki was touting. In keeping with his mistrust of the British military, the prime minister had insisted to Petraeus that he wanted British Major General Chris Hughes of the FSEC to stay far away from the project; instead, the team sent from Baghdad included Colonel Marty Stanton, Major Joel Rayburn, and Captain Seth Moulton and Sergeant Alex Lemons of Team Phoenix. What this group found was that Maliki had done very little to actually implement the promises he made to the sheikhs. There were actually just two tribal battalions, not five, and no one was paying them.

40. Weekly report from General David Petraeus to Defense Secretary Robert Gates (SECRET), week of 31 March–6 April 2008; Embassy Baghdad cable classified by Ryan Crocker, "Iran Managing the Post-Basrah Backlash" (SECRET), 23 April 2008.

41. The DIA report "Shedding Light on Operation Charge of the Knights" attempted to tease out the motivations of the various parties involved in the March 30 cease-fire deal: Maliki, Sadr, and Iran. Maliki's reasons were fairly clear; he had gotten in over his head in Basra, and wanted to be able to extricate himself in a way that still made him appear strong, something the agreement accomplished. Sadr, having made the point that the Mahdi·Army could still challenge the government, wanted his movement to survive; in every previous instance, twice in 2004 and then in 2007, that had meant eventually declaring a cease-fire, and the spring 2008 uprising was no exception. Moreover, he was under Iranian pressure to come to terms. "Muqtada al-Sadr's decision to halt JAM operations appears to have been influenced by a desire to prevent the Basrah conflict from escalating further, media reports portraying the Sadrists

as instigators of instability rather than victims of government aggression, and Iranian pressure to accept a cease-fire," the report said.

As for Iran, the report noted that the country had worked hard to arrange the cease-fire, even though it was Iranian-supplied arms that facilitated Mahdi Army and Special Groups violence. "Iran appears to have devoted its main thrust during this crisis to facilitating cease-fire negotiations between the OMS and the GoI," the report stated. "DIA assesses Tehran sought to halt intra-Shia violence among its various Iraqi allies, to prevent JAM from losing its retaliatory capabilities against CF and preserve Shia unity at least through the upcoming Iraqi provincial elections."

42. Embassy Baghdad cable classified by Matt Tueller, "Maliki Scores Big at April 5 PCNS Meeting" (CONFIDENTIAL), 7 April 2008.

CHAPTER 26 *March Madness*

1. Although Maliki was able to present Basra as a political victory as soon as he returned to Baghdad, his departure from the city did not mean the end of the fighting there. In fact, reinforced by fresh units and American advisers with their link to air power and medevac, the Iraqi forces in Basra were just gathering steam when Maliki left them on April 1. Nightly strikes by Iraqi commandos and their American advisers, joined by raids by three Iraqi Army battalions with 82nd Airborne advisers, kept up the pressure on militia strongholds like Hayyaniyah during early April, and Iraqi C-130s had been bringing fresh troops straight from training centers in the north.

Then on April 12 and 13, Iraqi troops cordoned Hayyaniyah off and the Anbar-based 1st Brigade, 1st Division, and its Marine advisers took up positions between that district and another militia stronghold, Qibla. On April 13, two Iraqi brigades, including six partially rehabilitated companies from the 14th Division, pushed successfully into Qibla. During the next stage of the Basra offensive British 155mm howitzers fired satellite-guided Excalibur shells at four points along Hayyaniyah's unpopulated outskirts and American B-1 swing-wing bombers dropped two-thousand-pound satellite-guided bombs. The next morning, two brigades, one advised by American Marines and one by teams of British infantrymen, pushed through Hayyaniyah from north to south with little incident. Nearly three weeks after Maliki left, the Iraqi military operations he had so sloppily initiated in Basra ended successfully.

2. Interviews with Iraqi and American officials; embassy Baghdad cable classified by Ryan Crocker, "Sami al-Askeri Describes January 19 Attack on NSA Rubaie" (SECRET), 23 January 2008.

3. Defense Intelligence Digest, "Iraq: IRGC-QF Surveillance Against U.S. Embassy and Bases" (SECRET), 3 June 2008.

4. Notes of a meeting participant.

5. Weekly report from General David Petraeus to Defense Secretary Robert Gates (SECRET), week of 28 January–3 February 2008.

6. Embassy Baghdad cable classified by Robert Waller, "Baha al-Araji: Lack of Timeline Is Biggest U.S. Mistake" (CONFIDENTIAL), 17 March 2008.

7. Weekly report from General David Petraeus to Defense Secretary Robert Gates (SECRET), week of 3–9 March 2008.

8. Multi-National Division—Baghdad, "Combined Sadr City Operations Update" (SECRET), 30 March 2008.

9. Interview, U.S. Army officer.

10. "Intel in Support of LAOTF in the Prosecution of JAM/SG Members Involved in 23MAR08-01APR08 IDF Attacks in Baghdad That Injured Iraqi Civilians" (SECRET), April 2008.

11. This account of the battle along Route Gold is based on the author's own observations while embedded with 3rd Brigade Combat Team, 4th Infantry Division; interviews with commanders and soldiers in the brigade; and Major Tom Sills and Commander Doreen Fussman, "Battle of Phase Line Gold, Sadr City, Iraq" (SECRET), a report on the battle by division and corps historians.

12. Weekly report from General David Petraeus to Defense Secretary Robert Gates (SECRET), week of 24–30 March 2008.

13. The spring fighting in Baghdad was the first large-scale combat test for the MRAP, the V-hulled armored vehicle that was replacing Humvees across all American combat units. The fighting showed that MRAPs were not invulnerable. Through March, no roadside bomb, not even an EFP, had been able to penetrate an MRAP (although soldiers had died when large IEDs flipped the vehicles). During the April fighting, though, some militants began to mount EFPs on vertical surfaces like walls or at upward angles so that they would hit the vehicles' sides instead of their V-shaped hulls. On April 12 and 14, two soldiers were killed in the first successful penetrations of MRAP armor, one in East Baghdad and one in West Baghdad, when EFPs punched through their vehicles' doors.

14. Quoted in Sills and Fussman, "Battle of Phase Line Gold, Sadr City, Iraq."

15. United States Senate, Committee on Armed Forces, "The Situation in Iraq and the Progress Made by the Government of Iraq in Meeting Benchmarks and Achieving Reconciliation," Hearing 110–635, 8–10 April 2008, 100th Congress, Second Session, Washington: GPO, 2008.

16. ABC News, *Good Morning America,* anchored by Diane Sawyer and Robin Roberts, 8 April 2008, transcript obtained via Nexis. Clinton's full proclamation on the surge read as follows: "I have the greatest respect for General Petraeus and Ambassador Crocker. They are, you know, working under very difficult circumstances. But let's remember what we were told about this surge a year ago, that the whole purpose for it was to give the Iraqi government the space and time to do what it needed to do when it came to allocating oil revenues, improving services, coming to some political reconciliation. That hasn't happened. We know, in the last few days, we've seen fighting in the streets of Basra, now in Sadr City in Baghdad. So clearly, the surge hasn't worked. Now, our military has done a superb job in quelling the violence. That is something that, you know, we're very proud of. But the point of the surge, its stated rationale, has not been fulfilled."

17. United States Senate, Committee on Foreign Relations, "Iraq After the Surge," Hearing 110-757, 2–10 April 2008, 100th Congress, Second Session, Washington: GPO, 2008.

18. Michael R. Gordon, "Iraqi Unit Flees Post, Despite American's Plea," *New York Times,* 16 April 2008.

19. CBS News, *60 Minutes,* anchored by Lesley Stahl, 12 October 2008. The segment began by declaring, "For years, insurgents in Iraq have been stymieing U.S. troops with homemade, low-tech weapons, like car bombs and improvised roadside explosives. But in the battle of Sadr City, as we learned in a high-level debriefing with the U.S. commander in Iraq, the Americans overpowered the

Shiite militias with high-tech, the most advanced, sophisticated whiz-bang hardware and software on earth: electronics, lasers, high-resolution cameras that can literally cut through the fog of war."

20. Sills and Fussman, "Battle of Phase Line Gold, Sadr City, Iraq."

21. Interviews, U.S. military officers.

22. The Hellfire strike did the trick, but the division directed that a 15-6 investigation be opened on Hort and the pilots for use of excessive force. In the end, the investigation found that neither Hort nor the pilots had done anything wrong, and Grimsley concurred. But Hammond insisted on issuing Hort and the pilots official letters of reprimand for the incident and also for an instance in which Hort had called in Apaches to fire their 30mm guns down Route Gold to clear IEDs near the new JSS Thawra II. Yet at the same time, the division had specifically authorized the use of tanks' and Bradleys' heavy machine guns to clear IEDs, and was actively encouraging Hort to fire mortars at targets north of the wall, something he refused to do because of the high likelihood that the unguided shells would kill or wound civilians.

23. The plan for a larger, combined U.S.-Iraqi assault on Sadr City, using the 2nd Stryker Brigade Combat Team, 25th Infantry Division, from Taji as the main effort, was detailed in "Multi-National Division—Baghdad: Defeat Special Groups Criminals" (SECRET), 1 May 2008.

24. Notes of a meeting participant.

25. Sills and Fussman, "Battle of Phase Line Gold, Sadr City, Iraq"; military history detachment interview, SEAL officer.

26. Interview, U.S. military officer.

27. Weekly report from General David Petraeus to Defense Secretary Robert Gates (SECRET), week of 24–30 March 2008.

28. Notes of meeting participants.

29. Interview, Mowaffak al-Rubaie.

30. Multi-National Corps—Iraq daily intelligence summary, 12 June 2008 (SECRET). The huge rifles that fired these rounds were called "anti-matériel rifles" because they were designed to destroy vehicles and ordnance rather than people—American engineers in Sadr City used them to explode IEDs—but they could also easily penetrate body armor, and their presence in the hands of Shiite militiamen represented an especially dangerous instance of Iranian lethal aid. By mid-June 2008, five unlicensed Iranian copies of the Austrian rifles had been found in insurgent hands in Iraq and Afghanistan, including one in a Mahdi Army cache in April in Basra during Charge of the Knights. Nine months later, in January 2009, American troops found another Iranian HS .50 copy, mated with a German-built Schmidt & Bender PM II telescopic sight, in a militia cache in the border province of Maysan.

31. Embassy Baghdad cable classified by Ryan Crocker, "Analysis of May 12 16-Point Sadr City Ceasefire Agreement" (SECRET), 14 May 2008.

32. Interview, Colonel John Hort.

33. Weekly report from General David Petraeus to Defense Secretary Robert Gates (SECRET), week of 14–20 April 2008. As Mahdi Army and Special Groups leaders fled Basra and Sadr City, those who did not go straight to Iran converged on Maysan, an impoverished and Sadrist-dominated border province devoid of Western troops that provided an open avenue from the Iranian border to Highway 1, Iraq's main north-south artery. Its capital, Amara, had close

tribal links to Sadr City. Since the British had rushed Maysan to premature PIC a year before, the province had acted as a safe haven for militants passing between Iraq and Iran, and had also been the subject of heavy Iranian economic development. Even though Maysan was one of Iraq's poorest provinces, compared to next-door Dhi Qar it had more paved roads and more streetlights; American troops described the nongovernmental organizations responsible for this development as "Iranian PRTs," a joke that went along with calling PIC "Provincial Iranian Control."

In late April, the Iraqi special operations brigade and its American advisers began a series of raids in Maysan, the first since the fall. In June they were joined by troops from Task Force 17. In the second week of June, the 1st Iraqi Army Division—now known widely as the "QRF Division" for the role it had played in Basra and Sadr City—arrived in the province to prepare for a push into Amara. The American military was not in a good position to support the move; although a pair of Army battalions was slotted to begin moving into Maysan over the summer to establish the first real American military presence there of the entire war, they would not arrive in time for the Iraqi push into Amara. Only advisers from the Marines and the 82nd Airborne—the same teams that had helped save the day in Basra—and Special Forces accompanied the Iraqi push on June 19. The 82nd Airborne advisers asked to have Western reporters embedded with them, but were told no by the corps headquarters in Baghdad. As in Basra, the military was worried about the media showing the American support that the Iraqis were relying on.

34. Interview, Lieutenant Colonel Joe McLamb.
35. Notes of a meeting participant. A puzzling incident around the same time pointed to Iran's continued influence not just over the Sadrists but in the government. Engineer Ahmed, the Badr intelligence veteran with strong links to Iran who had run the Jadriya Bunker prison, had been removed from his duties at the Interior Ministry more than a year before, but he remained on Maliki's staff at OCINC, and one day in the spring he showed up at the central facility in Karada of the Interior Ministry's in-house intelligence arm—with Ali Reza Hassan Kazemi-Qomi, the Quds Force officer who was Iran's ambassador in Baghdad. The visit was a quick one, and American officials never got an explanation for it: Ahmed and Kazemi-Qomi entered the building, downloaded an unknown amount of data from the computers there onto a thumb drive, and left, a particularly brazen instance of Iran's deep reach into Iraq's most sensitive governmental institutions.
36. Weekly report from General David Petraeus to Defense Secretary Robert Gates (SECRET), week of 9–15 June 2008.
37. Embassy Baghdad cable classified by Patricia Butenis, "PM Maliki Recounts His June 7–9 Visit to Tehran" (SECRET), 14 June 2008.
38. Notes of a meeting attendee.

CHAPTER 27 *Strange Justice*

1. Notes of Multi-National Force—Iraq Commanders' Conference (SECRET), 19 April 2008.
2. Damien Cave, "The Reach of War: Iraq's No. 2 Health Official Is Held and Accused of Financing Shiite Militants," *New York Times,* 9 February 2007;

Michael R. Gordon and Alissa J. Rubin, "Shiite Ex-Officials Face Trial in Hundreds of Sunni Deaths," *New York Times*, 5 November 2007.

3. Interview, Captain Matthew Albertus.
4. Interview, Ali al-Saffar.
5. "Malign Actors Exploitation Cell Meeting 7 Aug 07" (SECRET), 7 August 2007.
6. U.S. intelligence assessment prepared for Nuri al-Maliki and Mowaffak al-Rubaie, "Dr. Adel Mohsin (aka Adel Muhsin Abdullah al Khazali), Inspector General for the Ministry of Health; Head of the Prime Minister's Anti-Corruption Advisory Commission" (SECRET), 15 January 2008.
7. Michael R. Gordon, "Iraqi Premier Wants Trial of 2 Shiites in Killings," *New York Times*, 16 November 2007.
8. Interview, Ali al-Saffar.
9. Marc Santora and Michael R. Gordon, "Murky Candidacy Stokes Iraq's Sectarian Fears," *New York Times*, 3 March 2010.
10. Governance Assessment Team final report (SECRET), 24 April 2008.
11. Weekly report from General David Petraeus to Defense Secretary Robert Gates (SECRET), week of 19–25 May 2008.
12. Embassy Baghdad cable classified by Marcie Ries, "Recent Iranian Economic Involvement in Iraq" (SECRET), 13 January 2008.
13. Embassy Baghdad cable classified by Ryan Crocker, "NSA Rubai on Ahmedi-Nejad's Visit" (SECRET), 24 March 2008.
14. Embassy Baghdad cable classified by Matt Tueller, "Foreign Minister: Iran Will Escalate Confrontation with US in Iraq" (SECRET), 5 April 2008.
15. Embassy Baghdad cable classified by Patricia Butenis, "PM Maliki Recounts His June 7–9 Visit to Tehran" (SECRET), 14 June 2008.
16. "Israel: Increased Signaling of Potential Iran Strike" (TOP SECRET), 9 June 2008; JIOCEUR Analytic Center, EUCOM, "Israel/Iran: Limited Potential for a Strike on Iran" (TOP SECRET), 12 June 2008; Joint Staff J2, "Iran: Operational Mishaps by Air Defense Units" (TOP SECRET), 21 June 2008; Defense Intelligence Digest, "Iran: Air Defense at Heightened Alert" (TOP SECRET), 27 June 2008.
17. Embassy Baghdad cable classified by Ryan Crocker, "VP Abdel Mehdi and Ambassador Review Key Legislation and Iran Talks" (SECRET), 31 May 2007.
18. Weekly report from General David Petraeus to Defense Secretary Robert Gates (SECRET), week of 24–30 March 2008.
19. Interview, U.S. military officer.
20. Notes of a meeting participant.
21. Notes of meeting participants.
22. Weekly report from General David Petraeus to Defense Secretary Robert Gates (SECRET), week of 30 June–6 July 2008.
23. Notes of a meeting attendee.

CHAPTER 28 *Let's Make a Deal*

1. U.N. Security Council members disagreed on whether the U.S. and Britain had the authority under previous resolutions to invade Iraq, but a series of subsequent U.N. Security Council Resolutions (UNSCRs) established and reaffirmed the legal mandate for coalition forces. This process began with UNSCR

1511, which recognized the CPA in October 2003. Shortly before the CPA was dissolved in June 2004, the Security Council passed Resolution 1546, which extended the protections but also stipulated that "the mandate for the multinational force shall be reviewed at the request of the Government of Iraq or twelve months from the date of this resolution." This mandate was subsequently renewed by UNSCR 1637 in 2005, UNSCR 1723 in 2006, and UNSCR 1790 in 2007. See R. Chuck Mason, U.S.-Iraq-Withdrawal/Status of Forces Agreement: Issues for Congressional Oversight, Congressional Research Service, 13 July 2009.

2. Interviews, Ambassador Robert Loftis and multiple State Department and NSC officials.
3. Interviews, U.S. government officials.
4. United States House of Representatives, Committee on Foreign Affairs, *Report on Iraq to the House Committee on Foreign Affairs*, Hearing 110-195, 110th Congress, Second Session, 9 April 2008. Washington: GPO, 2008, p. 91.
5. Fallon announced his resignation after an *Esquire* article painted him as the only obstacle standing between the Bush administration and war with Iran. In fact, after months of tension over the pace of Iraq withdrawals, the administration had already decided to cut Fallon loose early from CENTCOM (he had been in command only a year) when the *Esquire* article appeared. His replacement would be Petraeus, and on February 27 the NSC discussed who should take over from Petraeus in Iraq when the time came later in the year; candidates included Ray Odierno and Stan McChrystal. After the article came out, portraying Fallon as borderline insubordinate, he announced his resignation on March 11. "I did what I thought was appropriate," he told Petraeus and his staff during a visit to Baghdad the next day. "The atmosphere in DC is not appropriate for mission focus, as it needs to be." It was too soon for Petraeus to leave Iraq to replace the admiral, so in the meantime, Fallon's three-star deputy, Marty Dempsey, would be acting commander of CENTCOM, outranked by his four-star nominal subordinate Petraeus.
6. Interview, Ambassador Robert Loftis.
7. Loftis later explained his unyielding position on jurisdictions over U.S. soldiers by saying, "Given all of my experience in what we had done everywhere else, it was not an area which I was prepared to compromise."
8. Notes of a meeting participant.
9. Notes of a meeting participant.
10. Interview, Ambassador Robert Loftis.
11. Notes of a participant.
12. Steven Lee Myers, "Bush, in a Shift, Accepts Concept of Iraq Timetable," *New York Times*, 19 July 2008.
13. *Der Spiegel*, "Interview with Iraqi Leader Nouri al-Maliki: 'The Tenure of Coalition Troops in Iraq Should Be Limited,' " 19 July 2008.
14. Weekly report from General David Petraeus to Defense Secretary Robert Gates (SECRET), week of 14–20 July 2008.
15. Notes of a participant. While Maliki agreed to let the British stay in Iraq beyond 2008, it was only so they could complete their planned withdrawal by the end of July 2009. Instead of a complete SOFA, Maliki agreed to an exchange of diplomatic notes that approved basic authorities for the British to operate during the first half of 2009.

16. Weekly report from General David Petraeus to Defense Secretary Robert Gates (SECRET), week of 14–20 July 2008.
17. George W. Bush White House Archives, "Press Conference with Dana Perino," 21 July 2008.
18. Interview, NSC official.
19. Account of a participant.
20. Notes of a participant.
21. Condoleezza Rice, *No Higher Honor: A Memoir of My Years in Washington* (New York: Crown, 2011), p. 695.
22. Weekly report from General David Petraeus to Defense Secretary Robert Gates (SECRET), week of 25–31 August 2008.
23. Notes of a meeting participant.

CHAPTER 29 *The Home Stretch*

1. Classified initial incident reports from 1-1 Attack Reconnaissance Battalion and 2-2 Stryker Cavalry Regiment.
2. Notes of a meeting participant.
3. Interview with Major General Mark Hertling by Captain Wendy Wright, 54th Military History Detachment.
4. Embassy Baghdad cable classified by Robert Ford, "Confidant to Sunni Arab Vice President Blasts PM Maliki" (CONFIDENTIAL), 22 August 2008.
5. Weekly report from General David Petraeus to Defense Secretary Robert Gates (SECRET), week of 11–17 August 2008.
6. Interview, Major General Mark Hertling.
7. Interview with Major General Mark Hertling by Captain Wendy Wright, 54th Military History Detachment.
8. Interview, Lieutenant General Michael Barbero.
9. Interviews, State Department and other U.S. government officials.
10. The "Concentric Circles Paper" noted that the "concurrent jurisdiction" in the Japan, South Korea, and NATO SOFAs meant that the host nation "retains exclusive jurisdiction over all criminal offenses punishable under host nation laws, but not U.S. laws; and all criminal offenses punishable under host nation and U.S. law not arising 'in the performance of official duty.' " In contrast, the Iraqis were seeking only to have jurisdiction over "heinous rape or murder committed off duty or off base." Along with the three additional safeguards explained in the text, the paper also suggested that the government could "limit legal risk by forbidding personnel to travel off agreed facilities while off duty."

The paper also drew on a previous SOFA arrangement to point out where other exceptions had been made in the past in the Middle East. The 1981 SOFA with Egypt agreed to "full concurrent jurisdiction in principle (using the Japanese language verbatim) but ensured that no U.S. soldier ever fell under Egyptian jurisdiction in practice." The paper concluded with several talking points to different audiences concerned with the new language, which included U.S. military personnel and associated civilians, Congress, and other nations who might seek to incorporate similar language into their own status of forces agreements.

As the negotiations over the SOFA language proceeded beyond September, the negotiating team was able to add another provision that would safeguard

U.S. troops. The final language deliberately refused to define a list of "grave premeditated felonies" that would be subject to Iraqi jurisdiction, preferring instead to leave it up to a joint U.S. and Iraqi committee to be appointed at a later date. Until this joint body defined which crimes could be prosecuted, the Iraqis could not assert jurisdiction over any offense. According to a government official involved in crafting the agreement, this joint committee was never convened.

11. Interviews, meeting participants.
12. Embassy Baghdad cable classified by Ryan Crocker, "Amb, CG and PM Discuss SOFA, SOI, Ambassador's Trip to Erbil, GOI/KRG Relations and Elections Law" (SECRET), 21 September 2008.
13. Account of a participant.
14. Interview, Colin Kahl.
15. Interview, Kurdish official.
16. Notes of a meeting participant.
17. No longer the formidable blend of terrorist networks embedded within a much broader insurgency, Al-Qaeda in Iraq was on its way to being an underground terrorist group, more like a tougher version of Al-Qaeda's franchises in other Arab countries. A June 1 briefing at the main intelligence center at Camp Victory concluded: "AQI has been reduced by half and is falling." In Mosul, though, the group remained strong. With IEDs now much harder to plant due to the presence of new outposts and more patrols and trash-cleanup efforts, Al-Qaeda increased its emphasis on car bombs in the city. One in July tried and failed to kill the commander of the Nineveh Operations Command, while another in August rammed the MRAP in which Brigadier General Tony Thomas, the senior American officer in Mosul, and Lieutenant General Frank Helmick, commander of MNSTC-I, were traveling. Soon after the two generals' MRAP had left the gates of Camp Marez, a sedan packed with five hundred pounds of explosive rammed it, but the vehicle's heavy armor protected them from serious harm.

At Balad, Bill McRaven was beginning to shift JSOC's focus to Afghanistan, but the commandos' strike forces in Iraq remained active, particularly in Mosul. Over the summer, JSOC's conventional squadron, Task Force Ghost, fought in the Mosul area before leaving Iraq, and in August, commandos captured Al-Qaeda in Iraq's financial emir in the city. That capture led to the discovery of a tunnel that the group was digging under Mosul's provincial hall in order to blow it up, Guy Fawkes–style. Then, in October, a raid killed Abu Qaswara, also known as Muhammad Moumou, the Moroccan-born Swedish national who acted as Al-Qaeda's overall leader for northern Iraq. Abu Qaswara was close both to Abu Ayyub al-Masri and to the cell of the group that collected its finances, as evidence collected at the raid site showed. A ledger in his possession provided a valuable rundown of Al-Qaeda in Iraq's finances: in one month, the ledger showed, the group's senior leadership had collected $1.1 million in revenue, of which $400,000 had come from various companies in northern Iraq that made money for the group, and most of the rest from oil smuggling.
18. Notes, Wesley Morgan.
19. Interviews, multiple meeting participants.
20. Alissa Rubin and Campbell Robertson, "Iraq Backs Deal That Sets End of U.S. Role," *New York Times*, 28 November 2008.
21. Alissa Rubin and Campbell Robertson, "Iraq Backs Deal That Sets End of U.S.

Role," *New York Times,* 28 November 2008; Sudarsan Raghavan, "Security Accord Approved in Iraq," *Washington Post,* 28 November 2008.
22. Alissa Rubin and Campbell Robertson, "Iraq Backs Deal That Sets End of U.S. Role," *New York Times,* 28 November 2008.

CHAPTER 30 *Change at the Top*

1. Interview, meeting participant.
2. This and all subsequent meetings come from accounts of participants.
3. Interviews, U.S. officials.
4. Interviews, military officials.
5. Interview, U.S. official.
6. "Options for a Responsible Drawdown in Iraq," MNF-I/US Embassy Baghdad report reviewed by the authors.
7. Interviews, current and former U.S. officials.
8. Interviews, U.S. officials.
9. Zinni recalls that the op-ed was supplied by Scott Gration, a retired Air Force major general who emerged as a close adviser to Obama during the campaign, and Denis McDonough, who initially served as the NSC director of strategic communications and was later promoted to deputy national security adviser. Gration did not respond to a request for comment and the White House said that McDonough did not recall the episode.
10. Interview, General (Retired) Anthony Zinni.
11. Interviews, U.S. officials.
12. Interviews, U.S. officials.
13. Embassy Baghdad cable classified by Patricia Butenis, "CDA, CG and PM Discuss Drawdown on U.S. Forces in Iraq, Intercept of an Iranian UAV, and Arab-Kurd Tensions" (SECRET), 27 February 2009.
14. Interview, U.S. official.
15. Embassy Damascus cable classified by Maura Connelly, "UK Foreign Secretary Miliband's Nov. 17–18 Trip to Damascus" (SECRET), 19 November 2008.
16. Embassy Damascus cable classified by Maura Connelly, "Kerry-Asad: Dividing Iraq and Unifying Iran" (CONFIDENTIAL), 27 February 2009.
17. Embassy Damascus cable classified by Maura Connelly, "May 7 Feltman-Shapiro Meeting in Damascus: FM Muallim Questions U.S. Commitment to Real Engagement" (SECRET), 12 May 2009.
18. Embassy Baghdad cable classified by Patricia Butenis, "CDA, CG and PM Discuss Initial Drawdown of US Forces, Foreign Fighters, Airport Development and Recent Visit by Former Iranian President Rafsanjani" (SECRET), 8 March 2009.
19. Embassy Baghdad cable classified by Patricia Butenis, "CDA, CG and PM Discuss Evolving Security Concerns, the Budget, Oil Contracts; CDA Delivers Demarche on Camp Ashraf" (SECRET), 23 March 2009.

CHAPTER 31 *The Odd Couple*

1. Glenn Kessler, "Longtime Statesman Puts Best Face Forward for U.S.," *Washington Post,* 21 September 2005.

2. A U.S. official reports hearing Hill make that comment, but Hill denies that he ever said it.

3. Several U.S. officials reported that Hill made disparaging remarks about Emma Sky, but Hill denies making the comments.

4. Embassy Baghdad cable classified by Ryan Crocker, "PM Maliki: Strengthened Center or Emerging Strongman?" (CONFIDENTIAL), 13 February 2009.

5. Embassy Baghdad cable classified by Christopher Hill, "PM Tells Ambassador That Iraq Wants Strong Relationship with Obama Administration" (SECRET), 12 May 2009.

6. Embassy Baghdad cable, "U/S Burns' and U/S Flournoy's Meeting VP Hashemi and the IIP" (CONFIDENTIAL), 20 May 2009.

7. Dr. Bianca Adams, "2009 Command Report: Multi-National Division—Baghdad, 1st Cavalry Division," 2010.

8. Embassy Baghdad cable classified by John Fox, "Iraq After June 30: The View From Sadr City" (CONFIDENTIAL), June 29, 2009.

9. Office of the Secretary of Defense for Public Affairs, "Official Department of Defense News Briefing with General Ray Odierno," transcript, 8 May 2009.

10. Embassy Baghdad cable classified by Patricia Butenis, "Iraqi National Security Council Discusses CF Withdrawals, Security Ops" (CONFIDENTIAL), 12 May 2009.

11. Dr. Bianca Adams, "2009 Command Report: Multi-National Division—Baghdad, 1st Cavalry Division," 2010.

12. Interview, Major General Robert Caslen.

13. Embassy Baghdad cable classified by Patricia Butenis, "Arrest of Sunni Leader Highlights Challenges on Many Fronts" (SECRET), 18 May 2009.

14. 3rd Stryker Brigade Combat Team, 2nd Infantry Division, "Identifying the Sunni Breaking Point" (SECRET), 24 December 2009.

15. Human Terrain Analysis Team—Baghdad, "Baghdad SOI Transition Study, 2010."

16. Human Terrain Analysis Team—Baghdad, "Baghdad SOI Transition Study, 2010."

17. Strike Force Fusion Cell, "Target: Adil al Karim Ali al Mashhadani aka Abu Muhannad aka Abu Umar, TGT#UA0578" (SECRET), 9 February 2007. "Adil al Karim Ali al Mashhadani is the [Army of the Victorious Sect] leader in the Fadl District, Rusafa," the file noted. "His group was implicated in two separate reports to be involved in the downing of a Blackwater helicopter and execution of its crew members on 23 JAN 2007."

18. "Nightly FAIO Consolidated Roll-Up" (SECRET), 11 May 2007. Though the circumstances of Zembiec's death were kept secret—the Pentagon announcement had his unit as "Headquarters Battalion, Marine Corps National Capital Region"—months later the landing pad at Camp Victory that Petraeus and other senior officers used would be renamed in his honor. Petraeus spoke at the renaming ceremony, as did a Marine captain who read aloud a letter from one of the other Americans on Zembiec's final raid. "What came over the radio was 'five wounded and one martyred,' " the letter said of the initial report placed by an Iraqi team member. "They didn't say whether it was Iraqi or American." Alissa Rubin, "Comrades Speak of Fallen Marine and Ties That Bind," *New York Times*, 1 February 2008.

19. Embassy Baghdad cable classified by Michael Corbin, "CDA, CG and PM

Discuss Contracts, Reconciliation, the MEK and Arab-Kurd Tensions" (SECRET), 20 February 2009; Embassy Baghdad cable classified by Patricia Butenis, "CDA, CG and PM Discuss Evolving Security Concerns, the Budget, Oil Contracts; CDA Delivers Demarche on Camp Ashraf," 23 March 2009.

20. Notes of a participant.
21. Embassy Baghdad cable classified by Robert Ford, "Maliki Courts the Sadrists: Strategy, Fear and Loathing" (SECRET), 17 March 2009.
22. Embassy Baghdad cable classified by Christopher Hill, "Prime Minister Maliki's Visit: Launching the Strategic Framework Agreement" (CONFIDENTIAL), 16 July 2009.
23. Account by U.S. and Iraqi officials. Also see Michael R. Gordon, "Meddling Neighbors Undercut Iraq Stability," *New York Times*, 29 June 2009.

CHAPTER 32 *Trouble Up North*

1. Multi-National Corps—Iraq, "Arab Kurd Tabletop Rehearsal Exsum" (SECRET), 5 April 2009.
2. Embassy Baghdad cable classified by Patricia Butenis, "Arab-Kurd Conflict Narrowly Averted May 8" (SECRET), 10 May 2009.
3. Dr. Bianca Adams, "2009 Command Report: Multi-National Division— Baghdad, 1st Cavalry Division," 2010.
4. United States Senate, Committee on Foreign Relations, *Iraq: Report from the Field*, Hearing 111-220, 111th Congress, First Session, 10 September 2009 (Washington: GPO, 2009), p. 3.
5. Embassy Baghdad cable classified by Christopher Hill, "Prime Minister Accuses Syria of Military Actions Targeting Iraq" (SECRET), 24 September 2009.
6. Dr. Bianca Adams, "2009 Command Report: Multi-National Division— Baghdad, 1st Cavalry Division," 2010.
7. Embassy Baghdad cable classified by Robert Ford, "Dec 8 Bombings Result in Finger Pointing, New Intel Committee" (SECRET), 22 December 2009.
8. Embassy Baghdad cable classified by Gary Grappo, "Press Reports of Sunni MP Candidate's Disqualification Overblown" (CONFIDENTIAL), 8 January 2010.
9. Interview, Emma Sky.

CHAPTER 33 *Crises of Confidence*

1. Account of participants.
2. Notes of a meeting participant.
3. At one point after the electoral results, an Iraqiya delegation had traveled to Tehran and met with Saeed Jalili, the head of Iran's Supreme National Security Council. The Iraqiya officials hoped to introduce themselves to the Iranians and explain their platform and interests. But during the meetings, the Iranians continually asserted that there were 159 parliamentarians in "our bloc." Puzzled, the Iraqiya officials interjected to correct their host. "We told them, no, they are 89 and 70," recalled a member of the delegation nearly a year later. Jalili and others, however, forecasted with confidence that the two blocs would eventually unify. "We said there is a big problem between the two blocs. They said, 'This is not your job, this is our job. They will unify.' " The Iranians informed the visitors that a candidate from a unified Shiite bloc would be the

next prime minister, and the largest bloc in parliament would be a 159-member coalition. "It happened exactly like what they told us," the Iraqiya member recalled.

4. PRT Maysan cable classified by Stephen Banks, "Ali al-Sharqi Operation Spurs Public and Political Backlash and Election Rhetoric" (SECRET), 19 February 2010.

5. Embassy Baghdad cable classified by Robert Ford, "Prime Minister Inserts Himself Into Authorization of Joint Special Ops" (SECRET), 16 February 2010.

6. Embassy Baghdad cable classified by Robert Ford, "Detainee Releases and Targeting Approval Changes Round Out Maysan Operation Fallout" (SECRET), 24 February 2010.

7. Account of a meeting participant.

8. Interview, coalition official.

9. Interviews, U.S. officials.

CHAPTER 34 *Team of Rivals*

1. "The Coordinating Council on National Strategic Policy," paper obtained by the authors.

2. Interviews, Kenneth Pollack and Ambassador Christopher Hill.

3. Interview, American official.

4. Interviews, Iraqi officials.

5. Interview, James Steinberg.

6. Interview, U.S. diplomat.

7. Accounts of participants. After describing his Christmas card list, Hill added, "This place is a nightmare."

8. Correspondence provided by Anthony Shadid.

9. Michael R. Gordon and Elisabeth Bumiller, "In Baghdad, U.S. Officials Take Note of Milestone," *New York Times,* 1 September 2010.

10. Michael R. Gordon, "In Iraq, Clearer Image of U.S. Support," *New York Times,* 13 September 2010. In all, the Army would award 4.600 soldiers with combat service badges for their "post-combat" service in Operation New Dawn, including 646 Combat Infantryman Badges.

11. Michael R. Gordon and Anthony Shadid, "Transcript: Vice President Biden on Progress and Lingering Threats in Iraq," *New York Times,* 9 September 2010, At War Blog.

12. Interviews, American officials.

13. Embassy Baghdad cable classified by Christopher Hill, "Secretary of Defense Meeting with the Government of Iraq Presidency Council on December 10" (CONFIDENTIAL), 15 December 2009.

14. Steven Lee Myers, "Accord Paves Way for Election of New Premier," *New York Times,* 1 October 2010.

15. Reidar Visser, "Muqtada al-Sadr Preparing His Supporters for the Dirty Game of Politics," *Gulf Analysis,* 29 September 2010.

16. Interviews, Iraqi officials.

17. Martin Chulov, "How Iran Brokered a Secret Deal to Put Its Ally in Power in Baghdad," *Guardian,* 17 October 2010; Martin Chulov, "Iraq Brokers Behind-the-Scenes Deal for Pro-Tehran Government in Iraq," *Guardian,* 17 October 2010.

18. The most important Kurdish demands related to Article 140, the provision of the Iraqi constitution that governed disputed territories in the north between the Arabs and Kurds. Iraqiya billed itself as a nonsectarian party, but many of its members were Sunnis who were unprepared to compromise on this point. The full list of demands read:

1. Commitment to the Iraq Constitution and all its clauses and complete protection of the democratic federal system.

2. Formation of a government of national partnership that represents the core components of Iraq.

3. The principle of partnership and participation in the resolution, and through:

   (a) The establishment of a National Security Council through legislation.

   (b) Adopt rules and procedures for the Council of Ministers to establish the references of the National Security Council and commit to collective decision-making on the distribution of administrative and financial powers between the prime minister and his deputies.

   (c) Abide by the principle of consensus.

4. The formation of the Federal Council during the first calendar year of the parliament, where the president and his two vice presidents hold veto power.

5. Amending the election law so as to achieve equitable representation of Iraqis.

6. Conduct and hold the population census on time.

7. Reconsider and reorganize the armed forces and security forces and the adoption and implementation of the principle of balance.

8. The application of the principle of balance in all state institutions, ministries, and independent bodies.

9. The application of Article 140 of the Constitution and the provision of a budget for its implementation during a timeframe not to exceed two years.

10. Approval of the bill of financial resources during the first calendar year of the Parliament (according to the latest draft agreed).

11. Ratification of the draft law of oil and gas during the first calendar year of the Parliament (according to the latest draft agreed).

12. Funding and equipping the Regional Guard (Peshmerga) as part of the system of national defense of Iraq.

13. Support for the Kurdish coalition's candidate for the Iraqi Presidency.

14. Quick and just compensation for victims of former regime members, including those of the Anfal Campaign and the chemical attack in Halabja and other areas.

15. Kurdish representation in the key ministries and the Council of Ministers, as well as the bodies of all state institutions in a fair and balanced manner according to a quota system.

16. Reserving the right for Kurds to decide on candidates in key and sovereign ministries relevant to the Kurdistan Region.

17. The Secretary-General of the Council of Ministers should be from the Kurdish coalition bloc.

18. Consider the coalition government resigned if the Secretary-General withdraws from the Council of Ministers because of a clear violation of the Constitution or nonimplementation of the agreed programs.

19. Committed to block the Prime Minister in Parliament and the Council of Ministers in support of the above-mentioned projects.
Hemin Baban, "Who Wins Kurdish Support: Maliki or Allawi?" *Rudaw,* 28 October 2010.

19. Accounts provided by multiple participants.

20. Interview, U.S. official.

21. Jon Lee Anderson, "Profiles: Mr. Big," *The New Yorker,* 5 February 2007.

22. Interviews, meeting participants.

CHAPTER 35 *The Numbers Game*

1. Jason Horowitz, "Tom Donilon: Political Wunderkind to Policy Trailblazer," *Washington Post,* 20 December 2010; interviews, current and former U.S. officials.

2. The ISOF's two brigades, along with the Interior Ministry's Emergency Response Brigade, were by far the most capable Iraqi units the United States was leaving behind in Iraq, trained and advised for nearly eight years by elite American Special Forces and SEALs. But, as ISOF commander Fadhil Barwari had predicted when OCINC began to press for more control over his troops in December 2006, the Iraqi commando units also had trouble at the top.

   By mid-2011, American Special Forces support to the Emergency Response Brigade had come to an abrupt end after the March arrest of the unit's commander, Brigadier General Numan Dakhil Jawad, on charges of having taken a $50,000 bribe during a videotaped sting operation. U.S. officials were skeptical of the motivations behind Numan's arrest, since an Interior Ministry investigation cleared him and he—a Shiite—had run afoul of the government by participating in raids not only against Al-Qaeda targets but also against Shiite militias. When American investigators tried to look into Numan's situation, though, the head of the Integrity Commission complained to James Jeffrey, and one of the American officials was sent home from Iraq. In April, American Special Forces troops got into a confrontation at the Green Zone jail where Numan was being held when, trying to visit him in his cell to say their goodbyes, they were denied entry by Iraqi guards. In Numan's place, the government installed a new officer whom the Americans believed had Sadrist leanings. The Emergency Response Brigade's operations against Shiite targets dropped off, and by summer the Special Forces adviser teams had stopped working with the brigade.

   The larger 1st and 2nd ISOF Brigades retained their advisers, but only for a while—unless a troop extension was negotiated, the American Special Forces were going to have to end their advising mission completely in the fall. By 2011 the ISOF was further than ever under the sway of its masters at the Counter-Terrorism Service, an offshoot of Maliki's OCINC. The Americans called the units the ISOF, for Iraqi special operations forces, but many Iraqis knew them as the Dirty Brigades or the Fedayeen Maliki, after the Fedayeen Saddam. As the American Special Forces headquarters in Iraq prepared to leave for good, its officers worried that their eight years of effort were being undercut as the Counter-Terrorism Service fired seasoned commando leaders and prevented the organization from going after Shiite targets—a reality that forced American special operators to launch a number of unilateral raids, without their Iraqi counterparts, after the summer's IRAM attacks. "If the target is

Shia, unless he is a low-level guy, they're not going to action it," the Special Forces major assigned to advise the 1st ISOF Brigade told an Army interviewer at the end of the summer. An unclassified journal article by an Army team that went to Iraq in August to evaluate the end of the Special Forces mission there elaborated (Major Dave Butler, "Lights Out: ARSOF Reflect on Eight Years in Iraq," *Special Warfare*, January–March 2012):

> Another reason for seeking to maintain a presence at the higher levels of ISOF is the underlying theme of corruption, which hampers operations. Often, effective Iraqi leaders will be replaced suddenly, without notice or obvious reason, causing disruption in the ranks and reducing effectiveness. "Since we got here, we are working with a new brigade commander and all new battalion commanders. Whether that's an initiative on their part, I don't know; we felt that at the ODA level," said the team leader of ODA 2134. . . . Prior to any operation, Iraqi units will build a warrant package to submit through the military and judicial systems for approval. Those warrant packages are often delayed or disapproved for no apparent reason. The details about the target can also be leaked, giving the targeted individual early warning and allowing him to escape.

3. Interviews, administration officials.
4. Interviews, senior administration officials.
5. Interviews, senior administration officials.
6. Interviews, current and former American officials. National Security Adviser Tom Donilon declined to be interviewed.
7. Interviews, current and former administration officials.
8. Interview, Lindsey Graham.
9. Sahar Issa and Roy Gutman, "Iraq's Maliki Signals He May Let U.S. Troops Extend Their Stay," *McClatchy Newspapers*, 12 May 2011; Jack Healy and Yasir Ghazi, "Iraqis to Weigh Asking Some U.S. Troops to Stay," *New York Times*, 12 May 2011.
10. Interview, Lindsey Graham.
11. Interviews, administration officials.
12. Jane Arraf, "Iraq Agrees to Discuss U.S. Security Role," Al-Jazeera English video last updated 5 August 2011. "Now we have an almost unanimous decision by all the political leaders for negotiation on the Iraqi need for trainers, for weapons systems, for boosting the capabilities of Iraqi military or security forces," Hoshyar Zebari, Iraq's foreign minister, said in an interview later in the segment. "Then the next thing will come—what are the needs, the numbers; what are the missions." Zebari later explained that the decision was "almost unanimous" because the Sadrists were likely to vote against any proposal to keep American troops.
13. White House, "Press Briefing by Press Secretary Jay Carney," 4 August 2011.
14. Interviews, administration officials.
15. Interview, administration official.

CHAPTER 36 *Mission Accomplished*

1. Ramzy Mardini, "Maliki Arrests Potential Opposition," backgrounder, Institute for the Study of War, 12 December 2011.

2. Accounts of participants.

3. Accounts of participants.

4. White House transcript, "Remarks by President Obama and Prime Minister al-Maliki of Iraq in a Joint Press Conference," 12 December 2011.

5. Interviews, Iraqi officials. Although Maliki was concerned about appeasing the protesters, he was also preoccupied with protecting his public image as a guarantor of security. At one point, Maliki spokesman Ali al-Dabbagh asked his next-door neighbor Major General Qasim Atta, the spokesman for the Baghdad Operations Command, to come with him to Baghdad's Tahrir Square and do a TV interview to show that the protests had subsided. Responding to criticisms from an American official that the Iraqi security forces had quelled the "Day of Rage" only by detaining large numbers of demonstrators, including journalists, the prime minister said, "I think the security did extremely well in Baghdad. This is what happens when you have protests."

6. Ramzy Mardini, "Iraq's First Post-Withdrawal Crisis," Institute for the Study of War Backgrounder, 19 December 2011.

7. Interview, Iraqi official. Though the plane was delayed, that was no fault of the former national security adviser, who was powerless to prevent the pilot from taking off.

8. Interview, Tariq al-Hashimi.

9. Interview, American official.

10. Interview, Faraj al-Haydari.

11. International Crisis Group, "Iraq and the Kurds: The High-Stakes Hydrocarbons Gambit," Middle East Report No. 120, 19 April 2012, p. 1.

12. Interview, Fuad Hussein.

13. Agence France-Presse, "Kurd President Urges No F-16s for Iraq," *Defense News,* 23 April 2012. In the interview, Barzani also alleged that Maliki had discussed his plans to use the fighter planes against the Kurds in a military meeting. "They talked about problems between Baghdad and Arbil," Barzani said of the generals in the meeting. "They told him, 'Sir, just give us the authority, and we would kick [the Kurds] out of Arbil.' [Maliki] answered: 'Wait until the arrival of the F-16.' "

14. Interview, American official. Ahmed Rasheed and Peg Mackey, "Iraq Asks Obama to Halt Exxon's Kurdish Deal," Reuters, 19 June 2012. Maliki's move contradicted the Iraqi government's previous position, which recognized that the United States government had a limited ability to control the dealings of ExxonMobil. "This contract that was signed by ExxonMobil will not undermine [the] Iraq-US relationship," former oil minister Hussein al-Shahristani said. "Both countries have taken a very clear position that such contracts will have to be done with the approval of the central government, and we don't expect anything more than that from the US government. They have given the right advice to the companies." Ben Van Heuevelen, "Q&A: Hussein al-Shahristani," *Iraq Oil Report,* 22 December 2011.

15. International Crisis Group, "Iraq and the Kurds: The High-Stakes Hydrocarbons Gambit," Middle East Report No. 120, 19 April 2012, p. 12.

16. Massoud Barzani hinted that in the event of such a showdown, the Kurds might soon have a powerful lobby in Washington. "If ExxonMobil came" to Kurdistan, Barzani said in a press conference, "it would be equivalent to 10 American military divisions. . . . They will defend the area if their interests

are there." Agence France-Presse, "Kurd President Urges No F-16s for Iraq," *Defense News*, 23 April 2012.

17. Elizabeth O'Bagy and Stephen Wicken, "Ali Mussa Daqduq," Institute for the Study of War Fact Sheet, 14 May 2012.

18. "Extradition Treaty Signed Between the United States and Iraq, signed 7 June 1934," published in *Foreign Relations*, no. 907, vol. 2, 1934.

19. Interview, Jalal Talabani.

20. Interview, Ayad Allawi.

21. Interview, Adil Abd al-Mahdi.

22. Interview, Barham Salih.

23. Interview, American official.

EPILOGUE

1. Interview, Vice President Joseph Biden.

Index

ALSO BY MICHAEL R. GORDON AND
GENERAL BERNARD E. TRAINOR

"Excellent. . . . Cobra II *is everything that the Bush
administration's plan for the war was not. It is meticulously
organized, shuns bluff and bombast for lapidary statements,
and is largely impervious to attack.*"
—The New York Times Book Review

COBRA II
The Inside Story of the Invasion and Occupation of Iraq

Written by the chief military correspondent of *The New York
Times* and a prominent retired Marine general, this is the
definitive account of the invasion of Iraq. A stunning work of
investigative journalism, *Cobra II* describes in riveting detail
how the American rush to Baghdad provided the opportunity for the virulent insurgency that followed. As Gordon and
Trainor show, the brutal aftermath was not inevitable and was a
surprise to the generals on both sides. Based on access to unseen
documents and exclusive interviews with the men and women
at the heart of the war, *Cobra II* provides firsthand accounts of
the fighting on the ground and the high-level planning behind
the scenes. Now with a new afterword that addresses what
transpired after the fateful events of the summer of 2003, this
is a peerless re-creation and analysis of the central event of our
times.

Political Science/Military

VINTAGE BOOKS
Available wherever books are sold.
www.vintagebooks.com